PEARSON CUSTOM

MATHEMATICS

Pre Statistics

PEARSON

Cover Art: "Close-up Shoot of Keyboard," "Financial Stat Arrow," "The Winning Formula," "Business Data Analyzing," "Teacher Writing Formula on Blackboard in Crowded Computer Room," "Stock Market Analysis," "Student Solving a Problem," "Market Analyze," "Annual Report," "Calculator Close-up," "Financial Stock Chart Tablet Computer," courtesy of iStockphoto; "Drawing Tools Background," courtesy of tuja66/Veer/Corbis Images; "Numbers," courtesy of iStockphoto; "Modern Glass Ceiling," courtesy of iStockphoto; "Pencils," courtesy of Shane White/Veer/Corbis Images; "Perspective Angle of Business Skyscraper" and "Modern Glass Architecture," courtesy of iStockphoto; "Perspective Angle of Business Skyscraper," courtesy of iStockphoto. Additional images courtesy of Pearson Learning Solutions, Photodisc/Getty Images.

This special edition published in cooperation with Pearson Learning Solutions.

Printed in the United States of America.

V0CR

Please visit our website at *www.pearsonlearningsolutions.com.*

Attention bookstores: For permission to return any unsold stock, contact us at *pe-uscustomreturns@pearson.com*.

Pearson Learning Solutions, 501 Boylston Street, Suite 900, Boston, MA 02116
A Pearson Education Company
www.pearsoned.com

ISBN 10: 1-256-56688-8
ISBN 13: 978-1-256-56688-5

Table of Contents

Variables, Real Numbers, and Mathematical Models

What can algebra possibly tell me about

- the rising cost of movie ticket prices over the years?
- how I can stretch or shrink my life span?
- the widening imbalance between numbers of women and men on college campuses?
- the number of calories I need to maintain energy balance?
- how much I can expect to earn at my first job after college?

In this chapter, you will learn how the special language of algebra describes your world.

Here's where you will find these applications:

- Movie ticket prices: Exercise Set 1, Exercises 83–84
- Stretching or shrinking my life span: Exercise Set 6, Exercises 101–110
- College gender imbalance: Section 7, Example 9
- Caloric needs: Section 8, Example 12; Exercise Set 8, Exercises 97–98
- Anticipated earnings at my first job after college: Exercise Set 8, Exercises 99–100.

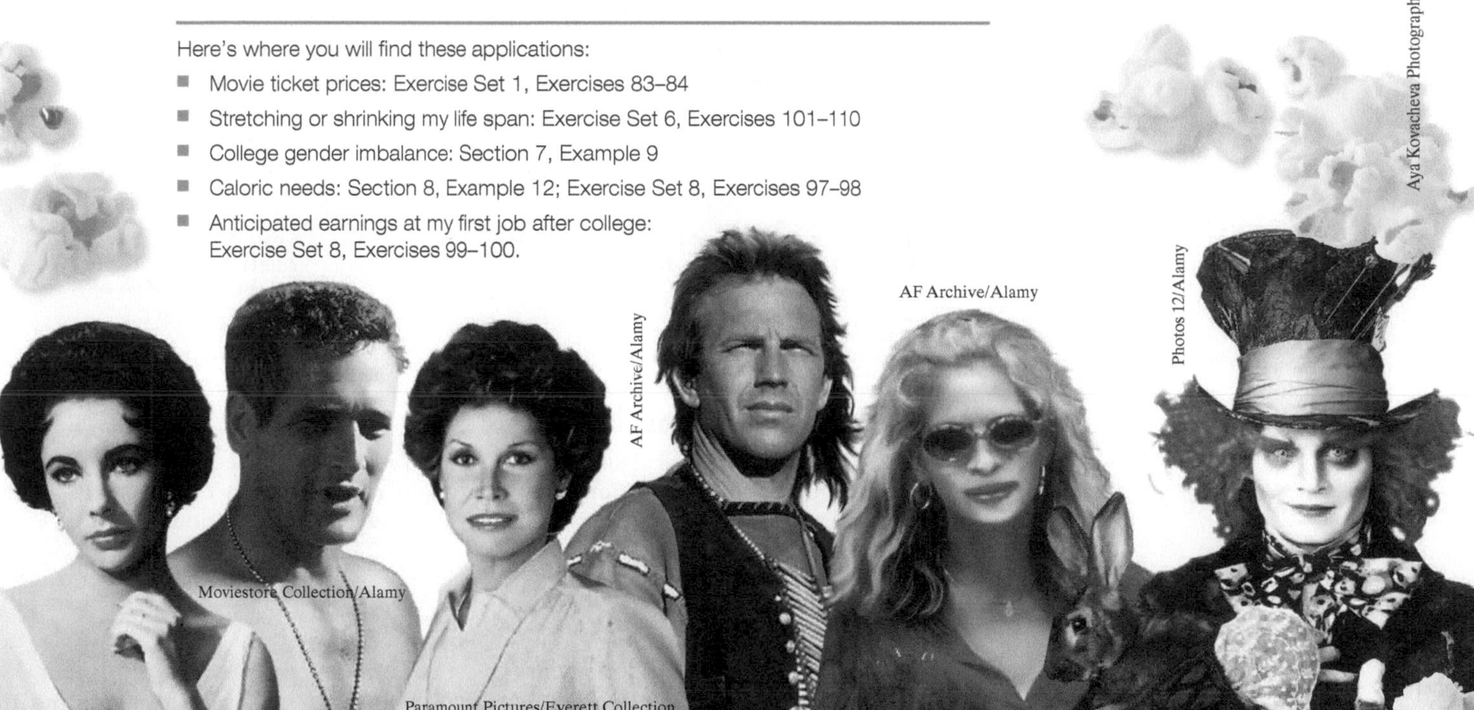

1958	1967	1980	1990	2000	2010
Cat on a Hot Tin Roof TICKET PRICE $0.68	Cool Hand Luke TICKET PRICE $1.22	Ordinary People TICKET PRICE $2.69	Dances with Wolves TICKET PRICE $4.23	Erin Brockovich TICKET PRICE $5.39	Alice in Wonderland TICKET PRICE $7.85

Sources: Motion Picture Association of America, National Association of Theater Owners (NATO), and Bureau of Labor Statistics (BLS)

SECTION 1

Introduction to Algebra: Variables and Mathematical Models

Objectives

1. Evaluate algebraic expressions.
2. Translate English phrases into algebraic expressions.
3. Determine whether a number is a solution of an equation.
4. Translate English sentences into algebraic equations.
5. Evaluate formulas.

You are thinking about buying a high-definition television. How much distance should you allow between you and the TV for pixels to be undetectable and the image to appear smooth?

Algebraic Expressions

Let's see what the distance between you and your TV has to do with algebra. The biggest difference between arithmetic and algebra is the use of *variables* in algebra. A **variable** is a letter that represents a variety of different numbers. For example, we can let x represent the diagonal length, in inches, of a high-definition television. The industry rule for most of the current HDTVs on the market is to multiply this diagonal length by 2.5 to get the distance, in inches, at which a person with perfect vision can see a smooth image. This can be written $2.5 \cdot x$, but it is usually expressed as $2.5x$. Placing a number and a letter next to one another indicates multiplication.

Notice that $2.5x$ combines the number 2.5 and the variable x using the operation of multiplication. A combination of variables and numbers using the operations of addition, subtraction, multiplication, or division, as well as powers or roots, is called an **algebraic expression**. Here are some examples of algebraic expressions:

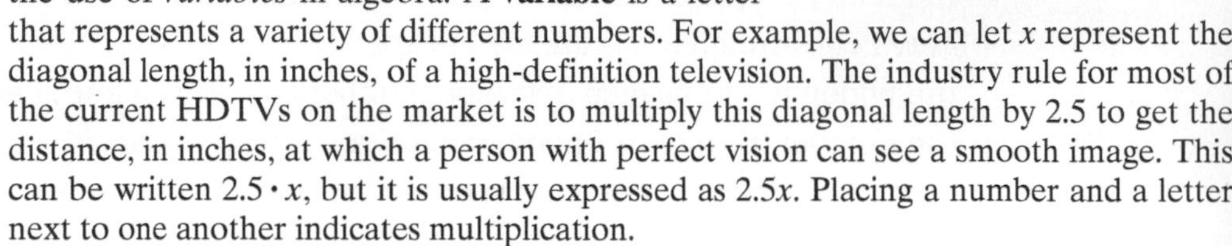

Great Question!

Are variables always represented by *x*?

No. As you progress through algebra, you will often see x, y, and z used, but any letter can be used to represent a variable. For example, if we use l to represent a TV's diagonal length, your ideal distance from the screen is described by the algebraic expression $2.5l$.

1 Evaluate algebraic expressions.

Evaluating Algebraic Expressions

We can replace a variable that appears in an algebraic expression by a number. We are **substituting** the number for the variable. The process is called **evaluating the expression**. For example, we can evaluate $2.5x$ (the ideal distance between you and your x-inch TV) for $x = 50$. We substitute 50 for x. We obtain $2.5 \cdot 50$, or 125. This means that if the diagonal length of your TV is 50 inches, your distance from the screen should be 125 inches. Because 12 inches = 1 foot, this distance is $\frac{125}{12}$ feet, or approximately 10.4 feet.

Many algebraic expressions involve more than one operation. The order in which we add, subtract, multiply, and divide is important. In Section 8, we will discuss the rules for the order in which operations should be done. For now, follow this order:

A First Look at Order of Operations

1. Perform all operations within grouping symbols, such as parentheses.
2. Do all multiplications in the order in which they occur from left to right.
3. Do all additions and subtractions in the order in which they occur from left to right.

Great Question!

What am I supposed to do with the worked examples?

Study the step-by-step solutions in these examples. Reading the solutions slowly and with great care will prepare you for success with the exercises in the Exercise Sets.

EXAMPLE 1 Evaluating Expressions

Evaluate each algebraic expression for $x = 5$:

a. $3 + 4x$ **b.** $4(x + 3)$.

Solution

a. We begin by substituting 5 for x in $3 + 4x$. Then we follow the order of operations: Multiply first, and then add.

$$3 + 4x$$

Replace x with 5.

$$= 3 + 4 \cdot 5$$

$$= 3 + 20 \quad \text{Perform the multiplication: } 4 \cdot 5 = 20.$$

$$= 23 \quad \text{Perform the addition.}$$

Great Question!

Why is it so important to work each of the text's Check Points?

You learn best by doing. Do not simply look at the worked examples and conclude that you know how to solve them. To be sure you understand the worked examples, try each Check Point. Check your answer in the answer section before continuing your reading. Expect to read this text with pencil and paper handy to work the Check Points.

b. We begin by substituting 5 for x in $4(x + 3)$. Then we follow the order of operations: Perform the addition in parentheses first, and then multiply.

$$4(x + 3)$$

Replace x with 5.

$$= 4(5 + 3)$$

$$= 4(8) \quad \text{Perform the addition inside the parentheses: } 5 + 3 = 8. \ 4(8) \text{ can also be written as } 4 \cdot 8.$$

$$= 32 \quad \text{Multiply.}$$ ■

✓ **CHECK POINT 1** Evaluate each expression for $x = 10$:

a. $6 + 2x$ **b.** $2(x + 6)$.

Example 2 illustrates that algebraic expressions can contain more than one variable.

EXAMPLE 2 Evaluating Expressions

Evaluate each algebraic expression for $x = 6$ and $y = 4$:

a. $5x - 3y$ **b.** $\dfrac{3x + 5y + 2}{2x - y}$.

Solution

a. $5x - 3y$ — This is the given algebraic expression.

Replace x with 6. Replace y with 4.

$= 5 \cdot 6 - 3 \cdot 4$ — We are evaluating the expression for $x = 6$ and $y = 4$.

$= 30 - 12$ — Multiply: $5 \cdot 6 = 30$ and $3 \cdot 4 = 12$.

$= 18$ — Subtract.

b. $\dfrac{3x + 5y + 2}{2x - y}$ — This is the given algebraic expression.

Replace x with 6. Replace y with 4.

$= \dfrac{3 \cdot 6 + 5 \cdot 4 + 2}{2 \cdot 6 - 4}$ — We are evaluating the expression for $x = 6$ and $y = 4$.

$= \dfrac{18 + 20 + 2}{12 - 4}$ — Multiply: $3 \cdot 6 = 18$, $5 \cdot 4 = 20$, and $2 \cdot 6 = 12$.

$= \dfrac{40}{8}$ — Add in the numerator. Subtract in the denominator.

$= 5$ — Simplify by dividing 40 by 8. ■

✓ **CHECK POINT 2** Evaluate each algebraic expression for $x = 3$ and $y = 8$:

a. $7x + 2y$ **b.** $\dfrac{6x - y}{2y - x - 8}$.

2 Translate English phrases into algebraic expressions.

Translating to Algebraic Expressions

Problem solving in algebra often requires the ability to translate word phrases into algebraic expressions. **Table 1** lists some key words associated with the operations of addition, subtraction, multiplication, and division.

Table 1 Key Words for Addition, Subtraction, Multiplication, and Division

Operation	Addition (+)	Subtraction (−)	Multiplication (×)	Division (÷)
Key words	plus	minus	times	divide
	sum	difference	product	quotient
	more than	less than	twice	ratio
	increased by	decreased by	multiplied by	divided by

EXAMPLE 3 Translating English Phrases into Algebraic Expressions

Write each English phrase as an algebraic expression. Let the variable x represent the number.

a. the sum of a number and 7

b. ten less than a number

c. twice a number, decreased by 6

d. the product of 8 and a number

e. three more than the quotient of a number and 11

Solution

a. The sum of | a number and 7

$x + 7$

The algebraic expression for "the sum of a number and 7" is $x + 7$.

b. Ten less than | a number

$x - 10$

The algebraic expression for "ten less than a number" is $x - 10$.

c. Twice a number, | decreased by 6

$2x - 6$

The algebraic expression for "twice a number, decreased by 6" is $2x - 6$.

d. The product of | 8 and a number

$8 \cdot x$

The algebraic expression for "the product of 8 and a number" is $8 \cdot x$, or $8x$.

e. Three more than | the quotient of a number and 11

$\frac{x}{11} + 3$

The algebraic expression for "three more than the quotient of a number and 11" is $\frac{x}{11} + 3$. ■

Great Question!

Are there any helpful hints I can use when writing algebraic expressions for English phrases involving subtraction?

Yes. Pay close attention to order when translating phrases involving subtraction.

Phrase	Translation
A number decreased by 7	$x - 7$
A number subtracted from 7	$7 - x$
Seven less than a number	$x - 7$
Seven less a number	$7 - x$

Think carefully about what is expressed in English before you translate into the language of algebra.

✓ **CHECK POINT 3** Write each English phrase as an algebraic expression. Let the variable x represent the number.

a. the product of 6 and a number

b. a number added to 4

c. three times a number, increased by 5

d. twice a number subtracted from 12

e. the quotient of 15 and a number

3 Determine whether a number is a solution of an equation.

Equations

An **equation** is a statement that two algebraic expressions are equal. **An equation always contains the equality symbol ·.** Here are some examples of equations:

$$6x + 16 = 46 \qquad 4y + 2 = 2y + 6 \qquad 2(z + 1) = 5(z - 2).$$

Solutions of an equation are values of the variable that make the equation a true statement. To determine whether a number is a solution, substitute that number for the variable and evaluate each side of the equation. If the values on both sides of the equation are the same, the number is a solution.

EXAMPLE 4 Determining Whether Numbers Are Solutions of Equations

Determine whether the given number is a solution of the equation.

a. $6x + 16 = 46; 5$ **b.** $2(z + 1) = 5(z - 2); 7$

Solution

a.

$6x + 16 = 46$ This is the given equation.

Is 5 a solution?

$6 \cdot 5 + 16 \stackrel{?}{=} 46$ To determine whether 5 is a solution, substitute 5 for x. The question mark over the equal sign indicates that we do not yet know if the statement is true.

$30 + 16 \stackrel{?}{=} 46$ Multiply: $6 \cdot 5 = 30$.

This statement is true. $46 = 46$ Add: $30 + 16 = 46$.

Because the values on both sides of the equation are the same, the number 5 is a solution of the equation.

b.

$2(z + 1) = 5(z - 2)$ This is the given equation.

Is 7 a solution?

$2(7 + 1) \stackrel{?}{=} 5(7 - 2)$ To determine whether 7 is a solution, substitute 7 for z.

$2(8) \stackrel{?}{=} 5(5)$ Perform operations in parentheses: $7 + 1 = 8$ and $7 - 2 = 5$.

This statement is false. $16 = 25$ Multiply: $2 \cdot 8 = 16$ and $5 \cdot 5 = 25$.

Because the values on both sides of the equation are not the same, the number 7 is not a solution of the equation. ■

✓ **CHECK POINT 4** Determine whether the given number is a solution of the equation.

a. $9x - 3 = 42; 6$ **b.** $2(y + 3) = 5y - 3; 3$

4 Translate English sentences into algebraic equations.

Translating to Equations

Earlier in the section, we translated English phrases into algebraic expressions. Now we will translate English sentences into equations. You'll find that there are a number of different words and phrases for an equation's equality symbol.

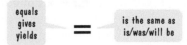

EXAMPLE 5 Translating English Sentences into Algebraic Equations

Write each sentence as an equation. Let the variable x represent the number.

a. The product of 6 and a number is 30.

b. Seven less than 3 times a number gives 17.

Solution

a.

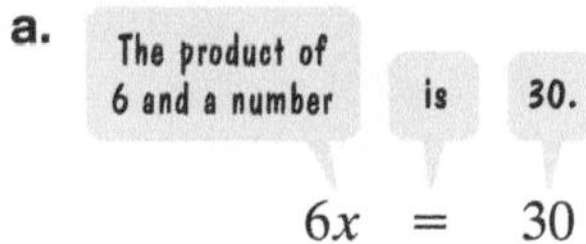

The equation for "the product of 6 and a number is 30" is $6x = 30$.

b.

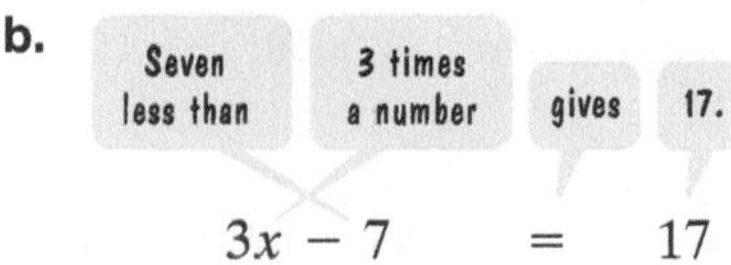

The equation for "seven less than 3 times a number gives 17" is $3x - 7 = 17$. ■

✓ **CHECK POINT 5** Write each sentence as an equation. Let the variable x represent the number.

a. The quotient of a number and 6 is 5.

b. Seven decreased by twice a number yields 1.

Great Question!

When translating English sentences containing commas into algebraic equations, should I pay attention to the commas?

Commas make a difference. In English, sentences and phrases can take on different meanings depending on the way words are grouped with commas. Some examples:

These are meant to be amusing.

- Woman, without her man, is nothing.
  Woman, without her, man is nothing.
- Do not break your bread or roll in your soup.
  Do not break your bread, or roll in your soup.

Algebraically, this is the important item.

- The product of 6 and a number increased by 5 is 30: $6(x + 5) = 30$.
  The product of 6 and a number, increased by 5, is 30: $6x + 5 = 30$.

5 Evaluate formulas.

Formulas and Mathematical Models

One aim of algebra is to provide a compact, symbolic description of the world. These descriptions involve the use of *formulas*. A **formula** is an equation that expresses a relationship between two or more variables. For example, one variety of crickets chirps faster as the temperature rises. You can calculate the temperature by counting the number of times a cricket chirps per minute and applying the following formula:

$$T = 0.3n + 40.$$

In the formula, T is the temperature, in degrees Fahrenheit, and n is the number of cricket chirps per minute. We can use this formula to determine the temperature if you are sitting on your porch and count 80 chirps per minute. Here is how to do so:

$T = 0.3n + 40$	This is the given formula.
$T = 0.3(80) + 40$	Substitute 80 for n.
$T = 24 + 40$	Multiply: $0.3(80) = 24$.
$T = 64.$	Add.

When there are 80 cricket chirps per minute, the temperature is 64 degrees.

The process of finding formulas to describe real-world phenomena is called **mathematical modeling**. Such formulas, together with the meaning assigned to the variables, are called **mathematical models**. We often say that these formulas model, or describe, the relationship among the variables.

In creating mathematical models, we strive for both accuracy and simplicity. For example, the formula $T = 0.3n + 40$ is relatively simple to use. However, you should not get upset if you count 80 cricket chirps and the actual temperature is 62 degrees, rather than 64 degrees, as predicted by the formula. Many mathematical models give an approximate, rather than an exact, description of the relationship between variables.

Sometimes a mathematical model gives an estimate that is not a good approximation or is extended to include values of the variable that do not make sense. In these cases, we say that **model breakdown** has occurred. Here is an example:

Use the mathematical model $T = 0.3n + 40$ with $n = 1200$ (1200 cricket chirps per minute).

$$T = 0.3(1200) + 40 = 360 + 40 = 400$$

At 400° F, forget about 1200 chirps per minute! At this temperature, the cricket would "cook" and, alas, all chirping would cease.

EXAMPLE 6 Age at Marriage and the Probability of Divorce

Divorce rates are considerably higher for couples who marry in their teens. The line graphs in **Figure 1** show the percentages of marriages ending in divorce based on the wife's age at marriage.

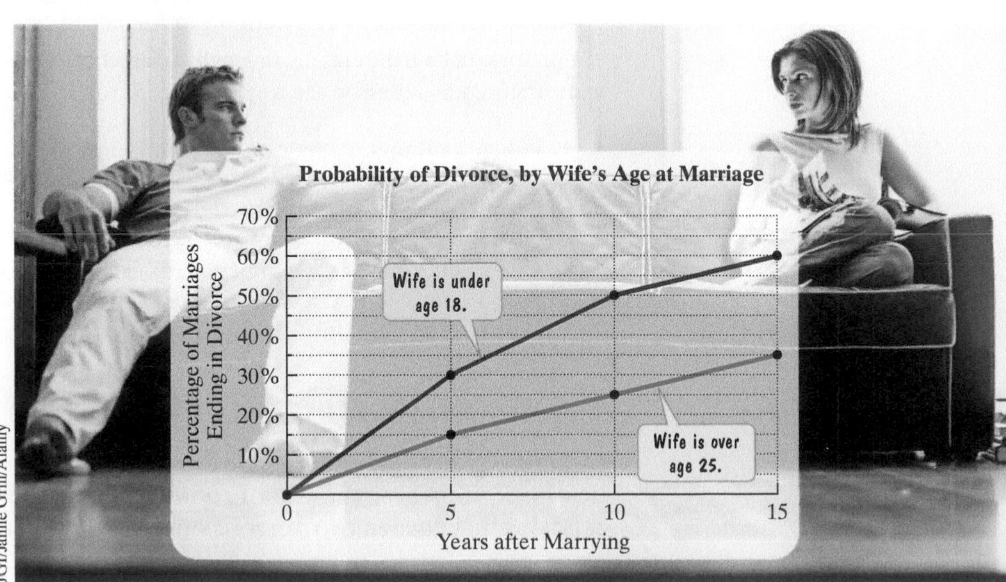

Figure 1

Source: B. E. Pruitt et al., *Human Sexuality*, Prentice Hall, 2007

Here are two mathematical models that approximate the data displayed by the line graphs:

Wife is under 18 at time of marriage.
Wife is over 25 at time of marriage.

$$d = 4n + 5 \qquad d = 2.3n + 1.5.$$

In each model, the variable n is the number of years after marriage and the variable d is the percentage of marriages ending in divorce.

a. Use the appropriate formula to determine the percentage of marriages ending in divorce after 10 years when the wife is over 25 at the time of marriage.

b. Use the appropriate line graph in **Figure 1** to determine the percentage of marriages ending in divorce after 10 years when the wife is over 25 at the time of marriage.

c. Does the value given by the mathematical model underestimate or overestimate the actual percentage of marriages ending in divorce after 10 years as shown by the graph? By how much?

Solution

a. Because the wife is over 25 at the time of marriage, we use the formula on the right, $d = 2.3n + 1.5$. To find the percentage of marriages ending in divorce after 10 years, we substitute 10 for n and evaluate the formula.

$d = 2.3n + 1.5$ — This is one of the two given mathematical models.

$d = 2.3(10) + 1.5$ — Replace n with 10.

$d = 23 + 1.5$ — Multiply: $2.3(10) = 23$.

$d = 24.5$ — Add.

The model indicates that 24.5% of marriages end in divorce after 10 years when the wife is over 25 at the time of marriage.

b. Now let's use the line graph that shows the percentage of marriages ending in divorce when the wife is over 25 at the time of marriage. The graph is shown again in **Figure 2**. To find the percentage of marriages ending in divorce after 10 years:

- Locate 10 on the horizontal axis and locate the point above 10.
- Read across to the corresponding percent on the vertical axis.

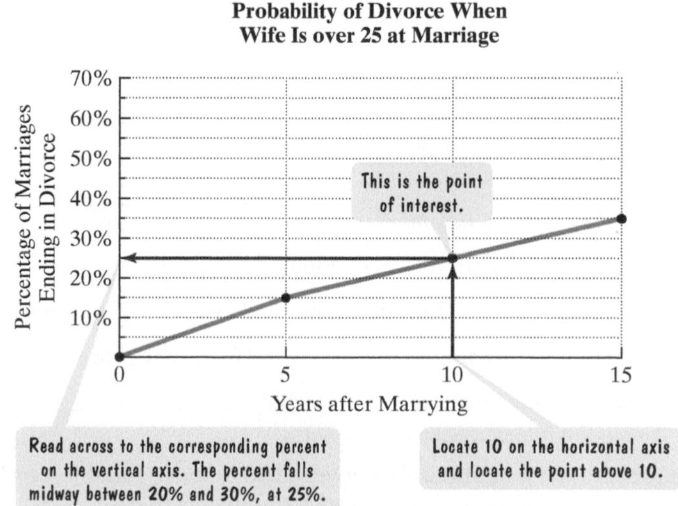
Probability of Divorce When Wife Is over 25 at Marriage
Percentage of Marriages Ending in Divorce
70%
60%
50%
40%
30%
20%
10%
0
5
10
15
Years after Marrying
This is the point of interest.
Read across to the corresponding percent on the vertical axis. The percent falls midway between 20% and 30%, at 25%.
Locate 10 on the horizontal axis and locate the point above 10.

Figure 2

The actual data displayed by the graph indicate that 25% of these marriages end in divorce after 10 years.

c. Here's a summary of what we found in parts (a) and (b).

Percentage of Marriages Ending in Divorce after 10 Years (Wife over 25 at Marriage)
Mathematical model: 24.5%
Actual data displayed by graph: 25.0%

The value obtained by evaluating the mathematical model, 24.5%, is close to, but slightly less than, the actual percentage of divorces, 25.0%. The difference between these percents is 25.0% − 24.5%, or 0.5%. The value given by the mathematical model underestimates the actual percent by only 0.5%, providing a fairly accurate description of the data. ■

✓ **CHECK POINT 6**

a. Use the appropriate formula from Example 6 to determine the percentage of marriages ending in divorce after 15 years when the wife is under 18 at the time of marriage.

b. Use the appropriate line graph in **Figure 1** to determine the percentage of marriages ending in divorce after 15 years when the wife is under 18 at the time of marriage.

c. Does the value given by the mathematical model underestimate or overestimate the actual percentage of marriages ending in divorce after 15 years as shown by the graph? By how much?

Achieving Success

Practice! Practice! Practice!

The way to learn algebra is by seeing solutions to examples and **doing exercises**. This means working the Check Points and the assigned exercises in the Exercise Sets. There are no alternatives. It's easy to read a solution, or watch your professor solve an example, and believe you know what to do. However, learning algebra requires that you actually **perform solutions by yourself**. Get in the habit of working exercises every day. The more time you spend solving exercises, the easier the process becomes. It's okay to take a short break after class, but start reviewing and working the assigned homework as soon as possible.

CONCEPT AND VOCABULARY CHECK

Fill in each blank so that the resulting statement is true.

1. A letter that represents a variety of different numbers is called a/an ____________.
2. A combination of numbers, letters that represent numbers, and operation symbols is called an algebraic ____________.
3. By replacing x with 60 in $2.5x$, we are ____________ 60 for x. The process of finding $2.5 \cdot 60$ is called ____________ $2.5x$ for $x = 60$.
4. A statement that two algebraic expressions are equal is called a/an ____________. A value of the variable that makes such a statement true is called a/an ____________.
5. A statement that expresses a relationship between two or more variables, such as $T = 0.3x + 40$, is called a/an ____________. The process of finding such statements to describe real-world phenomena is called mathematical ____________. Such statements, together with the meaning assigned to the variables, are called mathematical ____________.

1 EXERCISE SET

MyMathLab®

Watch the videos in MyMathLab

Download the MyDashBoard App

Practice Exercises

In Exercises 1–14, evaluate each expression for $x = 4$.

1. $x + 8$
2. $x + 10$
3. $12 - x$
4. $16 - x$
5. $5x$
6. $6x$
7. $\frac{28}{x}$
8. $\frac{36}{x}$
9. $5 + 3x$
10. $3 + 5x$
11. $2(x + 5)$
12. $5(x + 3)$
13. $\frac{12x - 8}{2x}$
14. $\frac{5x + 52}{3x}$

In Exercises 15–24, evaluate each expression for $x = 7$ and $y = 5$.

15. $2x + y$
16. $3x + y$
17. $2(x + y)$
18. $3(x + y)$
19. $4x - 3y$
20. $5x - 4y$
21. $\frac{21}{x} + \frac{35}{y}$
22. $\frac{50}{y} - \frac{14}{x}$
23. $\frac{2x - y + 6}{2y - x}$
24. $\frac{2y - x + 24}{2x - y}$

In Exercises 25–42, write each English phrase as an algebraic expression. Let the variable x represent the number.

25. four more than a number
26. six more than a number
27. four less than a number
28. six less than a number
29. the sum of a number and 4
30. the sum of a number and 6
31. nine subtracted from a number
32. three subtracted from a number
33. nine decreased by a number
34. three decreased by a number
35. three times a number, decreased by 5
36. five times a number, decreased by 3
37. one less than the product of 12 and a number
38. three less than the product of 13 and a number
39. the sum of 10 divided by a number and that number divided by 10
40. the sum of 20 divided by a number and that number divided by 20
41. six more than the quotient of a number and 30
42. four more than the quotient of 30 and a number

In Exercises 43–58, determine whether the given number is a solution of the equation.

43. $x + 14 = 20; 6$
44. $x + 17 = 22; 5$
45. $30 - y = 10; 20$
46. $50 - y = 20; 30$
47. $4z = 20; 10$
48. $5z = 30; 8$
49. $\frac{r}{6} = 8; 48$
50. $\frac{r}{9} = 7; 63$
51. $4m + 3 = 23; 6$
52. $3m + 4 = 19; 6$
53. $5a - 4 = 2a + 5; 3$
54. $5a - 3 = 2a + 6; 3$
55. $6(p - 4) = 3p; 8$
56. $4(p + 3) = 6p; 6$
57. $2(w + 1) = 3(w - 1); 7$
58. $3(w + 2) = 4(w - 3); 10$

In Exercises 59–74, write each sentence as an equation. Let the variable x represent the number.

59. Four times a number is 28.
60. Five times a number is 35.
61. The quotient of 14 and a number is $\frac{1}{2}$.
62. The quotient of a number and 8 is $\frac{1}{4}$.
63. The difference between 20 and a number is 5.
64. The difference between 40 and a number is 10.
65. The sum of twice a number and 6 is 16.
66. The sum of twice a number and 9 is 29.
67. Five less than 3 times a number gives 7.
68. Three less than 4 times a number gives 29.
69. The product of 4 and a number, increased by 5, is 33.
70. The product of 6 and a number, increased by 3, is 33.
71. The product of 4 and a number increased by 5 is 33.
72. The product of 6 and a number increased by 3 is 33.
73. Five times a number is equal to 24 decreased by the number.
74. Four times a number is equal to 25 decreased by the number.

Practice PLUS

75. Evaluate $\frac{x - y}{4}$ when x is 2 more than 7 times y and $y = 5$.
76. Evaluate $\frac{x - y}{3}$ when x is 2 more than 5 times y and $y = 4$.

77. Evaluate $4x + 3(y + 5)$ when x is 1 less than the quotient of y and 4 and $y = 12$.

78. Evaluate $3x + 4(y + 6)$ when x is 1 less than the quotient of y and 3, and $y = 15$.

79. **a.** Evaluate $2(x + 3y)$ for $x = 4$ and $y = 1$.

b. Is the number you obtained in part (a) a solution of $5z - 30 = 40$?

80. **a.** Evaluate $3(2x + y)$ for $x = 1$ and $y = 5$.

b. Is the number you obtained in part (a) a solution of $4z - 30 = 54$?

81. **a.** Evaluate $6x - 2y$ for $x = 3$ and $y = 6$.

b. Is the number you obtained in part (a) a solution of $7w = 45 - 2w$?

82. **a.** Evaluate $5x - 14y$ for $x = 3$ and $y = \frac{1}{2}$.

b. Is the number you obtained in part (a) a solution of $4w = 54 - 5w$?

Application Exercises

We opened the chapter with what it would have cost to see six classic movies on the big screen. The bar graph shows the average price of a movie ticket for selected years from 1980 through 2010.

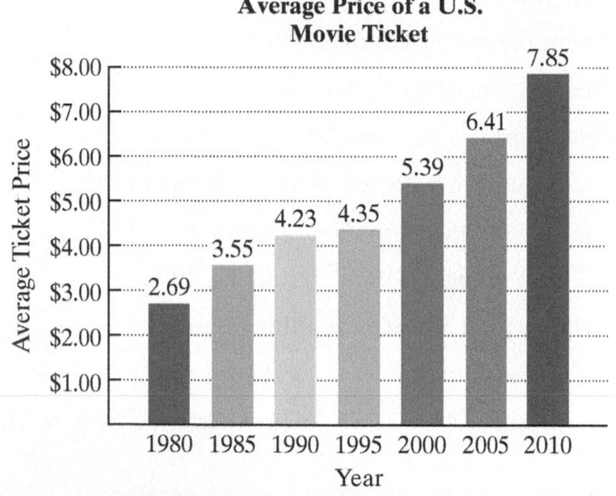

Sources: Motion Picture Association of America, National Association of Theater Owners (NATO), and Bureau of Labor Statistics (BLS)

Here is a mathematical model that approximates the data displayed by the bar graph:

$$T = 0.15n + 2.72.$$

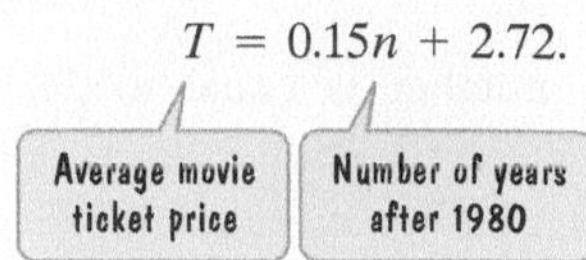

Use this formula to solve Exercises 83–84.

83. **a.** Use the formula to find the average ticket price 10 years after 1980, or in 1990. Does the mathematical model underestimate or overestimate the average ticket price shown by the bar graph for 1990? By how much?

b. Does the mathematical model underestimate or overestimate the average ticket price shown by the bar graph for 2010? By how much?

84. **a.** Use the formula to find the average ticket price 5 years after 1980, or in 1985. Does the mathematical model underestimate or overestimate the average ticket price shown by the bar graph in the previous column for 1985? By how much?

b. Does the mathematical model underestimate or overestimate the average ticket price shown by the bar graph for 2005? By how much?

We're just not that into marriage. *Among the 2691 American adults surveyed by the Pew Research Center in 2010, 39% said marriage is optional and becoming obsolete, up from 28% who responded to the same survey in 1978. The bar graph shows the percentage of Americans for four selected ages who say that marriage is obsolete.*

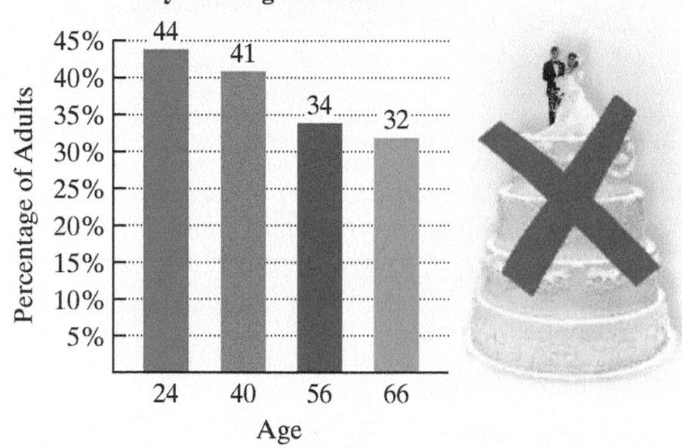

Source: Pew Research Center, "For Millennials, Parenthood Trumps Marriage," March 9, 2011 (www.pewresearch.org)

Here is a mathematical model that approximates the data displayed by the bar graph:

$$p = 52 - 0.3a.$$

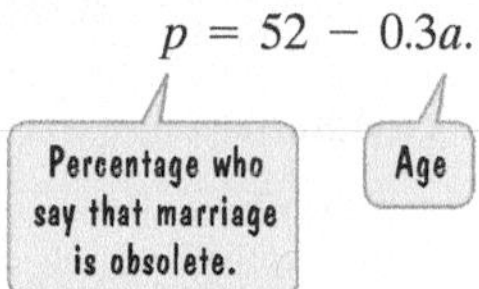

Use this formula to solve Exercises 85–86.

85. Does the mathematical model underestimate or overestimate the percentage of 24-year-olds who say that marriage is obsolete? By how much?

86. Does the mathematical model underestimate or overestimate the percentage of 66-year-olds who say that marriage is obsolete? By how much?

A bowler's handicap, H, is often found using the following formula:

$$H = 0.8(200 - A).$$

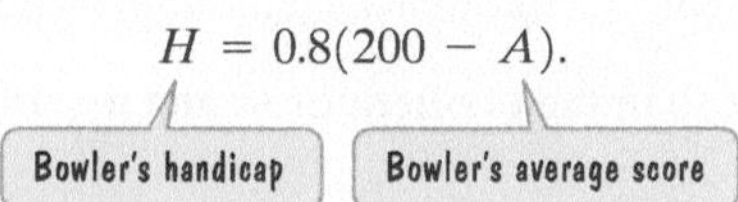

A bowler's final score for a game is the score for that game increased by the handicap.

Use this information and the formula at the bottom of the previous page to solve Exercises 87–88.

87. a. If your average bowling score is 145, what is your handicap?

b. What would your final score be if you bowled 120 in a game?

88. a. If your average bowling score is 165, what is your handicap?

b. What would your final score be if you bowled 140 in a game?

Writing in Mathematics

Writing about mathematics will help you to learn mathematics. For all writing exercises in this text, use complete sentences to respond to the questions. Some writing exercises can be answered in a sentence; others require a paragraph or two. You can decide how much you need to write as long as your writing clearly and directly answers the question in the exercise. Standard references such as a dictionary and a thesaurus should be helpful.

89. What is a variable?

90. What is an algebraic expression?

91. Explain how to evaluate $2 + 5x$ for $x = 3$.

92. If x represents the number, explain the difference between translating the following phrases:
a number decreased by 5
a number subtracted from 5.

93. What is an equation?

94. How do you tell the difference between an algebraic expression and an equation?

95. How do you determine whether a given number is a solution of an equation?

96. What is a mathematical model?

97. The bar graph for Exercises 85–86 shows a decline with increasing age in the percentage of Americans who say that marriage is obsolete. What explanations can you offer for this trend?

98. In Exercises 87–88, we used the formula $H = 0.8(200 - A)$ to find a bowler's handicap, H, where the variable A represents the bowler's average score. Describe what happens to the handicap when the average score is 200.

Critical Thinking Exercises

Make Sense? *In Exercises 99–102, determine whether each statement "makes sense" or "does not make sense" and explain your reasoning.*

99. As I read this book, I write questions in the margins that I might ask in class.

100. I'm solving a problem that requires me to determine if 5 is a solution of $4x + 7$.

101. The model $T = 0.15n + 2.72$ describes the average movie ticket price, T, n years after 1980, so I can use it to estimate the average movie ticket price in 1980.

102. Because there are four quarters in a dollar, I can use the formula $q = 4d$ to determine the number of quarters, q, in d dollars.

In Exercises 103–106, determine whether each statement is true or false. If the statement is false, make the necessary change(s) to produce a true statement.

103. The algebraic expression for "3 less than a number" is the same as the algebraic expression for "a number decreased by 3."

104. Some algebraic expressions contain the equality symbol, =.

105. The algebraic expressions $3 + 2x$ and $(3 + 2)x$ do not mean the same thing.

106. The algebraic expression for "the quotient of a number and 6" is the same as the algebraic expression for "the quotient of 6 and a number."

In Exercises 107–108, define variables and write a formula that describes the relationship in each table.

107.

Number of Hours Worked	Salary
3	\$60
4	\$80
5	\$100
6	\$120

108.

Number of Workers	Number of Televisions Assembled
3	30
4	40
5	50
6	60

Preview Exercises

Exercises 109–111 will help you prepare for the material covered in the next section. In each exercise, use the given formula to perform the indicated operation with the two fractions.

109. $\frac{a}{b} \cdot \frac{c}{d} = \frac{a \cdot c}{b \cdot d}$; $\frac{3}{7} \cdot \frac{2}{5}$

110. $\frac{a}{b} \div \frac{c}{d} = \frac{a}{b} \cdot \frac{d}{c} = \frac{a \cdot d}{b \cdot c}$; $\frac{2}{3} \div \frac{7}{5}$

111. $\frac{a}{b} - \frac{c}{b} = \frac{a - c}{b}$; $\frac{9}{17} - \frac{5}{17}$

SECTION 2

Fractions in Algebra

Objectives

1 Convert between mixed numbers and improper fractions.
2 Write the prime factorization of a composite number.
3 Reduce or simplify fractions.
4 Multiply fractions.
5 Divide fractions.
6 Add and subtract fractions with identical denominators.
7 Add and subtract fractions with unlike denominators.
8 Solve problems involving fractions in algebra.

Kris Ubach and Quim Roser/Cultura/Alamy

Erik Isakson/Tetra Images/Alamy

Had a good workout lately? If so, could you tell from your heart rate if you were overdoing it or not pushing yourself hard enough?

Couch-Potato Exercise

$$H = \frac{2}{5}(220 - a)$$

H: Heart rate, in beats per minute; a: Age

Working It

$$H = \frac{9}{10}(220 - a)$$

H: Heart rate, in beats per minute; a: Age

The fractions $\frac{2}{5}$ and $\frac{9}{10}$ provide the difference between these formulas. Recall that in a fraction, the number that is written above the fraction bar is called the **numerator**. The number below the fraction bar is called the **denominator**.

$$\frac{2}{5} \qquad \frac{9}{10}$$

Numerator; Fraction bar; Denominator

The numerators and denominators of these fractions, 2, 5, 9, and 10, are examples of *natural numbers*. The **natural numbers** are the numbers that we use for counting.

Natural numbers: $1, 2, 3, 4, 5, \ldots$

The three dots after the 5 indicate that the list continues in the same manner without ending.

Fractions appear throughout algebra. The first part of this section provides a review of the arithmetic of fractions. Later in the section, we focus on fractions in algebra.

1 Convert between mixed numbers and improper fractions.

Mixed Numbers and Improper Fractions

A **mixed number** consists of the sum of a natural number and a fraction, expressed without the use of an addition sign. Here is an example of a mixed number:

$$3\frac{4}{5}.$$

The natural number is 3 and the fraction is $\frac{4}{5}$. $3\frac{4}{5}$ means $3 + \frac{4}{5}$.

An **improper fraction** is a fraction whose numerator is greater than its denominator. An example of an improper fraction is $\frac{19}{5}$.

The mixed number $3\frac{4}{5}$ can be converted to the improper fraction $\frac{19}{5}$ using the following procedure:

Converting a Mixed Number to an Improper Fraction

1. Multiply the denominator of the fraction by the natural number and add the numerator to this product.
2. Place the result from step 1 over the denominator of the original mixed number.

EXAMPLE 1 Converting from Mixed Number to Improper Fraction

Convert $3\frac{4}{5}$ to an improper fraction.

Solution

$$3\frac{4}{5} = \frac{5 \cdot 3 + 4}{5}$$

Multiply the denominator by the natural number and add the numerator.

Place the result over the mixed number's denominator.

$$= \frac{15 + 4}{5} = \frac{19}{5}$$

■

Great Question!

I'm a visual learner. How can I "see" that $3\frac{4}{5}$ and $\frac{19}{5}$ represent the same number?

Figure 3 illustrates that shading $3\frac{4}{5}$ circles is the same as shading $\frac{19}{5}$ of the circles.

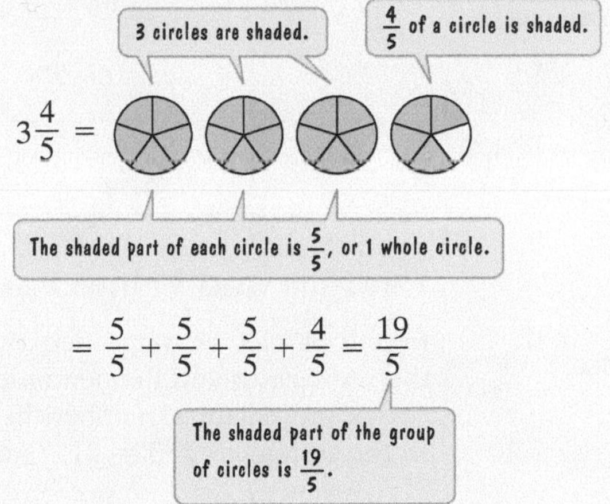

Figure 3 Supporting the conclusion that $3\frac{4}{5} = \frac{19}{5}$

✓ **CHECK POINT 1** Convert $2\frac{5}{8}$ to an improper fraction.

An **improper fraction** can be converted to a mixed number using the following procedure:

Converting an Improper Fraction to a Mixed Number

1. Divide the denominator into the numerator. Record the quotient (the result of the division) and the remainder.
2. Write the mixed number using the following form:

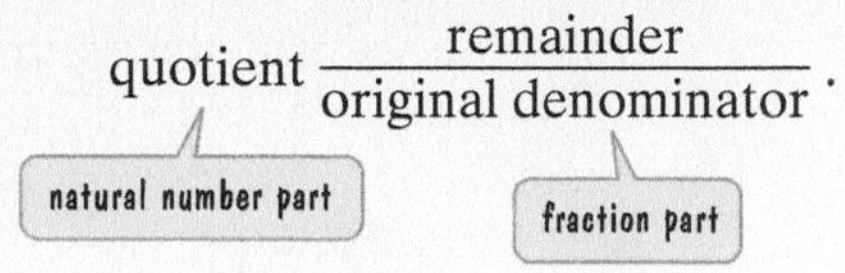

quotient $\dfrac{\text{remainder}}{\text{original denominator}}$.
natural number part
fraction part

EXAMPLE 2 Converting from Improper Fraction to Mixed Number

Convert $\frac{42}{5}$ to a mixed number.

Solution We use two steps to convert $\frac{42}{5}$ to a mixed number.

Step 1. Divide the denominator into the numerator.

$$5\overline{)42} = 8 \text{ (quotient)}, \quad 42 - 40 = 2 \text{ (remainder)}$$

Step 2. Write the mixed number using quotient $\dfrac{\textbf{remainder}}{\textbf{original denominator}}$. Thus,

$$\frac{42}{5} = 8\frac{2}{5}.$$

(quotient: 8; remainder: 2; original denominator: 5) ■

Great Question!

Should I express a fraction whose numerator is greater than its denominator as a mixed number or as an improper fraction?

In applied problems, answers are usually expressed as mixed numbers, which many people find more meaningful than improper fractions. Improper fractions are often easier to work with when performing operations with fractions.

✓ **CHECK POINT 2** Convert $\frac{5}{3}$ to a mixed number. 1

2 Write the prime factorization of a composite number.

Factors and Prime Factorizations

Fractions can be simplified by first factoring the natural numbers that make up the numerator and the denominator. To **factor** a natural number means to write it as two or more natural numbers being multiplied. For example, 21 can be factored as $7 \cdot 3$. In the statement $7 \cdot 3 = 21$, 7 and 3 are called the **factors** and 21 is the **product**.

$$7 \cdot 3 = 21$$

(7 is a factor of 21. 3 is a factor of 21. The product of 7 and 3 is 21.)

Are 7 and 3 the only factors of 21? The answer is no because 21 can also be factored as $1 \cdot 21$. Thus, 1 and 21 are also factors of 21. The factors of 21 are 1, 3, 7, and 21.

Unlike the number 21, some natural numbers have only two factors: the number itself and 1. For example, the number 7 has only two factors: 7 (the number itself) and 1. The only way to factor 7 is $1 \cdot 7$ or, equivalently, $7 \cdot 1$. For this reason, 7 is called a *prime number*.

Prime Numbers

A **prime number** is a natural number greater than 1 that has only itself and 1 as factors.

The first ten prime numbers are

$$2, 3, 5, 7, 11, 13, 17, 19, 23, \text{ and } 29.$$

Can you see why the natural number 15 is not in this list? In addition to having 15 and 1 as factors $(15 = 1 \cdot 15)$, it also has factors of 3 and $5 (15 = 3 \cdot 5)$. The number 15 is an example of a *composite number*.

Great Question!

Is 1 a prime number or a composite number?

It's neither. The number 1 is the only natural number that is neither a prime number nor a composite number.

Composite Numbers

A **composite number** is a natural number greater than 1 that is not a prime number.

Every composite number can be expressed as the product of prime numbers. For example, the composite number 45 can be expressed as

$$45 = 3 \cdot 3 \cdot 5.$$

This product contains only prime numbers: 3 and 5.

Expressing a composite number as the product of prime numbers is called the **prime factorization** of that composite number. The prime factorization of 45 is $3 \cdot 3 \cdot 5$. The order in which we write these factors does not matter. This means that

$$45 = 3 \cdot 3 \cdot 5 \quad \text{or} \quad 45 = 5 \cdot 3 \cdot 3 \quad \text{or} \quad 45 = 3 \cdot 5 \cdot 3.$$

To find the prime factorization of a composite number, begin by selecting any two numbers, excluding 1 and the number itself, whose product is the number to be factored. If one or both of the factors are not prime numbers, continue by factoring each composite number. Stop when all numbers in the factorization are prime.

EXAMPLE 3 Prime Factorization of a Composite Number

Find the prime factorization of 100.

Solution Begin by selecting any two numbers, excluding 1 and 100, whose product is 100. Here is one possibility:

$$100 = 4 \cdot 25.$$

Because the factors 4 and 25 are not prime, we factor each of these composite numbers.

$$100 = 4 \cdot 25 \qquad \text{This is our first factorization.}$$
$$= 2 \cdot 2 \cdot 5 \cdot 5 \qquad \text{Factor 4 and 25.}$$

Notice that 2 and 5 are both prime. The prime factorization of 100 is $2 \cdot 2 \cdot 5 \cdot 5$. ■

✓ **CHECK POINT 3** Find the prime factorization of 36.

3 Reduce or simplify fractions.

Reducing Fractions

Two fractions are **equivalent** if they represent the same value. Writing a fraction as an equivalent fraction with a smaller denominator is called **reducing a fraction.** A fraction is **reduced to its lowest terms** when the numerator and denominator have no common factors other than 1.

Figure 4

Look at the rectangle in **Figure 4**. Can you see that it is divided into 6 equal parts? Of these 6 parts, 4 of the parts are red. Thus, $\frac{4}{6}$ of the rectangle is red.

The rectangle in **Figure 4** is also divided into 3 equal stacks and 2 of the stacks are red. Thus, $\frac{2}{3}$ of the rectangle is red. Because both $\frac{4}{6}$ and $\frac{2}{3}$ of the rectangle are red, we can conclude that $\frac{4}{6}$ and $\frac{2}{3}$ are equivalent fractions.

How can we show that $\frac{4}{6} = \frac{2}{3}$ without using **Figure 4**? Prime factorizations of 4 and 6 play an important role in the process. So does the **Fundamental Principle of Fractions**.

Fundamental Principle of Fractions

In words: The value of a fraction does not change if both the numerator and the denominator are divided (or multiplied) by the same nonzero number.

In algebraic language: If $\frac{a}{b}$ is a fraction and c is a nonzero number, then

$$\frac{a \cdot c}{b \cdot c} = \frac{a}{b}.$$

We use prime factorizations and the Fundamental Principle to reduce $\frac{4}{6}$ to its lowest terms as follows:

$$\frac{4}{6} = \frac{2 \cdot 2}{3 \cdot 2} = \frac{2}{3}.$$

Write prime factorizations of 4 and 6.

Divide the numerator and the denominator by the common prime factor, 2.

Here is a procedure for writing a fraction in lowest terms:

Reducing a Fraction to Its Lowest Terms

1. Write the prime factorizations of the numerator and the denominator.
2. Divide the numerator and the denominator by the greatest common factor, the product of all factors common to both.

Division lines can be used to show dividing out common factors from a fraction's numerator and denominator:

$$\frac{4}{6} = \frac{2 \cdot \cancel{2}}{3 \cdot \cancel{2}} = \frac{2}{3}.$$

Great Question!

When can I divide out numbers that are common to a fraction's numerator and denominator?

When reducing a fraction to its lowest terms, only *factors* that are common to the numerator and the denominator can be divided out. **If you have not factored** and expressed the numerator and denominator in terms of multiplication, **do not divide out.**

Correct:

$$\frac{2 \cdot \cancel{2}}{3 \cdot \cancel{2}} = \frac{2}{3}$$

Incorrect:

$$\frac{2 + \cancel{2}}{3 + \cancel{2}} = \frac{2}{3}$$

Note that $\frac{2+2}{3+2} = \frac{4}{5}$, not $\frac{2}{3}$.

EXAMPLE 4 Reducing Fractions

Reduce each fraction to its lowest terms:

a. $\frac{6}{14}$ **b.** $\frac{15}{75}$ **c.** $\frac{25}{11}$ **d.** $\frac{11}{33}$.

Solution For each fraction, begin with the prime factorization of the numerator and the denominator.

a. $\frac{6}{14} = \frac{3 \cdot \cancel{2}}{7 \cdot \cancel{2}} = \frac{3}{7}$ 2 is the greatest common factor of 6 and 14. Divide the numerator and the denominator by 2.

Including 1 as a factor is helpful when all other factors can be divided out.

b. $\frac{15}{75} = \frac{3 \cdot 5}{3 \cdot 25} = \frac{1 \cdot \cancel{3} \cdot \cancel{5}}{\cancel{3} \cdot \cancel{5} \cdot 5} = \frac{1}{5}$ $3 \cdot 5$, or 15, is the greatest common factor of 15 and 75. Divide the numerator and the denominator by $3 \cdot 5$.

c. $\frac{25}{11} = \frac{5 \cdot 5}{1 \cdot 11}$

Because 25 and 11 share no common factor (other than 1), $\frac{25}{11}$ is already reduced to its lowest terms.

d. $\frac{11}{33} = \frac{1 \cdot \cancel{11}}{3 \cdot \cancel{11}} = \frac{1}{3}$ 11 is the greatest common factor of 11 and 33. Divide the numerator and denominator by 11. ■

When reducing fractions, it may not always be necessary to write prime factorizations. In some cases, you can use inspection to find the greatest common factor of the numerator and the denominator. For example, when reducing $\frac{15}{75}$, you can use 15 rather than $3 \cdot 5$:

$$\frac{15}{75} = \frac{1 \cdot \cancel{15}}{5 \cdot \cancel{15}} = \frac{1}{5}.$$

✓ **CHECK POINT 4** Reduce each fraction to its lowest terms:

a. $\frac{10}{15}$ **b.** $\frac{42}{24}$ **c.** $\frac{13}{15}$ **d.** $\frac{9}{45}$.

---

4 Multiply fractions.

Multiplying Fractions

The result of multiplying two fractions is called their **product**.

Multiplying Fractions

In words: The product of two or more fractions is the product of their numerators divided by the product of their denominators.

In algebraic language: If $\frac{a}{b}$ and $\frac{c}{d}$ are fractions, then

$$\frac{a}{b} \cdot \frac{c}{d} = \frac{a \cdot c}{b \cdot d}.$$

Here is an example that illustrates the rule in the previous box:

$$\frac{3}{8} \cdot \frac{5}{11} = \frac{3 \cdot 5}{8 \cdot 11} = \frac{15}{88}.$$

The product of $\frac{3}{8}$ and $\frac{5}{11}$ is $\frac{15}{88}$.

Multiply numerators and multiply denominators.

EXAMPLE 5 Multiplying Fractions

Multiply. If possible, reduce the product to its lowest terms:

a. $\frac{3}{7}\cdot\frac{2}{5}$ **b.** $5\cdot\frac{7}{12}$ **c.** $\frac{2}{3}\cdot\frac{9}{4}$ **d.** $\left(3\frac{2}{3}\right)\left(1\frac{1}{4}\right)$.

Solution

a. $\frac{3}{7}\cdot\frac{2}{5}=\frac{3\cdot 2}{7\cdot 5}=\frac{6}{35}$ Multiply numerators and multiply denominators.

b. $5\cdot\frac{7}{12}=\frac{5}{1}\cdot\frac{7}{12}=\frac{5\cdot 7}{1\cdot 12}=\frac{35}{12}$ or $2\frac{11}{12}$ Write 5 as $\frac{5}{1}$. Then multiply numerators and multiply denominators.

c. $\frac{2}{3}\cdot\frac{9}{4}=\frac{2\cdot 9}{3\cdot 4}=\frac{18}{12}=\frac{3\cdot\cancel{6}}{2\cdot\cancel{6}}=\frac{3}{2}$ or $1\frac{1}{2}$

Simplify $\frac{18}{12}$; 6 is the greatest common factor of 18 and 12.

d. $\left(3\frac{2}{3}\right)\left(1\frac{1}{4}\right)=\frac{11}{3}\cdot\frac{5}{4}=\frac{11\cdot 5}{3\cdot 4}=\frac{55}{12}$ or $4\frac{7}{12}$ ■

✓ **CHECK POINT 5** Multiply. If possible, reduce the product to its lowest terms:

a. $\frac{4}{11}\cdot\frac{2}{3}$ **b.** $6\cdot\frac{3}{5}$ **c.** $\frac{3}{7}\cdot\frac{2}{3}$ **d.** $\left(3\frac{2}{5}\right)\left(1\frac{1}{2}\right)$.

Great Question!

Can I divide numerators and denominators by common factors before I multiply fractions?

Yes, you can divide numerators and denominators by common factors before performing multiplication. Then multiply the remaining factors in the numerators and multiply the remaining factors in the denominators. For example,

$$\frac{7}{15}\cdot\frac{20}{21}=\frac{\cancel{7}\cdot 1}{\cancel{5}\cdot 3}\cdot\frac{\cancel{5}\cdot 4}{\cancel{7}\cdot 3}=\frac{1\cdot 4}{3\cdot 3}=\frac{4}{9}.$$

7 is the greatest common factor of 7 and 21.

5 is the greatest common factor of 15 and 20.

The divisions involving the common factors, 7 and 5, are often shown as follows:

$$\frac{7}{15}\cdot\frac{20}{21}=\frac{\overset{1}{\cancel{7}}}{\underset{3}{\cancel{15}}}\cdot\frac{\overset{4}{\cancel{20}}}{\underset{3}{\cancel{21}}}=\frac{1\cdot 4}{3\cdot 3}=\frac{4}{9}.$$

Divide by 7.

Divide by 5.

5 Divide fractions.

Dividing Fractions

The result of dividing two fractions is called their **quotient**. A geometric figure is useful for developing a process for determining the quotient of two fractions.

Consider the division

$$\frac{4}{5}\div\frac{1}{10}.$$

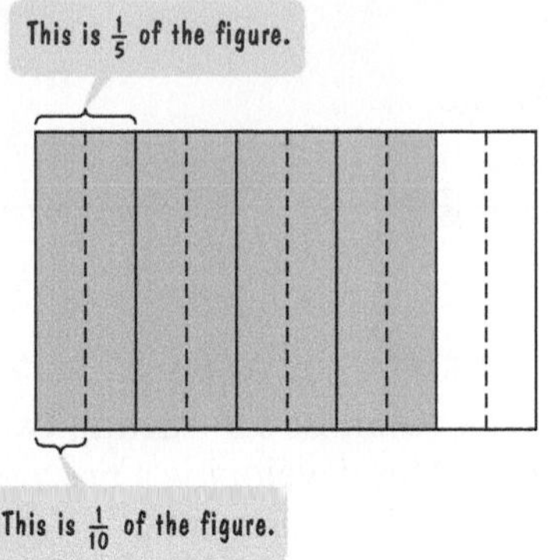
This is $\frac{1}{5}$ of the figure.
This is $\frac{1}{10}$ of the figure.

Figure 5

We want to know how many $\frac{1}{10}$'s are in $\frac{4}{5}$. We can use **Figure 5** to find this quotient. The rectangle is divided into fifths. The dashed lines further divide the rectangle into tenths.

Figure 5 shows that $\frac{4}{5}$ of the rectangle is red. How many $\frac{1}{10}$'s of the rectangle does this include? Can you see that this includes eight of the $\frac{1}{10}$ pieces? Thus, there are eight $\frac{1}{10}$'s in $\frac{4}{5}$:

$$\frac{4}{5} \div \frac{1}{10} = 8.$$

We can obtain the quotient 8 in the following way:

$$\frac{4}{5} \div \frac{1}{10} = \frac{4}{5} \cdot \frac{10}{1} = \frac{4 \cdot 10}{5 \cdot 1} = \frac{40}{5} = 8.$$

Change the division to multiplication.

Invert the divisor, $\frac{1}{10}$.

By inverting the divisor, $\frac{1}{10}$, and obtaining $\frac{10}{1}$, we are writing the divisor's *reciprocal*. Two fractions are **reciprocals** of each other if their product is 1. Thus, $\frac{1}{10}$ and $\frac{10}{1}$ are reciprocals because $\frac{1}{10} \cdot \frac{10}{1} = 1$.

Generalizing from the result above and using the word *reciprocal*, we obtain the following rule for dividing fractions:

Dividing Fractions

In words: The quotient of two fractions is the first fraction multiplied by the reciprocal of the second fraction.

In algebraic language: If $\frac{a}{b}$ and $\frac{c}{d}$ are fractions and $\frac{c}{d}$ is not 0, then

$$\frac{a}{b} \div \frac{c}{d} = \frac{a}{b} \cdot \frac{d}{c}.$$

Change division to multiplication.

Invert $\frac{c}{d}$ and write its reciprocal.

EXAMPLE 6 Dividing Fractions

a. $\frac{2}{3} \div \frac{7}{15}$ **b.** $\frac{3}{4} \div 5$ **c.** $4\frac{3}{4} \div 1\frac{1}{2}$.

Solution

a. $$\frac{2}{3} \div \frac{7}{15} = \frac{2}{3} \cdot \frac{15}{7} = \frac{2 \cdot 15}{3 \cdot 7} = \frac{30}{21} = \frac{10 \cdot \cancel{3}}{7 \cdot \cancel{3}} = \frac{10}{7} \text{ or } 1\frac{3}{7}$$

Change division to multiplication.

Invert $\frac{7}{15}$ and write its reciprocal.

Simplify: 3 is the greatest common factor of 30 and 21.

b. $$\frac{3}{4} \div 5 = \frac{3}{4} \div \frac{5}{1} = \frac{3}{4} \cdot \frac{1}{5} = \frac{3 \cdot 1}{4 \cdot 5} = \frac{3}{20}$$

Change division to multiplication.

Invert $\frac{5}{1}$ and write its reciprocal.

c. $$4\frac{3}{4} \div 1\frac{1}{2} = \frac{19}{4} \div \frac{3}{2} = \frac{19}{4} \cdot \frac{2}{3} = \frac{19 \cdot 2}{4 \cdot 3} = \frac{38}{12} = \frac{19 \cdot \cancel{2}}{6 \cdot \cancel{2}} = \frac{19}{6} \text{ or } 3\frac{1}{6}$$ ■

✓ CHECK POINT 6 Divide:

a. $\frac{5}{4} \div \frac{3}{8}$ b. $\frac{2}{3} \div 3$ c. $3\frac{3}{8} \div 2\frac{1}{4}$

6 Add and subtract fractions with identical denominators.

Adding and Subtracting Fractions with Identical Denominators

The result of adding two fractions is called their **sum**. The result of subtracting two fractions is called their **difference**. A geometric figure is useful for developing a process for determining the sum or difference of two fractions with identical denominators.

Consider the addition

$$\frac{3}{7} + \frac{2}{7}.$$

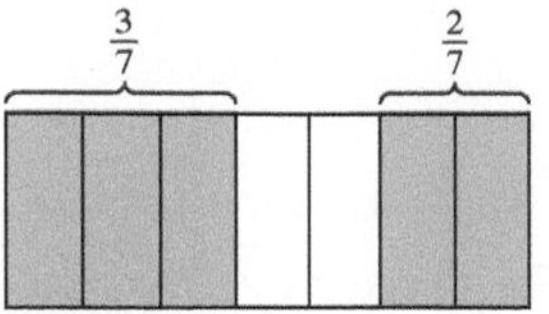

Figure 6

We can use **Figure 6** to find this sum. The rectangle is divided into sevenths. On the left, $\frac{3}{7}$ of the rectangle is red. On the right, $\frac{2}{7}$ of the rectangle is red. Including both the left and the right, a total of $\frac{5}{7}$ of the rectangle is red. Thus,

$$\frac{3}{7} + \frac{2}{7} = \frac{5}{7}.$$

We can obtain the sum $\frac{5}{7}$ in the following way:

$$\frac{3}{7} + \frac{2}{7} = \frac{3+2}{7} = \frac{5}{7}.$$

Add numerators and put this result over the common denominator.

Generalizing from this result gives us the following rule:

Adding and Subtracting Fractions with Identical Denominators

In words: The sum or difference of two fractions with identical denominators is the sum or difference of their numerators over the common denominator.

In algebraic language: If $\frac{a}{b}$ and $\frac{c}{b}$ are fractions, then

$$\frac{a}{b} + \frac{c}{b} = \frac{a+c}{b} \quad \text{and} \quad \frac{a}{b} - \frac{c}{b} = \frac{a-c}{b}.$$

EXAMPLE 7 Adding and Subtracting Fractions with Identical Denominators

Perform the indicated operations:

a. $\frac{3}{11} + \frac{4}{11}$ b. $\frac{11}{12} - \frac{5}{12}$ c. $5\frac{1}{4} - 2\frac{3}{4}$.

Solution

a. $\frac{3}{11} + \frac{4}{11} = \frac{3+4}{11} = \frac{7}{11}$

b. $\frac{11}{12} - \frac{5}{12} = \frac{11-5}{12} = \frac{6}{12} = \frac{1\cdot\cancel{6}}{2\cdot\cancel{6}} = \frac{1}{2}$

c. $5\frac{1}{4} - 2\frac{3}{4} = \frac{21}{4} - \frac{11}{4} = \frac{21-11}{4} = \frac{10}{4} = \frac{\cancel{2}\cdot 5}{\cancel{2}\cdot 2} = \frac{5}{2}$ or $2\frac{1}{2}$ ■

✓ **CHECK POINT 7** Perform the indicated operations:

a. $\frac{2}{11} + \frac{3}{11}$ **b.** $\frac{5}{6} - \frac{1}{6}$ **c.** $3\frac{3}{8} - 1\frac{1}{8}$.

---

7 Add and subtract fractions with unlike denominators.

Adding and Subtracting Fractions with Unlike Denominators

How do we add or subtract fractions with different denominators? We must first rewrite them as equivalent fractions with the same denominator. We do this by using the Fundamental Principle of Fractions: The value of a fraction does not change if the numerator and the denominator are multiplied by the same nonzero number. Thus, if $\frac{a}{b}$ is a fraction and c is a nonzero number, then

$$\frac{a}{b} = \frac{a \cdot c}{b \cdot c}.$$

EXAMPLE 8 Writing an Equivalent Fraction

Write $\frac{3}{4}$ as an equivalent fraction with a denominator of 16.

Solution To obtain a denominator of 16, we must multiply the denominator of the given fraction, $\frac{3}{4}$, by 4. So that we do not change the value of the fraction, we also multiply the numerator by 4.

$$\frac{3}{4} = \frac{3 \cdot 4}{4 \cdot 4} = \frac{12}{16}$$ ■

✓ **CHECK POINT 8** Write $\frac{2}{3}$ as an equivalent fraction with a denominator of 21.

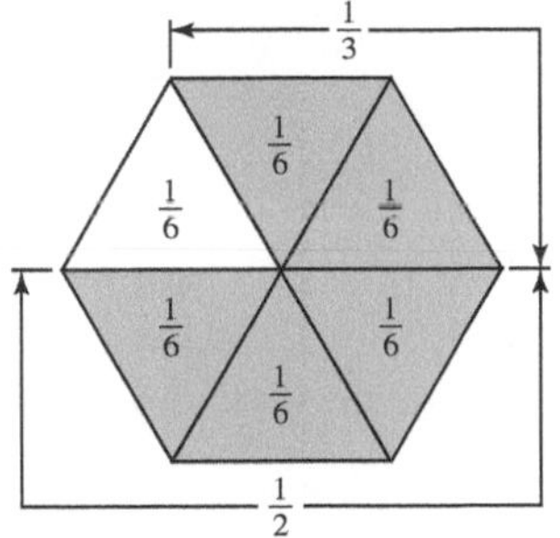

Figure 7 $\frac{1}{2} + \frac{1}{3} = \frac{5}{6}$

Equivalent fractions can be used to add fractions with different denominators, such as $\frac{1}{2}$ and $\frac{1}{3}$. **Figure 7** indicates that the sum of half the whole figure and one-third of the whole figure results in 5 parts out of 6, or $\frac{5}{6}$, of the figure. Thus,

$$\frac{1}{2} + \frac{1}{3} = \frac{5}{6}.$$

We can obtain the sum $\frac{5}{6}$ if we rewrite each fraction as an equivalent fraction with a denominator of 6.

$$\frac{1}{2} + \frac{1}{3} = \frac{1 \cdot 3}{2 \cdot 3} + \frac{1 \cdot 2}{3 \cdot 2}$$ Rewrite each fraction as an equivalent fraction with a denominator of 6.

$$= \frac{3}{6} + \frac{2}{6}$$ Perform the multiplications. We now have a common denominator.

$$= \frac{3 + 2}{6}$$ Add the numerators and place this sum over the common denominator.

$$= \frac{5}{6}$$ Perform the addition.

When adding $\frac{1}{2}$ and $\frac{1}{3}$, there are many common denominators that we can use, such as 6, 12, 18, and so on. The given denominators, 2 and 3, divide into all of these numbers. However, the denominator 6 is the smallest number that 2 and 3 divide into. For this reason, 6 is called the *least common denominator*, abbreviated LCD.

Adding and Subtracting Fractions with Unlike Denominators

1. Rewrite the fractions as equivalent fractions with the least common denominator.
2. Add or subtract the numerators, putting this result over the common denominator.

EXAMPLE 9 Adding and Subtracting Fractions with Unlike Denominators

Perform the indicated operation:

a. $\frac{1}{5} + \frac{3}{4}$ **b.** $\frac{3}{4} - \frac{1}{6}$ **c.** $2\frac{7}{15} - 1\frac{4}{5}$.

Solution

a. Just by looking at $\frac{1}{5} + \frac{3}{4}$, can you tell that the smallest number divisible by both 5 and 4 is 20? Thus, the least common denominator for the denominators 5 and 4 is 20. We rewrite both fractions as equivalent fractions with the least common denominator, 20.

$$\frac{1}{5} + \frac{3}{4} = \frac{1 \cdot 4}{5 \cdot 4} + \frac{3 \cdot 5}{4 \cdot 5}$$ To obtain denominators of 20, multiply the numerator and denominator of the first fraction by 4 and the second fraction by 5.

$$= \frac{4}{20} + \frac{15}{20}$$ Perform the multiplications.

$$= \frac{4 + 15}{20}$$ Add the numerators and put this sum over the least common denominator.

$$= \frac{19}{20}$$ Perform the addition.

Discover for Yourself

Try Example 9(a), $\frac{1}{5} + \frac{3}{4}$, using a common denominator of 40. Because both 5 and 4 divide into 40, 40 is a common denominator, although not the least common denominator. Describe what happens. What is the advantage of using the least common denominator?

b. By looking at $\frac{3}{4} - \frac{1}{6}$, can you tell that the smallest number divisible by both 4 and 6 is 12? Thus, the least common denominator for the denominators 4 and 6 is 12. We rewrite both fractions as equivalent fractions with the least common denominator, 12.

$$\frac{3}{4} - \frac{1}{6} = \frac{3 \cdot 3}{4 \cdot 3} - \frac{1 \cdot 2}{6 \cdot 2}$$ To obtain denominators of 12, multiply the numerator and denominator of the first fraction by 3 and the second fraction by 2.

$$= \frac{9}{12} - \frac{2}{12}$$ Perform the multiplications.

$$= \frac{9 - 2}{12}$$ Subtract the numerators and put this difference over the least common denominator.

$$= \frac{7}{12}$$ Perform the subtraction.

c. $2\frac{7}{15} - 1\frac{4}{5} = \frac{37}{15} - \frac{9}{5}$ Convert each mixed number to an improper fraction.

The smallest number divisible by both 15 and 5 is 15. Thus, the least common denominator for the denominators 15 and 5 is 15. Because the first fraction already has a denominator of 15, we only have to rewrite the second fraction.

$= \frac{37}{15} - \frac{9 \cdot 3}{5 \cdot 3}$ To obtain a denominator of 15, multiply the numerator and denominator of the second fraction by 3.

$= \frac{37}{15} - \frac{27}{15}$ Perform the multiplications.

$= \frac{37 - 27}{15}$ Subtract the numerators and put this difference over the common denominator.

$= \frac{10}{15}$ Perform the subtraction.

$= \frac{2 \cdot \cancel{5}}{3 \cdot \cancel{5}} = \frac{2}{3}$ Reduce to lowest terms. ■

✓ **CHECK POINT 9** Perform the indicated operation:

a. $\frac{1}{2} + \frac{3}{5}$ **b.** $\frac{4}{3} - \frac{3}{4}$ **c.** $3\frac{1}{6} - 1\frac{11}{12}$.

EXAMPLE 10 Using Prime Factorizations to Find the LCD

Perform the indicated operation: $\frac{1}{15} + \frac{7}{24}$.

Solution We need to find the least common denominator first. Using inspection, it is difficult to determine the smallest number divisible by both 15 and 24. We will use their prime factorizations to find the least common denominator:

$$15 = 5 \cdot 3 \qquad \text{and} \qquad 24 = 8 \cdot 3 = 2 \cdot 2 \cdot 2 \cdot 3.$$

The different prime factors are 5, 3, and 2. The least common denominator is obtained by using the greatest number of times each factor appears in any prime factorization. Because 5 and 3 appear as prime factors and 2 is a factor of 24 three times, the least common denominator is

$$5 \cdot 3 \cdot 2 \cdot 2 \cdot 2 = 5 \cdot 3 \cdot 8 = 120.$$

Now we can rewrite both fractions as equivalent fractions with the least common denominator, 120.

$\frac{1}{15} + \frac{7}{24} = \frac{1 \cdot 8}{15 \cdot 8} + \frac{7 \cdot 5}{24 \cdot 5}$ To obtain denominators of 120, multiply the numerator and denominator of the first fraction by 8 and the second fraction by 5.

$= \frac{8}{120} + \frac{35}{120}$ Perform the multiplications.

$= \frac{8 + 35}{120}$ Add the numerators and put this sum over the least common denominator.

$= \frac{43}{120}$ Perform the addition. ■

Great Question!

I see that least common denominators are used to add and subtract fractions with unlike denominators. Is it ever necessary to use least common denominators when multiplying or dividing fractions?

No. You do not need least common denominators to multiply or divide fractions.

✓ **CHECK POINT 10** Perform the indicated operation: $\frac{3}{10} + \frac{7}{12}$.

---

8 Solve problems involving fractions in algebra.

Fractions in Algebra

Fractions appear throughout algebra. Operations with fractions can be used to determine whether a particular fraction is a solution of an equation.

EXAMPLE 11 Determining Whether Fractions Are Solutions of Equations

Determine whether the given number is a solution of the equation.

a. $x + \frac{1}{4}x = 7; 6\frac{2}{5}$ **b.** $\frac{1}{7} - w = \frac{1}{2}w; \frac{2}{21}$

Solution

a. To determine whether $6\frac{2}{5}$ is a solution of $x + \frac{1}{4}x = 7$, we begin by converting $6\frac{2}{5}$ from a mixed number to an improper fraction.

$$6\frac{2}{5} = \frac{5 \cdot 6 + 2}{5} = \frac{30 + 2}{5} = \frac{32}{5}$$

Now we substitute $\frac{32}{5}$ for x.

$$x + \frac{1}{4}x = 7$$ This is the given equation.

Is $\frac{32}{5}$ a solution?

$$\frac{32}{5} + \frac{1}{4} \cdot \frac{32}{5} \stackrel{?}{=} 7$$ Substitute $\frac{32}{5}$ for x.

$$\frac{32}{5} + \frac{8}{5} \stackrel{?}{=} 7$$ Multiply: $\frac{1}{\not{4}_1} \cdot \frac{\not{32}^8}{5} = \frac{1 \cdot 8}{5} = \frac{8}{5}$.

$$\frac{40}{5} \stackrel{?}{=} 7$$ Add: $\frac{32}{5} + \frac{8}{5} = \frac{32 + 8}{5} = \frac{40}{5}$.

This statement is false.

$$8 = 7$$ Simplify: $\frac{40}{5} = 8$.

Because the values on both sides of the equation are not the same, the fraction $\frac{32}{5}$, or equivalently $6\frac{2}{5}$, is not a solution of the equation.

b.

$$\frac{1}{7} - w = \frac{1}{2}w$$ This is the given equation.

Is $\frac{2}{21}$ a solution?

$$\frac{1}{7} - \frac{2}{21} \stackrel{?}{=} \frac{1}{2} \cdot \frac{2}{21}$$ Substitute $\frac{2}{21}$ for w.

$$\frac{1}{7} - \frac{2}{21} \stackrel{?}{=} \frac{1}{21}$$ Multiply: $\frac{1}{\not{2}_1} \cdot \frac{\not{2}^1}{21} = \frac{1 \cdot 1}{1 \cdot 21} = \frac{1}{21}$.

$$\frac{1 \cdot 3}{7 \cdot 3} - \frac{2}{21} \stackrel{?}{=} \frac{1}{21}$$ Turn to the subtraction. The LCD is 21, so multiply the numerator and denominator of the first fraction by 3.

$$\frac{3}{21} - \frac{2}{21} \stackrel{?}{=} \frac{1}{21}$$ Perform the multiplications.

This statement is true.

$$\frac{1}{21} = \frac{1}{21}$$ Subtract: $\frac{3}{21} - \frac{2}{21} = \frac{3 - 2}{21} = \frac{1}{21}$.

Because the values on both sides of the equation are the same, the fraction $\frac{2}{21}$ is a solution of the equation. ■

✓ **CHECK POINT 11** Determine whether the given number is a solution of the equation.

a. $x - \frac{2}{9}x = 1; 1\frac{2}{7}$ **b.** $\frac{1}{5} - w = \frac{1}{3}w; \frac{3}{20}$

In Section 1, we translated phrases into algebraic expressions and sentences into equations. When these phrases and sentences involve fractions, the word *of* frequently appears. **When used with fractions, the word *of* represents multiplication.** For example, the phrase "$\frac{2}{5}$ of a number" can be represented by the algebraic expression $\frac{2}{5} \cdot x$, or $\frac{2}{5}x$.

EXAMPLE 12 Algebraic Representations of Phrases and Sentences with Fractions

Translate from English to an algebraic expression or equation, whichever is appropriate. Let the variable x represent the number.

a. $\frac{1}{3}$ of a number increased by 5 is half of that number.

b. $\frac{1}{4}$ of a number, decreased by 7

Solution Part (a) is a sentence, so we will translate into an equation. Part (b) is a phrase, so we will translate into an algebraic expression.

a.

$\frac{1}{3}$	of	a number increased by 5	is	half	of	that number.
$\frac{1}{3}$	$\cdot$	$(x + 5)$	$=$	$\frac{1}{2}$	$\cdot$	x

The equation for "$\frac{1}{3}$ of a number increased by 5 is half of that number" is $\frac{1}{3}(x + 5) = \frac{1}{2}x$.

b.

$\frac{1}{4}$	of	a number,	decreased by 7
$\frac{1}{4}$	$\cdot$	x	$- \; 7$

The algebraic expression for "$\frac{1}{4}$ of a number, decreased by 7" is $\frac{1}{4}x - 7$. ■

✓ **CHECK POINT 12** Translate from English to an algebraic expression or equation, whichever is appropriate. Let the variable x represent the number.

a. $\frac{2}{3}$ of a number decreased by 6

b. $\frac{3}{4}$ of a number, decreased by 2, is $\frac{1}{5}$ of that number.

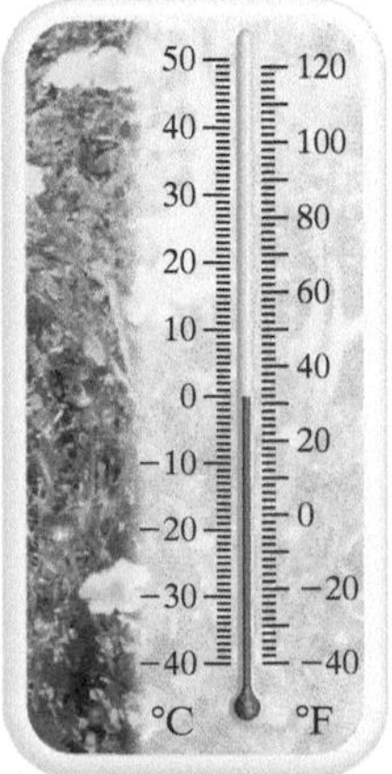

Figure 8 The Celsius scale is on the left and the Fahrenheit scale is on the right.

Many formulas and mathematical models contain fractions. For example, consider temperatures on the Celsius scale and on the Fahrenheit scale, as shown in **Figure 8**. The formula $C = \frac{5}{9}(F - 32)$ expresses the relationship between Fahrenheit temperature, F, and Celsius temperature, C.

The Formula	What the Formula Tells Us
$C = \frac{5}{9}(F - 32)$	If 32 is subtracted from the Fahrenheit temperature, $F - 32$, and this difference is multiplied by $\frac{5}{9}$, the resulting product, $\frac{5}{9}(F - 32)$, gives the Celsius temperature.

EXAMPLE 13 Evaluating a Formula Containing a Fraction

The temperature on a warm summer day is 86°F. Use the formula $C = \frac{5}{9}(F - 32)$ to find the equivalent temperature on the Celsius scale.

Solution Because the temperature is 86°F, we substitute 86 for F in the given formula. Then we determine the value of C.

$$C = \frac{5}{9}(F - 32)$$ This is the given formula.

$$C = \frac{5}{9}(86 - 32)$$ Replace F with 86.

$$C = \frac{5}{9}(54)$$ Work inside parentheses first: $86 - 32 = 54$.

$$C = 30$$ Multiply: $\frac{5}{9}(54) = \frac{5}{\cancel{9}_1} \cdot \frac{\cancel{54}^6}{1} = \frac{5 \cdot 6}{1 \cdot 1} = \frac{30}{1} = 30$.

Thus, 86°F is equivalent to 30°C. ■

✓ **CHECK POINT 13** The temperature on a warm spring day is 77°F. Use the formula $C = \frac{5}{9}(F - 32)$ to find the equivalent temperature on the Celsius scale.

CONCEPT AND VOCABULARY CHECK

Fill in each blank so that the resulting statement is true.

1. In the fraction $\frac{2}{5}$, the number 2 is called the ____________ and the number 5 is called the ____________.
2. The number $3\frac{2}{5}$ is called a/an ____________ number and the number $\frac{17}{5}$ is called a/an ____________ fraction.
3. The number $3\frac{2}{5}$ can be converted to $\frac{17}{5}$ by multiplying ____________ and ____________, adding ____________, and placing the result over ____________.
4. The numbers that we use for counting (1, 2, 3, 4, 5, . . .) are called ____________ numbers.
5. Among the numbers 1, 2, 3, 4, 5, . . . , a number greater than 1 that has only itself and 1 as factors is called a/an ____________ number.
6. In $7 \cdot 5 = 35$, the numbers 7 and 5 are called ____________ of 35 and the number 35 is called the ____________ of 7 and 5.
7. If $\frac{a}{b}$ is a fraction and c is a nonzero number, then $\frac{a \cdot c}{b \cdot c} =$ ____________.
8. If $\frac{a}{b}$ and $\frac{c}{d}$ are fractions, then $\frac{a}{b} \cdot \frac{c}{d} =$ ____________.
9. Two fractions whose product is 1, such as $\frac{2}{3}$ and $\frac{3}{2}$, are called ____________ of each other.
10. If $\frac{a}{b}$ and $\frac{c}{d}$ are fractions and $\frac{c}{d}$ is not 0, then $\frac{a}{b} \div \frac{c}{d} = \frac{a}{b} \cdot$ ____________.
11. If $\frac{a}{b}$ and $\frac{c}{b}$ are fractions, then $\frac{a}{b} + \frac{c}{b} =$ ____________.
12. In order to add $\frac{1}{5}$ and $\frac{3}{4}$, we use 20 as the ____________.

2 EXERCISE SET

MyMathLab®

Watch the videos in MyMathLab

Download the MyDashBoard App

Practice Exercises

In Exercises 1–6, convert each mixed number to an improper fraction.

1. $2\frac{3}{8}$ **2.** $2\frac{7}{9}$ **3.** $7\frac{3}{5}$

4. $6\frac{2}{5}$ **5.** $8\frac{7}{16}$ **6.** $9\frac{5}{16}$

In Exercises 7–12, convert each improper fraction to a mixed number.

7. $\frac{23}{5}$ **8.** $\frac{47}{8}$ **9.** $\frac{76}{9}$

10. $\frac{59}{9}$ **11.** $\frac{711}{20}$ **12.** $\frac{788}{25}$

In Exercises 13–28, identify each natural number as prime or composite. If the number is composite, find its prime factorization.

13. 22 **14.** 15 **15.** 20

16. 75 **17.** 37 **18.** 23

19. 36 **20.** 100 **21.** 140

22. 110 **23.** 79 **24.** 83

25. 81 **26.** 64

27. 240 **28.** 360

In Exercises 29–40, simplify each fraction by reducing it to its lowest terms.

29. $\frac{10}{16}$ **30.** $\frac{8}{14}$ **31.** $\frac{15}{18}$ **32.** $\frac{18}{45}$

33. $\frac{35}{50}$ **34.** $\frac{45}{50}$ **35.** $\frac{32}{80}$ **36.** $\frac{75}{80}$

37. $\frac{44}{50}$ **38.** $\frac{38}{50}$ **39.** $\frac{120}{86}$ **40.** $\frac{116}{86}$

In Exercises 41–90, perform the indicated operation. Where possible, reduce the answer to its lowest terms.

41. $\frac{2}{5}\cdot\frac{1}{3}$ **42.** $\frac{3}{7}\cdot\frac{1}{4}$ **43.** $\frac{3}{8}\cdot\frac{7}{11}$

44. $\frac{5}{8}\cdot\frac{3}{11}$ **45.** $9\cdot\frac{4}{7}$ **46.** $8\cdot\frac{3}{7}$

47. $\frac{1}{10}\cdot\frac{5}{6}$ **48.** $\frac{1}{8}\cdot\frac{2}{3}$ **49.** $\frac{5}{4}\cdot\frac{6}{7}$

50. $\frac{7}{4}\cdot\frac{6}{11}$ **51.** $\left(3\frac{3}{4}\right)\left(1\frac{3}{5}\right)$

52. $\left(2\frac{4}{5}\right)\left(1\frac{1}{4}\right)$ **53.** $\frac{5}{4}\div\frac{4}{3}$

54. $\frac{7}{8}\div\frac{2}{3}$ **55.** $\frac{18}{5}\div 2$ **56.** $\frac{12}{7}\div 3$

57. $2\div\frac{18}{5}$ **58.** $3\div\frac{12}{7}$ **59.** $\frac{3}{4}\div\frac{1}{4}$

60. $\frac{3}{7}\div\frac{1}{7}$ **61.** $\frac{7}{6}\div\frac{5}{3}$ **62.** $\frac{7}{4}\div\frac{3}{8}$

63. $\frac{1}{14}\div\frac{1}{7}$ **64.** $\frac{1}{8}\div\frac{1}{4}$ **65.** $6\frac{3}{5}\div 1\frac{1}{10}$

66. $1\frac{3}{4}\div 2\frac{5}{8}$ **67.** $\frac{2}{11}+\frac{4}{11}$ **68.** $\frac{5}{13}+\frac{2}{13}$

69. $\frac{7}{12}+\frac{1}{12}$ **70.** $\frac{5}{16}+\frac{1}{16}$ **71.** $\frac{5}{8}+\frac{5}{8}$

72. $\frac{3}{8}+\frac{3}{8}$ **73.** $\frac{7}{12}-\frac{5}{12}$ **74.** $\frac{13}{18}-\frac{5}{18}$

75. $\frac{16}{7}-\frac{2}{7}$ **76.** $\frac{17}{5}-\frac{2}{5}$ **77.** $\frac{1}{2}+\frac{1}{5}$

78. $\frac{1}{3}+\frac{1}{5}$ **79.** $\frac{3}{4}+\frac{3}{20}$ **80.** $\frac{2}{5}+\frac{2}{15}$

81. $\frac{3}{8}+\frac{5}{12}$ **82.** $\frac{3}{10}+\frac{2}{15}$ **83.** $\frac{11}{18}-\frac{2}{9}$

84. $\frac{17}{18}-\frac{4}{9}$ **85.** $\frac{4}{3}-\frac{3}{4}$ **86.** $\frac{3}{2}-\frac{2}{3}$

87. $\frac{7}{10}-\frac{3}{16}$ **88.** $\frac{7}{30}-\frac{5}{24}$

89. $3\frac{3}{4}-2\frac{1}{3}$ **90.** $3\frac{2}{3}-2\frac{1}{2}$

In Exercises 91–102, determine whether the given number is a solution of the equation.

91. $\frac{7}{2}x = 28; 8$ **92.** $\frac{5}{3}x = 30; 18$

93. $w - \frac{2}{3} = \frac{3}{4}; 1\frac{5}{12}$

94. $w - \frac{3}{4} = \frac{7}{4}; 2\frac{1}{2}$

95. $20 - \frac{1}{3}z = \frac{1}{2}z; 12$

96. $12 - \frac{1}{4}z = \frac{1}{2}z; 20$

97. $\frac{2}{9}y + \frac{1}{3}y = \frac{3}{7}; \frac{27}{35}$

98. $\frac{2}{3}y + \frac{5}{6}y = 2; 1\frac{1}{3}$

99. $\frac{1}{3}(x-2) = \frac{1}{5}(x+4) + 3; 26$

100. $\frac{1}{2}(x-2) + 3 = \frac{3}{8}(3x-4); 4$

101. $(y \div 6) + \frac{2}{3} = (y \div 2) - \frac{7}{9}; 4\frac{1}{3}$

102. $(y \div 6) + \frac{1}{3} = (y \div 2) - \frac{5}{9}; 2\frac{2}{3}$

In Exercises 103–114, translate from English to an algebraic expression or equation, whichever is appropriate. Let the variable x represent the number.

103. $\frac{1}{5}$ of a number

104. $\frac{1}{6}$ of a number

105. A number decreased by $\frac{1}{4}$ of itself

106. A number decreased by $\frac{1}{3}$ of itself

107. A number decreased by $\frac{1}{4}$ is half of that number.

108. A number decreased by $\frac{1}{3}$ is half of that number.

109. The sum of $\frac{1}{7}$ of a number and $\frac{1}{8}$ of that number gives 12.

110. The sum of $\frac{1}{9}$ of a number and $\frac{1}{10}$ of that number gives 15.

111. The product of $\frac{2}{3}$ and a number increased by 6

112. The product of $\frac{3}{4}$ and a number increased by 9

113. The product of $\frac{2}{3}$ and a number, increased by 6, is 3 less than the number.

114. The product of $\frac{3}{4}$ and a number, increased by 9, is 2 less than the number.

Practice PLUS

In Exercises 115–118, perform the indicated operation. Write the answer as an algebraic expression.

115. $\frac{3}{4} \cdot \frac{a}{5}$

116. $\frac{2}{3} \div \frac{a}{7}$

117. $\frac{11}{x} + \frac{9}{x}$

118. $\frac{10}{y} - \frac{6}{y}$

In Exercises 119–120, perform the indicated operations. Begin by performing operations in parentheses.

119. $\left(\frac{1}{2} - \frac{1}{3}\right) \div \frac{5}{8}$

120. $\left(\frac{1}{2} + \frac{1}{4}\right) \div \left(\frac{1}{2} + \frac{1}{3}\right)$

In Exercises 121–122, determine whether the given number is a solution of the equation.

121. $\frac{1}{5}(x + 2) = \frac{1}{2}\left(x - \frac{1}{5}\right); \frac{5}{8}$

122. $12 - 3(x - 2) = 4x - (x + 3); 3\frac{1}{2}$

Application Exercises

The formula

$$C = \frac{5}{9}(F - 32)$$

expresses the relationship between Fahrenheit temperature, F, and Celsius temperature, C. In Exercises 123–124, use the formula to convert the given Fahrenheit temperature to its equivalent temperature on the Celsius scale.

123. 68°F

124. 41°F

The maximum heart rate, in beats per minute, that you should achieve during exercise is 220 minus your age:

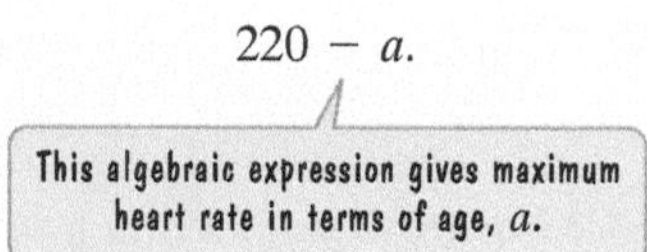

220 − a.
This algebraic expression gives maximum heart rate in terms of age, a.

The bar graph shows the target heart rate ranges for four types of exercise goals. The lower and upper limits of these ranges are fractions of the maximum heart rate, 220 − a. Exercises 125–128 are based on the information in the graph.

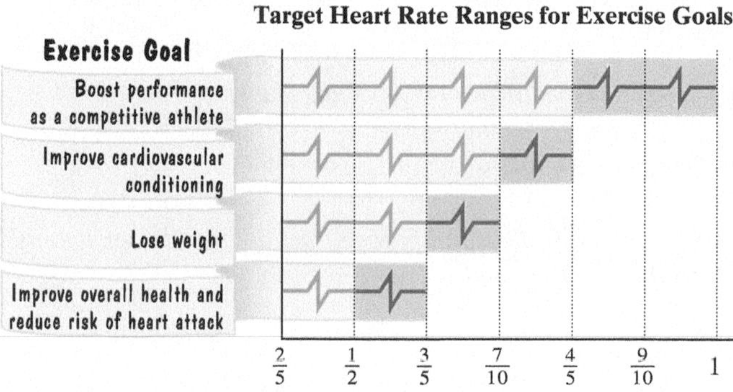

125. If your exercise goal is to improve cardiovascular conditioning, the graph shows the following range for target heart rate, H, in beats per minute:

Lower limit of range: $H = \frac{7}{10}(220 - a)$

Upper limit of range: $H = \frac{4}{5}(220 - a).$

a. What is the lower limit of the heart range, in beats per minute, for a 20-year-old with this exercise goal?

b. What is the upper limit of the heart range, in beats per minute, for a 20-year-old with this exercise goal?

126. If your exercise goal is to improve overall health, the graph on the previous page shows the following range for target heart rate, H, in beats per minute:

Lower limit of range $H = \frac{1}{2}(220 - a)$

Upper limit of range $H = \frac{3}{5}(220 - a).$

a. What is the lower limit of the heart range, in beats per minute, for a 30-year-old with this exercise goal?

b. What is the upper limit of the heart range, in beats per minute, for a 30-year-old with this exercise goal?

127. a. Write a formula that models the heart rate, H, in beats per minute, for a person who is a years old and would like to achieve $\frac{9}{10}$ of maximum heart rate during exercise.

b. Use your formula from part (a) to find the heart rate during exercise for a 40-year-old with this goal.

128. a. Write a formula that models the heart rate, H, in beats per minute, for a person who is a years old and would like to achieve $\frac{7}{8}$ of maximum heart rate during exercise.

b. Use your formula from part (a) to find the heart rate during exercise for a 20-year-old with this goal.

Making a list and trimming it twice. *The graph shows the average number of holiday presents bought by U.S. shoppers from 2007 through 2010.*

Source: Deloitte's 25th Annual Holiday Survey, © 2010 Deloitte Development LLC

Here is a mathematical model that approximates the data displayed by the bar graph:

$$P = 23\tfrac{1}{5} - 2\tfrac{1}{5}n.$$

Average number of holiday presents (P); Number of years after 2007 (n)

Use the formula at the bottom of the previous column to solve Exercises 129–130.

129. Use the formula to find the average number of holiday presents bought by U.S. shoppers in 2008. Does the mathematical model underestimate or overestimate the actual number shown in the bar graph for 2008? By how much?

130. Use the formula to find the average number of holiday presents bought by U.S. shoppers in 2010. Does the mathematical model underestimate or overestimate the actual number shown in the bar graph for 2010? By how much?

Writing in Mathematics

131. Explain how to convert a mixed number to an improper fraction and give an example.

132. Explain how to convert an improper fraction to a mixed number and give an example.

133. Describe the difference between a prime number and a composite number.

134. What is meant by the prime factorization of a composite number?

135. What is the Fundamental Principle of Fractions?

136. Explain how to reduce a fraction to its lowest terms. Give an example with your explanation.

137. Explain how to multiply fractions and give an example.

138. Explain how to divide fractions and give an example.

139. Describe how to add or subtract fractions with identical denominators. Provide an example with your description.

140. Explain how to add fractions with different denominators. Use $\frac{5}{6} + \frac{1}{2}$ as an example.

Critical Thinking Exercises

Make Sense? *In Exercises 141–144, determine whether each statement "makes sense" or "does not make sense" and explain your reasoning.*

141. I find it easier to multiply $\frac{1}{5}$ and $\frac{3}{4}$ than to add them.

142. Fractions frustrated me in arithmetic, so I'm glad I won't have to use them in algebra.

143. I need to be able to perform operations with fractions to determine whether $\frac{3}{2}$ is a solution of $8x = 12\left(x - \frac{1}{2}\right)$.

144. I saved money by buying a computer for $\frac{3}{2}$ of its original price.

In Exercises 145–148, determine whether each statement is true or false. If the statement is false, make the necessary change(s) to produce a true statement.

145. $\frac{1}{2} + \frac{1}{5} = \frac{2}{7}$

146. $\frac{1}{2} \div 4 = 2$

147. Every fraction has infinitely many equivalent fractions.

148. $\frac{3+7}{30} = \frac{\overset{1}{\cancel{3}}+7}{\underset{10}{\cancel{30}}} = \frac{8}{10} = \frac{4}{5}$

149. Shown below is a short excerpt from "The Star-Spangled Banner." The time is $\frac{3}{4}$, which means that each measure must contain notes that add up to $\frac{3}{4}$. The values of the different notes tell musicians how long to hold each note.

𝅝 = 1 𝅗𝅥 = $\frac{1}{2}$ ♩ = $\frac{1}{4}$ ♪ = $\frac{1}{8}$

Use vertical lines to divide this line of "The Star-Spangled Banner" into measures.

say does that Star-span-gled Ban-ner yet wave O'er the

Preview Exercises

Exercises 150–152 will help you prepare for the material covered in the next section. Consider the following "infinite ruler" that shows numbers that lie to the left and to the right of zero.

(c) (b) (a)

−5 −4 −3 −2 −1 0 1 2 3 4 5

150. What number is represented by point (a)?

151. What number is represented by point (b)? Express the number as an improper fraction.

152. What number is represented by point (c)?

SECTION 3

The Real Numbers

Objectives

1. Define the sets that make up the real numbers.
2. Graph numbers on a number line.
3. Express rational numbers as decimals.
4. Classify numbers as belonging to one or more sets of the real numbers.
5. Understand and use inequality symbols.
6. Find the absolute value of a real number.

The United Nations Building in New York was designed to represent its mission of promoting world harmony. Viewed from the front, the building looks like three rectangles stacked upon each other. In each rectangle, the ratio of the width to height is $\sqrt{5} + 1$ to 2, approximately 1.618 to 1. The ancient Greeks believed that such a rectangle, called a **golden rectangle**, was the most visually pleasing of all rectangles.

The ratio 1.618 to 1 is approximate because $\sqrt{5}$ is an irrational number, a special kind of real number. Irrational? Real? Let's make sense of all this by describing the kinds of numbers you will encounter in this course.

The U.N. building is designed with three golden rectangles.

Alan Schein/Alamy

1 Define the sets that make up the real numbers.

Natural Numbers and Whole Numbers

Before we describe the set of real numbers, let's be sure you are familiar with some basic ideas about sets. A **set** is a collection of objects whose contents can be clearly determined. The objects in a set are called the **elements** of the set. For example, the set of numbers used for counting can be represented by

$$\{1, 2, 3, 4, 5, \ldots\}.$$

The braces, $\{\ \}$, indicate that we are representing a set. This form of representing a set uses commas to separate the elements of the set. Remember that the three dots after the 5 indicate that there is no final element and that the listing goes on forever.

We have seen that the set of numbers used for counting is called the set of **natural numbers**. When we combine the number 0 with the natural numbers, we obtain the set of **whole numbers**.

Natural Numbers and Whole Numbers

The set of **natural numbers** is $\{1, 2, 3, 4, 5, \ldots\}$.

The set of **whole numbers** is $\{0, 1, 2, 3, 4, 5, \ldots\}$.

Integers and the Number Line

The whole numbers do not allow us to describe certain everyday situations. For example, if the balance in your checking account is \$30 and you write a check for \$35, your checking account is overdrawn by \$5. We can write this as −5, read *negative* 5. The set consisting of the natural numbers, 0, and the negatives of the natural numbers is called the set of **integers**.

Integers

The set of **integers** is

$$\{\underbrace{\ldots, -4, -3, -2, -1,}_{\text{Negative integers}}\ 0,\ \underbrace{1, 2, 3, 4. \ldots}_{\text{Positive integers}}\}.$$

Notice that the term **positive integers** is another name for the natural numbers. The positive integers can be written in two ways:

1. Use a "+" sign. For example, +4 is "positive four."
2. Do not write any sign. For example, 4 is assumed to be "positive four."

EXAMPLE 1 Practical Examples of Negative Integers

Write a negative integer that describes each of the following situations:

a. A debt of \$10
b. The shore surrounding the Dead Sea is 1312 feet below sea level.

Solution

a. A debt of \$10 can be expressed by the negative integer −10 (negative ten).
b. The shore surrounding the Dead Sea is 1312 feet below sea level, expressed as −1312. ■

✓ CHECK POINT 1 Write a negative integer that describes each of the following situations:

a. A debt of $500

b. Death Valley, the lowest point in North America, is 282 feet below sea level.

---

2 Graph numbers on a number line.

The **number line** is a graph we use to visualize the set of integers, as well as other sets of numbers. The number line is shown in **Figure 9**.

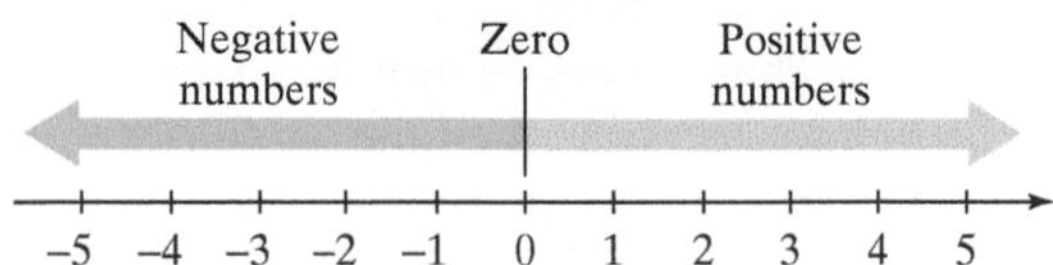

Figure 9 The number line

The number line extends indefinitely in both directions. Zero separates the positive numbers from the negative numbers on the number line. The positive integers are located to the right of 0, and the negative integers are located to the left of 0. Zero is neither positive nor negative. For every positive integer on a number line, there is a corresponding negative integer on the opposite side of 0.

Integers are graphed on a number line by placing a dot at the correct location for each number.

EXAMPLE 2 Graphing Integers on a Number Line

Graph:

a. -3 **b.** 4 **c.** 0.

Solution Place a dot at the correct location for each integer.

(a) (c) (b)

−5 −4 −3 −2 −1 0 1 2 3 4 5 ■

✓ CHECK POINT 2 Graph: **a.** -4 **b.** 0 **c.** 3.

Rational Numbers

If two integers are added, subtracted, or multiplied, the result is always another integer. This, however, is not always the case with division. For example, 10 divided by 5 is the integer 2. By contrast, 5 divided by 10 is $\frac{1}{2}$, and $\frac{1}{2}$ is not an integer. To permit divisions such as $\frac{5}{10}$, we enlarge the set of integers, calling the new collection the *rational numbers*. The set of **rational numbers** consists of all the numbers that can be expressed as a quotient of two integers, with the denominator not 0.

The Rational Numbers

The set of **rational numbers** is the set of all numbers that can be expressed in the form $\frac{a}{b}$, where a and b are integers and b is not equal to 0, written $b \neq 0$. The integer a is called the **numerator** and the integer b is called the **denominator**.

Great Question!

Is there another way to express the rational number $\frac{-3}{4}$?

In Section 7, you will learn that a negative number divided by a positive number gives a negative result. Thus, $\frac{-3}{4}$ can also be written as $-\frac{3}{4}$.

Here are two examples of rational numbers:

- $\frac{1}{2}$ — $a = 1$, $b = 2$
- $\frac{-3}{4}$ — $a = -3$, $b = 4$

Is the integer 5 another example of a rational number? Yes. The integer 5 can be written with a denominator of 1.

$$5 = \frac{5}{1}$$ ($a = 5$, $b = 1$)

All integers are also rational numbers because they can be written with a denominator of 1.

How can we express a negative mixed number, such as $-2\frac{3}{4}$, in the form $\frac{a}{b}$? Copy the negative sign and then follow the procedure discussed in the previous section:

$$-2\frac{3}{4} = -\frac{4 \cdot 2 + 3}{4} = -\frac{8 + 3}{4} = -\frac{11}{4} = \frac{-11}{4}.$$ ($a = -11$, $b = 4$)

Copy the negative sign from step to step and convert $2\frac{3}{4}$ to an improper fraction.

Rational numbers are graphed on a number line by placing a dot at the correct location for each number.

EXAMPLE 3 Graphing Rational Numbers on a Number Line

Graph: **a.** $\frac{7}{2}$ **b.** -4.6.

Solution Place a dot at the correct location for each rational number.

a. Because $\frac{7}{2} = 3\frac{1}{2}$, its graph is midway between 3 and 4.

b. Because $-4.6 = -4\frac{6}{10}$, its graph is $\frac{6}{10}$, or $\frac{3}{5}$, of a unit to the left of -4.

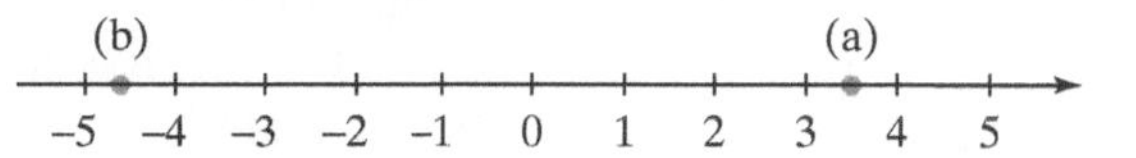

■

✓ **CHECK POINT 3** Graph: **a.** $\frac{9}{2}$ **b.** -1.2.

---

3 Express rational numbers as decimals.

Every rational number can be expressed as a fraction and as a decimal. To express the fraction $\frac{a}{b}$ as a decimal, divide the denominator, b, into the numerator, a.

Using Technology

Calculators and Decimals

Given a rational number, $\frac{a}{b}$, you can express it as a decimal by entering

a ÷ b

into a calculator. In the case of a repeating decimal, the calculator rounds off in the final decimal place displayed.

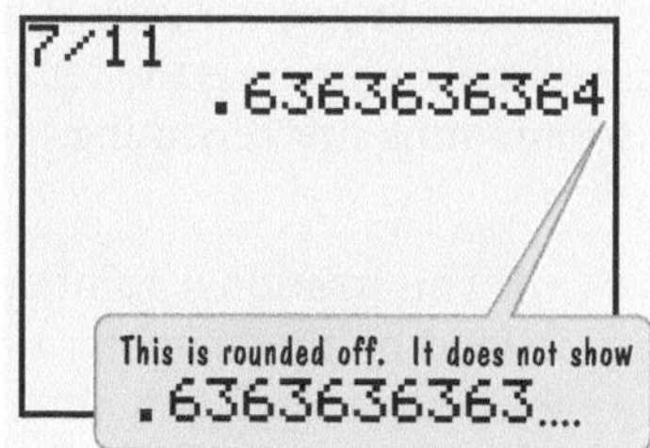

EXAMPLE 4 Expressing Rational Numbers as Decimals

Express each rational number as a decimal:

a. $\frac{5}{8}$ **b.** $\frac{7}{11}$.

Solution In each case, divide the denominator into the numerator.

a.
```
   0.625
8)5.000
  4 8
    20
    16
     40
     40
      0
```

b.
```
     0.6363 . . .
11)7.0000 . . .
   6 6
     40
     33
      70
      66
       40
       33
        70
         ⋮
```
■

In Example 4, the decimal for $\frac{5}{8}$, namely 0.625, stops and is called a **terminating decimal**. Other examples of terminating decimals are

$$\tfrac{1}{4} = 0.25, \quad \tfrac{2}{5} = 0.4, \quad \text{and} \quad \tfrac{7}{8} = 0.875.$$

By contrast, the division process for $\frac{7}{11}$ results in 0.6363. . . , with the digits 63 repeating over and over indefinitely. To indicate this, write a bar over the digits that repeat. Thus,

$$\tfrac{7}{11} = 0.\overline{63}.$$

The decimal for $\frac{7}{11}$, $0.\overline{63}$, is called a **repeating decimal**. Other examples of repeating decimals are

$$\tfrac{1}{3} = 0.333\ldots = 0.\overline{3} \quad \text{and} \quad \tfrac{2}{3} = 0.666\ldots = 0.\overline{6}.$$

Rational Numbers and Decimals

Any rational number can be expressed as a decimal. The resulting decimal will either terminate (stop), or it will have a digit that repeats or a block of digits that repeat.

✓ **CHECK POINT 4** Express each rational number as a decimal:

a. $\frac{3}{8}$ **b.** $\frac{5}{11}$.

Irrational Numbers

Can you think of a number that, when written in decimal form, neither terminates nor repeats? An example of such a number is $\sqrt{2}$ (read: "the square root of 2"). The number $\sqrt{2}$ is a number that can be multiplied by itself to obtain 2. No terminating or repeating decimal can be multiplied by itself to get 2. However, some approximations come close to 2.

- 1.4 is an approximation of $\sqrt{2}$:

$$1.4 \times 1.4 = 1.96.$$

- 1.41 is an approximation of $\sqrt{2}$:

$$1.41 \times 1.41 = 1.9881.$$

- 1.4142 is an approximation of $\sqrt{2}$:

$$1.4142 \times 1.4142 = 1.99996164.$$

Can you see how each approximation in the list is getting better? This is because the products are getting closer and closer to 2.

The number $\sqrt{2}$, whose decimal representation does not come to an end and does not have a block of repeating digits, is an example of an **irrational number**.

The Irrational Numbers

Any number that can be represented on the number line that is not a rational number is called an **irrational number**. Thus, the set of irrational numbers is the set of numbers whose decimal representations are neither terminating nor repeating.

Perhaps the best known of all the irrational numbers is π (pi). This irrational number represents the distance around a circle (its circumference) divided by the diameter of the circle. In the *Star Trek* episode "Wolf in the Fold," Spock foils an evil computer by telling it to "compute the last digit in the value of π." Because π is an irrational number, there is no last digit in its decimal representation:

$$\pi = 3.14159265358979323846264338327 95 \ldots .$$

Because irrational numbers cannot be represented by decimals that come to an end, mathematicians use symbols such as $\sqrt{2}$, $\sqrt{3}$, and π to represent these numbers. However, **not all square roots are irrational**. For example, $\sqrt{25} = 5$ because 5 multiplied by itself is 25. Thus, $\sqrt{25}$ is a natural number, a whole number, an integer, and a rational number $\left(\sqrt{25} = \frac{5}{1}\right)$.

Using Technology

You can obtain decimal approximations for irrational numbers using a calculator. For example, to approximate $\sqrt{2}$, use the following keystrokes:

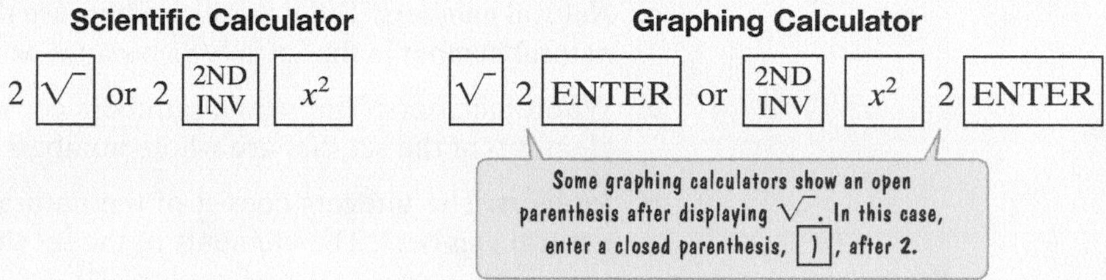

The display may read 1.41421356237, although your calculator may show more or fewer digits. Between which two integers would you graph $\sqrt{2}$ on a number line?

4 Classify numbers as belonging to one or more sets of the real numbers.

The Set of Real Numbers

All numbers that can be represented by points on the number line are called **real numbers.** Thus, the set of real numbers is formed by combining the rational numbers and the irrational numbers. Every real number is either rational or irrational.

The sets that make up the real numbers are summarized in **Table 2**. Notice the use of the symbol $\approx$ in the examples of irrational numbers. The symbol $\approx$ means "is approximately equal to."

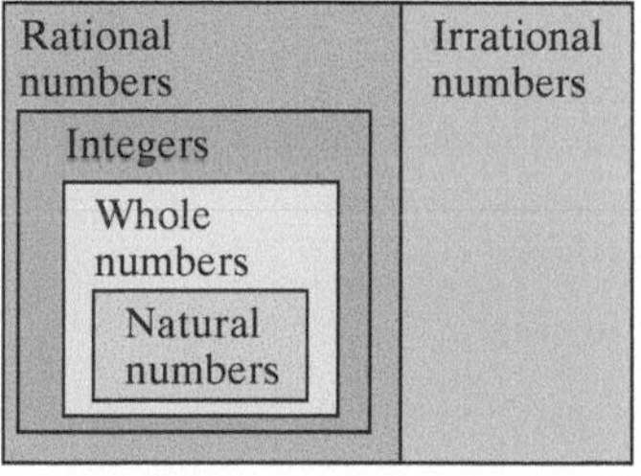

This diagram shows that every real number is rational or irrational.

Table 2 The Sets that Make Up the Real Numbers

Name	Description	Examples
Natural numbers	$\{1, 2, 3, 4, 5, \ldots\}$ These numbers are used for counting.	2, 3, 5, 17
Whole numbers	$\{0, 1, 2, 3, 4, 5, \ldots\}$ The set of whole numbers is formed by adding 0 to the set of natural numbers.	0, 2, 3, 5, 17
Integers	$\{\ldots, -5, -4, -3, -2, -1, 0, 1, 2, 3, 4, 5, \ldots\}$ The set of integers is formed by adding negatives of the natural numbers to the set of whole numbers.	$-17, -5, -3, -2, 0,$ 2, 3, 5, 17
Rational numbers	The set of rational numbers is the set of all numbers that can be expressed in the form $\frac{a}{b}$, where a and b are integers and b is not equal to 0, written $b \neq 0$. Rational numbers can be expressed as terminating or repeating decimals.	$-17 = \frac{-17}{1}, -5 = \frac{-5}{1}, -3, -2,$ 0, 2, 3, 5, 17, $\frac{2}{5} = 0.4,$ $\frac{-2}{3} = -0.6666\cdots = -0.\overline{6}$
Irrational numbers	The set of irrational numbers is the set of all numbers whose decimal representations are neither terminating nor repeating. Irrational numbers cannot be expressed as a quotient of integers.	$\sqrt{2} \approx 1.414214$ $-\sqrt{3} \approx -1.73205$ $\pi \approx 3.142$ $-\frac{\pi}{2} \approx -1.571$

EXAMPLE 5 Classifying Real Numbers

Consider the following set of numbers:

$$\left\{-7, -\frac{3}{4}, 0, 0.\overline{6}, \sqrt{5}, \pi, 7.3, \sqrt{81}\right\}.$$

List the numbers in the set that are

a. natural numbers. **b.** whole numbers. **c.** integers.
d. rational numbers. **e.** irrational numbers. **f.** real numbers.

Solution

a. Natural numbers: The natural numbers are the numbers used for counting. The only natural number in the set is $\sqrt{81}$ because $\sqrt{81} = 9$. (9 multiplied by itself is 81.)

b. Whole numbers: The whole numbers consist of the natural numbers and 0. The elements of the set that are whole numbers are 0 and $\sqrt{81}$.

c. Integers: The integers consist of the natural numbers, 0, and the negatives of the natural numbers. The elements of the set that are integers are $\sqrt{81}$, 0, and -7.

d. Rational numbers: All numbers in the set that can be expressed as the quotient of integers are rational numbers. These include $-7\left(-7 = \frac{-7}{1}\right), -\frac{3}{4}, 0\left(0 = \frac{0}{1}\right)$, and $\sqrt{81}\left(\sqrt{81} = \frac{9}{1}\right)$. Furthermore, all numbers in the set that are terminating or repeating decimals are also rational numbers. These include $0.\overline{6}$ and 7.3.

e. Irrational numbers: The irrational numbers in the set are $\sqrt{5}\left(\sqrt{5} \approx 2.236\right)$ and $\pi\,(\pi \approx 3.14)$. Both $\sqrt{5}$ and π are only approximately equal to 2.236 and 3.14, respectively. In decimal form, $\sqrt{5}$ and π neither terminate nor have blocks of repeating digits.

f. Real numbers: All the numbers in the given set are real numbers. ■

✓ **CHECK POINT 5** Consider the following set of numbers:

$$\left\{-9, -1.3, 0, 0.\overline{3}, \frac{\pi}{2}, \sqrt{9}, \sqrt{10}\right\}.$$

List the numbers in the set that are

a. natural numbers. **b.** whole numbers.
c. integers. **d.** rational numbers.
e. irrational numbers. **f.** real numbers.

---

5 Understand and use inequality symbols.

Ordering the Real Numbers

On the real number line, the real numbers increase from left to right. The lesser of two real numbers is the one farther to the left on a number line. The greater of two real numbers is the one farther to the right on a number line.

Look at the number line in **Figure 10**. The integers 2 and 5 are graphed. Observe that 2 is to the left of 5 on the number line. This means that 2 is less than 5.

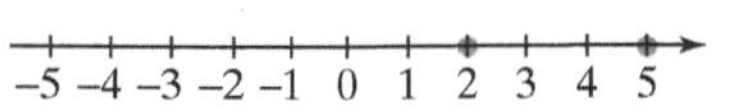

Figure 10

$2 < 5$: 2 is less than 5 because 2 is to the *left* of 5 on the number line.

In **Figure 10**, we can also observe that 5 is to the *right* of 2 on the number line. This means that 5 is greater than 2.

$5 > 2$: 5 is greater than 2 because 5 is to the *right* of 2 on the number line.

The symbols $<$ and $>$ are called **inequality symbols**. These symbols always point to the lesser of the two real numbers when the inequality is true.

2 is less than 5. — $2 < 5$ — The symbol points to 2, the lesser number.

5 is greater than 2. — $5 > 2$ — The symbol points to 2, the lesser number.

EXAMPLE 6 Using Inequality Symbols

Insert either $<$ or $>$ in the shaded area between each pair of numbers to make a true statement:

a. $3 \; \square \; 17$ **b.** $-4.5 \; \square \; 1.2$ **c.** $-5 \; \square \; -83$ **d.** $\frac{4}{5} \; \square \; \frac{2}{3}$.

Solution In each case, mentally compare the graph of the first number to the graph of the second number. If the first number is to the left of the second number, insert the symbol $<$ for "is less than." If the first number is to the right of the second number, insert the symbol $>$ for "is greater than."

a. Compare the graphs of 3 and 17 on the number line.

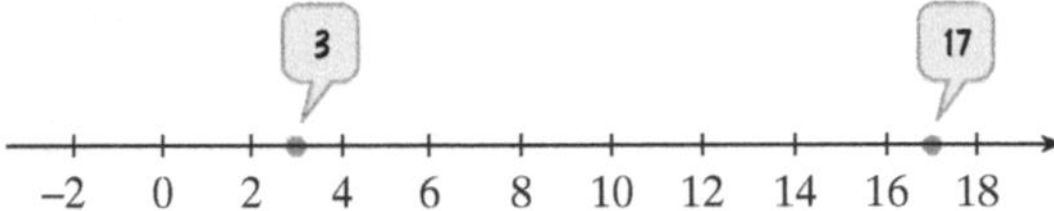

Because 3 is to the left of 17, this means that 3 is less than 17: $3 < 17$.

b. Compare the graphs of -4.5 and 1.2.

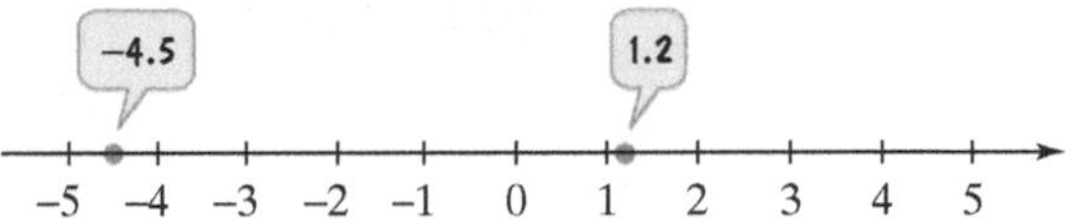

Because -4.5 is to the left of 1.2, this means that -4.5 is less than 1.2: $-4.5 < 1.2$.

c. Compare the graphs of -5 and -83.

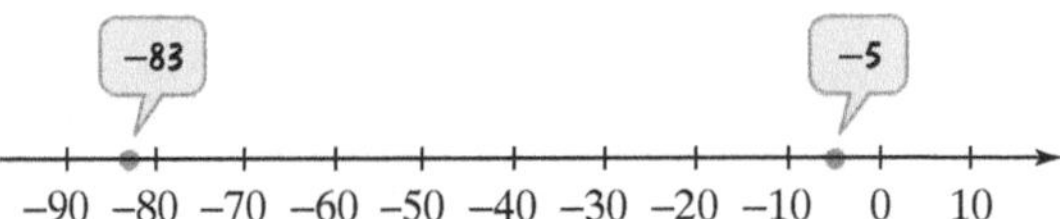

Because -5 is to the right of -83, this means that -5 is greater than -83: $-5 > -83$.

d. Compare the graphs of $\frac{4}{5}$ and $\frac{2}{3}$. To do so, convert to decimal notation or use a common denominator. Using decimal notation, $\frac{4}{5} = 0.8$ and $\frac{2}{3} = 0.\overline{6}$.

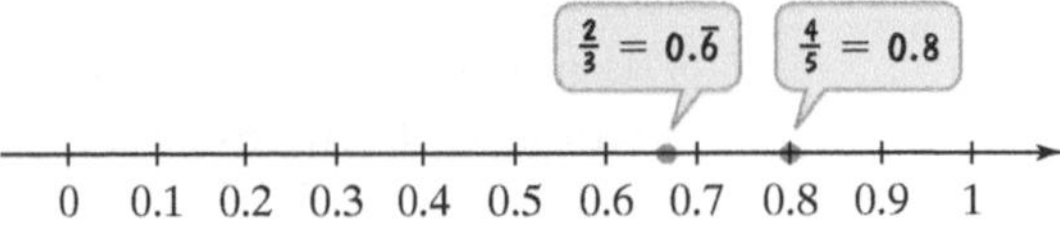

Because 0.8 is to the right of $0.\overline{6}$, this means that $\frac{4}{5}$ is greater than $\frac{2}{3}$: $\frac{4}{5} > \frac{2}{3}$. ■

CHECK POINT 6 Insert either $<$ or $>$ in the shaded area between each pair of numbers to make a true statement:

a. 14 ▒ 5 **b.** −5.4 ▒ 2.3 **c.** −19 ▒ −6 **d.** $\frac{1}{4}$ ▒ $\frac{1}{2}$.

The symbols $<$ and $>$ may be combined with an equal sign, as shown in the table.

This inequality is true if either the < part or the = part is true.

This inequality is true if either the > part or the = part is true.

Symbols	Meaning	Examples	Explanation
$a \le b$	a is less than or equal to b.	$3 \le 7$ $7 \le 7$	Because $3 < 7$ Because $7 = 7$
$b \ge a$	b is greater than or equal to a.	$7 \ge 3$ $-5 \ge -5$	Because $7 > 3$ Because $-5 = -5$

When using the symbol $\le$ (is less than or equal to), the inequality is a true statement if either the $<$ part or the $=$ part is true. When using the symbol $\ge$ (is greater than or equal to), the inequality is a true statement if either the $>$ part or the $=$ part is true.

EXAMPLE 7 Using Inequality Symbols

Determine whether each inequality is true or false:

a. $-7 \le 4$ **b.** $-7 \le -7$ **c.** $-9 \ge 6$.

Solution

a. $-7 \le 4$ is true because $-7 < 4$ is true.

b. $-7 \le -7$ is true because $-7 = -7$ is true.

c. $-9 \ge 6$ is false because neither $-9 > 6$ nor $-9 = 6$ is true. ■

CHECK POINT 7 Determine whether each inequality is true or false:

a. $-2 \le 3$ **b.** $-2 \ge -2$ **c.** $-4 \ge 1$.

6 Find the absolute value of real number.

Absolute Value

Absolute value describes distance from 0 on a number line. If a represents a real number, the symbol $|a|$ represents its absolute value, read "the absolute value of a." For example,

$$|-5| = 5.$$

The absolute value of −5 is 5 because −5 is 5 units from 0 on a number line.

Absolute Value

The **absolute value** of a real number a, denoted by $|a|$, is the distance from 0 to a on a number line. Because absolute value describes a distance, it is never negative.

EXAMPLE 8 Finding Absolute Value

Find the absolute value:

a. $|-3|$ **b.** $|5|$ **c.** $|0|$.

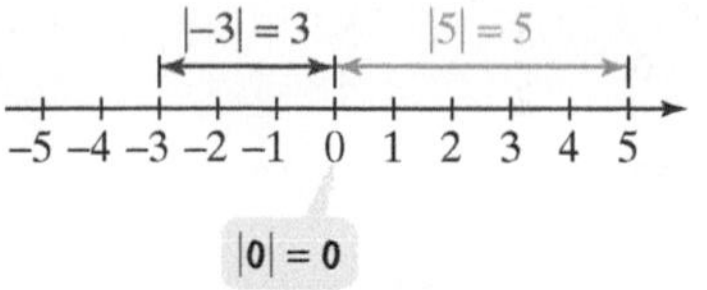

Figure 11 Absolute value describes distance from 0 on a number line.

Solution The solution is illustrated in **Figure 11**.

a. $|-3| = 3$ The absolute value of -3 is 3 because -3 is 3 units from 0.

b. $|5| = 5$ 5 is 5 units from 0.

c. $|0| = 0$ 0 is 0 units from itself. ■

Example 8 illustrates that the absolute value of a positive real number or 0 is the number itself. The absolute value of a negative real number, such as -3, is the number without the negative sign. Zero is the only real number whose absolute value is 0: $|0| = 0$. **The absolute value of any real number other than 0 is always positive.**

✓ **CHECK POINT 8** Find the absolute value:

a. $|-4|$ **b.** $|6|$ **c.** $|-\sqrt{2}|$.

Achieving Success

Check! Check! Check!

After completing each Check Point or odd-numbered exercise, compare your answer with the one given in the answer section. If your answer is different from the one given in the answer section, try to figure out your mistake. Then correct the error. If you cannot determine what went wrong, show your work to your professor. **By recording each step neatly and using as much paper as you need**, your professor will find it easier to determine where you had trouble.

CONCEPT AND VOCABULARY CHECK

Fill in each blank so that the resulting statement is true.

1. The set $\{1, 2, 3, 4, 5, \ldots\}$ is called the set of ____________ numbers.
2. The set $\{0, 1, 2, 3, 4, 5, \ldots\}$ is called the set of ____________ numbers.
3. The set $\{\ldots, -4, -3, -2, -1, 0, 1, 2, 3, 4, \ldots\}$ is called the set of ____________.
4. The set of numbers in the form $\frac{a}{b}$, where a and b belong to the set in statement 3 above and $b \neq 0$, is called the set of ____________ numbers.
5. The set of numbers whose decimal representations are neither terminating nor repeating is called the set of ____________ numbers.
6. Every real number is either a /an ____________ number or a/an ____________ number.
7. The notation $2 < 5$ means that 2 is to the ____________ of 5 on a number line.
8. The distance from 0 to a on a number line is called the ____________ of a, denoted by ____________.

3 EXERCISE SET

MyMathLab®

Watch the videos in MyMathLab

Download the MyDashBoard App

Practice Exercises

In Exercises 1–8, write a positive or negative integer that describes each situation.

1. Meteorology: 20° below zero
2. Navigation: 65 feet above sea level
3. Health: A gain of 8 pounds
4. Economics: A loss of \$12,500.00
5. Banking: A withdrawal of \$3000.00
6. Physics: An automobile slowing down at a rate of 3 meters per second each second
7. Economics: A budget deficit of 4 billion dollars
8. Football: A 14-yard loss

In Exercises 9–20, start by drawing a number line that shows integers from −5 to 5. Then graph each real number on your number line.

9. 2 **10.** 5 **11.** -5 **12.** -2 **13.** $3\frac{1}{2}$ **14.** $2\frac{1}{4}$

15. $\frac{11}{3}$ **16.** $\frac{7}{3}$ **17.** -1.8 **18.** -3.4 **19.** $-\frac{16}{5}$ **20.** $-\frac{11}{5}$

In Exercises 21–32, express each rational number as a decimal.

21. $\frac{3}{4}$ **22.** $\frac{3}{5}$ **23.** $\frac{7}{20}$

24. $\frac{3}{20}$ **25.** $\frac{7}{8}$ **26.** $\frac{5}{16}$

27. $\frac{9}{11}$ **28.** $\frac{3}{11}$ **29.** $-\frac{1}{2}$

30. $-\frac{1}{4}$ **31.** $-\frac{5}{6}$ **32.** $-\frac{7}{6}$

In Exercises 33–36, list all numbers from the given set that are: **a.** *natural numbers,* **b.** *whole numbers,* **c.** *integers,* **d.** *rational numbers,* **e.** *irrational numbers,* **f.** *real numbers.*

33. $\{-9, -\frac{4}{5}, 0, 0.25, \sqrt{3}, 9.2, \sqrt{100}\}$

34. $\{-7, -0.\bar{6}, 0, \sqrt{49}, \sqrt{50}\}$

35. $\{-11, -\frac{5}{6}, 0, 0.75, \sqrt{5}, \pi, \sqrt{64}\}$

36. $\{-5, -0.\bar{3}, 0, \sqrt{2}, \sqrt{4}\}$

37. Give an example of a whole number that is not a natural number.

38. Give an example of an integer that is not a whole number.

39. Give an example of a rational number that is not an integer.

40. Give an example of a rational number that is not a natural number.

41. Give an example of a number that is an integer, a whole number, and a natural number.

42. Give an example of a number that is a rational number, an integer, and a real number.

43. Give an example of a number that is an irrational number and a real number.

44. Give an example of a number that is a real number, but not an irrational number.

In Exercises 45–62, insert either $<$ *or* $>$ *in the shaded area between each pair of numbers to make a true statement.*

45. $\frac{1}{2}$ ▒ 2 **46.** 4 ▒ -3

47. 3 ▒ $-\frac{5}{2}$ **48.** 3 ▒ $\frac{3}{2}$

49. -4 ▒ -6 **50.** $-\frac{5}{2}$ ▒ $-\frac{5}{3}$

51. -2.5 ▒ 1.5 **52.** -1.25 ▒ -0.5

53. $-\frac{3}{4}$ ▒ $-\frac{5}{4}$ **54.** 0 ▒ $-\frac{1}{2}$

55. -4.5 ▒ 3 **56.** -5.5 ▒ 2.5

57. $\sqrt{2}$ ▒ 1.5 **58.** $\sqrt{3}$ ▒ 2

59. $0.\bar{3}$ ▒ 0.3 **60.** 0.6 ▒ $0.\bar{6}$

61. $-\pi$ ▒ -3.5 **62.** $-\frac{\pi}{2}$ ▒ -2.3

In Exercises 63–70, determine whether each inequality is true or false.

63. $-5 \ge -13$ **64.** $-5 \le -8$

65. $-9 \ge -9$ **66.** $-14 \le -14$

67. $0 \ge -6$ **68.** $0 \ge -13$

69. $-17 \ge 6$ **70.** $-14 \ge 8$

In Exercises 71–78, find each absolute value.

71. $|6|$ **72.** $|3|$ **73.** $|-7|$

74. $|-9|$ **75.** $\left|\frac{5}{6}\right|$ **76.** $\left|\frac{4}{5}\right|$

77. $|-\sqrt{11}|$ **78.** $|-\sqrt{29}|$

Practice PLUS

In Exercises 79–86, insert either $<$, $>$, *or* $=$ *in the shaded area to make a true statement.*

79. $|-6|$ ▒ $|-3|$ **80.** $|-20|$ ▒ $|-50|$

81. $\left|\frac{3}{5}\right|$ ▒ $|-0.6|$ **82.** $\left|\frac{5}{2}\right|$ ▒ $|-2.5|$

83. $\frac{30}{40} - \frac{3}{4}$ ▒ $\frac{14}{15} \cdot \frac{15}{14}$ **84.** $\frac{17}{18} \cdot \frac{18}{17}$ ▒ $\frac{50}{60} - \frac{5}{6}$

85. $\frac{8}{13} \div \frac{8}{13}$ ▒ $|-1|$ **86.** $|-2|$ ▒ $\frac{4}{17} \div \frac{4}{17}$

Application Exercises

In Exercises 87–94, determine whether natural numbers, whole numbers, integers, rational numbers, or all real numbers are appropriate for each situation.

87. Shoe sizes of students on campus

88. Recorded heights of students on campus

89. Temperatures in weather reports

90. Class sizes of algebra courses

91. Values of d given by the formula $d = \sqrt{1.5h}$, where d is the distance, in miles, that you can see to the horizon from a height of h feet

92. Values of C given by the formula $C = 2\pi r$, where C is the circumference of a circle with radius r

93. The number of pets a person has

94. The number of siblings a person has

95. The table shows the record low temperatures for five U.S. states.

State	Record Low (°F)	Date
Florida	−2	Feb. 13, 1899
Georgia	−17	Jan. 27, 1940
Hawaii	12	May 17, 1979
Louisiana	−16	Feb. 13, 1899
Rhode Island	−25	Feb. 5, 1996

Source: National Climatic Data Center

a. Graph the five record low temperatures on a number line.

b. Write the names of the states in order from the coldest record low to the warmest record low.

96. The table shows the record low temperatures for five U.S. states.

State	Record Low (°F)	Date
Virginia	−30	Jan. 22, 1985
Washington	−48	Dec. 30, 1968
West Virginia	−37	Dec. 30, 1917
Wisconsin	−55	Feb. 4, 1996
Wyoming	−66	Feb. 9, 1933

Source: National Climatic Data Center

a. Graph the five record low temperatures on a number line.

b. Write the names of the states in order from the coldest record low to the warmest record low.

Writing in Mathematics

97. What is a set?

98. What are the natural numbers?

99. What are the whole numbers?

100. What are the integers?

101. How does the set of integers differ from the set of whole numbers?

102. Describe how to graph a number on the number line.

103. What is a rational number?

104. Explain how to express $\frac{3}{8}$ as a decimal.

105. Describe the difference between a rational number and an irrational number.

106. If you are given two different real numbers, explain how to determine which one is the lesser.

107. Describe what is meant by the absolute value of a number. Give an example with your explanation.

Critical Thinking Exercises

Make Sense? *In Exercises 108–111, determine whether each statement "makes sense" or "does not make sense" and explain your reasoning.*

108. The humor in this joke is based on the fact that the football will never be hiked.

Foxtrot copyright © 2003, 2009 by Bill Amend/Distributed by Universal Uclick

109. *Titanic* came to rest 12,500 feet below sea level and *Bismarck* came to rest 15,617 feet below sea level, so *Bismarck's* resting place is higher than *Titanic's*.

110. I expressed a rational number as a decimal and the decimal neither terminated nor repeated.

111. I evaluated the formula $d = \sqrt{1.5h}$ for a value of h that resulted in a rational number for d.

In Exercises 112–117, determine whether each statement is true or false. If the statement is false, make the necessary change(s) to produce a true statement.

112. Every rational number is an integer.

113. Some whole numbers are not integers.

114. Some rational numbers are not positive.

115. Irrational numbers cannot be negative.

116. Some real numbers are not rational numbers.

117. Some integers are not rational numbers.

In Exercises 118–119, write each phrase as an algebraic expression.

118. a loss of $\frac{1}{3}$ of an investment of d dollars

119. a loss of half of an investment of d dollars

Technology Exercises

In Exercises 120–123, use a calculator to find a decimal approximation for each irrational number, correct to three decimal places. Between which two integers should you graph each of these numbers on the number line?

120. $\sqrt{3}$

121. $-\sqrt{12}$

122. $1 - \sqrt{2}$

123. $2 - \sqrt{5}$

Preview Exercises

Exercises 124–126 will help you prepare for the material covered in the next section. In each exercise, evaluate both expressions for $x = 4$. What do you observe?

124. $3(x + 5)$; $3x + 15$

125. $3x + 5x$; $8x$

126. $9x - 2x$; $7x$

SECTION 4

Basic Rules of Algebra

Objectives

1 Understand and use the vocabulary of algebraic expressions.
2 Use commutative properties.
3 Use associative property.
4 Use the distributive property.
5 Combine like terms.
6 Simplify algebraic expressions.

Starting as a link among U.S. research scientists, more than 1.8 billion people worldwide now use the Internet. Some random Internet factoids:

- Projected number of Facebook users by 2012: one billion
- Peak time for sex-related searches: 11 P.M.
- Fraction of people who use the word "password" as their password: $\frac{1}{8}$
- Vanity searchers: Fraction of people who typed their own name into a search engine: $\frac{1}{4}$
- Social interactions on Facebook every minute: 231,605 messages sent; 135,849 photos added; 98,604 friendships approved

(*Sources*: Facebook; Paul Grobman, *Vital Statistics*, Plume, 2005)

fStop/Alamy

In this section, we move from these quirky tidbits to mathematical models that describe the remarkable growth of the Internet in the United States and worldwide. To use these models efficiently (you'll work with them in the Exercise Set), they should be simplified using basic rules of algebra. Before turning to these rules, we open the section with a closer look at algebraic expressions.

1 Understand and use the vocabulary of algebraic expressions.

The Vocabulary of Algebraic Expressions

We have seen that an algebraic expression combines numbers and variables. Here is an example of an algebraic expression:

$$7x + 3.$$

The **terms** of an algebraic expression are those parts that are separated by addition. For example, the algebraic expression $7x + 3$ contains two terms, namely $7x$ and 3. Notice that a term is a number, a variable, or a number multiplied by one or more variables.

The numerical part of a term is called its **coefficient**. In the term $7x$, the 7 is the coefficient. If a term containing one or more variables is written without a coefficient, the coefficient is understood to be 1. Thus, x means $1x$ and ab means $1ab$.

A term that consists of just a number is called a **constant term**. The constant term of $7x + 3$ is 3.

The parts of each term that are multiplied are called the **factors of the term**. The factors of the term $7x$ are 7 and x.

Like terms are terms that have exactly the same variable factors. Here are two examples of like terms:

$7x$ and $3x$ These terms have the same variable factor, x.

$4y$ and $9y$. These terms have the same variable factor, y.

By contrast, here are some examples of terms that are not like terms. These terms do not have the same variable factor.

$7x$ and 3 The variable factor of the first term is x. The second term has no variable factor.

$7x$ and $3y$ The variable factor of the first term is x. The variable factor of the second term is y.

Constant terms are like terms. Thus, the constant terms 7 and -12 are like terms.

EXAMPLE 1 Using the Vocabulary of Algebraic Expressions

Use the algebraic expression

$$4x + 7 + 5x$$

to answer the following questions:

a. How many terms are there in the algebraic expression?

b. What is the coefficient of the first term?

c. What is the constant term?

d. What are the like terms in the algebraic expression?

Solution

a. Because terms are separated by addition, the algebraic expression $4x + 7 + 5x$ contains three terms.

$$4x + 7 + 5x$$

First term | Second term | Third term

b. The coefficient of the first term, $4x$, is 4.

c. The constant term in $4x + 7 + 5x$ is 7.

d. The like terms in $4x + 7 + 5x$ are $4x$ and $5x$. These terms have the same variable factor, x. ■

✓ **CHECK POINT 1** Use the algebraic expression $6x + 2x + 11$ to answer each of the four questions in Example 1.

Equivalent Algebraic Expressions

In Example 1, we considered the algebraic expression

$$4x + 7 + 5x.$$

Let's compare this expression with a second algebraic expression

$$9x + 7.$$

Evaluate each expression for some choice of x. We will select $x = 2$.

$4x + 7 + 5x$	$9x + 7$
Replace x with 2.	Replace x with 2.
$= 4 \cdot 2 + 7 + 5 \cdot 2$	$= 9 \cdot 2 + 7$
$= 8 + 7 + 10$	$= 18 + 7$
$= 25$	$= 25$

Both algebraic expressions have the same value when $x = 2$. Regardless of what number you select for x, the algebraic expressions $4x + 7 + 5x$ and $9x + 7$ will have the same value. These expressions are called *equivalent algebraic expressions*. Two algebraic expressions that have the same value for all replacements are called **equivalent algebraic expressions**. Because $4x + 7 + 5x$ and $9x + 7$ are equivalent algebraic expressions, we write

$$4x + 7 + 5x = 9x + 7.$$

Properties of Real Numbers and Algebraic Expressions

We now turn to basic properties, or rules, that you know from past experiences in working with whole numbers and fractions. These properties will be extended to include all real numbers and algebraic expressions. We will give each property a name so that we can refer to it throughout the study of algebra.

2 Use commutative properties.

The Commutative Properties

The addition or multiplication of two real numbers can be done in any order. For example, $3 + 5 = 5 + 3$ and $3 \cdot 5 = 5 \cdot 3$. Changing the order does not change the answer of a sum or a product. These facts are called **commutative properties.**

Great Question!

Are there commutative properties for subtraction and division?

No. The commutative property does not hold for subtraction or division.

$$6 - 1 \neq 1 - 6$$
$$8 \div 4 \neq 4 \div 8$$

The Commutative Properties

Let a and b represent real numbers, variables, or algebraic expressions.

Commutative Property of Addition

$$a + b = b + a$$

Changing order when adding does not affect the sum.

Commutative Property of Multiplication

$$ab = ba$$

Changing order when multiplying does not affect the product.

EXAMPLE 2 Using the Commutative Properties

Use the commutative properties to write an algebraic expression equivalent to each of the following:

a. $y + 6$ **b.** $5x$.

Solution

a. By the commutative property of addition, an algebraic expression equivalent to $y + 6$ is $6 + y$. Thus,

$$y + 6 = 6 + y.$$

b. By the commutative property of multiplication, an algebraic expression equivalent to $5x$ is $x5$. Thus,

$$5x = x5. \blacksquare$$

✓ **CHECK POINT 2** Use the commutative properties to write an algebraic expression equivalent to each of the following:

a. $x + 14$ **b.** $7y$.

EXAMPLE 3 Using the Commutative Properties

Write an algebraic expression equivalent to $13x + 8$ using

a. the commutative property of addition.

b. the commutative property of multiplication.

Solution

a. By the commutative property of addition, we change the order of the terms being added. This means that an algebraic expression equivalent to $13x + 8$ is $8 + 13x$:

$$13x + 8 = 8 + 13x.$$

b. By the commutative property of multiplication, we change the order of the factors being multiplied. This means that an algebraic expression equivalent to $13x + 8$ is $x13 + 8$:

$$13x + 8 = x13 + 8. \quad \blacksquare$$

✓ **CHECK POINT 3** Write an algebraic expression equivalent to $5x + 17$ using

a. the commutative property of addition.

b. the commutative property of multiplication.

Blitzer Bonus

Commutative Words and Sentences

The commutative property states that a change in order produces no change in the answer. The words and sentences listed here suggest a characteristic of the commutative property; they read the same from left to right and from right to left!

- dad
- repaper
- never odd or even
- Go deliver a dare, vile dog!
- May a moody baby doom a yam?
- Madam, in Eden I'm Adam.
- Ma is a nun, as I am.
- A man, a plan, a canal: Panama
- Was it a rat I saw?
- Six is a six is a six is a six is a six is . . . .
- Deb sat in Anita's bed.
Ned sat in Anita's den.
But Anita sat in a tub.
- Ed, is Nik inside?
Ed, is Deb bedside?
Ed is busy—subside!

3 Use associative properties.

The Associative Properties

Parentheses indicate groupings. As we have seen, we perform operations within the parentheses first. For example,

$$(2 + 5) + 10 = 7 + 10 = 17$$

and

$$2 + (5 + 10) = 2 + 15 = 17.$$

In general, the way in which three numbers are grouped does not change their sum. It also does not change their product. These facts are called the **associative properties**.

The Associative Properties

Let a, b, and c represent real numbers, variables, or algebraic expressions.

Associative Property of Addition

$$(a + b) + c = a + (b + c)$$

Changing grouping when adding does not affect the sum.

Associative Property of Multiplication

$$(ab)c = a(bc)$$

Changing grouping when multiplying does not affect the product.

Great Question!

Are there associative properties for subtraction and division?

No. The associative property does not hold for subtraction or division.

$$(6 - 3) - 1 \neq 6 - (3 - 1)$$
$$(8 \div 4) \div 2 \neq 8 \div (4 \div 2)$$

The associative properties can be used to simplify some algebraic expressions by removing the parentheses.

EXAMPLE 4 Simplifying Using the Associative Properties

Simplify:

a. $3 + (8 + x)$ **b.** $8(4x)$.

Solution

a. $3 + (8 + x)$ This is the given algebraic expression.

$= (3 + 8) + x$ Use the associative property of addition to group the first two numbers.

$= 11 + x$ Add within parentheses.

Using the commutative property of addition, this simplified algebraic expression can also be written as $x + 11$.

b. $8(4x)$ This is the given algebraic expression.

$= (8 \cdot 4)x$ Use the associative property of multiplication to group the first two numbers.

$= 32x$ Multiply within parentheses.

We can use the commutative property of multiplication to write this simplified algebraic expression as $x32$ or $x \cdot 32$. However, it is customary to express a term with its coefficient on the left. Thus, we use $32x$ as the simplified form of the algebraic expression. ■

✓ **CHECK POINT 4** Simplify:

a. $8 + (12 + x)$ **b.** $6(5x)$.

The next example involves the use of both basic properties to simplify an algebraic expression.

Great Question!

Is there an easy way to distinguish between the commutative and associative properties?

Commutative: changes *order*

Associative: changes *grouping*

EXAMPLE 5 Using the Commutative and Associative Properties

Simplify: $7 + (x + 2)$.

Solution

$7 + (x + 2)$ This is the given algebraic expression.

$= 7 + (2 + x)$ Use the commutative property to change the order of the addition.

$= (7 + 2) + x$ Use the associative property to group the first two numbers.

$= 9 + x$ Add within parentheses.

Using the commutative property of addition, an equivalent algebraic expression is $x + 9$. ■

✓ **CHECK POINT 5** Simplify: $8 + (x + 4)$.

4 Use the distributive property.

The Distributive Property

The **distributive property** involves both multiplication and addition. The property shows how to multiply the sum of two numbers by a third number. Consider, for example, $4(7 + 3)$, which can be calculated in two ways. One way is to perform the addition within the grouping symbols and then multiply:

$$4(7 + 3) = 4(10) = 40.$$

The other way to find $4(7 + 3)$ is to *distribute* the multiplication by 4 over the addition: First multiply each number within the parentheses by 4 and then add:

$$4 \cdot 7 + 4 \cdot 3 = 28 + 12 = 40.$$

The result in both cases is 40. Thus,

$$4(7 + 3) = 4 \cdot 7 + 4 \cdot 3.$$ Multiplication distributes over addition.

The distributive property allows us to rewrite the product of a number and a sum as the sum of two products.

The Distributive Property

Let a, b, and c represent real numbers, variables, or algebraic expressions.

$$a(b + c) = ab + ac$$

Multiplication distributes over addition.

Great Question!

Can you give examples so that I don't confuse the distributive property with the associative property of multiplication?

Distributive:

$$4(5 + x) = 4 \cdot 5 + 4x = 20 + 4x$$

Associative:

$$4(5 \cdot x) = (4 \cdot 5)x = 20x$$

EXAMPLE 6 Using the Distributive Property

Multiply: $6(x + 4)$.

Solution Multiply *each term* inside the parentheses, x and 4, by the multiplier outside, 6.

$$6(x + 4) = 6x + 6 \cdot 4$$ Use the distributive property to remove parentheses.

$$= 6x + 24$$ Multiply: $6 \cdot 4 = 24$. ■

✓ **CHECK POINT 6** Multiply: $5(x + 3)$.

EXAMPLE 7 Using the Distributive Property

Multiply: $5(3y + 7)$.

Solution Multiply *each term* inside the parentheses, $3y$ and 7, by the multiplier outside, 5.

$$5(3y + 7) = 5 \cdot 3y + 5 \cdot 7$$ Use the distributive property to remove parentheses.

$$= 15y + 35$$ Multiply. Use the associative property of multiplication to find $5 \cdot 3y$: $5 \cdot 3y = (5 \cdot 3)y = 15y$. ■

✓ **CHECK POINT 7** Multiply: $6(4y + 7)$.

Great Question!

What's the bottom line when using the distributive property?

When using the distributive property to remove parentheses, be sure to multiply *each term* inside the parentheses by the multiplier outside.

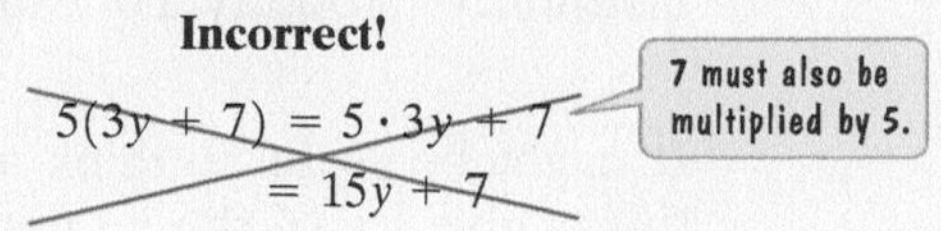

Table 3 shows a number of other forms of the distributive property.

Table 3 Other Forms of the Distributive Property

Property	Meaning	Example
$a(b - c) = ab - ac$	Multiplication distributes over subtraction.	$5(4x - 3) = 5 \cdot 4x - 5 \cdot 3$ $= 20x - 15$
$a(b + c + d) = ab + ac + ad$	Multiplication distributes over three or more terms in parentheses.	$4(x + 10 + 3y)$ $= 4x + 4 \cdot 10 + 4 \cdot 3y$ $= 4x + 40 + 12y$
$(b + c)a = ba + ca$	Multiplication on the right distributes over addition (or subtraction).	$(x + 7)9 = x \cdot 9 + 7 \cdot 9$ $= 9x + 63$

5 Combine like terms.

Combining Like Terms

The distributive property

$$a(b + c) = ab + ac$$

lets us add and subtract like terms. To do this, we will usually apply the property in the form

$$ax + bx = (a + b)x$$

and then combine a and b. For example,

$$3x + 7x = (3 + 7)x = 10x.$$

This process is called **combining like terms.**

EXAMPLE 8 Combining Like Terms

Combine like terms:

a. $4x + 15x$ **b.** $7a - 2a$.

Solution

a. $4x + 15x$ These are like terms because 4x and 15x have identical variable factors.

$= (4 + 15)x$ Apply the distributive property.

$= 19x$ Add within parentheses.

b. $7a - 2a$ These are like terms because 7a and 2a have identical variable factors.

$= (7 - 2)a$ Apply the distributive property.

$= 5a$ Subtract within parentheses. ■

✓ **CHECK POINT 8** Combine like terms:

a. $7x + 3x$ **b.** $9a - 4a$.

When combining like terms, you may find yourself leaving out the details of the distributive property. For example, you may simply write

$$7x + 3x = 10x.$$

It might be useful to think along these lines: Seven things plus three of the (same) things give ten of those things. To add like terms, add the coefficients and copy the common variable.

Combining Like Terms Mentally

1. Add or subtract the coefficients of the terms.
2. Use the result of step 1 as the coefficient of the term's variable factor.

When an expression contains three or more terms, use the commutative and associative properties to group like terms. Then combine the like terms.

EXAMPLE 9 Grouping and Combining Like Terms

Simplify:

a. $7x + 5 + 3x + 8$ **b.** $4x + 7y + 2x + 3y$.

Solution

a. $7x + 5 + 3x + 8$

$= (7x + 3x) + (5 + 8)$ Rearrange terms and group the like terms using the commutative and associative properties. This step is often done mentally.

$= 10x + 13$ Combine like terms: $7x + 3x = 10x$. Combine constant terms: $5 + 8 = 13$.

b. $4x + 7y + 2x + 3y$

$= (4x + 2x) + (7y + 3y)$ Group like terms.

$= 6x + 10y$ Combine like terms by adding coefficients and keeping the variable factor. ■

✓ **CHECK POINT 9** Simplify:

a. $8x + 7 + 10x + 3$ **b.** $9x + 6y + 5x + 2y$.

Great Question!

What do like objects, such as apples and apples, have to do with like terms?

Combining like terms should remind you of adding and subtracting numbers of like objects.

7 apples + 3 apples = 10 apples — $7a + 3a = 10a$

9 feet − 5 feet = 4 feet — $9f - 5f = 4f$

6 apples + 10 feet = ? — $6a$ and $10f$ are not like terms and cannot be added.

6 Simplify algebraic expressions.

Simplifying Algebraic Expressions

An algebraic expression is **simplified** when parentheses have been removed and like terms have been combined.

Simplifying Algebraic Expressions

1. Use the distributive property to remove parentheses.
2. Rearrange terms and group like terms using the commutative and associative properties. This step may be done mentally.
3. Combine like terms by combining the coefficients of the terms and keeping the same variable factor.

EXAMPLE 10 Simplifying an Algebraic Expression

Simplify: $5(3x + 7) + 6x$.

Solution

$$5(3x + 7) + 6x$$

$= 5 \cdot 3x + 5 \cdot 7 + 6x$ Use the distributive property to remove the parentheses.

$= 15x + 35 + 6x$ Multiply.

$= (15x + 6x) + 35$ Group like terms.

$= 21x + 35$ Combine like terms. ■

✓ **CHECK POINT 10** Simplify: $7(2x + 3) + 11x$.

EXAMPLE 11 Simplifying an Algebraic Expression

Simplify: $6(2x + 4y) + 10(4x + 3y)$.

Solution

$$6(2x + 4y) + 10(4x + 3y)$$

$= 6 \cdot 2x + 6 \cdot 4y + 10 \cdot 4x + 10 \cdot 3y$ Use the distributive property to remove the parentheses.

$= 12x + 24y + 40x + 30y$ Multiply.

$= (12x + 40x) + (24y + 30y)$ Group like terms.

$= 52x + 54y$ Combine like terms. ■

✓ **CHECK POINT 11** Simplify: $7(4x + 3y) + 2(5x + y)$.

Great Question!

Do I need to use the distributive property to simplify an algebraic expression such as 4(3x + 5x) that contains like terms within the parentheses?

Use the distributive property to remove parentheses when the terms inside parentheses are not like terms:

$$4(3x + 5y) = 4 \cdot 3x + 4 \cdot 5y = 12x + 20y.$$

$3x$ and $5y$ are not like terms.

It is not necessary to use the distributive property to remove parentheses when the terms inside parentheses are like terms:

$$4(3x + 5x) = 4(8x) = 32x.$$

$3x$ and $5x$ are like terms and can be combined: $3x + 5x = 8x$.

We mentally applied the associative property: $4(8x) = (4 \cdot 8)x = 32x$.

CONCEPT AND VOCABULARY CHECK

Fill in each blank so that the resulting statement is true.

1. Terms that have the same variable factors, such as $7x$ and $5x$, are called ______________ terms.
2. If a and b are real numbers, the commutative property of addition states that $a + b =$ ______________.
3. If a and b are real numbers, the commutative property of multiplication states that ______________ $= ba$.
4. If a, b, and c are real numbers, the associative property of addition states that $(a + b) + c =$ ______________.
5. If a, b, and c are real numbers, the associative property of multiplication states that ______________ $= a(bc)$.
6. If a, b, and c are real numbers, the distributive property states that $a(b + c) =$ ______________.
7. An algebraic expression is ______________ when parentheses have been removed and like terms have been combined.

4 EXERCISE SET

MyMathLab®

Watch the videos in MyMathLab

Download the MyDashBoard App

Practice Exercises

In Exercises 1–6, an algebraic expression is given. Use each expression to answer the following questions.

a. *How many terms are there in the algebraic expression?*
b. *What is the numerical coefficient of the first term?*
c. *What is the constant term?*
d. *Does the algebraic expression contain like terms? If so, what are the like terms?*

1. $3x + 5$
2. $9x + 4$
3. $x + 2 + 5x$
4. $x + 6 + 7x$
5. $4y + 1 + 3x$
6. $8y + 1 + 10x$

In Exercises 7–14, use the commutative property of addition to write an equivalent algebraic expression.

7. $y + 4$
8. $x + 7$
9. $5 + 3x$
10. $4 + 9x$
11. $4x + 5y$
12. $10x + 9y$
13. $5(x + 3)$
14. $6(x + 4)$

In Exercises 15–22, use the commutative property of multiplication to write an equivalent algebraic expression.

15. $9x$
16. $8x$
17. $x + y6$
18. $x + y7$
19. $7x + 23$
20. $13x + 11$
21. $5(x + 3)$
22. $6(x + 4)$

In Exercises 23–26, use an associative property to rewrite each algebraic expression. Once the grouping has been changed, simplify the resulting algebraic expression.

23. $7 + (5 + x)$
24. $9 + (3 + x)$
25. $7(4x)$
26. $8(5x)$

In Exercises 27–46, use a form of the distributive property to rewrite each algebraic expression without parentheses.

27. $3(x + 5)$
28. $4(x + 6)$
29. $8(2x + 3)$
30. $9(2x + 5)$
31. $\frac{1}{3}(12 + 6r)$
32. $\frac{1}{4}(12 + 8r)$
33. $5(x + y)$
34. $7(x + y)$
35. $3(x - 2)$
36. $4(x - 5)$
37. $2(4x - 5)$
38. $6(3x - 2)$
39. $\frac{1}{2}(5x - 12)$
40. $\frac{1}{3}(7x - 21)$
41. $(2x + 7)4$
42. $(5x + 3)6$
43. $6(x + 3 + 2y)$
44. $7(2x + 4 + y)$
45. $5(3x - 2 + 4y)$
46. $4(5x - 3 + 7y)$

In Exercises 47–64, simplify each algebraic expression.

47. $7x + 10x$
48. $5x + 13x$
49. $11a - 3a$
50. $14b - 5b$
51. $3 + (x + 11)$
52. $7 + (x + 10)$
53. $5y + 3 + 6y$
54. $8y + 7 + 10y$
55. $2x + 5 + 7x - 4$
56. $7x + 8 + 2x - 3$
57. $11a + 12 + 3a + 2$
58. $13a + 15 + 2a + 11$
59. $5(3x + 2) - 4$
60. $2(5x + 4) - 3$
61. $12 + 5(3x - 2)$
62. $14 + 2(5x - 1)$
63. $7(3a + 2b) + 5(4a + 2b)$
64. $11(6a + 3b) + 4(12a + 5b)$

Practice PLUS

In Exercises 65–66, name the property used to go from step to step each time that "(why?)" occurs.

65. $7 + 2(x + 9)$
$= 7 + (2x + 18)$ (why?)
$= 7 + (18 + 2x)$ (why?)
$= (7 + 18) + 2x$ (why?)
$= 25 + 2x$
$= 2x + 25$ (why?)

66. $5(x + 4) + 3x$
$= (5x + 20) + 3x$ (why?)
$= (20 + 5x) + 3x$ (why?)
$= 20 + (5x + 3x)$ (why?)
$= 20 + (5 + 3)x$ (why?)
$= 20 + 8x$
$= 8x + 20$ (why?)

In Exercises 67–76, write each English phrase as an algebraic expression. Then simplify the expression. Let x represent the number.

67. the sum of 7 times a number and twice the number
68. the sum of 8 times a number and twice the number
69. the product of 3 and a number, which is then subtracted from the product of 12 and a number
70. the product of 5 and a number, which is then subtracted from the product of 11 and a number
71. six times the product of 4 and a number
72. nine times the product of 3 and a number
73. six times the sum of 4 and a number
74. nine times the sum of 3 and a number
75. eight increased by the product of 5 and one less than a number
76. nine increased by the product of 3 and 2 less than a number

Application Exercises

The graph shows the number of Internet users in the United States and worldwide for four selected years. Exercises 77–78 involve mathematical models for the data.

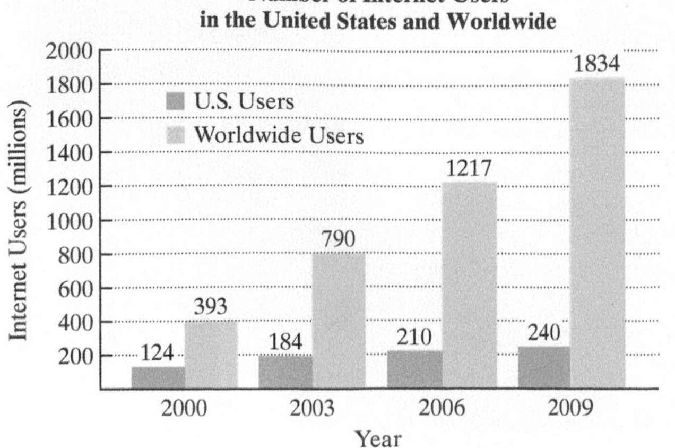

Source: International Telecommunication Union

77. The number of Internet users in the United States, U, in millions, n years after 2000 can be modeled by the formula
$$U = 4(2n + 32) + 5(n + 1).$$
   a. Simplify the formula.
   b. Use the simplified form of the mathematical model to find the number of Internet users in the United States in 2006. Does the model underestimate or overestimate the actual number shown by the bar graph for 2006? By how much?

78. The number of worldwide Internet users, W, in millions, n years after 2000 can be modeled by the formula
$$W = 2(19n + 38) + 3(40n + 90).$$
   a. Simplify the formula.
   b. Use the simplified form of the mathematical model to find the number of worldwide Internet users in 2009. Does the model underestimate or overestimate the actual number shown by the bar graph for 2009? By how much?

Writing in Mathematics

79. What is a term? Provide an example with your description.
80. What are like terms? Provide an example with your description.
81. What are equivalent algebraic expressions?
82. State a commutative property and give an example.
83. State an associative property and give an example.
84. State a form of the distributive property and give an example.
85. Explain how to add like terms. Give an example.
86. What does it mean to simplify an algebraic expression?
87. An algebra student incorrectly used the distributive property and wrote $3(5x + 7) = 15x + 7$. If you were that student's teacher, what would you say to help the student avoid this kind of error?
88. You can transpose the letters in the word "conversation" to form the phrase "voices rant on." From "total abstainers" we can form "sit not at ale bars." What two algebraic properties do each of these transpositions (called *anagrams*) remind you of? Explain your answer.

Critical Thinking Exercises

Make Sense? *In Exercises 89–92, determine whether each statement "makes sense" or "does not make sense" and explain your reasoning.*

89. I applied the commutative property and rewrote $x - 4$ as $4 - x$.
90. Just as the commutative properties change groupings, the associative properties change order.
91. I did not use the distributive property to simplify $3(2x + 5x)$.
92. The commutative, associative, and distributive properties remind me of the rules of a game.

In Exercises 93–96, determine whether each statement is true or false. If the statement is false, make the necessary change(s) to produce a true statement.

93. $(24 \div 6) \div 2 = 24 \div (6 \div 2)$

94. $2x + 5 = 5x + 2$

95. $a + (bc) = (a + b)(a + c)$; in words, addition can be distributed over multiplication.

96. Like terms contain the same coefficients.

Preview Exercises

Exercises 97–99 will help you prepare for the material covered in the next section. In each exercise, write an integer that is the result of the given situation.

97. You earn \$150, but then you misplace \$90.

98. You lose \$50 and then you misplace \$10.

99. The temperature is 30 degrees, and then it drops by 35 degrees.

MID-CHAPTER CHECK POINT Section 1–Section 4

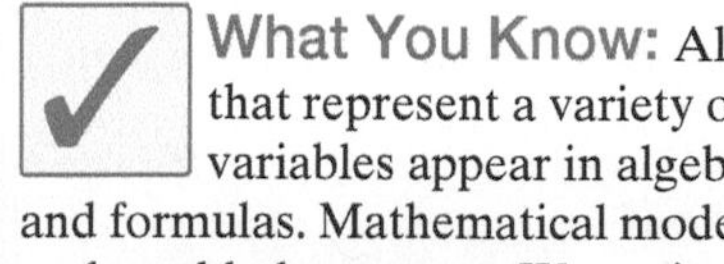

What You Know: Algebra uses variables, or letters, that represent a variety of different numbers. These variables appear in algebraic expressions, equations, and formulas. Mathematical models use variables to describe real-world phenomena. We reviewed operations with fractions and saw how fractions are used in algebra. We defined the real numbers and represented them as points on a number line. Finally, we introduced some basic rules of algebra and used the commutative, associative, and distributive properties to simplify algebraic expressions.

1. Evaluate for $x = 6$: $2 + 10x$

2. Evaluate for $x = \frac{3}{5}$: $10x - 4$.

3. Evaluate for $x = 3$ and $y = 10$:

$$\frac{xy}{2} + 4(y - x).$$

In Exercises 4–5, translate from English to an algebraic expression or equation, whichever is appropriate. Let the variable x represent the number.

4. Two less than $\frac{1}{4}$ of a number

5. Five more than the quotient of a number and 6 gives 19.

In Exercises 6–7, determine whether the given number is a solution of the equation.

6. $3(x + 2) = 4x - 1$; 6

7. $8y = 12\left(y - \frac{1}{2}\right)$; $\frac{3}{4}$

8. The average number of miles that a passenger car is driven per year is declining. The bar graph shows the average number of miles per car in the United States for four selected years.

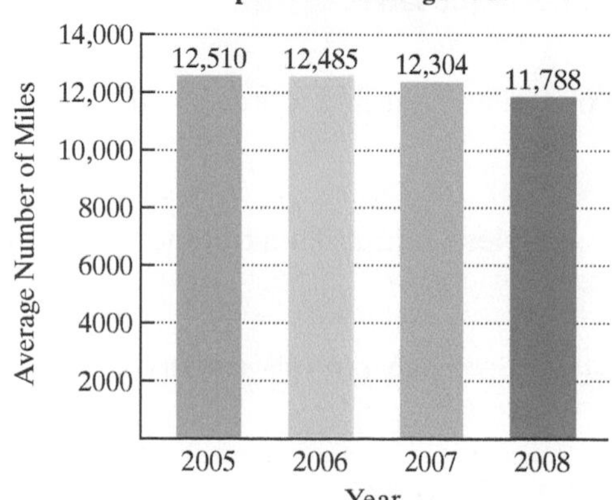

Source: Energy Information Administration

Here is a mathematical model that approximates the data displayed by the bar graph:

$$M = 12{,}624 - 235n.$$

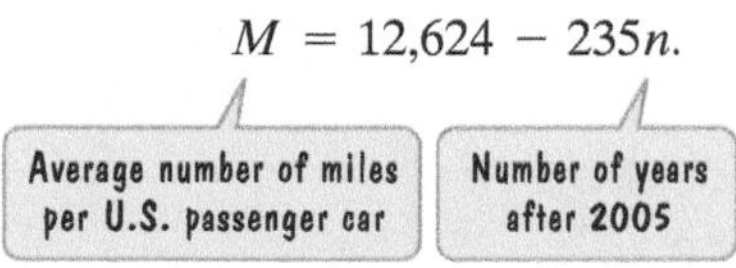

a. Use the formula to find the average number of miles per passenger car in 2008. Does the mathematical model underestimate or overestimate the actual number shown by the bar graph for 2008? By how much?

b. If trends from 2005 through 2008 continue, use the formula to project the average number of miles per U.S passenger car in 2015.

In Exercises 9–15, perform the indicated operation. Where possible, reduce answers to lowest terms.

9. $\frac{7}{10} - \frac{8}{15}$

10. $\frac{2}{3} \cdot \frac{3}{4}$

11. $\frac{5}{22} + \frac{5}{33}$

12. $\frac{3}{5} \div \frac{9}{10}$

13. $\frac{23}{105} - \frac{2}{105}$

14. $2\frac{7}{9} \div 3$

15. $5\frac{2}{9} - 3\frac{1}{6}$

16. The formula $C = \frac{5}{9}(F - 32)$ expresses the relationship between Fahrenheit temperature, F, and Celsius temperature, C. If the temperature is 50°F, use the formula to find the equivalent temperature on the Celsius scale.

17. Insert either < or > in the shaded area to make a true statement:

$$-8000 \;\square\; -8\frac{1}{4}.$$

18. Express $\frac{1}{11}$ as a decimal.

19. Find the absolute value: $|-19.3|$.

20. List all the rational numbers in this set:

$$\left\{-11, -\frac{3}{7}, 0, 0.45, \sqrt{23}, \sqrt{25}\right\}.$$

In Exercises 21–23, rewrite $5(x + 3)$ as an equivalent expression using the given property.

21. the commutative property of multiplication

22. the commutative property of addition

23. the distributive property

In Exercises 24–25, simplify each algebraic expression.

24. $7(9x + 3) + \frac{1}{3}(6x)$

25. $2(3x + 5y) + 4(x + 6y)$

SECTION 5

Addition of Real Numbers

Objectives

1. Add numbers with a number line.
2. Find sums using identity and inverse properties.
3. Add numbers without a number line.
4. Use addition rules to simplify algebraic expressions.
5. Solve applied problems using a series of additions.

It has not been a good day! First, you lost your wallet with \$50 in it. Then, to get through the day, you borrowed \$10, which you somehow misplaced. Your loss of \$50 followed by a loss of \$10 is an overall loss of \$60. This can be written

$$-50 + (-10) = -60.$$

Djarvik/Dreamstime

Kelly Richardson/Shutterstock

The result of adding two or more numbers is called the **sum** of the numbers. The sum of -50 and -10 is -60. You can think of gains and losses of money to find sums. For example, to find $17 + (-13)$, think of a gain of \$17 followed by a loss of \$13. There is an overall gain of \$4. Thus, $17 + (-13) = 4$. In the same way, to find $-17 + 13$, think of a loss of \$17 followed by a gain of \$13. There is an overall loss of \$4, so $-17 + 13 = -4$.

Adding with a Number Line

1 Add numbers with a number line.

We use the number line to help picture the addition of real numbers. Here is the procedure for finding $a + b$, the sum of a and b, using the number line:

Using the Number Line to Find a Sum

Let a and b represent real numbers. To find $a + b$ using a number line,

1. Start at a.
2. **a.** If b is **positive**, move b units to the **right**.
   b. If b is **negative**, move $|b|$ units to the **left**.
   c. If b is **0, stay** at a.
3. The number where we finish on the number line represents the sum of a and b.

This procedure is illustrated in Examples 1 and 2. Think of moving to the right as a gain and moving to the left as a loss.

EXAMPLE 1 Adding Real Numbers Using a Number Line

Find the sum using a number line:

$$3 + (-5).$$

Solution We find $3 + (-5)$ using the number line in **Figure 12**.

Step 1. We consider 3 to be the first number, represented by a in the box on the previous page. We start at a, or 3.

Step 2. We consider -5 to be the second number, represented by b. Because this number is negative, we move 5 units to the left.

Step 3. We finish at -2 on the number line. The number where we finish represents the sum of 3 and -5. Thus,

$$3 + (-5) = -2.$$

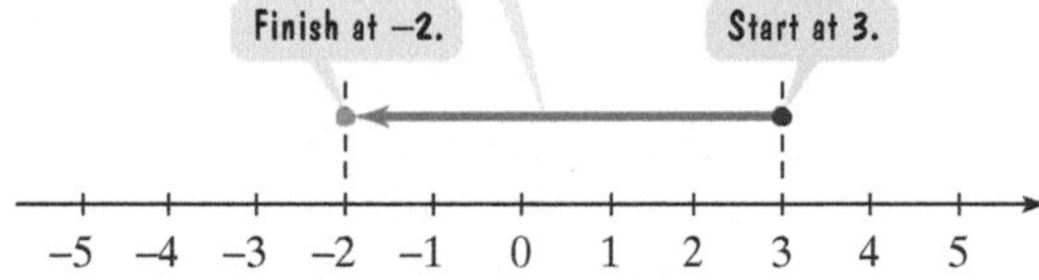

Figure 12 $3 + (-5) = -2$

Observe that if there is a gain of $3 followed by a loss of $5, there is an overall loss of $2. ■

✓ **CHECK POINT 1** Find the sum using a number line:

$$4 + (-7).$$

EXAMPLE 2 Adding Real Numbers Using a Number Line

Find each sum using a number line:

a. $-3 + (-4)$ **b.** $-6 + 2$.

Solution

a. To find $-3 + (-4)$, start at -3. Move 4 units to the left. We finish at -7. Thus,

$$-3 + (-4) = -7.$$

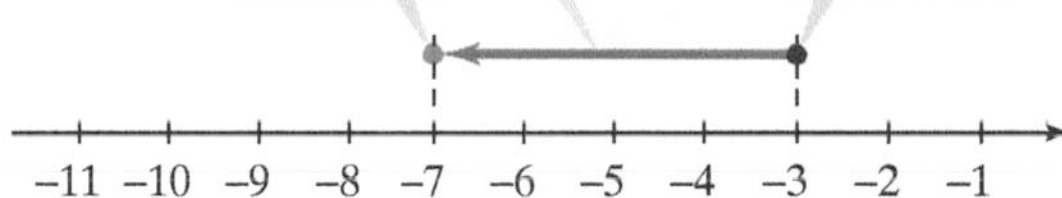

Observe that if there is a loss of $3 followed by a loss of $4, there is an overall loss of $7.

b. To find $-6 + 2$, start at -6. Move 2 units to the right because 2 is positive. We finish at -4. Thus,

$$-6 + 2 = -4.$$

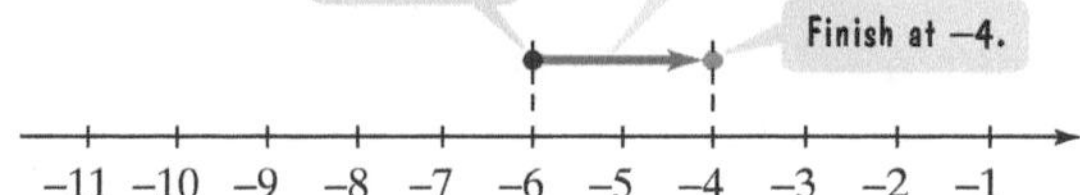

Observe that if there is a loss of $6 followed by a gain of $2, there is an overall loss of $4. ■

✓ **CHECK POINT 2** Find each sum using a number line:

a. $-1 + (-3)$ **b.** $-5 + 3$.

---

2 Find sums using identity and inverse properties.

The Number Line and Properties of Addition

The number line can be used to picture some useful properties of addition. For example, let's see what happens if we add two numbers with different signs but the same absolute value. Two such numbers are 3 and −3. To find $3 + (-3)$ on a number line, we start at 3 and move 3 units to the left. We finish at 0. Thus,

$$3 + (-3) = 0.$$

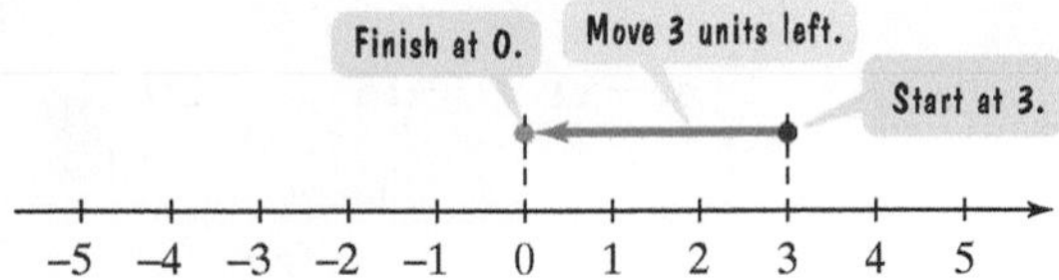

Numbers that differ only in sign, such as 3 and −3, are called *additive inverses*. **Additive inverses**, also called **opposites**, are pairs of real numbers that are the same number of units from zero on the number line, but are on opposite sides of zero. Thus, −3 is the additive inverse, or opposite, of 3, and 5 is the additive inverse, or opposite, of −5. The additive inverse of 0 is 0. Other additive inverses come in pairs.

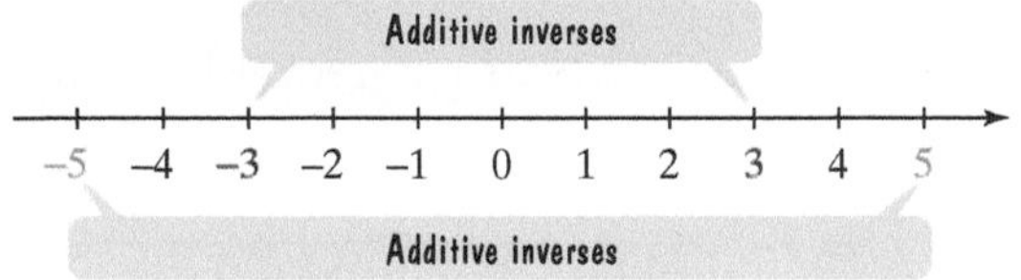

In general, the sum of any real number, denoted by a, and its additive inverse, denoted by $-a$, is zero:

$$a + (-a) = 0.$$

This property is called the **inverse property of addition**.

Table 4 shows the identity and inverse properties of addition.

Table 4 Identity and Inverse Properties of Addition

Let *a* be a real number, a variable, or an algebraic expression.

Property	Meaning	Examples
Identity Property of Addition	Zero can be deleted from a sum. $a + 0 = a$ $0 + a = a$	• $4 + 0 = 4$ • $-3x + 0 = -3x$ • $0 + (5a + b) = 5a + b$
Inverse Property of Addition	The sum of a real number and its additive inverse, or opposite, gives 0, the additive identity. $a + (-a) = 0$ $(-a) + a = 0$	• $6 + (-6) = 0$ • $3x + (-3x) = 0$ • $[-(2y + 1)] + (2y + 1) = 0$

3 Add numbers without a number line.

Adding without a Number Line

Now that we can picture the addition of real numbers, we look at two rules for using absolute value to add signed numbers.

Adding Two Numbers with the Same Sign

1. Add the absolute values.
2. Use the common sign as the sign of the sum.

EXAMPLE 3 Adding Real Numbers

Add without using a number line:

a. $-11 + (-15)$ **b.** $-0.2 + (-0.8)$ **c.** $-\frac{3}{4} + \left(-\frac{1}{2}\right)$.

Solution In each part of this example, we are adding numbers with the same sign.

a. $-11 + (-15) = -26$

Add absolute values: $11 + 15 = 26$.

Use the common sign.

b. $-0.2 + (-0.8) = -1$

Add absolute values: $0.2 + 0.8 = 1.0$ or 1.

Use the common sign.

c. $-\frac{3}{4} + \left(-\frac{1}{2}\right) = -\frac{5}{4}$

Add absolute values: $\frac{3}{4} + \frac{1}{2} = \frac{3}{4} + \frac{2}{4} = \frac{5}{4}$.

Use the common sign. ■

✓ **CHECK POINT 3** Add without using a number line:

a. $-10 + (-25)$ **b.** $-0.3 + (-1.2)$ **c.** $-\frac{2}{3} + \left(-\frac{1}{6}\right)$.

We also use absolute value to add two real numbers with different signs.

Adding Two Numbers with Different Signs

1. Subtract the smaller absolute value from the greater absolute value.
2. Use the sign of the number with the greater absolute value as the sign of the sum.

EXAMPLE 4 Adding Real Numbers

Add without using a number line:

a. $-13 + 4$ **b.** $-0.2 + 0.8$ **c.** $-\frac{3}{4} + \frac{1}{2}$.

Solution In each part of this example, we are adding numbers with different signs.

a. $-13 + 4 = -9$

Subtract absolute values: $13 - 4 = 9$.

Use the sign of the number with the greater absolute value.

b. $-0.2 + 0.8 = 0.6$

Subtract absolute values: $0.8 - 0.2 = 0.6$.

Use the sign of the number with the greater absolute value. The sign is assumed to be positive.

c. $-\frac{3}{4} + \frac{1}{2} = -\frac{1}{4}$

Subtract absolute values: $\frac{3}{4} - \frac{1}{2} = \frac{3}{4} - \frac{2}{4} = \frac{1}{4}$.

Use the sign of the number with the greater absolute value. ■

Using Technology

You can use a calculator to add signed numbers. Here are the keystrokes for finding $-11 + (-15)$:

Scientific Calculator

11 [+/−] [+] 15 [+/−] [=]

Graphing Calculator

[(−)] 11 [+] [(−)] 15 [ENTER]

Here are the keystrokes for finding $-13 + 4$:

Scientific Calculator

13 [+/−] [+] 4 [+]

Graphing Calculator

[(−)] 13 [+] 4 [ENTER]

✓ **CHECK POINT 4** Add without using a number line:

a. $-15 + 2$ **b.** $-0.4 + 1.6$ **c.** $-\frac{2}{3} + \frac{1}{6}$.

Great Question!

What's the bottom line for determining the sign of a sum?

- The sum of two positive numbers is always positive.
  Example: $0.8 + 0.3$ is a positive number.
- The sum of two negative numbers is always negative.
  Example: $-0.8 + (-0.3)$ is a negative number.
- The sum of two numbers with different signs may be positive or negative. The sign of the sum is the sign of the number with the greater absolute value.
  Examples: $-0.8 + 0.3$ is a negative number.
  $0.8 + (-0.3)$ is a positive number.
- The sum of a number and its additive inverse, or opposite, is always zero.
  Example: $0.8 + (-0.8) = 0$.

4 Use addition rules to simplify algebraic expressions.

Algebraic Expressions

The rules for adding real numbers can be used to simplify certain algebraic expressions.

EXAMPLE 5 Simplifying Algebraic Expressions

Simplify:

a. $-11x + 7x$ **b.** $7y + (-12z) + (-9y) + 15z$ **c.** $3(7x + 8) + (-25x)$.

Solution

a. $-11x + 7x$ The given algebraic expression has two like terms: $-11x$ and $7x$ have identical variable factors.

$= (-11 + 7)x$ Apply the distributive property.

$= -4x$ Add within parentheses: $-11 + 7 = -4$.

b. $7y + (-12z) + (-9y) + 15z$ The colors indicate that there are two pairs of like terms.

$= 7y + (-9y) + (-12z) + 15z$ Arrange like terms so that they are next to one another.

$= [7 + (-9)]y + [(-12) + 15]z$ Apply the distributive property.

$= -2y + 3z$ Add within the grouping symbols: $7 + (-9) = -2$ and $-12 + 15 = 3$.

c. $3(7x + 8) + (-25x)$

$= 3 \cdot 7x + 3 \cdot 8 + (-25x)$ Use the distributive property to remove the parentheses.

$= 21x + 24 + (-25x)$ Multiply.

$= 21x + (-25x) + 24$ Arrange like terms so that they are next to one another.

$= [21 + (-25)]x + 24$ Apply the distributive property.

$= -4x + 24$ Add within the grouping symbols: $21 + (-25) = -4$. ■

✓ **CHECK POINT 5** Simplify:

a. $-20x + 3x$

b. $3y + (-10z) + (-10y) + 16z$

c. $5(2x + 3) + (-30x)$

5 Solve applied problems using a series of additions.

Applications

Positive and negative numbers are used in everyday life to represent such things as gains and losses in the stock market, rising and falling temperatures, deposits and withdrawals on bank statements, and ascending and descending motion. Positive and negative numbers are used to solve applied problems involving a series of additions.

One way to add a series of positive and negative numbers is to use the commutative and associative properties.

- Add all the positive numbers.
- Add all the negative numbers.
- Add the sums obtained in the first two steps.

The next example illustrates this idea.

EXAMPLE 6 An Application of Adding Signed Numbers

A glider was towed 1000 meters into the air and then let go. It descended 70 meters into a thermal (rising bubble of warm air), which took it up 2100 meters. At this point it dropped 230 meters into a second thermal. Then it rose 1200 meters. What was its altitude at that point?

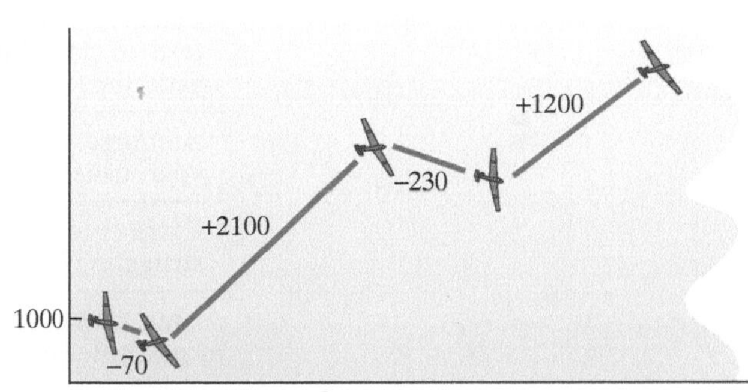

Solution We use the problem's conditions to write a sum. The altitude of the glider is expressed by the following sum:

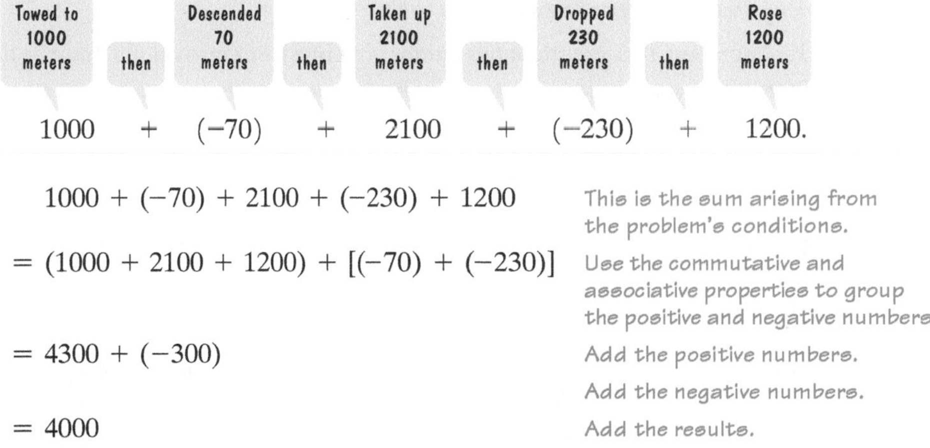

$$1000 + (-70) + 2100 + (-230) + 1200.$$

$1000 + (-70) + 2100 + (-230) + 1200$ — This is the sum arising from the problem's conditions.

$= (1000 + 2100 + 1200) + [(-70) + (-230)]$ — Use the commutative and associative properties to group the positive and negative numbers.

$= 4300 + (-300)$ — Add the positive numbers. Add the negative numbers.

$= 4000$ — Add the results.

The altitude of the glider is 4000 meters. ■

Discover for Yourself

Try working Example 6 by adding from left to right. You should still obtain 4000 for the sum. Which method do you find easier?

✓ CHECK POINT 6 The water level of a reservoir is measured over a five-month period. During this time, the level rose 2 feet, then fell 4 feet, then rose 1 foot, then fell 5 feet, and then rose 3 feet. What was the change in the water level at the end of the five months?

Achieving Success

Some of the difficulties facing students who take a college math class for the first time are a result of the differences between a high school math class and a college math course. It is helpful to understand these differences throughout your college math courses.

High School Math Class	College Math Course
Attendance is required.	Attendance may be optional.
Teachers monitor progress and performance closely.	Students receive grades, but may not be informed by the professor if they are in trouble.
There are frequent tests, as well as make-up tests if grades are poor.	There are usually no more than three or four tests per semester. Make-up tests are rarely allowed.
Grades are often based on participation and effort.	Grades are usually based exclusively on test grades.
Students have contact with their instructor every day.	Students usually meet with their instructor two or three times per week.
Teachers cover all material for tests in class through lectures and activities.	Students are responsible for information whether or not it is covered in class.
A course is covered over the school year, usually ten months.	A course is covered in a semester, usually four months.
Extra credit is often available for struggling students.	Extra credit is almost never offered.

Source: BASS, ALAN, *MATH STUDY SKILLS*, 1st, © 2008. Printed and Electronically reproduced by permission of Pearson Education, Inc., Upper Saddle River, New Jersey.

CONCEPT AND VOCABULARY CHECK

Fill in each blank so that the resulting statement is true.

1. Pairs of real numbers that are the same number of units from zero on the number line, but are on opposite sides of zero, are called opposites or ____________.
2. The sum of any real number and its opposite is always ____________.

In the remaining items, state whether each sum is a positive number, a negative number, or 0. Do not actually find the sum.

3. $-20 + (-18)$ ____________
4. $-20 + 28$ ____________
5. $-0.8 + 0.8$ ____________
6. $-\frac{4}{5} + \frac{1}{2}$ ____________
7. $-1.3 + 2.7$ ____________
8. $-\frac{2}{5} + \frac{2}{5}$ ____________

5 EXERCISE SET

MyMathLab®

Watch the videos in MyMathLab

Download the MyDashBoard App

Practice Exercises

In Exercises 1–8, find each sum using a number line.

1. $7 + (-3)$
2. $7 + (-2)$
3. $-2 + (-5)$
4. $-1 + (-5)$
5. $-6 + 2$
6. $-8 + 3$
7. $3 + (-3)$
8. $5 + (-5)$

In Exercises 9–46, find each sum without the use of a number line.

9. $-7 + 0$
10. $-5 + 0$

11. $30 + (-30)$

12. $15 + (-15)$

13. $-30 + (-30)$

14. $-15 + (-15)$

15. $-8 + (-10)$

16. $-4 + (-6)$

17. $-0.4 + (-0.9)$

18. $-1.5 + (-5.3)$

19. $-\frac{7}{10} + \left(-\frac{3}{10}\right)$

20. $-\frac{7}{8} + \left(-\frac{1}{8}\right)$

21. $-9 + 4$

22. $-7 + 3$

23. $12 + (-8)$

24. $13 + (-5)$

25. $6 + (-9)$

26. $3 + (-11)$

27. $-3.6 + 2.1$

28. $-6.3 + 5.2$

29. $-3.6 + (-2.1)$

30. $-6.3 + (-5.2)$

31. $\frac{9}{10} + \left(-\frac{3}{5}\right)$

32. $\frac{7}{10} + \left(-\frac{2}{5}\right)$

33. $-\frac{5}{8} + \frac{3}{4}$

34. $-\frac{5}{6} + \frac{1}{3}$

35. $-\frac{3}{7} + \left(-\frac{4}{5}\right)$

36. $-\frac{3}{8} + \left(-\frac{2}{3}\right)$

37. $4 + (-7) + (-5)$

38. $10 + (-3) + (-8)$

39. $85 + (-15) + (-20) + 12$

40. $60 + (-50) + (-30) + 25$

41. $17 + (-4) + 2 + 3 + (-10)$

42. $19 + (-5) + 1 + 8 + (-13)$

43. $-45 + \left(-\frac{3}{7}\right) + 25 + \left(-\frac{4}{7}\right)$

44. $-50 + \left(-\frac{7}{9}\right) + 35 + \left(-\frac{11}{9}\right)$

45. $3.5 + (-45) + (-8.4) + 72$

46. $6.4 + (-35) + (-2.6) + 14$

In Exercises 47–60, simplify each algebraic expression.

47. $-10x + 2x$

48. $-19x + 10x$

49. $25y + (-12y)$

50. $26y + (-14y)$

51. $-8a + (-15a)$

52. $-9a + (-13a)$

53. $4y + (-13z) + (-10y) + 17z$

54. $5y + (-11z) + (-15y) + 20z$

55. $-7b + 10 + (-b) + (-6)$

56. $-10b + 13 + (-b) + (-4)$

57. $7x + (-5y) + (-9x) + 19y$

58. $13x + (-9y) + (-17x) + 20y$

59. $8(4y + 3) + (-35y)$

60. $7(3y + 5) + (-25y)$

Practice PLUS

In Exercises 61–64, find each sum.

61. $|-3 + (-5)| + |2 + (-6)|$

62. $|4 + (-11)| + |-3 + (-4)|$

63. $-20 + [-|15 + (-25)|]$

64. $-25 + [-|18 + (-26)|]$

In Exercises 65–66, insert either $<$, $>$, or $=$ in the shaded area to make a true statement.

65. $6 + [2 + (-13)]$ ▒ $-3 + [4 + (-8)]$

66. $[(-8) + (-6)] + 10$ ▒ $-8 + [9 + (-2)]$

In Exercises 67–70, write each English phrase as an algebraic expression. Then simplify the expression. Let x represent the number.

67. The product of -6 and a number, which is then increased by the product of -13 and the number

68. The product of -9 and a number, which is then increased by the product of -11 and the number

69. The quotient of -20 and a number, increased by the quotient of 3 and the number

70. The quotient of -15 and a number, increased by the quotient of 4 and the number

Application Exercises

Solve Exercises 71–78 by writing a sum of signed numbers and adding.

71. The greatest temperature variation recorded in a day is 100 degrees in Browning, Montana, on January 23, 1916. The low temperature was -56°F. What was the high temperature?

72. In Spearfish, South Dakota, on January 22, 1943, the temperature rose 49 degrees in two minutes. If the initial temperature was -4°F, what was the temperature two minutes later?

73. The Dead Sea is the lowest elevation on Earth, 1312 feet below sea level. What is the elevation of a person standing 712 feet above the Dead Sea?

74. Lake Assal in Africa is 512 feet below sea level. What is the elevation of a person standing 642 feet above Lake Assal?

75. The temperature at 8:00 A.M. was -7°F. By noon it had risen 15°F, but by 4:00 P.M. it had fallen 5°F. What was the temperature at 4:00 P.M.?

76. On three successive plays, a football team lost 15 yards, gained 13 yards, and then lost 4 yards. What was the team's total gain or loss for the three plays?

77. A football team started with the football at the 27-yard line, advancing toward the center of the field (the 50-yard line). Four successive plays resulted in a 4-yard gain, a 2-yard loss, an 8-yard gain, and a 12-yard loss. What was the location of the football at the end of the fourth play?

78. The water level of a reservoir is measured over a five-month period. At the beginning, the level is 20 feet. During this time, the level rose 3 feet, then fell 2 feet, then fell 1 foot, then fell 4 feet, and then rose 2 feet. What is the reservoir's water level at the end of the five months?

The bar graph shows that in 2000 and 2001, the U.S. government collected more in taxes than it spent, so there was a budget surplus for each of these years. By contrast, in 2002 through 2009, the government spent more than it collected, resulting in budget deficits. Exercises 79–80 involve these deficits.

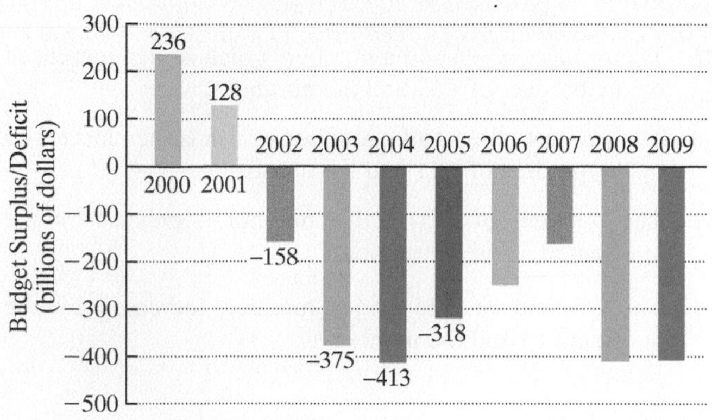

Source: Budget of the U.S. Government

79. a. In 2008, the government collected \$2521 billion and spent \$2931 billion. Find $2521 + (-2931)$ and determine the deficit, in billions of dollars, for 2008.

b. In 2009, the government collected \$2700 billion and spent \$3107 billion. Find the deficit, in billions of dollars, for 2009.

c. Use your answers from parts (a) and (b) to determine the combined deficit, in billions of dollars, for 2008 and 2009.

80. a. In 2006, the government collected \$2407 billion and spent \$2655 billion. Find $2407 + (-2655)$ and determine the deficit, in billions of dollars, for 2006.

b. In 2007, the government collected \$2568 billion and spent \$2730 billion. Find the deficit, in billions of dollars, for 2007.

c. Use your answers from part (a) and (b) to determine the combined deficit, in billions of dollars, for 2006 and 2007.

Writing in Mathematics

81. Explain how to add two numbers with a number line. Provide an example with your explanation.

82. What are additive inverses?

83. Describe how the inverse property of addition

$$a + (-a) = 0$$

can be shown on a number line.

84. Without using a number line, describe how to add two numbers with the same sign. Give an example.

85. Without using a number line, describe how to add two numbers with different signs. Give an example.

86. Write a problem that can be solved by finding the sum of at least three numbers, some positive and some negative. Then explain how to solve the problem.

87. Without a calculator, you can add numbers using a number line, using absolute value, or using gains and losses. Which method do you find most helpful? Why is this so?

Critical Thinking Exercises

Make Sense? *In Exercises 88–91, determine whether each statement "makes sense" or "does not make sense" and explain your reasoning.*

88. It takes me too much time to add real numbers with a number line.

89. I found the sum of -13 and 4 by thinking of temperatures above and below zero: If it's 13 below zero and the temperature rises 4 degrees, the new temperature will be 9 below zero, so $-13 + 4 = -9$.

90. I added two negative numbers and obtained a positive sum.

91. Without adding numbers, I can see that the sum of -227 and 319 is greater than the sum of 227 and -319.

In Exercises 92–95, determine whether each statement is true or false. If the statement is false, make the necessary change(s) to produce a true statement.

92. $\frac{3}{4} + \left(-\frac{3}{5}\right) = -\frac{3}{20}$

93. The sum of zero and a negative number is always a negative number.

94. If one number is positive and the other negative, then the absolute value of their sum equals the sum of their absolute values.

95. The sum of a positive number and a negative number is always a positive number.

In Exercises 96–99, use the number line to determine whether each expression is positive or negative.

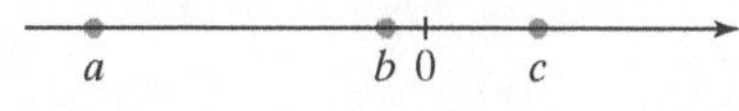

96. $a + b$ **97.** $a + c$

98. $b + c$ **99.** $|a + c|$

Technology Exercises

100. Use a calculator to verify any five of the sums that you found in Exercises 9–46.

101. Use a calculator to verify any three of the answers that you obtained in Application Exercises 71–78.

Review Exercises

From here on, each exercise set will contain three review exercises. It is essential to review previously covered topics to improve your understanding of the topics and to help maintain your mastery of the material. If you are not certain how to solve a review exercise, turn to the section and the worked example given in parentheses at the end of each exercise.

102. Consider the set

$$\{-6, -\pi, 0, 0.\overline{7}, \sqrt{3}, \sqrt{4}\}$$

List all numbers from the set that are **a.** natural numbers, **b.** whole numbers, **c.** integers, **d.** rational numbers, **e.** irrational numbers, **f.** real numbers. (Section 3, Example 5)

103. Determine whether this inequality is true or false: $19 \geq -18$. (Section 3, Example 7)

104. Determine whether 18 is a solution of $16 = 2(x - 1) - x$. (Section 1, Example 4)

Preview Exercises

Exercises 105–107 will help you prepare for the material covered in the next section. In each exercise, a subtraction is expressed as addition of an opposite. Find this sum, indicated by a question mark.

105. $7 - 10 = 7 + (-10) = ?$

106. $-8 - 13 = -8 + (-13) = ?$

107. $-8 - (-13) = -8 + 13 = ?$

SECTION 6

Subtraction of Real Numbers

Objectives

1. Subtract real numbers.
2. Simplify a series of additions and subtractions.
3. Use the definition of subtraction to identify terms.
4. Use the subtraction definition to simplify algebraic expressions.
5. Solve problems involving subtraction.

Everybody complains about the weather, but where is it really the worst? **Table 5** shows that in the United States, Alaska and Montana are the record-holders for the coldest temperatures.

Erik Peterson/The Bozeman Chronicle/AP Images

Table 5 Lowest Recorded U.S. Temperatures

State	Year	Temperature (°F)
Alaska	1971	−80
Montana	1954	−70

The table shows that Montana's record low temperature, −70, decreased by 10 degrees gives Alaska's record low temperature, −80. This can be expressed in two ways:

$$-70 - 10 = -80 \quad \text{or} \quad -70 + (-10) = -80.$$

This means that

$$-70 - 10 = -70 + (-10).$$

To subtract 10 from −70, we add −70 and the opposite, or additive inverse, of 10. Generalizing from this situation, we define subtraction as addition of an opposite.

Definition of Subtraction

For all real numbers a and b,

$$a - b = a + (-b).$$

In words: To subtract b from a, add the opposite, or additive inverse, of b to a. The result of subtraction is called the **difference**.

1 Subtract real numbers.

A Procedure for Subtracting Real Numbers

The definition of subtraction gives us a procedure for subtracting real numbers.

Subtracting Real Numbers

1. Change the subtraction operation to addition.
2. Change the sign of the number being subtracted.
3. Add, using one of the rules for adding numbers with the same sign or different signs.

Using Technology

You can use a calculator to subtract signed numbers. Here are the keystrokes for finding $5 - (-6)$:

Scientific Calculator

5 [−] 6 [+/−] [=]

Graphing Calculator

5 [−] [(−)] 6 [ENTER]

Here are the keystrokes for finding $-9 - (-3)$:

Scientific Calculator

9 [+/−] [−] 3 [+/−] [=]

Graphing Calculator

[(−)] 9 [−] [(−)] 3 [ENTER]

Don't confuse the subtraction key on a graphing calculator, [−], with the sign change or additive inverse key, [(−)]. What happens if you do?

EXAMPLE 1 Using the Definition of Subtraction

Subtract:

a. $7 - 10$ **b.** $5 - (-6)$ **c.** $-9 - (-3)$.

Solution

a. $7 - 10 = 7 + (-10) = -3$

Change the subtraction to addition. Replace 10 with its opposite.

b. $5 - (-6) = 5 + 6 = 11$

Change the subtraction to addition. Replace −6 with its opposite.

c. $-9 - (-3) = -9 + 3 = -6$

Change the subtraction to addition. Replace −3 with its opposite. ■

✓ **CHECK POINT 1** Subtract:

a. $3 - 11$ **b.** $4 - (-5)$ **c.** $-7 - (-2)$.

The definition of subtraction can be applied to real numbers that are not integers.

EXAMPLE 2 Using the Definition of Subtraction

Subtract:

a. $-5.2 - (-11.4)$ **b.** $-\frac{3}{4} - \frac{2}{3}$ **c.** $4\pi - (-9\pi)$.

Solution

a. $-5.2 - (-11.4) = -5.2 + 11.4 = 6.2$

Change the subtraction to addition. Replace −11.4 with its opposite.

b. $-\frac{3}{4} - \frac{2}{3} = -\frac{3}{4} + \left(-\frac{2}{3}\right) = -\frac{9}{12} + \left(-\frac{8}{12}\right) = -\frac{17}{12}$

Change the subtraction to addition. Replace $\frac{2}{3}$ with its opposite.

c. $4\pi - (-9\pi) = 4\pi + 9\pi = (4 + 9)\pi = 13\pi$

Change the subtraction to addition. Replace -9π with its opposite. ■

Reading the symbol "−" can be a bit tricky. The way you read it depends on where it appears. For example,

$$-5.2 - (-11.4)$$

is read "negative five point two minus negative eleven point four." Read parts (b) and (c) of Example 2 aloud. When is "−" read "negative" and when is it read "minus"?

✓ **CHECK POINT 2** Subtract:

a. $-3.4 - (-12.6)$ **b.** $-\frac{3}{5} - \frac{1}{3}$ **c.** $5\pi - (-2\pi)$.

2 Simplify a series of additions and subtractions.

Problems Containing a Series of Additions and Subtractions

In some problems, several additions and subtractions occur together. We begin by converting all subtractions to additions of opposites, or additive inverses.

Simplifying a Series of Additions and Subtractions

1. Change all subtractions to additions of opposites.
2. Group and then add all the positive numbers.
3. Group and then add all the negative numbers.
4. Add the results of steps 2 and 3.

EXAMPLE 3 Simplifying a Series of Additions and Subtractions

Simplify: $7 - (-5) - 11 - (-6) - 19$.

Solution

$7 - (-5) - 11 - (-6) - 19$

$= 7 + 5 + (-11) + 6 + (-19)$ — Write subtractions as additions of opposites.

$= (7 + 5 + 6) + [(-11) + (-19)]$ — Group the positive numbers. Group the negative numbers.

$= 18 + (-30)$ — Add the positive numbers. Add the negative numbers.

$= -12$ — Add the results. ■

✓ **CHECK POINT 3** Simplify: $10 - (-12) - 4 - (-3) - 6$.

3 Use the definition of subtraction to identify terms.

Subtraction and Algebraic Expressions

We know that the terms of an algebraic expression are separated by addition signs. Let's use this idea to identify the terms of the following algebraic expression:

$$9x - 4y - 5.$$

Because terms are separated by addition, we rewrite the subtractions in the algebraic expression as additions of opposites. Thus,

$$9x - 4y - 5 = 9x + (-4y) + (-5).$$

The three terms of the algebraic expression are $9x$, $-4y$, and -5.

EXAMPLE 4 Using the Definition of Subtraction to Identify Terms

Identify the terms of the algebraic expression:

$$2xy - 13y - 6.$$

Solution Rewrite the subtractions in the algebraic expression as additions of opposites.

$$2xy - 13y - 6 = 2xy + (-13y) + (-6)$$

First term; Second term; Third term

Because terms are separated by addition, the terms are $2xy$, $-13y$, and -6. ■

✓ **CHECK POINT 4** Identify the terms of the algebraic expression:

$$-6 + 4a - 7ab.$$

---

4 Use the subtraction definition to simplify algebraic expressions.

The procedure for subtracting real numbers can be used to simplify certain algebraic expressions that involve subtraction.

EXAMPLE 5 Simplifying Algebraic Expressions

Simplify:

a. $2 + 3x - 8x$ **b.** $-4x - 9y - 2x + 12y$.

Solution

a. $2 + 3x - 8x$ — This is the given algebraic expression.

$= 2 + 3x + (-8x)$ — Write the subtraction as the addition of an opposite.

$= 2 + [3 + (-8)]x$ — Apply the distributive property.

$= 2 + (-5x)$ — Add within the grouping symbols.

$= 2 - 5x$ — Be concise and express as subtraction.

b. $-4x - 9y - 2x + 12y$ — This is the given algebraic expression.

$= -4x + (-9y) + (-2x) + 12y$ — Write the subtractions as the additions of opposites.

$= -4x + (-2x) + (-9y) + 12y$ — Arrange like terms so that they are next to one another.

$= [-4 + (-2)]x + (-9 + 12)y$ — Apply the distributive property.

$= -6x + 3y$ — Add within the grouping symbols. ■

Great Question!

How can I speed up the process of subtracting like terms?

You can think of gains and losses of money to work some of the steps in Example 5 mentally:

- $3x - 8x = -5x$ A gain of 3 dollars followed by a loss of 8 dollars is a net loss of 5 dollars.
- $-9y + 12y = 3y$ A loss of 9 dollars followed by a gain of 12 dollars is a net gain of 3 dollars.

✓ **CHECK POINT 5** Simplify:

a. $4 + 2x - 9x$ **b.** $-3x - 10y - 6x + 14y$.

---

5 Solve problems involving subtraction.

Applications

Subtraction is used to solve problems in which the word *difference* appears. The difference between real numbers a and b is expressed as $a - b$.

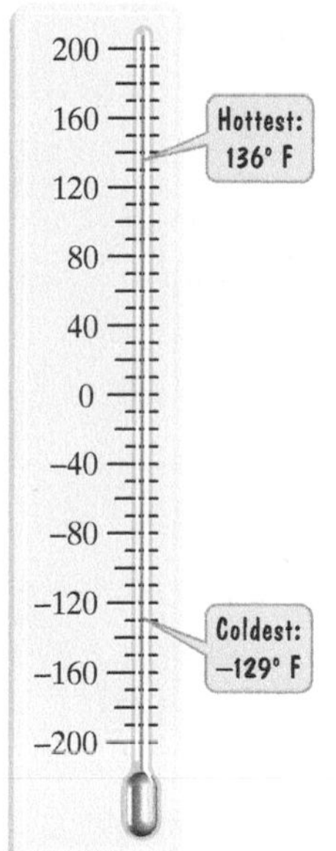

Figure 13

EXAMPLE 6 An Application of Subtraction Using the Word *Difference*

Figure 13 shows the hottest and coldest temperatures ever recorded on Earth. The record high was 136°F, recorded in Libya in 1922. The record low was −129°F, at the Vostok Scientific Station in Antarctica, in 1983. What is the difference between these highest and lowest temperatures? (*Source: The World Almanac Book of Records*, 2006)

Solution

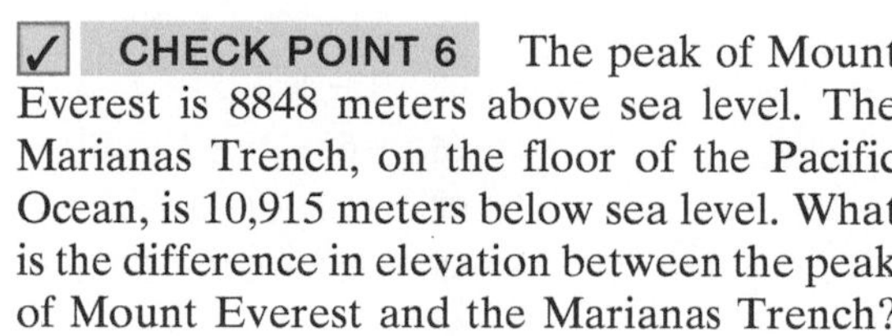

$$= 136 - (-129)$$
$$= 136 + 129 = 265$$

The difference between the two temperatures is 265°F. We can also say that the variation in temperature between these two world extremes is 265°F. ■

✓ **CHECK POINT 6** The peak of Mount Everest is 8848 meters above sea level. The Marianas Trench, on the floor of the Pacific Ocean, is 10,915 meters below sea level. What is the difference in elevation between the peak of Mount Everest and the Marianas Trench?

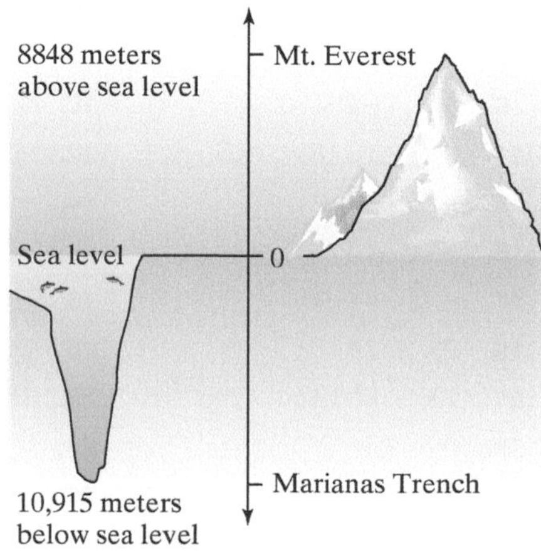

CONCEPT AND VOCABULARY CHECK

Fill in each blank so that the resulting statement is true.

1. $8 - 14 = 8 +$ ________
2. $8 - (-14) = 8 +$ ________
3. $-8 - (-14) = -8 +$ ________
4. $-8 - 14 =$ ________ $+$ ________
5. $7 - (-3) - 12 - 23 = 7 +$ ________ $+$ ________ $+$ ________
6. $9x - 4y - (-6) = 9x +$ ________ $+$ ________
7. The algebraic expression in Concept Check 6 contains ________ terms because terms are separated by ________.

6 EXERCISE SET

MyMathLab®

Watch the videos in MyMathLab

Download the MyDashBoard App

Practice Exercises

1. Consider the subtraction $5 - 12$.
   a. Find the opposite, or additive inverse, of 12.
   b. Rewrite the subtraction as the addition of the opposite of 12.
2. Consider the subtraction $4 - 10$.
   a. Find the opposite, or additive inverse, of 10.
   b. Rewrite the subtraction as the addition of the opposite of 10.
3. Consider the subtraction $5 - (-7)$.
   a. Find the opposite, or additive inverse, of -7.
   b. Rewrite the subtraction as the addition of the opposite of -7.
4. Consider the subtraction $2 - (-8)$.
   a. Find the opposite, or additive inverse, of -8.
   b. Rewrite the subtraction as the addition of the opposite of -8.

In Exercises 5–50, perform the indicated subtraction.

5. $14 - 8$
6. $15 - 2$
7. $8 - 14$
8. $2 - 15$
9. $3 - (-20)$
10. $5 - (-17)$
11. $-7 - (-18)$
12. $-5 - (-19)$
13. $-13 - (-2)$
14. $-21 - (-3)$
15. $-21 - 17$
16. $-29 - 21$
17. $-45 - (-45)$
18. $-65 - (-65)$
19. $23 - 23$
20. $26 - 26$
21. $13 - (-13)$
22. $15 - (-15)$
23. $0 - 13$
24. $0 - 15$
25. $0 - (-13)$
26. $0 - (-15)$
27. $\frac{3}{7} - \frac{5}{7}$
28. $\frac{4}{9} - \frac{7}{9}$
29. $\frac{1}{5} - \left(-\frac{3}{5}\right)$
30. $\frac{1}{7} - \left(-\frac{3}{7}\right)$
31. $-\frac{4}{5} - \frac{1}{5}$
32. $-\frac{4}{9} - \frac{1}{9}$
33. $-\frac{4}{5} - \left(-\frac{1}{5}\right)$
34. $-\frac{4}{9} - \left(-\frac{1}{9}\right)$
35. $\frac{1}{2} - \left(-\frac{1}{4}\right)$
36. $\frac{2}{5} - \left(-\frac{1}{10}\right)$
37. $\frac{1}{2} - \frac{1}{4}$
38. $\frac{2}{5} - \frac{1}{10}$
39. $9.8 - 2.2$
40. $5.7 - 3.3$
41. $-3.1 - (-1.1)$
42. $-4.6 - (-1.1)$
43. $1.3 - (-1.3)$
44. $1.4 - (-1.4)$
45. $-2.06 - (-2.06)$
46. $-3.47 - (-3.47)$
47. $5\pi - 2\pi$
48. $9\pi - 7\pi$
49. $3\pi - (-10\pi)$
50. $4\pi - (-12\pi)$

In Exercises 51–68, simplify each series of additions and subtractions.

51. $13 - 2 - (-8)$
52. $14 - 3 - (-7)$
53. $9 - 8 + 3 - 7$
54. $8 - 2 + 5 - 13$
55. $-6 - 2 + 3 - 10$
56. $-9 - 5 + 4 - 17$
57. $-10 - (-5) + 7 - 2$
58. $-6 - (-3) + 8 - 11$
59. $-23 - 11 - (-7) + (-25)$
60. $-19 - 8 - (-6) + (-21)$
61. $-823 - 146 - 50 - (-832)$
62. $-726 - 422 - 921 - (-816)$
63. $1 - \frac{2}{3} - \left(-\frac{5}{6}\right)$
64. $2 - \frac{3}{4} - \left(-\frac{7}{8}\right)$
65. $-0.16 - 5.2 - (-0.87)$
66. $-1.9 - 3 - (-0.26)$
67. $-\frac{3}{4} - \frac{1}{4} - \left(-\frac{5}{8}\right)$
68. $-\frac{1}{2} - \frac{2}{3} - \left(-\frac{1}{3}\right)$

In Exercises 69–72, identify the terms in each algebraic expression.

69. $-3x - 8y$ **70.** $-9a - 4b$

71. $12x - 5xy - 4$

72. $8a - 7ab - 13$

In Exercises 73–84, simplify each algebraic expression.

73. $3x - 9x$ **74.** $2x - 10x$

75. $4 + 7y - 17y$ **76.** $5 + 9y - 29y$

77. $2a + 5 - 9a$ **78.** $3a + 7 - 11a$

79. $4 - 6b - 8 - 3b$

80. $5 - 7b - 13 - 4b$

81. $13 - (-7x) + 4x - (-11)$

82. $15 - (-3x) + 8x - (-10)$

83. $-5x - 10y - 3x + 13y$

84. $-6x - 9y - 4x + 15y$

Practice PLUS

In Exercises 85–90, find the value of each expression.

85. $-|-9 - (-6)| - (-12)$

86. $-|-8 - (-2)| - (-6)$

87. $\frac{5}{8} - \left(\frac{1}{2} - \frac{3}{4}\right)$ **88.** $\frac{9}{10} - \left(\frac{1}{4} - \frac{7}{10}\right)$

89. $|-9 - (-3 + 7)| - |-17 - (-2)|$

90. $|24 - (-16)| - |-51 - (-31 + 2)|$

In Exercises 91–94, write each English phrase as an algebraic expression. Then simplify the expression. Let x represent the number.

91. The difference between 6 times a number and -5 times the number

92. The difference between 9 times a number and -4 times the number

93. The quotient of -2 and a number, subtracted from the quotient of -5 and the number

94. The quotient of -7 and a number, subtracted from the quotient of -12 and the number

Application Exercises

95. The peak of Mount Kilimanjaro, the highest point in Africa, is 19,321 feet above sea level. Qattara Depression, Egypt, one of the lowest points in Africa, is 436 feet below sea level. What is the difference in elevation between the peak of Mount Kilimanjaro and the Qattara Depression?

96. The peak of Mount Whitney is 14,494 feet above sea level. Mount Whitney can be seen directly above Death Valley, which is 282 feet below sea level. What is the difference in elevation between these geographic locations?

The bar graph shows the average daily low temperature for each month in Fairbanks, Alaska. Use the graph to solve Exercises 97–100.

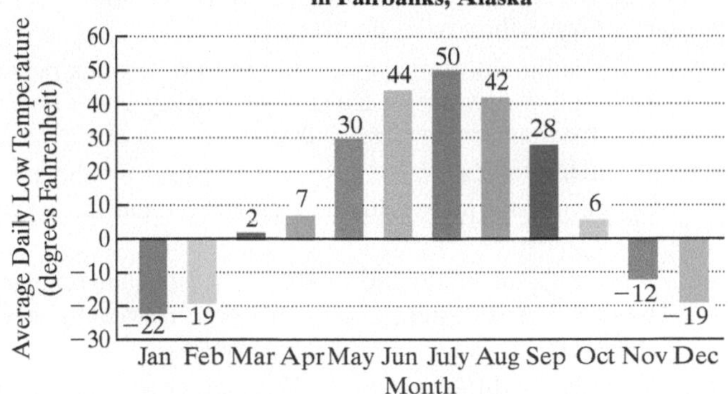

Source: The Weather Channel Enterprises, Inc.

97. What is the difference between the average daily low temperatures for March and February?

98. What is the difference between the average daily low temperatures for October and November?

99. How many degrees warmer is February's average low temperature than January's average low temperature?

100. How many degrees warmer is November's average low temperature than December's average low temperature?

Life expectancy for the average American man is 75.2 years; for a woman, it's 80.4 years. The number line, with points representing eight integers, indicates factors, many within our control, that can stretch or shrink one's probable life span. Use this information to solve Exercises 101–110.

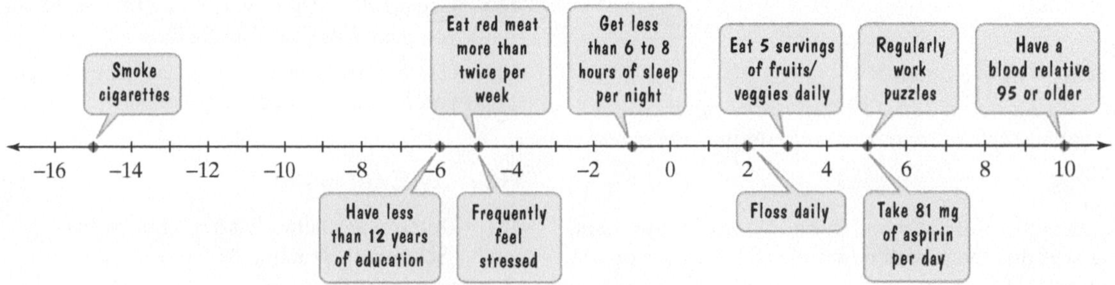

Source: Newsweek

(In Exercises 101–110, be sure to refer to the number line at the bottom of the previous page. Apologies from your author for this awkward, but unavoidable, page split.)

101. If you have a blood relative 95 or older and you smoke cigarettes, do you stretch or shrink your life span? By how many years?

102. If you floss daily and eat red meat more than twice per week, do you stretch or shrink your life span? By how many years?

103. If you frequently feel stressed and have less than 12 years of education, do you stretch or shrink your life span? By how many years?

104. If you get less than 6 to 8 hours of sleep per night and smoke cigarettes, do you stretch or shrink your life span? By how many years?

105. What is the difference in the life span between a person who regularly works puzzles and a person who eats red meat more than twice per week?

106. What is the difference in the life span between a person who eats 5 servings of fruits/veggies daily and a person who frequently feels stressed?

107. What happens to the life span for a person who takes 81 mg of aspirin per day and eats red meat more than twice per week?

108. What happens to the life span for a person who regularly works puzzles and a person who frequently feels stressed?

109. What is the difference in the life span between a person with less than 12 years of education and a person who smokes cigarettes?

110. What is the difference in the life span between a person who gets less than 6 to 8 hours of sleep per night and a person who smokes cigarettes?

Writing in Mathematics

111. Explain how to subtract real numbers.

112. How is $4 - (-2)$ read?

113. Explain how to simplify a series of additions and subtractions. Provide an example with your explanation.

114. Explain how to find the terms of the algebraic expression $5x - 2y - 7$.

115. Write a problem that can be solved by finding the difference between two numbers. At least one of the numbers should be negative. Then explain how to solve the problem.

Critical Thinking Exercises

Make Sense? *In Exercises 116–119, determine whether each statement "makes sense" or "does not make sense" and explain your reasoning.*

116. I already knew how to add positive and negative numbers, so there was not that much new to learn when it came to subtracting them.

117. I can find the closing price of stock PQR on Wednesday by subtracting the change in price, −1.23, from the closing price on Thursday, 47.19.

C3

STOCK PRICES

Thursday

Stock	Close	Change
ABC	31.54	0.47
XYZ	16.23	−0.87
PQR	47.19	−1.23
DEF	21.54	0.21

118. I found the variation in elevation between two heights by taking the difference between the high point and the low point.

119. I found the variation in U.S. temperature by subtracting the record low temperature, a negative number, from the record high temperature, a positive number.

In Exercises 120–123, determine whether each statement is true or false. If the statement is false, make the necessary change(s) to produce a true statement.

120. If a and b are negative numbers, then $a - b$ is sometimes a negative number.

121. $7 - (-2) = 5$

122. The difference between 0 and a negative number is always a positive number.

123. $|a - b| = |b - a|$

In Exercises 124–127, use the number line to determine whether each difference is positive or negative.

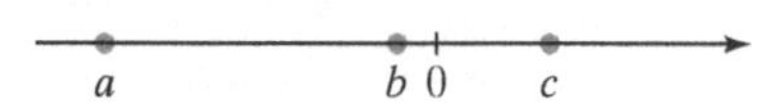

124. $c - a$

125. $a - b$

126. $b - c$

127. $0 - b$

128. Order the expressions $|x - y|$, $|x| - |y|$, and $|x + y|$ from least to greatest for $x = -6$ and $y = -8$.

Technology Exercises

129. Use a calculator to verify any five of the differences that you found in Exercises 5–46.

130. Use a calculator to verify any three of the answers that you found in Exercises 51–68.

Review Exercises

131. Determine whether 2 is a solution of $13x + 3 = 3(5x - 1)$. (Section 1, Example 4)

132. Simplify: $5(3x + 2y) + 6(5y)$. (Section 4, Example 11)

133. Give an example of an integer that is not a natural number. (Section 3; Example 5)

Preview Exercises

Exercises 134–136 will help you prepare for the material covered in the next section.

In Exercises 134–135, a multiplication is expressed as a repeated addition. Find this sum, indicated by a question mark.

134. $4(-3) = (-3) + (-3) + (-3) + (-3) = ?$

135. $3(-3) = (-3) + (-3) + (-3) = ?$

136. The list shows a pattern for various products.

$$
\begin{aligned}
2(-3) &= -6 \\
1(-3) &= -3 \\
0(-3) &= 0 \\
-1(-3) &= 3 \\
-2(-3) &= 6 \\
-3(-3) &= 9 \\
-4(-3) &= ?
\end{aligned}
$$

$2(-3) = (-3) + (-3) = -6$

Reading down the list, products keep increasing by 3.

Use this pattern to find $-4(-3)$.

SECTION 7

Multiplication and Division of Real Numbers

Objectives

1. Multiply real numbers.
2. Multiply more than two real numbers.
3. Find multiplicative inverses.
4. Use the definition of division.
5. Divide real numbers.
6. Simplify algebraic expressions involving multiplication.
7. Determine whether a number is a solution of an equation.
8. Use mathematical models involving multiplication and division.

Where the Boys Are, released in 1960, was the first college spring-break movie. Today, visitors to college campuses can't help but ask: Where are the boys?

Andres Rodriguez/Alamy

In 2007, 135 women received bachelor's degrees for every 100 men. In this section, we use data from a report by the U.S. Department of Education to develop mathematical models showing that this gender imbalance will widen in the coming years. Working with these models requires that we know how to multiply and divide real numbers.

Multiplying Real Numbers

Multiplication is repeated addition. For example, $5(-3)$ means that -3 is added five times:

$$5(-3) = (-3) + (-3) + (-3) + (-3) + (-3) = -15.$$

The result of the multiplication, -15, is called the **product** of 5 and -3. The numbers being multiplied, 5 and -3, are called the **factors** of the product.

Rules for multiplying real numbers are described in terms of absolute value. For example, $5(-3) = -15$ illustrates that the product of numbers with different signs is found by multiplying their absolute values. The product is negative.

$$5(-3) = -15$$

Multiply absolute values: $|5| \cdot |-3| = 5 \cdot 3 = 15$.

Factors have different signs and the product is negative.

The following rules are used to determine the sign of the product of two numbers:

1 Multiply real numbers.

The Product of Two Real Numbers

- The product of two real numbers with **different signs** is found by multiplying their absolute values. The product is **negative**.
- The product of two real numbers with the **same sign** is found by multiplying their absolute values. The product is **positive**.
- The product of 0 and any real number is 0. Thus, for any real number a,

$$a \cdot 0 = 0 \qquad \text{and} \qquad 0 \cdot a = 0.$$

EXAMPLE 1 Multiplying Real Numbers

Multiply:

a. $6(-3)$ **b.** $-\frac{1}{5} \cdot \frac{2}{3}$ **c.** $(-9)(-10)$ **d.** $(-1.4)(-2)$ **e.** $(-372)(0)$.

Solution

a. $6(-3) = -18$

Multiply absolute values: $6 \cdot 3 = 18$.

Different signs: negative product

b. $-\frac{1}{5} \cdot \frac{2}{3} = -\frac{2}{15}$

Multiply absolute values: $\frac{1}{5} \cdot \frac{2}{3} = \frac{1 \cdot 2}{5 \cdot 3} = \frac{2}{15}$.

Different signs: negative product

c. $(-9)(-10) = 90$

Multiply absolute values: $9 \cdot 10 = 90$.

Same sign: positive product

d. $(-1.4)(-2) = 2.8$

Multiply absolute values: $(1.4)(2) = 2.8$.

Same sign: positive product

e. $(-372)(0) = 0$

The product of 0 and any real number is 0: $a \cdot 0 = 0$. ■

✓ CHECK POINT 1 Multiply:

a. $8(-5)$ **b.** $-\frac{1}{3} \cdot \frac{4}{7}$ **c.** $(-12)(-3)$

d. $(-1.1)(-5)$ **e.** $(-543)(0)$.

2 Multiply more than two real numbers.

Multiplying More Than Two Numbers

How do we perform more than one multiplication, such as

$$-4(-3)(-2)?$$

Because of the associative and commutative properties, we can order and group the numbers in any manner. Each pair of negative numbers will produce a positive product. Thus, the product of an even number of negative numbers is always positive. By contrast, the product of an odd number of negative numbers is always negative.

$$-4(-3)(-2) = -24$$

Multiply absolute values: $4 \cdot 3 \cdot 2 = 24$.

Odd number of negative numbers (three): negative product

Multiplying More Than Two Numbers

1. Assuming that no factor is zero,
   - The product of an **even** number of **negative numbers** is **positive**.
   - The product of an **odd** number of **negative numbers** is **negative**.

   The multiplication is performed by multiplying the absolute values of the given numbers.
2. If any factor is 0, the product is 0.

EXAMPLE 2 Multiplying More Than Two Numbers

Multiply:

a. $(-3)(-1)(2)(-2)$ **b.** $(-1)(-2)(-2)(3)(-4)$.

Solution

a. $(-3)(-1)(2)(-2) = -12$

Multiply absolute values: $3 \cdot 1 \cdot 2 \cdot 2 = 12$.

Odd number of negative numbers (three): negative product

b. $(-1)(-2)(-2)(3)(-4) = 48$

Multiply absolute values: $1 \cdot 2 \cdot 2 \cdot 3 \cdot 4 = 48$.

Even number of negative numbers (four): positive product

■

✓ **CHECK POINT 2** Multiply:

a. $(-2)(3)(-1)(4)$ **b.** $(-1)(-3)(2)(-1)(5)$.

Is it always necessary to count the number of negative factors when multiplying more than two numbers? No. If any factor is 0, you can immediately write 0 for the product. For example,

$$(-37)(423)(0)(-55)(-3.7) = 0.$$

If any factor is 0, the product is 0.

3 Find multiplicative inverses.

The Meaning of Division

The result of dividing the real number a by the nonzero real number b is called the **quotient** of a and b. We can write this quotient as $a \div b$ or $\frac{a}{b}$.

We know that subtraction is defined in terms of addition of an additive inverse, or opposite:

$$a - b = a + (-b).$$

In a similar way, we can define division in terms of multiplication. For example, the quotient of 8 and 2 can be written as multiplication:

$$8 \div 2 = 8 \cdot \frac{1}{2}.$$

We call $\frac{1}{2}$ the *multiplicative inverse*, or *reciprocal*, of 2. Two numbers whose product is 1 are called **multiplicative inverses** or **reciprocals** of each other. Thus, the multiplicative inverse of 2 is $\frac{1}{2}$ and the multiplicative inverse of $\frac{1}{2}$ is 2 because $2 \cdot \frac{1}{2} = 1$.

EXAMPLE 3 Finding Multiplicative Inverses

Find the multiplicative inverse of each number:

a. 5 **b.** $\frac{1}{3}$ **c.** -4 **d.** $-\frac{4}{5}$.

Solution

a. The multiplicative inverse of 5 is $\frac{1}{5}$ because $5 \cdot \frac{1}{5} = 1$.

b. The multiplicative inverse of $\frac{1}{3}$ is 3 because $\frac{1}{3} \cdot 3 = 1$.

c. The multiplicative inverse of -4 is $-\frac{1}{4}$ because $(-4)\left(-\frac{1}{4}\right) = 1$.

d. The multiplicative inverse of $-\frac{4}{5}$ is $-\frac{5}{4}$ because $\left(-\frac{4}{5}\right)\left(-\frac{5}{4}\right) = 1$. ■

✓ **CHECK POINT 3** Find the multiplicative inverse of each number:

a. 7 **b.** $\frac{1}{8}$ **c.** -6 **d.** $-\frac{7}{13}$.

Can you think of a real number that has no multiplicative inverse? The number **0 has no multiplicative inverse** because 0 multiplied by any number is never 1, but always 0.

We now define division in terms of multiplication by a multiplicative inverse.

4 Use the definition of division.

Definition of Division

If a and b are real numbers and b is not 0, then the quotient of a and b is defined as

$$a \div b = a \cdot \frac{1}{b}.$$

In words: The quotient of two real numbers is the product of the first number and the multiplicative inverse of the second number.

EXAMPLE 4 Using the Definition of Division

Use the definition of division to find each quotient:

a. $-15 \div 3$ **b.** $\frac{-20}{-4}$.

Using Technology

You can use a calculator to multiply and divide signed numbers. Here are the keystrokes for finding

$$(-173)(-256):$$

Scientific Calculator

173 [+/−] [×] 256 [+/−] [=]

Graphing Calculator

[(−)] 173 [×] [(−)] 256 [ENTER]

The number 44288 should be displayed.
Division is performed in the same manner, using [÷] instead of [×]. What happens when you divide by 0? Try entering

8 [÷] 0

and pressing [=] or [ENTER].

Solution

a. $-15 \div 3 = -15 \cdot \frac{1}{3} = -5$

Change the division to multiplication. Replace 3 with its multiplicative inverse.

b. $\frac{-20}{-4} = -20 \cdot \left(-\frac{1}{4}\right) = 5$

Change the division to multiplication. Replace −4 with its multiplicative inverse. ■

✓ **CHECK POINT 4** Use the definition of division to find each quotient:

a. $-28 \div 7$ **b.** $\frac{-16}{-2}$.

---

5 Divide real numbers.

A Procedure for Dividing Real Numbers

Because the quotient $a \div b$ is defined as the product $a \cdot \frac{1}{b}$, the sign rules for dividing numbers are the same as the sign rules for multiplying them.

The Quotient of Two Real Numbers

- The quotient of two real numbers with **different signs** is found by dividing their absolute values. The quotient is **negative**.
- The quotient of two real numbers with the **same sign** is found by dividing their absolute values. The quotient is **positive**.
- Division of any number by zero is undefined.
- Any nonzero number divided into 0 is 0.

EXAMPLE 5 Dividing Real Numbers

Divide:

a. $\frac{8}{-2}$ **b.** $-\frac{3}{4} \div \left(-\frac{5}{9}\right)$ **c.** $\frac{-20.8}{4}$ **d.** $\frac{0}{-7}$.

Solution

a. $\frac{8}{-2} = -4$

Divide absolute values: $\frac{8}{2} = 4$.

Different signs: negative quotient

b. $-\frac{3}{4} \div \left(-\frac{5}{9}\right) = \frac{27}{20}$

Divide absolute values: $\frac{3}{4} \div \frac{5}{9} = \frac{3}{4} \cdot \frac{9}{5} = \frac{27}{20}$.

Same sign: positive quotient

c. $\frac{-20.8}{4} = -5.2$

Divide absolute values: $4\overline{)20.8}$ = 5.2.

Different signs: negative quotient

d. $\frac{0}{-7} = 0$

Any nonzero number divided into 0 is 0. ■

Great Question!

Why is zero under the line undefined?

Here's another reason why division by zero is undefined. We know that

$$\frac{12}{4} = 3 \text{ because } 3 \cdot 4 = 12.$$

Now think about $\frac{-7}{0}$. If

$$\frac{-7}{0} = ? \quad \text{then} \quad ? \cdot 0 = -7.$$

However, any real number multiplied by 0 is 0 and not −7. No matter what number we use to replace the question mark in $? \cdot 0 = -7$, we can never obtain −7.

Can you see why $\frac{0}{-7}$ must be 0? The definition of division tells us that

$$\frac{0}{-7} = 0 \cdot \left(-\frac{1}{7}\right)$$

and the product of 0 and any real number is 0. By contrast, the definition of division does not allow for division by 0 because 0 does not have a multiplicative inverse. It is incorrect to write

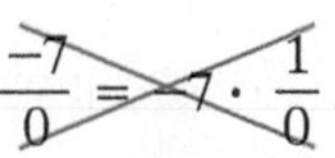

$$\frac{-7}{0} = -7 \cdot \frac{1}{0}.$$

0 does not have a multiplicative inverse.

Division by zero is not allowed, or not defined. Thus, $\frac{-7}{0}$ does not represent a real number. A real number can never have a denominator of 0.

✓ CHECK POINT 5 Divide:

a. $\frac{-32}{-4}$ **b.** $-\frac{2}{3} \div \frac{5}{4}$ **c.** $\frac{21.9}{-3}$ **d.** $\frac{0}{-5}$.

6 Simplify algebraic expressions involving multiplication.

Multiplication and Algebraic Expressions

In Section 4, we discussed the commutative and associative properties of multiplication. We also know that multiplication distributes over addition and subtraction. We now add some additional properties to our previous list (**Table 6**). These properties are frequently helpful in simplifying algebraic expressions.

Table 6 Additional Properties of Multiplication

Let *a* be a real number, a variable, or an algebraic expression.

Property	Meaning	Examples
Identity Property of Multiplication	1 can be deleted from a product. $a \cdot 1 = a$ $1 \cdot a = a$	• $\sqrt{3} \cdot 1 = \sqrt{3}$ • $1x = x$ • $1(2x + 3) = 2x + 3$
Inverse Property of Multiplication	If a is not 0: $a \cdot \frac{1}{a} = 1$ $\frac{1}{a} \cdot a = 1$ The product of a nonzero number and its multiplicative inverse, or reciprocal, gives 1, the multiplicative identity.	• $6 \cdot \frac{1}{6} = 1$ • $3x \cdot \frac{1}{3x} = 1$ (x is not 0.) • $\frac{1}{(y-2)} \cdot (y-2) = 1$ (y is not 2.)
Multiplication Property of −1	Negative 1 times a is the opposite, or additive inverse, of a. $-1 \cdot a = -a$ $a(-1) = -a$	• $-1 \cdot \sqrt{3} = -\sqrt{3}$ • $-1\left(-\frac{3}{4}\right) = \frac{3}{4}$ • $-1x = -x$ • $-(x + 4) = -1(x + 4) = -x - 4$
Double Negative Property	The opposite of $-a$ is a. $-(-a) = a$	• $-(-4) = 4$ • $-(-6y) = 6y$

In Table 6, we used two steps to remove the parentheses from $-(x + 4)$. First, we used the multiplication property of -1.

$$-(x + 4) = -1(x + 4)$$

Then we used the distributive property, distributing -1 to each term in parentheses.

$$-1(x + 4) = (-1)x + (-1)4 = -x + (-4) = -x - 4$$

There is a fast way to obtain $-(x + 4) = -x - 4$ in just one step.

Negative Signs and Parentheses

If a negative sign precedes parentheses, remove the parentheses and change the sign of every term within the parentheses.

Here are some examples that illustrate this method.

$$-(11x + 5) = -11x - 5$$
$$-(11x - 5) = -11x + 5$$
$$-(-11x + 5) = 11x - 5$$
$$-(-11x - 5) = 11x + 5$$

Discover for Yourself

Verify each simplification in Example 6 by substituting 5 for the variable. The value of the given expression should be the same as the value of the simplified expression. Which expression is easier to evaluate?

EXAMPLE 6 Simplifying Algebraic Expressions

Simplify:

a. $-2(3x)$ **b.** $6x + x$ **c.** $8a - 9a$ **d.** $-3(2x - 5)$ **e.** $-(3y - 8)$.

Solution We will show all steps in the solution process. However, you probably are working many of these steps mentally.

a. $-2(3x)$ — This is the given algebraic expression.
$= (-2 \cdot 3)x$ — Use the associative property and group the first two numbers.
$= -6x$ — Numbers with opposite signs have a negative product.

b. $6x + x$ — This is the given algebraic expression.
$= 6x + 1x$ — Use the multiplication property of 1.
$= (6 + 1)x$ — Apply the distributive property.
$= 7x$ — Add within parentheses.

c. $8a - 9a$ — This is the given algebraic expression.
$= (8 - 9)a$ — Apply the distributive property.
$= -1a$ — Subtract within parentheses: $8 - 9 = 8 + (-9) = -1$.
$= -a$ — Apply the multiplication property of -1.

d. $-3(2x - 5)$ — This is the given algebraic expression.
$= -3(2x) - (-3) \cdot (5)$ — Apply the distributive property.
$= -6x - (-15)$ — Multiply.
$= -6x + 15$ — Subtraction is the addition of an opposite.

e. $-(3y - 8)$ — This is the given algebraic expression.
$= -3y + 8$ — Remove parentheses by changing the sign of every term inside the parentheses. ■

✓ CHECK POINT 6 Simplify:

a. $-4(5x)$ **b.** $9x + x$ **c.** $13b - 14b$

d. $-7(3x - 4)$ **e.** $-(7y - 6)$.

EXAMPLE 7 Simplifying an Algebraic Expression

Simplify: $5(2y - 9) - (9y - 8)$.

Solution

$5(2y - 9) - (9y - 8)$	This is the given algebraic expression.
$= 5 \cdot 2y - 5 \cdot 9 - (9y - 8)$	Apply the distributive property over the first parentheses.
$= 10y - 45 - (9y - 8)$	Multiply.
$= 10y - 45 - 9y + 8$	Remove the remaining parentheses by changing the sign of each term within parentheses.
$= (10y - 9y) + (-45 + 8)$	Group like terms.
$= 1y + (-37)$	Combine like terms. For the variable terms, $10y - 9y = 10y + (-9y) = [10 + (-9)]y = 1y$.
$= y + (-37)$	Use the multiplication property of 1: $1y = y$.
$= y - 37$	Express addition of an opposite as subtraction. ■

✓ CHECK POINT 7 Simplify: $4(3y - 7) - (13y - 2)$.

A Summary of Operations with Real Numbers

Operations with real numbers are summarized in **Table 7**.

Table 7 Summary of Operations with Real Numbers

Signs of Numbers	Addition	Subtraction	Multiplication	Division
Both numbers are positive. Examples 8 and 2 2 and 8	Sum is always positive. $8 + 2 = 10$ $2 + 8 = 10$	Difference may be either positive or negative. $8 - 2 = 6$ $2 - 8 = -6$	Product is always positive. $8 \cdot 2 = 16$ $2 \cdot 8 = 16$	Quotient is always positive. $8 \div 2 = 4$ $2 \div 8 = \frac{1}{4}$
One number is positive and the other number is negative. Examples 8 and −2 −8 and 2	Sum may be either positive or negative. $8 + (-2) = 6$ $-8 + 2 = -6$	Difference may be either positive or negative. $8 - (-2) = 10$ $-8 - 2 = -10$	Product is always negative. $8(-2) = -16$ $-8(2) = -16$	Quotient is always negative. $8 \div (-2) = -4$ $-8 \div 2 = -4$
Both numbers are negative. Examples −8 and −2 −2 and −8	Sum is always negative. $-8 + (-2) = -10$ $-2 + (-8) = -10$	Difference may be either positive or negative. $-8 - (-2) = -6$ $-2 - (-8) = 6$	Product is always positive. $-8(-2) = 16$ $-2(-8) = 16$	Quotient is always positive. $-8 \div (-2) = 4$ $-2 \div (-8) = \frac{1}{4}$

7 Determine whether a number is a solution of an equation.

To determine if a number is a solution of an equation, it is often necessary to perform more than one operation with real numbers.

EXAMPLE 8 Determining Whether a Number Is a Solution of an Equation

Determine whether -3 is a solution of

$$6x + 14 = -7 - x.$$

Solution

$6x + 14 = -7 - x$ This is the given equation.

Is −3 a solution?

$6(-3) + 14 \stackrel{?}{=} -7 - (-3)$ Substitute −3 for x.

$-18 + 14 \stackrel{?}{=} -7 - (-3)$ Multiply: $6(-3) = -18$.

$-18 + 14 \stackrel{?}{=} -7 + 3$ Rewrite subtraction as addition of an opposite.

$-4 = -4$ This statement is true. Add: $-18 + 14 = -4$ and $-7 + 3 = -4$.

Because the values on both sides of the equation are the same, −3 is a solution of the equation. ■

✓ **CHECK POINT 8** Determine whether −3 is a solution of $2x - 5 = 8x + 7$.

---

8 Use mathematical models involving multiplication and division.

Applications

Mathematical models frequently involve multiplication and division.

EXAMPLE 9 Big (Lack of) Men on Campus

In 2007, 135 women received bachelor's degrees for every 100 men. According to the U.S. Department of Education, that gender imbalance will widen in the coming years, as shown by the bar graphs in **Figure 14**.

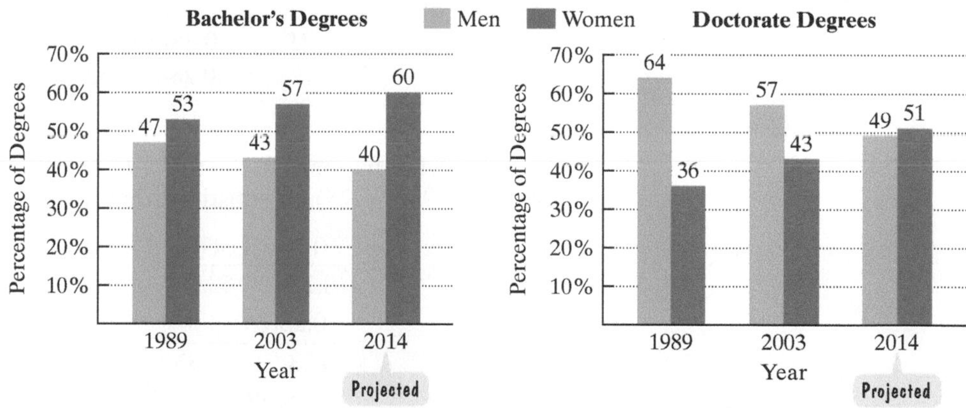

Figure 14

Source: U.S. Department of Education

The data for bachelor's degrees can be described by the following mathematical models:

$$M = -0.28n + 47$$

Percentage of bachelor's degrees awarded to men; Number of years after 1989

$$W = 0.28n + 53.$$

Percentage of bachelor's degrees awarded to women

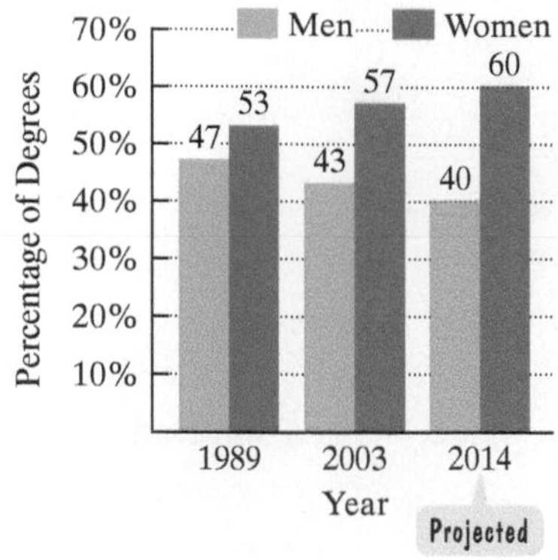

Figure 14 (repeated)

a. According to the first formula, $M = -0.28n + 47$, what percentage of bachelor's degrees were awarded to men in 2003? Does this underestimate or overestimate the actual percent shown in **Figure 14** for 2003? By how much?

b. A **ratio** is a comparison by division. Write a formula that describes the ratio of the percentage of bachelor's degrees received by men, $M = -0.28n + 47$, to the percentage of bachelor's degrees received by women, $W = 0.28n + 53$. Name this new mathematical model R, for ratio.

c. Use the formula for R to find the projected ratio of bachelor's degrees received by men to degrees received by women in 2014.

Solution

a. We are interested in the percentage of bachelor's degrees awarded to men in 2003. The year 2003 is 14 years after 1989: $2003 - 1989 = 14$. We substitute 14 for n in the formula for men and evaluate the formula.

$$M = -0.28n + 47$$ This is the model for the percentage of degrees awarded to men.

$$M = -0.28(14) + 47$$ Replace n with 14.

$$M = -3.92 + 47$$ Multiply: $-0.28(14) = -3.92$.

$$M = 43.08$$ Add. Use the sign of 47 and subtract absolute values:

$$\begin{array}{r} \overset{6\ 9\ 10}{47.\not{0}\not{0}} \\ -\ \ 3.92 \\ \hline 43.08 \end{array}$$

The model indicates that 43.08% of bachelor's degrees were awarded to men in 2003. Because the number displayed in **Figure 14** is 43%, the formula overestimates the actual percent by 0.08%.

b. Now we use division to write a model comparing the ratio, R, of bachelor's degrees received by men to degrees received by women.

$$R = \frac{M}{W} = \frac{-0.28n + 47}{0.28n + 53}$$

Formula for percentage of degrees awarded to men

Formula for percentage of degrees awarded to women

c. Let's see what happens to the ratio, R, in 2014. The year 2014 is 25 years after 1989 $(2014 - 1989 = 25)$, so substitute 25 for n.

$$R = \frac{-0.28n + 47}{0.28n + 53}$$ This is the model for the ratio of the percentage of degrees awarded to men and to women.

$$R = \frac{-0.28(25) + 47}{0.28(25) + 53}$$ Replace each occurrence of n with 25.

$$R = \frac{-7 + 47}{7 + 53}$$ Multiply: $-0.28(25) = -7$ and $0.28(25) = 7$.

$$R = \frac{40}{60}$$ Add: $-7 + 47 = 40$ and $7 + 53 = 60$.

The models for M and W give the projected percents for 2014 in **Figure 14.**

$$R = \frac{2}{3}$$ Reduce: $\frac{40}{60} = \frac{2 \cdot \not{20}}{3 \cdot \not{20}} = \frac{2}{3}$.

Our model for R, consistent with the actual data, shows that in 2014, the ratio of bachelor's degrees received by men to degrees received by women is projected to be 2 to 3. If model breakdown does not occur, three women will receive bachelor's degrees for every two men. ■

✓ **CHECK POINT 9** The data for doctorate degrees shown in **Figure 14** on page 81 can be described by $M = -0.6n + 64.4$, where M is the percentage of doctorate degrees awarded to men n years after 1989. According to this mathematical model, what percentage of doctorate degrees are projected to be received by men in 2014? Does this underestimate or overestimate the projection shown in **Figure 14**? By how much?

Achieving Success

Ask! Ask! Ask!

Do not be afraid to ask questions in class. Your professor may not realize that a concept is unclear until you raise your hand and ask a question. Other students who have problems asking questions in class will be appreciative that you have spoken up. Be polite and professional, but ask as many questions as required.

CONCEPT AND VOCABULARY CHECK

Use the choices below to fill in each blank so that the resulting statement is true:

positive   negative   0   undefined.

1. The product of two negative numbers is a/an ____________ number.
2. The product of a negative number and a positive number is a/an ____________ number.
3. The product of three negative numbers is a/an ____________ number.
4. The product of an even number of negative numbers is a/an ____________ number.
5. The product of two negative numbers and 0 is ____________.
6. The multiplicative inverse, or reciprocal, of a negative number is a/an ____________ number.
7. The quotient of a positive number and a negative number is a/an ____________ number.
8. The quotient of two negative numbers is a/an ____________ number.
9. The quotient of 0 and a negative number is ____________.
10. The quotient of a negative number and 0 is ____________.
11. The opposite of a negative number is a/an ____________ number.

7 EXERCISE SET

MyMathLab®

Watch the videos in MyMathLab

Download the MyDashBoard App

Practice Exercises

In Exercises 1–34, perform the indicated multiplication.

1. $5(-9)$
2. $10(-7)$
3. $(-8)(-3)$
4. $(-9)(-5)$
5. $(-3)(7)$
6. $(-4)(8)$
7. $(-19)(-1)$
8. $(-11)(-1)$
9. $0(-19)$
10. $0(-11)$
11. $\frac{1}{2}(-24)$
12. $\frac{1}{3}(-21)$
13. $\left(-\frac{3}{4}\right)(-12)$
14. $\left(-\frac{4}{5}\right)(-30)$
15. $-\frac{3}{5}\cdot\left(-\frac{4}{7}\right)$
16. $-\frac{5}{7}\cdot\left(-\frac{3}{8}\right)$
17. $-\frac{7}{9}\cdot\frac{2}{3}$
18. $-\frac{5}{11}\cdot\frac{2}{7}$
19. $3(-1.2)$
20. $4(-1.2)$
21. $-0.2(-0.6)$
22. $-0.3(-0.7)$
23. $(-5)(-2)(3)$
24. $(-6)(-3)(10)$
25. $(-4)(-3)(-1)(6)$ −72
26. $(-2)(-7)(-1)(3)$
27. $-2(-3)(-4)(-1)$
28. $-3(-2)(-5)(-1)$
29. $(-3)(-3)(-3)$
30. $(-4)(-4)(-4)$
31. $5(-3)(-1)(2)(3)$
32. $2(-5)(-2)(3)(1)$
33. $(-8)(-4)(0)(-17)(-6)$
34. $(-9)(-12)(-18)(0)(-3)$

In Exercises 35–42, find the multiplicative inverse of each number.

35. 4 **36.** 3 **37.** $\frac{1}{5}$

38. $\frac{1}{7}$ **39.** -10 **40.** -12

41. $-\frac{2}{5}$ **42.** $-\frac{4}{9}$

In Exercises 43–46,

a. *Rewrite the division as multiplication involving a multiplicative inverse.*

b. *Use the multiplication from part (a) to find the given quotient.*

43. $-32 \div 4$

44. $-18 \div 6$

45. $\frac{-60}{-5}$

46. $\frac{-30}{-5}$

In Exercises 47–76, perform the indicated division or state that the expression is undefined.

47. $\frac{12}{-4}$ **48.** $\frac{40}{-5}$ **49.** $\frac{-21}{3}$

50. $\frac{-60}{6}$ **51.** $\frac{-90}{-3}$ **52.** $\frac{-66}{-6}$

53. $\frac{0}{-7}$ **54.** $\frac{0}{-8}$ **55.** $\frac{7}{0}$

56. $\frac{-8}{0}$ **57.** $-15 \div 3$ **58.** $-80 \div 8$

59. $120 \div (-10)$ **60.** $130 \div (-10)$

61. $(-180) \div (-30)$ **62.** $(-150) \div (-25)$

63. $0 \div (-4)$ **64.** $0 \div (-10)$

65. $-4 \div 0$ **66.** $-10 \div 0$

67. $\frac{-12.9}{3}$ **68.** $\frac{-21.6}{3}$

69. $-\frac{1}{2} \div \left(-\frac{3}{5}\right)$ **70.** $-\frac{1}{2} \div \left(-\frac{7}{9}\right)$

71. $-\frac{14}{9} \div \frac{7}{8}$ **72.** $-\frac{5}{16} \div \frac{25}{8}$

73. $\frac{1}{3} \div \left(-\frac{1}{3}\right)$ **74.** $\frac{1}{5} \div \left(-\frac{1}{5}\right)$

75. $6 \div \left(-\frac{2}{5}\right)$ **76.** $8 \div \left(-\frac{2}{9}\right)$

In Exercises 77–96, simplify each algebraic expression.

77. $-5(2x)$ **78.** $-9(3x)$

79. $-4\left(-\frac{3}{4}y\right)$ **80.** $-5\left(-\frac{3}{5}y\right)$

81. $8x + x$ **82.** $12x + x$

83. $-5x + x$ **84.** $-6x + x$

85. $6b - 7b$ **86.** $12b - 13b$

87. $-y + 4y$ **88.** $-y + 9y$

89. $-4(2x - 3)$ **90.** $-3(4x - 5)$

91. $-3(-2x + 4)$ **92.** $-4(-3x + 2)$

93. $-(2y - 5)$ **94.** $-(3y - 1)$

95. $4(2y - 3) - (7y + 2)$

96. $5(3y - 1) - (14y - 2)$

In Exercises 97–108, determine whether the given number is a solution of the equation.

97. $4x = 2x - 10; -5$

98. $5x = 3x - 6; -3$

99. $-7y + 18 = -10y + 6; -4$

100. $-4y + 21 = -7y + 15; -2$

101. $5(w + 3) = 2w - 21; -10$

102. $6(w + 2) = 4w - 10; -9$

103. $4(6 - z) + 7z = 0; -8$

104. $5(7 - z) + 12z = 0; -5$

105. $14 - 2x = -4x + 7; -2\frac{1}{2}$

106. $16 - 4x = -2x + 21; -3\frac{1}{2}$

107. $\frac{5m - 1}{6} = \frac{3m - 2}{4}; -4$

108. $\frac{6m - 5}{11} = \frac{3m - 2}{5}; -1$

Practice PLUS

In Exercises 109–116, write a numerical expression for each phrase. Then simplify the numerical expression by performing the given operations.

109. 8 added to the product of 4 and -10

110. 14 added to the product of 3 and -15

111. The product of -9 and -3, decreased by -2

112. The product of -6 and -4, decreased by -5

113. The quotient of -18 and the sum of -15 and 12

114. The quotient of -25 and the sum of -21 and 16

115. The difference between -6 and the quotient of 12 and -4

116. The difference between -11 and the quotient of 20 and -5

Application Exercises

In Exercises 117–118, use the formula $C = \frac{5}{9}(F - 32)$ to express each Fahrenheit temperature, F, as its equivalent Celsius temperature, C.

117. -22°F

118. -31°F

In the years after warning labels were put on cigarettes packs, the number of smokers dropped from approximately two in five adults to one in five. The bar graph shows the percentage of American adults who smoked cigarettes for selected years from 1965 through 2009.

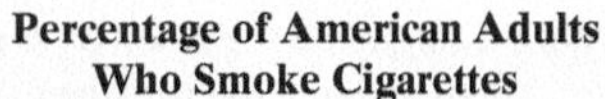

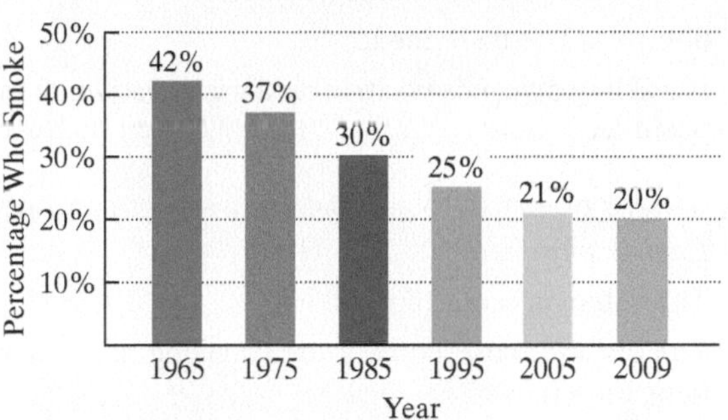

Source: Centers for Disease Control and Prevention

Here is a mathematical model that approximates the data displayed by the bar graph:

$$C = -0.5x + 41.$$

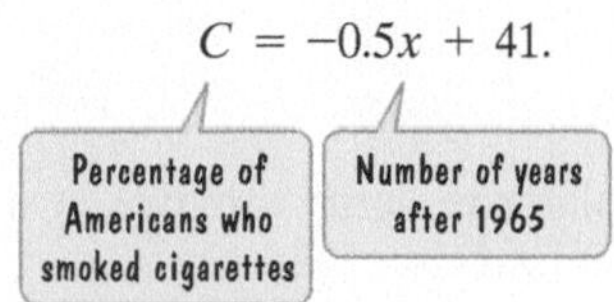

Use this formula to solve Exercises 119–120.

119. **a.** Does the mathematical model underestimate or overestimate the percentage of American adults who smoked cigarettes in 2009? By how much?

b. Use the mathematical model to project the percentage of American adults who will smoke cigarettes in 2015.

120. **a.** Use the mathematical model to determine the percentage of American adults who smoked cigarettes in 2005. How does this compare with the actual percentage displayed by the bar graph?

b. Use the mathematical model to project the percentage of American adults who will smoke cigarettes in 2019.

The graph shows the average number of hours per week women and men in the United States devoted to household chores and child care for five selected years from 1965 through 2005.

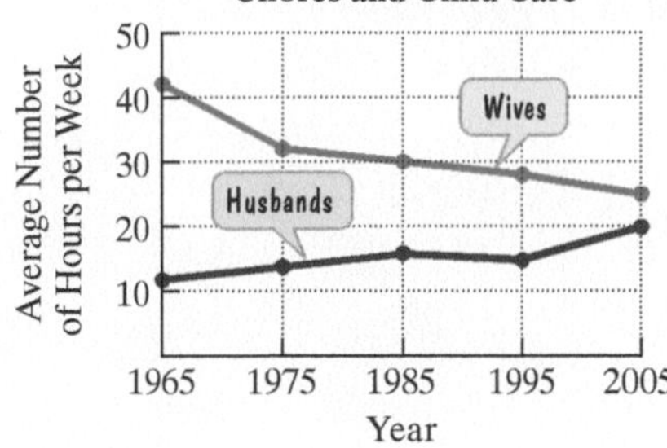

Source: Davis and Palladino, *Psychology*, Ninth Edition, Pearson, 2010.

The data can be described by the following mathematical models:

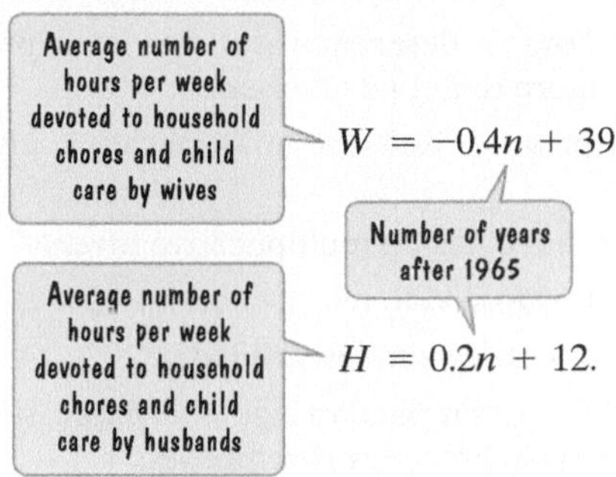

Use this information to solve Exercises 121–122.

121. **a.** Use the appropriate graph to estimate the average number of hours per week devoted to household chores and child care by wives in 2005.

b. Use the appropriate formula to determine the average number of hours per week devoted to household chores and child care by wives in 2005. How does this compare with your estimate in part (a)?

c. Write a formula that describes the difference between the average number of hours per week devoted to household chores and child care between wives and husbands n years after 1965. Name this new mathematical model D, for difference. Then simplify the algebraic expression in the model.

d. Use the simplified form of the mathematical model from part (c) to determine the difference in the number of hours per week women and men spent on household chores and child care in 2005. Does this overestimate or underestimate the difference displayed by the graphs?

122. **a.** Use the appropriate graph to estimate the average number of hours per week devoted to household chores and child care by wives in 1995.

b. Use the appropriate formula to determine the average number of hours per week devoted to household chores and child care by wives in 1995. How does this compare with your estimate in part (a)?

c. Write a formula that describes the ratio of the average number of hours per week devoted to household chores and child care by husbands to the average number of hours per week devoted by wives. Name this new mathematical model R, for ratio.

d. Use the mathematical model from part (c) to determine the fraction of time men spent on household chores and child care in 1995 compared with women. Express the fraction reduced to its lowest terms.

Writing in Mathematics

123. Explain how to multiply two real numbers. Provide examples with your explanation.

124. Explain how to determine the sign of a product that involves more than two numbers.

125. Explain how to find the multiplicative inverse of a number.

126. Why is it that 0 has no multiplicative inverse?

127. Explain how to divide real numbers.

128. Why is division by zero undefined?

129. Explain how to simplify an algebraic expression in which a negative sign precedes parentheses.

130. Do you believe that the trend in the graphs showing a decline in male college attendance (**Figure 14**) should be reversed by providing admissions preferences for men? Explain your position on this issue.

Critical Thinking Exercises

Make Sense? *In Exercises 131–134, determine whether each statement "makes sense" or "does not make sense" and explain your reasoning.*

131. I've noticed that the sign rules for dividing real numbers are slightly different than the sign rules for multiplying real numbers.

132. Just as two negative factors give a positive product, I've seen the same thing occur with double negatives in English:

That rumor is not unknown means That rumor is known.

133. This pattern suggests that multiplying two negative numbers results in a positive answer:

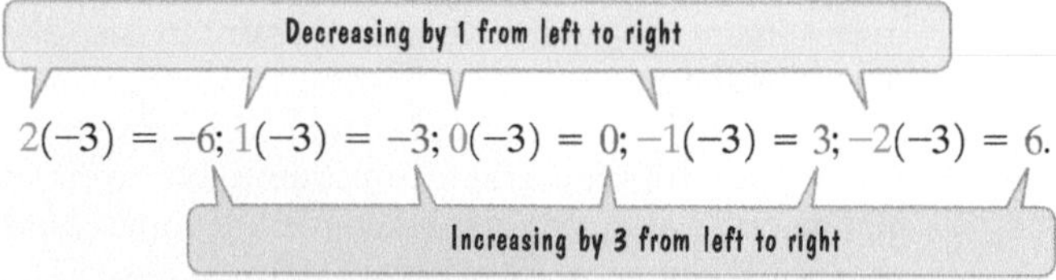

Decreasing by 1 from left to right
2(−3) = −6; 1(−3) = −3; 0(−3) = 0; −1(−3) = 3; −2(−3) = 6.
Increasing by 3 from left to right

134. When I used

$$R = \frac{M}{W} = \frac{-0.28n + 47}{0.28n + 53}$$

Number of years after 1989

to project the ratio of bachelor's degrees received by men to degrees received by women in 2020, I had to find the quotient of two negative numbers.

In Exercises 135–138, determine whether each statement is true or false. If the statement is false, make the necessary change(s) to produce a true statement.

135. Both the addition and the multiplication of two negative numbers result in a positive number.

136. Multiplying a negative number by a nonnegative number will always give a negative number.

137. $0 \div (-\sqrt{2})$ is undefined.

138. If a is negative, b is positive, and c is negative, then $\frac{a}{bc}$ is positive.

In Exercises 139–142, write an algebraic expression for the given English phrase.

139. The value, in cents, of x nickels

140. The distance covered by a car traveling at 50 miles per hour for x hours

141. The monthly salary, in dollars, for a person earning x dollars per year

142. The fraction of people in a room who are women if there are 40 women and x men in the room

Technology Exercises

143. Use a calculator to verify any five of the products that you found in Exercises 1–34.

144. Use a calculator to verify any five of the quotients that you found in Exercises 47–76.

145. Simplify using a calculator:

$$0.3(4.7x - 5.9) - 0.07(3.8x - 61).$$

146. Use your calculator to attempt to find the quotient of −3 and 0. Describe what happens. Does the same thing occur when finding the quotient of 0 and −3? Explain the difference. Finally, what happens when you enter the quotient of 0 and itself?

Review Exercises

In Exercises 147–149, perform the indicated operation.

147. $-6 + (-3)$ (Section 5, Example 3)

148. $-6 - (-3)$ (Section 6, Example 1)

149. $-6 \div (-3)$ (Section 7, Example 4)

Preview Exercises

Exercises 150–152 will help you prepare for the material covered in the next section. In each exercise, an expression with an exponent is written as a repeated multiplication. Find this product, indicated by a question mark.

150. $(-6)^2 = (-6)(-6) = ?$

151. $(-5)^3 = (-5)(-5)(-5) = ?$

152. $(-2)^4 = (-2)(-2)(-2)(-2) = ?$

SECTION 8

Exponents and Order of Operations

Objectives

1. Evaluate exponential expressions.
2. Simplify algebraic expressions with exponents.
3. Use the order of operations agreement.
4. Evaluate mathematical models.

Tony Freeman/PhotoEdit, Inc

Eat, drink, and be merry—for tomorrow we diet. But is there a way to avoid the extremes of merriment and dieting? In this section, we continue to see how mathematical models describe your world, including formulas that provide daily caloric needs for maintaining energy balance based on age and lifestyle.

1 Evaluate exponential expressions.

Natural Number Exponents

Although people do a great deal of talking, the total output since the beginning of gabble to the present day, including all baby talk, love songs, and congressional debates, only amounts to about 10 million billion words. This can be expressed as 16 factors of 10, or 10^{16} words.

Exponents such as 2, 3, 4, and so on are used to indicate repeated multiplication. For example,

$$10^2 = 10 \cdot 10 = 100,$$
$$10^3 = 10 \cdot 10 \cdot 10 = 1000, \quad 10^4 = 10 \cdot 10 \cdot 10 \cdot 10 = 10{,}000.$$

The 10 that is repeated when multiplying is called the **base**. The small numbers above and to the right of the base are called **exponents** or **powers**. The exponent tells the number of times the base is to be used when multiplying. In 10^3, the base is 10 and the exponent is 3.

Any number with an exponent of 1 is the number itself. Thus, $10^1 = 10$.

Multiplications that are expressed in exponential notation are read as follows:

10^1: "ten to the first power"

10^2: "ten to the second power" or "ten squared"

10^3: "ten to the third power" or "ten cubed"

10^4: "ten to the fourth power"

10^5: "ten to the fifth power"

etc.

Using Technology

You can use a calculator to evaluate exponential expressions. For example, to evaluate 5^3, press the following keys:

Many Scientific Calculators

5 [y^x] 3 [=]

Many Graphing Calculators

5 [∧] 3 [ENTER]

Although calculators have special keys to evaluate powers of ten and squaring bases, you can always use one of the sequences shown here.

Any real number can be used as the base. Thus,

$$7^2 = 7 \cdot 7 = 49 \quad \text{and} \quad (-3)^4 = (-3)(-3)(-3)(-3) = 81.$$

The bases are 7 and -3, respectively. Do not confuse $(-3)^4$ and -3^4.

$$-3^4 = -(3 \cdot 3 \cdot 3 \cdot 3) = -81$$

The negative is not taken to the power because it is not inside parentheses.

An exponent applies only to a base. A negative sign is not part of a base unless it appears in parentheses.

EXAMPLE 1 Evaluating Exponential Expressions

Evaluate:

a. 4^2 **b.** $(-5)^3$ **c.** $(-2)^4$ **d.** -2^4.

Solution

Exponent is 2.

a. $4^2 = 4 \cdot 4 = 16$ — The exponent indicates that the base is used as a factor two times.

Base is 4.

We read $4^2 = 16$ as "4 to the second power is 16" or "4 squared is 16."

Exponent is 3.

b. $(-5)^3 = (-5)(-5)(-5)$ — The exponent indicates that the base is used as a factor three times.

Base is −5.

$= -125$ — An odd number of negative factors yields a negative product.

We read $(-5)^3 = -125$ as "the number negative 5 to the third power is negative 125" or "negative 5 cubed is negative 125."

Exponent is 4.

c. $(-2)^4 = (-2)(-2)(-2)(-2)$ — The exponent indicates that the base is used as a factor four times.

Base is −2.

$= 16$ — An even number of negative factors yields a positive product.

We read $(-2)^4 = 16$ as "the number negative 2 to the fourth power is 16."

Exponent is 4.

d. $-2^4 = -(2 \cdot 2 \cdot 2 \cdot 2)$ — The negative is not inside parentheses and is not taken to the fourth power.

Base is 2.

$= -16$ — Multiply the twos and copy the negative.

We read $-2^4 = -16$ as "the negative of 2 raised to the fourth power is negative 16" or "the opposite, or additive inverse, of 2 raised to the fourth power is negative 16." ■

✓ **CHECK POINT 1** Evaluate:

a. 6^2 **b.** $(-4)^3$ **c.** $(-1)^4$ **d.** -1^4.

The formal algebraic definition of a natural number exponent summarizes our discussion:

Definition of a Natural Number Exponent

If b is a real number and n is a natural number,

Exponent

$$b^n = \underbrace{b \cdot b \cdot b \cdot \cdots \cdot b}_{b \text{ appears as a factor } n \text{ times.}}.$$

Base

b^n is read "the nth power of b" or "b to the nth power." Thus, the nth power of b is defined as the product of n factors of b. The expression b^n is called an **exponential expression.**

Furthermore, $b^1 = b$.

Blitzer Bonus

Integers, Karma, and Exponents

On Friday the 13th, are you a bit more careful crossing the street even if you don't consider yourself superstitious? Numerology, the belief that certain integers have greater significance and can be lucky or unlucky, is widespread in many cultures.

Integer	Connotation	Culture	Origin	Example
4	Negative	Chinese	The word for the number 4 sounds like the word for death.	Many buildings in China have floor-numbering systems that skip 40–49.
7	Positive	United States	In dice games, this prime number is the most frequently rolled number with two dice.	There was a spike in the number of couples getting married on 7/7/07.
8	Positive	Chinese	It's considered a sign of prosperity.	The Beijing Olympics began at 8 P.M. on 8/8/08.
13	Negative	Various	Various reasons, including the number of people at the Last Supper	Many buildings around the world do not label any floor "13."
18	Positive	Jewish	The Hebrew letters spelling *chai*, or living, are the 8th and 10th in the alphabet, adding up to 18	Monetary gifts for celebrations are often given in multiples of 18.
666	Negative	Christian	The New Testament's Book of Revelation identifies 666 as the "number of the beast," which some say refers to Satan.	In 2008, Reeves, Louisiana, eliminated 666 as the prefix of its phone numbers.

Although your author is not a numerologist, he is intrigued by curious exponential representations for 666:

$$666 = 6 + 6 + 6 + 6^3 + 6^3 + 6^3$$

$$666 = 1^3 + 2^3 + 3^3 + 4^3 + 5^3 + 6^3 + 5^3 + 4^3 + 3^3 + 2^3 + 1^3$$

$$666 = 2^2 + 3^2 + 5^2 + 7^2 + 11^2 + 13^2 + 17^2$$

Sum of the squares of the first seven prime numbers

$$666 = 1^6 - 2^6 + 3^6.$$

2 Simplify algebraic expressions with exponents.

Exponents and Algebraic Expressions

The distributive property can be used to simplify certain algebraic expressions that contain exponents. For example, we can use the distributive property to combine like terms in the algebraic expression $4x^2 + 6x^2$:

$$4x^2 + 6x^2 \quad = \quad (4 + 6)x^2 = 10x^2.$$

First term with variable factor x^2

Second term with variable factor x^2

The common variable factor is x^2.

Great Question!

When I add like terms, do I add exponents?

When adding algebraic expressions, if you have like terms you add only the numerical coefficients—not the exponents. **Exponents are never added when the operation is addition.** Avoid these common errors.

Incorrect

- ~~$7x^3 + 2x^3 = 9x^6$~~
- ~~$5x^2 + x^2 = 6x^4$~~
- ~~$3x^2 + 4x^3 = 7x^5$~~

EXAMPLE 2 Simplifying Algebraic Expressions

Simplify, if possible:

a. $7x^3 + 2x^3$ **b.** $5x^2 + x^2$ **c.** $3x^2 + 4x^3$.

Solution

a. $7x^3 + 2x^3$ There are two like terms with the same variable factor, namely x^3.

$= (7 + 2)x^3$ Apply the distributive property.

$= 9x^3$ Add within parentheses.

b. $5x^2 + x^2$ There are two like terms with the same variable factor, namely x^2.

$= 5x^2 + 1x^2$ Use the multiplication property of 1.

$= (5 + 1)x^2$ Apply the distributive property.

$= 6x^2$ Add within parentheses.

c. $3x^2 + 4x^3$ cannot be simplified. The terms $3x^2$ and $4x^3$ are not like terms because they have different variable factors, namely x^2 and x^3. ■

✓ **CHECK POINT 2** Simplify, if possible:

a. $16x^2 + 5x^2$ **b.** $7x^3 + x^3$ **c.** $10x^2 + 8x^3$.

---

3 Use the order of operations agreement.

Order of Operations

Suppose that you want to find the value of $3 + 7 \cdot 5$. Which procedure shown is correct?

$$3 + 7 \cdot 5 = 3 + 35 = 38 \quad \text{or} \quad 3 + 7 \cdot 5 = 10 \cdot 5 = 50$$

You know the answer because we introduced certain rules, called the **order of operations**, at the beginning of the chapter. One of these rules stated that if a problem contains no parentheses or other grouping symbols, perform multiplication before addition. Thus, the procedure on the left is correct because the multiplication of 7 and 5 is done first. Then the addition is performed. The correct answer is 38.

Some problems contain grouping symbols, such as parentheses, ( ); brackets, [ ]; braces, { }; absolute value symbols, | |; or fraction bars. These grouping symbols tell us what to do first. Here are two examples:

- $(3 + 7) \cdot 5 = 10 \cdot 5 = 50$
- $8|6 - 16| = 8|-10| = 8 \cdot 10 = 80.$

First, perform operations in grouping symbols.

Great Question!

How can I remember the order of operations?

This sentence may help: Please excuse my dear Aunt Sally.

Please	**P**arentheses
Excuse	**E**xponents
My	**M**ultiplication
Dear	**D**ivision
Aunt	**A**ddition
Sally	**S**ubtraction

Here are the rules for determining the order in which operations should be performed:

Order of Operations

1. Perform all operations within grouping symbols.
2. Evaluate all exponential expressions.
3. Do all multiplications and divisions in the order in which they occur, working from left to right.
4. Finally, do all additions and subtractions using one of the following procedures:
   a. Work from left to right and do additions and subtractions in the order in which they occur.

   or

   b. Rewrite subtractions as additions of opposites. Combine positive and negative numbers separately, and then add these results.

The last step in the order of operations indicates that you have a choice when working with additions and subtractions, although in this section we will perform these operations from left to right. However, when working with multiplications and divisions, you must perform these operations *as they occur* from left to right. For example,

$8 \div 4 \cdot 2 = 2 \cdot 2 = 4$ Do the division first because it occurs first.

$8 \cdot 4 \div 2 = 32 \div 2 = 16.$ Do the multiplication first because it occurs first.

EXAMPLE 3 Using the Order of Operations

Simplify: $18 + 2 \cdot 3 - 10.$

Solution There are no grouping symbols or exponential expressions. In cases like this, we multiply and divide before adding and subtracting.

$18 + 2 \cdot 3 - 10 = 18 + 6 - 10$ Multiply: $2 \cdot 3 = 6$.

$= 24 - 10$ Add and subtract from left to right: $18 + 6 = 24$.

$= 14$ Subtract: $24 - 10 = 14$. ■

✓ **CHECK POINT 3** Simplify: $20 + 4 \cdot 3 - 17.$

EXAMPLE 4 Using the Order of Operations

Simplify: $6^2 - 24 \div 2^2 \cdot 3 - 1.$

Solution There are no grouping symbols. Thus, we begin by evaluating exponential expressions. Then we multiply or divide. Finally, we add or subtract.

$6^2 - 24 \div 2^2 \cdot 3 - 1$

$= 36 - 24 \div 4 \cdot 3 - 1$ Evaluate exponential expressions: $6^2 = 6 \cdot 6 = 36$ and $2^2 = 2 \cdot 2 = 4$.

$= 36 - 6 \cdot 3 - 1$ Perform the multiplications and divisions from left to right. Start with $24 \div 4 = 6$.

$= 36 - 18 - 1$ Now do the multiplication: $6 \cdot 3 = 18$.

$= 18 - 1$ Finally, perform the subtraction from left to right: $36 - 18 = 18$.

$= 17$ Complete the subtraction: $18 - 1 = 17$. ■

✓ **CHECK POINT 4** Simplify: $7^2 - 48 \div 4^2 \cdot 5 - 2.$

EXAMPLE 5 Using the Order of Operations

Simplify:

a. $(2 \cdot 5)^2$ **b.** $2 \cdot 5^2$.

Solution

a. Because $(2 \cdot 5)^2$ contains grouping symbols, namely parentheses, we perform the operation within parentheses first.

$$(2 \cdot 5)^2 = 10^2 \quad \text{Multiply within parentheses: } 2 \cdot 5 = 10.$$
$$= 100 \quad \text{Evaluate the exponential expression: } 10^2 = 10 \cdot 10 = 100.$$

b. Because $2 \cdot 5^2$ does not contain grouping symbols, we begin by evaluating the exponential expression.

$$2 \cdot 5^2 = 2 \cdot 25 \quad \text{Evaluate the exponential expression: } 5^2 = 5 \cdot 5 = 25.$$
$$= 50 \quad \text{Now do the multiplication: } 2 \cdot 25 = 50. \blacksquare$$

✓ **CHECK POINT 5** Simplify:

a. $(3 \cdot 2)^2$ **b.** $3 \cdot 2^2$.

EXAMPLE 6 Using the Order of Operations

Simplify: $\left(\frac{1}{2}\right)^3 - \left(\frac{1}{2} - \frac{3}{4}\right)^2(-4)$.

Solution Because grouping symbols appear, we perform the operation within parentheses first.

$$\left(\frac{1}{2}\right)^3 - \left(\frac{1}{2} - \frac{3}{4}\right)^2(-4)$$

$$= \left(\frac{1}{2}\right)^3 - \left(-\frac{1}{4}\right)^2(-4) \quad \text{Work inside parentheses first: } \frac{1}{2} - \frac{3}{4} = \frac{2}{4} - \frac{3}{4} = \frac{2}{4} + \left(-\frac{3}{4}\right) = -\frac{1}{4}.$$

$$= \frac{1}{8} - \frac{1}{16}(-4) \quad \text{Evaluate exponential expressions: } \left(\frac{1}{2}\right)^3 = \frac{1}{2} \cdot \frac{1}{2} \cdot \frac{1}{2} = \frac{1}{8} \text{ and } \left(-\frac{1}{4}\right)^2 = \left(-\frac{1}{4}\right)\left(-\frac{1}{4}\right) = \frac{1}{16}.$$

$$= \frac{1}{8} - \left(-\frac{1}{4}\right) \quad \text{Multiply: } \frac{1}{16} \cdot \left(\frac{-4}{1}\right) = -\frac{4}{16} = -\frac{1}{4}.$$

$$= \frac{3}{8} \quad \text{Subtract: } \frac{1}{8} - \left(-\frac{1}{4}\right) = \frac{1}{8} + \frac{1}{4} = \frac{1}{8} + \frac{2}{8} = \frac{3}{8}. \blacksquare$$

✓ **CHECK POINT 6** Simplify: $\left(-\frac{1}{2}\right)^2 - \left(\frac{7}{10} - \frac{8}{15}\right)^2(-18)$.

Some expressions contain many grouping symbols. An example of such an expression is $2[5(4 - 7) + 9]$. The grouping symbols are the parentheses and the brackets.

The parentheses, the innermost grouping symbols, group $4 - 7$.

$$2[5(4 - 7) + 9]$$

The brackets, the outermost grouping symbols, group $5(4 - 7) + 9$.

When combinations of grouping symbols appear, **perform operations within the innermost grouping symbols first**. Then work to the outside, performing operations within the outermost grouping symbols.

EXAMPLE 7 Using the Order of Operations

Simplify: $2[5(4 - 7) + 9]$.

Solution

$2[5(4 - 7) + 9]$	
$= 2[5(-3) + 9]$	Work inside parentheses first: $4 - 7 = 4 + (-7) = -3$.
$= 2[-15 + 9]$	Work inside brackets and multiply: $5(-3) = -15$.
$= 2[-6]$	Add inside brackets: $-15 + 9 = -6$. The resulting problem can also be expressed as $2(-6)$.
$= -12$	Multiply: $2[-6] = -12$. ■

Parentheses can be used for both innermost and outermost grouping symbols. For example, the expression $2[5(4 - 7) + 9]$ can also be written $2(5(4 - 7) + 9)$. However, too many parentheses can be confusing. The use of both parentheses and brackets makes it easier to identify inner and outer groupings.

✓ **CHECK POINT 7** Simplify: $4[3(6 - 11) + 5]$.

EXAMPLE 8 Using the Order of Operations

Simplify: $18 \div 6 + 4[5 + 2(8 - 10)^3]$.

Solution

$18 \div 6 + 4[5 + 2(8 - 10)^3]$	
$= 18 \div 6 + 4[5 + 2(-2)^3]$	Work inside parentheses first: $8 - 10 = 8 + (-10) = -2$.
$= 18 \div 6 + 4[5 + 2(-8)]$	Work inside brackets and evaluate the exponential expression: $(-2)^3 = (-2)(-2)(-2) = -8$.
$= 18 \div 6 + 4[5 + (-16)]$	Work inside brackets and multiply: $2(-8) = -16$.
$= 18 \div 6 + 4[-11]$	Work inside brackets and add: $5 + (-16) = -11$.
$= 3 + 4[-11]$	Perform the multiplications and divisions from left to right. Start with $18 \div 6 = 3$.
$= 3 + (-44)$	Now do the multiplication: $4(-11) = -44$.
$= -41$	Finally, perform the addition: $3 + (-44) = -41$. ■

✓ **CHECK POINT 8** Simplify: $25 \div 5 + 3[4 + 2(7 - 9)^3]$.

Fraction bars are grouping symbols that separate expressions into two parts, the numerator and the denominator. Consider, for example,

$$\frac{2(3 - 12) + 6 \cdot 4}{2^4 + 1}.$$

The fraction bar is the grouping symbol.

The numerator is one part of the expression.

The denominator is the other part of the expression.

We can use brackets instead of the fraction bar. An equivalent expression for $\frac{2(3-12)+6\cdot 4}{2^4+1}$ is

$$[2(3-12)+6\cdot 4] \div [2^4+1].$$

The grouping suggests a method for simplifying expressions with fraction bars as grouping symbols:

- Simplify the numerator.
- Simplify the denominator.
- If possible, simplify the fraction.

EXAMPLE 9 Using the Order of Operations

Simplify: $\dfrac{2(3-12)+6\cdot 4}{2^4+1}$.

Solution

$$\frac{2(3-12)+6\cdot 4}{2^4+1}$$

$$=\frac{2(-9)+6\cdot 4}{16+1}$$

Work inside parentheses in the numerator: $3-12=3+(-12)=-9$. Evaluate the exponential expression in the denominator: $2^4=2\cdot 2\cdot 2\cdot 2=16$.

$$=\frac{-18+24}{16+1}$$

Multiply in the numerator: $2(-9)=-18$ and $6\cdot 4=24$.

$$=\frac{6}{17}$$

Perform the addition in the numerator and in the denominator. ■

✓ **CHECK POINT 9** Simplify: $\dfrac{5(4-9)+10\cdot 3}{2^3-1}$.

EXAMPLE 10 Using the Order of Operations

Evaluate: $-x^2-7x$ for $x=-2$.

Solution We begin by substituting -2 for each occurrence of x in the algebraic expression. Then we use the order of operations to evaluate the expression.

$$-x^2-7x$$

Replace x with -2. Place parentheses around -2.

$$=-(-2)^2-7(-2)$$

$$=-4-7(-2)$$

Evaluate the exponential expression: $(-2)^2=(-2)(-2)=4$.

$$=-4-(-14)$$

Multiply: $7(-2)=-14$.

$$=10$$

Subtract: $-4-(-14)=-4+14=10$. ■

✓ **CHECK POINT 10** Evaluate: $-x^2-4x$ for $x=-5$.

Some algebraic expressions contain two sets of grouping symbols. Using the order of operations, grouping symbols are removed from innermost (parentheses) to outermost (brackets).

EXAMPLE 11 Simplifying an Algebraic Expression

Simplify: $18x^2 + 4 - [6(x^2 - 2) + 5]$.

Solution

$$18x^2 + 4 - [6(x^2 - 2) + 5]$$

$= 18x^2 + 4 - [6x^2 - 12 + 5]$ Use the distributive property to remove parentheses: $6(x^2 - 2) = 6x^2 - 6 \cdot 2 = 6x^2 - 12$.

$= 18x^2 + 4 - [6x^2 - 7]$ Add inside brackets: $-12 + 5 = -7$.

$= 18x^2 + 4 - 6x^2 + 7$ Remove brackets by changing the sign of each term within brackets.

$= (18x^2 - 6x^2) + 4 + 7$ Group like terms.

$= 12x^2 + 11$ Combine like terms. ■

✓ **CHECK POINT 11** Simplify: $14x^2 + 5 - [7(x^2 - 2) + 4]$.

4 Evaluate mathematical models.

Applications

In Examples 12 and 13, we use the order of operations to evaluate mathematical models.

EXAMPLE 12 Modeling Caloric Needs

The bar graph in **Figure 15** shows the estimated number of calories per day needed to maintain energy balance for various gender and age groups for moderately active lifestyles. (Moderately active means a lifestyle that includes physical activity equivalent to walking 1.5 to 3 miles per day at 3 to 4 miles per hour, in addition to the light physical activity associated with typical day-to-day life.)

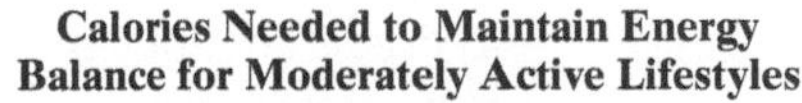

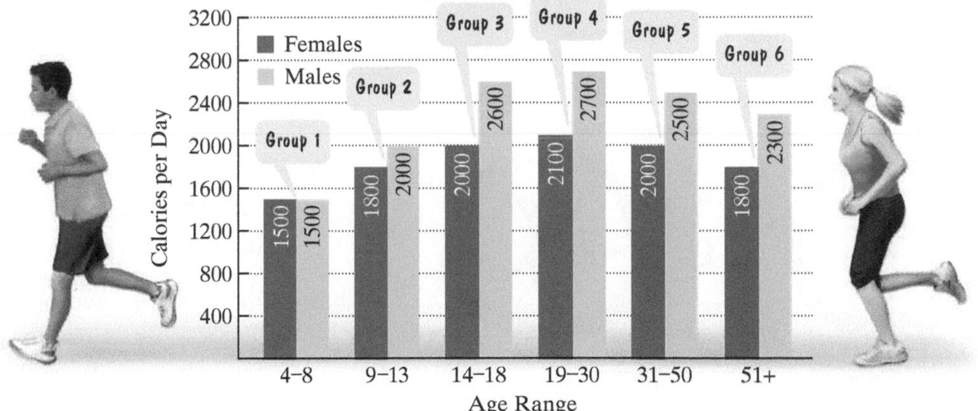

Figure 15

Source: U.S.D.A.

The mathematical model

$$F = -66x^2 + 526x + 1030$$

describes the number of calories needed per day, F, by females in age group x with moderately active lifestyles. According to the model, how many calories per day are needed by females between the ages of 19 and 30, inclusive, with this lifestyle? Does this underestimate or overestimate the number shown by the graph in **Figure 15**? By how much?

Solution Because the 19–30 age range is designated as group 4, we substitute 4 for x in the given model. Then we use the order of operations to find F, the number of calories needed per day by females between the ages of 19 and 30.

$F = -66x^2 + 526x + 1030$ — This is the given mathematical model.

$F = -66 \cdot 4^2 + 526 \cdot 4 + 1030$ — Replace each occurrence of x with 4.

$F = -66 \cdot 16 + 526 \cdot 4 + 1030$ — Evaluate the exponential expression: $4^2 = 4 \cdot 4 = 16$.

$F = -1056 + 2104 + 1030$ — Multiply from left to right: $-66 \cdot 16 = -1056$ and $526 \cdot 4 = 2104$.

$F = 2078$ — Add: $-1056 + 2104 = 1048$ and $1048 + 1030 = 2078$.

The formula indicates that females in the 19–30 age range with moderately active lifestyles need 2078 calories per day. **Figure 15** on the previous page indicates that 2100 calories are needed. Thus, the mathematical model underestimates caloric needs by 2100 − 2078 calories, or by 22 calories per day. ■

Great Question!

In the solution to Example 12, −1056 + 2104 + 1030 was simplified by performing the addition from left to right. Do I have to do it that way?

No. Here's another way to simplify the expression. First add the positive numbers

$$2104 + 1030 = 3134$$

and then add the negative number to that result:

$$3134 + (-1056) = 2078.$$

✓ **CHECK POINT 12** The mathematical model

$$M = -120x^2 + 998x + 590$$

describes the number of calories needed per day, M, by males in age group x with moderately active lifestyles. According to the model, how many calories per day are needed by males between the ages of 19 and 30, inclusive, with this lifestyle? Does this underestimate or overestimate the number shown by the graph in **Figure 15** on the previous page? By how much?

EXAMPLE 13 Shrinky-Dink Size without Rinky-Dink Style

A company has decided to jump into the pedal game with foldable, ultraportable bikes. Its fixed monthly costs are \$500,000 and it will cost \$400 to manufacture each bike. The average cost per bike, $\overline{C}$, for the company to manufacture x foldable bikes per month is modeled by

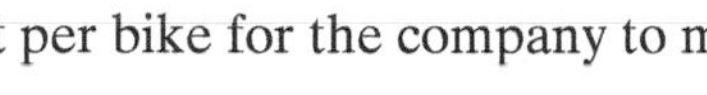

$$\overline{C} = \frac{400x + 500{,}000}{x}.$$

Find the average cost per bike for the company to manufacture

a. 10,000 bikes per month.

b. 50,000 bikes per month.

c. 100,000 bikes per month.

What happens to the average cost per bike as the production level increases?

Courtesy of Puma

Courtesy of Puma

Solution

a. We are interested in the average cost per bike for the company if 10,000 bikes are manufactured per month. Because x represents the number of bikes manufactured per month, we substitute 10,000 for x in the given mathematical model.

$$\overline{C} = \frac{400x + 500{,}000}{x} = \frac{400(10{,}000) + 500{,}000}{10{,}000} = \frac{4{,}000{,}000 + 500{,}000}{10{,}000}$$

$$= \frac{4{,}500{,}000}{10{,}000} = 450$$

The average cost per bike of producing 10,000 bikes per month is \$450.

b. Now, 50,000 bikes are manufactured per month. We find the average cost per bike by substituting 50,000 for x in the given mathematical model.

$$\overline{C} = \frac{400x + 500{,}000}{x} = \frac{400(50{,}000) + 500{,}000}{50{,}000} = \frac{20{,}000{,}000 + 500{,}000}{50{,}000}$$

$$= \frac{20{,}500{,}000}{50{,}000} = 410$$

The average cost per bike of producing 50,000 bikes per month is \$410.

c. Finally, the production level has increased to 100,000 bikes per month. We find the average cost per bike for the company by substituting 100,000 for x in the given mathematical model.

$$\overline{C} = \frac{400x + 500{,}000}{x} = \frac{400(100{,}000) + 500{,}000}{100{,}000} = \frac{40{,}000{,}000 + 500{,}000}{100{,}000}$$

$$= \frac{40{,}500{,}000}{100{,}000} = 405$$

The average cost per bike of producing 100,000 bikes per month is \$405.

As the production level increases, the average cost of producing each foldable bike decreases. This illustrates the difficulty with small businesses. It is nearly impossible to have competitively low prices when production levels are low. ■

The graph in **Figure 16** shows the relationship between production level and cost. The three points with the voice balloons illustrate our evaluations in Example 13. The other unlabeled points along the smooth blue curve represent the company's average costs for various production levels. The symbol ⫯ on the vertical axis indicates that there is a break in the values between 0 and 400. Thus, values for the average cost per bike begin at \$400.

The points that lie along the blue curve in **Figure 16** are falling from left to right. Can you see how this shows that the company's cost per foldable bike is decreasing as the production level increases?

Figure 16

✓ **CHECK POINT 13** A company that manufactures running shoes has weekly fixed costs of \$300,000 and it costs \$30 to manufacture each pair of running shoes. The average cost per pair of running shoes, $\overline{C}$, for the company to manufacture x pairs per week is modeled by

$$\overline{C} = \frac{30x + 300{,}000}{x}.$$

Find the average cost per pair of running shoes for the company to manufacture

a. 1000 pairs per week.

b. 10,000 pairs per week.

c. 100,000 pairs per week.

Achieving Success

Do not wait until the last minute to study for an exam. Cramming is a high-stress activity that forces your brain to make a lot of weak connections. No wonder crammers tend to forget everything they learned minutes after taking a test.

Preparing for Tests Using the Text

- Study the appropriate sections from the review chart in the Chapter Summary. The chart contains definitions, concepts, procedures, and examples. Review this chart and you'll know the most important material in each section!
- Work the assigned exercises from the Review Exercises. The Review Exercises contain the most significant problems for each of the chapter's sections.
- Find a quiet place to take the Chapter Test. Do not use notes, index cards, or any other resources. Check your answers and ask your professor to review any exercises you missed.

CONCEPT AND VOCABULARY CHECK

Fill in each blank so that the resulting statement is true.

1. In the expression b^n, b is called the ____________ and n is called the ____________.
2. The expression b^n is read ____________.

In the remaining items, use the choices below to fill in each blank:

add subtract multiply divide.

3. To simplify the expression $10 + 4 \cdot 5 - 30$, first ____________.
4. To simplify the expression $(10 + 4) \cdot 5 - 30$, first ____________.
5. To simplify the expression $36 - 24 \div 4 \cdot 3$, first ____________.
6. To simplify the expression $4[8 + 3(2 - 6)^2]$, first ____________.
7. To simplify the expression $8|5 - 4 \cdot 6|$, first ____________.

8 EXERCISE SET

MyMathLab®

Watch the videos in MyMathLab

Download the MyDashBoard App

Practice Exercises

In Exercises 1–14, evaluate each exponential expression.

1. 9^2
2. 3^2
3. 4^3
4. 6^3
5. $(-4)^2$
6. $(-10)^2$
7. $(-4)^3$
8. $(-10)^3$
9. $(-5)^4$
10. $(-1)^6$
11. -5^4
12. -1^6
13. -10^2
14. -8^2

In Exercises 15–28, simplify each algebraic expression, or explain why the expression cannot be simplified.

15. $7x^2 + 12x^2$
16. $6x^2 + 18x^2$
17. $10x^3 + 5x^3$
18. $14x^3 + 8x^3$
19. $8x^4 + x^4$
20. $14x^4 + x^4$
21. $26x^2 - 27x^2$
22. $29x^2 - 30x^2$
23. $27x^3 - 26x^3$
24. $30x^3 - 29x^3$
25. $5x^2 + 5x^3$
26. $8x^2 + 8x^3$
27. $16x^2 - 16x^2$
28. $34x^2 - x^2$

In Exercises 29–72, use the order of operations to simplify each expression.

29. $7 + 6 \cdot 3$
30. $3 + 4 \cdot 5$
31. $45 \div 5 \cdot 3$
32. $40 \div 4 \cdot 2$
33. $6 \cdot 8 \div 4$
34. $8 \cdot 6 \div 2$
35. $14 - 2 \cdot 6 + 3$
36. $36 - 12 \div 4 + 2$
37. $8^2 - 16 \div 2^2 \cdot 4 - 3$
38. $10^2 - 100 \div 5^2 \cdot 2 - 1$

39. $3(-2)^2 - 4(-3)^2$
40. $5(-3)^2 - 2(-4)^2$
41. $(4 \cdot 5)^2 - 4 \cdot 5^2$
42. $(3 \cdot 5)^2 - 3 \cdot 5^2$
43. $(2 - 6)^2 - (3 - 7)^2$
44. $(4 - 6)^2 - (5 - 9)^2$
45. $6(3 - 5)^3 - 2(1 - 3)^3$
46. $-3(-6 + 8)^3 - 5(-3 + 5)^3$
47. $[2(6 - 2)]^2$
48. $[3(4 - 6)]^3$
49. $2[5 + 2(9 - 4)]$
50. $3[4 + 3(10 - 8)]$
51. $[7 + 3(2^3 - 1)] \div 21$
52. $[11 - 4(2 - 3^3)] \div 37$
53. $\frac{10 + 8}{5^2 - 4^2}$
54. $\frac{6^2 - 4^2}{2 - (-8)}$
55. $\frac{37 + 15 \div (-3)}{2^4}$
56. $\frac{22 + 20 \div (-5)}{3^2}$
57. $\frac{(-11)(-4) + 2(-7)}{7 - (-3)}$
58. $\frac{-5(7 - 2) - 3(4 - 7)}{-13 - (-5)}$
59. $4|10 - (8 - 20)|$
60. $6|7 - 4 \cdot 3|$
61. $8(-10) + |4(-5)|$
62. $4(-15) + |3(-10)|$
63. $-2^2 + 4[16 \div (3 - 5)]$
64. $-3^2 + 2[20 \div (7 - 11)]$
65. $24 \div \frac{3^2}{8 - 5} - (-6)$
66. $30 \div \frac{5^2}{7 - 12} - (-9)$
67. $\frac{\frac{1}{4} - \frac{1}{2}}{\frac{1}{3}}$
68. $\frac{\frac{3}{5} - \frac{7}{10}}{\frac{1}{2}}$
69. $-\frac{9}{4}\left(\frac{1}{2}\right) + \frac{3}{4} \div \frac{5}{6}$
70. $\left[-\frac{4}{7} - \left(-\frac{2}{5}\right)\right]\left[-\frac{3}{8} + \left(-\frac{1}{9}\right)\right]$
71. $\frac{\frac{7}{9} - 3}{\frac{5}{6}} \div \frac{3}{2} + \frac{3}{4}$
72. $\frac{\frac{17}{25}}{\frac{3}{5} - 4} \div \frac{1}{5} + \frac{1}{2}$

In Exercises 73–80, evaluate each algebraic expression for the given value of the variable.

73. $x^2 + 5x; x = 3$
74. $x^2 - 2x; x = 6$
75. $3x^2 - 8x; x = -2$
76. $4x^2 - 2x; x = -3$
77. $-x^2 - 10x; x = -1$
78. $-x^2 - 14x; x = -1$
79. $\frac{6y - 4y^2}{y^2 - 15}; y = 5$
80. $\frac{3y - 2y^2}{y(y - 2)}; y = 5$

In Exercises 81–88, simplify each algebraic expression by removing parentheses and brackets.

81. $3[5(x - 2) + 1]$
82. $4[6(x - 3) + 1]$
83. $3[6 - (y + 1)]$
84. $5[2 - (y + 3)]$
85. $7 - 4[3 - (4y - 5)]$
86. $6 - 5[8 - (2y - 4)]$
87. $2(3x^2 - 5) - [4(2x^2 - 1) + 3]$
88. $4(6x^2 - 3) - [2(5x^2 - 1) + 1]$

Practice PLUS

In Exercises 89–92, express each sentence as a single numerical expression. Then use the order of operations to simplify the expression.

89. Cube −2. Subtract this exponential expression from −10.
90. Cube −5. Subtract this exponential expression from −100.
91. Subtract 10 from 7. Multiply this difference by 2. Square this product.
92. Subtract 11 from 9. Multiply this difference by 2. Raise this product to the fourth power.

In Exercises 93–96, let x represent the number. Express each sentence as a single algebraic expression. Then simplify the expression.

93. Multiply a number by 5. Add 8 to this product. Subtract this sum from the number.
94. Multiply a number by 3. Add 9 to this product. Subtract this sum from the number.
95. Cube a number. Subtract 4 from this exponential expression. Multiply this difference by 5.
96. Cube a number. Subtract 6 from this exponential expression. Multiply this difference by 4.

Application Exercises

The bar graph shows the estimated number of calories per day needed to maintain energy balance for various gender and age groups for sedentary lifestyles. (Sedentary means a lifestyle that includes only the light physical activity associated with typical day-to-day life.)

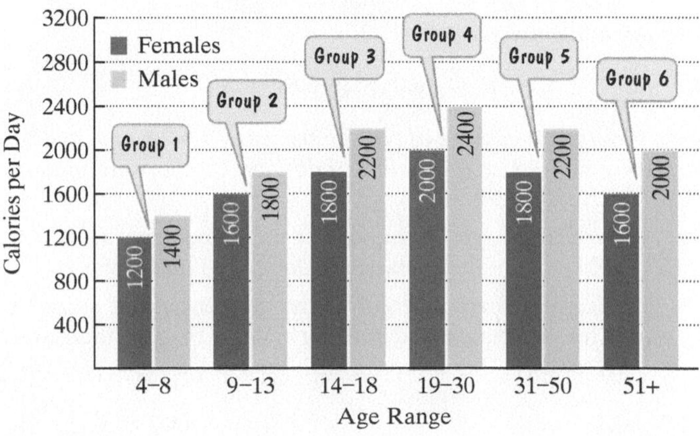

Source: U.S.D.A.

Use the appropriate information displayed by the graph at the bottom of the previous page to solve Exercises 97–98.

97. The mathematical model

$$F = -82x^2 + 654x + 620$$

describes the number of calories needed per day, F, by females in age group x with sedentary lifestyles. According to the model, how many calories per day are needed by females between the ages of 19 and 30, inclusive, with this lifestyle? Does this underestimate or overestimate the number shown by the graph? By how much?

98. The mathematical model

$$M = -96x^2 + 802x + 660$$

describes the number of calories needed per day, M, by males in age group x with sedentary lifestyles. According to the model, how many calories per day are needed by males between the ages of 19 and 30, inclusive, with this lifestyle? Does this underestimate or overestimate the number shown by the graph? By how much?

Salary after College. *In 2010, MonsterCollege surveyed 1250 U.S. college students expecting to graduate in the next several years. Respondents were asked the following question:*

> *What do you think your starting salary will be at your first job after college?*

The line graph shows the percentage of college students who anticipated various starting salaries.

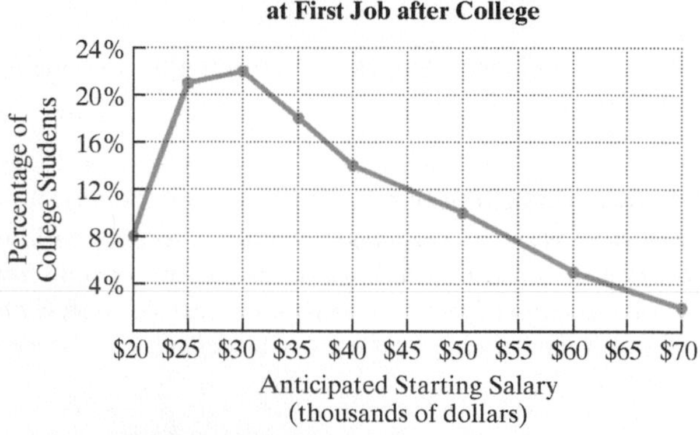

Source: MonsterCollege™

The mathematical model

$$p = -0.01s^2 + 0.8s + 3.7$$

describes the percentage of college students, p, who anticipated a starting salary s, in thousands of dollars. Use this information to solve Exercises 99–100.

99. **a.** Use the line graph to estimate the percentage of students who anticipated a starting salary of \$30 thousand.

b. Use the formula to find the percentage of students who anticipated a starting salary of \$30 thousand. How does this compare with your estimate in part (a)?

100. **a.** Use the line graph to estimate the percentage of students who anticipated a starting salary of \$40 thousand.

b. Use the formula to find the percentage of students who anticipated a starting salary of \$40 thousand. How does this compare with your estimate in part (a)?

In Palo Alto, California, a government agency ordered computer-related companies to contribute to a pool of money to clean up underground water supplies. (The companies had stored toxic chemicals in leaking underground containers.) The mathematical model

$$C = \frac{200x}{100 - x}$$

describes the cost, C, in tens of thousands of dollars, for removing x percent of the contaminants. Use this formula to solve Exercises 101–102.

101. **a.** Find the cost, in tens of thousands of dollars, for removing 50% of the contaminants.

b. Find the cost, in tens of thousands of dollars, for removing 80% of the contaminants.

c. Describe what is happening to the cost of the cleanup as the percentage of contaminant removed increases.

102. **a.** Find the cost, in tens of thousands of dollars, for removing 60% of the contaminants.

b. Find the cost, in tens of thousands of dollars, for removing 90% of the contaminants.

c. Describe what is happening to the cost of the cleanup as the percentage of contaminants removed increases.

Writing in Mathematics

103. Describe what it means to raise a number to a power. In your description, include a discussion of the difference between -5^2 and $(-5)^2$.

104. Explain how to simplify $4x^2 + 6x^2$. Why is the sum not equal to $10x^4$?

105. Why is the order of operations agreement needed?

Critical Thinking Exercises

Make Sense? *In Exercises 106–109, determine whether each statement "makes sense" or "does not make sense" and explain your reasoning.*

106. Without parentheses, an exponent has only the number next to it as its base.

107. I read that a certain star is 10^4 light-years from Earth, which means 100,000 light-years.

108. When I evaluated $(-1)^n$, I obtained positive numbers when n was even and negative numbers when n was odd.

109. The rules for the order of operations avoid the confusion of obtaining different results when I simplify the same expression.

In Exercises 110–113, determine whether each statement is true or false. If the statement is false, make the necessary change(s) to produce a true statement.

110. If x is -3, then the value of $-3x - 9$ is -18.

111. The algebraic expression $\frac{6x+6}{x+1}$ cannot have the same value when two different replacements are made for x such as $x = -3$ and $x = 2$.

112. The value of $\frac{|3-7| - 2^3}{(-2)(-3)}$ is the fraction that results when $\frac{1}{2}$ is subtracted from $-\frac{1}{3}$.

113. $-2(6 - 4^2)^3 = -2(6 - 16)^3$
$= -2(-10)^3 = (-20)^3 = -8000$

114. Simplify: $\frac{1}{4} - 6(2 + 8) \div \left(-\frac{1}{3}\right)\left(-\frac{1}{9}\right)$.

In Exercises 115–116, insert parentheses in each expression so that the resulting value is 45.

115. $2 \cdot 3 + 3 \cdot 5$

116. $2 \cdot 5 - \frac{1}{2} \cdot 10 \cdot 9$

Review Exercises

117. Simplify: $-8 - 2 - (-5) + 11$. (Section 6, Example 3)

118. Multiply: $-4(-1)(-3)(2)$. (Section 7, Example 2)

119. Give an example of a real number that is not an irrational number. (Section 3, Example 5).

Preview Exercises

In each exercise, determine whether the given number is a solution of the equation.

120. $-\frac{1}{2} = x - \frac{2}{3}; \frac{1}{6}$

121. $5y + 3 - 4y - 8 = 15; 20$

122. $4x + 2 = 3(x - 6) + 8; -11$

GROUP PROJECT

One measure of physical fitness is your *resting heart rate*. Generally speaking, the more fit you are, the lower your resting heart rate. The best time to take this measurement is when you first awaken in the morning, before you get out of bed. Lie on your back with no body parts crossed and take your pulse in your neck or wrist. Use your index and second fingers and count your pulse beat for one full minute to get your resting heart rate. A resting heart rate under 48 to 57 indicates high fitness, 58 to 62, above average fitness, 63 to 70, average fitness, 71 to 82, below average fitness, and 83 or more, low fitness.

Another measure of physical fitness is your percentage of body fat. You can estimate your body fat using the following formulas:

For men: Body fat $= -98.42 + 4.15w - 0.082b$

For women: Body fat $= -76.76 + 4.15w - 0.082b$

where w = waist measurement, in inches, and b = total body weight, in pounds. Then divide your body fat by your total weight to get your body fat percentage. For men, less than 15% is considered athletic, 25% about average. For women, less than 22% is considered athletic, 30% about average.

Each group member should bring his or her age, resting heart rate, and body fat percentage to the group. Using the data, the group should create three graphs.

a. Create a graph that shows age and resting heart rate for group members.

b. Create a graph that shows age and body fat percentage for group members.

c. Create a graph that shows resting heart rate and body fat percentage for group members.

For each graph, select the style (line or bar) that is most appropriate.

Summary

Definitions and Concepts	Examples

Section 1 Introduction to Algebra: Variables and Mathematical Models

A letter that represents a variety of different numbers is called a variable. An algebraic expression is a combination of variables, numbers, and operation symbols. To evaluate an algebraic expression, substitute a given number for the variable and simplify:

1. Perform calculations within parentheses first.
2. Perform multiplication before addition or subtraction.

(A more detailed order of operations is given in Section 8.)

Evaluate $6(x - 3) + 4x$ for $x = 5$.

Replace x with 5.

$$6(5 - 3) + 4 \cdot 5$$
$$= 6(2) + 4 \cdot 5$$
$$= 12 + 20$$
$$= 32$$

Here are some key words for translating into algebraic expressions:

- Addition: plus, sum, more than, increased by
- Subtraction: minus, difference, less than, decreased by
- Multiplication: times, product, twice, multiplied by
- Division: divide, quotient, ratio, divided by

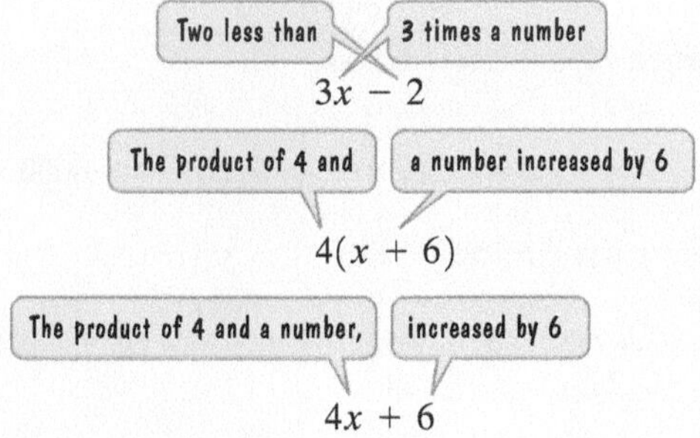

An equation is a statement that two algebraic expressions are equal. Solutions of an equation are values of the variable that make the equation a true statement. To determine whether a number is a solution, substitute that number for the variable and evaluate each side of the equation. If the values on both sides of the equation are the same, the number is a solution.

Is 5 a solution of

$$3(3x + 5) = 10x + 10?$$

Substitute 5 for x.

$$3(3 \cdot 5 + 5) \stackrel{?}{=} 10 \cdot 5 + 10$$
$$3(15 + 5) \stackrel{?}{=} 50 + 10$$
$$3(20) \stackrel{?}{=} 60$$
$$60 = 60, \quad \text{true}$$

The true statement indicates that 5 is a solution.

A formula is an equation that expresses a relationship between two or more variables. The process of finding formulas to describe real-world phenomena is called mathematical modeling. Such formulas, together with the meaning assigned to the variables, are called mathematical models. These formulas model, or describe, the relationship among the variables.

The formulas

$$M = 0.2n + 12$$

and

$$W = -0.4n + 39$$

model the time each week that men, M, and women, W, devoted to housework n years after 1965.

Definitions and Concepts	Examples

Section 2 Fractions in Algebra

Mixed Numbers and Improper Fractions

A mixed number consists of the addition of a natural number (1, 2, 3, . . .) and a fraction, expressed without the use of an addition sign. An improper fraction has a numerator that is greater than its denominator. To convert a mixed number to an improper fraction, multiply the denominator by the natural number and add the numerator. Then place this result over the original denominator.

To convert an improper fraction to a mixed number, divide the denominator into the numerator and write the mixed number using

$$\text{quotient}\,\frac{\text{remainder}}{\text{original denominator}}.$$

Convert $5\frac{3}{7}$ to an improper fraction.

$$5\frac{3}{7} = \frac{7\cdot5+3}{7} = \frac{35+3}{7} = \frac{38}{7}$$

Convert $\frac{14}{3}$ to a mixed number.

$$\frac{14}{3} = 4\frac{2}{3} \qquad \begin{array}{r} 4 \\ 3\overline{)14} \\ \underline{12} \\ 2 \end{array}$$

A prime number is a natural number greater than 1 that has only itself and 1 as factors. A composite number is a natural number greater than 1 that is not a prime number. The prime factorization of a composite number is the expression of the composite number as the product of prime numbers.

Find the prime factorization:

$$\begin{aligned} 60 &= 6\cdot10 \\ &= 2\cdot3\cdot2\cdot5 \end{aligned}$$

A fraction is reduced to its lowest terms when the numerator and denominator have no common factors other than 1. To reduce a fraction to its lowest terms, divide both the numerator and the denominator by their greatest common factor. The greatest common factor can be found by inspection or prime factorizations of the numerator and the denominator.

Reduce to lowest terms:

$$\frac{8}{14} = \frac{\cancel{2}\cdot4}{\cancel{2}\cdot7} = \frac{4}{7}$$

Multiplying Fractions

The product of two or more fractions is the product of their numerators divided by the product of their denominators.

Multiply:

$$\frac{2}{7}\cdot\frac{5}{9} = \frac{2\cdot5}{7\cdot9} = \frac{10}{63}$$

Dividing Fractions

The quotient of two fractions is the first multiplied by the reciprocal (or multiplicative inverse) of the second.

Divide:

$$\frac{4}{9}\div\frac{3}{7} = \frac{4}{9}\cdot\frac{7}{3} = \frac{4\cdot7}{9\cdot3} = \frac{28}{27}$$

Adding and Subtracting Fractions with Identical Denominators

Add or subtract numerators. Put this result over the common denominator.

Subtract:

$$\frac{5}{8}-\frac{3}{8} = \frac{5-3}{8} = \frac{2}{8} = \frac{\cancel{2}\cdot1}{\cancel{2}\cdot4} = \frac{1}{4}$$

Adding and Subtracting Fractions with Unlike Denominators

Rewrite the fractions as equivalent fractions with the least common denominator. Then add or subtract numerators, putting this result over the common denominator.

Add:

$$\begin{aligned} \frac{3}{8}+\frac{5}{12} &= \frac{3\cdot3}{8\cdot3}+\frac{5\cdot2}{12\cdot2} \\ &= \frac{9}{24}+\frac{10}{24} = \frac{19}{24} \end{aligned}$$

The LCD is 24.

Definitions and Concepts	Examples

Section 2 Fractions in Algebra (continued)

Fractions appear throughout algebra. Many formulas and mathematical models contain fractions. Operations with fractions can be used to determine whether a particular fraction is a solution of an equation. When used with fractions, the word *of* represents multiplication.

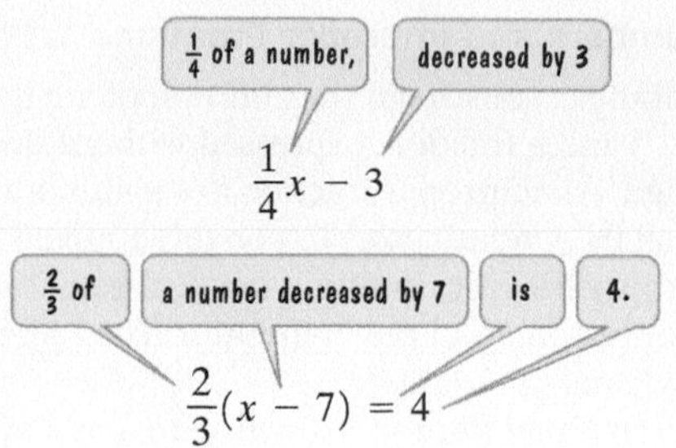

Section 3 The Real Numbers

A set is a collection of objects, called elements, whose contents can be clearly determined.

$\{a, b, c\}$

A line used to visualize numbers is called a number line.

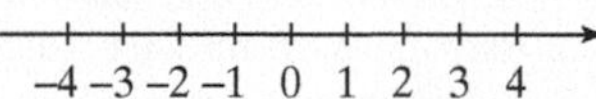

Real Numbers: the set of all numbers that can be represented by points on the number line

The Sets That Make Up the Real Numbers

- Natural Numbers: $\{1, 2, 3, 4, \ldots\}$
- Whole Numbers: $\{0, 1, 2, 3, 4, \ldots\}$
- Integers: $\{\ldots, -3, -2, -1, 0, 1, 2, 3, \ldots\}$
- Rational Numbers: the set of numbers that can be expressed as the quotient of an integer and a nonzero integer; can be expressed as terminating or repeating decimals
- Irrational Numbers: the set of numbers that cannot be expressed as the quotient of integers; decimal representations neither terminate nor repeat.

Given the set

$$\left\{-1.4, 0, 0.\overline{7}, \frac{9}{10}, \sqrt{2}, \sqrt{4}\right\}$$

list the

- natural numbers: $\sqrt{4}$, or 2
- whole numbers: 0, $\sqrt{4}$
- integers: 0, $\sqrt{4}$
- rational numbers: $-1.4, 0, 0.\overline{7}, \frac{9}{10}, \sqrt{4}$
- irrational numbers: $\sqrt{2}$
- real numbers:

$$-1.4, 0, 0.\overline{7}, \frac{9}{10}, \sqrt{2}, \sqrt{4}$$

For any two real numbers, a and b, a is less than b if a is to the left of b on the number line.

Inequality Symbols

$<$: is less than	$>$: is greater than
$\leq$: is less than or equal to	$\geq$: is greater than or equal to

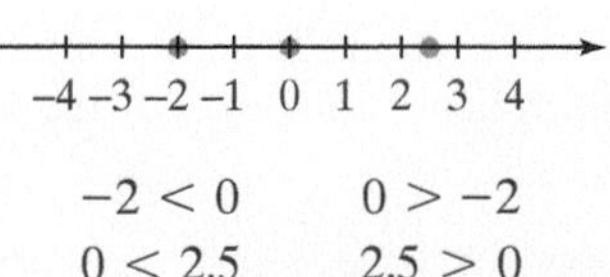

$-2 < 0$ $\quad$ $0 > -2$

$0 < 2.5$ $\quad$ $2.5 > 0$

The absolute value of a, written $|a|$, is the distance from 0 to a on the number line.

$|4| = 4 \quad |0| = 0 \quad |-6| = 6$

Definitions and Concepts	Examples

Section 4 Basic Rules of Algebra

Terms of an algebraic expression are separated by addition. The parts of each term that are multiplied are its factors. The numerical part of a term is its coefficient. Like terms have the same variable factors raised to the same powers.

- An expression with three terms:

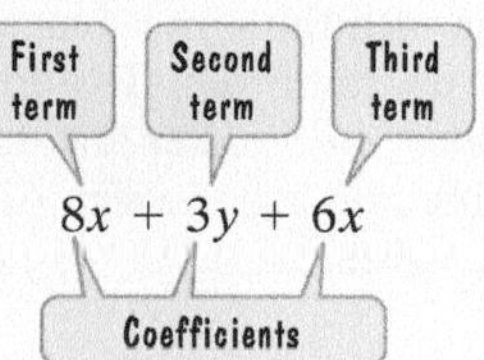

The like terms are $8x$ and $6x$.

Properties of Real Numbers and Algebraic Expressions

- Commutative Properties:

$$a + b = b + a$$
$$ab = ba$$

- Associative Properties:

$$(a + b) + c = a + (b + c)$$
$$(ab)c = a(bc)$$

- Distributive Properties:

$$a(b + c) = ab + ac$$
$$(b + c)a = ba + ca$$
$$a(b - c) = ab - ac$$
$$(b - c)a = ba - ca$$
$$a(b + c + d) = ab + ac + ad$$

Commutative of Addition:

$$5x + 4 = 4 + 5x$$

Commutative of Multiplication:

$$5x + 4 = x5 + 4$$

Associative of Addition:

$$6 + (4 + x) = (6 + 4) + x = 10 + x$$

Associative of Multiplication:

$$7(10x) = (7 \cdot 10)x = 70x$$

Distributive:

$$8(x + 5 + 4y) = 8x + 40 + 32y$$

Distributive to Combine Like Terms:

$$8x + 12x = (8 + 12)x = 20x$$

Simplifying Algebraic Expressions

Use the distributive property to remove grouping symbols. Then combine like terms.

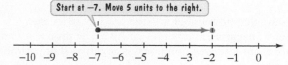

$$4(5x + 7) + 13x$$
$$= 20x + 28 + 13x$$
$$= (20x + 13x) + 28$$
$$= 33x + 28$$

Section 5 Addition of Real Numbers

Sums on a Number Line

To find $a + b$, the sum of a and b, on a number line, start at a. If b is positive, move b units to the right. If b is negative, move $|b|$ units to the left. If b is 0, stay at a. The number where we finish on the number line represents $a + b$.

$$-7 + 5 = -2$$

Start at −7. Move 5 units to the right.

−10 −9 −8 −7 −6 −5 −4 −3 −2 −1 0

Additive inverses, or opposites, are pairs of real numbers that are the same number of units from zero on the number line, but on opposite sides of zero.

- Identity Property of Addition:

$$a + 0 = 0 \qquad 0 + a = a$$

- Inverse Property of Addition:

$$a + (-a) = 0 \qquad (-a) + a = 0$$

The additive inverse (or opposite) of 4 is -4.
The additive inverse of -1.7 is 1.7.

Identity Property of Addition:

$$4x + 0 = 4x$$

Inverse Property of Addition:

$$4x + (-4x) = 0$$

Definitions and Concepts	Examples

Section 5 Addition of Real Numbers (continued)

Addition without a Number Line

To add two numbers with the same sign, add their absolute values and use their common sign. To add two numbers with different signs, subtract the smaller absolute value from the greater absolute value and use the sign of the number with the greater absolute value.

Add:

$$10 + 4 = 14$$
$$-4 + (-6) = -10$$
$$-30 + 5 = -25$$
$$12 + (-8) = 4$$

To add a series of positive and negative numbers, add all the positive numbers and add all the negative numbers. Then add the resulting positive and negative sums.

$$\begin{aligned} &5 + (-3) + (-7) + 2 \\ &= (5 + 2) + [(-3) + (-7)] \\ &= 7 + (-10) \\ &= -3 \end{aligned}$$

Section 6 Subtraction of Real Numbers

To subtract b from a, add the opposite, or additive inverse, of b to a:

$$a - b = a + (-b).$$

The result is called the difference between a and b.

Subtract:

$$-7 - (-5) = -7 + 5 = -2$$
$$\begin{aligned} -\frac{3}{4} - \frac{1}{2} &= -\frac{3}{4} + \left(-\frac{1}{2}\right) \\ &= -\frac{3}{4} + \left(-\frac{2}{4}\right) = -\frac{5}{4} \end{aligned}$$

To simplify a series of additions and subtractions, change all subtractions to additions of opposites. Then use the procedure for adding a series of positive and negative numbers.

Simplify:

$$\begin{aligned} &-6 - 2 - (-3) + 10 \\ &= -6 + (-2) + 3 + 10 \\ &= -8 + 13 \\ &= 5 \end{aligned}$$

Section 7 Multiplication and Division of Real Numbers

The result of multiplying a and b, ab, is called the product of a and b. If the two numbers have different signs, the product is negative. If the two numbers have the same sign, the product is positive. If either number is 0, the product is 0.

Multiply:

$$-5(-10) = 50$$
$$\frac{3}{4}\left(-\frac{5}{7}\right) = -\frac{3}{4}\cdot\frac{5}{7} = -\frac{15}{28}$$

Assuming that no number is 0, the product of an even number of negative numbers is positive. The product of an odd number of negative numbers is negative. If any number is 0, the product is 0.

Multiply:

$$(-3)(-2)(-1)(-4) = 24$$
$$(-3)(2)(-1)(-4) = -24$$

The result of dividing the real number a by the nonzero real number b is called the quotient of a and b. If two numbers have different signs, their quotient is negative. If two numbers have the same sign, their quotient is positive. Division by zero is undefined.

Divide:

$$\frac{21}{-3} = -7$$
$$-\frac{1}{3} \div (-3) = \frac{1}{3}\cdot\frac{1}{3} = \frac{1}{9}$$

Definitions and Concepts	Examples

Section 7 Multiplication and Division of Real Numbers (continued)

Two numbers whose product is 1 are called multiplicative inverses, or reciprocals, of each other. The number 0 has no multiplicative inverse.

- Identity Property of Multiplication

$$a \cdot 1 = a \qquad 1 \cdot a = a$$

- Inverse Property of Multiplication
  If a is not 0:

$$a \cdot \frac{1}{a} = 1 \qquad \frac{1}{a} \cdot a = 1$$

- Multiplication Property of -1

$$-1a = -a \qquad a(-1) = -a$$

- Double Negative Property

$$-(-a) = a$$

The multiplicative inverse of 4 is $\frac{1}{4}$.

The multiplicative inverse of $-\frac{1}{3}$ is -3.

Simplify:

$$1x = x$$

$$7x \cdot \frac{1}{7x} = 1, \quad x \neq 0$$

$$4x - 5x = -1x = -x$$

$$-(-7y) = 7y$$

If a negative sign precedes parentheses, remove parentheses and change the sign of every term within parentheses.

Simplify:

$$-(7x - 3y + 2) = -7x + 3y - 2$$

Section 8 Exponents and Order of Operations

If b is a real number and n is a natural number, b^n, the nth power of b, is the product of n factors of b. Furthermore, $b^1 = b$.

Evaluate:

$$8^2 = 8 \cdot 8 = 64$$

$$(-5)^3 = (-5)(-5)(-5) = -125$$

Order of Operations

1. Perform operations within grouping symbols, starting with the innermost grouping symbols. Grouping symbols include parentheses, brackets, fraction bars, and absolute value symbols.
2. Evaluate exponential expressions.
3. Multiply and divide, from left to right.
4. Add and subtract. In this step, you have a choice. You can add and subtract in order from left to right. You can also rewrite subtractions as additions of opposites, combine positive and negative numbers separately, and then add these results.

Simplify:

$$\begin{aligned} &5(4 - 6)^2 - 2(1 - 3)^3 \\ &= 5(-2)^2 - 2(-2)^3 \\ &= 5(4) - 2(-8) \\ &= 20 - (-16) \\ &= 20 + 16 = 36 \end{aligned}$$

Some algebraic expressions contain two sets of grouping symbols: parentheses, the inner grouping symbols, and brackets, the outer grouping symbols. To simplify such expressions, use the order of operations and remove grouping symbols from innermost (parentheses) to outermost (brackets).

Simplify:

$$\begin{aligned} &5 - 3[2(x + 1) - 7] \\ &= 5 - 3[2x + 2 - 7] \\ &= 5 - 3[2x - 5] \\ &= 5 - 6x + 15 \\ &= -6x + 20 \end{aligned}$$

CHAPTER REVIEW EXERCISES

1 *In Exercises 1–2, evaluate each expression for $x = 6$.*

1. $10 + 5x$

2. $8(x - 2) + 3x$

In Exercises 3–4, evaluate each expression for $x = 8$ and $y = 10$.

3. $\frac{40}{x} - \frac{y}{5}$

4. $3(2y + x)$

In Exercises 5–8, translate from English to an algebraic expression or equation, whichever is appropriate. Let the variable x represent the number.

5. Six subtracted from the product of 7 and a number

6. The quotient of a number and 5, decreased by 2, is 18.

7. Nine less twice a number is 14.

8. The product of 3 and 7 more than a number

In Exercises 9–11, determine whether the given number is a solution of the equation.

9. $4x + 5 = 13; 3$

10. $2y + 7 = 4y - 5; 6$

11. $3(w + 1) + 11 = 2(w + 8); 2$

Exercises 12–13 involve an experiment on memory. Students in a language class are asked to memorize 40 vocabulary words in Latin, a language with which they are not familiar. After studying the words for one day, students are tested each day after to see how many words they remember. The class average is taken and the results are shown as ten points on a line graph.

Average Number of Words Remembered Over Time

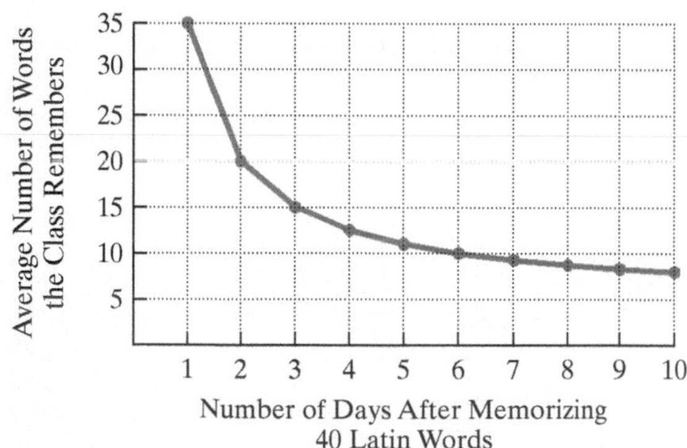

12. Use the line graph to estimate the average number of Latin words the class remembered after 5 days.

13. The mathematical model

$$L = \frac{5n + 30}{n}$$

describes the average number of Latin words remembered by the students, L, after n days. Use the formula to find the average number of words remembered after 5 days. How well does this compare with your estimate from Exercise 12?

14. Average annual premiums for employer-sponsored family health policies more than doubled in the past decade. The bar graph shows the average cost of a family health insurance plan in the United States for six selected years from 2000 through 2009.

Average Cost of a Family Health Insurance Plan

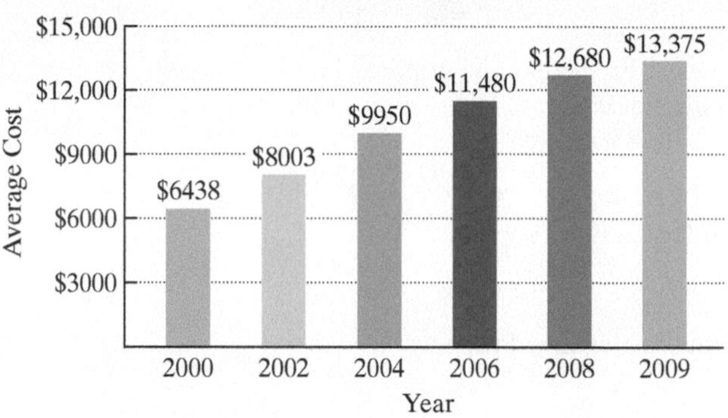

Source: Kaiser Family Foundation

Here is a mathematical model that approximates the data displayed by the bar graph:

$$C = 783n + 6522.$$

Average cost of a family health insurance plan (C)

Number of years after 2000 (n)

a. Use the formula to find the average cost of a family health insurance plan in 2009. Does the mathematical model underestimate or overestimate the actual cost shown by the bar graph? By how much?

b. If trends from 2000 through 2009 continue, use the formula to project the average cost of a family health insurance plan in 2020.

2 *In Exercises 15–16, convert each mixed number to an improper fraction.*

15. $3\frac{2}{7}$

16. $5\frac{9}{11}$

In Exercises 17–18, convert each improper fraction to a mixed number.

17. $\frac{17}{9}$

18. $\frac{27}{5}$

In Exercises 19–21, identify each natural number as prime or composite. If the number is composite, find its prime factorization.

19. 60

20. 63

21. 67

In Exercises 22–23, simplify each fraction by reducing it to its lowest terms.

22. $\frac{15}{33}$

23. $\frac{40}{75}$

In Exercises 24–29, perform the indicated operation. Where possible, reduce the answer to its lowest terms.

24. $\frac{3}{5} \cdot \frac{7}{10}$ **25.** $\frac{4}{5} \div \frac{3}{10}$ **26.** $1\frac{2}{3} \div 6\frac{2}{3}$

27. $\frac{2}{9} + \frac{4}{9}$ **28.** $\frac{5}{6} + \frac{7}{9}$ **29.** $\frac{3}{4} - \frac{2}{15}$

In Exercises 30–31, determine whether the given number is a solution of the equation.

30. $x - \frac{3}{4} = \frac{7}{4}; 2\frac{1}{2}$

31. $\frac{2}{3}w = \frac{1}{15}w + \frac{3}{5}; 2$

In Exercises 32–33, translate from English to an algebraic expression or equation, whichever is appropriate. Let the variable x represent the number.

32. Two decreased by half of a number is $\frac{1}{4}$ of the number.

33. $\frac{3}{5}$ of a number increased by 6

34. Suppose that the target heart rate, H, in beats per minute, for your exercise goal is given by

$$H = \frac{4}{5}(220 - a),$$

where a is your age. If you are 30 years old, what is your target heart rate?

3 *In Exercises 35–36, graph each real number on a number line.*

35. -2.5 **36.** $4\frac{3}{4}$

In Exercises 37–38, express each rational number as a decimal.

37. $\frac{5}{8}$ **38.** $\frac{3}{11}$

39. Consider the set

$$\left\{-17, -\frac{9}{13}, 0, 0.75, \sqrt{2}, \pi, \sqrt{81}\right\}.$$

List all numbers from the set that are: **a.** natural numbers, **b.** whole numbers, **c.** integers, **d.** rational numbers, **e.** irrational numbers, **f.** real numbers.

40. Give an example of an integer that is not a natural number.

41. Give an example of a rational number that is not an integer.

42. Give an example of a real number that is not a rational number.

In Exercises 43–46, insert either < or > in the shaded area between each pair of numbers to make a true statement.

43. -93 ▒ 17 **44.** -2 ▒ -200

45. 0 ▒ $-\frac{1}{3}$ **46.** $-\frac{1}{4}$ ▒ $-\frac{1}{5}$

In Exercises 47–48, determine whether each inequality is true or false.

47. $-13 \geq -11$ **48.** $-126 \leq -126$

In Exercises 49–50, find each absolute value.

49. $|-58|$ **50.** $|2.75|$

4

51. Use the commutative property of addition to write an equivalent algebraic expression: $7 + 13y$.

52. Use the commutative property of multiplication to write an equivalent algebraic expression: $9(x + 7)$.

In Exercises 53–54, use an associative property to rewrite each algebraic expression. Then simplify the resulting algebraic expression.

53. $6 + (4 + y)$

54. $7(10x)$

55. Use the distributive property to rewrite without parentheses: $6(4x - 2 + 5y)$.

In Exercises 56–57, simplify each algebraic expression.

56. $4a + 9 + 3a - 7$

57. $6(3x + 4) + 5(2x - 1)$

5

58. Use a number line to find the sum: $-6 + 8$.

In Exercises 59–61, find each sum without the use of a number line.

59. $8 + (-11)$

60. $-\frac{3}{4} + \frac{1}{5}$

61. $7 + (-5) + (-13) + 4$

In Exercises 62–63, simplify each algebraic expression.

62. $8x + (-6y) + (-12x) + 11y$

63. $10(3y + 4) + (-40y)$

64. The Dead Sea is the lowest elevation on Earth, 1312 feet below sea level. If a person is standing 512 feet above the Dead Sea, what is that person's elevation?

65. The water level of a reservoir is measured over a five-month period. At the beginning, the level is 25 feet. During this time, the level fell 3 feet, then rose 2 feet, then rose 1 foot, then fell 4 feet, and then rose 2 feet. What is the reservoir's water level at the end of the five months?

6

66. Rewrite $9 - 13$ as the addition of an opposite.

In Exercises 67–69, perform the indicated subtraction.

67. $-9 - (-13)$ **68.** $-\frac{7}{10} - \frac{1}{2}$

69. $-3.6 - (-2.1)$

In Exercises 70–71, simplify each series of additions and subtractions.

70. $-7 - (-5) + 11 - 16$

71. $-25 - 4 - (-10) + 16$

72. Simplify: $3 - 6a - 8 - 2a$.

73. What is the difference in elevation between a plane flying 26,500 feet above sea level and a submarine traveling 650 feet below sea level?

7 *In Exercises 74–76, perform the indicated multiplication.*

74. $-7(-12)$ **75.** $\frac{3}{5}\left(-\frac{5}{11}\right)$

76. $5(-3)(-2)(-4)$

In Exercises 77–79, perform the indicated division or state that the expression is undefined.

77. $\frac{45}{-5}$ **78.** $-17 \div 0$

79. $-\frac{4}{5} \div \left(-\frac{2}{5}\right)$

In Exercises 80–81, simplify each algebraic expression.

80. $-4\left(-\frac{3}{4}x\right)$ **81.** $-3(2x - 1) - (4 - 5x)$

In Exercises 82–83, determine whether the given number is a solution of the equation.

82. $5x + 16 = -8 - x; -6$

83. $2(x + 3) - 18 = 5x; -4$

84. Are you expecting a tax refund this year? The bar graph shows the percentage of taxpayers expecting a tax refund for six selected ages.

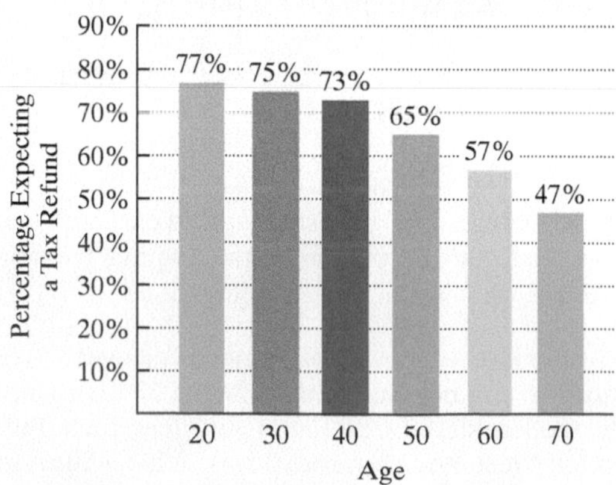

The percentage of U.S. taxpayers expecting a tax refund, p, can be described by the mathematical model

$$p = -0.6a + 93,$$

where a is the age of the taxpayer. Use the formula to find the percentage of 20-year-old taxpayers expecting a refund. Does the mathematical model underestimate or overestimate the actual percent shown by the bar graph? By how much?

8 *In Exercises 85–87, evaluate each exponential expression.*

85. $(-6)^2$ **86.** -6^2 **87.** $(-2)^5$

In Exercises 88–89, simplify each algebraic expression, or explain why the expression cannot be simplified.

88. $4x^3 + 2x^3$ **89.** $4x^3 + 4x^2$

In Exercises 90–98, use the order of operations to simplify each expression.

90. $-40 \div 5 \cdot 2$ **91.** $-6 + (-2) \cdot 5$

92. $6 - 4(-3 + 2)$ **93.** $28 \div (2 - 4^2)$

94. $36 - 24 \div 4 \cdot 3 - 1$ **95.** $-8[-4 - 5(-3)]$

96. $\frac{6(-10 + 3)}{2(-15) - 9(-3)}$

97. $\left(\frac{1}{2} + \frac{1}{3}\right) \div \left(\frac{1}{4} - \frac{3}{8}\right)$

98. $\frac{1}{2} - \frac{2}{3} \div \frac{5}{9} + \frac{3}{10}$

In Exercises 99–100, evaluate each algebraic expression for the given value of the variable.

99. $x^2 - 2x + 3; x = -1$ **100.** $-x^2 - 7x; x = -2$

In Exercises 101–102, simplify each algebraic expression.

101. $4[7(a - 1) + 2]$ **102.** $-6[4 - (y + 2)]$

103. The bar graph shows the percentage of people 25 years of age and older who were college graduates in the United States for seven selected years.

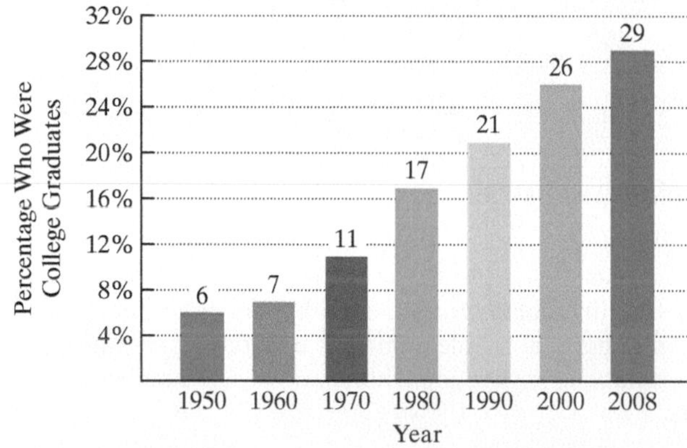

The percentage of people 25 years of age and older who were college graduates in the United States, p, can be described by the mathematical model

$$p = 0.002n^2 + 0.3n + 5,$$

where n is the number of years after 1950.

a. Does the mathematical model underestimate or overestimate the percentage of college graduates in 2000? By how much?

b. If the trend shown by the graph continues, use the formula to project the percentage of people 25 years of age and older who will be college graduates in 2020.

CHAPTER TEST

Step-by-step test solutions are found on the Chapter Test Prep Videos available in MyMathLab® or on YouTube® (search "BlitzerIntroAlg" and click on "Channels").

In Exercises 1–10, perform the indicated operation or operations.

1. $1.4 - (-2.6)$
2. $-9 + 3 + (-11) + 6$
3. $3(-17)$
4. $\left(-\frac{3}{7}\right) \div \left(-\frac{15}{7}\right)$
5. $\left(3\frac{1}{3}\right)\left(-1\frac{3}{4}\right)$
6. $-50 \div 10$
7. $-6 - (5 - 12)$
8. $(-3)(-4) \div (7 - 10)$
9. $(6 - 8)^2(5 - 7)^3$
10. $\dfrac{3(-2) - 2(2)}{-2(8 - 3)}$

In Exercises 11–13, simplify each algebraic expression.

11. $11x - (7x - 4)$
12. $5(3x - 4y) - (2x - y)$
13. $6 - 2[3(x + 1) - 5]$
14. List all the rational numbers in this set.
$$\left\{-7, -\frac{4}{5}, 0, 0.25, \sqrt{3}, \sqrt{4}, \frac{22}{7}, \pi\right\}$$
15. Insert either < or > in the shaded area to make a true statement: -1 ▒ -100.
16. Find the absolute value: $|-12.8|$.

In Exercises 17–18, evaluate each algebraic expression for the given value of the variable.

17. $5(x - 7); x = 4$
18. $x^2 - 5x; x = -10$
19. Use the commutative property of addition to write an equivalent algebraic expression: $2(x + 3)$.
20. Use the associative property of multiplication to rewrite $-6(4x)$. Then simplify the expression.
21. Use the distributive property to rewrite without parentheses: $7(5x - 1 + 2y)$.
22. What is the difference in elevation between a plane flying 16,200 feet above sea level and a submarine traveling 830 feet below sea level?

In Exercises 23–24, determine whether the given number is a solution of the equation.

23. $\frac{1}{5}(x + 2) = \frac{1}{10}x + \frac{3}{5}; 3$
24. $3(x + 2) - 15 = 4x; -9$

In Exercises 25–26, translate from English to an algebraic expression or equation, whichever is appropriate. Let the variable x represent the number.

25. $\frac{1}{4}$ of a number, decreased by 5, is 32.
26. Seven subtracted from the product of 5 and 4 more than a number
27. In 2009, Marian Robinson, President Obama's mother-in-law, moved into the White House, creating a multigenerational first family. The bar graph shows the number of multigenerational households in the United States for selected years from 1950 through 2008.

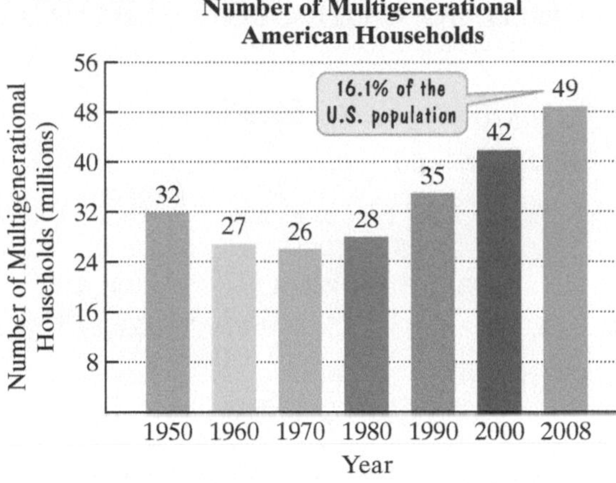

Source: Pew Research Center

The number of multigenerational American households, H, in millions, can be described by the mathematical model

$$H = 0.01n^2 - 0.5n + 31,$$

where n is the number of years after 1950. Does the mathematical model underestimate or overestimate the actual number of multigenerational households shown by the graph in 1970? By how many million?

28. Electrocardiograms are used in exercise stress tests to determine a person's fitness for strenuous exercise. The target heart rate, in beats per minute, for such tests depends on a person's age. The line graph shows target heart rates for stress tests for people of various ages.

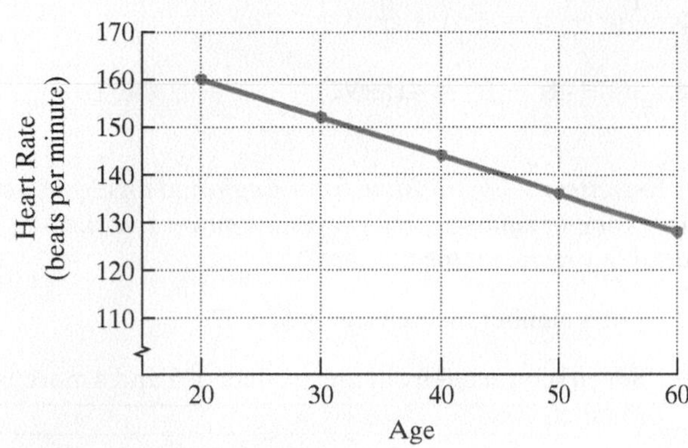

Use the graph to estimate the target heart rate for a 40-year-old taking a stress test.

29. The formula $H = \frac{4}{5}(220 - a)$ gives the target heart rate, H, in beats per minute, on a stress test for a person of age a. Use the formula to find the target heart rate for a 40-year-old. How does this compare with your estimate from Exercise 28?

Answers to Selected Exercises

Section 1 Check Point Exercises

1. a. 26 **b.** 32 **2. a.** 37 **b.** 2 **3. a.** $6x$ **b.** $4 + x$ **c.** $3x + 5$ **d.** $12 - 2x$ **e.** $\frac{15}{x}$ **4. a.** not a solution **b.** solution **5. a.** $\frac{x}{6} = 5$ **b.** $7 - 2x = 1$ **6. a.** 65% **b.** 60% **c.** overestimates by 5%

Concept and Vocabulary Check

1. variable **2.** expression **3.** substituting; evaluating **4.** equation; solution **5.** formula; modeling; models

Exercise Set 1

1. 12 **3.** 8 **5.** 20 **7.** 7 **9.** 17 **11.** 18 **13.** 5 **15.** 19 **17.** 24 **19.** 13 **21.** 10 **23.** 5 **25.** $x + 4$ **27.** $x - 4$ **29.** $x + 4$ **31.** $x - 9$ **33.** $9 - x$ **35.** $3x - 5$ **37.** $12x - 1$ **39.** $\frac{10}{x} + \frac{x}{10}$ **41.** $\frac{x}{30} + 6$ **43.** solution **45.** solution **47.** not a solution **49.** solution **51.** not a solution **53.** solution **55.** solution **57.** not a solution **59.** $4x = 28$ **61.** $\frac{14}{x} = \frac{1}{2}$ **63.** $20 - x = 5$ **65.** $2x + 6 = 16$ **67.** $3x - 5 = 7$ **69.** $4x + 5 = 33$ **71.** $4(x + 5) = 33$ **73.** $5x = 24 - x$ **75.** 8 **77.** 59 **79. a.** 14 **b.** yes **81. a.** 6 **b.** no **83. a.** \$4.22; underestimates by \$0.01 **b.** underestimates by \$0.63 **85.** overestimates by 0.8% **87. a.** 44 **b.** 164 **99.** makes sense **101.** makes sense **103.** true **105.** true **107.** Choices of variables may vary. Example: h = hours worked, s = salary; $s = 20h$ **109.** $\frac{6}{35}$ **110.** $\frac{10}{21}$ **111.** $\frac{4}{17}$

Section 2 Check Point Exercises

1. $\frac{21}{8}$ **2.** $1\frac{2}{3}$ **3.** $2 \cdot 2 \cdot 3 \cdot 3$ **4. a.** $\frac{2}{3}$ **b.** $\frac{7}{4}$ **c.** $\frac{13}{15}$ **d.** $\frac{1}{5}$ **5. a.** $\frac{8}{33}$ **b.** $\frac{18}{5}$ or $3\frac{3}{5}$ **c.** $\frac{2}{7}$ **d.** $\frac{51}{10}$ or $5\frac{1}{10}$ **6. a.** $\frac{10}{3}$ or $3\frac{1}{3}$ **b.** $\frac{2}{9}$ **c.** $\frac{3}{2}$ or $1\frac{1}{2}$ **7. a.** $\frac{5}{11}$ **b.** $\frac{2}{3}$ **c.** $\frac{9}{4}$ or $2\frac{1}{4}$ **8.** $\frac{14}{21}$ **9. a.** $\frac{11}{10}$ or $1\frac{1}{10}$ **b.** $\frac{7}{12}$ **c.** $\frac{5}{4}$ or $1\frac{1}{4}$ **10.** $\frac{53}{60}$ **11. a.** solution **b.** solution **12. a.** $\frac{2}{3}(x - 6)$ **b.** $\frac{3}{4}x - 2 = \frac{1}{5}x$ **13.** 25°C

Concept and Vocabulary Check

1. numerator; denominator **2.** mixed; improper **3.** 5; 3; 2; 5 **4.** natural **5.** prime **6.** factors; product **7.** $\frac{a}{b}$ **8.** $\frac{a \cdot c}{b \cdot d}$ **9.** reciprocals **10.** $\frac{d}{c}$ **11.** $\frac{a + c}{b}$ **12.** least common denominator

Exercise Set 2

1. $\frac{19}{8}$ **3.** $\frac{38}{5}$ **5.** $\frac{135}{16}$ **7.** $4\frac{3}{5}$ **9.** $8\frac{4}{9}$ **11.** $35\frac{11}{20}$ **13.** $2 \cdot 11$ **15.** $2 \cdot 2 \cdot 5$ **17.** prime **19.** $2 \cdot 2 \cdot 3 \cdot 3$ **21.** $2 \cdot 2 \cdot 5 \cdot 7$

23. prime **25.** $3 \cdot 3 \cdot 3 \cdot 3$ **27.** $2 \cdot 2 \cdot 2 \cdot 2 \cdot 3 \cdot 5$ **29.** $\frac{5}{8}$ **31.** $\frac{5}{6}$ **33.** $\frac{7}{10}$ **35.** $\frac{2}{5}$ **37.** $\frac{22}{25}$ **39.** $\frac{60}{43}$ **41.** $\frac{2}{15}$ **43.** $\frac{21}{88}$

45. $\frac{36}{7}$ **47.** $\frac{1}{12}$ **49.** $\frac{15}{14}$ **51.** 6 **53.** $\frac{15}{16}$ **55.** $\frac{9}{5}$ **57.** $\frac{5}{9}$ **59.** 3 **61.** $\frac{7}{10}$ **63.** $\frac{1}{2}$ **65.** 6 **67.** $\frac{6}{11}$ **69.** $\frac{2}{3}$ **71.** $\frac{5}{4}$

73. $\frac{1}{6}$ **75.** 2 **77.** $\frac{7}{10}$ **79.** $\frac{9}{10}$ **81.** $\frac{19}{24}$ **83.** $\frac{7}{18}$ **85.** $\frac{7}{12}$ **87.** $\frac{41}{80}$ **89.** $1\frac{5}{12}$ or $\frac{17}{12}$ **91.** solution **93.** solution

95. not a solution **97.** solution **99.** not a solution **101.** solution **103.** $\frac{1}{5}x$ **105.** $x - \frac{1}{4}x$ **107.** $x - \frac{1}{4} = \frac{1}{2}x$ **109.** $\frac{1}{7}x + \frac{1}{8}x = 12$

111. $\frac{2}{3}(x + 6)$ **113.** $\frac{2}{3}x + 6 = x - 3$ **115.** $\frac{3a}{20}$ **117.** $\frac{20}{x}$ **119.** $\frac{4}{15}$ **121.** not a solution **123.** 20°C **125. a.** 140 beats per minute

b. 160 beats per minute **127. a.** $H = \frac{9}{10}(220 - a)$ **b.** 162 beats per minute **129.** 21; underestimates by $\frac{1}{2}$ present

141. makes sense **143.** makes sense **145.** false **147.** true

149.

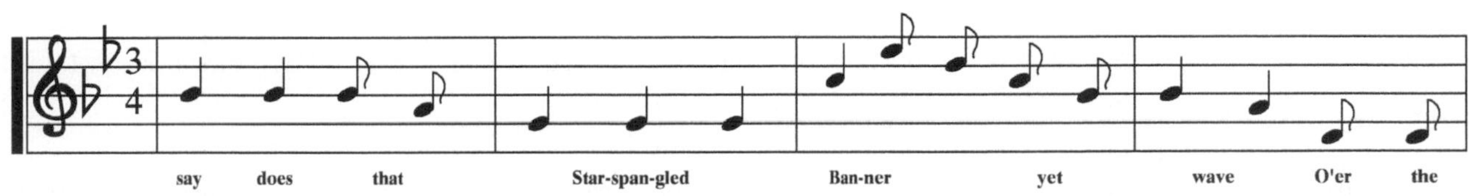
say
does
that
Star-span-gled
Ban-ner
yet
wave
O'er
the

150. 5 **151.** $\frac{5}{2}$ **152.** -4

Section 3 Check Point Exercises

1. a. -500 **b.** -282 **2.** (a), (b), (c) plotted on number line from -5 to 5 **3.** (b), (a) plotted on number line from -5 to 5

4. a. 0.375 **b.** $0.\overline{45}$ **5. a.** $\sqrt{9}$ **b.** $0, \sqrt{9}$ **c.** $-9, 0, \sqrt{9}$ **d.** $-9, -1.3, 0, 0.\overline{3}, \sqrt{9}$ **e.** $\frac{\pi}{2}, \sqrt{10}$ **f.** $-9, -1.3, 0, 0.\overline{3}, \frac{\pi}{2}, \sqrt{9}, \sqrt{10}$

6. a. $>$ **b.** $<$ **c.** $<$ **d.** $<$ **7. a.** true **b.** true **c.** false **8. a.** 4 **b.** 6 **c.** $\sqrt{2}$

Concept and Vocabulary Check

1. natural **2.** whole **3.** integers **4.** rational **5.** irrational **6.** rational; irrational **7.** left **8.** absolute value; $|a|$

Exercise Set 3

1. -20 **3.** 8 **5.** -3000 **7.** -4 billion **9–19.** -5, $-\frac{16}{5}$, -1.8, 2, $3\frac{1}{2}$, $\frac{11}{3}$ plotted on number line from -5 to 5 **21.** 0.75 **23.** 0.35 **25.** 0.875 **27.** $0.\overline{81}$

29. -0.5 **31.** $-0.8\overline{3}$ **33. a.** $\sqrt{100}$ **b.** $0, \sqrt{100}$ **c.** $-9, 0, \sqrt{100}$ **d.** $-9, -\frac{4}{5}, 0, 0.25, 9.2, \sqrt{100}$ **e.** $\sqrt{3}$

f. $-9, -\frac{4}{5}, 0, 0.25, \sqrt{3}, 9.2, \sqrt{100}$ **35. a.** $\sqrt{64}$ **b.** $0, \sqrt{64}$ **c.** $-11, 0, \sqrt{64}$ **d.** $-11, -\frac{5}{6}, 0, 0.75, \sqrt{64}$ **e.** $\sqrt{5}, \pi$

f. $-11, -\frac{5}{6}, 0, 0.75, \sqrt{5}, \pi, \sqrt{64}$ **37.** 0 **39.** Answers will vary; $\frac{1}{2}$ is an example. **41.** Answers will vary; 6 is an example.

43. Answers will vary; π is an example. **45.** $<$ **47.** $>$ **49.** $>$ **51.** $<$ **53.** $>$ **55.** $<$ **57.** $<$ **59.** $>$

61. $>$ **63.** true **65.** true **67.** true **69.** false **71.** 6 **73.** 7 **75.** $\frac{5}{6}$ **77.** $\sqrt{11}$ **79.** $>$ **81.** $=$ **83.** $<$ **85.** $=$

87. rational numbers **89.** integers **91.** all real numbers **93.** whole numbers

95. a. -25, -17, -16, -2, 12 plotted on number line from -30 to 20 **b.** Rhode Island, Georgia, Louisiana, Florida, Hawaii

109. does not make sense **111.** makes sense **113.** false **115.** false **117.** false **119.** $-\frac{1}{2}d$ **121.** -3.464; -4 and -3

123. -0.236; -1 and 0 **124.** 27; 27; Both expressions have the same value. **125.** 32; 32; Both expressions have the same value.
126. 28; 28; Both expressions have the same value.

Section 4 Check Point Exercises

1. a. 3 terms **b.** 6 **c.** 11 **d.** $6x$ and $2x$ **2. a.** $14 + x$ **b.** $y7$ **3. a.** $17 + 5x$ **b.** $x5 + 17$ **4. a.** $20 + x$ or $x + 20$ **b.** $30x$ **5.** $12 + x$ or $x + 12$ **6.** $5x + 15$ **7.** $24y + 42$ **8. a.** $10x$ **b.** $5a$ **9. a.** $18x + 10$ **b.** $14x + 8y$ **10.** $25x + 21$ **11.** $38x + 23y$

Concept and Vocabulary Check

1. like **2.** $b + a$ **3.** ab **4.** $a + (b + c)$ **5.** $(ab)c$ **6.** $ab + ac$ **7.** simplified

Exercise Set 4

1. a. 2 **b.** 3 **c.** 5 **d.** no **3. a.** 3 **b.** 1 **c.** 2 **d.** yes; x and $5x$ **5. a.** 3 **b.** 4 **c.** 1 **d.** no **7.** $4 + y$ **9.** $3x + 5$ **11.** $5y + 4x$ **13.** $5(3 + x)$ **15.** $x9$ **17.** $x + 6y$ **19.** $x7 + 23$ **21.** $(x + 3)5$ **23.** $(7 + 5) + x = 12 + x$ **25.** $(7 \cdot 4)x = 28x$ **27.** $3x + 15$ **29.** $16x + 24$ **31.** $4 + 2r$ **33.** $5x + 5y$ **35.** $3x - 6$ **37.** $8x - 10$ **39.** $\frac{5}{2}x - 6$ **41.** $8x + 28$ **43.** $6x + 18 + 12y$ **45.** $15x - 10 + 20y$ **47.** $17x$ **49.** $8a$ **51.** $14 + x$ **53.** $11y + 3$ **55.** $9x + 1$ **57.** $14a + 14$ **59.** $15x + 6$ **61.** $15x + 2$ **63.** $41a + 24b$ **65.** Distributive property; Commutative property of addition; Associative property of addition; Commutative property of addition **67.** $7x + 2x$; $9x$ **69.** $12x - 3x$; $9x$ **71.** $6(4x)$; $24x$ **73.** $6(4 + x)$; $24 + 6x$ **75.** $8 + 5(x - 1)$; $5x + 3$ **77. a.** $U = 13n + 133$ **b.** 211 million; overestimates by 1 million **89.** does not make sense **91.** makes sense **93.** false **95.** false **97.** 60 **98.** -60 **99.** -5

Mid-Chapter Check Point Exercises

1. 62 **2.** 2 **3.** 43 **4.** $\frac{1}{4}x - 2$ **5.** $\frac{x}{6} + 5 = 19$ **6.** not a solution **7.** not a solution **8. a.** 11,919; overestimates by 131 miles **b.** 10,274 **9.** $\frac{1}{6}$ **10.** $\frac{1}{2}$ **11.** $\frac{25}{66}$ **12.** $\frac{2}{3}$ **13.** $\frac{1}{5}$ **14.** $\frac{25}{27}$ **15.** $\frac{37}{18}$ or $2\frac{1}{8}$ **16.** 10°C **17.** $<$ **18.** $0.\overline{09}$ **19.** 19.3 **20.** $-11, -\frac{3}{7}, 0, 0.45, \sqrt{25}$ **21.** $(x + 3)5$ **22.** $5(3 + x)$ **23.** $5x + 15$ **24.** $65x + 21$ **25.** $10x + 34y$

Section 5 Check Point Exercises

1. $4 + (-7) = -3$ **2. a.** $-1 + (-3) = -4$

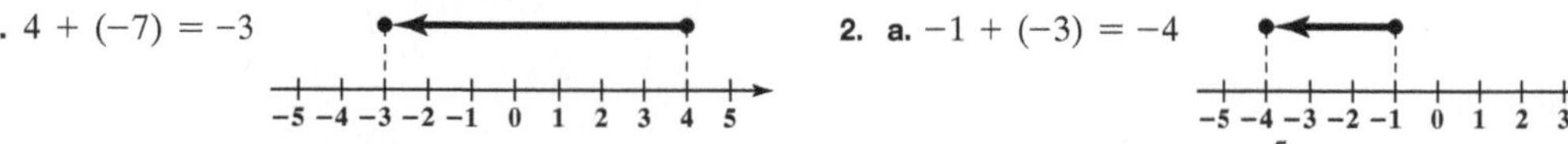

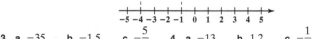

b. $-5 + 3 = -2$ **3. a.** -35 **b.** -1.5 **c.** $-\frac{5}{6}$ **4. a.** -13 **b.** 1.2 **c.** $-\frac{1}{2}$ **5. a.** $-17x$ **b.** $-7y + 6z$ **c.** $-20x + 15$ **6.** down 3 ft

Concept and Vocabulary Check

1. additive inverses **2.** zero **3.** negative number **4.** positive number **5.** 0 **6.** negative number **7.** positive number **8.** 0

Exercise Set 5

1. 4 **3.** -7 **5.** -4 **7.** 0

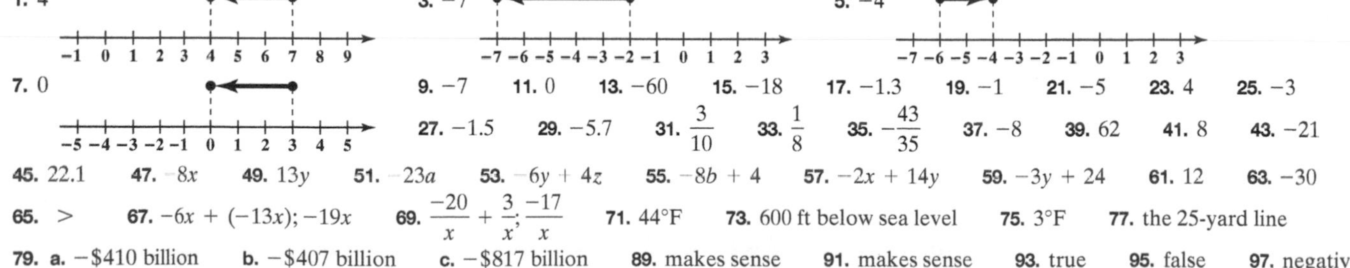

9. -7 **11.** 0 **13.** -60 **15.** -18 **17.** -1.3 **19.** -1 **21.** -5 **23.** 4 **25.** -3 **27.** -1.5 **29.** -5.7 **31.** $\frac{3}{10}$ **33.** $\frac{1}{8}$ **35.** $-\frac{43}{35}$ **37.** -8 **39.** 62 **41.** 8 **43.** -21 **45.** 22.1 **47.** $-8x$ **49.** $13y$ **51.** $-23a$ **53.** $-6y + 4z$ **55.** $-8b + 4$ **57.** $-2x + 14y$ **59.** $-3y + 24$ **61.** 12 **63.** -30 **65.** $>$ **67.** $-6x + (-13x)$; $-19x$ **69.** $\frac{-20}{x} + \frac{3}{x}$; $\frac{-17}{x}$ **71.** 44°F **73.** 600 ft below sea level **75.** 3°F **77.** the 25-yard line **79. a.** $-\$410$ billion **b.** $-\$407$ billion **c.** $-\$817$ billion **89.** makes sense **91.** makes sense **93.** true **95.** false **97.** negative **99.** positive **102. a.** $\sqrt{4}$ **b.** $0, \sqrt{4}$ **c.** $-6, 0, \sqrt{4}$ **d.** $-6, 0, 0.\overline{7}, \sqrt{4}$ **e.** $-\pi, \sqrt{3}$ **f.** $-6, \pi, 0, 0.\overline{7}, \sqrt{3}, \sqrt{4}$ **103.** true **104.** solution **105.** -3 **106.** -21 **107.** 5

Section 6 Check Point Exercises

1. a. -8 **b.** 9 **c.** -5 **2. a.** 9.2 **b.** $-\frac{14}{15}$ **c.** 7π **3.** 15 **4.** $-6, 4a, -7ab$ **5. a.** $4 - 7x$ **b.** $-9x + 4y$ **6.** 19,763 m

Concept and Vocabulary Check

1. (-14) **2.** 14 **3.** 14 **4.** -8; (-14) **5.** 3; (-12); (-23) **6.** $(-4y)$; 6 **7.** three; addition

Exercise Set 6

1. a. -12 **b.** $5 + (-12)$ **3. a.** 7 **b.** $5 + 7$ **5.** 6 **7.** -6 **9.** 23 **11.** 11 **13.** -11 **15.** -38 **17.** 0 **19.** 0 **21.** 26 **23.** -13 **25.** 13 **27.** $-\frac{2}{7}$ **29.** $\frac{4}{5}$ **31.** -1 **33.** $-\frac{3}{5}$ **35.** $\frac{3}{4}$ **37.** $\frac{1}{4}$ **39.** 7.6 **41.** -2 **43.** 2.6 **45.** 0 **47.** 3π

49. 13π **51.** 19 **53.** −3 **55.** −15 **57.** 0 **59.** −52 **61.** −187 **63.** $\frac{7}{6}$ **65.** −4.49 **67.** $-\frac{3}{8}$ **69.** $-3x, -8y$
71. $12x, -5xy, -4$ **73.** $-6x$ **75.** $4 - 10y$ **77.** $5 - 7a$ **79.** $-4 - 9b$ **81.** $24 + 11x$ **83.** $3y - 8x$ **85.** 9 **87.** $\frac{7}{8}$
89. −2 **91.** $6x - (-5x)$; $11x$ **93.** $\frac{-5}{x} - \left(\frac{-2}{x}\right)$; $\frac{-3}{x}$ **95.** 19,757 ft **97.** 21°F **99.** 3°F **101.** shrink by 5 years
103. shrink by 11 years **105.** 10 years **107.** no change **109.** 9 years **117.** makes sense **119.** makes sense **121.** false **123.** true
125. negative **127.** positive **131.** not a solution **132.** $15x + 40y$ **133.** Answers will vary; −1 is an example. **134.** −12 **135.** −9 **136.** 12

Section 7 Check Point Exercises

1. a. −40 **b.** $-\frac{4}{21}$ **c.** 36 **d.** 5.5 **e.** 0 **2. a.** 24 **b.** −30 **3. a.** $\frac{1}{7}$ **b.** 8 **c.** $-\frac{1}{6}$ **d.** $-\frac{13}{7}$ **4. a.** −4 **b.** 8
5. a. 8 **b.** $-\frac{8}{15}$ **c.** −7.3 **d.** 0 **6. a.** $-20x$ **b.** $10x$ **c.** $-b$ **d.** $-21x + 28$ **e.** $-7y + 6$ **7.** $-y - 26$
8. not a solution **9.** 49.4%; overestimates by 0.4%

Concept and Vocabulary Check

1. positive **2.** negative **3.** negative **4.** positive **5.** 0 **6.** negative **7.** negative **8.** positive **9.** 0
10. undefined **11.** positive

Exercise Set 7

1. −45 **3.** 24 **5.** −21 **7.** 19 **9.** 0 **11.** −12 **13.** 9 **15.** $\frac{12}{35}$ **17.** $-\frac{14}{27}$ **19.** −3.6 **21.** 0.12 **23.** 30 **25.** −72
27. 24 **29.** −27 **31.** 90 **33.** 0 **35.** $\frac{1}{4}$ **37.** 5 **39.** $-\frac{1}{10}$ **41.** $-\frac{5}{2}$ **43. a.** $-32 \cdot \left(\frac{1}{4}\right)$ **b.** −8 **45. a.** $-60 \cdot \left(-\frac{1}{5}\right)$
b. 12 **47.** −3 **49.** −7 **51.** 30 **53.** 0 **55.** undefined **57.** −5 **59.** −12 **61.** 6 **63.** 0 **65.** undefined **67.** −4.3
69. $\frac{5}{6}$ **71.** $-\frac{16}{9}$ **73.** −1 **75.** −15 **77.** $-10x$ **79.** $3y$ **81.** $9x$ **83.** $-4x$ **85.** $-b$ **87.** $3y$ **89.** $-8x + 12$
91. $6x - 12$ **93.** $-2y + 5$ **95.** $y - 14$ **97.** solution **99.** solution **101.** not a solution **103.** solution **105.** not a solution
107. solution **109.** $4(-10) + 8 = -32$ **111.** $(-9)(-3) - (-2) = 29$ **113.** $\frac{-18}{-15 + 12} = 6$ **115.** $-6 - \left(\frac{12}{-4}\right) = -3$ **117.** −30°C
119. a. underestimates by 1% **b.** 16% **121. a.** 25 hours **b.** 23 hours; it's less than the estimate.
c. $D = -0.4n + 39 - (0.2n + 12)$; $D = -0.6n + 27$ **d.** 3 hours; underestimates **131.** does not make sense **133.** makes sense
135. false **137.** false **139.** $5x$ **141.** $\frac{x}{12}$ **145.** $1.144x + 2.5$ **147.** −9 **148.** −3 **149.** 2 **150.** 36 **151.** −125 **152.** 16

Section 8 Check Point Exercises

1. a. 36 **b.** −64 **c.** 1 **d.** −1 **2. a.** $21x^2$ **b.** $8x^3$ **c.** cannot simplify **3.** 15 **4.** 32 **5. a.** 36 **b.** 12 **6.** $\frac{3}{4}$ **7.** −40
8. −31 **9.** $\frac{5}{7}$ **10.** −5 **11.** $7x^2 + 15$ **12.** 2662 calories; underestimates by 38 calories **13. a.** \$330 **b.** \$60 **c.** \$33

Concept and Vocabulary Check

1. base; exponent **2.** b to the nth power **3.** multiply **4.** add **5.** divide **6.** subtract **7.** multiply

Exercise Set 8

1. 81 **3.** 64 **5.** 16 **7.** −64 **9.** 625 **11.** −625 **13.** −100 **15.** $19x^2$ **17.** $15x^3$ **19.** $9x^4$ **21.** $-x^2$ **23.** x^3
25. cannot be simplified **27.** 0 **29.** 25 **31.** 27 **33.** 12 **35.** 5 **37.** 45 **39.** −24 **41.** 300 **43.** 0 **45.** −32 **47.** 64
49. 30 **51.** $\frac{4}{3}$ **53.** 2 **55.** 2 **57.** 3 **59.** 88 **61.** −60 **63.** −36 **65.** 14 **67.** $-\frac{3}{4}$ **69.** $-\frac{9}{40}$ **71.** $-\frac{37}{36}$ or $-1\frac{1}{36}$
73. 24 **75.** 28 **77.** 9 **79.** −7 **81.** $15x - 27$ **83.** $15 - 3y$ **85.** $16y - 25$ **87.** $-2x^2 - 9$ **89.** $-10 - (-2)^3 = -2$
91. $[2(7 - 10)]^2 = 36$ **93.** $x - (5x + 8) = -4x - 8$ **95.** $5(x^3 - 4) = 5x^3 - 20$ **97.** 1924 calories; underestimates by 76 calories **99. a.** 22%
b. 18.7%; less than the estimate **101. a.** \$2,000,000 (or \$200 tens of thousands) **b.** \$8,000,000 (or \$800 tens of thousands) **c.** Cost inceases.
107. does not make sense **109.** makes sense **111.** false **113.** false **115.** $(2 \cdot 3 + 3) \cdot 5 = 45$ **117.** 6 **118.** −24
119. Answers will vary; −3 is an example. **120.** solution **121.** solution **122.** not a solution

Review Exercises

1. 40 **2.** 50 **3.** 3 **4.** 84 **5.** $7x - 6$ **6.** $\frac{x}{5} - 2 = 18$ **7.** $9 - 2x = 14$ **8.** $3(x + 7)$ **9.** not a solution **10.** solution
11. solution **12.** 11, although answers may vary by ±1 **13.** 11 Latin words; very well; It is the same. **14. a.** \$13,569; overestimates by \$194
b. \$22,182 **15.** $\frac{23}{7}$ **16.** $\frac{64}{11}$ **17.** $1\frac{8}{9}$ **18.** $5\frac{2}{5}$ **19.** $2 \cdot 2 \cdot 3 \cdot 5$ **20.** $3 \cdot 3 \cdot 7$ **21.** prime **22.** $\frac{5}{11}$ **23.** $\frac{8}{15}$ **24.** $\frac{21}{50}$ **25.** $\frac{8}{3}$

26. $\frac{1}{4}$ **27.** $\frac{2}{3}$ **28.** $\frac{29}{18}$ **29.** $\frac{37}{60}$ **30.** solution **31.** not a solution **32.** $2 - \frac{1}{2}x = \frac{1}{4}x$ **33.** $\frac{3}{5}(x + 6)$ **34.** 152 beats per minute

35.

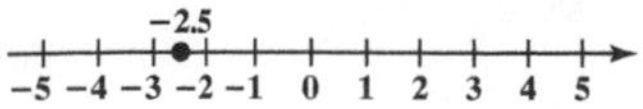

36.

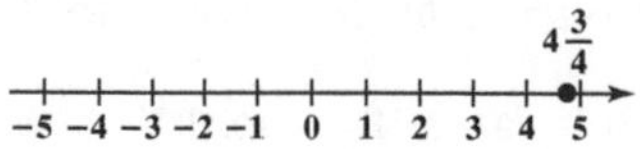

37. 0.625 **38.** $0.\overline{27}$ **39. a.** $\sqrt{81}$ **b.** $0, \sqrt{81}$ **c.** $-17, 0, \sqrt{81}$ **d.** $-17, -\frac{9}{13}, 0, 0.75, \sqrt{81}$ **e.** $\sqrt{2}, \pi$ **f.** $-17, -\frac{9}{13}, 0, 0.75, \sqrt{2}, \pi, \sqrt{81}$

40. Answers will vary; −2 is an example. **41.** Answers will vary; $\frac{1}{2}$ is an example. **42.** Answers will vary; π is an example. **43.** $<$

44. $>$ **45.** $>$ **46.** $<$ **47.** false **48.** true **49.** 58 **50.** 2.75 **51.** $13y + 7$ **52.** $(x + 7)9$ **53.** $(6 + 4) + y = 10 + y$
54. $(7 \cdot 10)x = 70x$ **55.** $24x - 12 + 30y$ **56.** $7a + 2$ **57.** $28x + 19$

58. 2

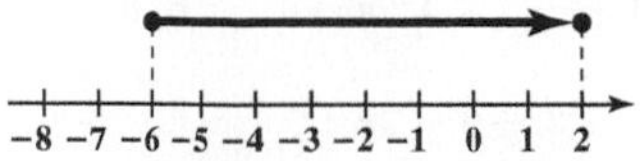

59. −3 **60.** $-\frac{11}{20}$ **61.** −7 **62.** $-4x + 5y$ or $5y - 4x$ **63.** $-10y + 40$ or $40 - 10y$
64. 800 ft below sea level **65.** 23 ft **66.** $9 + (-13)$ **67.** 4

68. $-\frac{6}{5}$ **69.** −1.5 **70.** −7 **71.** −3 **72.** $-5 - 8a$ **73.** 27,150 ft **74.** 84 **75.** $-\frac{3}{11}$ **76.** −120 **77.** −9 **78.** undefined
79. 2 **80.** $3x$ **81.** $-x - 1$ **82.** not a solution **83.** solution **84.** 81%; overestimates by 4% **85.** 36 **86.** −36 **87.** −32
88. $6x^3$ **89.** cannot be simplified **90.** −16 **91.** −16 **92.** 10 **93.** −2 **94.** 17 **95.** −88 **96.** 14
97. $-\frac{20}{3}$ **98.** $-\frac{2}{5}$ **99.** 6 **100.** 10 **101.** $28a - 20$ **102.** $6y - 12$ **103. a.** underestimates by 1% **b.** 35.8%

Chapter Test

1. 4 **2.** −11 **3.** −51 **4.** $\frac{1}{5}$ **5.** $-\frac{35}{6}$ or $-5\frac{5}{6}$ **6.** −5 **7.** 1 **8.** −4 **9.** −32 **10.** 1 **11.** $4x + 4$ **12.** $13x - 19y$
13. $10 - 6x$ **14.** $-7, -\frac{4}{5}, 0, 0.25, \sqrt{4}, \frac{22}{7}$ **15.** $>$ **16.** 12.8 **17.** −15 **18.** 150 **19.** $2(3 + x)$ **20.** $(-6 \cdot 4)x = -24x$
21. $35x - 7 + 14y$ **22.** 17,030 ft **23.** not a solution **24.** solution **25.** $\frac{1}{4}x - 5 = 32$ **26.** $5(x + 4) - 7$
27. underestimates by 1 million **28.** 144 beats per minute, although answers may vary by ±1 **29.** 144 beats per minute; very well; It is the same.

Linear Equations and Inequalities in One Variable

The belief that humor and laughter can have positive effects on our lives is not new. The Bible tells us, "A merry heart doeth good like a medicine, but a broken spirit drieth the bones." **(Proverbs 17:22)**

Some random humor factoids: ■ The average adult laughs 15 times each day. **(*Newhouse News Service*)** ■ Forty-six percent of people who are telling a joke laugh more than the people they are telling it to. **(*U.S. News and World Report*)** ■ Eighty percent of adult laughter does not occur in response to jokes or funny situations. **(*Independent*)** ■ Algebra can be used to model the influence that humor plays in our responses to negative life events. **(Bob Blitzer, *Introductory Algebra*)**

That last tidbit that your author threw into the list is true. Based on our sense of humor, there is actually a formula that predicts how we will respond to difficult life events.

Formulas can be used to explain what is happening in the present and to make predictions about what might occur in the future. In this chapter, you will learn to use formulas in new ways that will help you to recognize patterns, logic, and order in a world that can appear chaotic to the untrained eye.

A mathematical model that includes sense of humor as a variable is developed in Example 8 of Section 3.

KRT/Newscom

SECTION

1

The Addition Property of Equality

Objectives

1. Identify linear equations in one variable.
2. Use the addition property of equality to solve equations.
3. Solve applied problems using formulas.

Credit cards: Are they convenient tools or snakes in your wallet? Before President Obama signed legislation that prohibited issuing credit cards to college students younger than 21, the average credit-card debt for college seniors exceeded $4000. In this section's Exercise Set, you will work with a mathematical model that describes credit-card debt. Your work with this model will involve solving linear equations.

Inbj/Dreamstime

Martin Harvey/Alamy

Linear Equations in One Variable

An equation is a statement that two algebraic expressions are equal. We determine whether a given number is an equation's solution by substituting that number for each occurrence of the variable. When the substitution results in a true statement, that number is a solution. When the substitution results in a false statement, that number is not a solution.

In the next three sections, we will study how to solve equations in one variable. **Solving an equation** is the process of finding the number (or numbers) that make the equation a true statement. These numbers are called the **solutions**, or **roots**, of the equation, and we say that they **satisfy** the equation.

In this chapter, you will learn to solve the simplest type of equation, called a *linear equation in one variable.*

1 Identify linear equations in one variable.

Definition of a Linear Equation in One Variable

A **linear equation in one variable x** is an equation that can be written in the form

$$ax + b = c,$$

where a, b, and c are real numbers, and $a \neq 0$ (a is not equal to 0).

Linear Equations in One Variable (x)

$3x + 7 = 9$	$-15x = 45$	$x = 6.8$
$ax + b = c$, with $a = 3$, $b = 7$, and $c = 9$	$ax + b = c$, with $a = -15$, $b = 0$, and $c = 45$	$ax + b = c$ $(1x + 0 = 6.8)$, with $a = 1$, $b = 0$, and $c = 6.8$

Nonlinear Equations in One Variable (x)

$3x^2 + 7 = 9$	$-\dfrac{15}{x} = 45$	$\lvert x \rvert = 6.8$
Nonlinear because x is squared	Nonlinear because x is in the denominator	Nonlinear because of the absolute value bars around x

The adjective *linear* contains the word *line*. Linear equations are related to graphs whose points lie along a straight line.

2 Use the addition property of equality to solve equations.

Using the Addition Property of Equality to Solve Equations

Consider the equation

$$x = 11.$$

By inspection, we can see that the solution to this equation is 11. If we substitute 11 for x, we obtain the true statement $11 = 11$.

Now consider the equation

$$x - 3 = 8.$$

If we substitute 11 for x, we obtain $11 - 3 \stackrel{?}{=} 8$. Subtracting on the left side, we get the true statement $8 = 8$.

The equations $x - 3 = 8$ and $x = 11$ both have the same solution, namely 11, and are called *equivalent equations*. **Equivalent equations** are equations that have the same solution.

The idea in solving a linear equation is to get an equivalent equation with the variable (the letter) by itself on one side of the equal sign and a number by itself on the other side. For example, consider the equation $x - 3 = 8$. To get x by itself on the left side, add 3 to the left side, because $x - 3 + 3$ gives $x + 0$, or just x. You must then add 3 to the right side also. By doing this, we are using the **addition property of equality**.

The Addition Property of Equality

The same real number (or algebraic expression) may be added to both sides of an equation without changing the equation's solution. This can be expressed symbolically as follows:

$$\text{If } a = b, \text{ then } a + c = b + c.$$

EXAMPLE 1 Solving an Equation Using the Addition Property

Solve the equation: $x - 3 = 8$.

Solution We can isolate the variable, x, by adding 3 to both sides of the equation.

$x - 3 = 8$	This is the given equation.
$x - 3 + 3 = 8 + 3$	Add 3 to both sides.
$x + 0 = 11$	This step is often done mentally and not listed.
$x = 11$	

By inspection, we can see that the solution to $x = 11$ is 11. To check this proposed solution, replace x with 11 in the original equation.

Check

$x - 3 = 8$	This is the original equation.
$11 - 3 \stackrel{?}{=} 8$	Substitute 11 for x.
This statement is true. $8 = 8$	Subtract: $11 - 3 = 8$.

Because the check results in a true statement, we conclude that the solution to the given equation is 11. ■

Great Question!

Is there another way to show that I'm adding the same number to both sides of an equation?

Some people prefer to show the number below the equation:

$$\begin{array}{rcr} x - 3 & = & 8 \\ +3 & & +3 \\ \hline x & = & 11. \end{array}$$

Great Question!

In a high school algebra course, I remember my teacher talking about balancing an equation. What does the addition property of equality have to do with a balanced equation?

You can think of an equation as a balanced scale—balanced because its two sides are equal. To maintain this balance, whatever you do to one side must also be done to the other side.

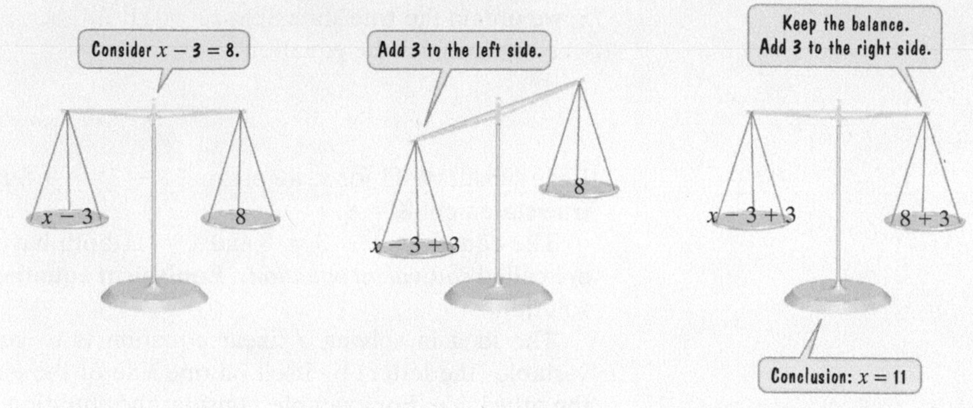

The set of an equation's solutions is called its **solution set**. Thus, the solution set of the equation in Example 1, $x - 3 = 8$, is $\{11\}$. The solution can be expressed as 11 or, using set notation, $\{11\}$.

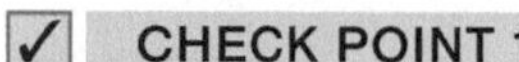

✓ **CHECK POINT 1** Solve the equation and check your proposed solution:

$$x - 5 = 12.$$

When we use the addition property of equality, we add the same number to both sides of an equation. We know that subtraction is the addition of an opposite, or additive inverse. Thus, the addition property also lets us subtract the same number from both sides of an equation without changing the equation's solution.

EXAMPLE 2 Subtracting the Same Number from Both Sides

Solve and check: $z + 1.4 = 2.06$.

Solution

$z + 1.4 = 2.06$ This is the given equation.

$z + 1.4 - 1.4 = 2.06 - 1.4$ Subtract 1.4 from both sides. This is equivalent to adding -1.4 to both sides.

$z = 0.66$ Subtracting 1.4 from both sides eliminates 1.4 on the left.

Can you see that the solution to $z = 0.66$ is 0.66? To check this proposed solution, replace z with 0.66 in the original equation.

Check $z + 1.4 = 2.06$ This is the original equation.

$0.66 + 1.4 \stackrel{?}{=} 2.06$ Substitute 0.66 for z.

$2.06 = 2.06$ This statement is true.

This true statement indicates that the solution is 0.66, or the solution set is $\{0.66\}$. ■

✓ **CHECK POINT 2** Solve and check: $z + 2.8 = 5.09$.

When isolating the variable, we can isolate it on either the left side or the right side of an equation.

EXAMPLE 3 Isolating the Variable on the Right

Solve and check: $-\frac{1}{2} = x - \frac{2}{3}$.

Solution We can isolate the variable, x, on the right side by adding $\frac{2}{3}$ to both sides of the equation.

$$-\frac{1}{2} = x - \frac{2}{3}$$ This is the given equation.

$$-\frac{1}{2} + \frac{2}{3} = x - \frac{2}{3} + \frac{2}{3}$$ Add $\frac{2}{3}$ to both sides, isolating x on the right.

$$-\frac{3}{6} + \frac{4}{6} = x$$ Rewrite each fraction as an equivalent fraction with a denominator of 6: $-\frac{1}{2} + \frac{2}{3} = -\frac{1}{2}\cdot\frac{3}{3} + \frac{2}{3}\cdot\frac{2}{2} = -\frac{3}{6} + \frac{4}{6}$.

$$\frac{1}{6} = x$$ Add on the left side: $-\frac{3}{6} + \frac{4}{6} = \frac{-3+4}{6} = \frac{1}{6}$.

Take a moment to check the proposed solution, $\frac{1}{6}$. Substitute $\frac{1}{6}$ for x in the original equation. You should obtain $-\frac{1}{2} = -\frac{1}{2}$. This true statement indicates that the solution is $\frac{1}{6}$, or the solution set is $\{\frac{1}{6}\}$. ■

Great Question!

Am I allowed to "flip" the two sides of an equation?

The equations $a = b$ and $b = a$ have the same meaning. If you prefer, you can solve

$$-\frac{1}{2} = x - \frac{2}{3}$$

by reversing the two sides and solving

$$x - \frac{2}{3} = -\frac{1}{2}.$$

✓ **CHECK POINT 3** Solve and check: $-\frac{1}{2} = x - \frac{3}{4}$.

In Example 4, we combine like terms before using the addition property.

EXAMPLE 4 Combining Like Terms before Using the Addition Property

Solve and check: $5y + 3 - 4y - 8 = 6 + 9$.

Solution

$$5y + 3 - 4y - 8 = 6 + 9$$ This is the given equation.

$$y - 5 = 15$$ Combine like terms: $5y - 4y = y$, $3 - 8 = -5$, and $6 + 9 = 15$.

$$y - 5 + 5 = 15 + 5$$ Add 5 to both sides.

$$y = 20$$ Simplify.

To check the proposed solution, 20, replace y with 20 in the original equation.

Check $5y + 3 - 4y - 8 = 6 + 9$ Be sure to use the original equation and not the simplified form from the second step above. (Why?)

$$5(20) + 3 - 4(20) - 8 \stackrel{?}{=} 6 + 9$$ Substitute 20 for y.

$$100 + 3 - 80 - 8 \stackrel{?}{=} 6 + 9$$ Multiply on the left.

$$103 - 88 \stackrel{?}{=} 6 + 9$$ Combine positive numbers and combine negative numbers on the left.

$$15 = 15$$ This statement is true.

This true statement verifies that the solution is 20, or the solution set is {20}. ■

✓ **CHECK POINT 4** Solve and check: $8y + 7 - 7y - 10 = 6 + 4$.

Adding and Subtracting Variable Terms on Both Sides of an Equation

In some equations, variable terms appear on both sides. Here is an example:

$$4x = 7 + 3x.$$

A variable term, $4x$, is on the left side.

A variable term, $3x$, is on the right side.

Our goal is to isolate all the variable terms on one side of the equation. We can use the addition property of equality to do this. The property allows us to add or subtract the same variable term on both sides of an equation without changing the solution. Let's see how we can use this idea to solve $4x = 7 + 3x$.

EXAMPLE 5 Using the Addition Property to Isolate Variable Terms

Solve and check: $4x = 7 + 3x$.

Solution In the given equation, variable terms appear on both sides. We can isolate them on one side by subtracting $3x$ from both sides of the equation.

$4x = 7 + 3x$	This is the given equation.
$4x - 3x = 7 + 3x - 3x$	Subtract $3x$ from both sides and isolate variable terms on the left.
$x = 7$	Subtracting $3x$ from both sides eliminates $3x$ on the right. On the left, $4x - 3x = 1x = x$.

To check the proposed solution, 7, replace x with 7 in the original equation.

Check

$4x = 7 + 3x$	Use the original equation.
$4(7) \stackrel{?}{=} 7 + 3(7)$	Substitute 7 for x.
$28 \stackrel{?}{=} 7 + 21$	Multiply: $4(7) = 28$ and $3(7) = 21$.
$28 = 28$	This statement is true.

This true statement verifies that the solution is 7, or the solution set is $\{7\}$. ■

✓ **CHECK POINT 5** Solve and check: $7x = 12 + 6x$.

EXAMPLE 6 Solving an Equation by Isolating the Variable

Solve and check: $3y - 9 = 2y + 6$.

Solution Our goal is to isolate variable terms on one side and constant terms on the other side. Let's begin by isolating the variable on the left.

$3y - 9 = 2y + 6$	This is the given equation.
$3y - 2y - 9 = 2y - 2y + 6$	Isolate the variable terms on the left by subtracting $2y$ from both sides.
$y - 9 = 6$	Subtracting $2y$ from both sides eliminates $2y$ on the right. On the left, $3y - 2y = 1y = y$.

Now we isolate the constant terms on the right by adding 9 to both sides.

$y - 9 + 9 = 6 + 9$	Add 9 to both sides.
$y = 15$	Simplify.

Check

$$3y - 9 = 2y + 6 \quad \text{Use the original equation.}$$
$$3(15) - 9 \stackrel{?}{=} 2(15) + 6 \quad \text{Substitute 15 for } y.$$
$$45 - 9 \stackrel{?}{=} 30 + 6 \quad \text{Multiply: } 3(15) = 45 \text{ and } 2(15) = 30.$$
$$36 = 36 \quad \text{This statement is true.}$$

The solution is 15, or the solution set is $\{15\}$. ■

✓ **CHECK POINT 6** Solve and check: $3x - 6 = 2x + 5$.

---

3 Solve applied problems using formulas.

Applications

Our next example shows how the addition property of equality can be used to find the value of a variable in a mathematical model.

EXAMPLE 7 An Application: Vocabulary and Age

There is a relationship between the number of words in a child's vocabulary, V, and the child's age, A, in months, for ages between 15 and 50 months, inclusive. This relationship can be modeled by the formula

$$V + 900 = 60A.$$

Use the formula to find the number of words in a child's vocabulary at the age of 30 months.

Solution In the formula, A represents the child's age, in months. We are interested in a 30-month-old child. Thus, we substitute 30 for A. Then we use the addition property of equality to find V, the number of words in the child's vocabulary.

$$V + 900 = 60A \quad \text{This is the given formula.}$$
$$V + 900 = 60(30) \quad \text{Substitute 30 for } A.$$
$$V + 900 = 1800 \quad \text{Multiply: } 60(30) = 1800.$$
$$V + 900 - 900 = 1800 - 900 \quad \text{Subtract 900 from both sides and solve for } V.$$
$$V = 900$$

At the age of 30 months, a child has a vocabulary of 900 words. ■

✓ **CHECK POINT 7** Use the formula $V + 900 = 60A$ to find the number of words in a child's vocabulary at the age of 50 months.

The line graph in **Figure 1** allows us to "see" the formula $V + 900 = 60A$. The two points labeled with voice balloons illustrate what we learned about vocabulary and age by solving equations in Example 7 and Check Point 7.

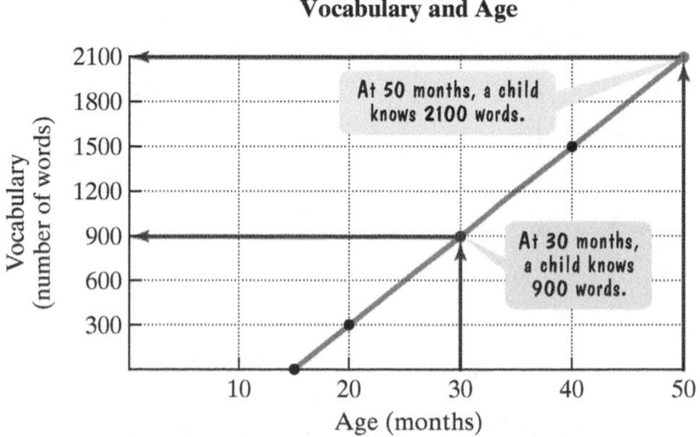

Figure 1

Linear equations are related to models whose graphs are straight lines, like the one in **Figure 1**. For this reason, these equations are called *linear* equations.

Achieving Success

Algebra is cumulative. This means that the topics build on one another. Understanding each topic depends on understanding the previous material. Do not let yourself fall behind.

CONCEPT AND VOCABULARY CHECK

Fill in each blank so that the resulting statement is true.

1. The process of finding the number or numbers that make an equation a true statement is called ______________ the equation.
2. An equation in the form $ax + b = c$, such as $7x + 9 = 13$, is called a/an ______________ equation in one variable.
3. Equations that have the same solution are called ______________ equations.
4. The addition property of equality states that if $a = b$, then $a + c =$ ______________.
5. The addition property of equality lets us add or ______________ the same number on both sides of an equation without changing the equation's ______________.
6. The equation $x - 7 = 13$ can be solved by ______________ to both sides.
7. The equation $7x = 5 + 6x$ can be solved by ______________ from both sides.

1 EXERCISE SET

MyMathLab®

Watch the videos in MyMathLab

Download the MyDashBoard App

Practice Exercises

In Exercises 1–10, identify the linear equations in one variable.

1. $x - 9 = 13$
2. $x - 15 = 20$
3. $x^2 - 9 = 13$
4. $x^2 - 15 = 20$
5. $\frac{9}{x} = 13$
6. $\frac{15}{x} = 20$
7. $\sqrt{2}x + \pi = 0.\overline{3}$
8. $\sqrt{3}x + \pi = 0.\overline{6}$
9. $|x + 2| = 5$
10. $|x + 5| = 8$

Solve each equation in Exercises 11–54 using the addition property of equality. Be sure to check your proposed solutions.

11. $x - 4 = 19$
12. $y - 5 = -18$
13. $z + 8 = -12$
14. $z + 13 = -15$
15. $-2 = x + 14$
16. $-13 = x + 11$
17. $-17 = y - 5$
18. $-21 = y - 4$
19. $7 + z = 11$
20. $18 + z = 14$
21. $-6 + y = -17$
22. $-8 + y = -29$
23. $x + \frac{1}{3} = \frac{7}{3}$
24. $x + \frac{7}{8} = \frac{9}{8}$
25. $t + \frac{5}{6} = -\frac{7}{12}$
26. $t + \frac{2}{3} = -\frac{7}{6}$
27. $x - \frac{3}{4} = \frac{9}{2}$
28. $x - \frac{3}{5} = \frac{7}{10}$
29. $-\frac{1}{5} + y = -\frac{3}{4}$
30. $-\frac{1}{8} + y = -\frac{1}{4}$
31. $3.2 + x = 7.5$
32. $-2.7 + w = -5.3$
33. $x + \frac{3}{4} = -\frac{9}{2}$
34. $r + \frac{3}{5} = -\frac{7}{10}$
35. $5 = -13 + y$
36. $-11 = 8 + x$
37. $-\frac{3}{5} = -\frac{3}{2} + s$
38. $\frac{7}{3} = -\frac{5}{2} + z$
39. $830 + y = 520$
40. $-90 + t = -35$
41. $r + 3.7 = 8$
42. $x + 10.6 = -9$
43. $-3.7 + m = -3.7$
44. $y + \frac{7}{11} = \frac{7}{11}$
45. $6y + 3 - 5y = 14$
46. $-3x - 5 + 4x = 9$
47. $7 - 5x + 8 + 2x + 4x - 3 = 2 + 3 \cdot 5$
48. $13 - 3r + 2 + 6r - 2r - 1 = 3 + 2 \cdot 9$
49. $7y + 4 = 6y - 9$
50. $4r - 3 = 5 + 3r$
51. $12 - 6x = 18 - 7x$
52. $20 - 7s = 26 - 8s$
53. $4x + 2 = 3(x - 6) + 8$
54. $7x + 3 = 6(x - 1) + 9$

Practice PLUS

The equations in Exercises 55–58 contain small geometric figures that represent real numbers. Use the addition property of equality to isolate x on one side of the equation and the geometric figures on the other side.

55. $x - \square = \triangle$

56. $x + \square = \triangle$

57. $2x + \triangle = 3x + \square$

58. $6x - \triangle = 7x - \square$

In Exercises 59–62, use the given information to write an equation. Let x represent the number described in each exercise. Then solve the equation and find the number.

59. If 12 is subtracted from a number, the result is -2. Find the number.

60. If 23 is subtracted from a number, the result is -8. Find the number.

61. The difference between $\frac{2}{5}$ of a number and 8 is $\frac{7}{5}$ of that number. Find the number.

62. The difference between 3 and $\frac{2}{7}$ of a number is $\frac{5}{7}$ of that number. Find the number.

Application Exercises

Formulas frequently appear in the business world. For example, the cost, C, of an item (the price paid by a retailer) plus the markup, M, on that item (the retailer's profit) equals the selling price, S, of the item. The formula is

$$C + M = S.$$

Use the formula to solve Exercises 63–64.

63. The selling price of a computer is \$1850. If the markup on the computer is \$150, find the cost to the retailer for the computer.

64. The selling price of a television is \$650. If the cost to the retailer for the television is \$520, find the markup.

The bar graph shows the average credit-card debt per U.S. household for selected years from 2000 through 2008.

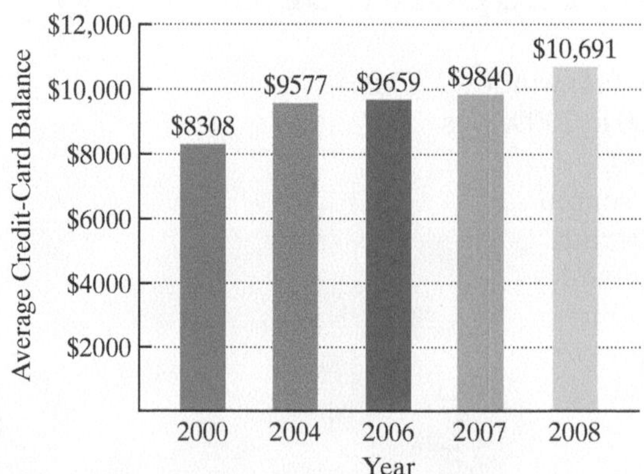

Source: CardTrak.com

The data displayed by the bar graph can be described by the mathematical model

$$d - 257x = 8328,$$

where d is the average credit-card debt per U.S. household x years after 2000. Use this information to solve Exercises 65–66.

65. According to the formula at the bottom of the previous column, what was the average credit-card debt per U.S. household for 2008? Does this underestimate or overestimate the number displayed by the bar graph? By how much?

66. According to the formula at the bottom of the previous column, what was the average credit-card debt per U.S. household for 2007? Does this underestimate or overestimate the number displayed by the bar graph? By how much?

Diversity Index. *The diversity index, from 0 (no diversity) to 100, measures the chance that two randomly selected people are a different race or ethnicity. The diversity index in the United States varies widely from region to region, from as high as 79 in Hawaii and 68 in California to as low as 10 in Maine and Vermont and 13 in West Virginia. The line graph shows the national diversity index for the United States for four years in the period from 1980 through 2009.*

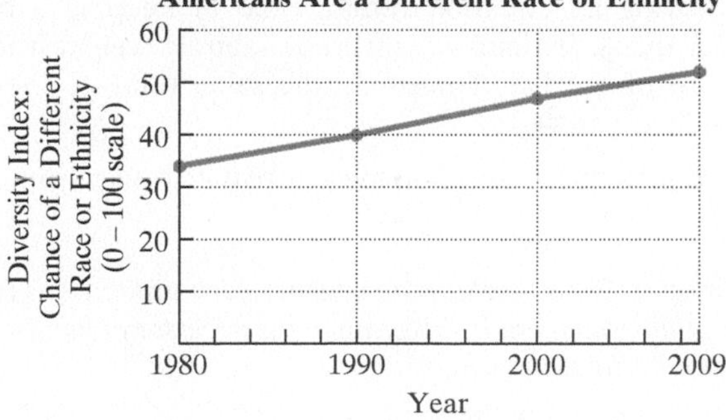

Source: USA Today

The data displayed by the line graph can be described by the mathematical model

$$I - 0.6x = 34,$$

where I is the national diversity index in the United States x years after 1980. Use this information to solve Exercises 67–68.

67. **a.** Use the line graph to estimate the U.S. diversity index in 2009.

b. Use the formula to determine the U.S. diversity index in 2009. How does this compare with your graphical estimate from part (a)?

68. **a.** Use the line graph to estimate the U.S. diversity index in 2000.

b. Use the formula to determine the U.S. diversity index in 2000. How does this compare with your graphical estimate from part (a)?

Writing in Mathematics

69. State the addition property of equality and give an example.

70. Explain why $x + 2 = 9$ and $x + 2 = -6$ are not equivalent equations.

71. What is the difference between solving an equation such as

$$5y + 3 - 4y - 8 = 6 + 9$$

and simplifying an algebraic expression such as

$$5y + 3 - 4y - 8?$$

If there is a difference, which topic should be taught first? Why?

72. Look, again, at the graph for Exercises 67–68 that shows the diversity index in the United States over time. You used a *linear* equation to solve Exercise 67 or 68. What does the adjective *linear* have to do with the relationship among the four data points in the graph?

Critical Thinking Exercises

Make Sense? *In Exercises 73–76, determine whether each statement "makes sense" or "does not make sense" and explain your reasoning.*

73. The book is teaching me totally different things than my instructor: The book adds the number to both sides beside the equation, but my instructor adds the number underneath.

74. There are times that I prefer to check an equation's solution in my head and not show the check.

75. Solving an equation reminds me of keeping a barbell balanced: If I add weight to or subtract weight from one side of the bar, I must do the same thing to the other side.

76. I used a linear equation to explore data points lying on the same line.

In Exercises 77–80, determine whether each statement is true or false. If the statement is false, make the necessary change(s) to produce a true statement.

77. If $y - a = -b$, then $y = a + b$.

78. If $y + 7 = 0$, then $y = 7$.

79. If $2x - 5 = 3x$, then $x = -5$.

80. If $3x = 18$, then $x = 18 - 3$.

81. Write an equation with a negative solution that can be solved by adding 100 to both sides.

Technology Exercises

Use a calculator to solve each equation in Exercises 82–83.

82. $x - 7.0463 = -9.2714$

83. $6.9825 = 4.2296 + y$

Review Exercises

84. Write as an algebraic expression in which x represents the number: the quotient of 9 and a number, decreased by 4 times the number.

85. Simplify: $-16 - 8 \div 4 \cdot (-2)$.

86. Simplify: $3[7x - 2(5x - 1)]$.

Preview Exercises

Exercises 87–89 will help you prepare for the material covered in the next section.

87. Multiply and simplify: $5 \cdot \frac{x}{5}$.

88. Divide and simplify: $\frac{-7y}{-7}$.

89. Is 4 a solution of $3x - 14 = -2x + 6$?

SECTION 2

The Multiplication Property of Equality

Objectives

1. Use the multiplication property of equality to solve equations.
2. Solve equations in the form $-x = c$.
3. Use the addition and multiplication properties to solve equations.
4. Solve applied problems using formulas.

How much was that doggie in the window? This purebred Westie, selling for $2000 in 2009, was a real bargain for $50 back in 1940.

Prices and salaries have soared over the decades. If present trends continue, what will you spend and earn in the future? In this section, we introduce a new property for solving equations to address these questions.

Yoshio Tomii/SuperStock

1 Use the multiplication property of equality to solve equations.

Using the Multiplication Property of Equality to Solve Equations

Can the addition property of equality be used to solve every linear equation in one variable? No. For example, consider the equation

$$\frac{x}{5} = 9.$$

We cannot isolate the variable x by adding or subtracting 5 on both sides. To get x by itself on the left side, multiply the left side by 5:

$$5 \cdot \frac{x}{5} = \left(5 \cdot \frac{1}{5}\right)x = 1x = x.$$

5 is the multiplicative inverse of $\frac{1}{5}$.

You must then multiply the right side by 5 also. By doing this, we are using the **multiplication property of equality**.

The Multiplication Property of Equality

The same nonzero real number (or algebraic expression) may multiply both sides of an equation without changing the solution. This can be expressed symbolically as follows:

If $a = b$ and $c \neq 0$, then $ac = bc$.

EXAMPLE 1 Solving an Equation Using the Multiplication Property

Solve the equation: $\frac{x}{5} = 9.$

Solution We can isolate the variable, x, by multiplying both sides of the equation by 5.

$\frac{x}{5} = 9$	This is the given equation.
$5 \cdot \frac{x}{5} = 5 \cdot 9$	Multiply both sides by 5.
$1x = 45$	Simplify.
$x = 45$	$1x = x$

By substituting 45 for x in the original equation, we obtain the true statement $9 = 9$. This verifies that the solution is 45, or the solution set is $\{45\}$. ■

✓ **CHECK POINT 1** Solve the equation: $\frac{x}{3} = 12.$

When we use the multiplication property of equality, we multiply both sides of an equation by the same nonzero number. We know that division is multiplication by a multiplicative inverse. Thus, the multiplication property also lets us divide both sides of an equation by a nonzero number without changing the solution.

EXAMPLE 2 Dividing Both Sides by the Same Nonzero Number

Solve: **a.** $6x = 30$ **b.** $-7y = 56$ **c.** $-18.9 = 3z$.

Solution In each equation, the variable is multiplied by a number. We can isolate the variable by dividing both sides of the equation by that number.

a.

$6x = 30$ This is the given equation.

$\frac{6x}{6} = \frac{30}{6}$ Divide both sides by 6.

$1x = 5$ Simplify.

$x = 5$ $1x = x$

By substituting 5 for x in the original equation, we obtain the true statement $30 = 30$. The solution is 5, or the solution set is $\{5\}$.

b.

$-7y = 56$ This is the given equation.

$\frac{-7y}{-7} = \frac{56}{-7}$ Divide both sides by -7.

$1y = -8$ Simplify.

$y = -8$ $1y = y$

By substituting -8 for y in the original equation, we obtain the true statement $56 = 56$. The solution is -8, or the solution set is $\{-8\}$.

c.

$-18.9 = 3z$ This is the given equation.

$\frac{-18.9}{3} = \frac{3z}{3}$ Divide both sides by 3.

$-6.3 = 1z$ Simplify.

$-6.3 = z$ $1z = z$

By substituting -6.3 for z in the original equation, we obtain the true statement $-18.9 = -18.9$. The solution is -6.3, or the solution set is $\{-6.3\}$. ■

✓ **CHECK POINT 2** Solve:

a. $4x = 84$ **b.** $-11y = 44$

c. $-15.5 = 5z$.

Some equations have a variable term with a fractional coefficient. Here is an example:

$$\frac{3}{4}y = 12.$$

The coefficient of the term $\frac{3}{4}y$ is $\frac{3}{4}$.

To isolate the variable, multiply both sides of the equation by the multiplicative inverse of the fraction. For the equation $\frac{3}{4}y = 12$, the multiplicative inverse of $\frac{3}{4}$ is $\frac{4}{3}$. Thus, we solve $\frac{3}{4}y = 12$ by multiplying both sides by $\frac{4}{3}$.

EXAMPLE 3 Using the Multiplication Property to Eliminate a Fractional Coefficient

Solve: **a.** $\frac{3}{4}y = 12$ **b.** $9 = -\frac{3}{5}x$.

Solution

a. $\frac{3}{4}y = 12$ — This is the given equation.

$\frac{4}{3}\left(\frac{3}{4}y\right) = \frac{4}{3}\cdot 12$ — Multiply both sides by $\frac{4}{3}$, the multiplicative inverse of $\frac{3}{4}$.

$1y = 16$ — On the left, $\frac{4}{3}\left(\frac{3}{4}y\right) = \left(\frac{4}{3}\cdot\frac{3}{4}\right)y = 1y$. On the right, $\frac{4}{3}\cdot\frac{12}{1} = \frac{48}{3} = 16$.

$y = 16$ — $1y = y$

By substituting 16 for y in the original equation, we obtain the true statement $12 = 12$. The solution is 16, or the solution set is $\{16\}$.

b. $9 = -\frac{3}{5}x$ — This is the given equation.

$-\frac{5}{3}\cdot 9 = -\frac{5}{3}\left(-\frac{3}{5}x\right)$ — Multiply both sides by $-\frac{5}{3}$, the multiplicative inverse of $-\frac{3}{5}$.

$-15 = 1x$ — Simplify.

$-15 = x$ — $1x = x$

By substituting -15 for x in the original equation, we obtain the true statement $9 = 9$. The solution is -15, or the solution set is $\{-15\}$. ■

✓ CHECK POINT 3 Solve:

a. $\frac{2}{3}y = 16$ **b.** $28 = -\frac{7}{4}x$.

---

2 Solve equations in the form $-x = c$.

Equations and Coefficients of −1

How do we solve an equation in the form $-x = c$, such as $-x = 4$? Because the equation means $-1x = 4$, we have not yet obtained a solution. The solution of an equation is obtained from the form $x =$ some number. The equation $-x = 4$ is not yet in this form. We still need to isolate x. We can do this by multiplying or dividing both sides of the equation by -1. We will multiply by -1.

EXAMPLE 4 Solving Equations in the Form $-x = c$

Solve: **a.** $-x = 4$ **b.** $-x = -7$.

Solution We multiply both sides of each equation by -1. This will isolate x on the left side.

a. $-x = 4$ — This is the given equation.

$-1x = 4$ — Rewrite $-x$ as $-1x$.

$(-1)(-1x) = (-1)(4)$ — Multiply both sides by -1.

$1x = -4$ — On the left, $(-1)(-1) = 1$. On the right, $(-1)(4) = -4$.

$x = -4$ — $1x = x$

Check $-x = 4$ — This is the original equation.

$-(-4) \stackrel{?}{=} 4$ — Substitute -4 for x.

$4 = 4$ — $-(-a) = a$, so $-(-4) = 4$.

This true statement indicates that the solution is -4, or the solution set is $\{-4\}$.

b.

$$
\begin{aligned}
-x &= -7 && \text{This is the given equation.}\\
-1x &= -7 && \text{Rewrite } -x \text{ as } -1x.\\
(-1)(-1x) &= (-1)(-7) && \text{Multiply both sides by } -1.\\
1x &= 7 && (-1)(-1) = 1 \text{ and } (-1)(-7) = 7.\\
x &= 7 && 1x = x
\end{aligned}
$$

By substituting 7 for x in the original equation, we obtain the true statement $-7 = -7$. The solution is 7, or the solution set is $\{7\}$. ■

Great Question!

Is there a fast way to solve equations in the form $-x = c$?

If $-x = c$, then the equation's solution is the opposite, or additive inverse, of c. For example, the solution of $-x = -7$ is the opposite of -7, which is 7.

✓ **CHECK POINT 4** Solve: **a.** $-x = 5$ **b.** $-x = -3$.

3 Use the addition and multiplication properties to solve equations.

Equations Requiring Both the Addition and Multiplication Properties

When an equation does not contain fractions, we will often use the addition property of equality before the multiplication property of equality. Our overall goal is to isolate the variable with a coefficient of 1 on either the left or right side of the equation.

Here is the procedure that we will be using to solve the equations in the next three examples:

- Use the addition property of equality to isolate the variable term.
- Use the multiplication property of equality to isolate the variable.

EXAMPLE 5 Using Both the Addition and Multiplication Properties

Solve: $3x + 1 = 7$.

Solution We first isolate the variable term, $3x$, by subtracting 1 from both sides. Then we isolate the variable, x, by dividing both sides by 3.

- **Use the addition property of equality to isolate the variable term.**

$$
\begin{aligned}
3x + 1 &= 7 && \text{This is the given equation.}\\
3x + 1 - 1 &= 7 - 1 && \text{Use the addition property, subtracting 1 from both sides.}\\
3x &= 6 && \text{Simplify.}
\end{aligned}
$$

- **Use the multiplication property of equality to isolate the variable.**

$$
\begin{aligned}
\frac{3x}{3} &= \frac{6}{3} && \text{Divide both sides of } 3x = 6 \text{ by 3.}\\
x &= 2 && \text{Simplify.}
\end{aligned}
$$

By substituting 2 for x in the original equation, $3x + 1 = 7$, we obtain the true statement $7 = 7$. The solution is 2, or the solution set is $\{2\}$. ■

✓ **CHECK POINT 5** Solve: $4x + 3 = 27$.

EXAMPLE 6 Using Both the Addition and Multiplication Properties

Solve: $-2y - 28 = 4$.

Solution We first isolate the variable term, $-2y$, by adding 28 to both sides. Then we isolate the variable, y, by dividing both sides by -2.

- **Use the addition property of equality to isolate the variable term.**

$$-2y - 28 = 4 \quad \text{This is the given equation.}$$
$$-2y - 28 + 28 = 4 + 28 \quad \text{Use the addition property, adding 28 to both sides.}$$
$$-2y = 32 \quad \text{Simplify.}$$

- **Use the multiplication property of equality to isolate the variable.**

$$\frac{-2y}{-2} = \frac{32}{-2} \quad \text{Divide both sides by } -2.$$
$$y = -16 \quad \text{Simplify.}$$

Take a moment to substitute -16 for y in the given equation. Do you obtain the true statement $4 = 4$? The solution is -16, or the solution set is $\{-16\}$. ■

✓ **CHECK POINT 6** Solve: $-4y - 15 = 25$.

EXAMPLE 7 Using Both the Addition and Multiplication Properties

Solve: $3x - 14 = -2x + 6$.

Solution We will use the addition property to collect all terms involving x on the left and all numerical terms on the right. Then we will isolate the variable, x, by dividing both sides by its coefficient.

- **Use the addition property of equality to isolate the variable term.**

$$3x - 14 = -2x + 6 \quad \text{This is the given equation.}$$
$$3x + 2x - 14 = -2x + 2x + 6 \quad \text{Add 2x to both sides.}$$
$$5x - 14 = 6 \quad \text{Simplify.}$$
$$5x - 14 + 14 = 6 + 14 \quad \text{Add 14 to both sides.}$$
$$5x = 20 \quad \text{Simplify. The variable term, 5x, is isolated on the left. The numerical term, 20, is isolated on the right.}$$

- **Use the multiplication property of equality to isolate the variable.**

$$\frac{5x}{5} = \frac{20}{5} \quad \text{Divide both sides by 5.}$$
$$x = 4 \quad \text{Simplify.}$$

Check

$$3x - 14 = -2x + 6 \quad \text{Use the original equation.}$$
$$3(4) - 14 \stackrel{?}{=} -2(4) + 6 \quad \text{Substitute the proposed solution, 4, for x.}$$
$$12 - 14 \stackrel{?}{=} -8 + 6 \quad \text{Multiply.}$$
$$-2 = -2 \quad \text{Simplify.}$$

The true statement $-2 = -2$ verifies that the solution is 4, or the solution set is $\{4\}$. ■

✓ **CHECK POINT 7** Solve: $2x - 15 = -4x + 21$.

---

4 Solve applied problems using formulas.

Applications

Most, but not all, salaries and prices have soared over the decades. To make it easier to compare, **Figure 2** converts historical prices into today's dollars, with adjustments based on the consumer price index. Our next example, as well as forthcoming exercises, shows how solving linear equations can be used to explore mathematical models based on some of the data displayed by the bar graphs.

Comparing Salaries and Prices Using Today's Dollars

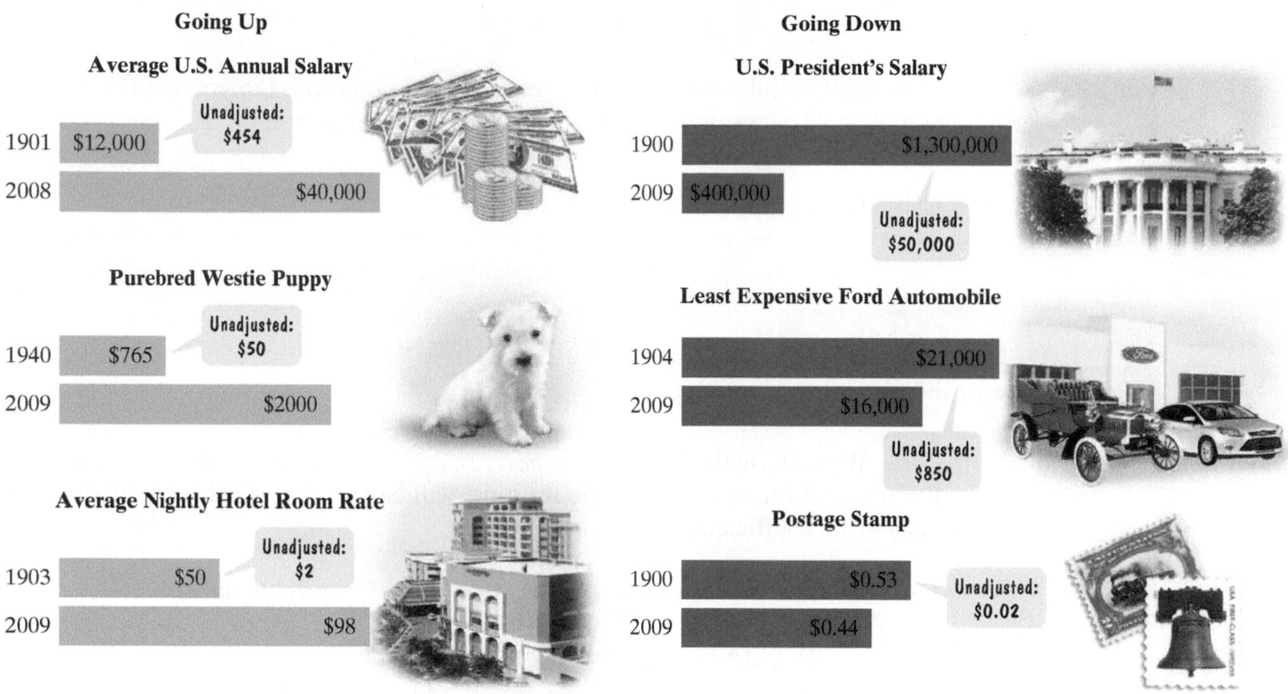

Figure 2

Source: Newsweek

EXAMPLE 8 Average Annual Salary

The data in **Figure 2** for average annual salary can be described by the mathematical model

$$S = 262n + 12{,}000,$$

where S is the average U.S. annual salary, in dollars, n years after 1901.

a. Does the formula underestimate or overestimate the average annual salary in 2008? By how much?

b. If trends shown by the formula continue, when will the average annual salary be \$43,000? Round to the nearest year.

Solution

a. **Figure 2** indicates that the average annual salary was \$40,000 in 2008. Let's see if the formula underestimates or overestimates this value. The year 2008 is 107 years after 1901 ($2008 - 1901 = 107$), so we substitute 107 for n.

$S = 262n + 12{,}000$ — This is the given formula.

$S = 262(107) + 12{,}000$ — Replace n with 107.

$S = 28{,}034 + 12{,}000$ — Multiply: $262(107) = 28{,}034$.

$S = 40{,}034$ — Add: $28{,}034 + 12{,}000 = 40{,}034$.

The model indicates that the average annual salary was \$40,034 in 2008. This overestimates the number displayed by the graph, \$40,000, by \$34.

b. We are interested in when the average annual salary will be \$43,000. We substitute 43,000 for the average annual salary, S, in the given formula. Then we solve for n, the number of years after 1901.

$$S = 262n + 12{,}000$$ This is the given formula.

$$43{,}000 = 262n + 12{,}000$$ Replace S with 43,000.

Our goal is to isolate n.

$$43{,}000 - 12{,}000 = 262n + 12{,}000 - 12{,}000$$ Isolate the term containing n by subtracting 12,000 from both sides.

$$31{,}000 = 262n$$ Simplify.

$$\frac{31{,}000}{262} = \frac{262n}{262}$$ Divide both sides by 262.

$$118 \approx n$$ Simplify: $\frac{31{,}000}{262} \approx 118.3 \approx 118$.

The formula indicates that approximately 118 years after 1901, or in 2019 $(1901 + 118 = 2019)$, the average annual salary in the United States will be \$43,000. ■

Great Question!

In Example 8, did you use the formula $S = 262n + 12{,}000$ in two different ways?

Good observation! In Example 8(a), we substituted a value for n and used the order of operations to determine S. In Example 8(b), we substituted a value for S and solved a linear equation to determine n.

✓ **CHECK POINT 8** The data in **Figure 2** for the price of a Westie puppy can be described by the mathematical model

$$P = 18n + 765,$$

where P is the puppy's price n years after 1940.

a. Does the formula underestimate or overestimate the price of a Westie puppy in 2009? By how much?

b. If trends shown by the formula continue, when will the price of a Westie puppy be \$2151?

CONCEPT AND VOCABULARY CHECK

Fill in each blank so that the resulting statement is true.

1. The multiplication property of equality states that if $a = b$ and $c \neq 0$, then $ac =$ ________.
2. The multiplication property of equality lets us multiply or ________ both sides of an equation by the same nonzero number.
3. The equation $\frac{x}{7} = 13$ can be solved by ________ both sides by ________.
4. The equation $-8y = 32$ can be solved by ________ both sides by ________.
5. The equation $\frac{3}{5}x = 20$ can be solved by ________ both sides by ________.
6. The equation $-x = 12$ can be solved by ________ both sides by ________.
7. The equation $5x + 2 = 17$ can be solved by first ________ from both sides and then ________ both sides by ________.

2 EXERCISE SET

MyMathLab®

Watch the videos in MyMathLab

Download the MyDashBoard App

Practice Exercises

Solve each equation in Exercises 1–28 using the multiplication property of equality. Be sure to check your proposed solutions.

1. $\frac{x}{6} = 5$

2. $\frac{x}{7} = 4$

3. $\frac{x}{-3} = 11$

4. $\frac{x}{-5} = 8$

5. $5y = 35$

6. $6y = 42$

7. $-7y = 63$

8. $-4y = 32$

9. $-28 = 8z$

10. $-36 = 8z$

11. $-18 = -3z$

12. $-54 = -9z$

13. $-8x = 6$

14. $-8x = 4$

15. $17y = 0$

16. $-16y = 0$

17. $\frac{2}{3}y = 12$

18. $\frac{3}{4}y = 15$

19. $28 = -\frac{7}{2}x$

20. $20 = -\frac{5}{8}x$

21. $-x = 17$

22. $-x = 23$

23. $-47 = -y$

24. $-51 = -y$

25. $-\frac{x}{5} = -9$

26. $-\frac{x}{5} = -1$

27. $2x - 12x = 50$

28. $8x - 3x = -45$

Solve each equation in Exercises 29–54 using both the addition and multiplication properties of equality. Check proposed solutions.

29. $2x + 1 = 11$

30. $2x + 5 = 13$

31. $2x - 3 = 9$

32. $3x - 2 = 9$

33. $-2y + 5 = 7$

34. $-3y + 4 = 13$

35. $-3y - 7 = -1$

36. $-2y - 5 = 7$

37. $12 = 4z + 3$

38. $14 = 5z - 21$

39. $-x - 3 = 3$

40. $-x - 5 = 5$

41. $6y = 2y - 12$

42. $8y = 3y - 10$

43. $3z = -2z - 15$

44. $2z = -4z + 18$

45. $-5x = -2x - 12$

46. $-7x = -3x - 8$

47. $8y + 4 = 2y - 5$

48. $5y + 6 = 3y - 6$

49. $6z - 5 = z + 5$

50. $6z - 3 = z + 2$

51. $6x + 14 = 2x - 2$

52. $9x + 2 = 6x - 4$

53. $-3y - 1 = 5 - 2y$

54. $-3y - 2 = -5 - 4y$

Practice PLUS

The equations in Exercises 55–58 contain small geometric figures that represent nonzero real numbers. Use the multiplication property of equality to isolate x on one side of the equation and the geometric figures on the other side.

55. $\frac{x}{\square} = \triangle$

56. $\triangle = \square x$

57. $\triangle = -x$

58. $\frac{-x}{\square} = \triangle$

In Exercises 59–66, use the given information to write an equation. Let x represent the number described in each exercise. Then solve the equation and find the number.

59. If a number is multiplied by 6, the result is 10. Find the number.

60. If a number is multiplied by -6, the result is 20. Find the number.

61. If a number is divided by -9, the result is 5. Find the number.

62. If a number is divided by -7, the result is 8. Find the number.

63. Eight subtracted from the product of 4 and a number is 56.

64. Ten subtracted from the product of 3 and a number is 23.

65. Negative three times a number, increased by 15, is -6.

66. Negative five times a number, increased by 11, is -29.

Application Exercises

The formula

$$M = \frac{n}{5}$$

models your distance, M, in miles, from a lightning strike in a thunderstorm if it takes n seconds to hear thunder after seeing the lightning. Use this formula to solve Exercises 67–68.

Leonid/Shutterstock

67. If you are 2 miles away from the lightning flash, how long will it take the sound of thunder to reach you?

68. If you are 3 miles away from the lightning flash, how long will it take the sound of thunder to reach you?

The Mach number is a measurement of speed, named after the man who suggested it, Ernst Mach (1838–1916). The formula

$$M = \frac{A}{740}$$

indicates that the speed of an aircraft, A, in miles per hour, divided by the speed of sound, approximately 740 miles per hour, results in the Mach number, M. Use the formula to determine the speed, in miles per hour, of the aircrafts in Exercises 69–70. (Note: When an aircraft's speed increases beyond Mach 1, it is said to have broken the sound barrier.)

69.

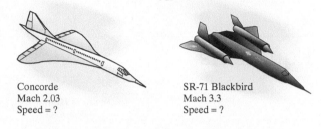

Concorde
Mach 2.03
Speed = ?

70.

SR-71 Blackbird
Mach 3.3
Speed = ?

In Exercises 71–72, we continue with our historical comparisons using today's dollars.

71. **Least Expensive Ford Automobile**

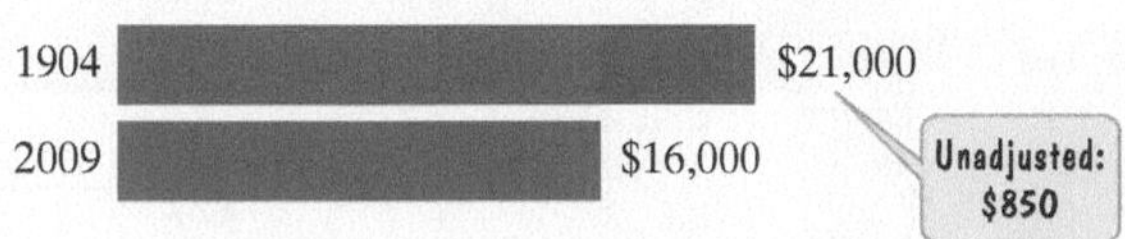

Using today's dollars, the data in the bar graph can be described by the mathematical model

$$F = -48n + 21{,}000,$$

where F is the price of the least expensive Ford n years after 1904.

a. Does the formula underestimate or overestimate the price of the least expensive Ford in 2009? By how much?

b. If trends shown by the formula continue, when will the least expensive Ford cost $15,000?

72. **Average Nightly Hotel Room Rate**

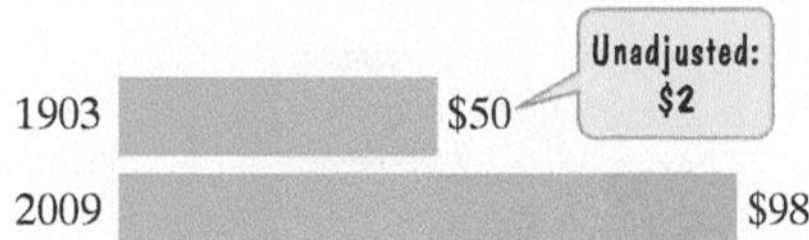

Using today's dollars, the data in the bar graph can be described by the mathematical model

$$H = 0.5n + 50,$$

where H is the average nightly hotel room rate n years after 1903.

a. Does the formula underestimate or overestimate the average nightly hotel room rate in 2009? By how much?

b. If trends shown by the formula continue, when will the average nightly hotel room rate cost $110?

Writing in Mathematics

73. State the multiplication property of equality and give an example.

74. Explain how to solve the equation $-x = -50$.

75. Explain how to solve the equation $2x + 8 = 5x - 3$.

Critical Thinking Exercises

Make Sense? *In Exercises 76–79, determine whether each statement "makes sense" or "does not make sense" and explain your reasoning.*

76. I used the addition and multiplication properties of equality to solve $3x = 20 + 4$.

77. I used the addition and multiplication properties of equality to solve $12 - 3x = 15$ as follows:

$$\begin{aligned} 12 - 3x &= 15 \\ 3x &= 3 \\ x &= 1. \end{aligned}$$

78. When I use the addition and multiplication properties to solve $2x + 5 = 17$, I undo the operations in the opposite order in which they are performed.

79. The model $P = 18n + 765$ describes the price of a Westie puppy, P, n years after 1940, so I have to solve a linear equation to determine the puppy's price in 2009.

In Exercises 80–83, determine whether each statement is true or false. If the statement is false, make the necessary change(s) to produce a true statement.

80. If $7x = 21$, then $x = 21 - 7$.

81. If $3x - 4 = 16$, then $3x = 12$.

82. If $3x + 7 = 0$, then $x = \frac{7}{3}$.

83. The solution of $6x = 0$ is not a natural number.

In Exercises 84–85, write an equation with the given characteristics.

84. The solution is a positive integer and the equation can be solved by dividing both sides by -60.

85. The solution is a negative integer and the equation can be solved by multiplying both sides by $\frac{4}{5}$.

Technology Exercises

Solve each equation in Exercises 86–87. Use a calculator to help with the arithmetic. Check your solution using the calculator.

86. $3.7x - 19.46 = -9.988$

87. $-72.8y - 14.6 = -455.43 - 4.98y$

Review Exercises

88. Evaluate: $(-10)^2$.

89. Evaluate: -10^2.

90. Evaluate $x^3 - 4x$ for $x = -1$.

Preview Exercises

Exercises 91–93 will help you prepare for the material covered in the next section.

91. Simplify: $13 - 3(x + 2)$.

92. Is 6 a solution of $2(x - 3) - 17 = 13 - 3(x + 2)$?

93. Multiply and simplify: $10\left(\frac{x}{5} - \frac{39}{5}\right)$.

SECTION 3

Solving Linear Equations

Objectives

1. Solve linear equations.
2. Solve linear equations containing fractions.
3. Solve linear equations containing decimals.
4. Identify equations with no solution or infinitely many solutions.
5. Solve applied problems using formulas.

20th Century FoxTV/Album/Newscom

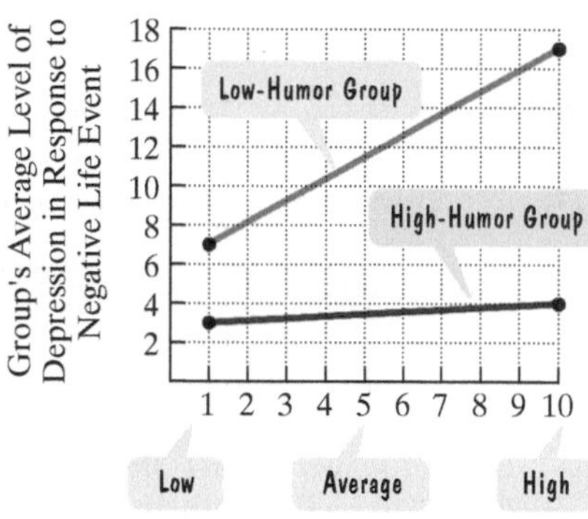

Figure 3

Source: Steven Davis and Joseph Palladino. *Psychology*, Fifth Edition, Prentice Hall, 2007.

The belief that humor and laughter can have positive benefits on our lives is not new. The graphs in **Figure 3** indicate that persons with a low sense of humor have higher levels of depression in response to negative life events than those with a high sense of humor. In this section, we will see how algebra models these relationships. To use these mathematical models, it would be helpful to have a systematic procedure for solving linear equations. We open this section with such a procedure.

1 Solve linear equations.

A Step-by-Step Procedure for Solving Linear Equations

Here is a step-by-step procedure for solving a linear equation in one variable. Not all of these steps are necessary to solve every equation.

Solving a Linear Equation

1. Simplify the algebraic expression on each side.
2. Collect all the variable terms on one side and all the constant terms on the other side.
3. Isolate the variable and solve.
4. Check the proposed solution in the original equation.

EXAMPLE 1 Solving a Linear Equation

Solve and check: $2x - 8x + 40 = 13 - 3x - 3$.

Solution

Step 1. Simplify the algebraic expression on each side.

$$2x - 8x + 40 = 13 - 3x - 3 \qquad \text{This is the given equation.}$$

$$-6x + 40 = 10 - 3x \qquad \text{Combine like terms: } 2x - 8x = -6x \text{ and } 13 - 3 = 10.$$

Discover for Yourself

Solve the equation in Example 1 by collecting terms with the variable on the right and numbers on the left. What do you observe?

Step 2. Collect variable terms on one side and constant terms on the other side. The simplified equation is $-6x + 40 = 10 - 3x$. We will collect variable terms on the left by adding $3x$ to both sides. We will collect the numbers on the right by subtracting 40 from both sides.

$$-6x + 40 + 3x = 10 - 3x + 3x \qquad \text{Add } 3x \text{ to both sides.}$$

$$-3x + 40 = 10 \qquad \text{Simplify: } -6x + 3x = -3x.$$

$$-3x + 40 - 40 = 10 - 40 \qquad \text{Subtract 40 from both sides.}$$

$$-3x = -30 \qquad \text{Simplify.}$$

Step 3. Isolate the variable and solve. We isolate the variable, x, by dividing both sides by -3.

$$\frac{-3x}{-3} = \frac{-30}{-3} \qquad \text{Divide both sides by } -3.$$

$$x = 10 \qquad \text{Simplify.}$$

Step 4. Check the proposed solution in the original equation. Substitute 10 for x in the original equation.

$$2x - 8x + 40 = 13 - 3x - 3 \qquad \text{This is the original equation.}$$

$$2 \cdot 10 - 8 \cdot 10 + 40 \stackrel{?}{=} 13 - 3 \cdot 10 - 3 \qquad \text{Substitute 10 for } x.$$

$$20 - 80 + 40 \stackrel{?}{=} 13 - 30 - 3 \qquad \text{Perform the indicated multiplications.}$$

$$-60 + 40 \stackrel{?}{=} -17 - 3 \qquad \text{Subtract: } 20 - 80 = -60 \text{ and } 13 - 30 = -17.$$

$$-20 = -20 \qquad \text{Simplify.}$$

By substituting 10 for x in the original equation, we obtain the true statement $-20 = -20$. This verifies that the solution is 10, or the solution set is $\{10\}$. ■

✓ **CHECK POINT 1** Solve and check: $-7x + 25 + 3x = 16 - 2x - 3$.

EXAMPLE 2 Solving a Linear Equation

Solve and check: $5x = 8(x + 3)$.

Solution

Step 1. Simplify the algebraic expression on each side. Use the distributive property to remove parentheses on the right.

$$5x = 8(x + 3) \qquad \text{This is the given equation.}$$

$$5x = 8x + 24 \qquad \text{Use the distributive property.}$$

Step 2. Collect variable terms on one side and constant terms on the other side. We will work with $5x = 8x + 24$ and collect variable terms on the left by subtracting $8x$ from both sides. The only constant term, 24, is already on the right.

$$5x - 8x = 8x + 24 - 8x \qquad \text{Subtract } 8x \text{ from both sides.}$$

$$-3x = 24 \qquad \text{Simplify: } 5x - 8x = -3x.$$

Step 3. Isolate the variable and solve. We isolate the variable, x, by dividing both sides of $-3x = 24$ by -3.

$$\frac{-3x}{-3} = \frac{24}{-3} \quad \text{Divide both sides by } -3.$$

$$x = -8 \quad \text{Simplify.}$$

Step 4. Check the proposed solution in the original equation. Substitute -8 for x in the original equation.

$$5x = 8(x + 3) \quad \text{This is the original equation.}$$

$$5(-8) \stackrel{?}{=} 8(-8 + 3) \quad \text{Substitute } -8 \text{ for } x.$$

$$5(-8) \stackrel{?}{=} 8(-5) \quad \text{Perform the addition in parentheses: } -8 + 3 = -5.$$

$$-40 = -40 \quad \text{Multiply.}$$

The true statement $-40 = -40$ verifies that -8 is the solution, or the solution set is $\{-8\}$. ■

✓ **CHECK POINT 2** Solve and check: $8x = 2(x + 6)$.

EXAMPLE 3 Solving a Linear Equation

Solve and check: $2(x - 3) - 17 = 13 - 3(x + 2)$.

Solution

Step 1. Simplify the algebraic expression on each side.

Do not begin with 13 – 3. Multiplication (the distributive property) is applied before subtraction.

$$2(x - 3) - 17 = 13 - 3(x + 2) \quad \text{This is the given equation.}$$

$$2x - 6 - 17 = 13 - 3x - 6 \quad \text{Use the distributive property.}$$

$$2x - 23 = -3x + 7 \quad \text{Combine like terms.}$$

Step 2. Collect variable terms on one side and constant terms on the other side. We will collect variable terms on the left by adding $3x$ to both sides. We will collect the numbers on the right by adding 23 to both sides.

$$2x - 23 + 3x = -3x + 7 + 3x \quad \text{Add } 3x \text{ to both sides.}$$

$$5x - 23 = 7 \quad \text{Simplify: } 2x + 3x = 5x.$$

$$5x - 23 + 23 = 7 + 23 \quad \text{Add 23 to both sides.}$$

$$5x = 30 \quad \text{Simplify.}$$

Step 3. Isolate the variable and solve. We isolate the variable, x, by dividing both sides by 5.

$$\frac{5x}{5} = \frac{30}{5} \quad \text{Divide both sides by 5.}$$

$$x = 6 \quad \text{Simplify.}$$

Step 4. Check the proposed solution in the original equation. Substitute 6 for x in the original equation.

$$2(x - 3) - 17 = 13 - 3(x + 2) \quad \text{This is the original equation.}$$

$$2(6 - 3) - 17 \stackrel{?}{=} 13 - 3(6 + 2) \quad \text{Substitute 6 for } x.$$

$$2(3) - 17 \stackrel{?}{=} 13 - 3(8) \quad \text{Simplify inside parentheses.}$$

$$6 - 17 \stackrel{?}{=} 13 - 24 \quad \text{Multiply.}$$

$$-11 = -11 \quad \text{Subtract.}$$

The true statement $-11 = -11$ verifies that 6 is the solution, or the solution set is $\{6\}$. ■

✓ **CHECK POINT 3** Solve and check: $4(2x + 1) - 29 = 3(2x - 5)$.

2 Solve linear equations containing fractions.

Linear Equations with Fractions

Equations are easier to solve when they do not contain fractions. How do we remove fractions from an equation? We begin by multiplying both sides of the equation by the least common denominator of any fractions in the equation. The least common denominator is the smallest number that all denominators will divide into. Multiplying every term on both sides of the equation by the least common denominator will eliminate the fractions in the equation. Example 4 shows how we "clear an equation of fractions."

EXAMPLE 4 Solving a Linear Equation Involving Fractions

Solve and check: $\frac{3x}{2} = \frac{x}{5} - \frac{39}{5}$.

Solution The denominators are 2, 5, and 5. The smallest number that is divisible by 2, 5, and 5 is 10. We begin by multiplying both sides of the equation by 10, the least common denominator.

$$\frac{3x}{2} = \frac{x}{5} - \frac{39}{5}$$ This is the given equation.

$$10 \cdot \frac{3x}{2} = 10\left(\frac{x}{5} - \frac{39}{5}\right)$$ Multiply both sides by 10.

$$10 \cdot \frac{3x}{2} = 10 \cdot \frac{x}{5} - 10 \cdot \frac{39}{5}$$ Use the distributive property. Be sure to multiply all terms by 10.

$$\overset{5}{\cancel{10}} \cdot \frac{3x}{\underset{1}{\cancel{2}}} = \overset{2}{\cancel{10}} \cdot \frac{x}{\underset{1}{\cancel{5}}} - \overset{2}{\cancel{10}} \cdot \frac{39}{\underset{1}{\cancel{5}}}$$ Divide out common factors in the multiplications.

$$15x = 2x - 78$$ Complete the multiplications. The fractions are now cleared.

At this point, we have an equation similar to those we previously have solved. Collect the variable terms on one side and the constant terms on the other side.

$$15x - 2x = 2x - 2x - 78$$ Subtract $2x$ to get the variable terms on the left.

$$13x = -78$$ Simplify.

Isolate x by dividing both sides by 13.

$$\frac{13x}{13} = \frac{-78}{13}$$ Divide both sides by 13.

$$x = -6$$ Simplify.

Check

$$\frac{3x}{2} = \frac{x}{5} - \frac{39}{5}$$ This is the original equation.

$$\frac{3(-6)}{2} \stackrel{?}{=} \frac{-6}{5} - \frac{39}{5}$$ Substitute -6 for x.

$$-9 \stackrel{?}{=} \frac{-6}{5} - \frac{39}{5}$$ Simplify the left side: $\frac{3(-6)}{2} = \frac{-18}{2} = -9$.

$$-9 \stackrel{?}{=} \frac{-45}{5}$$ Subtract on the right side: $\frac{-6}{5} - \frac{39}{5} = \frac{-6}{5} + \left(\frac{-39}{5}\right) = \frac{-45}{5}$.

$$-9 = -9$$ Simplify: $\frac{-45}{5} = -9$.

The true statement $-9 = -9$ verifies that -6 is the solution, or the solution set is $\{-6\}$. ■

✓ **CHECK POINT 4** Solve and check: $\frac{x}{4} = \frac{2x}{3} + \frac{5}{6}$.

---

3 Solve linear equations containing decimals.

Linear Equations with Decimals

It is not a requirement to clear decimals in an equation. However, if you are not using a calculator, eliminating decimal numbers can make calculations easier.

Multiplying a decimal number by 10^n, where n is a positive integer, has the effect of moving the decimal point n places to the right. For example,

$$0.3 \times 10 = 3 \qquad 0.37 \times 10^2 = 37 \qquad 0.408 \times 10^3 = 408.$$

One decimal place — Two decimal places — Three decimal places

These numerical examples suggest a procedure for clearing decimals in an equation.

Clearing an Equation of Decimals

Multiply every term on both sides of the equation by a power of 10. The exponent on 10 will equal the greatest number of decimal places in the equation.

EXAMPLE 5 Solving a Linear Equation Involving Decimals

Solve and check: $0.3(x - 6) = 0.37x - 1.1$.

Solution We will first apply the distributive property to remove parentheses on the left. Then we will clear the equation of decimals.

$$0.3(x - 6) = 0.37x - 1.1$$ This is the given equation.

$$0.3x - 0.3(6) = 0.37x - 1.1$$ Use the distributive property.

$$0.3x - 1.8 = 0.37x - 1.1$$ Multiply: $0.3(6) = 1.8$.

The number 0.37 has two decimal places, the greatest number of decimal places in the equation. Multiply both sides by 10^2, or 100, to clear the decimals.

$$100(0.3x - 1.8) = 100(0.37x - 1.1)$$ Multiply both sides by 100.

$$100(0.3x) - 100(1.8) = 100(0.37x) - 100(1.1)$$ Use the distributive property.

$$30x - 180 = 37x - 110$$ Simplify by moving decimal points two places to the right.

At this point, we have an equation similar to those we previously solved. We will solve $30x - 180 = 37x - 110$ by collecting the variable terms on one side and the constant terms on the other side.

$30x - 37x - 180 = 37x - 37x - 110$	Subtract $37x$ to get the variable terms on the left.
$-7x - 180 = -110$	Simplify.
$-7x - 180 + 180 = -110 + 180$	Add 180 to get the constant terms on the right.
$-7x = 70$	Simplify.
$\frac{7x}{-7} = \frac{70}{-7}$	Isolate x by dividing both sides by -7.
$x = -10$	Simplify.

Check

$0.3(x - 6) = 0.37x - 1.1$	This is the original equation.
$0.3(-10 - 6) = 0.37(-10) - 1.1$	Substitute -10 for x.
$0.3(-16) = 0.37(-10) - 1.1$	Simplify the left side: $-10 - 6 = -16$.
$-4.8 = -3.7 - 1.1$	Multiply: $0.3(-16) = -4.8$ and $0.37(-10) = -3.7$.
$-4.8 = -4.8$	Subtract on the right side: $-3.7 - 1.1 = -3.7 + (-1.1) = -4.8$.

The true statement $-4.8 = -4.8$ verifies that -10 is the solution, or the solution set is $\{-10\}$. ■

Great Question!

In the solution to Example 5, you simplified using the distributive property. Then you multiplied by 100 and cleared the equation of decimals. Can I clear the equation of decimals before using the distributive property?

Yes. Decimals can be cleared at any step in the process of solving an equation. Here's how it works for the equation in Example 5:

$0.3(x - 6) = 0.37x - 1.1$	This is the given equation.
$100[0.3(x - 6)] = 100(0.37x - 1.1)$	Multiply both sides by 100.

0.3$(x - 6)$ is one term with two factors, 0.3 and $x - 6$. To multiply the term by 100, we need only multiply one factor, in this case 0.3, by 100.

$[100(0.3)](x - 6) = 100(0.37x) - 100(1.1)$	Use the associative property on the left and the distributive property on the right.
$30(x - 6) = 37x - 110$	Simplify by moving decimal points two places to the right.
$30x - 180 = 37x - 110.$	Use the distributive property.

This last equation, $30x - 180 = 37x - 110$, is the same equation cleared of decimals that we obtained in the solution to Example 5.

✓ **CHECK POINT 5** Solve and check: $0.48x + 3 = 0.2(x - 6)$.

4 Identify equations with no solution or infinitely many solutions.

Equations with No Solution or Infinitely Many Solutions

Thus far, each equation that we have solved has had a single solution. However, some equations are not true for even one real number. Such an equation is called an **inconsistent equation**. Here is an example of such an equation:

$$x = x + 4.$$

There is no number that is equal to itself plus 4. This equation has no solution.

You can express the fact that an equation has no solution using words or set notation.

- Use the phrase "no solution."
- Use set notation: $\varnothing$.

This symbol stands for the empty set, a set with no elements.

An equation that is true for all real numbers is called an **identity**. An example of an identity is

$$x + 3 = x + 2 + 1.$$

Every number plus 3 is equal to that number plus 2 plus 1. Every real number is a solution to this equation.

You can express the fact that every real number is a solution of an equation using words or set notation.

- Use the phrase "all real numbers."
- Use set notation: $\{x \mid x \text{ is a real number}\}$.

The set of | all x | such that | x is a real number

Recognizing Inconsistent Equations and Identities

If you attempt to solve an equation with no solution or one that is true for every real number, you will eliminate the variable.

- An inconsistent equation with no solution results in a false statement, such as $2 = 5$.
- An identity that is true for every real number results in a true statement, such as $4 = 4$.

EXAMPLE 6 Solving an Equation

Solve: $2x + 6 = 2(x + 4)$.

Solution

$$2x + 6 = 2(x + 4) \quad \text{This is the given equation.}$$

$$2x + 6 = 2x + 8 \quad \text{Use the distributive property.}$$

$$2x + 6 - 2x = 2x + 8 - 2x \quad \text{Subtract 2x from both sides.}$$

$$6 = 8 \quad \text{Simplify.}$$

Keep reading. $6 = 8$ is not the solution.

The original equation is equivalent to the statement $6 = 8$, which is false for every value of x. The equation is inconsistent and has no solution. You can express this by writing "no solution" or using the symbol for the empty set, $\varnothing$. ■

✓ **CHECK POINT 6** Solve: $3x + 7 = 3(x + 1)$.

EXAMPLE 7 Solving an Equation

Solve: $-3x + 5 + 5x = 4x - 2x + 5$.

Solution

$$-3x + 5 + 5x = 4x - 2x + 5 \quad \text{This is the given equation.}$$

$$2x + 5 = 2x + 5 \quad \text{Combine like terms: } -3x + 5x = 2x \text{ and } 4x - 2x = 2x.$$

$$2x + 5 - 2x = 2x + 5 - 2x \quad \text{Subtract } 2x \text{ from both sides.}$$

Keep reading. $5 = 5$ is not the solution.

$$5 = 5 \quad \text{Simplify.}$$

The original equation is equivalent to the statement $5 = 5$, which is true for every value of x. The equation is an identity and all real numbers are solutions. You can express this by writing "all real numbers" or using set notation: $\{x \mid x \text{ is a real number}\}$. ■

✓ **CHECK POINT 7** Solve: $3(x - 1) + 9 = 8x + 6 - 5x$.

---

5 Solve applied problems using formulas.

Applications

The next example shows how our procedure for solving equations with fractions can be used to find the value of a variable in a mathematical model.

EXAMPLE 8 An Application: Responding to Negative Life Events

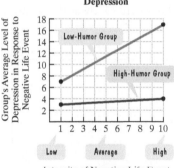

Sense of Humor and Depression

Group's Average Level of Depression in Response to Negative Life Event

Low-Humor Group

High-Humor Group

Low · Average · High

Intensity of Negative Life Event

Figure 3 (repeated)

In the section opener, we introduced line graphs, repeated in **Figure 3**, indicating that persons with a low sense of humor have higher levels of depression in response to negative life events than those with a high sense of humor. These graphs can be modeled by the following formulas:

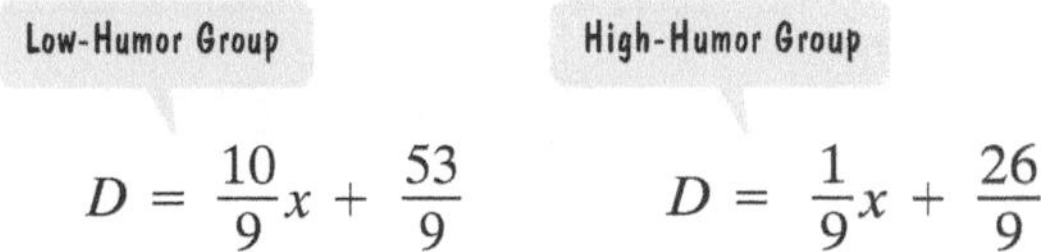

$$D = \frac{10}{9}x + \frac{53}{9} \qquad D = \frac{1}{9}x + \frac{26}{9}.$$

In each formula, x represents the intensity of a negative life event (from 1, low, to 10, high) and D is the level of depression in response to that event. If the high-humor group averages a level of depression of 3.5, or $\frac{7}{2}$, in response to a negative life event, what is the intensity of that event? How is the solution shown on the red line graph in **Figure 3**?

Solution We are interested in the intensity of a negative life event with an average level of depression of $\frac{7}{2}$ for the high-humor group. We substitute $\frac{7}{2}$ for D in the high-humor model and solve for x, the intensity of the negative life event.

$$D = \frac{1}{9}x + \frac{26}{9} \quad \text{This is the given formula for the high-humor group.}$$

$$\frac{7}{2} = \frac{1}{9}x + \frac{26}{9} \quad \text{Replace } D \text{ with } \frac{7}{2}.$$

$$18 \cdot \frac{7}{2} = 18\left(\frac{1}{9}x + \frac{26}{9}\right) \quad \text{Multiply both sides by 18, the least common denominator.}$$

$$18 \cdot \frac{7}{2} = 18 \cdot \frac{1}{9}x + 18 \cdot \frac{26}{9} \quad \text{Use the distributive property.}$$

$$\overset{9}{\cancel{18}} \cdot \frac{7}{\underset{1}{\cancel{2}}} = \overset{2}{\cancel{18}} \cdot \frac{1}{\underset{1}{\cancel{9}}}x + \overset{2}{\cancel{18}} \cdot \frac{26}{\underset{1}{\cancel{9}}} \quad \text{Divide out common factors in the multiplications.}$$

$63 = 2x + 52$	Complete the multiplications. The fractions are now cleared.
$63 - 52 = 2x + 52 - 52$	Subtract 52 from both sides to get constants on the left.
$11 = 2x$	Simplify.
$\frac{11}{2} = \frac{2x}{2}$	Divide both sides by 2.
$\frac{11}{2} = x$	Simplify.

The formula indicates that if the high-humor group averages a level of depression of 3.5 in response to a negative life event, the intensity of that event is $\frac{11}{2}$, or 5.5. This is illustrated on the line graph for the high-humor group in **Figure 4**.

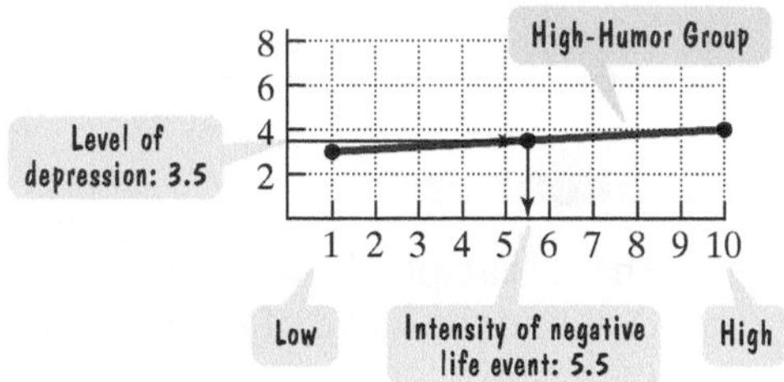

Figure 4

✓ CHECK POINT 8 Use the model for the low-humor group given in Example 8 to solve this problem. If the low-humor group averages a level of depression of 10 in response to a negative life event, what is the intensity of that event? How is the solution shown on the blue line graph in **Figure 3**?

Achieving Success

FoxTrot

Because concepts in mathematics build on each other, **it is extremely important that you complete all homework assignments**. This requires more than attempting a few of the assigned exercises. When it comes to assigned homework, you need to do four things and to do these things consistently throughout any math course:

1. Attempt to work *every* assigned problem.
2. Check your answers.
3. Correct your errors.
4. Ask for help with the problems you have attempted but do not understand.

Having said this, **don't panic at the length of the Exercise Sets**. You are not expected to work all, or even most, of the problems. Your professor will provide guidance on which exercises to work by assigning those problems that are consistent with the goals and objectives of your course.

CONCEPT AND VOCABULARY CHECK

Fill in each blank so that the resulting statement is true.

1. The first step in solving $3x - 9x + 30 = 15 - 2x - 4$ is to ______________.
2. The equation $\frac{x}{5} - \frac{1}{2} = \frac{x}{6}$ can be cleared of fractions by multiplying both sides by ______________.
3. The equation $0.9x - 4.3 = 0.47$ can be cleared of decimals by multiplying both sides by ______________.
4. A linear equation that is not true for even one real number, and therefore has no solution, is called a/an ______________ equation.
5. A linear equation that is true for all real numbers is called a/an ______________.
6. In solving an equation, if you eliminate the variable and obtain a false statement such as $2 = 5$, the equation is a/an ______________ equation.
7. In solving an equation, if you eliminate the variable and obtain a true statement such as $5 = 5$, the equation is a/an ______________.

3 EXERCISE SET

MyMathLab®

Watch the videos in MyMathLab

Download the MyDashBoard App

Practice Exercises

In Exercises 1–30, solve each equation. Be sure to check your proposed solution by substituting it for the variable in the original equation.

1. $5x + 3x - 4x = 10 + 2$
2. $4x + 8x - 2x = 20 - 15$
3. $4x - 9x + 22 = 3x + 30$
4. $3x + 2x + 64 = 40 - 7x$
5. $3x + 6 - x = 8 + 3x - 6$
6. $3x + 2 - x = 6 + 3x - 8$
7. $4(x + 1) = 20$
8. $3(x - 2) = -6$
9. $7(2x - 1) = 42$
10. $4(2x - 3) = 32$
11. $38 = 30 - 2(x - 1)$
12. $20 = 44 - 8(2 - x)$
13. $2(4z + 3) - 8 = 46$
14. $3(3z + 5) - 7 = 89$
15. $6x - (3x + 10) = 14$
16. $5x - (2x + 14) = 10$
17. $5(2x + 1) = 12x - 3$
18. $3(x + 2) = x + 30$
19. $3(5 - x) = 4(2x + 1)$
20. $3(3x - 1) = 4(3 + 3x)$
21. $8(y + 2) = 2(3y + 4)$
22. $8(y + 3) = 3(2y + 12)$
23. $3(x + 1) = 7(x - 2) - 3$
24. $5x - 4(x + 9) = 2x - 3$
25. $5(2x - 8) - 2 = 5(x - 3) + 3$
26. $7(3x - 2) + 5 = 6(2x - 1) + 24$
27. $6 = -4(1 - x) + 3(x + 1)$
28. $100 = -(x - 1) + 4(x - 6)$
29. $10(z + 4) - 4(z - 2) = 3(z - 1) + 2(z - 3)$
30. $-2(z - 4) - (3z - 2) = -2 - (6z - 2)$

Solve each equation and check your proposed solution in Exercises 31–46. Begin your work by rewriting each equation without fractions.

31. $\frac{x}{5} - 4 = -6$
32. $\frac{x}{2} + 13 = -22$
33. $\frac{2x}{3} - 5 = 7$
34. $\frac{3x}{4} - 9 = -6$
35. $\frac{2y}{3} - \frac{3}{4} = \frac{5}{12}$
36. $\frac{3y}{4} - \frac{2}{3} = \frac{7}{12}$
37. $\frac{x}{3} + \frac{x}{2} = \frac{5}{6}$
38. $\frac{x}{4} - \frac{x}{5} = 1$
39. $20 - \frac{z}{3} = \frac{z}{2}$
40. $\frac{z}{5} - \frac{1}{2} = \frac{z}{6}$
41. $\frac{y}{3} + \frac{2}{5} = \frac{y}{5} - \frac{2}{5}$
42. $\frac{y}{12} + \frac{1}{6} = \frac{y}{2} - \frac{1}{4}$
43. $\frac{3x}{4} - 3 = \frac{x}{2} + 2$
44. $\frac{3x}{5} - \frac{2}{5} = \frac{x}{3} + \frac{2}{5}$
45. $\frac{x - 3}{5} - 1 = \frac{x - 5}{4}$
46. $\frac{x - 2}{3} - 4 = \frac{x + 1}{4}$

Solve each equation and check your proposed solution in Exercises 47–58.

47. $3.6x = 2.9x + 6.3$

48. $1.2x - 3.6 = 2.4 - 0.3x$

49. $0.92y + 2 = y - 0.4$

50. $0.15y - 0.1 = 2.5y - 1.04$

51. $0.3x - 4 = 0.1(x + 10)$

52. $0.1(x + 80) = 14 - 0.2x$

53. $0.4(2z + 6) + 0.1 = 0.5(2z - 3)$

54. $1.4(z - 5) - 0.2 = 0.5(6z - 8)$

55. $0.01(x + 4) - 0.04 = 0.01(5x + 4)$

56. $0.02(x - 2) = 0.06 - 0.01(x + 1)$

57. $0.6(x + 300) = 0.65x - 205$

58. $0.05(7x + 36) = 0.4x + 1.2$

In Exercises 59–78, solve each equation. Use words or set notation to identify equations that have no solution, or equations that are true for all real numbers.

59. $3x - 7 = 3(x + 1)$

60. $2(x - 5) = 2x + 10$

61. $2(x + 4) = 4x + 5 - 2x + 3$

62. $3(x - 1) = 8x + 6 - 5x - 9$

63. $7 + 2(3x - 5) = 8 - 3(2x + 1)$

64. $2 + 3(2x - 7) = 9 - 4(3x + 1)$

65. $4x + 1 - 5x = 5 - (x + 4)$

66. $5x - 5 = 3x - 7 + 2(x + 1)$

67. $4(x + 2) + 1 = 7x - 3(x - 2)$

68. $5x - 3(x + 1) = 2(x + 3) - 5$

69. $3 - x = 2x + 3$

70. $5 - x = 4x + 5$

71. $\frac{x}{3} + 2 = \frac{x}{3}$

72. $\frac{x}{4} + 3 = \frac{x}{4}$

73. $\frac{x}{2} - \frac{x}{4} + 4 = x + 4$

74. $\frac{x}{2} + \frac{2x}{3} + 3 = x + 3$

75. $\frac{2}{3}x = 2 - \frac{5}{6}x$

76. $\frac{2}{3}x = \frac{1}{4}x - 8$

77. $0.06(x + 5) = 0.03(2x + 7) + 0.09$

78. $0.04(x - 2) = 0.02(6x - 3) - 0.02$

Practice PLUS

The equations in Exercises 79–80 contain small figures (□, △, and \$) that represent nonzero real numbers. Use properties of equality to isolate x on one side of the equation and the small figures on the other side.

79. $\frac{x}{\square} + \triangle = \$$

80. $\frac{x}{\square} - \triangle = -\$$

81. If $\frac{x}{5} - 2 = \frac{x}{3}$, evaluate $x^2 - x$.

82. If $\frac{3x}{2} + \frac{3x}{4} = \frac{x}{4} - 4$, evaluate $x^2 - x$.

In Exercises 83–86, use the given information to write an equation. Let x represent the number described in each exercise. Then solve the equation and find the number.

83. When one-third of a number is added to one-fifth of the number, the sum is 16. What is the number?

84. When two-fifths of a number is added to one-fourth of the number, the sum is 13. What is the number?

85. When 3 is subtracted from three-fourths of a number, the result is equal to one-half of the number. What is the number?

86. When 30 is subtracted from seven-eighths of a number, the result is equal to one-half of the number. What is the number?

Application Exercises

In Massachusetts, speeding fines are determined by the formula

$$F = 10(x - 65) + 50,$$

where F is the cost, in dollars, of the fine if a person is caught driving x miles per hour. Use this formula to solve Exercises 87–88.

87. If a fine comes to \$250, how fast was that person driving?

88. If a fine comes to \$400, how fast was that person driving?

The latest guidelines, which apply to both men and women, give healthy weight ranges, rather than specific weights, for your height. The further you are above the upper limit of your range, the greater are the risks of developing weight-related health problems. The bar graph shows these ranges for various heights for people between the ages of 19 and 34, inclusive.

Healthy Weight Ranges for Men and Women, Ages 19 to 34

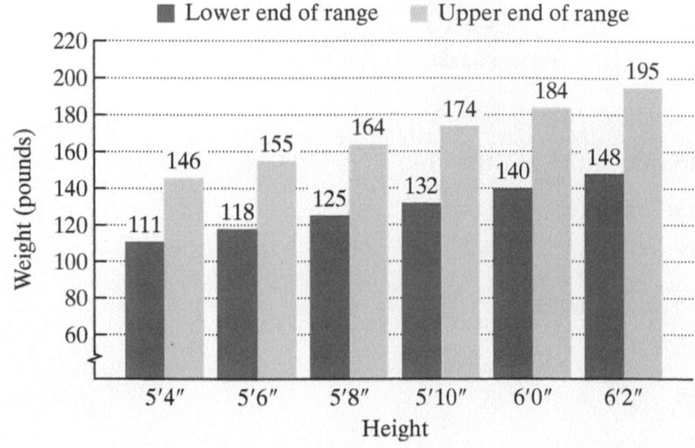

Source: U.S. Department of Health and Human Services

The mathematical model

$$\frac{W}{2} - 3H = 53$$

describes a weight, W, in pounds, that lies within the healthy weight range for a person whose height is H inches over 5 feet. Use this information to solve Exercises 89–90.

89. Use the formula to find a healthy weight for a person whose height is 5′6″. (*Hint*: $H = 6$ because this person's height is 6 inches over 5 feet.) How many pounds is this healthy weight below the upper end of the range shown by the bar graph?

90. Use the formula to find a healthy weight for a person whose height is 6′0″. (*Hint*: $H = 12$ because this person's height is 12 inches over 5 feet.) How many pounds is this healthy weight below the upper end of the range shown by the bar graph?

The formula

$$p = 15 + \frac{5d}{11}$$

describes the pressure of sea water, p, in pounds per square foot, at a depth of d feet below the surface. Use the formula to solve Exercises 91–92.

JonMilnes/Shutterstock

91. The record depth for breath-held diving, by Francisco Ferreras (Cuba) off Grand Bahama Island, on November 14, 1993, involved pressure of 201 pounds per square foot. To what depth did Ferreras descend on this ill-advised venture? (He was underwater for 2 minutes and 9 seconds!)

92. At what depth is the pressure 20 pounds per square foot?

Writing in Mathematics

93. In your own words, describe how to solve a linear equation.

94. Explain how to solve a linear equation containing fractions.

95. Suppose that you solve $\frac{x}{5} - \frac{x}{2} = 1$ by multiplying both sides by 20, rather than the least common denominator, 10. Describe what happens. If you get the correct solution, why do you think we clear the equation of fractions by multiplying by the *least* common denominator?

96. Explain how to clear decimals in a linear equation.

97. Suppose you are an algebra teacher grading the following solution on an examination:

Solve: $-3(x - 6) = 2 - x$

Solution: $-3x - 18 = 2 - x$

$-2x - 18 = 2$

$-2x = -16$

$x = 8.$

You should note that 8 checks, and the solution is 8. The student who worked the problem therefore wants full credit. Can you find any errors in the solution? If full credit is 10 points, how many points should you give the student? Justify your position.

Critical Thinking Exercises

Make Sense? *In Exercises 98–101, determine whether each statement "makes sense" or "does not make sense" and explain your reasoning.*

98. Although I can solve $3x + \frac{1}{5} = \frac{1}{4}$ by first subtracting $\frac{1}{5}$ from both sides, I find it easier to begin by multiplying both sides by 20, the least common denominator.

99. I can use any common denominator to clear an equation of fractions, but using the least common denominator makes the arithmetic easier.

100. When I substituted 5 for x in the equation

$$4x + 6 = 6(x + 1) - 2x$$

I obtained a true statement, so the equation's solution is 5.

101. I cleared the equation $0.5x + 8.3 = 12.4$ of decimals by multiplying both sides by 100.

In Exercises 102–105, determine whether each statement is true or false. If the statement is false, make the necessary change(s) to produce a true statement.

102. The equation $3(x + 4) = 3(4 + x)$ has precisely one solution.

103. The equation $2y + 5 = 0$ is equivalent to $2y = 5$.

104. If $2 - 3y = 11$ and the solution to the equation is substituted into $y^2 + 2y - 3$, a number results that is neither positive nor negative.

105. The equation $x + \frac{1}{3} = \frac{1}{2}$ is equivalent to $x + 2 = 3$.

106. A woman's height, h, is related to the length of her femur, f (the bone from the knee to the hip socket), by the formula $f = 0.432h - 10.44$. Both h and f are measured in inches. A partial skeleton is found of a woman in which the femur is 16 inches long. Police find the skeleton in an area where a woman slightly over 5 feet tall has been missing for over a year. Can the partial skeleton be that of the missing woman? Explain.

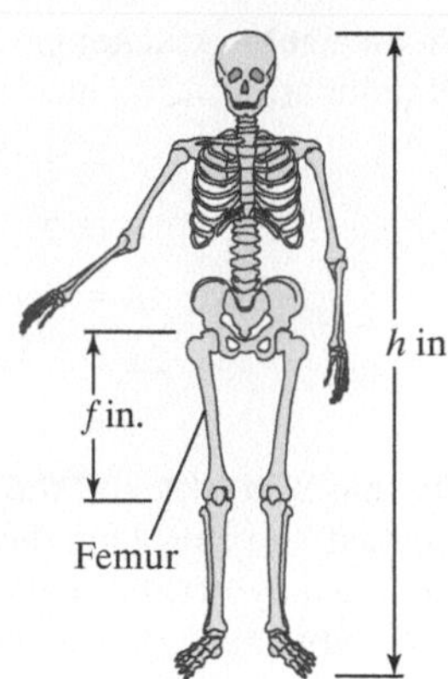

Solve each equation in Exercises 107–108.

107. $\frac{2x-3}{9} + \frac{x-3}{2} = \frac{x+5}{6} - 1$

108. $2(3x + 4) = 3x + 2[3(x - 1) + 2]$

Review Exercises

In Exercises 109–110, insert either $<$ or $>$ in the shaded area between each pair of numbers to make a true statement.

109. $-24 \ \blacksquare \ -20$

110. $-\frac{1}{3} \ \blacksquare \ -\frac{1}{5}$

111. Simplify: $-9 - 11 + 7 - (-3)$.

Preview Exercises

Exercises 112–114 will help you prepare for the material covered in the next section.

112. Consider the formula

$$T = D + pm.$$

a. Subtract D from both sides and write the resulting formula.

b. Divide both sides of your formula from part (a) by p and write the resulting formula.

113. Solve: $4 = 0.25B$.

114. Solve: $1.3 = P \cdot 26$.

SECTION 4

Formulas and Percents

Objectives

1. Solve a formula for a variable.
2. Use the percent formula.
3. Solve applied problems involving percent change.

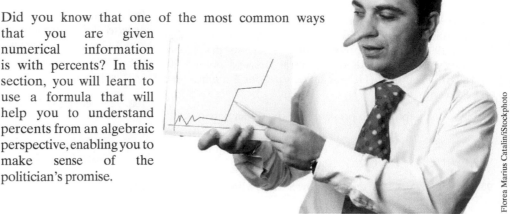

"And, if elected, it is my solemn pledge to cut your taxes by 10% for each of my first three years in office, for a total cut of 30%."

Did you know that one of the most common ways that you are given numerical information is with percents? In this section, you will learn to use a formula that will help you to understand percents from an algebraic perspective, enabling you to make sense of the politician's promise.

Florea Marius Catalin/iStockphoto

1 Solve a formula for a variable.

Solving a Formula for One of Its Variables

We know that solving an equation is the process of finding the number (or numbers) that make the equation a true statement. All of the equations we have solved contained only one letter, such as x or y.

By contrast, the formulas we have seen contain two or more letters, representing two or more variables. Here is an example:

$$C + M = S.$$

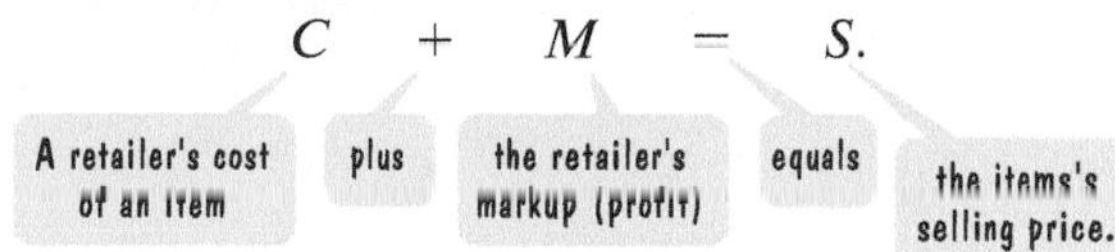
A retailer's cost of an item
plus
the retailer's markup (profit)
equals
the items's selling price.

We say that this formula is solved for the variable S because S is alone on one side of the equation and the other side does not contain an S.

Solving a formula for a variable means rewriting the formula so that the variable is isolated on one side of the equation. It does not mean obtaining a numerical value for that variable.

The addition and multiplication properties of equality are used to solve a formula for one of its variables. Consider the retailer's formula, $C + M = S$. How do we solve this formula for C? Use the addition property to isolate C by subtracting M from both sides:

We need to isolate C.

$$C + M = S \quad \text{This is the given formula.}$$
$$C + M - M = S - M \quad \text{Subtract } M \text{ from both sides.}$$
$$C = S - M \quad \text{Simplify.}$$

Solved for C, the formula $C = S - M$ tells us that the cost of an item for a retailer is the item's selling price minus its markup.

To solve a formula for one of its variables, treat that variable as if it were the only variable in the equation. Think of the other variables as if they were numbers. Use the addition property of equality to isolate all terms with the specified variable on one side of the equation and all terms without the specified variable on the other side. Then use the multiplication property of equality to get the specified variable alone.

Our first example involves the formula for the area of a rectangle. The **area of a two-dimensional figure** is the number of square units it takes to fill the interior of the figure. A **square unit** is a square, each of whose sides is one unit in length, as illustrated in **Figure 5**. The figure shows that there are 12 square units contained within the rectangle. The area of the rectangle is 12 square units. Notice that the area can be determined in the following manner:

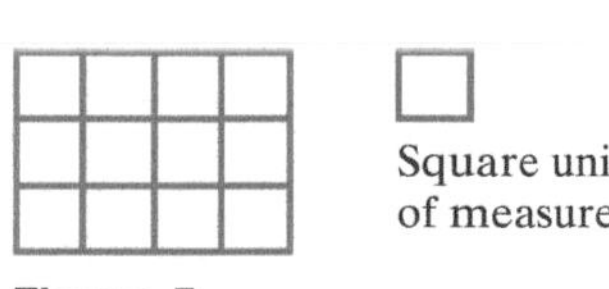
Square unit of measure

Figure 5

Across · Down

$$4 \text{ units} \cdot 3 \text{ units} = 4 \cdot 3 \text{ units} \cdot \text{units} = 12 \text{ square units.}$$

The area of a rectangle is the product of the distance across, its length, and the distance down, its width.

Area of a Rectangle

The area, A, of a rectangle with length l and width w is given by the formula

$$A = lw.$$

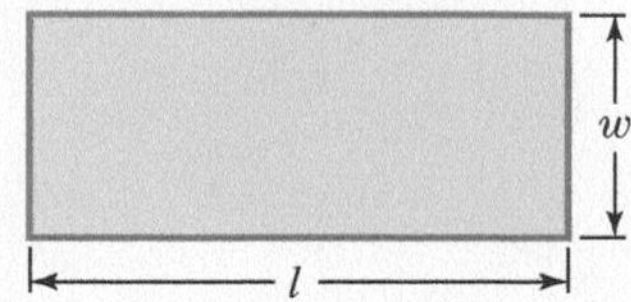
w
l

EXAMPLE 1 Solving a Formula for a Variable

Solve the formula $A = lw$ for w.

Solution Our goal is to get w by itself on one side of the formula. There is only one term with w, lw, and it is already isolated on the right side. We isolate w on the right by using the multiplication property of equality and dividing both sides by l.

We need to isolate w.

$A = lw$ This is the given formula.

$\frac{A}{l} = \frac{lw}{l}$ Isolate w by dividing both sides by l.

$\frac{A}{l} = w$ Simplify: $\frac{lw}{l} = 1w = w$.

The formula solved for w is $\frac{A}{l} = w$ or $w = \frac{A}{l}$. Thus, the area of a rectangle divided by its length is equal to its width. ■

✓ **CHECK POINT 1** Solve the formula $A = lw$ for l.

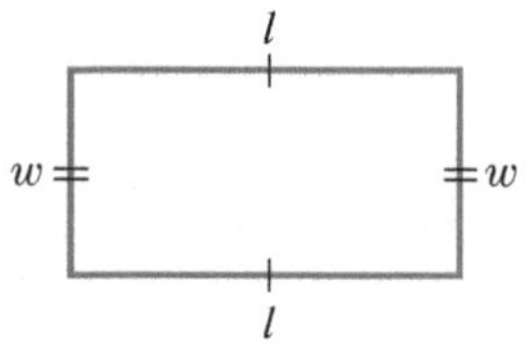

The **perimeter of a two-dimensional figure** is the sum of the lengths of its sides. Perimeter is measured in linear units, such as inches, feet, yards, meters, or kilometers.

Example 2 involves the perimeter, P, of a rectangle. Because perimeter is the sum of the lengths of the sides, the perimeter of the rectangle shown in **Figure 6** is $l + w + l + w$. This can be expressed as

$$P = 2l + 2w.$$

Figure 6 A rectangle with length l and width w

Perimeter of a Rectangle

The perimeter, P, of a rectangle with length l and width w is given by the formula

$$P = 2l + 2w.$$

The perimeter of a rectangle is the sum of twice the length and twice the width.

EXAMPLE 2 Solving a Formula for a Variable

Solve the formula $2l + 2w = P$ for w.

Solution First, isolate $2w$ on the left by subtracting $2l$ from both sides. Then solve for w by dividing both sides by 2.

We need to isolate w.

$2l + 2w = P$ This is the given formula.

$2l - 2l + 2w = P - 2l$ Isolate $2w$ by subtracting $2l$ from both sides.

$2w = P - 2l$ Simplify.

$\frac{2w}{2} = \frac{P - 2l}{2}$ Isolate w by dividing both sides by 2.

$w = \frac{P - 2l}{2}$ Simplify. ■

✓ **CHECK POINT 2** Solve the formula $2l + 2w = P$ for l.

EXAMPLE 3 Solving a Formula for a Variable

The total price of an article purchased on a monthly deferred payment plan is described by the following formula:

$$T = D + pm.$$

In this formula, T is the total price, D is the down payment, p is the amount of the monthly payment, and m is the number of payments. Solve the formula for p.

Solution First, isolate pm on the right by subtracting D from both sides. Then isolate p from pm by dividing both sides of the formula by m.

We need to isolate p.

$$T = D + pm$$ This is the given formula. We want p alone.

$$T - D = D - D + pm$$ Isolate pm by subtracting D from both sides.

$$T - D = pm$$ Simplify.

$$\frac{T - D}{m} = \frac{pm}{m}$$ Now isolate p by dividing both sides by m.

$$\frac{T - D}{m} = p$$ Simplify: $\frac{pm}{m} = \frac{p\cancel{m}}{\cancel{m}} = p \cdot 1 = p$. ■

✓ CHECK POINT 3 Solve the formula $T = D + pm$ for m.

The next example has a formula that contains a fraction. To solve for a variable in a formula involving fractions, we begin by multiplying both sides by the least common denominator of all fractions in the formula. This will eliminate the fractions. Then we solve for the specified variable.

EXAMPLE 4 Solving a Formula Containing a Fraction for a Variable

Solve the formula $\frac{W}{2} - 3H = 53$ for W.

Solution Do you remember seeing this formula in the last section's Exercise Set? It models a person's healthy weight, W, where H represents that person's height, in inches, in excess of 5 feet. We begin by multiplying both sides of the formula by 2 to eliminate the fraction. Then we isolate the variable W.

$$\frac{W}{2} - 3H = 53$$ This is the given formula.

$$2\left(\frac{W}{2} - 3H\right) = 2 \cdot 53$$ Multiply both sides by 2.

$$2 \cdot \frac{W}{2} - 2 \cdot 3H = 2 \cdot 53$$ Use the distributive property.

We need to isolate W.

$$W - 6H = 106$$ Simplify.

$$W - 6H + 6H = 106 + 6H$$ Isolate W by adding $6H$ to both sides.

$$W = 106 + 6H$$ Simplify.

This form of the formula makes it easy to find a person's healthy weight, W, if we know that person's height, H, in inches, in excess of 5 feet. ■

✓ **CHECK POINT 4** Solve for x: $\frac{x}{3} - 4y = 5$.

2 Use the percent formula.

A Formula Involving Percent

Great Question!

Before presenting this formula involving percent, can you briefly review what I should already know about the basics of percent?

- **Percents** are the result of expressing numbers as part of 100. The word *percent* means *per hundred.* For example, the bar graph in **Figure 7** shows that 47% of Americans find "whatever" most annoying in conversation. Thus, 47 out of every 100 Americans are most annoyed by "whatever" in conversation: $47\% = \frac{47}{100}$.

Which Is Most Annoying In Conversation?

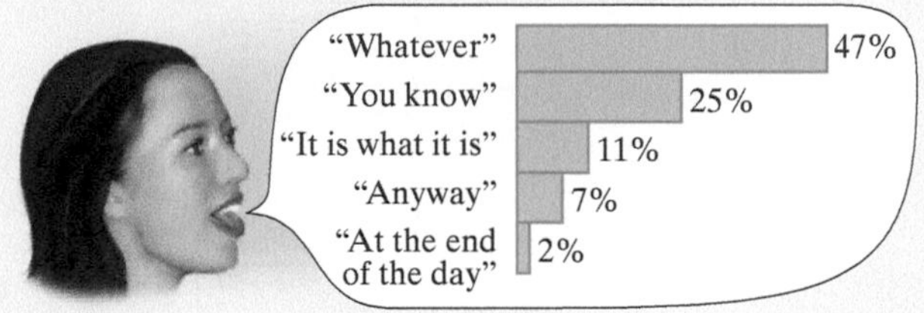

Figure 7

Source: Marist Poll Survey of 938 Americans ages 16 and older, August 3–6, 2010.

- To convert a number from percent form to decimal form, move the decimal point two places to the left and drop the percent sign. Example:

$$47\% = 47.\% = 0.47\%$$

Thus, $47\% = 0.47$.

- To convert a number from decimal form to a percent, move the decimal point two places to the right and attach a percent sign.

$$0.86 = 086.\%$$

Thus, $0.86 = 86\%$.

- Dictionaries indicate that the word *percentage* has the same meaning as the word *percent.* Use the word that sounds better in a given circumstance.

Percents are useful in comparing two numbers. To compare the number A to the number B using a percent P, the following formula is used:

A is *P* percent of *B*.

$$A = P \cdot B.$$

In the formula

$$A = PB,$$

$B =$ the base number, $P =$ the percent (in decimal form), and $A =$ the number being compared to B.

There are three basic types of percent problems that can be solved using the percent formula

$$A = PB. \quad \text{A is P percent of B.}$$

Question	Given	Percent Formula
What is P percent of B?	P and B	Solve for A.
A is P percent of what?	A and P	Solve for B.
A is what percent of B?	A and B	Solve for P.

Let's look at an example of each type of problem.

EXAMPLE 5 Using the Percent Formula: What Is P Percent of B?

What is 8% of 20?

Solution We use the formula $A = PB$: A is P percent of B. We are interested in finding the quantity A in this formula.

What | is | 8% | of | 20?

$A = 0.08 \cdot 20$ Express 8% as 0.08.

$A = 1.6$ Multiply: $\begin{array}{r} 0.08 \\ \times\ 20 \\ \hline 1.60 \end{array}$

Thus, 1.6 is 8% of 20. The answer is 1.6. ■

✓ **CHECK POINT 5** What is 9% of 50?

EXAMPLE 6 Using the Percent Formula: A Is P Percent of What?

4 is 25% of what?

Solution We use the formula $A = PB$: A is P percent of B. We are interested in finding the quantity B in this formula.

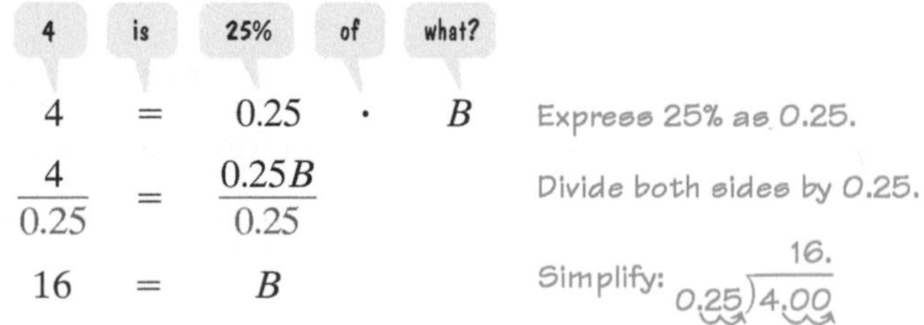

$4 = 0.25 \cdot B$ Express 25% as 0.25.

$\dfrac{4}{0.25} = \dfrac{0.25B}{0.25}$ Divide both sides by 0.25.

$16 = B$ Simplify: $0.25\overline{)4.00}$ = 16.

Thus, 4 is 25% of 16. The answer is 16. ■

✓ **CHECK POINT 6** 9 is 60% of what?

EXAMPLE 7 Using the Percent Formula: *A* Is What Percent of *B*?

1.3 is what percent of 26?

Solution We use the formula $A = PB$: A is P percent of B. We are interested in finding the quantity P in this formula.

1.3 | is | what percent | of | 26?

$$1.3 = P \cdot 26$$

$$\frac{1.3}{26} = \frac{P \cdot 26}{26} \quad \text{Divide both sides by 26.}$$

$$0.05 = P \quad \text{Simplify: } 26\overline{)1.30} = 0.05$$

We change 0.05 to a percent by moving the decimal point two places to the right and adding a percent sign: $0.05 = 5\%$. Thus, 1.3 is 5% of 26. The answer is 5%. ■

✓ **CHECK POINT 7** 18 is what percent of 50?

---

3 Solve applied problems involving percent change.

Applications

Percents are used for comparing changes, such as increases or decreases in sales, population, prices, and production. If a quantity changes, its percent increase or percent decrease can be determined by asking the following question:

The change is what percent of the original amount?

The question is answered using the percent formula as follows:

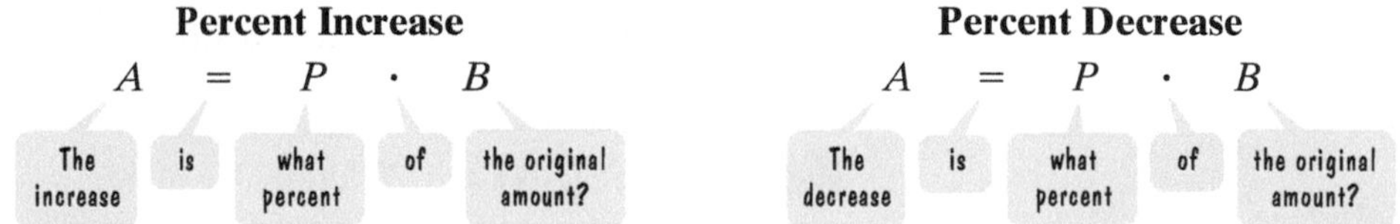
Percent Increase
A = P · B
The increase
is
what percent
of
the original amount?
Percent Decrease
A = P · B
The decrease
is
what percent
of
the original amount?

EXAMPLE 8 Finding Percent Decrease

A jacket regularly sells for \$135.00. The sale price is \$60.75. Find the percent decrease in the jacket's price.

Solution The percent decrease in price can be determined by asking the following question:

The price decrease is what percent of the original price (\$135.00)?

The price decrease is the difference between the original price and the sale price (\$60.75):

$$\$135.00 - \$60.75 = \$74.25.$$

Now we use the percent formula to find the percent decrease.

The price decrease | is | what percent | of | the original price?

$$74.25 = P \cdot 135$$

$$\frac{74.25}{135} = \frac{P \cdot 135}{135} \quad \text{Divide both sides by 135.}$$

$$0.55 = P \quad \text{Simplify: } 135\overline{)74.25} = 0.55$$

We change 0.55 to a percent by moving the decimal point two places to the right and adding a percent sign: $0.55 = 55\%$. Thus, the percent decrease in the jacket's price is 55%. ■

✓ **CHECK POINT 8** A television regularly sells for \$940. The sale price is \$611. Find the percent decrease in the television's price.

In our next example, we look at one of the many ways that percent can be used incorrectly.

EXAMPLE 9 Promises of a Politician

A politician states, "If you elect me to office, I promise to cut your taxes for each of my first three years in office by 10% each year, for a total reduction of 30%." Evaluate the accuracy of the politician's statement.

Solution To make things simple, let's assume that a taxpayer paid \$100 in taxes in the year previous to the politician's election. A 10% reduction during year 1 is 10% of \$100.

$$10\% \text{ of previous year's tax} = 10\% \text{ of } \$100 = 0.10 \cdot \$100 = \$10$$

With a 10% reduction the first year, the taxpayer will pay only \$100 − \$10, or \$90, in taxes during the politician's first year in office.

The table below shows how we calculate the new, reduced tax for each of the first three years in office.

Year	Tax Paid the Year Before	10% Reduction	Taxes Paid This Year
1	\$100	$0.10 \cdot \$100 = \$10$	$\$100 - \$10 = \$90$
2	\$ 90	$0.10 \cdot \$90 = \$9$	$\$90 - \$9 = \$81$
3	\$ 81	$0.10 \cdot \$81 = \$8.10$	$\$81 - \$8.10 = \$72.90$

The tax reduction is the amount originally paid, \$100.00, minus the amount paid during the politician's third year in office, \$72.90:

$$\$100.00 - \$72.90 = \$27.10.$$

Now we use the percent formula to determine the percent decrease in taxes over the three years.

The tax decrease | is | what percent | of | the original tax?

$$27.1 = P \cdot 100$$

$$\frac{27.1}{100} = \frac{P \cdot 100}{100} \quad \text{Divide both sides by 100.}$$

$$0.271 = P \quad \text{Simplify.}$$

Change 0.271 to a percent: 0.271 = 27.1%. The percent decrease is 27.1%. The taxes decline by 27.1%, not by 30%. The politician is ill-informed in saying that three consecutive 10% cuts add up to a total tax cut of 30%. In our calculation, which serves as a counterexample to the promise, the total tax cut is only 27.1%. ■

✓ **CHECK POINT 9** Suppose you paid \$1200 in taxes. During year 1, taxes decrease by 20%. During year 2, taxes increase by 20%.

a. What do you pay in taxes for year 2?

b. How do your taxes for year 2 compare with what you originally paid, namely \$1200? If the taxes are not the same, find the percent increase or decrease.

CONCEPT AND VOCABULARY CHECK

Fill in each blank so that the resulting statement is true.

1. Solving a formula for a variable means rewriting the formula so that the variable is ______________.
2. The area, A, of a rectangle with length l and width w is given by the formula ______________.
3. The perimeter, P, of a rectangle with length l and width w is given by the formula ______________.
4. The sentence "A is P percent of B" is expressed by the formula ______________.
5. In order to solve $y = mx + b$ for x, we first ______________ and then ______________.

4 EXERCISE SET

MyMathLab®

Watch the videos in MyMathLab

Download the MyDashBoard App

Practice Exercises

In Exercises 1–26, solve each formula for the specified variable. Do you recognize the formula? If so, what does it describe?

1. $d = rt$ for r
2. $d = rt$ for t
3. $I = Prt$ for P
4. $I = Prt$ for r
5. $C = 2\pi r$ for r
6. $C = \pi d$ for d
7. $E = mc^2$ for m
8. $V = \pi r^2 h$ for h
9. $y = mx + b$ for m
10. $y = mx + b$ for x
11. $T = D + pm$ for D
12. $P = C + MC$ for M
13. $A = \frac{1}{2}bh$ for b
14. $A = \frac{1}{2}bh$ for h
15. $M = \frac{n}{5}$ for n
16. $M = \frac{A}{740}$ for A
17. $\frac{c}{2} + 80 = 2F$ for c
18. $p = 15 + \frac{5d}{11}$ for d
19. $A = \frac{1}{2}(a + b)$ for a
20. $A = \frac{1}{2}(a + b)$ for b
21. $S = P + Prt$ for r
22. $S = P + Prt$ for t
23. $A = \frac{1}{2}h(a + b)$ for b
24. $A = \frac{1}{2}h(a + b)$ for a
25. $Ax + By = C$ for x
26. $Ax + By = C$ for y

Use the percent formula, $A = PB$: A is P percent of B, to solve Exercises 27–42.

27. What is 3% of 200?
28. What is 8% of 300?
29. What is 18% of 40?
30. What is 16% of 90?
31. 3 is 60% of what?
32. 8 is 40% of what?
33. 24% of what number is 40.8?
34. 32% of what number is 51.2?
35. 3 is what percent of 15?
36. 18 is what percent of 90?
37. What percent of 2.5 is 0.3?
38. What percent of 7.5 is 0.6?
39. If 5 is increased to 8, the increase is what percent of the original number?
40. If 5 is increased to 9, the increase is what percent of the original number?
41. If 4 is decreased to 1, the decrease is what percent of the original number?
42. If 8 is decreased to 6, the decrease is what percent of the original number?

Practice PLUS

In Exercises 43–50, solve each equation for x.

43. $y = (a + b)x$

44. $y = (a - b)x$

45. $y = (a - b)x + 5$

46. $y = (a + b)x - 8$

47. $y = cx + dx$

48. $y = cx - dx$

49. $y = Ax - Bx - C$

50. $y = Ax + Bx + C$

Application Exercises

51. The average, or mean, A, of three exam grades, x, y, and z, is given by the formula

$$A = \frac{x + y + z}{3}.$$

a. Solve the formula for z.

b. Use the formula in part (a) to solve this problem. On your first two exams, your grades are 86% and 88%: $x = 86$ and $y = 88$. What must you get on the third exam to have an average of 90%?

52. The average, or mean, A, of four exam grades, x, y, z, and w, is given by the formula

$$A = \frac{x + y + z + w}{4}.$$

a. Solve the formula for w.

b. Use the formula in part (a) to solve this problem. On your first three exams, your grades are 76%, 78%, and 79%: $x = 76$, $y = 78$, and $z = 79$. What must you get on the fourth exam to have an average of 80%?

53. If you are traveling in your car at an average rate of r miles per hour for t hours, then the distance, d, in miles, that you travel is described by the formula $d = rt$: distance equals rate times time.

a. Solve the formula for t.

b. Use the formula in part (a) to find the time that you travel if you cover a distance of 100 miles at an average rate of 40 miles per hour.

54. The formula $F = \frac{9}{5}C + 32$ expresses the relationship between Celsius temperature, C, and Fahrenheit temperature, F.

a. Solve the formula for C.

b. Use the formula from part (a) to find the equivalent Celsius temperature for a Fahrenheit temperature of 59°.

An Adecco survey of 1800 workers asked participants about taboo topics to discuss at work. The circle graph shows the results. Use this information to solve Exercises 55–56.

What Is the Most Taboo Topic to Discuss at Work?

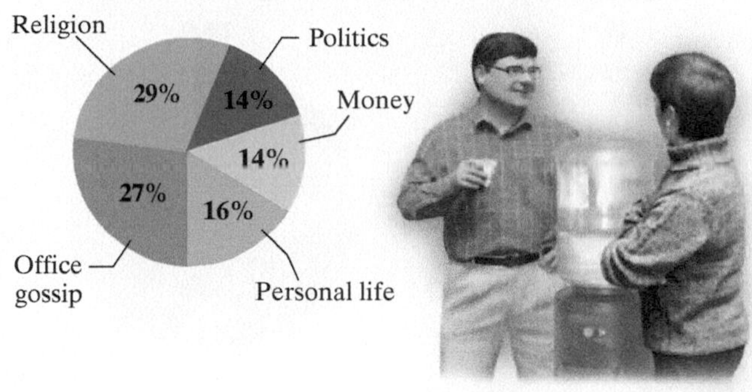

Source: Adecco

55. Among the 1800 workers who participated in the poll, how many stated that religion is the most taboo topic to discuss at work?

56. Among the 1800 workers who participated in the poll, how many stated that politics is the most taboo topic to discuss at work?

The graph shows the composition of a typical American community's trash. Use this information to solve Exercises 57–58.

Types of Trash in an American Community by Percentage of Total Weight

Source: U.S. Environmental Protection Agency

57. Across the United States, people generate approximately 175 billion pounds of trash in the form of paper each year. (That's approximately 580 pounds per person per year.) How many billions of pounds of trash do we throw away each year?

58. Across the United States, people generate approximately 55 billion pounds of trash in the form of plastic each year. (That's approximately 180 pounds per person per year.) How many billions of pounds of trash do we throw away each year?

The circle graphs show the number of free, partly free, and not free countries in 1974 and 2009. Use this information to solve Exercises 59–60. Round answers to the nearest percent.

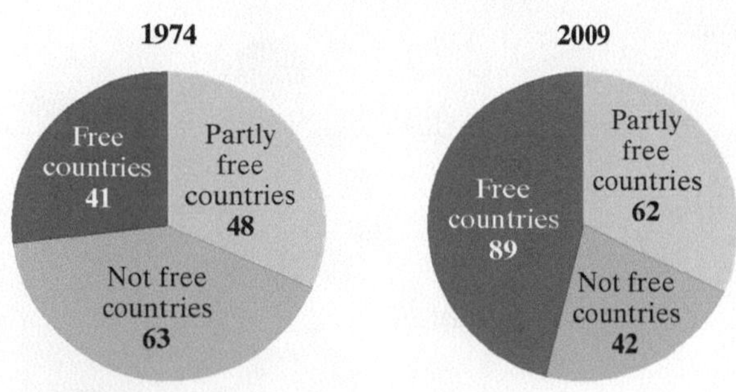

59. **a.** What percentage of the world's countries were free in 1974?

b. What percentage of the world's countries were free in 2009?

c. Find the percent increase in the number of free countries from 1974 to 2009.

60. **a.** What percentage of the world's countries were not free in 1974?

b. What percentage of the world's countries were not free in 2009?

c. Find the percent decrease in the number of not free countries from 1974 to 2009.

61. A charity has raised \$7500, with a goal of raising \$60,000. What percent of the goal has been raised?

62. A charity has raised \$225,000, with a goal of raising \$500,000. What percent of the goal has been raised?

63. A restaurant bill came to \$60. If 15% of this amount was left as a tip, how much was the tip?

64. If income tax is \$3502 plus 28% of taxable income over \$23,000, how much is the income tax on a taxable income of \$35,000?

65. Suppose that the local sales tax rate is 6% and you buy a car for \$16,800.

a. How much tax is due?

b. What is the car's total cost?

66. Suppose that the local sales tax rate is 7% and you buy a graphing calculator for \$96.

a. How much tax is due?

b. What is the calculator's total cost?

67. An exercise machine with an original price of \$860 is on sale at 12% off.

a. What is the discount amount?

b. What is the exercise machine's sale price?

68. A dictionary that normally sells for \$16.50 is on sale at 40% off.

a. What is the discount amount?

b. What is the dictionary's sale price?

69. A sofa regularly sells for \$840. The sale price is \$714. Find the percent decrease in the sofa's price.

70. A fax machine regularly sells for \$380. The sale price is \$266. Find the percent decrease in the machine's price.

71. Suppose that you put \$10,000 in a rather risky investment recommended by your financial advisor. During the first year, your investment decreases by 30% of its original value. During the second year, your investment increases by 40% of its first-year value. Your advisor tells you that there must have been a 10% overall increase of your original \$10,000 investment. Is your financial advisor using percentages properly? If not, what is the actual percent gain or loss on your original \$10,000 investment?

72. The price of a color printer is reduced by 30% of its original price. When it still does not sell, its price is reduced by 20% of the reduced price. The salesperson informs you that there has been a total reduction of 50%. Is the salesperson using percentages properly? If not, what is the actual percent reduction from the original price?

Writing in Mathematics

73. Explain what it means to solve a formula for a variable.

74. What does the percent formula, $A = PB$, describe? Give an example of how the formula is used.

Critical Thinking Exercises

Make Sense? *In Exercises 75–78, determine whether each statement "makes sense" or "does not make sense" and explain your reasoning.*

75. To help me get started, I circle the variable that I need to solve for in a formula.

76. By solving a formula for one of its variables, I find a numerical value for that variable.

77. I have \$100 and my restaurant bill comes to \$80, which is not enough to leave a 20% tip.

78. I found the percent decrease in a jacket's price to be 120%.

In Exercises 79–82, determine whether each statement is true or false. If the statement is false, make the necessary change(s) to produce a true statement.

79. If $ax + b = 0$, then $x = \frac{b}{a}$.

80. If $A = lw$, then $w = \frac{l}{A}$.

81. If $A = \frac{1}{2}bh$, then $b = \frac{A}{2h}$.

82. Solving $x - y = -7$ for y gives $y = x + 7$.

83. In psychology, an intelligence quotient, Q, also called IQ, is measured by the formula

$$Q = \frac{100M}{C},$$

where M = mental age and C = chronological age. Solve the formula for C.

Review Exercises

84. Solve and check: $5x + 20 = 8x - 16$. (Section 2, Example 7)

85. Solve and check: $5(2y - 3) - 1 = 4(6 + 2y)$. (Section 3, Example 3)

86. Simplify: $x - 0.3x$.

Preview Exercises

Exercises 87–89 will help you prepare for the material covered in the next section. In each exercise, let x represent the number and write the phrase as an algebraic expression.

87. The quotient of 13 and a number, decreased by 7 times the number

88. Eight times the sum of a number and 14

89. Nine times the difference of a number and 5

MID-CHAPTER CHECK POINT Section 1–Section 4

What You Know: We learned a step-by-step procedure for solving linear equations, including equations with fractions and decimals. We saw that some equations have no solution, whereas others have all real numbers as solutions. We used the addition and multiplication properties of equality to solve formulas for variables. Finally, we worked with the percent formula $A = PB$: A is P percent of B.

1. Solve: $\frac{x}{2} = 12 - \frac{x}{4}$.

2. Solve: $5x - 42 = -57$.

3. Solve for C: $H = \frac{EC}{825}$.

4. What is 6% of 140?

5. Solve: $\frac{-x}{10} = -3$.

6. Solve: $1 - 3(y - 5) = 4(2 - 3y)$.

7. Solve for r: $S = 2\pi rh$.

8. 12 is 30% of what?

9. Solve: $\frac{3y}{5} + \frac{y}{2} = \frac{5y}{4} - 3$.

10. Solve: $2.4x + 6 = 1.4x + 0.5(6x - 9)$

11. Solve: $5z + 7 = 6(z - 2) - 4(2z - 3)$.

12. Solve for x: $Ax - By = C$.

13. Solve: $6y + 7 + 3y = 3(3y - 1)$.

14. Solve: $10\left(\frac{1}{2}x + 3\right) = 10\left(\frac{3}{5}x - 1\right)$.

15. 50 is what percent of 400?

16. Solve: $\frac{3(m + 2)}{4} = 2m + 3$.

17. If 40 is increased to 50, the increase is what percent of the original number?

18. Solve: $12x - 4 + 8x - 4 = 4(5x - 2)$.

19. The bar graph indicates that reading books for fun loses value as kids age.

Percentage of U.S. Kids Who Believe Reading Books Not Required for School Is Important

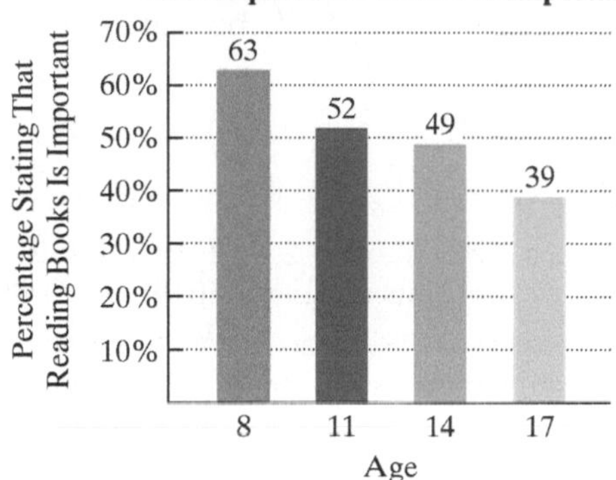

Source of data: Scholastic Kids and Family Reading Report 2010, Scholastic Inc.

The data can be described by the mathematical model

$$B = -\frac{5}{2}a + 82,$$

where B is the percentage at age a who believe that reading books is important.

a. Does the formula underestimate or overestimate the percentage of 14-year-olds who believe that reading books is important? By how much?

b. If trends shown by the formula continue, at which age will 22% believe that reading books is important?

SECTION 5

An Introduction to Problem Solving

Objectives

1. Translate English phrases into algebraic expressions.
2. Solve algebraic word problems using linear equations.

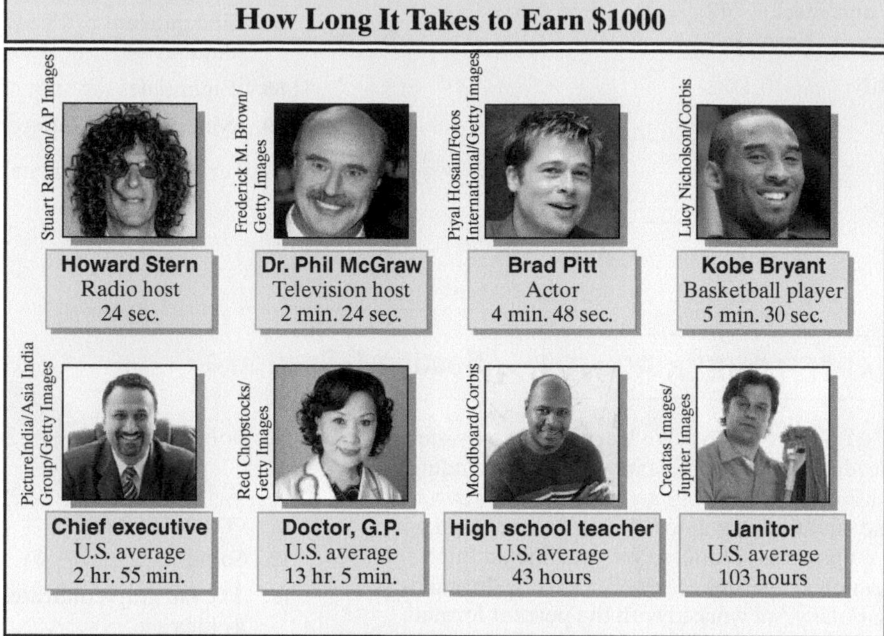

Source of data: TIME Magazine, October 30, 2006

In this section, you'll see examples and exercises focused on how much money Americans earn. These situations illustrate a step-by-step strategy for solving problems. As you become familiar with this strategy, you will learn to solve a wide variety of problems.

1 Translate English phrases into algebric expressions.

Algebraic Expressions for English Phrases

The hardest thing about word problems is writing an equation that translates, or models, the problem's conditions. **Table 1** summarizes many algebraic expressions written for conditions about numbers. We are using x to represent the variable, but we can use any letter.

Great Question!

Table 1 looks long and intimidating. What's the best way to get through the table?

Cover the right column with a sheet of paper and attempt to formulate the algebraic expression for the English phrase in the left column on your own. Then slide the paper down and check your answer. Work through the entire table in this manner.

Table 1 Algebraic Translations of English Phrases

English Phrase	Algebraic Expression
Addition	
The sum of a number and 7	$x + 7$
Five more than a number; a number plus 5	$x + 5$
A number increased by 6; 6 added to a number	$x + 6$
Subtraction	
A number minus 4	$x - 4$
A number decreased by 5	$x - 5$
A number subtracted from 8	$8 - x$
The difference between a number and 6	$x - 6$
The difference between 6 and a number	$6 - x$
Seven less than a number	$x - 7$
Seven minus a number	$7 - x$
Nine fewer than a number	$x - 9$

Table 1 continued

English Phrase	Algebraic Expression
Multiplication	
Five times a number	$5x$
The product of 3 and a number	$3x$
Two-thirds of a number (used with fractions)	$\frac{2}{3}x$
Seventy-five percent of a number (used with decimals)	$0.75x$
Thirteen multiplied by a number	$13x$
A number multiplied by 13	$13x$
Twice a number	$2x$
Division	
A number divided by 3	$\frac{x}{3}$
The quotient of 7 and a number	$\frac{7}{x}$
The quotient of a number and 7	$\frac{x}{7}$
The reciprocal of a number	$\frac{1}{x}$
More than one operation	
The sum of twice a number and 7	$2x + 7$
Twice the sum of a number and 7	$2(x + 7)$
Three times the sum of 1 and twice a number	$3(1 + 2x)$
Nine subtracted from 8 times a number	$8x - 9$
Twenty-five percent of the sum of 3 times a number and 14	$0.25(3x + 14)$
Seven times a number, increased by 24	$7x + 24$
Seven times the sum of a number and 24	$7(x + 24)$

A Strategy for Solving Word Problems Using Equations

Here are some general steps we will follow in solving word problems:

Strategy for Solving Word Problems

Step 1. Read the problem carefully several times until you can state in your own words what is given and what the problem is looking for. Let x (or any variable) represent one of the unknown quantities in the problem.

Step 2. If necessary, write expressions for any other unknown quantities in the problem in terms of x.

Step 3. Write an equation in x that translates, or models, the conditions of the problem.

Step 4. Solve the equation and answer the problem's question.

Step 5. Check the solution *in the original wording* of the problem, not in the equation obtained from the words.

Great Question!

Why are word problems important?

There is great value in reasoning through the steps for solving a word problem. This value comes from the problem-solving skills that you will attain and is often more important than the specific problem or its solution.

2 Solve algebraic word problems using linear equations.

Applying the Strategy for Solving Word Problems

Now that you've read why word problems are important, let's apply our five-step strategy for solving these problems.

EXAMPLE 1 Solving a Word Problem

Nine subtracted from eight times a number is 39. Find the number.

Solution

Step 1. Let x represent one of the quantities. Because we are asked to find a number, let

$$x = \text{the number.}$$

Step 2. Represent other unknown quantities in terms of x. There are no other unknown quantities to find, so we can skip this step.

Step 3. Write an equation in x that models the conditions.

Nine subtracted from | eight times a number | is | 39.

$$8x \quad - 9 \quad = \quad 39$$

Step 4. Solve the equation and answer the question.

$$8x - 9 = 39 \quad \text{This is the equation that models the problem's conditions.}$$
$$8x - 9 + 9 = 39 + 9 \quad \text{Add 9 to both sides.}$$
$$8x = 48 \quad \text{Simplify.}$$
$$\frac{8x}{8} = \frac{48}{8} \quad \text{Divide both sides by 8.}$$
$$x = 6 \quad \text{Simplify.}$$

The number is 6.

Step 5. Check the proposed solution in the original wording of the problem. "Nine subtracted from eight times a number is 39." The proposed number is 6. Eight times 6 is $8 \cdot 6$, or 48. Nine subtracted from 48 is $48 - 9$, or 39. The proposed solution checks in the problem's wording, verifying that the number is 6. ■

✓ **CHECK POINT 1** Four subtracted from six times a number is 68. Find the number.

EXAMPLE 2 Starting Salaries for College Graduates with Undergraduate Degrees

The bar graph in **Figure 8** shows the ten most popular college majors with median, or middlemost, starting salaries for recent college graduates.

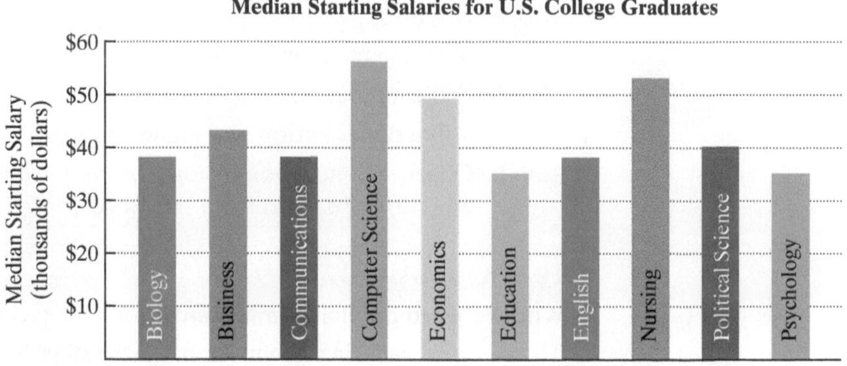

Figure 8

Source: PayScale (2010 data)

The median starting salary of a nursing major exceeds that of a business major by \$10 thousand. Combined, their median starting salaries are \$96 thousand. Determine the median starting salaries of business and nursing majors with bachelor's degrees.

Solution

Step 1. Let x represent one of the quantities. We know something about the median starting salary of a nursing major: It exceeds that of a business major by \$10 thousand. This means that nursing majors with bachelor's degrees earn \$10 thousand more than business majors. We will let

x = the median starting salary, in thousands of dollars, of business majors.

Step 2. Represent other unknown quantities in terms of x. The other unknown quantity is the median starting salary of nursing majors. Because it is \$10 thousand more than that of business majors, let

$x + 10$ = the median starting salary, in thousands of dollars, of nursing majors.

Step 3. Write an equation in x that models the conditions. Combined, the median starting salaries for business and nursing majors are \$96 thousand.

The median starting salary for business majors	plus	the median starting salary for nursing majors	is	\$96 thousand.
x	$+$	$(x + 10)$	$=$	96

Step 4. Solve the equation and answer the question.

$x + (x + 10) = 96$	This is the equation that models the problem's conditions.
$2x + 10 = 96$	Regroup and combine like terms on the left side.
$2x + 10 - 10 = 96 - 10$	Subtract 10 from both sides.
$2x = 86$	Simplify.
$\frac{2x}{2} = \frac{86}{2}$	Divide both sides by 2.
$x = 43$	Simplify.

Because x represents the median starting salary, in thousands of dollars, of business majors, we see that business majors with bachelor's degrees have a median starting salary of \$43 thousand, or \$43,000. Because $x + 10$ represents the median starting salary, in thousands of dollars, of nursing majors, their median starting salary is $43 + 10$, or \$53 thousand (\$53,000).

Step 5. Check the proposed solution in the original wording of the problem. The problem states that combined, the median starting salaries are \$96 thousand. By adding \$43 thousand, the median starting salary of business majors, and \$53 thousand, the median starting salary of nursing majors, we do, indeed, obtain a sum of \$96 thousand. ■

Great Question!

Example 2 involves using the word *exceeds* to represent one of the unknown quantities. Can you help me to write algebraic expressions for quantities described using *exceeds*?

Modeling with the word *exceeds* can be a bit tricky. It's helpful to identify the smaller quantity. Then add to this quantity to represent the larger quantity. For example, suppose that Tim's height exceeds Tom's height by a inches. Tom is the shorter person. If Tom's height is represented by x, then Tim's height is represented by $x + a$.

✓ **CHECK POINT 2** Two of the bars in **Figure 8** represent starting salaries of computer science and English majors. The median starting salary of a computer science major exceeds that of an English major by \$18 thousand. Combined, their median starting salaries are \$94 thousand. Determine the median starting salaries of English and computer science majors with bachelor's degrees.

EXAMPLE 3 Consecutive Integers and the Super Bowl

Only once, in 1991, were the winning and losing scores in the Super Bowl consecutive integers. The New York Giants beat the Buffalo Bills in a nearly error-free game. If the sum of the scores was 39, determine the points scored by the losing team, the Bills, and the winning team, the Giants.

Solution

Step 1. Let x represent one of the quantities. We will let

$$x = \text{points scored by the losing team, the Bills.}$$

Step 2. Represent other unknown quantities in terms of x. The other unknown quantity involves points scored by the winning team, the Giants. Because the scores were consecutive integers, the winning team scored one point more than the losing team. Thus,

$$x + 1 = \text{points scored by the winning team, the Giants.}$$

Step 3. Write an equation in x that models the conditions. We are told that the sum of the scores was 39.

Points scored by the losing team | plus | points scored by the winning team | result in | 39 points.

$$x + (x + 1) = 39$$

Step 4. Solve the equation and answer the question.

$$x + (x + 1) = 39 \quad \text{This is the equation that models the problem's conditions.}$$
$$2x + 1 = 39 \quad \text{Regroup and combine like terms.}$$
$$2x + 1 - 1 = 39 - 1 \quad \text{Subtract 1 from both sides.}$$
$$2x = 38 \quad \text{Simplify.}$$
$$\frac{2x}{2} = \frac{38}{2} \quad \text{Divide both sides by 2.}$$
$$x = 19 \quad \text{Simplify.}$$

Thus,

$$\text{points scored by the losing team, the Bills} = x = 19$$

and

$$\text{points scored by the winning team, the Giants} = x + 1 = 20.$$

With the closest final score in Super Bowl history, the Giants scored 20 points and the Bills scored 19 points.

Step 5. Check the proposed solution in the original wording of the problem. The problem states that the sum of the scores was 39. With a final score of 20 to 19, we see that the sum of these numbers is, indeed, 39. ■

✓ **CHECK POINT 3** Page numbers on facing pages of a book are consecutive integers. Two pages that face each other have 145 as the sum of their page numbers. What are the page numbers?

Example 3 and Check Point 3 involved consecutive integers. By contrast, some word problems involve consecutive odd integers, such as 5, 7, and 9. Other word problems involve consecutive even integers, such as 6, 8, and 10. When working with consecutive even or consecutive odd integers, we must continually add 2 to move from one integer to the next successive integer in the list.

Table 2 should be helpful in solving consecutive integer problems.

Table 2 Consecutive Integers

English Phrase	Algebraic Expressions	Example
Two consecutive integers	$x, x + 1$	13, 14
Three consecutive integers	$x, x + 1, x + 2$	$-8, -7, -6$
Two consecutive even integers	$x, x + 2$	40, 42
Two consecutive odd integers	$x, x + 2$	$-37, -35$
Three consecutive even integers	$x, x + 2, x + 4$	30, 32, 34
Three consecutive odd integers	$x, x + 2, x + 4$	9, 11, 13

Wesley Hitt/Alamy

EXAMPLE 4 Renting a Car

Rent-a-Heap Agency charges \$125 per week plus \$0.20 per mile to rent a small car. How many miles can you travel for \$335?

Solution

Step 1. Let x represent one of the quantities. Because we are asked to find the number of miles we can travel for \$335, let

$$x = \text{the number of miles.}$$

Step 2. Represent other unknown quantities in terms of x. There are no other unknown quantities to find, so we can skip this step.

Step 3. Write an equation in x that models the conditions. Before writing the equation, let us consider a few specific values for the number of miles traveled. The rental charge is \$125 plus \$0.20 for each mile.

3 miles: The rental charge is \$125 + \$0.20(3).

30 miles: The rental charge is \$125 + \$0.20(30).

100 miles: The rental charge is \$125 + \$0.20(100).

x miles: The rental charge is \$125 + \$0.20x.

The weekly charge of \$125 | plus | the charge of \$0.20 per mile for x miles | equals | the total \$335 rental charge.

$$125 + 0.20x = 335$$

Step 4. Solve the equation and answer the question.

$$125 + 0.20x = 335$$ This is the equation that models the conditions of the problem.

$$125 + 0.20x - 125 = 335 - 125$$ Subtract 125 from both sides.

$$0.20x = 210$$ Simplify.

$$\frac{0.20x}{0.20} = \frac{210}{0.20}$$ Divide both sides by 0.20.

$$x = 1050$$ Simplify.

You can travel 1050 miles for \$335.

Step 5. Check the proposed solution in the original wording of the problem. Traveling 1050 miles should result in a total rental charge of \$335. The mileage charge of \$0.20 per mile is

$$\$0.20(1050) = \$210.$$

Adding this to the \$125 weekly charge gives a total rental charge of

$$\$125 + \$210 = \$335.$$

Because this results in the given rental charge of \$335, this verifies that you can travel 1050 miles. ■

✓ **CHECK POINT 4** A taxi charges \$2.00 to turn on the meter plus \$0.25 for each eighth of a mile. If you have \$10.00, how many eighths of a mile can you go? How many miles is that?

We will be using the formula for the perimeter of a rectangle, $P = 2l + 2w$, in our next example. Twice the rectangle's length plus twice the rectangle's width is its perimeter.

EXAMPLE 5 Finding the Dimensions of a Soccer Field

A rectangular soccer field is twice as long as it is wide. If the perimeter of a soccer field is 300 yards, what are the field's dimensions?

Solution

Step 1. Let x represent one of the quantities. We know something about the length; the field is twice as long as it is wide. We will let

$$x = \text{the width.}$$

Step 2. Represent other unknown quantities in terms of x. Because the field is twice as long as it is wide, let

$$2x = \text{the length.}$$

Figure 9 illustrates the soccer field and its dimensions.

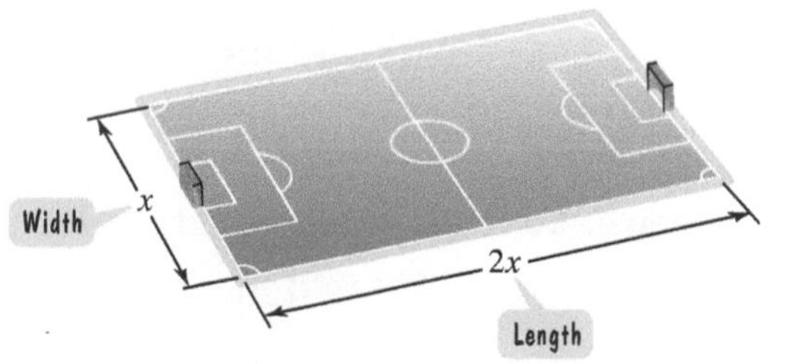

Figure 9

Great Question!

Should I draw pictures like Figure 9 when solving geometry problems?

When solving word problems, particularly problems involving geometric figures, drawing a picture of the situation is often helpful. Label x on your drawing and, where appropriate, label other parts of the drawing in terms of x.

Step 3. Write an equation in x that models the conditions. Because the perimeter of a soccer field is 300 yards,

Twice the length	plus	twice the width	is	the perimeter.
$2 \cdot 2x$	$+$	$2 \cdot x$	$=$	300.

Step 4. Solve the equation and answer the question.

$$2 \cdot 2x + 2 \cdot x = 300 \quad \text{This is the equation that models the problem's conditions.}$$
$$4x + 2x = 300 \quad \text{Multiply.}$$
$$6x = 300 \quad \text{Combine like terms.}$$
$$\frac{6x}{6} = \frac{300}{6} \quad \text{Divide both sides by 6.}$$
$$x = 50 \quad \text{Simplify.}$$

Thus,
$$\text{width} = x = 50$$
$$\text{length} = 2x = 2(50) = 100.$$

The dimensions of a soccer field are 50 yards by 100 yards.

Step 5. Check the proposed solution in the original wording of the problem. The perimeter of the soccer field, using the dimensions that we found, is 2(50 yards) + 2(100 yards) = 100 yards + 200 yards, or 300 yards. Because the problem's wording tells us that the perimeter is 300 yards, our dimensions are correct. ■

✓ **CHECK POINT 5** A rectangular swimming pool is three times as long as it is wide. If the perimeter of the pool is 320 feet, what are the pool's dimensions?

EXAMPLE 6 A Price Reduction

Your local computer store is having a sale. After a 30% price reduction, you purchase a new computer for $980. What was the computer's price before the reduction?

Solution

Step 1. Let x represent one of the quantities. We will let

x = the original price of the computer.

Step 2. Represent other unknown quantities in terms of x. There are no other unknown quantities to find, so we can skip this step.

Step 3. Write an equation in x that models the conditions. The computer's original price minus the 30% reduction is the reduced price, $980.

Original price	minus	the reduction (30% of the original price)	is	the reduced price, $980.
x	$-$	$0.3x$	$=$	980

Great Question!

Is there a common error that I can avoid when solving problems about price reductions?

Yes. In Example 6, notice that the original price, x, reduced by 30% is $x - 0.3x$ and *not* $x - 0.3$.

Step 4. Solve the equation and answer the question.

$$x - 0.3x = 980 \quad \text{This is the equation that models the problem's conditions.}$$
$$0.7x = 980 \quad \text{Combine like terms: } x - 0.3x = 1x - 0.3x = 0.7x.$$
$$\frac{0.7x}{0.7} = \frac{980}{0.7} \quad \text{Divide both sides by 0.7.}$$
$$x = 1400 \quad \text{Simplify: } 0.7\overline{)980.0} = 1400$$

The computer's price before the reduction was $1400.

Step 5. Check the proposed solution in the original wording of the problem. The price before the reduction, $1400, minus the reduction in price should equal the reduced price given in the original wording, $980. The reduction in price is equal to 30% of the price before the reduction, \$1400. To find the reduction, we multiply the decimal equivalent of 30%, 0.30 or 0.3, by the original price, \$1400:

$$30\% \text{ of } \$1400 = (0.3)(\$1400) = \$420.$$

Now we can determine whether the calculation for the price before the reduction, \$1400, minus the reduction, \$420, is equal to the reduced price given in the problem, \$980. We subtract:

$$\$1400 - \$420 = \$980.$$

This verifies that the price of the computer before the reduction was \$1400. ■

Great Question!

Can I solve the equation in Example 6, $x - 0.3x = 980$, by first clearing the decimal?

Yes. Because 0.3 has one decimal place, the greatest number of decimal places in the equation, multiply both sides by 10^1, or 10, to clear the decimal.

$$x - 0.3x = 980$$ This is the equation that models the conditions in Example 6.

$$10(x - 0.3x) = 10(980)$$ Multiply both sides by 10.

$$10x - 10(0.3x) = 10(980)$$ Use the distributive property.

$$10x - 3x = 9800$$ Simplify by moving decimal points one place to the right.

$$7x = 9800$$ Combine like terms.

$$\frac{7x}{7} = \frac{9800}{7}$$ Divide both sides by 7.

$$x = 1400$$ Simplify.

This is the same value for x that we obtained in Example 6 when we did not clear the decimal. Which method do you prefer?

✓ **CHECK POINT 6** After a 40% price reduction, an exercise machine sold for \$564. What was the exercise machine's price before this reduction?

Achieving Success

Do not expect to solve every word problem immediately. As you read each problem, underline the important parts. It's a good idea to read the problem at least twice. Be persistent, but use the **"Ten Minutes of Frustration" Rule**. If you have exhausted every possible means for solving a problem and you are still bogged down, stop after ten minutes. Put a question mark by the exercise and move on. When you return to class, ask your professor for assistance.

CONCEPT AND VOCABULARY CHECK

Fill in each blank so that the resulting statement is true.

1. If x represents a number, six subtracted from four times the number can be represented by ____________.
2. According to *Forbes* magazine, the top-earning dead celebrities in 2010 were Michael Jackson and Elvis Presley. Jackson's earnings exceeded Presley's earnings by \$215 million. If x represents Presley's earnings, in millions of dollars, Jackson's earnings can be represented by ____________.
3. If the number of any left-hand page in this book is represented by x, the number on the facing page can be represented by ____________.
4. I can rent a car for \$125 per week plus \$0.15 for each mile driven. If I drive x miles in a week, the cost for the rental can be represented by ____________.
5. If x represents a rectangle's width and $4x$ represents its length, the perimeter of the rectangle can be represented by ____________.
6. I purchased a computer after a 35% price reduction. If x represents the computer's original price, the reduced price can be represented by ____________.

5 EXERCISE SET

MyMathLab®

Practice Exercises

In Exercises 1–20, let x represent the number. Use the given conditions to write an equation. Solve the equation and find the number.

1. A number increased by 60 is equal to 410. Find the number.
2. The sum of a number and 43 is 107. Find the number.
3. A number decreased by 23 is equal to 214. Find the number.
4. The difference between a number and 17 is 96. Find the number.
5. The product of 7 and a number is 126. Find the number.
6. The product of 8 and a number is 272. Find the number.
7. The quotient of a number and 19 is 5. Find the number.
8. The quotient of a number and 14 is 8. Find the number.
9. The sum of four and twice a number is 56. Find the number.
10. The sum of five and three times a number is 59. Find the number.
11. Seven subtracted from five times a number is 178. Find the number.
12. Eight subtracted from six times a number is 298. Find the number.
13. A number increased by 5 is two times the number. Find the number.
14. A number increased by 12 is four times the number. Find the number.
15. Twice the sum of four and a number is 36. Find the number.
16. Three times the sum of five and a number is 48. Find the number.
17. Nine times a number is 30 more than three times that number. Find the number.
18. Five more than four times a number is that number increased by 35. Find the number.
19. If the quotient of three times a number and five is increased by four, the result is 34. Find the number.
20. If the quotient of three times a number and four is decreased by three, the result is nine. Find the number.

Application Exercises

In Exercises 21–46, use the five-step strategy to solve each problem.

How will you spend your average life expectancy of 78 years? The bar graph shows the average number of years you will devote to each of your most time-consuming activities. Exercises 21–22 are based on the data displayed by the graph.

How You Will Spend Your Average Life Expectancy of 78 Years

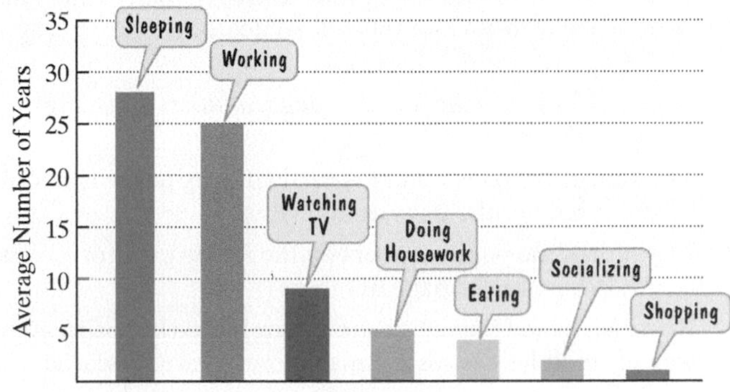

Source: U.S. Bureau of Labor Statistics

21. According to the American Bureau of Labor Statistics, you will devote 37 years to sleeping and watching TV. The number of years sleeping will exceed the number of years watching TV by 19. Over your lifetime, how many years will you spend on each of these activities?
22. According to the American Bureau of Labor Statistics, you will devote 32 years to sleeping and eating. The number of years sleeping will exceed the number of years eating by 24. Over your lifetime, how many years will you spend on each of these activities?

The bar graph shows average yearly earnings in the United States for people with a college education, by final degree earned. Exercises 23–24 are based on the data displayed by the graph.

Average Earnings of Full-Time Workers in the U.S., by Final Degree Earned

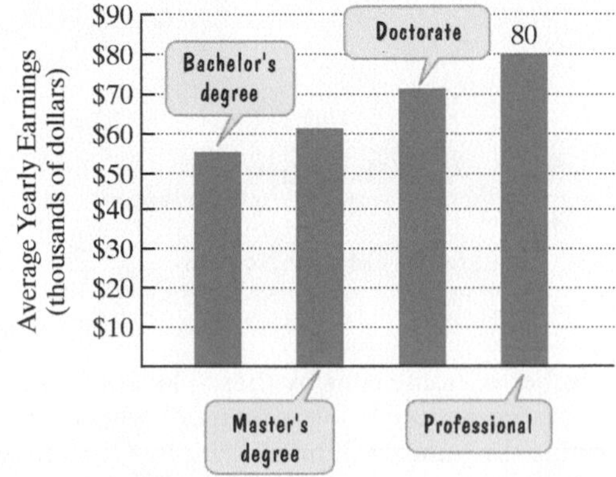

Source: U.S. Census Bureau

23. The average yearly salary of an American whose final degree is a master's is $49 thousand less than twice that of an American whose final degree is a bachelor's. Combined, two people with each of these educational attainments earn $116 thousand. Find the average yearly salary of Americans with each of these final degrees.

24. The average yearly salary of an American whose final degree is a doctorate is $39 thousand less than twice that of an American whose final degree is a bachelor's. Combined, two people with each of these educational attainments earn $126 thousand. Find the average yearly salary of Americans with each of these final degrees.

In Exercises 25–26, use the fact that page numbers on facing pages of a book are consecutive integers.

25. The sum of the page numbers on the facing pages of a book is 629. What are the page numbers?

26. The sum of the page numbers on the facing pages of a book is 525. What are the page numbers?

27. Roger Maris and Babe Ruth are among the ten baseball players with the most home runs in a major league baseball season.

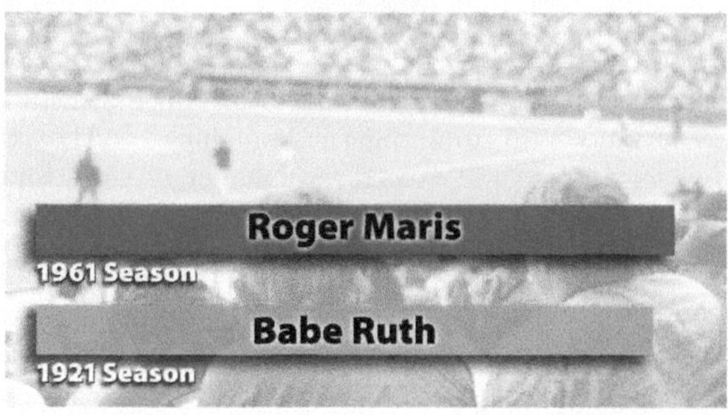

The number of home runs by these players for the seasons shown are consecutive odd integers whose sum is 120. Determine the number of homers hit by Ruth and by Maris.

28. Babe Ruth and Hank Greenberg are among the ten baseball players with the most home runs in a major league baseball season.

The number of home runs by these players for the seasons shown are consecutive even integers whose sum is 118. Determine the number of homers hit by Greenberg and by Ruth.

29. A car rental agency charges $200 per week plus $0.15 per mile to rent a car. How many miles can you travel in one week for $320?

30. A car rental agency charges $180 per week plus $0.25 per mile to rent a car. How many miles can you travel in one week for $395?

The bar graph shows that average rent and mortgage payments in the United States have increased since 1975, even after taking inflation into account. Exercises 31–32 are based on the information displayed by the graph.

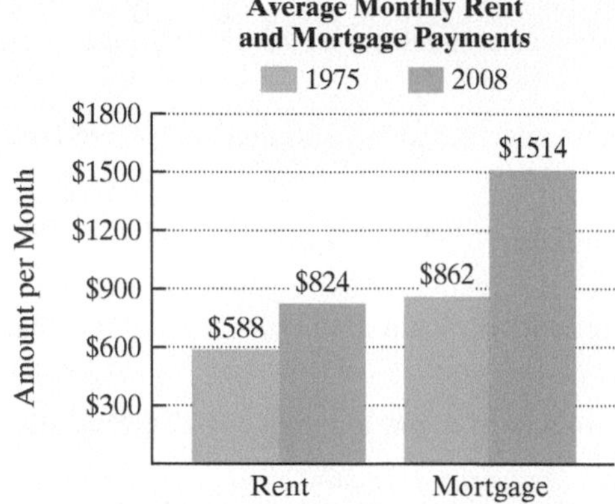

Source: U.S. Department of Housing and Urban Development

31. In 2008, mortgage payments averaged $1514 per month. For the period shown, monthly mortgage payments increased by approximately $20 per year. If this trend continues, how many years after 2008 will mortgage payments average $1714? In which year will this occur?

32. In 2008, rent payments averaged $824 per month. For the period shown, monthly rent payments increased by approximately $7 per year. If this trend continues, how many years after 2008 will rent payments average $929? In which year will this occur?

33. A rectangular field is four times as long as it is wide. If the perimeter of the field is 500 yards, what are the field's dimensions?

34. A rectangular field is five times as long as it is wide. If the perimeter of the field is 288 yards, what are the field's dimensions?

35. An American football field is a rectangle with a perimeter of 1040 feet. The length is 200 feet more than the width. Find the width and length of the rectangular field.

36. A basketball court is a rectangle with a perimeter of 86 meters. The length is 13 meters more than the width. Find the width and length of the basketball court.

37. A bookcase is to be constructed as shown in the figure. The length is to be 3 times the height. If 60 feet of lumber is available for the entire unit, find the length and height of the bookcase.

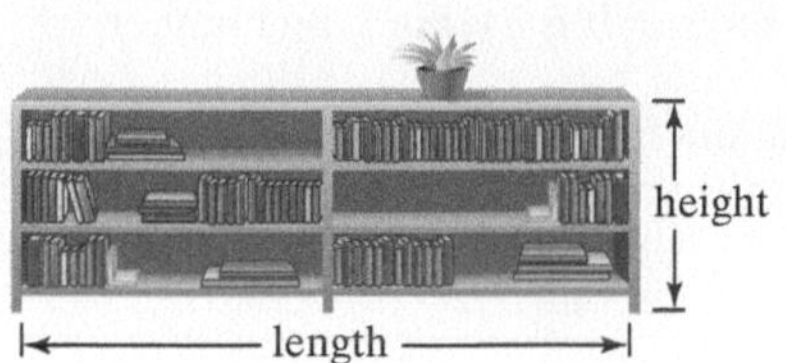

38. The height of the bookcase in the figure is 3 feet longer than the length of a shelf. If 18 feet of lumber is available for the entire unit, find the length and height of the unit.

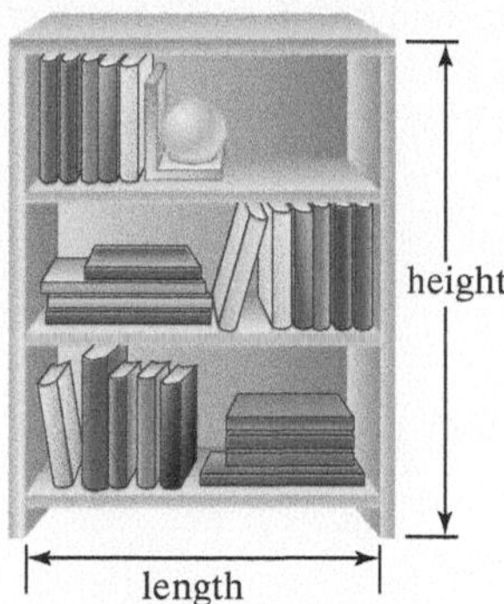

39. After a 20% reduction, you purchase a television for \$320. What was the television's price before the reduction?
40. After a 30% reduction, you purchase a DVD player for \$98. What was the price before the reduction?
41. This year's salary, \$50,220, is an 8% increase over last year's salary. What was last year's salary?
42. This year's salary, \$42,074, is a 9% increase over last year's salary. What was last year's salary?
43. Including 6% sales tax, a car sold for \$23,850. Find the price of the car before the tax was added.
44. Including 8% sales tax, a bed-and-breakfast inn charges \$172.80 per night. Find the inn's nightly cost before the tax is added.
45. An automobile repair shop charged a customer \$448, listing \$63 for parts and the remainder for labor. If the cost of labor is \$35 per hour, how many hours of labor did it take to repair the car?
46. A repair bill on a sailboat came to \$1603, including \$532 for parts and the remainder for labor. If the cost of labor is \$63 per hour, how many hours of labor did it take to repair the sailboat?

Writing in Mathematics

47. In your own words, describe a step-by-step approach for solving algebraic word problems.
48. Many students find solving linear equations much easier than solving algebraic word problems. Discuss some of the reasons why this is the case.
49. Did you have some difficulties solving some of the problems that were assigned in this Exercise Set? Discuss what you did if this happened to you. Did your course of action enhance your ability to solve algebraic word problems?
50. Write an original word problem that can be solved using a linear equation. Then solve the problem.

Critical Thinking Exercises

Make Sense? *In Exercises 51–54, determine whether each statement "makes sense" or "does not make sense" and explain your reasoning.*

51. Rather than struggling with the assigned word problems, I'll ask my instructor to solve them all in class and then study the solutions.
52. By reasoning through word problems, I can increase my problem-solving skills in general.
53. I find the hardest part in solving a word problem is writing the equation that models the verbal conditions.
54. I made a mistake when I used x and $x + 2$ to represent two consecutive odd integers, because 2 is even.

In Exercises 55–58, determine whether each statement is true or false. If the statement is false, make the necessary change(s) to produce a true statement.

55. Ten pounds less than Bill's weight, x, equals 160 pounds is modeled by $10 - x = 160$.
56. After a 35% reduction, a computer's price is \$780, so its original price, x, can be found by solving $x - 0.35 = 780$.
57. If the length of a rectangle is 6 inches more than its width, and its perimeter is 24 inches, the distributive property must be used to solve the equation that determines the length.
58. On a number line, consecutive integers do not have any other integers between them.
59. An HMO pamphlet contains the following recommended weight for women: "Give yourself 100 pounds for the first 5 feet plus 5 pounds for every inch over 5 feet tall." Using this description, which height corresponds to an ideal weight of 135 pounds?
60. The rate for a particular international telephone call is \$0.55 for the first minute and \$0.40 for each additional minute. Determine the length of a call that costs \$6.95.
61. In a film, the actor Charles Coburn played an elderly "uncle" character criticized for marrying a woman when he is 3 times her age. He wittily replies, "Ah, but in 20 years time I shall only be twice her age." How old is the "uncle" and the woman?
62. Answer the question in the following *Peanuts* cartoon strip. (*Note*: You may not use the answer given in the cartoon!)

Peanuts copyright © 1979, 2011 by United Features Syndicate, Inc.

Review Exercises

63. Solve and check: $\frac{4}{5}x = -16$. (Section 2, Example 3)

64. Solve and check: $6(y - 1) + 7 = 9y - y + 1$. (Section 3, Example 3)

65. Solve for w: $V = \frac{1}{3}lwh$. (Section 4, Example 4)

Preview Exercises

Exercises 66–68 will help you prepare for the material covered in the next section.

66. Use $A = \frac{1}{2}bh$ to find h if $A = 30$ and $b = 12$.

67. Evaluate $A = \frac{1}{2}h(a + b)$ for $a = 10$, $b = 16$, and $h = 7$.

68. Solve: $x = 4(90 - x) - 40$.

SECTION 6

Problem Solving in Geometry

Objectives

1. Solve problems using formulas for perimeter and area.
2. Solve problems using formulas for a circle's area and circumference.
3. Solve problems using formulas for volume.
4. Solve problems involving the angles of a triangle.
5. Solve problems involving complementary and supplementary angles.

Geometry is about the space you live in and the shapes that surround you. You're even made of it. The human lung consists of nearly 300 spherical air sacs, geometrically designed to provide the greatest surface area within the limited volume of our bodies. Viewed in this way, geometry becomes an intimate experience.

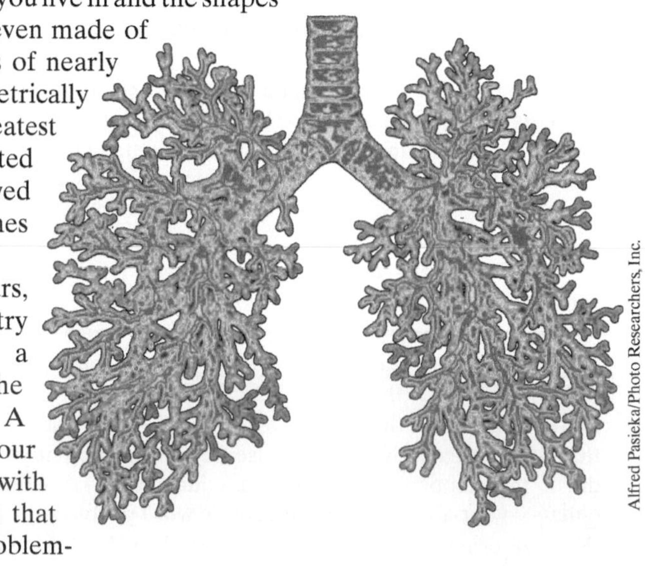

Alfred Pasieka/Photo Researchers, Inc.

For thousands of years, people have studied geometry in some form to obtain a better understanding of the world in which they live. A study of the shape of your world will provide you with many practical applications that will help to increase your problem-solving skills.

Geometric Formulas for Perimeter and Area

1 Solve problems using formulas for perimeter and area.

Solving geometry problems often requires using basic geometric formulas. Formulas for perimeter and area are summarized in **Table 3**. Remember that perimeter is measured in linear units, such as feet or meters, and area is measured in square units, such as square feet, ft^2, or square meters, m^2.

Table 3 Common Formulas for Perimeter and Area

Square	Rectangle	Triangle	Trapezoid
$A = s^2$	$A = lw$	$A = \frac{1}{2}bh$	$A = \frac{1}{2}h(a + b)$
$P = 4s$	$P = 2l + 2w$		

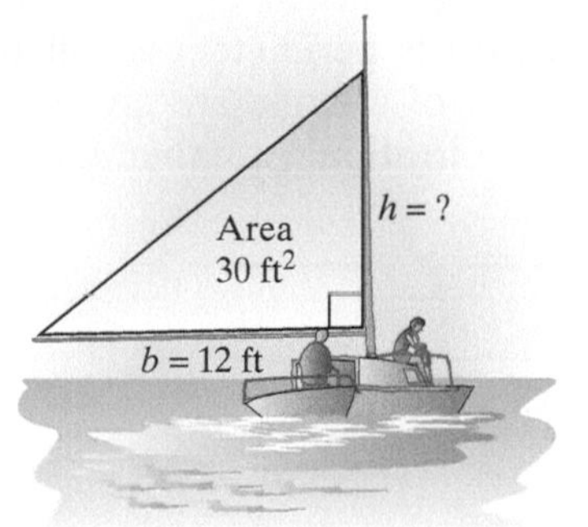

Figure 10 Finding the height of a triangular sail

EXAMPLE 1 Using the Formula for the Area of a Triangle

A sailboat has a triangular sail with an area of 30 square feet and a base that is 12 feet long. (See **Figure 10**.) Find the height of the sail.

Solution We begin with the formula for the area of a triangle given in **Table 3**.

$$A = \frac{1}{2}bh \quad \text{The area of a triangle is } \tfrac{1}{2} \text{ the product of its base and height.}$$

$$30 = \frac{1}{2}(12)h \quad \text{Substitute 30 for } A \text{ and 12 for } b.$$

$$30 = 6h \quad \text{Simplify.}$$

$$\frac{30}{6} = \frac{6h}{6} \quad \text{Divide both sides by 6.}$$

$$5 = h \quad \text{Simplify.}$$

The height of the sail is 5 feet.

Check
The area is $A = \frac{1}{2}bh = \frac{1}{2}(12 \text{ feet})(5 \text{ feet}) = 30$ square feet. ■

✓ **CHECK POINT 1** A sailboat has a triangular sail with an area of 24 square feet and a base that is 4 feet long. Find the height of the sail.

2 Solve problems using formulas for a circle's area and circumference.

Geometric Formulas for Circumference and Area of a Circle

It's a good idea to know your way around a circle. Clocks, angles, maps, and compasses are based on circles. Circles occur everywhere in nature: in ripples on water, patterns on a butterfly's wings, and cross sections of trees. Some consider the circle to be the most pleasing of all shapes.

Design Pics/SuperStock

The point at which a pebble hits a flat surface of water becomes the center of a number of circular ripples.

A **circle** is a set of points in the plane equally distant from a given point, its center. **Figure 11** shows two circles. A **radius** (plural: radii), r, is a line segment from the center to any point on the circle. For a given circle, all radii have the same length. A **diameter**, d, is a line segment through the center whose endpoints both lie on the circle. For a given circle, all diameters have the same length. In any circle, **the length of a diameter is twice the length of a radius.**

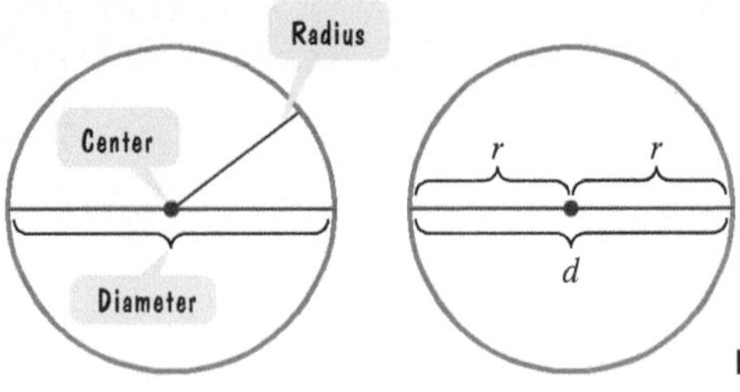

Figure 11

The words *radius* and *diameter* refer to both the line segments in **Figure 11** as well as their linear measures. The distance around a circle (its perimeter) is called its **circumference**. Formulas for the area and circumference of a circle are given in terms of π and appear in **Table 4**. We have seen that π is an irrational number and is approximately equal to 3.14.

Table 4 Formulas for Circles

Circle	Area	Circumference
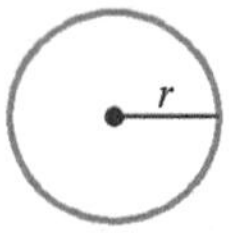	$A = \pi r^2$	$C = 2\pi r$

When computing a circle's area or circumference by hand, round π to 3.14. When using a calculator, use the $\boxed{\pi}$ key, which gives the value of π rounded to approximately 11 decimal places. In either case, calculations involving π give approximate answers. These answers can vary slightly depending on how π is rounded. The symbol $\approx$ (is approximately equal to) will be written in these calculations.

EXAMPLE 2 Finding the Area and Circumference of a Circle

Find the area and circumference of a circle with a diameter measuring 20 inches.

Solution The radius is half the diameter, so $r = \frac{20}{2} = 10$ inches.

$A = \pi r^2$	$C = 2\pi r$	Use the formulas for area and circumference of a circle.
$A = \pi(10)^2$	$C = 2\pi(10)$	Substitute 10 for r.
$A = 100\pi$	$C = 20\pi$	

The area of the circle is 100π square inches and the circumference is 20π inches. Using the fact that $\pi \approx 3.14$, the area is approximately 100(3.14), or 314 square inches. The circumference is approximately 20(3.14), or 62.8 inches. ■

✓ **CHECK POINT 2** The diameter of a circular landing pad for helicopters is 40 feet. Find the area and circumference of the landing pad. Express answers in terms of π. Then round answers to the nearest square foot and foot, respectively.

EXAMPLE 3 Problem Solving Using the Formula for a Circle's Area

Which one of the following is the better buy: a large pizza with a 16-inch diameter for \$15.00 or a medium pizza with an 8-inch diameter for \$7.50?

Solution The better buy is the pizza with the lower price per square inch. The radius of the large pizza is $\frac{1}{2}\cdot 16$ inches, or 8 inches, and the radius of the medium pizza is $\frac{1}{2}\cdot 8$ inches, or 4 inches. The area of the surface of each circular pizza is determined using the formula for the area of a circle.

$$\text{Large pizza: } A = \pi r^2 = \pi(8 \text{ in.})^2 = 64\pi \text{ in.}^2 \approx 201 \text{ in.}^2$$
$$\text{Medium pizza: } A = \pi r^2 = \pi(4 \text{ in.})^2 = 16\pi \text{ in.}^2 \approx 50 \text{ in.}^2$$

Using Technology

You can use your calculator to obtain the price per square inch for each pizza in Example 3. The price per square inch for the large pizza, $\frac{15}{64\pi}$, is approximated by one of the following keystrokes:

Many Scientific Calculators

15 [÷] [(] 64 [×] [π] [)] [=]

Many Graphing Calculators

15 [÷] [(] 64 [π] [)] [ENTER]

For each pizza, the price per square inch is found by dividing the price by the area:

$$\text{Price per square inch for large pizza} = \frac{\$15.00}{64\pi \text{ in.}^2} \approx \frac{\$15.00}{201 \text{ in.}^2} \approx \frac{\$0.07}{\text{in.}^2}$$
$$\text{Price per square inch for medium pizza} = \frac{\$7.50}{16\pi \text{ in.}^2} \approx \frac{\$7.50}{50 \text{ in.}^2} = \frac{\$0.15}{\text{in.}^2}.$$

The large pizza costs approximately \$0.07 per square inch and the medium pizza costs approximately \$0.15 per square inch. Thus, the large pizza is the better buy. ■

In Example 3, did you at first think that the price per square inch would be the same for the large and the medium pizzas? After all, the radius of the large pizza is twice that of the medium pizza, and the cost of the large is twice that of the medium. However, the large pizza's area, 64π square inches, is *four times the area* of the medium pizza, 16π square inches. Doubling the radius of a circle increases its area by four times the original amount.

✓ **CHECK POINT 3** Which one of the following is the better buy: a large pizza with an 18-inch diameter for \$20.00 or a medium pizza with a 14-inch diameter for \$14.00?

3 Solve problems using formulas for volume.

Geometric Formulas for Volume

A shoe box and a basketball are examples of three-dimensional figures. **Volume** refers to the amount of space occupied by such a figure. To measure this space, we begin by selecting a cubic unit. One such cubic unit, 1 cubic centimeter (cm^3), is shown in **Figure 12**.

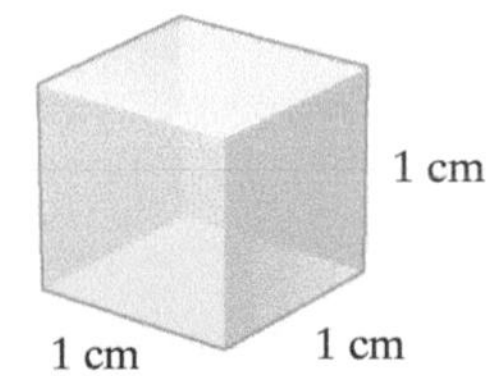

Figure 12

The edges of a cube all have the same length. Other cubic units used to measure volume include 1 cubic inch (in.^{3}) and 1 cubic foot (ft^3). The volume of a solid is the number of cubic units that can be contained in the solid.

Formulas for volumes of three-dimensional figures are given in **Table 5**.

Table 5 Common Formulas for Volume

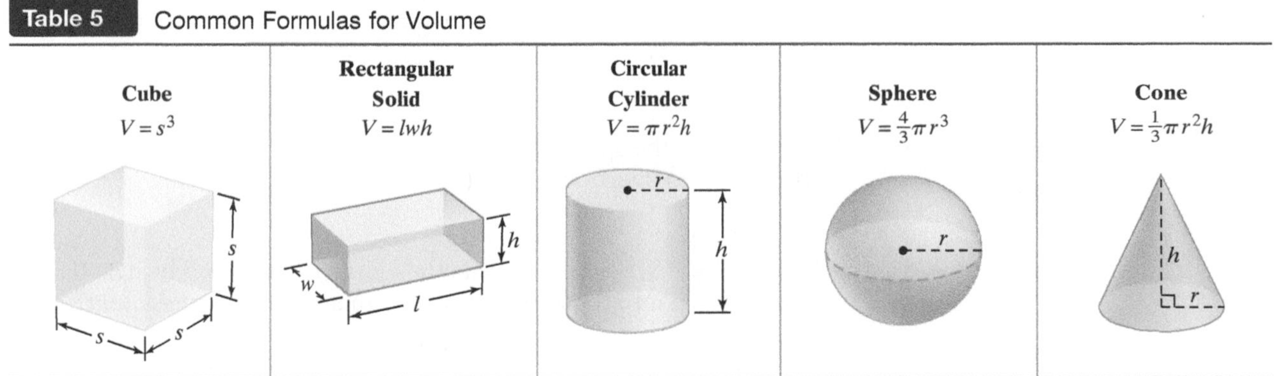

Cube
V = s³
s
s
s
Rectangular Solid
V = lwh
h
w
l
Circular Cylinder
V = πr²h
r
h
Sphere
V = (4/3)πr³
r
Cone
V = (1/3)πr²h
h
r

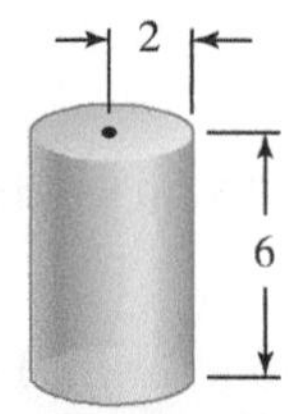

Radius: 2 inches
Height: 6 inches

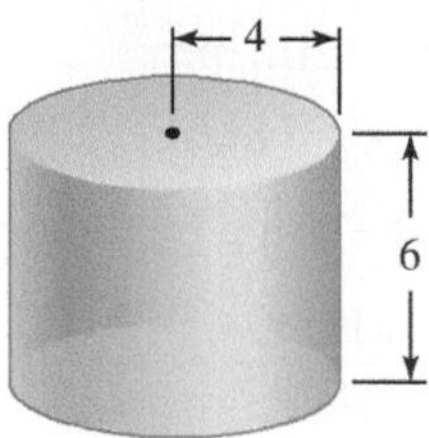

Radius: 4 inches
Height: 6 inches

Figure 13 Doubling a cylinder's radius

EXAMPLE 4 Using the Formula for the Volume of a Cylinder

A cylinder with a radius of 2 inches and a height of 6 inches has its radius doubled. (See **Figure 13.**) How many times greater is the volume of the larger cylinder than the volume of the smaller cylinder?

Solution We begin with the formula for the volume of a cylinder, $V = \pi r^2 h$, given on the previous page in **Table 5**. Find the volume of the smaller cylinder and the volume of the larger cylinder. To compare the volumes, divide the volume of the larger cylinder by the volume of the smaller cylinder.

$$V = \pi r^2 h$$ Use the formula for the volume of a cylinder.

Radius is doubled.

$$V_{\text{Smaller}} = \pi(2)^2(6) \quad V_{\text{Larger}} = \pi(4)^2(6)$$ Substitute the given values.

$$V_{\text{Smaller}} = \pi(4)(6) \quad V_{\text{Larger}} = \pi(16)(6)$$

$$V_{\text{Smaller}} = 24\pi \qquad V_{\text{Larger}} = 96\pi$$

The volume of the smaller cylinder is 24π cubic inches. The volume of the larger cylinder is 96π cubic inches. We use division to compare the volumes:

$$\frac{V_{\text{Larger}}}{V_{\text{Smaller}}} = \frac{96\pi}{24\pi} = \frac{4}{1}.$$

Thus, the volume of the larger cylinder is 4 times the volume of the smaller cylinder. ■

✓ **CHECK POINT 4** A cylinder with a radius of 3 inches and a height of 5 inches has its height doubled. How many times greater is the volume of the larger cylinder than the volume of the smaller cylinder?

EXAMPLE 5 Applying Volume Formulas

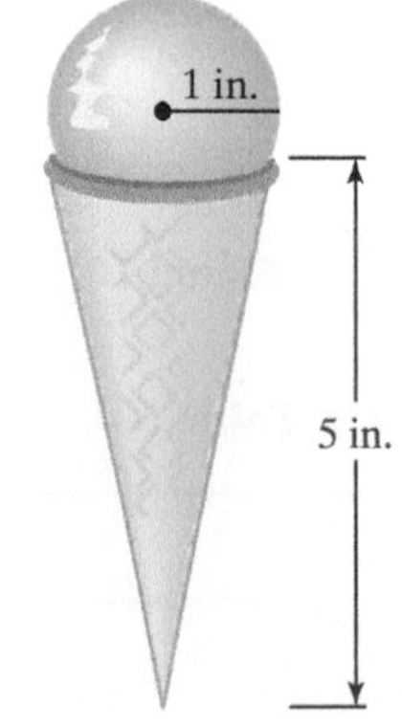

Figure 14

An ice cream cone is 5 inches deep and has a radius of 1 inch. A spherical scoop of ice cream also has a radius of 1 inch. (See **Figure 14.**) If the ice cream melts into the cone, will it overflow?

Solution The ice cream will overflow if the volume of the ice cream, a sphere, is greater than the volume of the cone. Find the volume of each.

$$V_{\text{cone}} = \frac{1}{3}\pi r^2 h = \frac{1}{3}\pi(1 \text{ in.})^2 \cdot 5 \text{ in.} = \frac{5\pi}{3}\text{in.}^3 \approx 5 \text{ in.}^3$$

$$V_{\text{sphere}} = \frac{4}{3}\pi r^3 = \frac{4}{3}\pi(1 \text{ in.})^3 = \frac{4\pi}{3}\text{in.}^3 \approx 4 \text{ in.}^3$$

The volume of the spherical scoop of ice cream is less than the volume of the cone, so there will be no overflow. ■

✓ **CHECK POINT 5** A basketball has a radius of 4.5 inches. If 350 cubic inches of air are pumped into the ball, is this enough air to fill it completely?

Blitzer Bonus

Deceptions in Visual Displays of Data

Graphs can be used to distort data, making it difficult for the viewer to learn the truth. One potential source of misunderstanding involves geometric figures whose lengths are in the correct ratios for the displayed data, but whose areas or volumes are then varied to create a misimpression about how the data are changing over time. Here are two examples of misleading visual displays.

Graphic Display	Presentation Problems
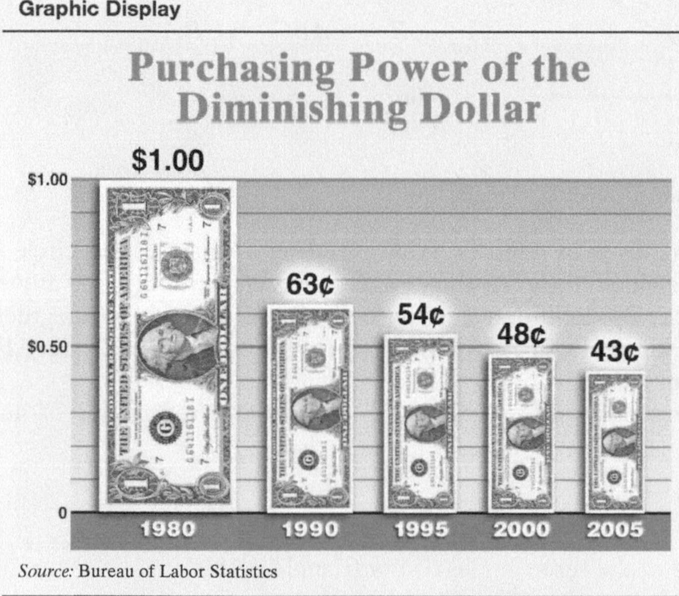 *Source:* Bureau of Labor Statistics	Although the length of each dollar bill is proportional to its spending power, the visual display varies both the length *and width* of the bills to show the diminishing power of the dollar over time. Because our eyes focus on the *areas* of the dollar-shaped bars, this creates the impression that the purchasing power of the dollar diminished even more than it really did. If the area of the dollar were drawn to reflect its purchasing power, the 2005 dollar would be approximately twice as large as the one shown in the graphic display.
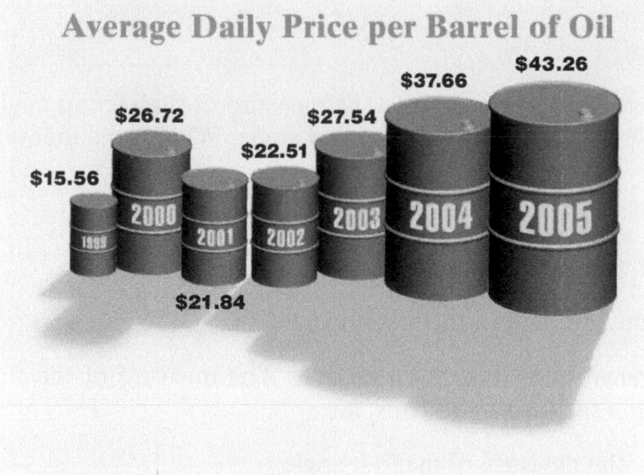 *Source:* U.S. Department of Energy	The height of each barrel is proportional to its price. However, the graph varies both the height *and radius* of the barrels to show the increase in the price of oil over time. Our eyes focus on the *volumes* of the cylinders: $V = \pi r^2 h$. By varying the radii, the volumes are not proportional to the barrel prices, creating the impression that oil prices increased even more than they really did. Cosmetic effects, including dates that are printed in different sizes and shadows under the barrels, further exaggerate how the data are changing over time.

4 Solve problems involving the angles of a triangle.

The Angles of a Triangle

The hour hand of a clock moves from 12 to 2. The hour hand suggests a **ray**, a part of a line that has only one endpoint and extends forever in the opposite direction. An *angle* is formed as the ray in **Figure 15** rotates from 12 to 2.

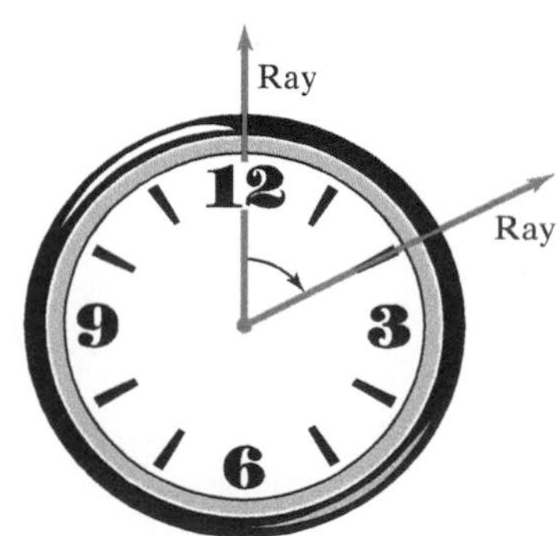

Figure 15 Clock with a ray rotating to form an angle

An **angle**, symbolized $\measuredangle$, is made up of two rays that have a common endpoint. **Figure 16** shows an angle. The common endpoint, B in the figure, is called the **vertex** of the angle. The two rays that form the angle are called its **sides**. The four ways of naming the angle are shown to the right of **Figure 16**.

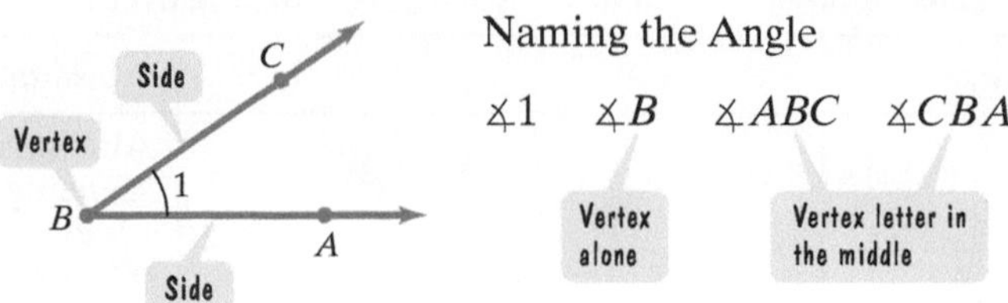

Figure 16 An angle: two rays with a common endpoint

One way to measure angles is in **degrees**, symbolized by a small, raised circle °. Think of the hour hand of a clock. From 12 noon to 12 midnight, the hour hand moves around in a complete circle. By definition, the ray has rotated through 360 degrees, or 360°. Using 360° as the amount of rotation of a ray back onto itself, **a degree, 1°, is $\frac{1}{360}$ of a complete rotation.**

Our next problem is based on the relationship among the three angles of any triangle.

The Angles of a Triangle

The sum of the measures of the three angles of any triangle is 180°.

EXAMPLE 6 Angles of a Triangle

In a triangle, the measure of the first angle is twice the measure of the second angle. The measure of the third angle is 20° less than the second angle. What is the measure of each angle?

Solution

Step 1. Let x represent one of the quantities. Let

$$x = \text{the measure of the second angle.}$$

Step 2. Represent other unknown quantities in terms of x. The measure of the first angle is twice the measure of the second angle. Thus, let

$$2x = \text{the measure of the first angle.}$$

The measure of the third angle is 20° less than the second angle. Thus, let

$$x - 20 = \text{the measure of the third angle.}$$

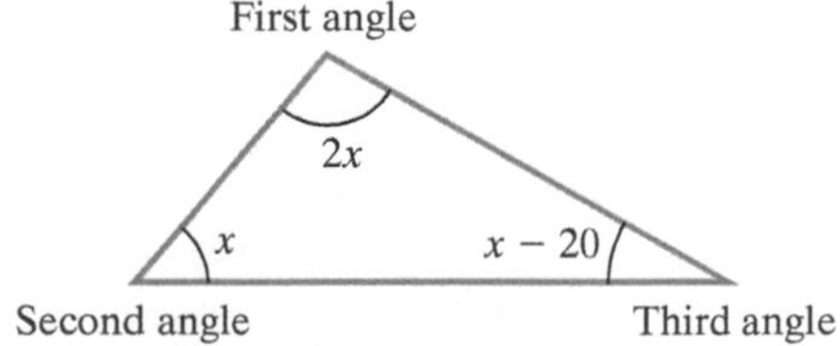

Step 3. Write an equation in x that models the conditions. Because we are working with a triangle, the sum of the measures of its three angles is 180°.

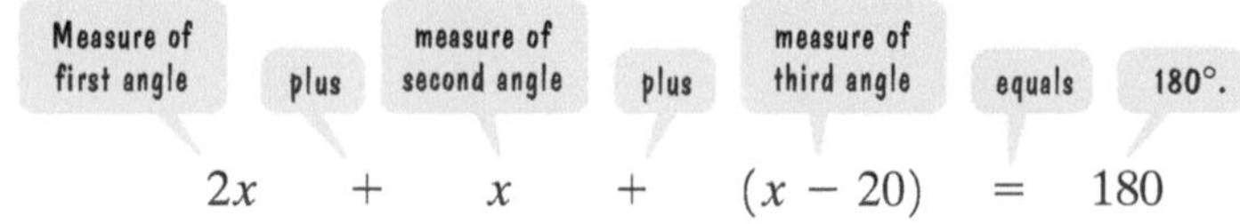

$$2x \quad + \quad x \quad + \quad (x - 20) \quad = \quad 180$$

Step 4. Solve the equation and answer the question.

$$2x + x + (x - 20) = 180$$ This is the equation that models the sum of the measures of the angles.

$$4x - 20 = 180$$ Regroup and combine like terms.

$$4x - 20 + 20 = 180 + 20$$ Add 20 to both sides.

$$4x = 200$$ Simplify.

$$\frac{4x}{4} = \frac{200}{4}$$ Divide both sides by 4.

$$x = 50$$ Simplify.

Measure of first angle $= 2x = 2 \cdot 50 = 100$

Measure of second angle $= x = 50$

Measure of third angle $= x - 20 = 50 - 20 = 30$

The angles measure 100°, 50°, and 30°.

Step 5. Check the proposed solution in the original wording of the problem. The problem tells us that we are working with a triangle's angles. Thus, the sum of the measures should be 180°. Adding the three measures, we obtain 100° + 50° + 30°, giving the required sum of 180°. ■

✓ **CHECK POINT 6** In a triangle, the measure of the first angle is three times the measure of the second angle. The measure of the third angle is 20° less than the second angle. What is the measure of each angle?

---

5 Solve problems involving complementary and supplementary angles.

Complementary and Supplementary Angles

Two angles with measures having a sum of 90° are called **complementary angles.** For example, angles measuring 70° and 20° are complementary angles because 70° + 20° = 90°. For angles such as those measuring 70° and 20°, each angle is a **complement** of the other: The 70° angle is the complement of the 20° angle and the 20° angle is the complement of the 70° angle. The measure of the complement can be found by subtracting the angle's measure from 90°. For example, we can find the complement of a 25° angle by subtracting 25° from 90°: 90° − 25° = 65°. Thus, an angle measuring 65° is the complement of one measuring 25°.

Two angles with measures having a sum of 180° are called **supplementary angles.** For example, angles measuring 110° and 70° are supplementary angles because 110° + 70° = 180°. For angles such as those measuring 110° and 70°, each angle is a **supplement** of the other: The 110° angle is the supplement of the 70° angle and the 70° angle is the supplement of the 110° angle. The measure of the supplement can be found by subtracting the angle's measure from 180°. For example, we can find the supplement of a 25° angle by subtracting 25° from 180°: 180° − 25° = 155°. Thus, an angle measuring 155° is the supplement of one measuring 25°.

Algebraic Expressions for Complements and Supplements

Measure of an angle: x

Measure of the angle's complement: $90 - x$

Measure of the angle's supplement: $180 - x$

EXAMPLE 7 Angle Measures and Complements

The measure of an angle is 40° less than four times the measure of its complement. What is the angle's measure?

Solution

Step 1. Let x represent one of the quantities. Let

$$x = \text{the measure of the angle.}$$

Step 2. Represent other unknown quantities in terms of x. Because this problem involves an angle and its complement, let

$$90 - x = \text{the measure of the complement.}$$

Step 3. Write an equation in x that models the conditions.

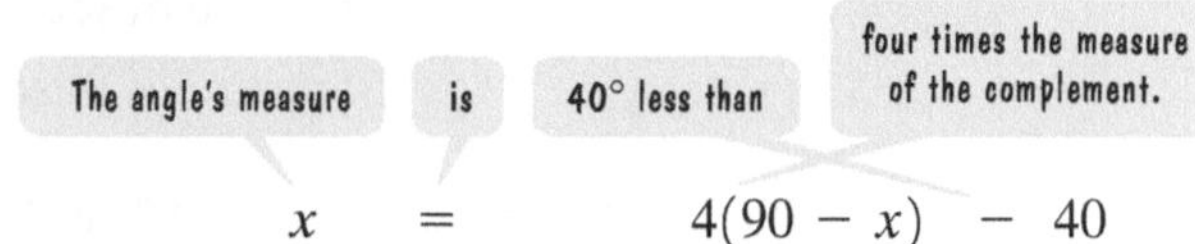
The angle's measure
is
40° less than
four times the measure of the complement.

$$x = 4(90 - x) - 40$$

Step 4. Solve the equation and answer the question.

$x = 4(90 - x) - 40$ This is the equation that models the problem's conditions.

$x = 360 - 4x - 40$ Use the distributive property.

$x = 320 - 4x$ Simplify: $360 - 40 = 320$.

$x + 4x = 320 - 4x + 4x$ Add 4x to both sides.

$5x = 320$ Simplify.

$\frac{5x}{5} = \frac{320}{5}$ Divide both sides by 5.

$x = 64$ Simplify.

The angle measures 64°.

Step 5. Check the proposed solution in the original wording of the problem. The measure of the complement is $90° - 64° = 26°$. Four times the measure of the complement is $4 \cdot 26°$, or 104°. The angle's measure, 64°, is 40° less than 104°: $104° - 40° = 64°$. As specified by the problem's wording, the angle's measure is 40° less than four times the measure of its complement. ■

✓ **CHECK POINT 7** The measure of an angle is twice the measure of its complement. What is the angle's measure?

CONCEPT AND VOCABULARY CHECK

Fill in each blank so that the resulting statement is true.

1. The area, A, of a triangle with base b and height h is given by the formula ______________.
2. The area, A, of a circle with radius r is given by the formula ______________.
3. The circumference, C, of a circle with radius r is given by the formula ______________.
4. In any circle, twice the length of the ______________ is the length of the ______________.
5. The volume, V, of a rectangular solid with length l, width w, and height h is given by the formula ______________.
6. The volume, V, of a circular cylinder with radius r and height h is given by the formula ______________.
7. The sum of the measures of the three angles of any triangle is ______________.
8. Two angles with measures having a sum of 90° are called ______________ angles.
9. Two angles with measures having a sum of 180° are called ______________ angles.
10. If the measure of an angle is represented by x, the measure of its complement is represented by ______________ and the measure of its supplement is represented by ______________.

6 EXERCISE SET

MyMathLab®

Watch the videos in MyMathLab

Download the MyDashBoard App

Practice Exercises

*Use the formulas for perimeter and area in **Table 3** to solve Exercises 1–12.*

In Exercises 1–2, find the perimeter and area of each rectangle.

1.

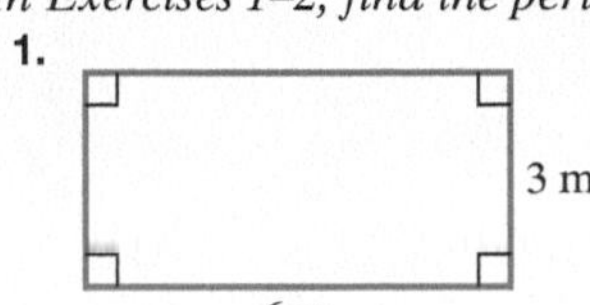

2.

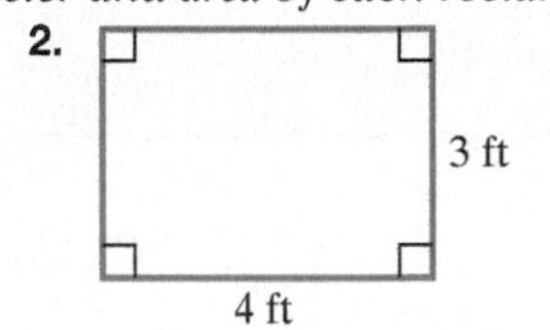

In Exercises 3–4, find the area of each triangle.

3.

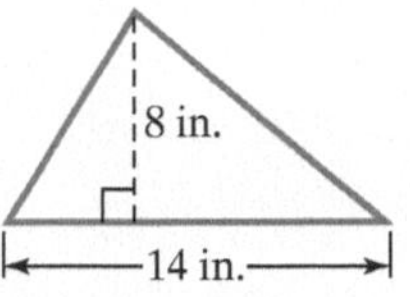

4.

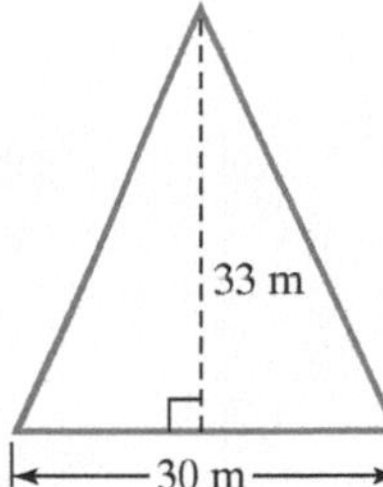

In Exercises 5–6, find the area of each trapezoid.

5.

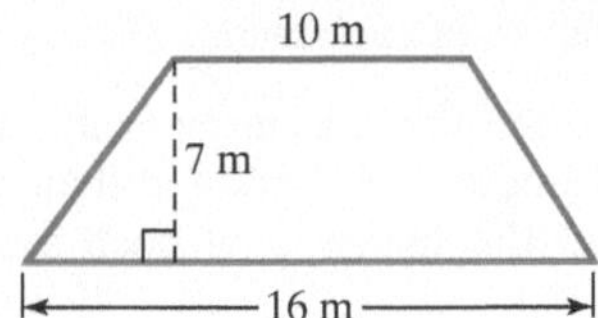

6.

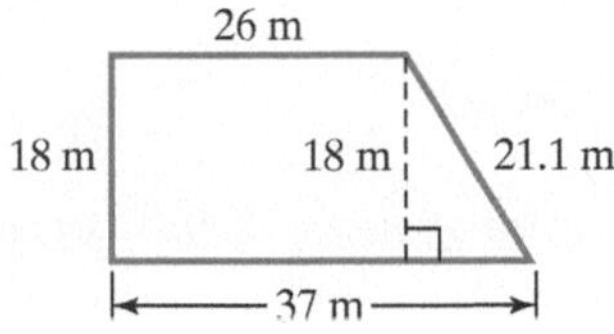

7. A rectangular swimming pool has a width of 25 feet and an area of 1250 square feet. What is the pool's length?

8. A rectangular swimming pool has a width of 35 feet and an area of 2450 square feet. What is the pool's length?

9. A triangle has a base of 5 feet and an area of 20 square feet. Find the triangle's height.

10. A triangle has a base of 6 feet and an area of 30 square feet. Find the triangle's height.

11. A rectangle has a width of 44 centimeters and a perimeter of 188 centimeters. What is the rectangle's length?

12. A rectangle has a width of 46 centimeters and a perimeter of 208 centimeters. What is the rectangle's length?

*Use the formulas for the area and circumference of a circle in **Table 4** to solve Exercises 13–18.*

In Exercises 13–16, find the area and circumference of each circle. Express answers in terms of π. Then round to the nearest whole number.

13.

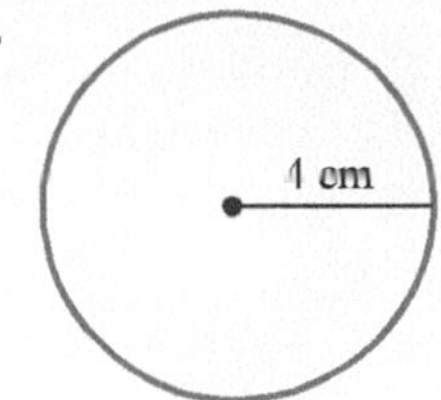

14.

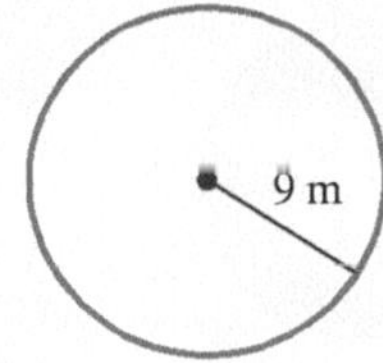

15.

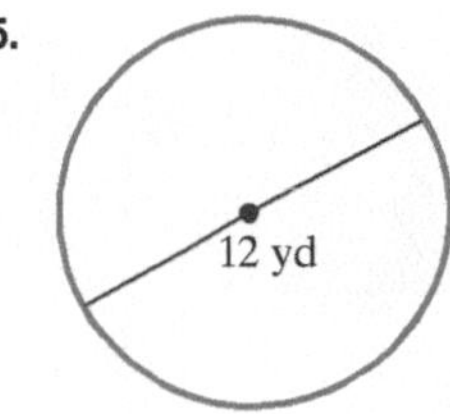

16.

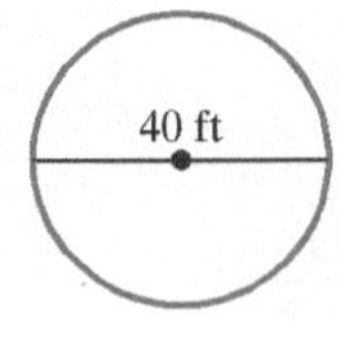

17. The circumference of a circle is 14π inches. Find the circle's radius and diameter.

18. The circumference of a circle is 16π inches. Find the circle's radius and diameter.

*Use the formulas for volume in **Table 5** to solve Exercises 19–30.*

In Exercises 19–26, find the volume of each figure. Where applicable, express answers in terms of π. Then round to the nearest whole number.

19.

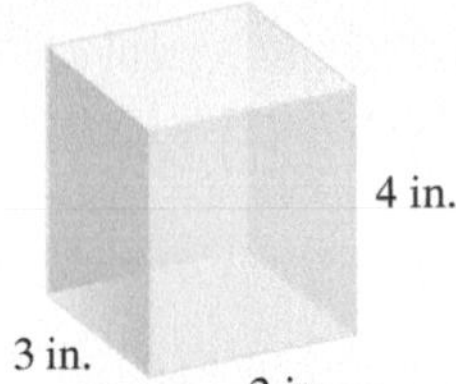

20.

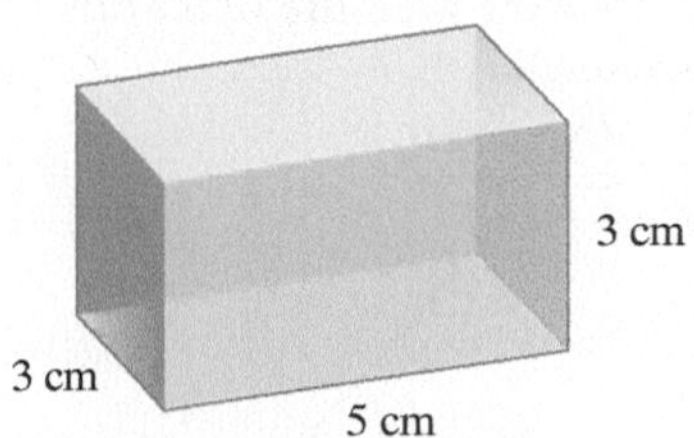

21.

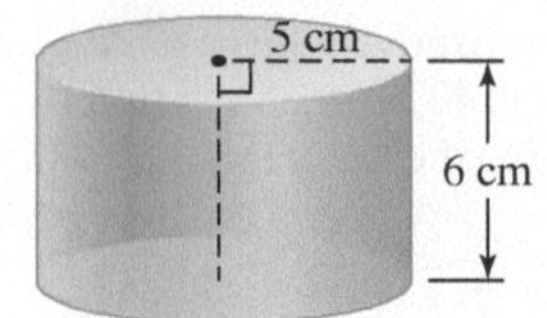

22. **23.** **24.**

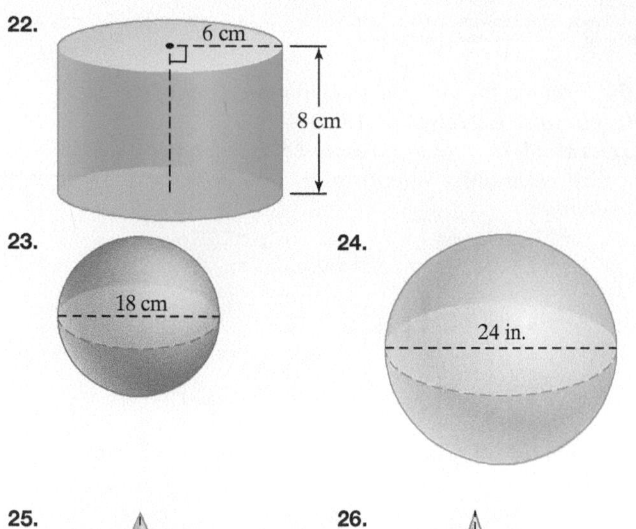

25.

9 m
4 m

26.

16 m
5 m

27. Solve the formula for the volume of a circular cylinder for h.

28. Solve the formula for the volume of a cone for h.

29. A cylinder with radius 3 inches and height 4 inches has its radius tripled. How many times greater is the volume of the larger cylinder than the smaller cylinder?

30. A cylinder with radius 2 inches and height 3 inches has its radius quadrupled. How many times greater is the volume of the larger cylinder than the smaller cylinder?

Use the relationship among the three angles of any triangle to solve Exercises 31–36.

31. Two angles of a triangle have the same measure and the third angle is 30° greater than the measure of the other two. Find the measure of each angle.

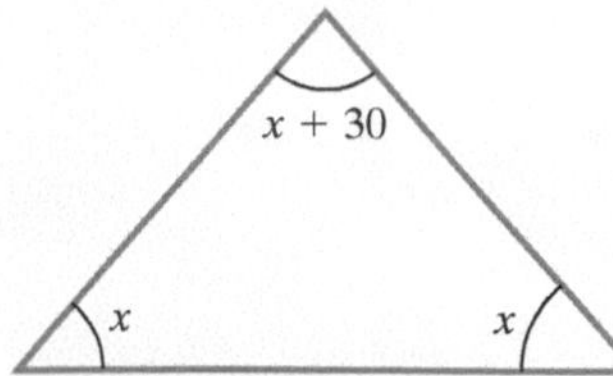

32. One angle of a triangle is three times as large as another. The measure of the third angle is 40° more than that of the smallest angle. Find the measure of each angle.

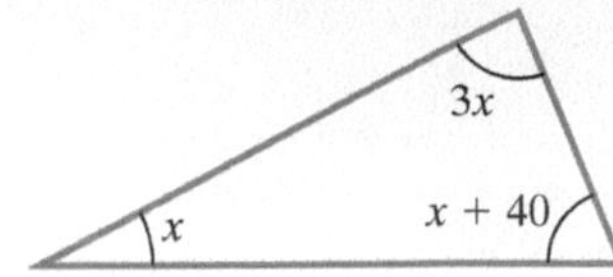

Find the measure of each angle whose degree measure is represented in terms of x in the triangles in Exercises 33–34.

33.

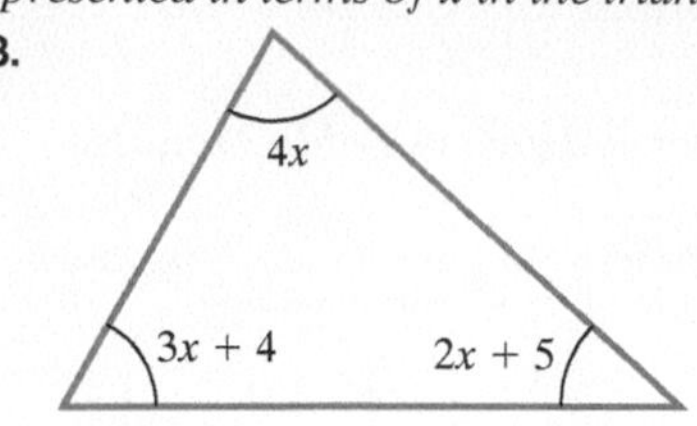

34.

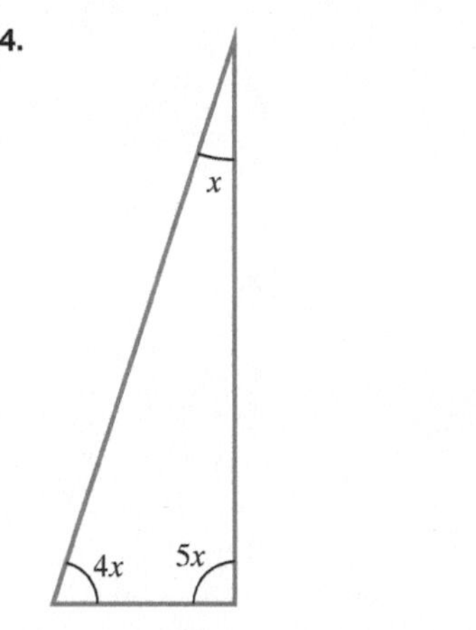

35. One angle of a triangle is twice as large as another. The measure of the third angle is 20° more than that of the smallest angle. Find the measure of each angle.

36. One angle of a triangle is three times as large as another. The measure of the third angle is 30° greater than that of the smallest angle. Find the measure of each angle.

In Exercises 37–40, find the measure of the complement of each angle.

37. 58° **38.** 41° **39.** 88° **40.** 2°

In Exercises 41–44, find the measure of the supplement of each angle.

41. 132° **42.** 93°

43. 90° **44.** 179.5°

In Exercises 45–50, use the five-step problem-solving strategy to find the measure of the angle described.

45. The angle's measure is 60° more than that of its complement.

46. The angle's measure is 78° less than that of its complement.

47. The angle's measure is three times that of its supplement.

48. The angle's measure is 16° more than triple that of its supplement.

49. The measure of the angle's supplement is 10° more than three times that of its complement.

50. The measure of the angle's supplement is 52° more than twice that of its complement.

Practice PLUS

In Exercises 51–53, find the area of each figure.

51.

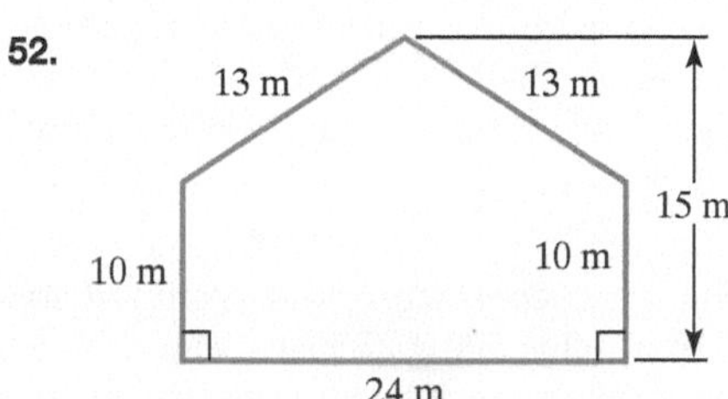

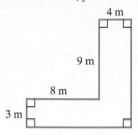

52.

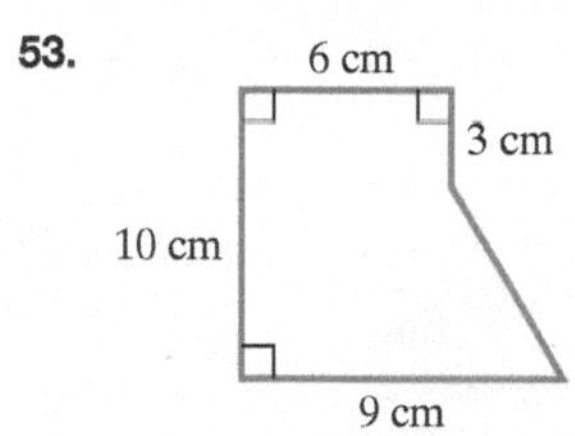

53.

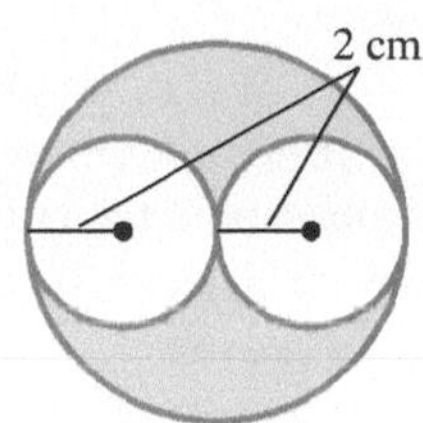

54. Find the area of the shaded region in terms of π.

55. Find the volume of the cement block in the figure shown.

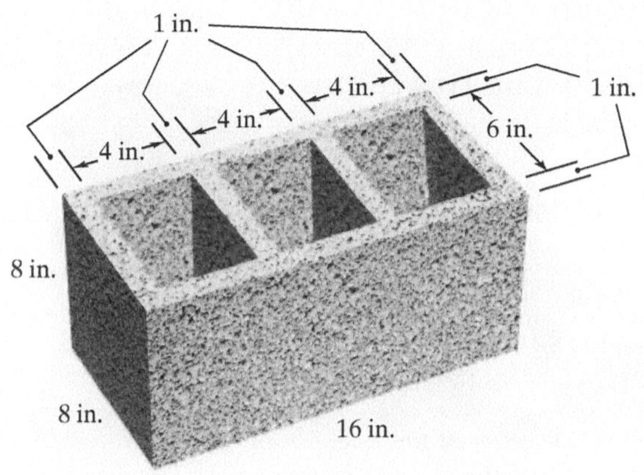

56. Find the volume of the darkly shaded region. Express the answer in terms of π.

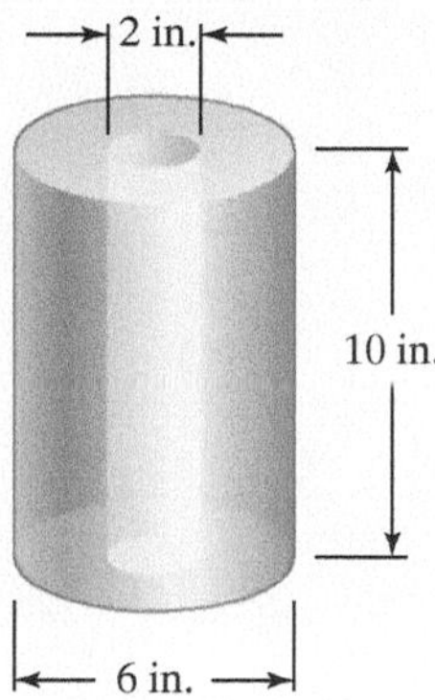

Application Exercises

*Use the formulas for perimeter and area in **Table 3** to solve Exercises 57–58.*

57. Taxpayers with an office in their home may deduct a percentage of their home-related expenses. This percentage is based on the ratio of the office's area to the area of the home. A taxpayer with a 2200-square-foot home maintains a 20-foot by 16-foot office. If the yearly electricity bills for the home come to \$4800, how much of this is deductible?

58. The lot in the figure shown, except for the house, shed, and driveway, is lawn. One bag of lawn fertilizer costs \$25.00 and covers 4000 square feet.

a. Determine the minimum number of bags of fertilizer needed for the lawn.

b. Find the total cost of the fertilizer.

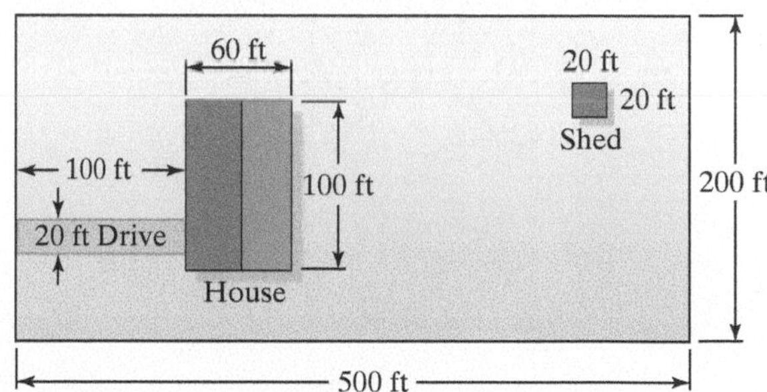

*Use the formulas for the area and the circumference of a circle in **Table 4** to solve Exercises 59–64. Unless otherwise indicated, round all circumference and area calculations to the nearest whole number.*

59. Which one of the following is a better buy: a large pizza with a 14-inch diameter for \$12.00 or a medium pizza with a 7-inch diameter for \$5.00?

60. Which one of the following is a better buy: a large pizza with a 16-inch diameter for \$12.00 or two small pizzas, each with a 10-inch diameter, for \$12.00?

61. If asphalt pavement costs \$0.80 per square foot, find the cost to pave the circular road in the figure shown. Round to the nearest dollar.

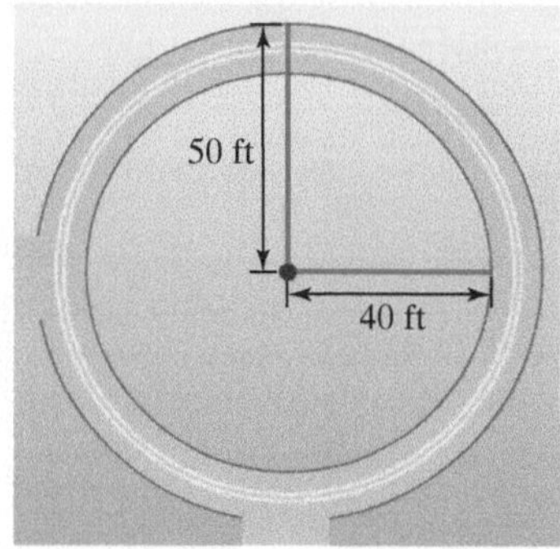

62. Hardwood flooring costs \$10.00 per square foot. How much will it cost (to the nearest dollar) to cover the dance floor shown in the figure with hardwood flooring?

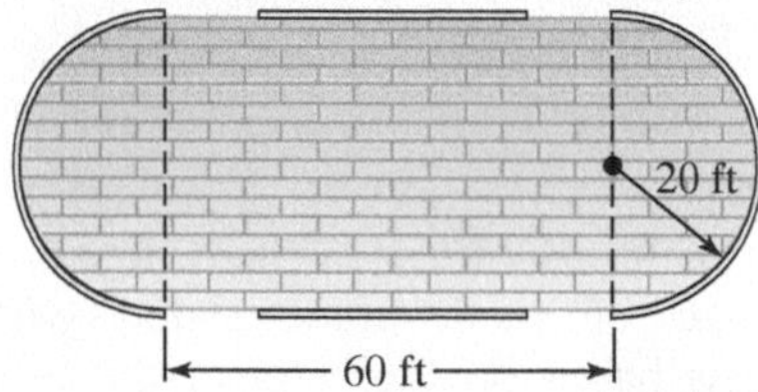

63. A glass window is to be placed in a house. The window consists of a rectangle, 6 feet high by 3 feet wide, with a semicircle at the top. Approximately how many feet of stripping, to the nearest tenth of a foot, will be needed to frame the window?

64. How many plants spaced every 6 inches are needed to surround a circular garden with a 30-foot radius?

Use the formulas for volume in ***Table 5*** *to solve Exercises 65–69. When necessary, round all volume calculations to the nearest whole number.*

65. A water reservoir is shaped like a rectangular solid with a base that is 50 yards by 30 yards, and a vertical height of 20 yards. At the start of a three-month period of no rain, the reservoir was completely full. At the end of this period, the height of the water was down to 6 yards. How much water was used in the three-month period?

66. A building contractor is to dig a foundation 4 yards long, 3 yards wide, and 2 yards deep for a toll booth's foundation. The contractor pays \$10 per load for trucks to remove the dirt. Each truck holds 6 cubic yards. What is the cost to the contractor to have all the dirt hauled away?

67. Two cylindrical cans of soup sell for the same price. One can has a diameter of 6 inches and a height of 5 inches. The other has a diameter of 5 inches and a height of 6 inches. Which can contains more soup and, therefore, is the better buy?

68. The tunnel under the English Channel that connects England and France is one of the world's longest tunnels. The Chunnel, as it is known, consists of three separate tunnels built side by side. Each is a half-cylinder that is 50,000 meters long and 4 meters high. How many cubic meters of dirt had to be removed to build the Chunnel?

69. You are about to sue your contractor who promised to install a water tank that holds 500 gallons of water. You know that 500 gallons is the capacity of a tank that holds 67 cubic feet. The cylindrical tank has a radius of 3 feet and a height of 2 feet 4 inches. Does the evidence indicate you can win the case against the contractor if it goes to court?

Writing in Mathematics

70. Using words only, describe how to find the area of a triangle.

71. Describe the difference between the following problems: How much fencing is needed to enclose a garden? How much fertilizer is needed for the garden?

72. Describe how volume is measured. Explain why linear or square units cannot be used.

73. What is an angle?

74. If the measures of two angles of a triangle are known, explain how to find the measure of the third angle.

75. Can a triangle contain two 90° angles? Explain your answer.

76. What are complementary angles? Describe how to find the measure of an angle's complement.

77. What are supplementary angles? Describe how to find the measure of an angle's supplement.

78. Describe what is misleading in this visual display of data.

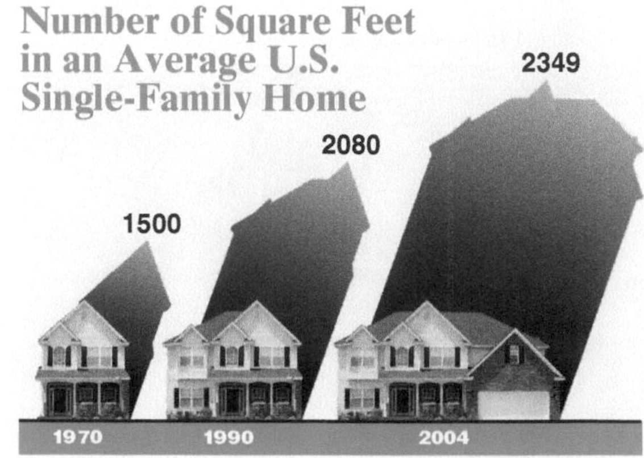

Source: National Association of Home Builders

Critical Thinking Exercises

Make Sense? *In Exercises 79–82, determine whether each statement "makes sense" or "does not make sense" and explain your reasoning.*

79. There is nothing that is misleading in this visual display of data.

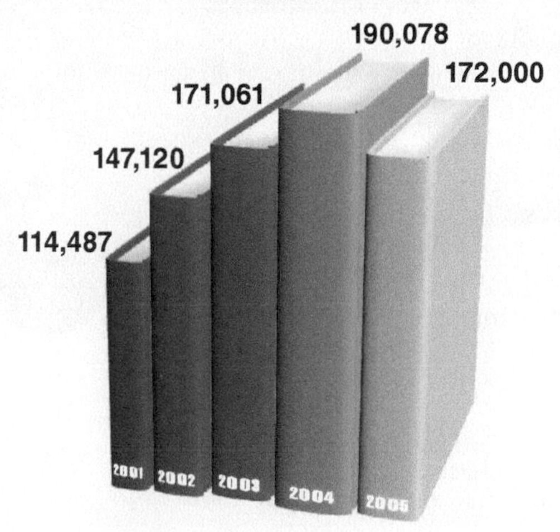

Source: R. R. Bowker

80. I solved a word problem and determined that a triangle had angles measuring 37°, 58°, and 86°.

81. I paid $10 for a pizza, so I would expect to pay approximately $20 for the same kind of pizza with twice the radius.

82. I find that my answers involving π can vary slightly depending on whether I round π mid-calculation or use the π key on my calculator and then round at the very end.

In Exercises 83–86, determine whether each statement is true or false. If the statement is false, make the necessary change(s) to produce a true statement.

83. It is possible to have a circle whose circumference is numerically equal to its area.

84. When the measure of a given angle is added to three times the measure of its complement, the sum equals the sum of the measures of the complement and supplement of the angle.

85. The complement of an angle that measures less than 90° is an angle that measures more than 90°.

86. Two complementary angles can be equal in measure.

87. Suppose you know the cost for building a rectangular deck measuring 8 feet by 10 feet. If you decide to increase the dimensions to 12 feet by 15 feet, by how many times will the cost increase?

88. A rectangular swimming pool measures 14 feet by 30 feet. The pool is surrounded on all four sides by a path that is 3 feet wide. If the cost to resurface the path is $2 per square foot, what is the total cost of resurfacing the path?

89. What happens to the volume of a sphere if its radius is doubled?

90. A scale model of a car is constructed so that its length, width, and height are each $\frac{1}{10}$ the length, width, and height of the actual car. By how many times does the volume of the car exceed its scale model?

91. Find the measure of the angle of inclination, denoted by x in the figure, for the road leading to the bridge.

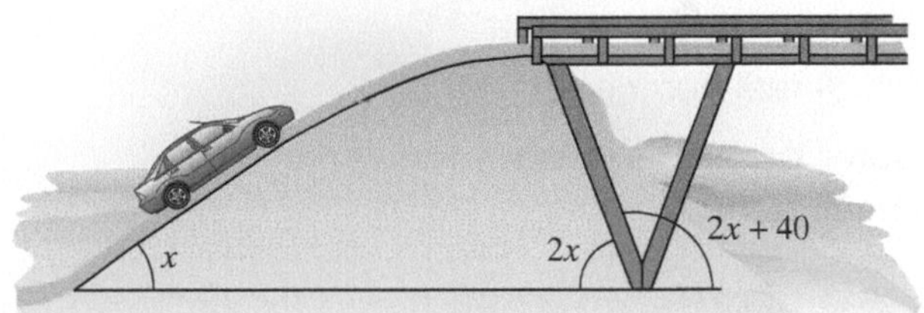

Review Exercises

92. Solve for s: $P = 2s + b$.
(Section 4, Example 3)

93. Solve for x: $\frac{x}{2} + 7 = 13 - \frac{x}{4}$.
(Section 3, Example 4)

94. Simplify: $[3(12 \div 2^2 - 3)^2]^2$.

Preview Exercises

Exercises 95–97 will help you prepare for the material covered in the next section.

95. Is 2 a solution of $x + 3 < 8$?

96. Is 6 a solution of $4y - 7 \geq 5$?

97. Solve: $2(x - 3) + 5x = 8(x - 1)$.

SECTION

7

Solving Linear Inequalities

Objectives

1. Graph the solutions of an inequality on a number line.
2. Use interval notation.
3. Understand properties used to solve linear inequalities.
4. Solve linear inequalities.
5. Identify inequalities with no solution or true for all real numbers.
6. Solve problems using linear inequalities.

Do you remember Rent-a-Heap, the car rental company that charged \$125 per week plus \$0.20 per mile to rent a small car? In Example 4 in Section 5, we asked the question: How many miles can you travel for \$335? We let x represent the number of miles and set up a linear equation as follows:

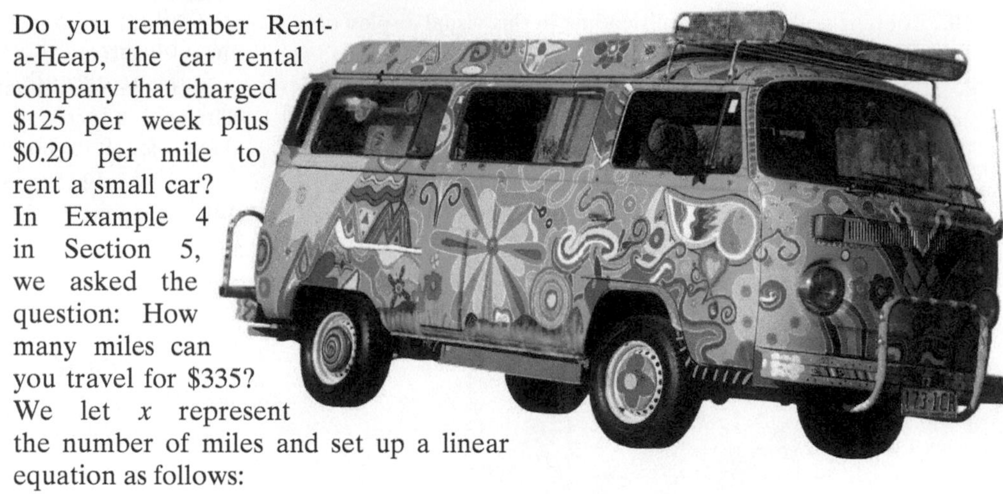

Doug Steley A/Alamy

The weekly charge of \$125	plus	the charge of \$0.20 per mile for x miles	equals	the total \$335 rental charge.
125	+	$0.20x$	=	335.

Because we are limited by how much money we can spend on everything from buying clothing to renting a car, it is also possible to ask: How many miles can you travel if you can spend *at most* \$335? We again let x represent the number of miles. Spending *at most* \$335 means that the amount spent on the weekly rental must be *less than or equal to* \$335:

The weekly charge of \$125	plus	the charge of \$0.20 per mile for x miles	must be less than or equal to	\$335.
125	+	$0.20x$	$\leq$	335.

Using the commutative property of addition, we can express this inequality as

$$0.20x + 125 \leq 335.$$

The form of this inequality is $ax + b \leq c$, with $a = 0.20$, $b = 125$, and $c = 335$. Any inequality in this form is called a **linear inequality in one variable**. The symbol between $ax + b$ and c can be $\leq$ (is less than or equal to), $<$ (is less than), $\geq$ (is greater than or equal to), or $>$ (is greater than). The greatest exponent on the variable in such an inequality is 1.

In this section, we will study how to solve linear inequalities such as $0.20x + 125 \leq 335$. **Solving an inequality** is the process of finding the set of numbers that will make the inequality a true statement. These numbers are called the **solutions** of the inequality, and we say that they **satisfy** the inequality. The set of all solutions is called the **solution set** of the inequality. We begin by discussing how to graph and how to represent these solution sets.

1 Graph the solutions of an inequality on a number line.

Graphs of Inequalities

There are infinitely many solutions to the inequality $x < 3$, namely, all real numbers that are less than 3. Although we cannot list all the solutions, we can make a drawing on a number line that represents these solutions. Such a drawing is called the **graph of the inequality**.

Graphs of solutions to linear inequalities are shown on a number line by shading all points representing numbers that are solutions. **Square brackets, [ ], indicate endpoints that are solutions. Parentheses, ( ), indicate endpoints that are not solutions.**

Great Question!

Is there another way that I can write $x < 3$?

Because an inequality symbol points to the smaller number, $x < 3$ (x is less than 3) may be expressed as $3 > x$ (3 is greater than x).

EXAMPLE 1 Graphing Inequalities

Graph the solutions of each inequality:

a. $x < 3$ **b.** $x \geq -1$ **c.** $-1 < x \leq 3$.

Solution

a. The solutions of $x < 3$ are all real numbers that are less than 3. They are graphed on a number line by shading all points to the left of 3. The parenthesis at 3 indicates that 3 is not a solution, but numbers such as 2.9999 and 2.6 are. The arrow shows that the graph extends indefinitely to the left.

−4 −3 −2 −1 0 1 2 3 4

b. The solutions of $x \geq -1$ are all real numbers that are greater than or equal to -1. We shade all points to the right of -1 and the point for -1 itself. The square bracket at -1 shows that -1 is a solution of the given inequality. The arrow shows that the graph extends indefinitely to the right.

−4 −3 −2 −1 0 1 2 3 4

c. The inequality $-1 < x \leq 3$ is read "-1 is less than x *and* x is less than or equal to 3," or "x is greater than -1 *and* less than or equal to 3." The solutions of $-1 < x \leq 3$ are all real numbers between -1 and 3, not including -1 but including 3. The parenthesis at -1 indicates that -1 is not a solution. The square bracket at 3 shows that 3 is a solution. Shading indicates the other solutions.

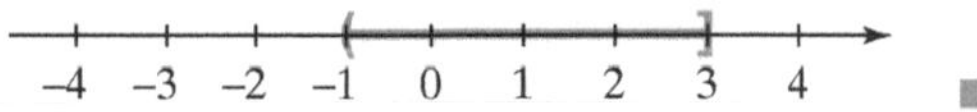

✓ **CHECK POINT 1** Graph the solutions of each inequality:

a. $x < 4$ **b.** $x \geq -2$ **c.** $-4 \leq x < 1$.

2 Use interval notation.

Interval Notation

The solutions of $x < 3$ are all real numbers that are less than 3:

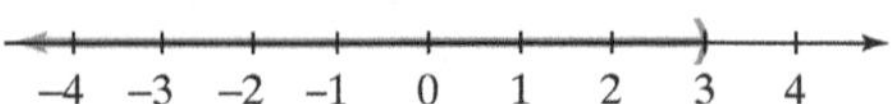

These numbers form an *interval* on the number line. The solution set of $x < 3$ can be expressed in **interval notation** as

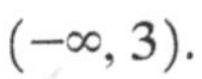

$$(-\infty, 3).$$

The negative infinity symbol indicates that the interval extends indefinitely to the left.

The parenthesis indicates that 3 is excluded from the interval.

The solution set of $x < 3$ can also be expressed in set-builder notation as

$$\{ x \mid x < 3 \}.$$

The set of | all x | such that | x is less than 3.

Table 6 shows four inequalities, their solution sets using interval and set-builder notations, and graphs of the solution sets.

Table 6 Solution Sets of Inequalities

Let a and b be real numbers.

Inequality	Interval Notation	Set-Builder Notation	Graph
$x > a$	(a, ∞)	$\{x \mid x > a\}$	a
$x \geq a$	$[a, \infty)$	$\{x \mid x \geq a\}$	a
$x < b$	$(-\infty, b)$	$\{x \mid x < b\}$	b
$x \leq b$	$(-\infty, b]$	$\{x \mid x \leq b\}$	b

Parentheses and Brackets in Interval Notation

Parentheses indicate endpoints that are not included in an interval. Square brackets indicate endpoints that are included in an interval. Parentheses are always used with ∞ or $-\infty$.

EXAMPLE 2 Using Interval Notation

Express the solution set of each inequality in interval notation and graph the interval:

a. $x \leq -1$ **b.** $x > 2$.

Solution

Inequality	Interval Notation	Graph
a. $x \leq -1$	$(-\infty, -1]$	–4 –3 –2 –1 0 1 2 3 4
x is less than or equal to –1.	The interval extends indefinitely to the left.	The square bracket on the graph and in interval notation shows –1 is included in the interval.
b. $x > 2$	$(2, \infty)$	–4 –3 –2 –1 0 1 2 3 4
x is greater than 2.	The interval extends indefinitely to the right.	The parenthesis on the graph and in interval notation shows 2 is excluded from the interval.

■

✓ **CHECK POINT 2** Express the solution set of each inequality in interval notation and graph the interval:

a. $x \geq 0$ **b.** $x < 5$.

---

3 Understand properties used to solve linear inequalities.

Properties Used to Solve Linear Inequalities

Back to our question that opened this section: How many miles can you drive your Rent-a-Heap car if you can spend at most \$335 per week? We answer the question by solving

$$0.20x + 125 \leq 335$$

for x. The solution procedure is nearly identical to that for solving

$$0.20x + 125 = 335.$$

Our goal is to get x by itself on the left side. We do this by first subtracting 125 from both sides to isolate $0.20x$:

$$0.20x + 125 \leq 335 \quad \text{This is the given inequality.}$$

$$0.20x + 125 - 125 \leq 335 - 125 \quad \text{Subtract 125 from both sides.}$$

$$0.20x \leq 210. \quad \text{Simplify.}$$

Finally, we isolate x from $0.20x$ by dividing both sides of the inequality by 0.20:

$$\frac{0.20x}{0.20} \leq \frac{210}{0.20} \quad \text{Divide both sides by 0.20.}$$

$$x \leq 1050. \quad \text{Simplify.}$$

Great Question!

What are some common English phrases and sentences that I can model with linear inequalities?

English phrases such as "at least" and "at most" can be represented by inequalities.

English Sentence	Inequality
x is at least 5.	$x \geq 5$
x is at most 5.	$x \leq 5$
x is no more than 5.	$x \leq 5$
x is no less than 5.	$x \geq 5$

With at most \$335 per week to spend, you can travel at most 1050 miles.

We started with the inequality $0.20x + 125 \leq 335$ and obtained the inequality $x \leq 1050$ in the final step. Both of these inequalities have the same solution set, namely $\{x | x \leq 1050\}$. Inequalities such as these, with the same solution set, are said to be **equivalent**.

We isolated x from $0.20x$ by dividing both sides of $0.20x \leq 210$ by 0.20, a positive number. Let's see what happens if we divide both sides of an inequality by a negative number. Consider the inequality $10 < 14$. Divide both 10 and 14 by -2:

$$\frac{10}{-2} = -5 \quad \text{and} \quad \frac{14}{-2} = -7.$$

Because -5 lies to the right of -7 on the number line, -5 is greater than -7:

$$-5 > -7.$$

Notice that the direction of the inequality symbol is reversed:

$$10 < 14$$

$$\updownarrow$$

$$-5 > -7.$$

Dividing by −2 changes the direction of the inequality symbol.

In general, **when we multiply or divide both sides of an inequality by a negative number, the direction of the inequality symbol is reversed**. When we reverse the direction of the inequality symbol, we say that we change the *sense* of the inequality.

We can isolate a variable in a linear inequality the same way we can isolate a variable in a linear equation. The following properties are used to create equivalent inequalities:

Properties of Inequalities

Property	The Property in Words	Example
The Addition Property of Inequality If $a < b$, then $a + c < b + c$. If $a < b$, then $a - c < b - c$.	If the same quantity is added to or subtracted from both sides of an inequality, the resulting inequality is equivalent to the original one.	$2x + 3 < 7$ Subtract 3: $2x + 3 - 3 < 7 - 3.$ Simplify: $2x < 4.$
The Positive Multiplication Property of Inequality If $a < b$ and c is positive, then $ac < bc$. If $a < b$ and c is positive, then $\frac{a}{c} < \frac{b}{c}$.	If we multiply or divide both sides of an inequality by the same positive quantity, the resulting inequality is equivalent to the original one.	$2x < 4$ Divide by 2: $\frac{2x}{2} < \frac{4}{2}.$ Simplify: $x < 2.$
The Negative Multiplication Property of Inequality If $a < b$ and c is negative, then $ac > bc$. If $a < b$ and c is negative, then $\frac{a}{c} > \frac{b}{c}$.	If we multiply or divide both sides of an inequality by the same negative quantity and reverse the direction of the inequality symbol, the resulting inequality is equivalent to the original one.	$-4x < 20$ Divide by -4 and reverse the direction of the inequality symbol: $\frac{-4x}{-4} > \frac{20}{-4}.$ Simplify: $x > -5.$

4 Solve linear inequalities.

Solving Linear Inequalities Involving Only One Property of Inequality

If you can solve a linear equation, it is likely that you can solve a linear inequality. Why? The procedure for solving linear inequalities is nearly the same as the procedure for solving linear equations, with one important exception: **When multiplying or dividing by a negative number, reverse the direction of the inequality symbol, changing the sense of the inequality.**

EXAMPLE 3 Solving a Linear Inequality

Solve and graph the solution set on a number line:

$$x + 3 < 8.$$

Solution Our goal is to isolate x. We can do this by using the addition property, subtracting 3 from both sides.

$$x + 3 < 8 \quad \text{This is the given inequality.}$$
$$x + 3 - 3 < 8 - 3 \quad \text{Subtract 3 from both sides.}$$
$$x < 5 \quad \text{Simplify.}$$

The solution set consists of all real numbers that are less than 5. We express this in interval notation as $(-\infty, 5)$, or in set-builder notation as $\{x \mid x < 5\}$. The graph of the solution set is shown as follows:

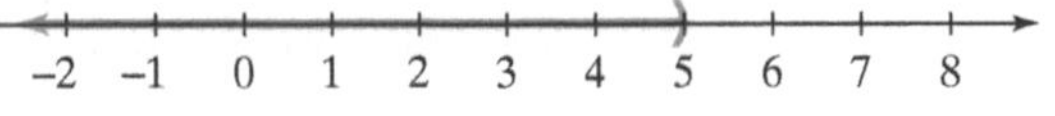

■

Discover for Yourself

Can you check all solutions to Example 3 in the given inequality? Is a partial check possible? Select a real number that is less than 5 and show that it satisfies $x + 3 < 8$.

✓ **CHECK POINT 3** Solve and graph the solution set on a number line:

$$x + 6 < 9.$$

EXAMPLE 4 Solving a Linear Inequality

Solve and graph the solution set on a number line:

$$4x - 1 \geq 3x - 6.$$

Solution Our goal is to isolate all terms involving x on one side and all numerical terms on the other side, exactly as we did when solving equations. Let's begin by using the addition property to isolate variable terms on the left.

$4x - 1 \geq 3x - 6$	This is the given inequality.
$4x - 3x - 1 \geq 3x - 3x - 6$	Subtract $3x$ from both sides.
$x - 1 \geq -6$	Simplify.

Now we isolate the numerical terms on the right. Use the addition property and add 1 to both sides.

$x - 1 + 1 \geq -6 + 1$	Add 1 to both sides.
$x \geq -5$	Simplify.

The solution set consists of all real numbers that are greater than or equal to -5. We express this in interval notation as $[-5, \infty)$, or in set-builder notation as $\{x \mid x \geq -5\}$.

The graph of the solution set is shown as follows:

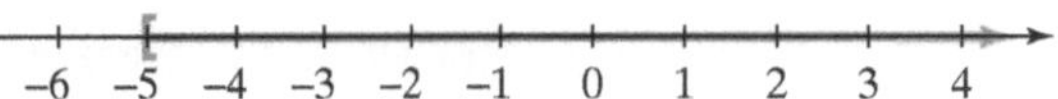

■

 **CHECK POINT 4** Solve and graph the solution set on a number line:

$$8x - 2 \geq 7x - 4.$$

We solved the inequalities in Examples 3 and 4 using the addition property of inequality. Now let's practice using the multiplication property of inequality. Do not forget to reverse the direction of the inequality symbol when multiplying or dividing both sides by a negative number.

EXAMPLE 5 Solving Linear Inequalities

Solve and graph the solution set on a number line:

a. $\frac{1}{3}x < 5$ **b.** $-3x < 21.$

Solution In each case, our goal is to isolate x. In the first inequality, this is accomplished by multiplying both sides by 3. In the second inequality, we can do this by dividing both sides by -3.

a.

$\frac{1}{3}x < 5$	This is the given inequality.
$3 \cdot \frac{1}{3}x < 3 \cdot 5$	Isolate x by multiplying by 3 on both sides. The symbol $<$ stays the same because we are multiplying both sides by a positive number.
$x < 15$	Simplify.

The solution set consists of all real numbers that are less than 15. We express this in interval notation as $(-\infty, 15)$, or in set-builder notation as $\{x \mid x < 15\}$. The graph of the solution set is shown as follows:

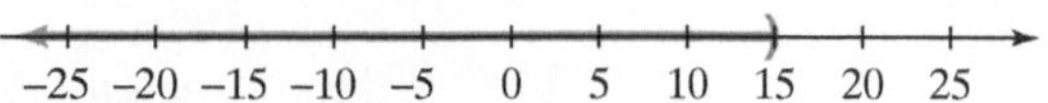

b. $-3x < 21$ This is the given inequality.

$\frac{-3x}{-3} > \frac{21}{-3}$ Isolate x by dividing by -3 on both sides. The symbol $<$ must be reversed because we are dividing both sides by a negative number.

$x > -7$ Simplify.

The solution set consists of all real numbers that are greater than -7. We express this in interval notation as $(-7, \infty)$, or in set-builder notation as $\{x \mid x > -7\}$. The graph of the solution set is shown as follows:

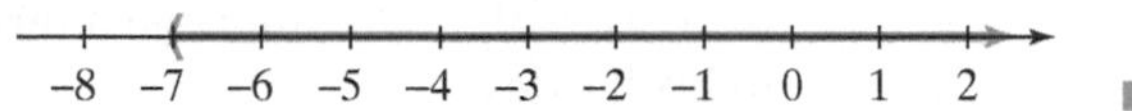

✓ **CHECK POINT 5** Solve and graph the solution set on a number line:

a. $\frac{1}{4}x < 2$ **b.** $-6x < 18$.

Inequalities Requiring Both the Addition and Multiplication Properties

If a linear inequality does not contain fractions, it can be solved using the following procedure. Notice, again, how similar this procedure is to the procedure for solving a linear equation.

Solving a Linear Inequality

1. Simplify the algebraic expression on each side.
2. Use the addition property of inequality to collect all the variable terms on one side and all the constant terms on the other side.
3. Use the multiplication property of inequality to isolate the variable and solve. Change the sense of the inequality when multiplying or dividing both sides by a negative number.
4. Express the solution set in interval or set-builder notation, and graph the solution set on a number line.

EXAMPLE 6 Solving a Linear Inequality

Solve and graph the solution set on a number line:

$$4y - 7 \geq 5.$$

Solution

Step 1. Simplify each side. Because each side is already simplified, we can skip this step.

Step 2. Collect variable terms on one side and constant terms on the other side. The only variable term, $4y$, is already on the left side of $4y - 7 \geq 5$. We will collect constant terms on the right by adding 7 to both sides.

$$4y - 7 \geq 5 \quad \text{This is the given inequality.}$$
$$4y - 7 + 7 \geq 5 + 7 \quad \text{Add 7 to both sides.}$$
$$4y \geq 12 \quad \text{Simplify.}$$

Step 3. Isolate the variable and solve. We isolate the variable, y, by dividing both sides by 4. Because we are dividing by a positive number, we do not reverse the inequality symbol.

$$\frac{4y}{4} \geq \frac{12}{4} \quad \text{Divide both sides by 4.}$$
$$y \geq 3 \quad \text{Simplify.}$$

Step 4. Express the solution set in interval or set-builder notation, and graph the set on a number line. The solution set consists of all real numbers that are greater than or equal to 3, expressed in interval notation as $[3, \infty)$, or in set-builder notation as $\{y \mid y \geq 3\}$. The graph of the solution set is shown as follows:

−5 −4 −3 −2 −1 0 1 2 3 4 5 ■

Great Question!

Is there a way to check that I obtained the correct solution set for a linear inequality?

It is possible to perform a partial check for an inequality. Select one number from the solution set. Substitute that number into the original inequality and perform the resulting computations. You should obtain a true statement.

✓ **CHECK POINT 6** Solve and graph the solution set on a number line:

$$5y - 3 \geq 17.$$

EXAMPLE 7 Solving a Linear Inequality

Solve and graph the solution set on a number line:

$$7x + 15 \geq 13x + 51.$$

Solution

Step 1. Simplify each side. Because each side is already simplified, we can skip this step.

Step 2. Collect variable terms on one side and constant terms on the other side. We will collect variable terms on the left and constant terms on the right.

$$7x + 15 \geq 13x + 51 \quad \text{This is the given inequality.}$$
$$7x + 15 - 13x \geq 13x + 51 - 13x \quad \text{Subtract } 13x \text{ from both sides.}$$
$$-6x + 15 \geq 51 \quad \text{Simplify.}$$
$$-6x + 15 - 15 \geq 51 - 15 \quad \text{Subtract 15 from both sides.}$$
$$-6x \geq 36 \quad \text{Simplify.}$$

Step 3. Isolate the variable and solve. We isolate the variable, x, by dividing both sides by -6. Because we are dividing by a negative number, we must reverse the inequality symbol.

$$\frac{-6x}{-6} \leq \frac{36}{-6} \quad \text{Divide both sides by } -6 \text{ and change the sense of the inequality.}$$
$$x \leq -6 \quad \text{Simplify.}$$

Step 4. Express the solution set in interval or set-builder notation, and graph the set on a number line. The solution set consists of all real numbers that are less than or equal to -6, expressed in interval notation as $(-\infty, -6]$, or in set-builder notation as $\{x \mid x \leq -6\}$. The graph of the solution set is shown as follows:

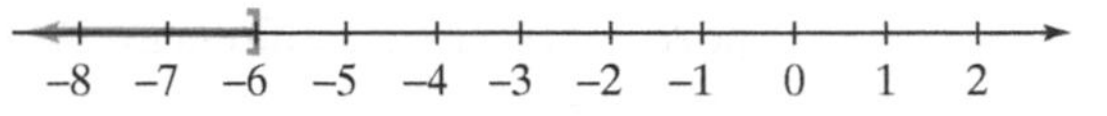

■

Great Question!

Do I have to solve the inequality in Example 7 by isolating the variable on the left?

No. You can solve

$$7x + 15 \geq 13x + 51$$

by isolating x on the right side. Subtract $7x$ from both sides:

$$7x + 15 - 7x \geq 13x + 51 - 7x$$
$$15 \geq 6x + 51.$$

Now subtract 51 from both sides:

$$15 - 51 \geq 6x + 51 - 51$$
$$-36 \geq 6x.$$

Finally, divide both sides by 6:

$$\frac{-36}{6} \geq \frac{6x}{6}$$
$$-6 \geq x.$$

This last inequality means the same thing as

$$x \leq -6.$$

✓ **CHECK POINT 7** Solve and graph the solution set: $6 - 3x \leq 5x - 2$.

EXAMPLE 8 Solving a Linear Inequality

Solve and graph the solution set on a number line:

$$2(x - 3) + 5x \leq 8(x - 1).$$

Solution

Step 1. Simplify each side. We use the distributive property to remove parentheses. Then we combine like terms.

$2(x - 3) + 5x \leq 8(x - 1)$	This is the given inequality.
$2x - 6 + 5x \leq 8x - 8$	Use the distributive property.
$7x - 6 \leq 8x - 8$	Add like terms on the left.

Step 2. Collect variable terms on one side and constant terms on the other side. We will collect variable terms on the left and constant terms on the right.

$7x - 8x - 6 \leq 8x - 8x - 8$	Subtract 8x from both sides.
$-x - 6 \leq -8$	Simplify.
$-x - 6 + 6 \leq -8 + 6$	Add 6 to both sides.
$-x \leq -2$	Simplify.

Step 3. Isolate the variable and solve. To isolate x in $-x \leq -2$, we must eliminate the negative sign in front of the x. Because $-x$ means $-1x$, we can do this by multiplying (or dividing) both sides of the inequality by -1. We are multiplying by a negative number. Thus, we must reverse the inequality symbol.

$(-1)(-x) \geq (-1)(-2)$	Multiply both sides of $-x \leq -2$ by -1 and change the sense of the inequality.
$x \geq 2$	Simplify.

Step 4. Express the solution set in interval or set-builder notation, and graph the set on a number line. The solution set consists of all real numbers that are greater than or equal to 2, expressed in interval notation as $[2, \infty)$, or in set-builder notation as $\{x \mid x \geq 2\}$. The graph of the solution set is shown as follows:

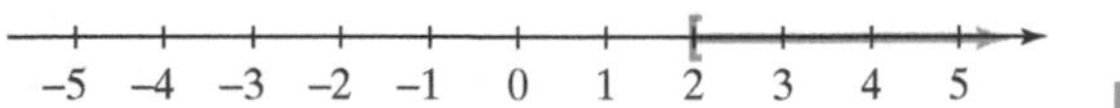

■

✓ **CHECK POINT 8** Solve and graph the solution set on a number line:

$$2(x - 3) - 1 \leq 3(x + 2) - 14.$$

---

5 Identify inequalities with no solution or true for all real numbers.

Inequalities with Unusual Solution Sets

We have seen that some equations have no solution. This is also true for some inequalities. An example of such an inequality is

$$x > x + 1.$$

There is no number that is greater than itself plus 1. This inequality has no solution. Its solution set is $\varnothing$, the empty set.

By contrast, some inequalities are true for all real numbers. An example of such an inequality is

$$x < x + 1.$$

Every real number is less than itself plus 1. The solution set is expressed in interval notation as $(-\infty, \infty)$, or in set-builder notation as $\{x \mid x \text{ is a real number}\}$.

Recognizing Inequalities with No Solution or True for All Real Numbers

If you attempt to solve an inequality with no solution or one that is true for every real number, you will eliminate the variable.

- An inequality with no solution results in a false statement, such as $0 > 1$. The solution set is $\varnothing$, the empty set.
- An inequality that is true for every real number results in a true statement, such as $0 < 1$. The solution set is $(-\infty, \infty)$ or $\{x \mid x \text{ is a real number}\}$.

EXAMPLE 9 Solving a Linear Inequality

Solve: $3(x + 1) > 3x + 5$.

Solution

$3(x + 1) > 3x + 5$	This is the given inequality.
$3x + 3 > 3x + 5$	Apply the distributive property.
$3x + 3 - 3x > 3x + 5 - 3x$	Subtract 3x from both sides.
$3 > 5$	Simplify.

Keep reading. $3 > 5$ is not the solution.

The original inequality is equivalent to the statement $3 > 5$, which is false for every value of x. The inequality has no solution. The solution set is $\varnothing$, the empty set. ■

✓ **CHECK POINT 9** Solve: $4(x + 2) > 4x + 15$.

EXAMPLE 10 Solving a Linear Inequality

Solve: $2(x + 5) \le 5x - 3x + 14$.

Solution

$2(x + 5) \le 5x - 3x + 14$	This is the given inequality.
$2x + 10 \le 5x - 3x + 14$	Apply the distributive property.
$2x + 10 \le 2x + 14$	Combine like terms.
$2x + 10 - 2x \le 2x + 14 - 2x$	Subtract 2x from both sides.
$10 \le 14$	Simplify.

Keep reading. $10 \le 14$ is not the solution.

The original inequality is equivalent to the statement $10 \le 14$, which is true for every value of x. The solution is the set of all real numbers, expressed in interval notation as $(-\infty, \infty)$, or in set-builder notation as $\{x \mid x \text{ is a real number}\}$. ■

✓ **CHECK POINT 10** Solve: $3(x + 1) \ge 2x + 1 + x$.

6 Solve problems using linear inequalities.

Applications

As you know, different professors may use different grading systems to determine your final course grade. Some professors require a final examination; others do not. In our next example, a final exam is required *and* it also counts as two grades.

EXAMPLE 11 An Application: Final Course Grade

To earn an A in a course, you must have a final average of at least 90%. On the first four examinations, you have grades of 86%, 88%, 92%, and 84%. If the final examination counts as two grades, what must you get on the final to earn an A in the course?

Solution We will use our five-step strategy for solving algebraic word problems.

Steps 1 and 2. Represent unknown quantities in terms of x. Let

$$x = \text{your grade on the final examination.}$$

Step 3. Write an inequality in x that models the conditions. The average of the six grades is found by adding the grades and dividing the sum by 6.

$$\text{Average} = \frac{86 + 88 + 92 + 84 + x + x}{6}$$

Because the final counts as two grades, the x (your grade on the final examination) is added twice. This is also why the sum is divided by 6.

To get an A, your average must be at least 90. This means that your average must be greater than or equal to 90.

Your average | must be greater than or equal to | 90.

$$\frac{86 + 88 + 92 + 84 + x + x}{6} \geq 90$$

Step 4. Solve the inequality and answer the problem's question.

$$\frac{86 + 88 + 92 + 84 + x + x}{6} \geq 90$$ This is the inequality that models the given conditions.

$$\frac{350 + 2x}{6} \geq 90$$ Combine like terms in the numerator.

$$6\left(\frac{350 + 2x}{6}\right) \geq 6(90)$$ Multiply both sides by 6, clearing the fraction.

$$350 + 2x \geq 540$$ Multiply.

$$350 + 2x - 350 \geq 540 - 350$$ Subtract 350 from both sides.

$$2x \geq 190$$ Simplify.

$$\frac{2x}{2} \geq \frac{190}{2}$$ Divide both sides by 2.

$$x \geq 95$$ Simplify.

You must get at least 95% on the final examination to earn an A in the course.

Step 5. Check. We can perform a partial check by computing the average with any grade that is at least 95. We will use 96. If you get 96% on the final examination, your average is

$$\frac{86 + 88 + 92 + 84 + 96 + 96}{6} = \frac{542}{6} = 90\frac{1}{3}.$$

Because $90\frac{1}{3} > 90$, you earn an A in the course. ■

✓ **CHECK POINT 11** To earn a B in a course, you must have a final average of at least 80%. On the first three examinations, you have grades of 82%, 74%, and 78%. If the final examination counts as two grades, what must you get on the final to earn a B in the course?

EXAMPLE 12 An Application: Staying within a Budget

You can spend at most $1000 to have a picnic catered. The caterer charges a $150 setup fee and $25 per person. How many people can you invite while staying within your budget?

Solution

Steps 1 and 2. Represent unknown quantities in terms of x. Let

x = the number of people you invite to the picnic.

Step 3. Write an inequality in x that models the conditions. You can spend at most $1000. This means that the caterer's setup fee plus the cost of the meals must be less than or equal to $1000.

The setup fee: $150 | plus | the cost of the meals: $25 per person for x people | must be less than or equal to | $1000.

$$150 \quad + \quad 25x \quad \leq \quad 1000$$

Step 4. Solve the inequality and answer the problem's question.

$$150 + 25x \leq 1000$$ This is the inequality that models the given conditions.

$$150 + 25x - 150 \leq 1000 - 150$$ Subtract 150 from both sides.

$$25x \leq 850$$ Simplify.

$$\frac{25x}{25} \leq \frac{850}{25}$$ Divide both sides by 25.

$$x \leq 34$$ Simplify.

You can invite at most 34 people to the picnic and still stay within your budget.

Step 5. Check. We can perform a partial check. Because $x \leq 34$, let's see if you stay within your $1000 budget by inviting 33 guests.

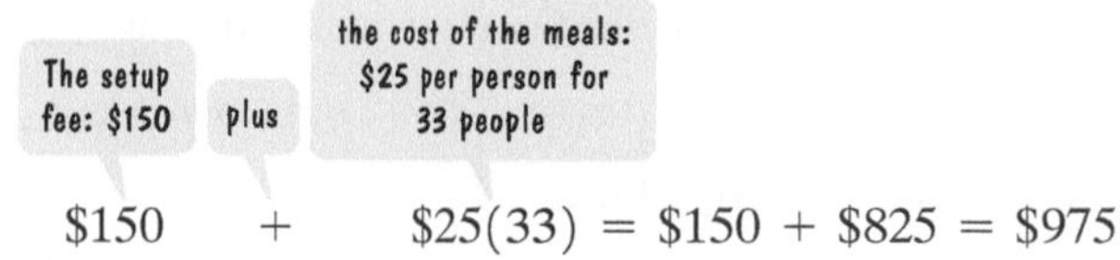
The setup fee: $150
plus
the cost of the meals: $25 per person for 33 people
$150 + $25(33) = $150 + $825 = $975

Inviting 33 people results in catering costs of $975, which is within your $1000 budget. ■

✓ **CHECK POINT 12** You can spend at most $1600 to have a picnic catered. The caterer charges a $95 setup fee and $35 per person. How many people can you invite while staying within your budget?

Achieving Success

Assuming that you have done very well preparing for an exam, **there are certain things you can do that will make you a better test taker**.

- Get a good sleep the night before the exam.
- Have a good breakfast that balances protein, carbohydrates, and fruit.
- Just before the exam, briefly review the relevant material in the chapter summary.
- Bring everything you need to the exam, including two pencils, an eraser, scratch paper (if permitted), a calculator (if you're allowed to use one), water, and a watch.
- Survey the entire exam quickly to get an idea of its length.
- Read the directions to each problem carefully. Make sure that you have answered the specific question asked.
- Work the easy problems first. Then return to the hard problems you are not sure of. Doing the easy problems first will build your confidence. If you get bogged down on any one problem, you may not be able to complete the exam and receive credit for the questions you can easily answer.
- Attempt every problem. There may be partial credit even if you do not obtain the correct answer.
- Work carefully. Show your step-by-step solutions neatly. Check your work and answers.
- Watch the time. Pace yourself and be aware of when half the time is up. Determine how much of the exam you have completed. This will indicate if you're moving at a good pace or need to speed up. Prepare to spend more time on problems worth more points.
- Never turn in a test early. Use every available minute you are given for the test. If you have extra time, double check your arithmetic and look over your solutions.

CONCEPT AND VOCABULARY CHECK

Fill in each blank so that the resulting statement is true.

1. The solution set of $x < 5$ can be expressed in interval notation as ______________.
2. The solution set of $x \geq 2$ can be expressed in interval notation as ______________.
3. The addition property of inequality states that if $a < b$, then $a + c$ ______________.
4. The positive multiplication property of inequality states that if $a < b$ and c is positive, then ac ______________.
5. The negative multiplication property of inequality states that if $a < b$ and c is negative, then ac ______________.
6. The linear inequality $-3x + 4 > 13$ can be solved by first ______________ from both sides and then ______________ both sides by ______________, which changes the ______________ of the inequality symbol from ______________ to ______________.
7. In solving an inequality, if you eliminate the variable and obtain a false statement such as $0 > 1$, the solution set is ______________.
8. In solving an inequality, if you eliminate the variable and obtain a true statement such as $0 < 1$, the solution set in interval notation is ______________.

7 EXERCISE SET

MyMathLab®

Watch the videos in MyMathLab

Download the MyDashBoard App

Practice Exercises

In Exercises 1–12, graph the solutions of each inequality on a number line.

1. $x > 5$
2. $x > -3$
3. $x < -2$
4. $x < 0$
5. $x \geq -4$
6. $x \geq -6$
7. $x \leq 4.5$
8. $x \leq 7.5$
9. $-2 < x \leq 6$
10. $-3 \leq x < 6$
11. $-1 < x < 3$
12. $-2 \leq x \leq 0$

In Exercises 13–20, express the solution set of each inequality in interval notation and graph the interval.

13. $x \leq 3$
14. $x \leq 5$
15. $x > \frac{5}{2}$
16. $x > \frac{7}{2}$
17. $x \leq 0$
18. $x \leq 1$
19. $x < 4$
20. $x < 5$

Use the addition property of inequality to solve each inequality in Exercises 21–38 and graph the solution set on a number line.

21. $x - 3 > 4$
22. $x + 1 < 6$
23. $x + 4 \leq 10$
24. $x - 5 \geq 2$
25. $y - 2 < 0$
26. $y + 3 \geq 0$
27. $3x + 4 \leq 2x + 7$
28. $2x + 9 \leq x + 2$
29. $5x - 9 < 4x + 7$
30. $3x - 8 < 2x + 11$
31. $7x - 7 > 6x - 3$
32. $8x - 9 > 7x - 3$
33. $x - \frac{2}{3} > \frac{1}{2}$
34. $x - \frac{1}{3} \geq \frac{5}{6}$
35. $y + \frac{7}{8} \leq \frac{1}{2}$
36. $y + \frac{1}{3} \leq \frac{3}{4}$
37. $-15y + 13 > 13 - 16y$
38. $-12y + 17 > 20 - 13y$

Use the multiplication property of inequality to solve each inequality in Exercises 39–56 and graph the solution set on a number line.

39. $\frac{1}{2}x < 4$
40. $\frac{1}{2}x > 3$
41. $\frac{x}{3} > -2$
42. $\frac{x}{4} < -1$
43. $4x < 20$
44. $6x < 18$
45. $3x \geq -21$
46. $7x \geq -56$
47. $-3x < 15$
48. $-7x > 21$
49. $-3x \geq 15$
50. $-7x \leq 21$
51. $-16x > -48$
52. $-20x > -140$
53. $-4y \leq \frac{1}{2}$
54. $-2y \leq \frac{1}{2}$
55. $-x < 4$
56. $-x > -3$

Use both the addition and multiplication properties of inequality to solve each inequality in Exercises 57–80 and graph the solution set on a number line.

57. $2x - 3 > 7$
58. $3x + 2 \leq 14$
59. $3x + 3 < 18$
60. $8x - 4 > 12$
61. $3 - 7x \leq 17$
62. $5 - 3x \geq 20$
63. $-2x - 3 < 3$
64. $-3x + 14 < 5$
65. $5 - x \leq 1$
66. $3 - x \geq -3$
67. $2x - 5 > -x + 6$
68. $6x - 2 \geq 4x + 6$
69. $2y - 5 < 5y - 11$
70. $4y - 7 > 9y - 2$
71. $3(2y - 1) < 9$
72. $4(2y - 1) > 12$
73. $3(x + 1) - 5 < 2x + 1$
74. $4(x + 1) + 2 \geq 3x + 6$
75. $8x + 3 > 3(2x + 1) - x + 5$
76. $7 - 2(x - 4) < 5(1 - 2x)$
77. $\frac{x}{3} - 2 \geq 1$
78. $\frac{x}{4} - 3 \geq 1$
79. $1 - \frac{x}{2} > 4$
80. $1 - \frac{x}{2} < 5$

In Exercises 81–90, solve each inequality.

81. $4x - 4 < 4(x - 5)$
82. $3x - 5 < 3(x - 2)$

83. $x + 3 < x + 7$

84. $x + 4 < x + 10$

85. $7x \leq 7(x - 2)$

86. $3x + 1 \leq 3(x - 2)$

87. $2(x + 3) > 2x + 1$

88. $5(x + 4) > 5x + 10$

89. $5x - 4 \leq 4(x - 1)$

90. $6x - 3 \leq 3(x - 1)$

Practice PLUS

In Exercises 91–94, use properties of inequality to rewrite each inequality so that x is isolated on one side.

91. $3x + a > b$

92. $-2x - a \leq b$

93. $y \leq mx + b$ and $m < 0$

94. $y > mx + b$ and $m > 0$

We know that $|x|$ represents the distance from 0 to x on a number line. In Exercises 95–98, use each sentence to describe all possible locations of x on a number line. Then rewrite the given sentence as an inequality involving $|x|$.

95. The distance from 0 to x on a number line is less than 2.

96. The distance from 0 to x on a number line is less than 3.

97. The distance from 0 to x on a number line is greater than 2.

98. The distance from 0 to x on a number line is greater than 3.

Application Exercises

An online test of English spelling looked at how well people spelled difficult words. The bar graph shows the percentage of people who spelled each word correctly. Let x represent the percentage who spelled a word correctly. In Exercises 99–104, write the word or words described by the given inequality. (Yes, spelling counts!)

Percentage of People Spelling Various Words Correctly

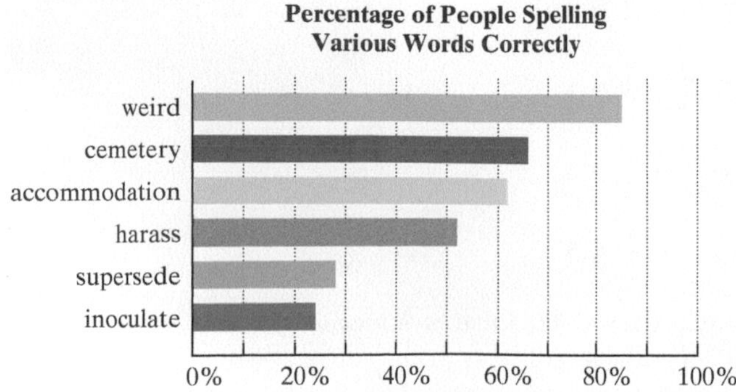

Source: Vivian Cook. *Accomodating Brocolli in the Cemetary or Why Can't Anybody Spell?*. Simon and Schuster, 2004.

99. $x > 55\%$

100. $x \geq 70\%$

101. $x \leq 30\%$

102. $x \leq 50\%$

103. $40\% \leq x < 60\%$

104. $50\% < x \leq 70\%$

The graph shows the decline in the number of stamped letters mailed in the United States from 2000 to 2010. The data shown by the graph can be modeled by

$$S = 55 - 2.5x,$$

where S is the number of stamped letters mailed, in billions, x years after 2000. Use this formula to solve Exercises 105–106.

Number of Stamped Letters Mailed in the United States

Source: U.S. Postal Service

105. Describe how many years after 2000 there will be no more than 15 billion stamped letters mailed in the United States. Which years are included in your description?

106. Describe how many years after 2000 there will be no more than 10 billion stamped letters mailed in the United States. Which years are included in your description?

107. On two examinations, you have grades of 86 and 88. There is an optional final examination, which counts as one grade. You decide to take the final in order to get a course grade of A, meaning a final average of at least 90.
   a. What must you get on the final to earn an A in the course?
   b. By taking the final, if you do poorly, you might risk the B that you have in the course based on the first two exam grades. If your final average is less than 80, you will lose your B in the course. Describe the grades on the final that will cause this to happen.

108. On three examinations, you have grades of 88, 78, and 86. There is still a final examination, which counts as one grade.
   a. In order to get an A, your average must be at least 90. If you get 100 on the final, compute your average and determine if an A in the course is possible.
   b. To earn a B in the course, you must have a final average of at least 80. What must you get on the final to earn a B in the course?

109. A car can be rented from Continental Rental for \$80 per week plus 25 cents for each mile driven. How many miles can you travel if you can spend at most \$400 for the week?

110. A car can be rented from Basic Rental for \$60 per week plus 50 cents for each mile driven. How many miles can you travel if you can spend at most \$600 for the week?

111. An elevator at a construction site has a maximum capacity of 3000 pounds. If the elevator operator weighs 245 pounds and each cement bag weighs 95 pounds, how many bags of cement can be safely lifted on the elevator in one trip?

112. An elevator at a construction site has a maximum capacity of 2800 pounds. If the elevator operator weighs 265 pounds and each cement bag weighs 65 pounds, how many bags of cement can be safely lifted on the elevator in one trip?

Writing in Mathematics

113. When graphing the solutions of an inequality, what is the difference between a parenthesis and a bracket?

114. When solving an inequality, when is it necessary to change the direction of the inequality symbol? Give an example.

115. Describe ways in which solving a linear inequality is similar to solving a linear equation.

116. Describe ways in which solving a linear inequality is different from solving a linear equation.

Critical Thinking Exercises

Make Sense? *In Exercises 117–120, determine whether each statement "makes sense" or "does not make sense" and explain your reasoning.*

117. I prefer interval notation over set-builder notation because it takes less space to write solution sets.

118. I can check inequalities by substituting 0 for the variable: When 0 belongs to the solution set, I should obtain a true statement, and when 0 does not belong to the solution set, I should obtain a false statement.

119. In an inequality such as $5x + 4 < 8x - 5$, I can avoid division by a negative number depending on which side I collect the variable terms and on which side I collect the constant terms.

120. I solved $-2x + 5 \geq 13$ and concluded that -4 is the greatest integer in the solution set.

In Exercises 121–124, determine whether each statement is true or false. If the statement is false, make the necessary change(s) to produce a true statement.

121. The inequality $x - 3 > 0$ is equivalent to $x < 3$.

122. The statement "x is at most 5" is written $x < 5$.

123. The inequality $-4x < -20$ is equivalent to $x > -5$.

124. The statement "the sum of x and 6% of x is at least 80" is modeled by $x + 0.06x \geq 80$.

125. A car can be rented from Basic Rental for \$260 per week with no extra charge for mileage. Continental charges \$80 per week plus 25 cents for each mile driven to rent the same car. How many miles should be driven in a week to make the rental cost for Basic Rental a better deal than Continental's?

126. Membership in a fitness club costs \$500 yearly plus \$1 per hour spent working out. A competing club charges \$440 yearly plus \$1.75 per hour for use of their equipment. How many hours must a person work out yearly to make membership in the first club cheaper than membership in the second club?

Technology Exercises

Solve each inequality in Exercises 127–128. Use a calculator to help with the arithmetic.

127. $1.45 - 7.23x > -1.442$

128. $126.8 - 9.4y \leq 4.8y + 34.5$

Review Exercises

129. 8 is 40% of what number? (Section 4, Example 6)

130. The length of a rectangle exceeds the width by 5 inches. The perimeter is 34 inches. What are the rectangle's dimensions? (Section 5, Example 5)

131. Solve and check: $5x + 16 = 3(x + 8)$. (Section 3, Example 2)

Preview Exercises

132. Is $x - 4y = 14$ a true statement for $x = 2$ and $y = -3$?

133. Is $x - 4y = 14$ a true statement for $x = 12$ and $y = 1$?

134. If $y = \frac{2}{3}x + 1$, find the value of y for $x = -6$.

GROUP PROJECT

One of the best ways to learn how to *solve* a word problem in algebra is to *design* word problems of your own. Creating a word problem makes you very aware of precisely how much information is needed to solve the problem. You must also focus on the best way to present information to a reader and on how much information to give. As you write your problem, you gain skills that will help you solve problems created by others.

The group should design five different word problems that can be solved using an algebraic equation. All of the problems should be on different topics. For example, the group should not have more than one problem on finding a number. The group should turn in both the problems and their algebraic solutions.

Summary

Definitions and Concepts	Examples
Section 1 The Addition Property of Equality	
A linear equation in one variable can be written in the form $ax + b = c$, where a is not zero.	$3x + 7 = 9$ is a linear equation.
Equivalent equations have the same solution.	$2x - 4 = 6$, $2x = 10$, and $x = 5$ are equivalent equations.
The Addition Property of Equality Adding the same number (or algebraic expression) to both sides of an equation or subtracting the same number (or algebraic expression) from both sides of an equation does not change its solution.	• $x - 3 = 8$ $x - 3 + 3 = 8 + 3$ $x = 11$ • $x + 4 = 10$ $x + 4 - 4 = 10 - 4$ $x = 6$
Section 2 The Multiplication Property of Equality	
The Multiplication Property of Equality Multiplying both sides of an equation or dividing both sides of an equation by the same nonzero real number (or algebraic expression) does not change the solution.	• $\frac{x}{-5} = 6$ $-5\left(\frac{x}{-5}\right) = -5(6)$ $x = -30$ • $-50 = -5y$ $\frac{-50}{-5} = \frac{-5y}{-5}$ $10 = y$
Equations and Coefficients of −1 If $-x = c$, multiply both sides by -1 to solve for x. The solution is the opposite, or additive inverse, of c.	$-x = -12$ $(-1)(-x) = (-1)(-12)$ $x = 12$

Definitions and Concepts	Examples

Section 2 The Multiplication Property of Equality (continued)

Using the Addition and Multiplication Properties

If an equation does not contain fractions,

- Use the addition property to isolate the variable term.
- Use the multiplication property to isolate the variable.

$$\begin{aligned} -2x - 5 &= 11 \\ -2x - 5 + 5 &= 11 + 5 \\ -2x &= 16 \\ \frac{-2x}{-2} &= \frac{16}{-2} \\ x &= -8 \end{aligned}$$

Section 3 Solving Linear Equations

Solving a Linear Equation

1. Simplify each side.

Solve: $7 - 4(x - 1) = x + 1.$

$$\begin{aligned} 7 - 4x + 4 &= x + 1 \\ -4x + 11 &= x + 1 \end{aligned}$$

2. Collect all the variable terms on one side and all the constant terms on the other side.

$$\begin{aligned} -4x - x + 11 &= x - x + 1 \\ -5x + 11 &= 1 \\ -5x + 11 - 11 &= 1 - 11 \\ -5x &= -10 \end{aligned}$$

3. Isolate the variable and solve. (If the variable is eliminated and a false statement results, the inconsistent equation has no solution. If a true statement results, all real numbers are solutions of the identity.)

$$\begin{aligned} \frac{-5x}{-5} &= \frac{-10}{-5} \\ x &= 2 \end{aligned}$$

4. Check the proposed solution in the original equation.

$$\begin{aligned} 7 - 4(x - 1) &= x + 1 \\ 7 - 4(2 - 1) &\stackrel{?}{=} 2 + 1 \\ 7 - 4(1) &\stackrel{?}{=} 2 + 1 \\ 7 - 4 &\stackrel{?}{=} 2 + 1 \\ 3 &= 3, \text{ true} \end{aligned}$$

The solution is 2, or the solution set is $\{2\}$.

Equations Containing Fractions

Multiply both sides (all terms) by the least common denominator. This clears the equation of fractions.

Solve: $\frac{x}{5} + \frac{1}{2} = \frac{x}{2} - 1.$

$$\begin{aligned} 10\left(\frac{x}{5} + \frac{1}{2}\right) &= 10\left(\frac{x}{2} - 1\right) \\ 10\cdot\frac{x}{5} + 10\cdot\frac{1}{2} &= 10\cdot\frac{x}{2} - 10\cdot 1 \\ 2x + 5 &= 5x - 10 \\ -3x &= -15 \\ x &= 5 \end{aligned}$$

The solution is 5, or the solution set is $\{5\}$.

Equations Containing Decimals

An equation may be cleared of decimals by multiplying every term on both sides by a power of 10. The exponent on 10 will equal the greatest number of decimal places in the equation.

Solve: $1.4(x - 5) = 3x - 3.8$

$$\begin{aligned} 1.4x - 7 &= 3x - 3.8 \\ 10(1.4x) - 10(7) &= 10(3x) - 10(3.8) \\ 14x - 70 &= 30x - 38 \\ -16x &= 32 \\ x &= -2 \end{aligned}$$

The solution is -2, or the solution set is $\{-2\}$.

Definitions and Concepts	Examples

Section 3 Solving Linear Equations (continued)

Inconsistent equations with no solution (solution set: $\varnothing$) result in false statements in the solution process. Identities, true for every real number (solution set: $\{x \mid x \text{ is a real number}\}$) result in true statements in the solution process.

Solve: $3x + 2 = 3(x + 5).$

$$\begin{aligned} 3x + 2 &= 3x + 15 \\ 3x + 2 - 3x &= 3x + 15 - 3x \\ 2 &= 15 \quad \text{(false)} \end{aligned}$$

No solution: $\varnothing$

Solve: $2(x + 4) = x + x + 8.$

$$\begin{aligned} 2x + 8 &= 2x + 8 \\ 2x + 8 - 2x &= 2x + 8 - 2x \\ 8 &= 8 \quad \text{(true)} \end{aligned}$$

$\{x \mid x \text{ is a real number}\}$

Section 4 Formulas and Percents

To solve a formula for one of its variables, use the steps for solving a linear equation and isolate the specified variable on one side of the equation.

Solve for l: $w = \dfrac{P - 2l}{2}.$

$$\begin{aligned} 2w &= 2\left(\frac{P - 2l}{2}\right) \\ 2w &= P - 2l \\ 2w - P &= P - P - 2l \\ 2w - P &= -2l \\ \frac{2w - P}{-2} &= \frac{-2l}{-2} \\ \frac{2w - P}{-2} &= l \end{aligned}$$

A Formula Involving Percent

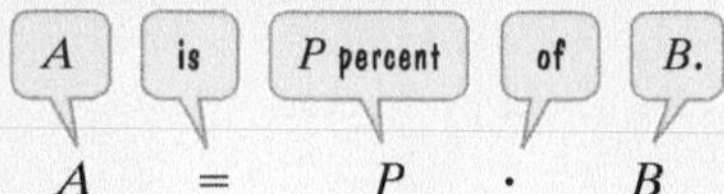

$A \quad = \quad P \quad \cdot \quad B$

In the formula $A = PB$, P is expressed as a decimal.

- What is 5% of 20?

  $A = 0.05 \cdot 20$

  $A = 1$

  Thus, 1 is 5% of 20.

- 6 is 30% of what?

  $6 = 0.3 \cdot B$

  $\dfrac{6}{0.3} = B$

  $20 = B$

  Thus, 6 is 30% of 20.

- 33 is what percent of 75?

  $33 = P \cdot 75$

  $\dfrac{33}{75} = P$

  $P = 0.44 = 44\%$

  Thus, 33 is 44% of 75.

Definitions and Concepts	Examples

Section 5 An Introduction to Problem Solving

Strategy for Solving Word Problems

Step 1. Let x represent one of the quantities.

Step 2. Represent other unknown quantities in terms of x.

Step 3. Write an equation that models the conditions.

Step 4. Solve the equation and answer the question.

Step 5. Check the proposed solution in the original wording of the problem.

The length of a rectangle exceeds the width by 3 inches. The perimeter is 26 inches. What are the rectangle's dimensions?

Let $x =$ the width.

$x + 3 =$ the length

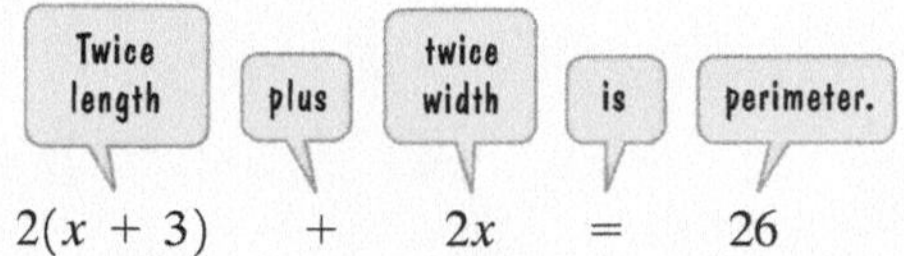

$$2(x + 3) \quad + \quad 2x \quad = \quad 26$$

$$2(x + 3) + 2x = 26$$

$$2x + 6 + 2x = 26$$

$$4x + 6 = 26$$

$$4x = 20$$

$$x = 5$$

The width (x) is 5 inches and the length ($x + 3$) is $5 + 3$, or 8 inches.

$$\text{Perimeter} = 2(5 \text{ in.}) + 2(8 \text{ in.})$$

$$= 10 \text{ in.} + 16 \text{ in.} = 26 \text{ in.}$$

This checks with the given perimeter.

Section 6 Problem Solving in Geometry

Solving geometry problems often requires using basic geometric formulas. Formulas for perimeter, area, circumference, and volume are given in **Table 3**, **Table 4**, and **Table 5** in Section 6.

A sailboat's triangular sail has an area of 24 ft^2 and a base of 8 ft. Find its height.

$$A = \frac{1}{2}bh$$

$$24 = \frac{1}{2}(8)h$$

$$24 = 4h$$

$$6 = h$$

The sail's height is 6 ft.

Definitions and Concepts	Examples

Section 6 Problem Solving in Geometry (continued)

The sum of the measures of the three angles of any triangle is 180°.

In a triangle, the first angle measures 3 times the second and the third measures 40° less than the second. Find each angle's measure.

$$\text{Second angle} = x$$
$$\text{First angle} = 3x$$
$$\text{Third angle} = x - 40$$

Sum of measures is 180°.

$$x + 3x + (x - 40) = 180$$
$$5x - 40 = 180$$
$$5x = 220$$
$$x = 44$$

The angles measure $x = 44$, $3x = 3 \cdot 44 = 132$, and $x - 40 = 44 - 40 = 4$.

The angles measure 44°, 132°, and 4°.

Two complementary angles have measures whose sum is 90°. Two supplementary angles have measures whose sum is 180°. If an angle measures x, its complement measures $90 - x$, and its supplement measures $180 - x$.

An angle measures five times its complement. Find the angle's measure.

$$x = \text{angle's measure}$$
$$90 - x = \text{measure of complement}$$
$$x = 5(90 - x)$$
$$x = 450 - 5x$$
$$6x = 450$$
$$x = 75$$

The angle measures 75°.

Section 7 Solving Linear Inequalities

A linear inequality in one variable can be written in one of these forms:

$$ax + b < c \qquad ax + b \le c.$$
$$ax + b > c \qquad ax + b \ge c.$$

$3x + 6 > 12$ is a linear inequality.

Graphs of solutions to linear inequalities are shown on a number line by shading all points representing numbers that are solutions. Square brackets, [ ], indicate endpoints that are solutions. Parentheses, ( ), indicate endpoints that are not solutions.

- Graph the solutions of $x < 4$.

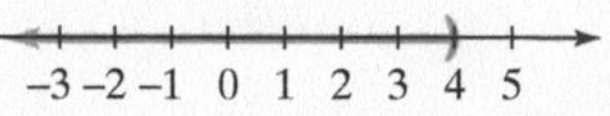

- Graph the solutions of $-2 < x \le 1$.

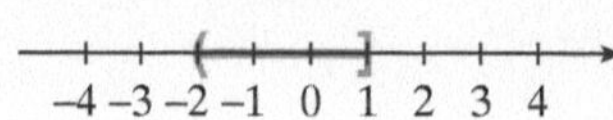

Definitions and Concepts	Examples

Section 7 Solving Linear Inequalities (continued)

Solutions of inequalities can be expressed in interval notation or set-builder notation.

Inequality	Interval Notation	Set-Builder Notation	Graph
$x > b$	(b, ∞)	$\{x \mid x > b\}$	a b
$x \leq a$	$(-\infty, a]$	$\{x \mid x \leq a\}$	a b

Express the solution set in interval notation and graph the interval:

- $x \leq 1$
  $(-\infty, 1]$
  −4 −3 −2 −1 0 1 2 3 4
- $x > -2$
  $(-2, \infty)$
  −4 −3 −2 −1 0 1 2 3 4

The Addition Property of Inequality

Adding the same number to both sides of an inequality or subtracting the same number from both sides of an inequality does not change the solutions.

$$x + 3 < 8$$
$$x + 3 - 3 < 8 - 3$$
$$x < 5$$

The Positive Multiplication Property of Inequality

Multiplying or dividing both sides of an inequality by the same positive number does not change the solutions.

$$\frac{x}{6} \geq 5$$
$$6 \cdot \frac{x}{6} \geq 6 \cdot 5$$
$$x \geq 30$$

The Negative Multiplication Property of Inequality

Multiplying or dividing both sides of an inequality by the same negative number and reversing the direction of the inequality sign does not change the solutions.

$$-3x \leq 12$$
$$\frac{-3x}{-3} \geq \frac{12}{-3}$$
$$x \geq -4$$

Solving Linear Inequalities

Use the procedure for solving linear equations. When multiplying or dividing by a negative number, reverse the direction of the inequality symbol. Express the solution set in interval or set-builder notation, and graph the set on a number line. If the variable is eliminated and a false statement results, the inequality has no solution. The solution set is ∅, the empty set. If a true statement results, the solution is the set of all real numbers: $(-\infty, \infty)$ or $\{x \mid x \text{ is a real number}\}$.

Solve:
$$x + 4 \geq 6x - 16$$
$$x + 4 - 6x \geq 6x - 16 - 6x$$
$$-5x + 4 \geq -16$$
$$-5x + 4 - 4 \geq -16 - 4$$
$$-5x \geq -20$$
$$\frac{-5x}{-5} \leq \frac{-20}{-5}$$
$$x \leq 4$$

Solution set: $(-\infty, 4]$ or $\{x \mid x \leq 4\}$

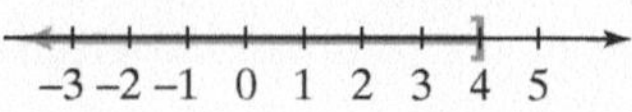

CHAPTER REVIEW EXERCISES

1 *Solve each equation in Exercises 1–5 using the addition property of equality. Be sure to check proposed solutions.*

1. $x - 10 = 22$

2. $-14 = y + 8$

3. $7z - 3 = 6z + 9$

4. $4(x + 3) = 3x - 10$

5. $6x - 3x - 9 + 1 = -5x + 7x - 3$

2 *Solve each equation in Exercises 6–13 using the multiplication property of equality. Be sure to check proposed solutions.*

6. $\frac{x}{8} = 10$

7. $\frac{y}{-8} = 7$

8. $7z = 77$

9. $-36 = -9y$

10. $\frac{3}{5}x = -9$

11. $30 = -\frac{5}{2}y$

12. $-x = 25$

13. $\frac{-x}{10} = -1$

Solve each equation in Exercises 14–18 using both the addition and multiplication properties of equality. Check proposed solutions.

14. $4x + 9 = 33$

15. $-3y - 2 = 13$

16. $5z + 20 = 3z$

17. $5x - 3 = x + 5$

18. $3 - 2x = 9 - 8x$

19. The percentage of tax returns filed electronically in the United States exceeded 50% for the first time in 2005. The bar graph shows the percentage of electronically filed tax returns from 2005 through 2010.

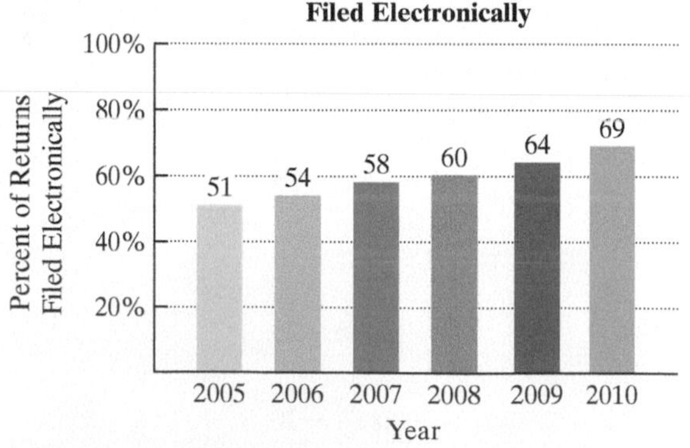

Source: IRS

The mathematical model

$$p = 3.5n + 51$$

describes the percentage of U.S. tax returns filed electronically, p, n years after 2005.

a. Does the formula underestimate or overestimate the percentage of tax returns filed electronically in 2009? By how much?

b. If trends shown by the formula continue, when will 93% of tax returns be filed electronically?

3 *Solve and check each equation in Exercises 20–30.*

20. $5x + 9 - 7x + 6 = x + 18$

21. $3(x + 4) = 5x - 12$

22. $1 - 2(6 - y) = 3y + 2$

23. $2(x - 4) + 3(x + 5) = 2x - 2$

24. $-2(y - 4) - (3y - 2) = -2 - (6y - 2)$

25. $\frac{2x}{3} = \frac{x}{6} + 1$

26. $\frac{x}{2} - \frac{1}{10} = \frac{x}{5} + \frac{1}{2}$

27. $0.5x + 8.75 = 13.25$

28. $0.1(x - 3) = 1.1 - 0.25x$

29. $3(8x - 1) = 6(5 + 4x)$

30. $4(2x - 3) + 4 = 8x - 8$

31. The formula $H = 0.7(220 - a)$ can be used to determine target heart rate during exercise, H, in beats per minute, by a person of age a. If the target heart rate is 133 beats per minute, how old is that person?

4 *In Exercises 32–36, solve each formula for the specified variable.*

32. $I = Pr$ for r

33. $V = \frac{1}{3}Bh$ for h

34. $P = 2l + 2w$ for w

35. $A = \frac{B + C}{2}$ for B

36. $T = D + pm$ for m

37. What is 8% of 120?

38. 90 is 45% of what?

39. 36 is what percent of 75?

40. If 6 is increased to 12, the increase is what percent of the original number?

41. If 5 is decreased to 3, the decrease is what percent of the original number?

42. A college that had 40 students for each lecture course increased the number to 45 students. What is the percent increase in the number of students in a lecture course?

43. Consider the following statement:

> My portfolio fell 10% last year, but then it rose 10% this year, so at least I recouped my losses.

Is this statement true? In particular, suppose you invested \$10,000 in the stock market last year. How much money would be left in your portfolio with a 10% fall and then a 10% rise? If there is a loss, what is the percent decrease in your portfolio?

44. The radius is one of two bones that connect the elbow and the wrist. The formula $r = \frac{h}{7}$ models the length of a woman's radius, r, in inches, and her height, h, in inches.

a. Solve the formula for h.

b. Use the formula in part (a) to find a woman's height if her radius is 9 inches long.

45. Every day, the average U.S. household uses 91 gallons of water flushing toilets. The circle graph shows that this represents 26% of the total number of gallons of water used per day. How many gallons of water does the average U.S. household use per day?

Where United States Households Use Water

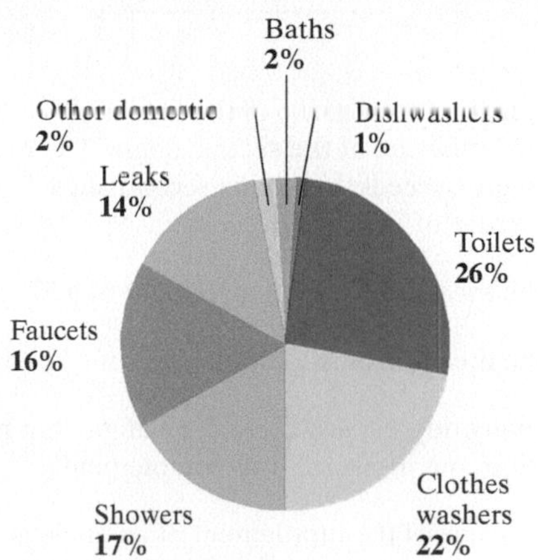

Source: American Water Works Association

5 *In Exercises 46–53, use the five-step strategy to solve each problem.*

46. Six times a number, decreased by 20, is four times the number. Find the number.

47. In 2010, the wealthiest Americans were Bill Gates and Warren Buffett. At that time, Gates's net worth exceeded that of Buffett's by $9 billion. Combined, the two men were worth $99 billion. Determine each man's net worth in 2010. (*Source: Forbes*)

48. Two pages that face each other in a book have 93 as the sum of their page numbers. What are the page numbers?

49. The graph shows the gender breakdown of the U.S. population at each end of the age spectrum.

Gender Breakdown of the American Population

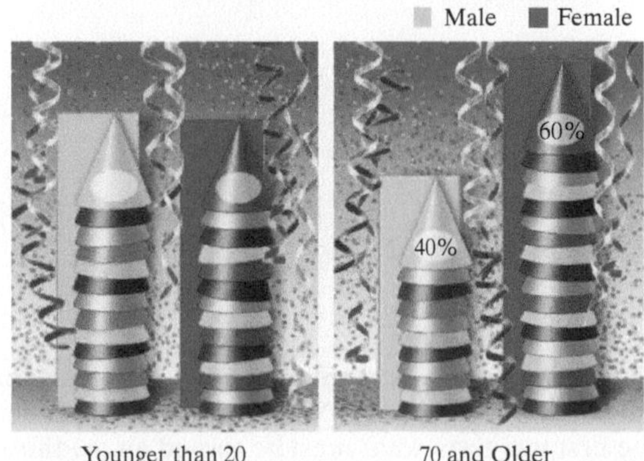

Source: U.S. Census Bureau

For Americans under 20, the percentage of males is greater than the percentage of females and these percents are consecutive odd integers. What percentage of Americans younger than 20 are females and what percentage are males?

50. In 2001, the U.S. defense budget was $316 billion, increasing by approximately $42 billion per year for the period shown by the bar graph. If this trend continues, in how many years after 2001 will the defense budget be $904 billion? In which year will that be?

U.S. Defense Budget

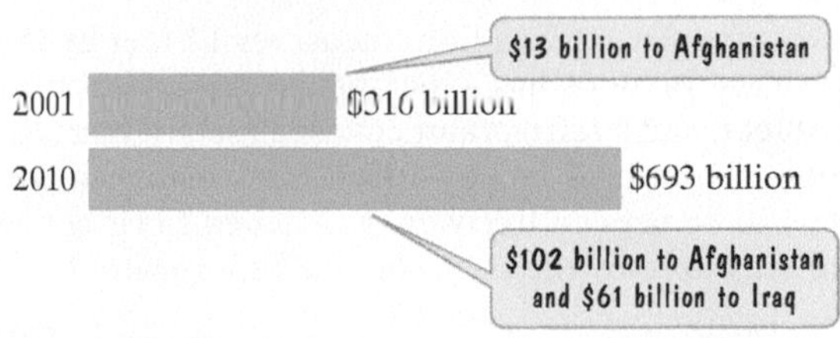

Source: Office of Management and Budget, www.whitehouse.gov <http://www.whitehouse.gov>

51. A bank's total monthly charge for a checking account is $6 plus $0.05 per check. If your total monthly charge is $6.90, how many checks did you write during that month?

52. A rectangular field is three times as long as it is wide. If the perimeter of the field is 400 yards, what are the field's dimensions?

53. After a 25% reduction, you purchase a table for $180. What was the table's price before the reduction?

6 *Use a formula for area to find the area of each figure in Exercises 54–57.*

54.

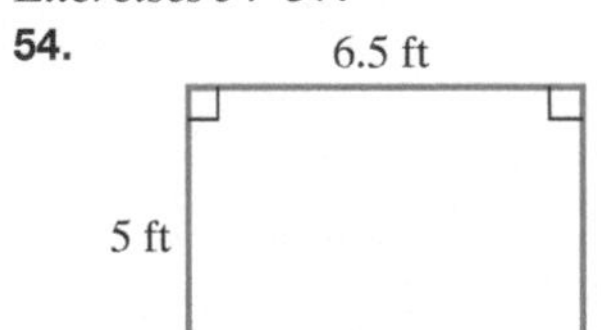

55.

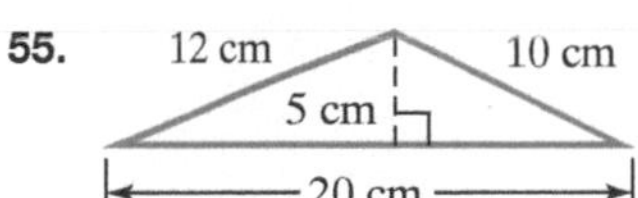

56.

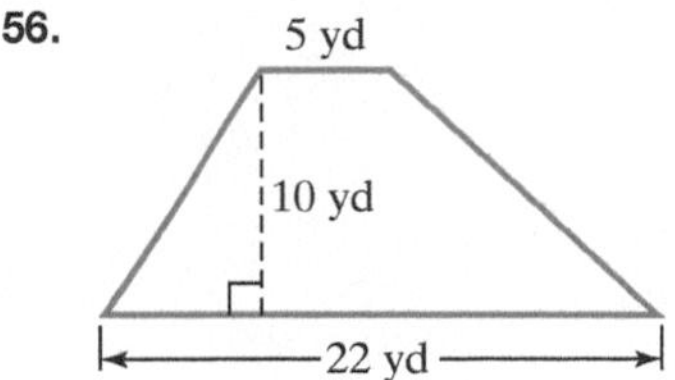

57.

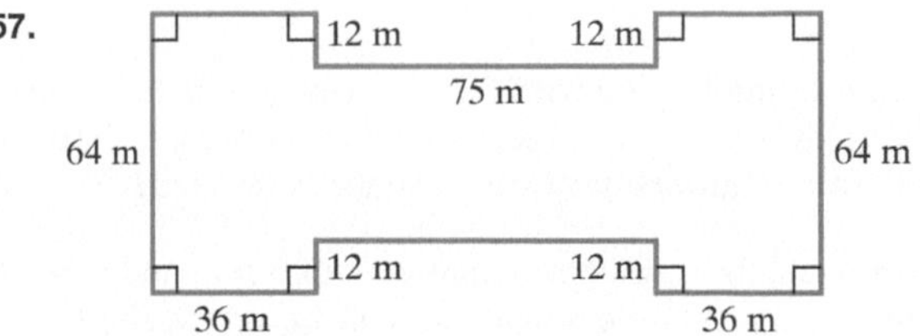

58. Find the circumference and the area of a circle with a diameter of 20 meters. Round answers to the nearest whole number.

59. A sailboat has a triangular sail with an area of 42 square feet and a base that measures 14 feet. Find the height of the sail.

60. A rectangular kitchen floor measures 12 feet by 15 feet. A stove on the floor has a rectangular base measuring 3 feet by 4 feet, and a refrigerator covers a rectangular area of the floor measuring 3 feet by 4 feet. How many square feet of tile will be needed to cover the kitchen floor not counting the area used by the stove and the refrigerator?

61. A yard that is to be covered with mats of grass is shaped like a trapezoid. The bases are 80 feet and 100 feet, and the height is 60 feet. What is the cost of putting the grass mats on the yard if the landscaper charges \$0.35 per square foot?

62. Which one of the following is a better buy: a medium pizza with a 14-inch diameter for \$6.00 or two small pizzas, each with an 8-inch diameter, for \$6.00?

Use a formula for volume to find the volume of each figure in Exercises 63–65. Where applicable, express answers in terms of π. Then round to the nearest whole number.

63.

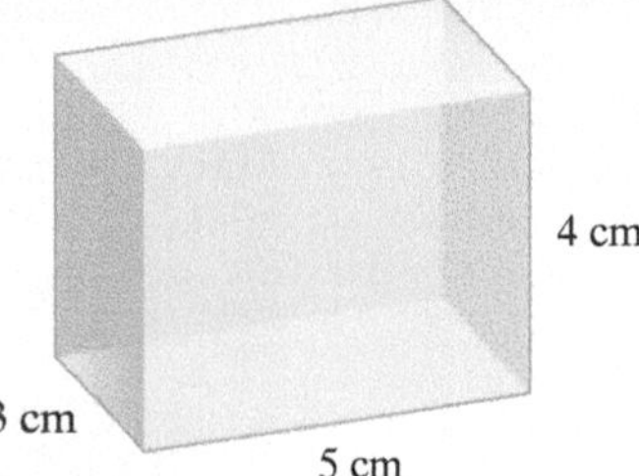

64.

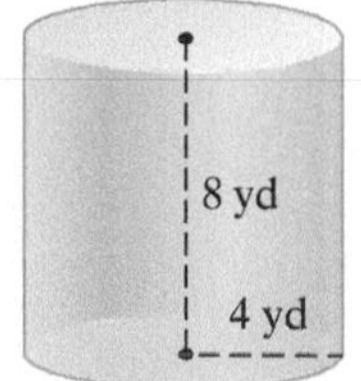

65.

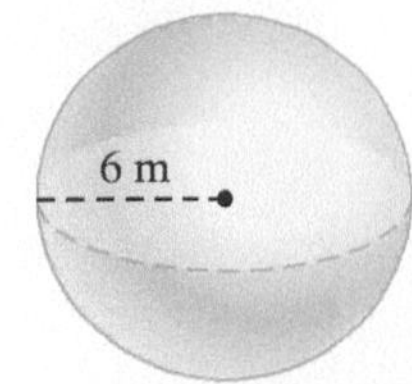

66. A train is being loaded with freight containers. Each box is 8 meters long, 4 meters wide, and 3 meters high. If there are 50 freight containers, how much space is needed?

67. A cylindrical fish tank has a diameter of 6 feet and a height of 3 feet. How many tropical fish can be put in the tank if each fish needs 5 cubic feet of water?

68. Find the measure of each angle of the triangle shown in the figure.

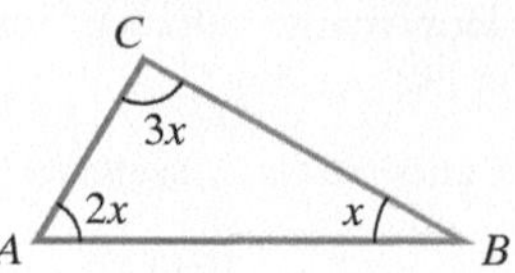

69. In a triangle, the measure of the first angle is 15° more than twice the measure of the second angle. The measure of the third angle exceeds that of the second angle by 25°. What is the measure of each angle?

70. Find the measure of the complement of a 57° angle.

71. Find the measure of the supplement of a 75° angle.

72. How many degrees are there in an angle that measures 25° more than the measure of its complement?

73. The measure of the supplement of an angle is 45° less than four times the measure of the angle. Find the measure of the angle and its supplement.

7 *In Exercises 74–75, graph the solution of each inequality on a number line.*

74. $x < -1$

75. $-2 < x \le 4$

In Exercises 76–77, express the solution set of each inequality in interval notation and graph the interval.

76. $x \ge \frac{3}{2}$

77. $x < 0$

In Exercises 78–85, solve each inequality and graph the solution set on a number line. It is not necessary to provide graphs if the inequality has no solution or is true for all real numbers.

78. $2x - 5 < 3$

79. $\frac{x}{2} > -4$

80. $3 - 5x \le 18$

81. $4x + 6 < 5x$

82. $6x - 10 \ge 2(x + 3)$

83. $4x + 3(2x - 7) \le x - 3$

84. $2(2x + 4) > 4(x + 2) - 6$

85. $-2(x - 4) \le 3x + 1 - 5x$

86. To pass a course, a student must have an average on three examinations of at least 60. If a student scores 42 and 74 on the first two tests, what must be earned on the third test to pass the course?

87. You can spend at most \$2000 for a catered party. The caterer charges a setup fee of \$350 and \$55 per person. How many people can you invite while staying within your budget?

CHAPTER TEST

CHAPTER Test Prep VIDEOS

Step-by-step test solutions are found on the Chapter Test Prep Videos available in MyMathLab® or on YouTube (search "BlitzerIntroAlg" and click on "Channels").

In Exercises 1–7, solve each equation.

1. $4x - 5 = 13$
2. $12x + 4 = 7x - 21$
3. $8 - 5(x - 2) = x + 26$
4. $3(2y - 4) = 9 - 3(y + 1)$
5. $\frac{3}{4}x = -15$
6. $\frac{x}{10} + \frac{1}{3} = \frac{x}{5} + \frac{1}{2}$
7. $9.2x - 80.1 = 21.3x - 19.6$
8. The formula $P = 2.4x + 180$ models U.S. population, P, in millions x years after 1960. How many years after 1960 is the U.S. population expected to reach 324 million? In which year is this expected to occur?

In Exercises 9–10, solve each formula for the specified variable.

9. $V = \pi r^2 h$ for h
10. $l = \frac{P - 2w}{2}$ for w
11. What is 6% of 140?
12. 120 is 80% of what?
13. 12 is what percent of 240?

In Exercises 14–18, solve each problem.

14. The product of 5 and a number, decreased by 9, is 306. What is the number?
15. Compared with other major countries, American employees have less vacation time. The bar graph shows the average number of vacation days per person for selected countries.

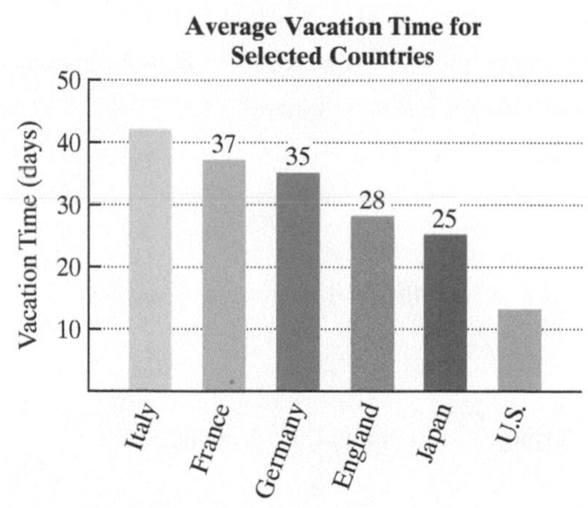

Source: World Development Indicators

The average time Italians spend on vacation exceeds the average American vacation time by 29 days. The combined average vacation time for Americans and Italians is 55 days. On average, how many days do Americans spend on vacation and how many days do Italians spend on vacation?

16. A phone plan has a monthly fee of \$15.00 and a rate of \$0.05 per minute. How many calling minutes can you use in a month for a total cost, including the \$15.00, of \$45.00?
17. A rectangular field is twice as long as it is wide. If the perimeter of the field is 450 yards, what are the field's dimensions?
18. After a 20% reduction, you purchase a new Stephen King novel for \$28. What was the book's price before the reduction?

In Exercises 19–21, find the area of each figure.

19.

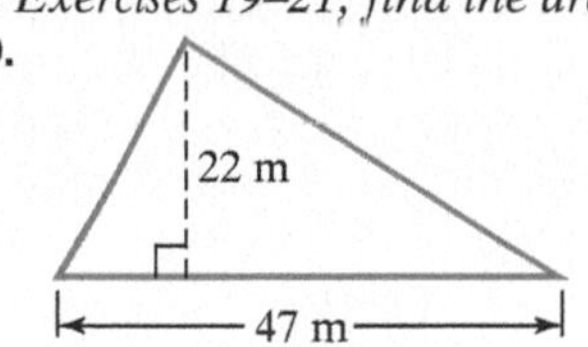

20.

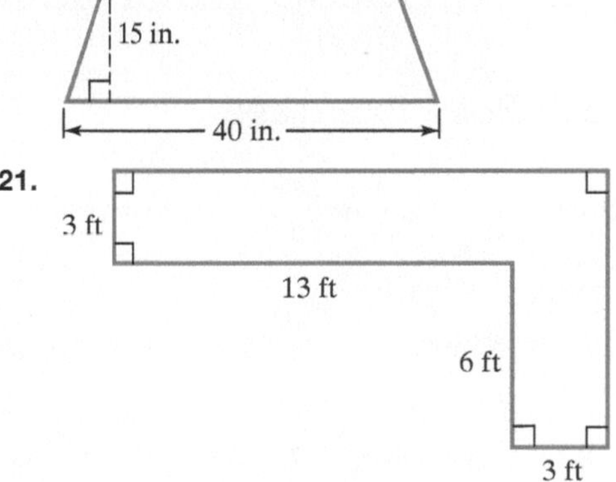

21.

3 ft
13 ft
6 ft
3 ft

In Exercises 22–23, find the volume of each figure. Where applicable, express answers in terms of π. Then round to the nearest whole number.

22.

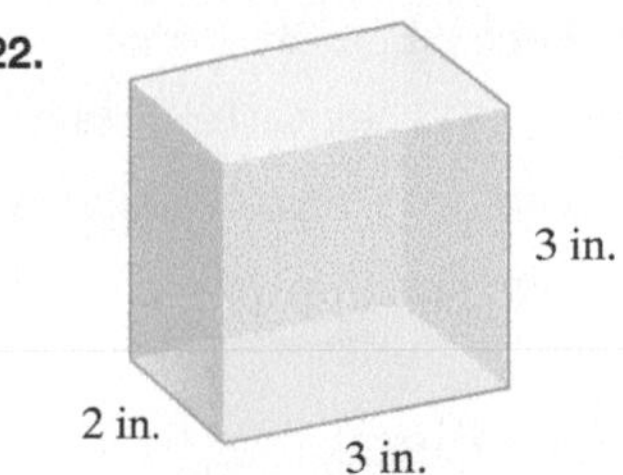

23.

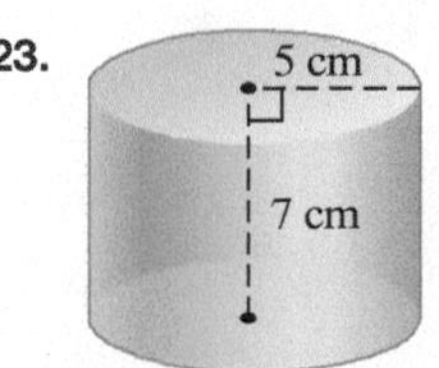

24. What will it cost to cover a rectangular floor measuring 40 feet by 50 feet with square tiles that measure 2 feet on each side if a package of 10 tiles costs \$13 per package?
25. A sailboat has a triangular sail with an area of 56 square feet and a base that measures 8 feet. Find the height of the sail.
26. In a triangle, the measure of the first angle is three times that of the second angle. The measure of the third angle is 30° less than the measure of the second angle. What is the measure of each angle?

27. How many degrees are there in an angle that measures 16° more than the measure of its complement?

In Exercises 28–29, express the solution set of each inequality in interval notation and graph the interval.

28. $x > -2$ **29.** $x \leq 3$

Solve each inequality in Exercises 30–32 and graph the solution set on a number line.

30. $\frac{x}{2} < -3$

31. $6 - 9x \geq 33$

32. $4x - 2 > 2(x + 6)$

33. A student has grades on three examinations of 76, 80, and 72. What must the student earn on a fourth examination to have an average of at least 80?

34. The length of a rectangle is 20 inches. For what widths is the perimeter greater than 56 inches?

Answers to Selected Exercises

Section 1 Check Point Exercises

1. 17 or {17} **2.** 2.29 or {2.29} **3.** $\frac{1}{4}$ or $\left\{\frac{1}{4}\right\}$ **4.** 13 or {13} **5.** 12 or {12} **6.** 11 or {11} **7.** 2100 words

Concept and Vocabulary Check

1. solving **2.** linear **3.** equivalent **4.** $b + c$ **5.** subtract; solution **6.** adding 7 **7.** subtracting $6x$

Exercise Set 1

1. linear **3.** not linear **5.** not linear **7.** linear **9.** not linear **11.** 23 or {23} **13.** −20 or {−20} **15.** −16 or {−16} **17.** −12 or {−12} **19.** 4 or {4} **21.** −11 or {−11} **23.** 2 or {2} **25.** $-\frac{17}{12}$ or $\left\{-\frac{17}{12}\right\}$ **27.** $\frac{21}{4}$ or $\left\{\frac{21}{4}\right\}$ **29.** $-\frac{11}{20}$ or $\left\{-\frac{11}{20}\right\}$ **31.** 4.3 or {4.3} **33.** $-\frac{21}{4}$ or $\left\{-\frac{21}{4}\right\}$ **35.** 18 or {18} **37.** $\frac{9}{10}$ or $\left\{\frac{9}{10}\right\}$ **39.** −310 or {−310} **41.** 4.3 or {4.3} **43.** 0 or {0} **45.** 11 or {11} **47.** 5 or {5} **49.** −13 or {−13} **51.** 6 or {6} **53.** −12 or {−12} **55.** $x = \triangle + \square$ **57.** $\triangle - \square = x$ **59.** $x - 12 = -2$; 10 **61.** $\frac{2}{5}x - 8 = \frac{7}{5}x$; −8 **63.** \$1700 **65.** \$10,384; underestimates by \$307 **67. a.** 52 ± 1 **b.** 51.4; very well **73.** does not make sense **75.** makes sense **77.** false **79.** true **81.** Answers will vary; example: $x - 100 = -101$. **83.** 2.7529 or {2.7529} **84.** $\frac{9}{x} - 4x$ **85.** −12 **86.** $6 - 9x$ **87.** x **88.** y **89.** yes

Section 2 Check Point Exercises

1. 36 or {36} **2. a.** 21 or {21} **b.** −4 or {−4} **c.** −3.1 or {−3.1} **3. a.** 24 or {24} **b.** −16 or {−16} **4. a.** −5 or {−5} **b.** 3 or {3} **5.** 6 or {6} **6.** −10 or {−10} **7.** 6 or {6} **8. a.** overestimates by \$7 **b.** 2017

Concept and Vocabulary Check

1. bc **2.** divide **3.** multiplying; 7 **4.** dividing/multiplying; $-8/-\frac{1}{8}$ **5.** multiplying; $\frac{5}{3}$ **6.** multiplying/dividing; −1 **7.** subtracting 2; dividing; 5

Exercise Set 2

1. 30 or {30} **3.** −33 or {−33} **5.** 7 or {7} **7.** −9 or {−9} **9.** $-\frac{7}{2}$ or $\left\{-\frac{7}{2}\right\}$ **11.** 6 or {6} **13.** $-\frac{3}{4}$ or $\left\{-\frac{3}{4}\right\}$ **15.** 0 or {0} **17.** 18 or {18} **19.** −8 or {−8} **21.** −17 or {−17} **23.** 47 or {47} **25.** 45 or {45} **27.** −5 or {−5} **29.** 5 or {5} **31.** 6 or {6} **33.** −1 or {−1} **35.** −2 or {−2} **37.** $\frac{9}{4}$ or $\left\{\frac{9}{4}\right\}$ **39.** −6 or {−6} **41.** −3 or {−3} **43.** −3 or {−3} **45.** 4 or {4} **47.** $-\frac{3}{2}$ or $\left\{-\frac{3}{2}\right\}$ **49.** 2 or {2} **51.** −4 or {−4} **53.** −6 or {−6} **55.** $x = \square \cdot \triangle$ **57.** $-\triangle = x$ **59.** $6x = 10$; $\frac{5}{3}$ **61.** $\frac{x}{-9} = 5$; −45 **63.** $4x - 8 = 56$; 16 **65.** $-3x + 15 = -6$; 7 **67.** 10 sec **69.** 1502.2 mph **71. a.** underestimates by \$40 **b.** 2029 **77.** does not make sense **79.** does not make sense **81.** false **83.** true **85.** Answers will vary; example: $\frac{5}{4}x = -20$. **87.** 6.5 or {6.5} **88.** 100 **89.** −100 **90.** 3 **91.** $-3x + 7$ **92.** yes **93.** $2x - 78$

Section 3 Check Point Exercises

1. 6 or {6} **2.** 2 or {2} **3.** 5 or {5} **4.** −2 or {−2} **5.** −15 or {−15} **6.** no solution or ∅ **7.** all real numbers or {$x|x$ is a real number} **8.** 3.7; shown as the point whose corresponding value on the vertical axis is 10 and whose value on the horizontal axis is 3.7

Concept and Vocabulary Check

1. simplifying each side; combining like terms **2.** 30 **3.** 100 **4.** inconsistent **5.** identity **6.** inconsistent **7.** identity

Exercise Set 3

1. 3 or {3} **3.** −1 or {−1} **5.** 4 or {4} **7.** 4 or {4} **9.** $\frac{7}{2}$ or $\left\{\frac{7}{2}\right\}$ **11.** −3 or {−3} **13.** 6 or {6} **15.** 8 or {8} **17.** 4 or {4} **19.** 1 or {1} **21.** −4 or {−4} **23.** 5 or {5} **25.** 6 or {6} **27.** 1 or {1} **29.** −57 or {−57} **31.** −10 or {−10} **33.** 18 or {18} **35.** $\frac{7}{4}$ or $\left\{\frac{7}{4}\right\}$ **37.** 1 or {1} **39.** 24 or {24} **41.** −6 or {−6} **43.** 20 or {20} **45.** −7 or {−7} **47.** 9 or {9} **49.** 30 or {30} **51.** 25 or {25} **53.** 20 or {20} **55.** −1 or {−1} **57.** 7700 or {7700} **59.** no solution or ∅ **61.** all real numbers or {$x|x$ is a real number} **63.** $\frac{2}{3}$ or $\left\{\frac{2}{3}\right\}$ **65.** all real numbers or {$x|x$ is a real number} **67.** no solution or ∅ **69.** 0 or {0} **71.** no solution or ∅ **73.** 0 or {0} **75.** $\frac{4}{3}$ or $\left\{\frac{4}{3}\right\}$ **77.** all real numbers or {$x|x$ is a real number} **79.** $x = \square\$ - \square\triangle$ **81.** 240 **83.** $\frac{x}{5} + \frac{x}{3} = 16$; 30 **85.** $\frac{3x}{4} - 3 = \frac{x}{2}$; 12 **87.** 85 mph **89.** 142 lb; 13 lb **91.** 409.2 ft **99.** makes sense **101.** does not make sense **103.** false **105.** false **107.** 3 or {3} **109.** < **110.** < **111.** −10 **112. a.** $T - D = pm$ **b.** $\frac{T - D}{p} = m$ **113.** 16 or {16} **114.** 0.05 or {0.05}

Section 4 Check Point Exercises

1. $l = \frac{A}{w}$ **2.** $l = \frac{P - 2w}{2}$ **3.** $m = \frac{T - D}{p}$ **4.** $x = 15 + 12y$ **5.** 4.5 **6.** 15 **7.** 36% **8.** 35% **9. a.** $1152 **b.** 4% decrease

Concept and Vocabulary Check

1. isolated on one side **2.** $A = lw$ **3.** $P = 2l + 2w$ **4.** $A = PB$ **5.** subtract b; divide by m

Exercise Set 4

1. $r = \frac{d}{t}$ **3.** $P = \frac{I}{rt}$ **5.** $r = \frac{C}{2\pi}$ **7.** $m = \frac{E}{c^2}$ **9.** $m = \frac{y - b}{x}$ **11.** $D = T - pm$ **13.** $b = \frac{2A}{h}$ **15.** $n = 5M$ **17.** $c = 4F - 160$ **19.** $a = 2A - b$ **21.** $r = \frac{S - P}{Pt}$ **23.** $b = \frac{2A}{h} - a$ **25.** $x = \frac{C - By}{A}$ **27.** 6 **29.** 7.2 **31.** 5 **33.** 170 **35.** 20% **37.** 12% **39.** 60% **41.** 75% **43.** $x = \frac{y}{a + b}$ **45.** $x = \frac{y - 5}{a - b}$ **47.** $x = \frac{y}{c + d}$ **49.** $x = \frac{y + C}{A - B}$ **51. a.** $z = 3A - x - y$ **b.** 96% **53. a.** $t = \frac{d}{r}$ **b.** 2.5 hr **55.** 522 **57.** 500 billion pounds **59. a.** 27% **b.** 46% **c.** 117% **61.** 12.5% **63.** $9 **65. a.** $1008 **b.** $17,808 **67. a.** $103.20 **b.** $756.80 **69.** 15% **71.** no; 2% loss **75.** makes sense **77.** does not make sense **79.** false **81.** false **83.** $C = \frac{100M}{Q}$ **84.** 12 or {12} **85.** 20 or {20} **86.** $0.7x$ **87.** $\frac{13}{x} - 7x$ **88.** $8(x + 14)$ **89.** $9(x - 5)$

Mid-Chapter Check Point Exercises

1. 16 or {16} **2.** −3 or {−3} **3.** $C = \frac{825H}{E}$ **4.** 8.4 **5.** 30 or {30} **6.** $-\frac{8}{9}$ or $\left\{-\frac{8}{9}\right\}$ **7.** $r = \frac{S}{2\pi h}$ **8.** 40 **9.** 20 or {20} **10.** 5.25 or {5.25} **11.** −1 or {−1} **12.** $x = \frac{By + C}{A}$ **13.** no solution or ∅ **14.** 40 or {40} **15.** 12.5% **16.** $-\frac{6}{5}$ or $\left\{-\frac{6}{5}\right\}$ **17.** 25% **18.** all real numbers or {$x|x$ is a real number} **19. a.** underestimates by 2% **b.** 24

Section 5 Check Point Exercises

1. 12 **2.** English: $38 thousand; computer science; $56 thousand **3.** pages 72 and 73 **4.** 32; 4 mi **5.** 40 ft wide and 120 ft long **6.** $940

Concept and Vocabulary Check

1. $4x - 6$ **2.** $x + 215$ **3.** $x + 1$ **4.** $125 + 0.15x$ **5.** $2x + 2 \cdot 4x$ or $2 \cdot 4x + 2x$ or $10x$ **6.** $x - 0.35x$ or $0.65x$

Exercise Set 5

1. $x + 60 = 410; 350$ **3.** $x - 23 = 214; 237$ **5.** $7x = 126; 18$ **7.** $\frac{x}{19} = 5; 95$ **9.** $4 + 2x = 56; 26$ **11.** $5x - 7 = 178; 37$ **13.** $x + 5 = 2x; 5$ **15.** $2(x + 4) = 36; 14$ **17.** $9x = 3x + 30; 5$ **19.** $\frac{3x}{5} + 4 = 34; 50$ **21.** TV: 9 years; sleeping: 28 years **23.** Bachelor's: $55 thousand; Master's: $61 thousand **25.** pages 314 and 315 **27.** Ruth: 59; Maris: 61 **29.** 800 mi **31.** 10 years after 2008; 2018 **33.** 50 yd wide and 200 yd long **35.** 160 ft wide and 360 ft long **37.** 12 ft long and 4 ft high **39.** $400 **41.** $46,500 **43.** $22,500 **45.** 11 hr **51.** does not make sense **53.** makes sense **55.** false **57.** true **59.** 5 ft 7 in. **61.** The uncle is 60 years old, and the woman is 20 years old. **63.** -20 or $\{20\}$ **64.** 0 or $\{0\}$ **65.** $w = \frac{3V}{lh}$ **66.** 5 **67.** 91 **68.** 64 or $\{64\}$

Section 6 Check Point Exercises

1. 12 ft **2.** $400\pi \text{ ft}^2 \approx 1256 \text{ ft}^2$ or 1257 ft^2; $40\pi \text{ ft} \approx 126$ ft **3.** large pizza **4.** 2 times **5.** no; About 32 more cubic inches are needed. **6.** first: 120°; second: 40°; third: 20° **7.** 60°

Concept and Vocabulary Check

1. $A = \frac{1}{2}bh$ **2.** $A = \pi r^2$ **3.** $C = 2\pi r$ **4.** radius; diameter **5.** $V = lwh$ **6.** $V = \pi r^2 h$ **7.** 180° **8.** complementary **9.** supplementary **10.** $90 - x; 180 - x$

Exercise Set 6

1. 18 m; 18 m^2 **3.** 56 in.^{2} **5.** 91 m^2 **7.** 50 ft **9.** 8 ft **11.** 50 cm **13.** $16\pi \text{ cm}^2 \approx 50 \text{ cm}^2$; $8\pi \text{ cm} \approx 25$ cm **15.** $36\pi \text{ yd}^2 \approx 113 \text{ yd}^2$; $12\pi \text{ yd} \approx 38$ yd **17.** 7 in.; 14 in. **19.** 36 in.^{3} **21.** $150\pi \text{ cm}^3 \approx 471 \text{ cm}^3$ **23.** $972\pi \text{ cm}^3 \approx 3052$ or 3054 cm^3 **25.** $48\pi \text{ m}^3 \approx 151 \text{ m}^3$ **27.** $h = \frac{V}{\pi r^2}$ **29.** 9 times **31.** $x = 50; x + 30 = 80$; 50°, 50°, 80° **33.** $4x = 76; 3x + 4 = 61; 2x + 5 = 43$; 76°, 61°, 43° **35.** 40°, 80°, 60° **37.** 32° **39.** 2° **41.** 48° **43.** 90° **45.** 75° **47.** 135° **49.** 50° **51.** 72 m^2 **53.** 70.5 cm^2 **55.** 448 in.^{3} **57.** $698.18 **59.** large pizza **61.** $2261 or $2262 **63.** approx 19.7 ft **65.** 21,000 yd^3 **67.** the can with diameter of 6 in. and height of 5 in. **69.** Yes, the water tank is a little over one cubic foot too small. **79.** does not make sense **81.** does not make sense **83.** true **85.** false **87.** 2.25 times **89.** Volume increases 8 times. **91.** 35° **92.** $s = \frac{P - b}{2}$ **93.** 8 or $\{8\}$ **94.** 0 **95.** yes **96.** yes **97.** 2 or $\{2\}$

Section 7 Check Point Exercises

1. a. −2 −1 0 1 2 3 4 5 6 7 8 **b.** −5 −4 −3 −2 −1 0 1 2 3 4 5 **c.** −5 −4 −3 −2 −1 0 1 2 3 4 5

2. a. $[0, \infty)$; −5 −4 −3 −2 −1 0 1 2 3 4 5 **b.** $(-\infty, 5)$; −5 −4 −3 −2 −1 0 1 2 3 4 5

3. $(-\infty, 3)$ or $\{x|x < 3\}$ −5 −4 −3 −2 −1 0 1 2 3 4 5 **4.** $[-2, \infty)$ or $\{x|x \geq -2\}$ −5 −4 −3 −2 −1 0 1 2 3 4 5

5. a. $(-\infty, 8)$ or $\{x|x < 8\}$ 0 1 2 3 4 5 6 7 8 9 10 **b.** $(-3, \infty)$ or $\{x|x > -3\}$ −8 −7 −6 −5 −4 −3 −2 −1 0 1 2

6. $[4, \infty)$ or $\{y|y \geq 4\}$ −2 −1 0 1 2 3 4 5 6 7 8 **7.** $[1, \infty)$ or $\{x|x \geq 1\}$ −5 −4 −3 −2 −1 0 1 2 3 4 5

8. $[1, \infty)$ or $\{x|x \geq 1\}$ −5 −4 −3 −2 −1 0 1 2 3 4 5 **9.** no solution or ∅ **10.** $(-\infty, \infty)$ or $\{x|x$ is a real number$\}$

11. at least 83% **12.** at most 43

Concept and Vocabulary Check

1. $(-\infty, 5)$ **2.** $[2, \infty)$ **3.** $< b + c$ **4.** $< bc$ **5.** $> bc$ **6.** subtracting 4; dividing; −3; direction; >; < **7.** ∅ or the empty set **8.** $(-\infty, \infty)$

Exercise Set 7

1. −2 −1 0 1 2 3 4 5 6 7 8 **3.** −6 −5 −4 −3 −2 −1 0 1 2 3 4 **5.** −8 −7 −6 −5 −4 −3 −2 −1 0 1 2

7. −2 −1 0 1 2 3 4 5 6 7 8 **9.** −3 −2 −1 0 1 2 3 4 5 6 7 **11.** −3 −2 −1 0 1 2 3 4 5 6 7

13. $(-\infty, 3]$ −5 −4 −3 −2 −1 0 1 2 3 4 5 **15.** $\left(\frac{5}{2}, \infty\right)$ $\frac{5}{2}$ −5 −4 −3 −2 −1 0 1 2 3 4 5

17. $(-\infty, 0]$ −5 −4 −3 −2 −1 0 1 2 3 4 5 **19.** $(-\infty, 4)$ −5 −4 −3 −2 −1 0 1 2 3 4 5

21. $(7, \infty)$ or $\{x|x > 7\}$ −1 0 1 2 3 4 5 6 7 8 9 **23.** $(-\infty, 6]$ or $\{x|x \leq 6\}$ −2 −1 0 1 2 3 4 5 6 7 8

25. $(-\infty, 2)$ or $\{y|y < 2\}$ −5 −4 −3 −2 −1 0 1 2 3 4 5 **27.** $(-\infty, 3]$ or $\{x|x \leq 3\}$ −2 −1 0 1 2 3 4 5 6 7 8

29. $(-\infty, 16)$ or $\{x \mid x < 16\}$

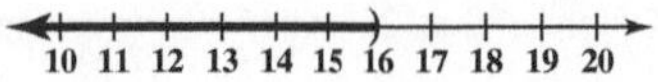

31. $(4, \infty)$ or $\{x \mid x > 4\}$

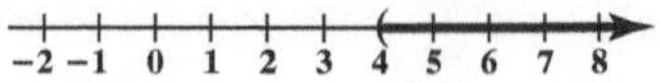

33. $\left(\frac{7}{6}, \infty\right)$ or $\left\{x \middle| x > \frac{7}{6}\right\}$

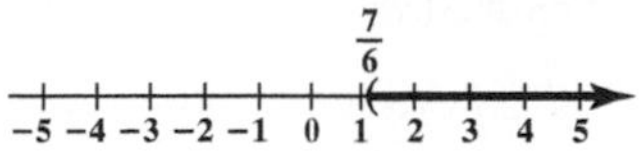

35. $\left(-\infty, -\frac{3}{8}\right]$ or $\left\{y \middle| y \le -\frac{3}{8}\right\}$

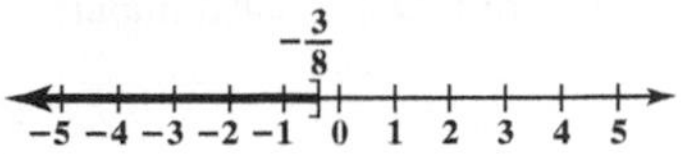

37. $(0, \infty)$ or $\{y \mid y > 0\}$

39. $(-\infty, 8)$ or $\{x \mid x < 8\}$

41. $(-6, \infty)$ or $\{x \mid x > -6\}$

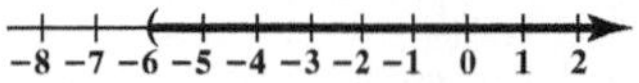

43. $(-\infty, 5)$ or $\{x \mid x < 5\}$

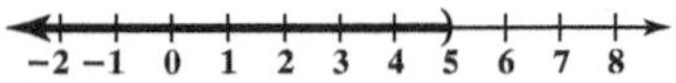

45. $[-7, \infty)$ or $\{x \mid x \ge -7\}$

47. $(-5, \infty)$ or $\{x \mid x > -5\}$

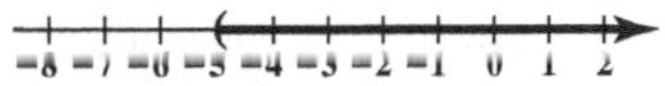

49. $(-\infty, -5]$ or $\{x \mid x \le -5\}$

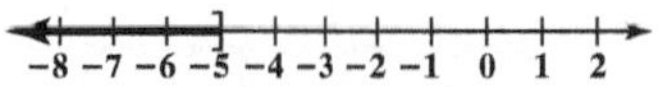

51. $(-\infty, 3)$ or $\{x \mid x < 3\}$

53. $\left[-\frac{1}{8}, \infty\right)$ or $\left\{y \middle| y \ge -\frac{1}{8}\right\}$

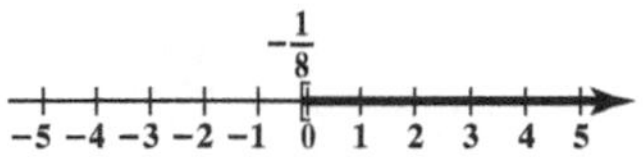

55. $(-4, \infty)$ or $\{x \mid x > -4\}$

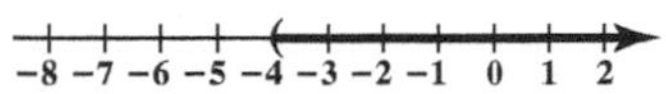

57. $(5, \infty)$ or $\{x \mid x > 5\}$

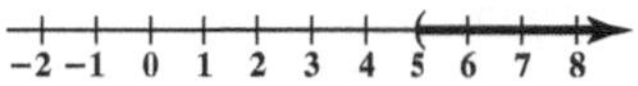

59. $(-\infty, 5)$ or $\{x \mid x < 5\}$

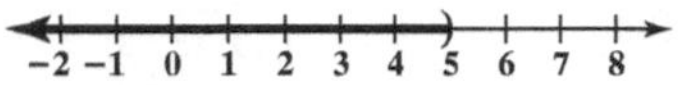

61. $[-2, \infty)$ or $\{x \mid x \ge -2\}$

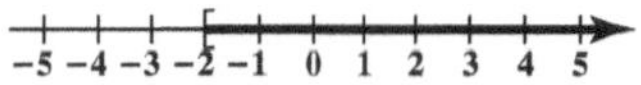

63. $(-3, \infty)$ or $\{x \mid x > -3\}$

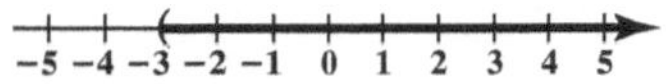

65. $[4, \infty)$ or $\{x \mid x \ge 4\}$

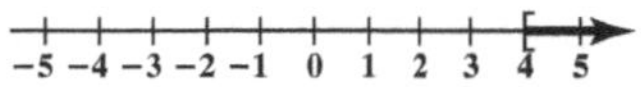

67. $\left(\frac{11}{3}, \infty\right)$ or $\left\{x \middle| x > \frac{11}{3}\right\}$

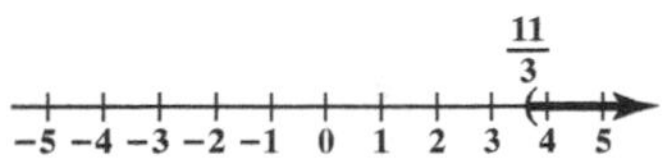

69. $(2, \infty)$ or $\{y \mid y > 2\}$

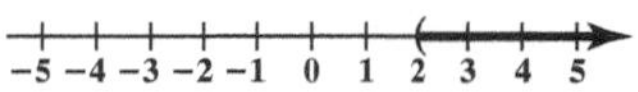

71. $(-\infty, 2)$ or $\{y \mid y < 2\}$

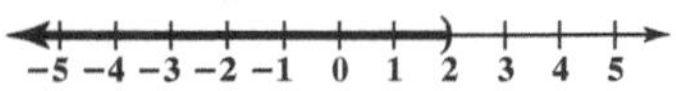

73. $(-\infty, 3)$ or $\{x \mid x < 3\}$

75. $\left(\frac{5}{3}, \infty\right)$ or $\left\{x \middle| x > \frac{5}{3}\right\}$

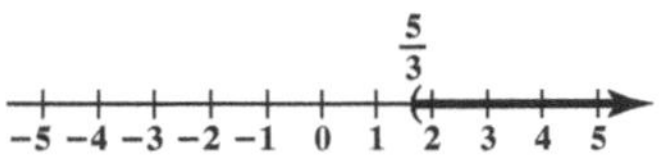

77. $[9, \infty)$ or $\{x \mid x \ge 9\}$

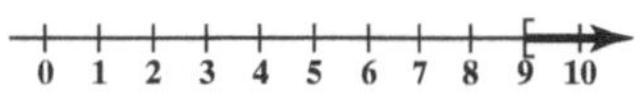

79. $(-\infty, -6)$ or $\{x \mid x < -6\}$

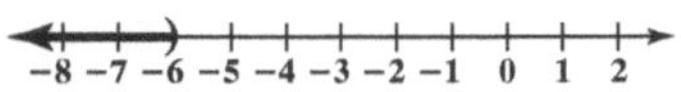

81. no solution or $\varnothing$ **83.** $(-\infty, \infty)$ or $\{x \mid x \text{ is a real number}\}$ **85.** no solution or $\varnothing$ **87.** $(-\infty, \infty)$ or $\{x \mid x \text{ is a real number}\}$
89. $(-\infty, 0]$ or $\{x \mid x \le 0\}$ **91.** $x > \frac{b-a}{3}$ **93.** $\frac{y-b}{m} \ge x$ **95.** x is between -2 and 2; $|x| < 2$
97. x is greater than 2 or less than -2; $|x| > 2$ **99.** weird, cemetery, accommodation **101.** supersede, inoculate **103.** harass
105. 16 years; from 2016 onward **107. a.** at least 96 **b.** if you get less than 66 on the final **109.** up to 1280 mi **111.** up to 29 bags of cement
117. makes sense **119.** makes sense **121.** false **123.** false **125.** more than 720 mi **127.** $(-\infty, 0.4)$ or $\{x \mid x < 0.4\}$ **129.** 20
130. length: 11 in.; width: 6 in. **131.** 4 or $\{4\}$ **132.** yes **133.** no **134.** -3

Review Exercises

1. 32 or $\{32\}$ **2.** -22 or $\{-22\}$ **3.** 12 or $\{12\}$ **4.** -22 or $\{-22\}$ **5.** 5 or $\{5\}$ **6.** 80 or $\{80\}$ **7.** -56 or $\{-56\}$ **8.** 11 or $\{11\}$
9. 4 or $\{4\}$ **10.** -15 or $\{-15\}$ **11.** -12 or $\{-12\}$ **12.** -25 or $\{-25\}$ **13.** 10 or $\{10\}$ **14.** 6 or $\{6\}$ **15.** -5 or $\{-5\}$ **16.** -10 or $\{-10\}$
17. 2 or $\{2\}$ **18.** 1 or $\{1\}$ **19. a.** overestimates by 1% **b.** 2017 **20.** -1 or $\{-1\}$ **21.** 12 or $\{12\}$ **22.** -13 or $\{-13\}$ **23.** -3 or $\{-3\}$
24. -10 or $\{-10\}$ **25.** 2 or $\{2\}$ **26.** 2 or $\{2\}$ **27.** 9 or $\{9\}$ **28.** 4 or $\{4\}$ **29.** no solution or $\varnothing$ **30.** all real numbers or $\{x \mid x \text{ is a real number}\}$ **31.** 30 years old **32.** $r = \frac{I}{P}$ **33.** $h = \frac{3V}{B}$ **34.** $w = \frac{P - 2l}{2}$ **35.** $B = 2A - C$ **36.** $m = \frac{T - D}{p}$ **37.** 9.6
38. 200 **39.** 48% **40.** 100% **41.** 40% **42.** 12.5% **43.** no; 1% **44. a.** $h = 7r$ **b.** 5 ft 3 in. **45.** 350 gallons **46.** 10
47. Gates: \$54 billion; Buffett: \$45 billion **48.** pages 46 and 47 **49.** females: 49%; males: 51% **50.** 14 yr; 2015 **51.** 18 checks
52. length: 150 yd; width: 50 yd **53.** \$240 **54.** 32.5 ft^2 **55.** 50 cm^2 **56.** 135 yd^2 **57.** 7608 m^2 **58.** 20π m $\approx$ 63 m; 100π m^2 $\approx$ 314 m^2
59. 6 ft **60.** 156 ft^2 **61.** \$1890 **62.** medium pizza **63.** 60 cm^3 **64.** 128π yd^3 $\approx$ 402 yd^3 **65.** 288π m^3 $\approx$ 905 m^3 **66.** 4800 m^3
67. 16 fish **68.** $x = 30, 3x = 90, 2x = 60$; 30°, 60°, 90° **69.** 85°, 35°, 60° **70.** 33° **71.** 105° **72.** 57.5° **73.** 45° and 135°

74.

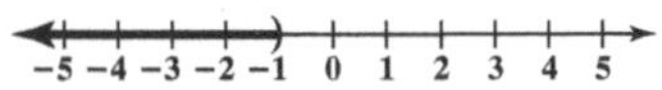

75.

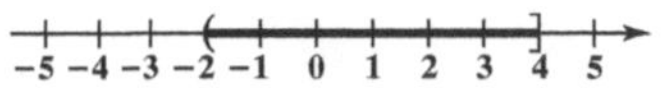

76. $\left[\frac{3}{2}, \infty\right)$

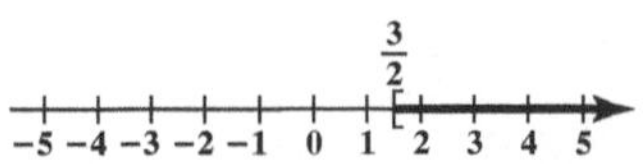

77. $(-\infty, 0)$

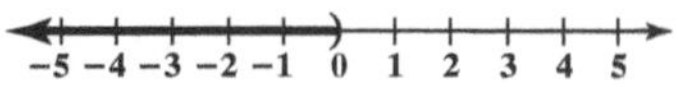

78. $(-\infty, 4)$ or $\{x \mid x < 4\}$

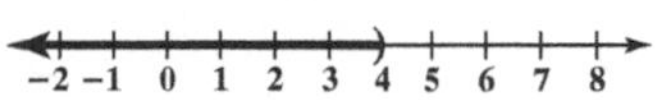

79. $(-8, \infty)$ or $\{x \mid x > -8\}$

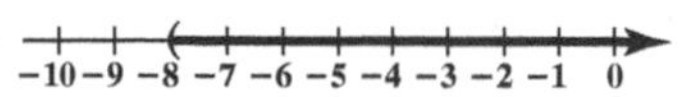

80. $[-3, \infty)$ or $\{x \mid x \ge -3\}$

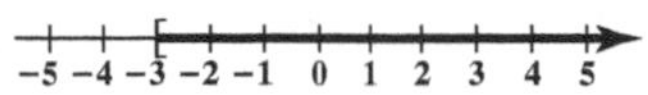

81. $(6, \infty)$ or $\{x \mid x > 6\}$

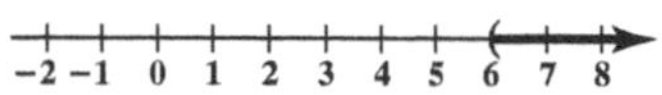

82. $[4, \infty)$ or $\{x|x \geq 4\}$ 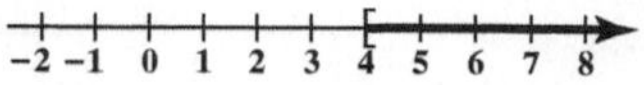 **83.** $(-\infty, 2]$ or $\{x|x \leq 2\}$ 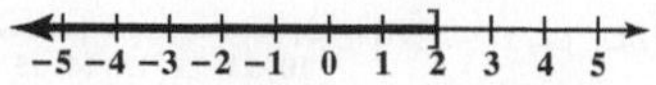

84. $(-\infty, \infty)$ or $\{x|x$ is a real number$\}$ **85.** no solution or $\varnothing$ **86.** at least 64 **87.** at most 30

Chapter Test

1. $\frac{9}{2}$ or $\left\{\frac{9}{2}\right\}$ **2.** -5 or $\{-5\}$ **3.** $-\frac{4}{3}$ or $\left\{-\frac{4}{3}\right\}$ **4.** 2 or $\{2\}$ **5.** -20 or $\{-20\}$ **6.** $-\frac{5}{3}$ or $\left\{-\frac{5}{3}\right\}$ **7.** -5 or $\{-5\}$ **8.** 60 yr; 2020 **9.** $h = \frac{V}{\pi r^2}$

10. $w = \frac{P - 2l}{2}$ **11.** 8.4 **12.** 150 **13.** 5% **14.** 63 **15.** Americans: 13 days; Italians: 42 days

16. 600 min **17.** length: 150 yd; width: 75 yd **18.** \$35 **19.** 517 m^2 **20.** 525 $in.^2$ **21.** 66 ft^2 **22.** 18 $in.^3$ **23.** 175π cm^3 $=$ 550 cm^3
24. \$650 **25.** 14 ft **26.** 126°, 42°, 12° **27.** 53°

28. $(-2, \infty)$ 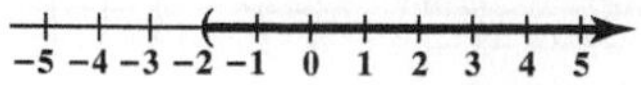 **29.** $(-\infty, 3]$ 

30. $(-\infty, -6)$ or $\{x|x < -6\}$ 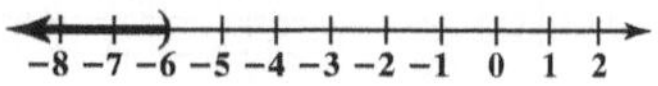 **31.** $(-\infty, -3]$ or $\{x|x \leq -3\}$ 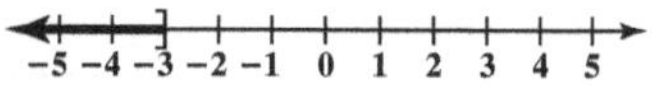

32. $(7, \infty)$ or $\{x|x > 7\}$ 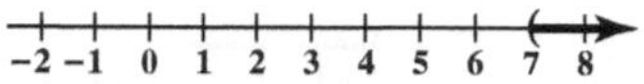 **33.** at least 92 **34.** widths greater than 8 in.

Linear Equations and Inequalities in Two Variables

These photos of presidential puffing indicate that the White House was not always a no-smoking zone. According to *Cigar Aficionado*, nearly half of U.S. Presidents have had a nicotine habit, from cigarettes to pipes to cigars. Franklin Roosevelt's stylish way with a cigarette holder was part of his mystique. Although Dwight Eisenhower quit his wartime four-pack-a-day habit before taking office, smoking in the residence was still common, with ashtrays on the tables at state dinners and free cigarettes for guests. In 1993, Hillary Clinton banned smoking in the White House, although Bill Clinton's cigars later made a sordid cameo in the Lewinsky scandal. Barack Obama quit smoking before entering the White House, but had "fallen off the wagon occasionally" as he admitted in a *Meet the Press* interview.

Changing attitudes toward smoking, both inside and outside the White House, date back to 1964 and an equation in two variables. In this chapter, you will learn graphing and modeling methods for situations involving two variables that will enable you to understand the mathematics behind this turning point in public health.

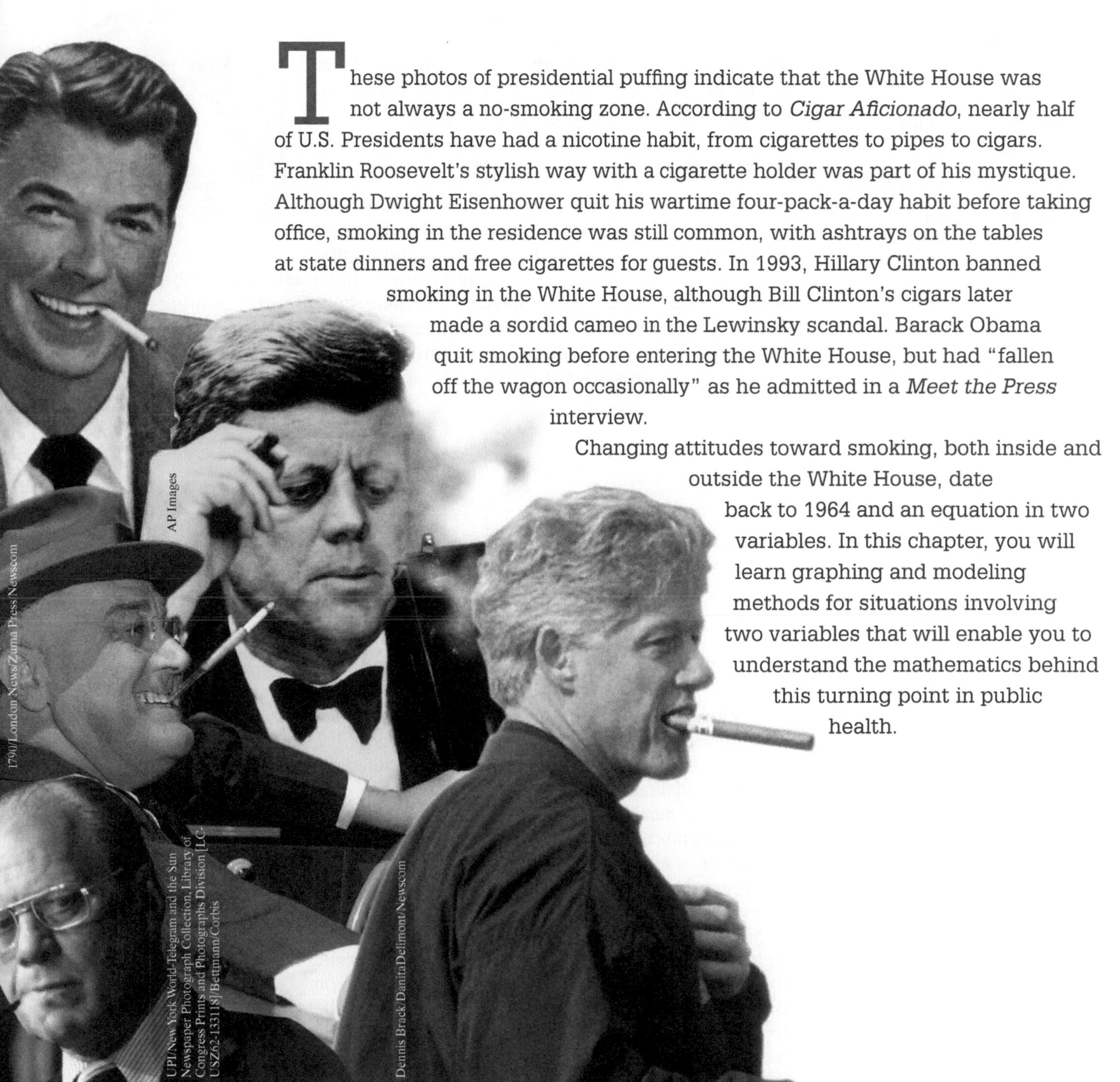

SECTION 1

Graphing Linear Equations in Two Variables

Objectives

1. Plot ordered pairs in the rectangular coordinate system.
2. Find coordinates of points in the rectangular coordinate system.
3. Determine whether an ordered pair is a solution of an equation.
4. Find solutions of an equation in two variables.
5. Use point plotting to graph linear equations.
6. Use graphs of linear equations to solve problems.

Despite high interest rates, fees, and penalties, American consumers are paying more with credit cards, and less with checks and cash. In this section, we will use geometric figures to visualize mathematical models describing our primary spending methods. The idea of visualizing equations as geometric figures was developed by the French philosopher and mathematician René Descartes (1596–1650). We begin by looking at Descartes's idea that brought together algebra and geometry, called the **rectangular coordinate system** or (in his honor) the **Cartesian coordinate system**.

Points and Ordered Pairs

1 Plot ordered pairs in the rectangular coordinate system.

The rectangular coordinate system consists of two number lines that intersect at right angles at their zero points, as shown in **Figure 1**. The horizontal number line is the ***x*-axis**. The vertical number line is the ***y*-axis**. The point of intersection of these axes is their zero points, called the **origin**. Positive numbers are shown to the right and above the origin. Negative numbers are shown to the left and below the origin. The axes divide the plane into four regions, called **quadrants**. The points located on the axes are not in any quadrant.

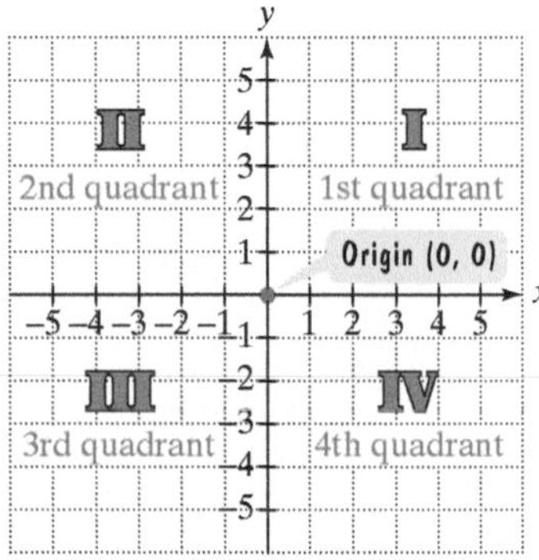

Figure 1 The rectangular coordinate system

Each point in the rectangular coordinate system corresponds to an **ordered pair** of real numbers, (x, y). Examples of such pairs are $(4, 2)$ and $(-5, -3)$. The first number in each pair, called the ***x*-coordinate**, denotes the distance and direction from the origin along the x-axis. The second number, called the ***y*-coordinate**, denotes vertical distance and direction along a line parallel to the y-axis or along the y-axis itself.

Figure 2 shows how we **plot**, or locate, the points corresponding to the ordered pairs $(4, 2)$ and $(-5, -3)$. We plot $(4, 2)$ by going 4 units from 0 to the right along the x-axis. Then we go 2 units up parallel to the y-axis. We plot $(-5, -3)$ by going 5 units from 0 to the left along the x-axis and 3 units down parallel to the y-axis. The phrase "the point corresponding to the ordered pair $(-5, -3)$" is often abbreviated as "the point $(-5, -3)$."

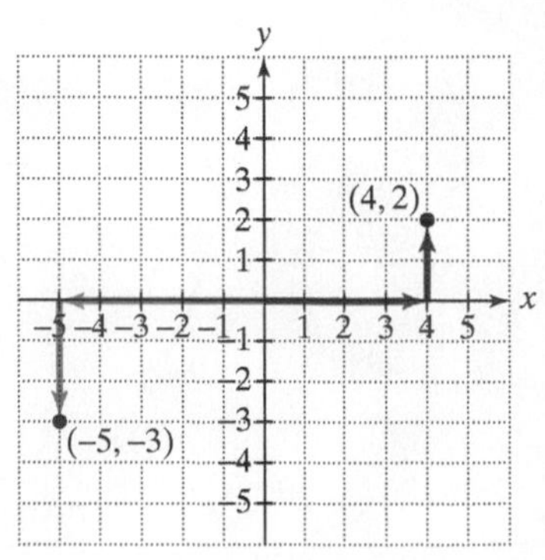

Figure 2 Plotting (4, 2) and (−5, −3)

EXAMPLE 1 Plotting Points in the Rectangular Coordinate System

Plot the points: $A(-3, 5)$, $B(2, -4)$, $C(5, 0)$, $D(-5, -2)$, $E(0, 4)$, and $F(0, 0)$.

Solution See **Figure 3**. We move from the origin and plot the points in the following way:

$A(-3, 5)$: 3 units left, 5 units up

$B(2, -4)$: 2 units right, 4 units down

$C(5, 0)$: 5 units right, 0 units up or down

$D(-5, -2)$: 5 units left, 2 units down

$E(0, 4)$: 0 units right or left, 4 units up

$F(0, 0)$: 0 units right or left, 0 units up or down

Notice that the origin is represented by (0, 0).

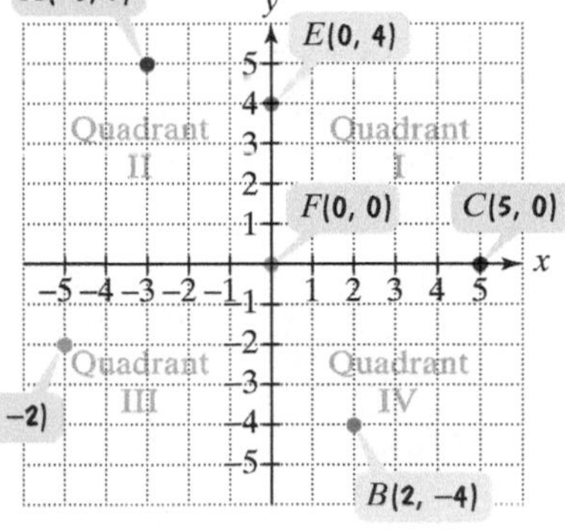

Figure 3 Plotting points

Great Question!

If a point is located on an axis, is one of its coordinates always zero?

Any point on the x-axis, such as (5, 0), has a y-coordinate of 0.
Any point on the y-axis, such as (0, 4), has an x-coordinate of 0.

The phrase *ordered pair* is used because **order is important**. For example, the points (2, 5) and (5, 2) are not the same. To plot (2, 5), move 2 units right and 5 units up. To plot (5, 2), move 5 units right and 2 units up. The points (2, 5) and (5, 2) are in different locations. **The order in which coordinates appear makes a difference in a point's location.**

✓ **CHECK POINT 1** Plot the points: $A(-2, 4)$, $B(4, -2)$, $C(-3, 0)$, and $D(0, -3)$.

2 Find coordinates of points in the rectangular coordinate system.

In the rectangular coordinate system, each ordered pair corresponds to exactly one point. Example 2 illustrates that each point in the rectangular coordinate system corresponds to exactly one ordered pair.

EXAMPLE 2 Finding Coordinates of Points

Determine the coordinates of points A, B, C, and D shown in **Figure 4**.

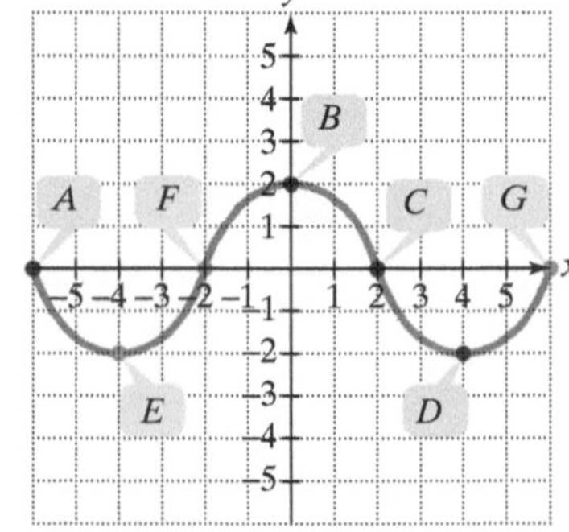

Figure 4 Finding coordinates of points

Solution

Point	Position from the Origin	Coordinates
A	6 units left, 0 units up or down	$(-6, 0)$
B	0 units right or left, 2 units up	$(0, 2)$
C	2 units right, 0 units up or down	$(2, 0)$
D	4 units right, 2 units down	$(4, -2)$

✓ **CHECK POINT 2** Determine the coordinates of points E, F, and G shown in **Figure 4**.

3 Determine whether an ordered pair is a solution of an equation.

Solutions of Equations in Two Variables

The rectangular coordinate system allows us to visualize relationships between two variables by connecting any equation in two variables with a geometric figure. Consider, for example, the following equation in two variables:

$$x + y = 10.$$

The sum of two numbers, x and y, is 10.

Many pairs of numbers fit the description in the voice balloon, such as $x = 1$ and $y = 9$, or $x = 3$ and $y = 7$. The phrase "$x = 1$ and $y = 9$" is abbreviated using the ordered pair (1, 9). Similarly, the phrase "$x = 3$ and $y = 7$" is abbreviated using the ordered pair (3, 7).

A **solution of an equation in two variables**, x and y, is an ordered pair of real numbers with the following property: When the x-coordinate is substituted for x and the y-coordinate is substituted for y in the equation, we obtain a true statement. For example, (1, 9) is a solution of the equation $x + y = 10$. When 1 is substituted for x and 9 is substituted for y, we obtain the true statement $1 + 9 = 10$, or $10 = 10$. Because there are infinitely many pairs of numbers that have a sum of 10, the equation $x + y = 10$ has infinitely many solutions. Each ordered-pair solution is said to **satisfy** the equation. Thus, (1, 9) satisfies the equation $x + y = 10$.

EXAMPLE 3 Deciding Whether an Ordered Pair Satisfies an Equation

Determine whether each ordered pair is a solution of the equation

$$x - 4y = 14:$$

a. $(2, -3)$ **b.** $(12, 1)$.

Solution

a. To determine whether $(2, -3)$ is a solution of the equation, we substitute 2 for x and -3 for y.

$$x - 4y = 14 \quad \text{This is the given equation.}$$

$$2 - 4(-3) \stackrel{?}{=} 14 \quad \text{Substitute 2 for x and } -3 \text{ for y.}$$

$$2 - (-12) \stackrel{?}{=} 14 \quad \text{Multiply: } 4(-3) = -12.$$

$$14 = 14 \quad \text{Subtract: } 2 - (-12) = 2 + 12 = 14.$$

This statement is true.

Because we obtain a true statement, we conclude that $(2, -3)$ is a solution of the equation $x - 4y = 14$. Thus, $(2, -3)$ satisfies the equation.

b. To determine whether (12, 1) is a solution of the equation, we substitute 12 for x and 1 for y.

$$x - 4y = 14 \quad \text{This is the given equation.}$$

$$12 - 4(1) \stackrel{?}{=} 14 \quad \text{Substitute 12 for x and 1 for y.}$$

$$12 - 4 \stackrel{?}{=} 14 \quad \text{Multiply: } 4(1) = 4.$$

$$8 = 14 \quad \text{Subtract: } 12 - 4 = 8.$$

This statement is false.

Because we obtain a false statement, we conclude that (12, 1) is not a solution of $x - 4y = 14$. The ordered pair (12, 1) does not satisfy the equation. ■

✓ **CHECK POINT 3** Determine whether each ordered pair is a solution of the equation $x - 3y = 9$:

a. $(3, -2)$ **b.** $(-2, 3)$.

In this chapter, we will use x and y to represent the variables of an equation in two variables. However, any two letters can be used. Solutions are still ordered pairs. Although it depends on the role variables play in equations, the first number in an ordered pair often replaces the variable that occurs first alphabetically. The second number in an ordered pair often replaces the variable that occurs last alphabetically.

4 Find solutions of an equation in two variables.

How do we find ordered pairs that are solutions of an equation in two variables, x and y?

- Select a value for one of the variables.
- Substitute that value into the equation and find the corresponding value of the other variable.
- Use the values of the two variables to form an ordered pair (x, y). This pair is a solution of the equation.

EXAMPLE 4 Finding Solutions of an Equation

Find five solutions of

$$y = 2x - 1.$$

Select integers for x, starting with -2 and ending with 2.

Solution We organize the process of finding solutions in the following table of values.

Start with these values of x.

Substitute x into $y = 2x - 1$ and compute y.

Use values for x and y to form an ordered-pair solution.

Any numbers can be selected for x. There is nothing special about integers from -2 to 2, inclusive. We chose these values to include two negative numbers, 0, and two positive numbers. We also wanted to keep the resulting computations for y relatively simple.

x	$y = 2x - 1$	(x, y)
-2	$y = 2(-2) - 1 = -4 - 1 = -5$	$(-2, -5)$
-1	$y = 2(-1) - 1 = -2 - 1 = -3$	$(-1, -3)$
0	$y = 2 \cdot 0 - 1 = 0 - 1 = -1$	$(0, -1)$
1	$y = 2 \cdot 1 - 1 = 2 - 1 = 1$	$(1, 1)$
2	$y = 2 \cdot 2 - 1 = 4 - 1 = 3$	$(2, 3)$

Look at the ordered pairs in the last column. Five solutions of $y = 2x - 1$ are $(-2, -5)$, $(-1, -3)$, $(0, -1)$, $(1, 1)$, and $(2, 3)$. ■

✓ **CHECK POINT 4** Find five solutions of $y = 3x + 2$. Select integers for x, starting with -2 and ending with 2.

---

5 Use point plotting to graph linear equations.

Graphing Linear Equations in the Form $y = mx + b$

In Example 4, we found five solutions of $y = 2x - 1$. We can generate as many ordered-pair solutions as desired to $y = 2x - 1$ by substituting numbers for x and then finding the corresponding values for y. The **graph of the equation** is the set of all points whose coordinates satisfy the equation.

One method for graphing an equation such as $y = 2x - 1$ is the **point-plotting method**.

The Point-Plotting Method for Graphing an Equation in Two Variables

1. Find several ordered pairs that are solutions of the equation.
2. Plot these ordered pairs as points in the rectangular coordinate system.
3. Connect the points with a smooth curve or line.

EXAMPLE 5 Graphing an Equation Using the Point-Plotting Method

Graph the equation: $y = 3x$.

Solution

Step 1. Find several ordered pairs that are solutions of the equation. Because there are infinitely many solutions, we cannot list them all. To find a few solutions of the equation, we select integers for x, starting with -2 and ending with 2.

Start with these values of x. | Substitute x into $y = 3x$ and compute y. | These are solutions of $y = 3x$.

x	$y = 3x$	(x, y)
-2	$y = 3(-2) = -6$	$(-2, -6)$
-1	$y = 3(-1) = -3$	$(-1, -3)$
0	$y = 3 \cdot 0 = 0$	$(0, 0)$
1	$y = 3 \cdot 1 = 3$	$(1, 3)$
2	$y = 3 \cdot 2 = 6$	$(2, 6)$

Step 2. Plot these ordered pairs as points in the rectangular coordinate system. The five ordered pairs in the table of values are plotted in **Figure 5(a)**.

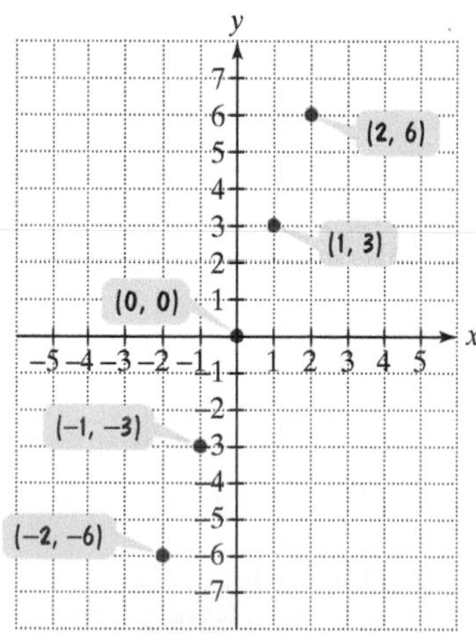

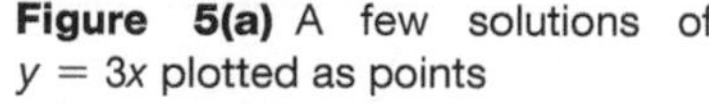
Figure 5(a) A few solutions of $y = 3x$ plotted as points

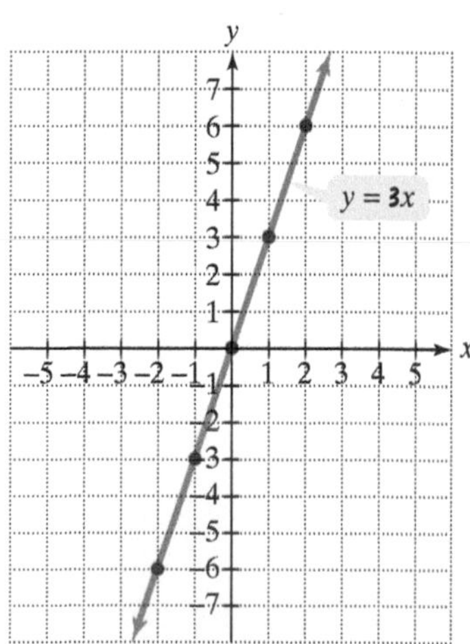

Figure 5(b) The graph of $y = 3x$

Step 3. Connect the points with a smooth curve or line. The points lie along a straight line. The graph of $y = 3x$ is shown in **Figure 5(b)**. The arrows on both ends of the line indicate that it extends indefinitely in both directions. ■

✓ **CHECK POINT 5** Graph the equation: $y = 2x$.

Equations like $y = 3x$ and $y = 2x$ are called **linear equations in two variables** because the graph of each equation is a line. Any equation that can be written in the form $y = mx + b$, where m and b are constants, is a linear equation in two variables. Here are examples of linear equations in two variables:

$$y = 3x \qquad\qquad y = 3x - 2$$

$$\text{or} \quad y = 3x + 0 \qquad\qquad \text{or} \quad y = 3x + (-2).$$

This is in the form of $y = mx + b$, with $m = 3$ and $b = 0$.

This is in the form of $y = mx + b$, with $m = 3$ and $b = -2$.

Great Question!

What's the big deal about the constants m and b in the linear equation $y = mx + b$?

In Section 4, you will see how these numbers affect the equation's graph in special ways. The number m determines the line's steepness. The number b determines the point where the line crosses the y-axis. Any real numbers can be used for m and b.

Can you guess how the graph of the linear equation $y = 3x - 2$ compares with the graph of $y = 3x$? In Example 5, we graphed $y = 3x$. Now, let's graph the equation $y = 3x - 2$.

EXAMPLE 6 Graphing a Linear Equation in Two Variables

Graph the equation: $y = 3x - 2$.

Solution

Step 1. Find several ordered pairs that are solutions of the equation. To find a few solutions, we select integers for x, starting with -2 and ending with 2.

Start with x. Compute y. Form the ordered pair (x, y).

x	$y = 3x - 2$	(x, y)
-2	$y = 3(-2) - 2 = -6 - 2 = -8$	$(-2, -8)$
-1	$y = 3(-1) - 2 = -3 - 2 = -5$	$(-1, -5)$
0	$y = 3 \cdot 0 - 2 = 0 - 2 = -2$	$(0, -2)$
1	$y = 3 \cdot 1 - 2 = 3 - 2 = 1$	$(1, 1)$
2	$y = 3 \cdot 2 - 2 = 6 - 2 = 4$	$(2, 4)$

Step 2. Plot these ordered pairs as points in the rectangular coordinate system. The five ordered pairs in the table of values are plotted in **Figure 6(a)**.

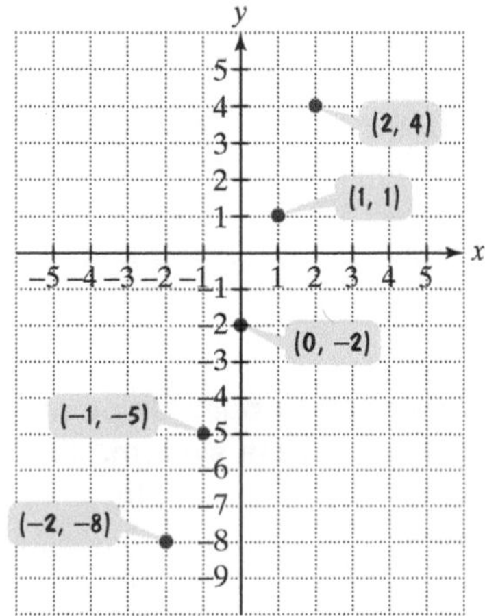

Figure 6(a) A few solutions of $y = 3x - 2$ plotted as points

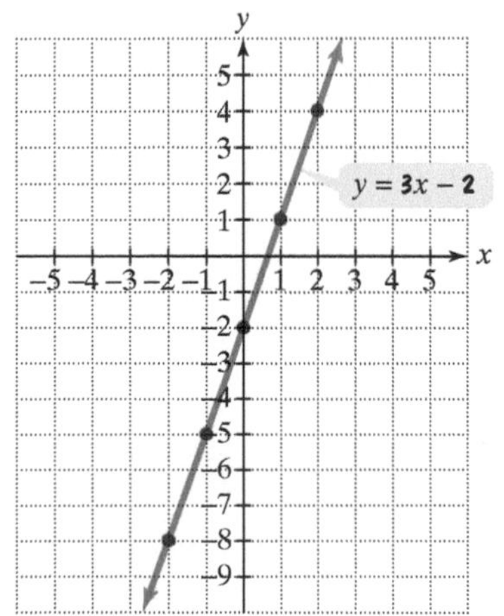

Figure 6(b) The graph of $y = 3x - 2$

Step 3. Connect the points with a smooth curve or line. The points lie along a straight line. The graph of $y = 3x - 2$ is shown in **Figure 6(b)**. ■

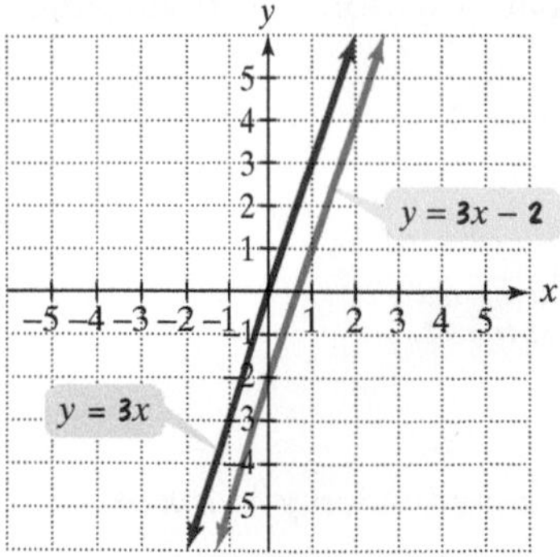

Figure 7

Now we are ready to compare the graphs of $y = 3x - 2$ and $y = 3x$. The graphs of both linear equations are shown in the same rectangular coordinate system in **Figure 7**. Can you see that the blue graph of $y = 3x - 2$ is parallel to the red graph of $y = 3x$ and 2 units lower than the graph of $y = 3x$? Instead of crossing the y-axis at (0, 0), the graph of $y = 3x - 2$ crosses the y-axis at (0, −2).

Comparing Graphs of Linear Equations

If the value of m does not change,

- The graph of $y = mx + b$ is the graph of $y = mx$ shifted b units up when b is a positive number.
- The graph of $y = mx + b$ is the graph of $y = mx$ shifted $|b|$ units down when b is a negative number.

✓ **CHECK POINT 6** Graph the equation: $y = 2x - 2$.

EXAMPLE 7 Graphing a Linear Equation in Two Variables

Graph the equation: $y = \frac{2}{3}x + 1$.

Solution

Step 1. Find several ordered pairs that are solutions of the equation. Notice that m, the coefficient of x, is $\frac{2}{3}$. When m is a fraction, we will select values of x that are multiples of the denominator. In this way, we can avoid values of y that are fractions. Because the denominator of $\frac{2}{3}$ is 3, we select multiples of 3 for x. Let's use −6, −3, 0, 3, and 6.

Start with multiples of 3 for x. Compute y. Form the ordered pair (x, y).

x	$y = \frac{2}{3}x + 1$	(x, y)
−6	$y = \frac{2}{3}(-6) + 1 = -4 + 1 = -3$	(−6, −3)
−3	$y = \frac{2}{3}(-3) + 1 = -2 + 1 = -1$	(−3, −1)
0	$y = \frac{2}{3} \cdot 0 + 1 = 0 + 1 = 1$	(0, 1)
3	$y = \frac{2}{3} \cdot 3 + 1 = 2 + 1 = 3$	(3, 3)
6	$y = \frac{2}{3} \cdot 6 + 1 = 4 + 1 = 5$	(6, 5)

Step 2. Plot these ordered pairs as points in the rectangular coordinate system. The five ordered pairs in the table of values are plotted in **Figure 8**.

Step 3. Connect the points with a smooth curve or line. The points lie along a straight line. The graph of $y = \frac{2}{3}x + 1$ is shown in **Figure 8**.

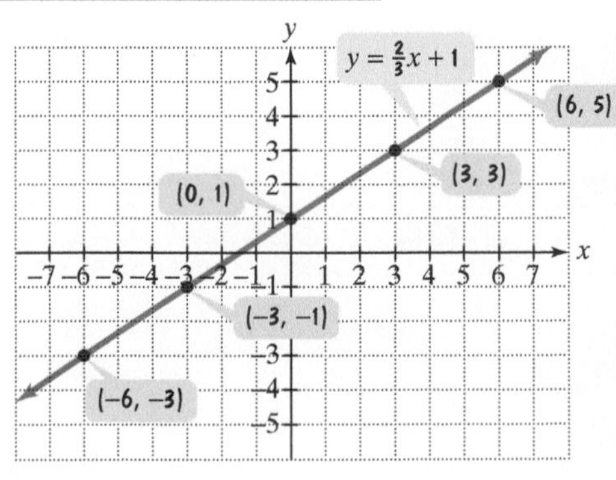

Figure 8 The graph of $y = \frac{2}{3}x + 1$ ■

✓ **CHECK POINT 7** Graph the equation: $y = \frac{1}{2}x + 2$.

6 Use graphs of linear equations to solve problems.

Applications

Part of the beauty of the rectangular coordinate system is that it allows us to "see" mathematical models and visualize the solution to a problem. This idea is demonstrated in Example 8.

EXAMPLE 8 Graphing a Mathematical Model

The graph in **Figure 9** shows that over time fewer consumers are paying with checks and cash, and more are paying with plastic.

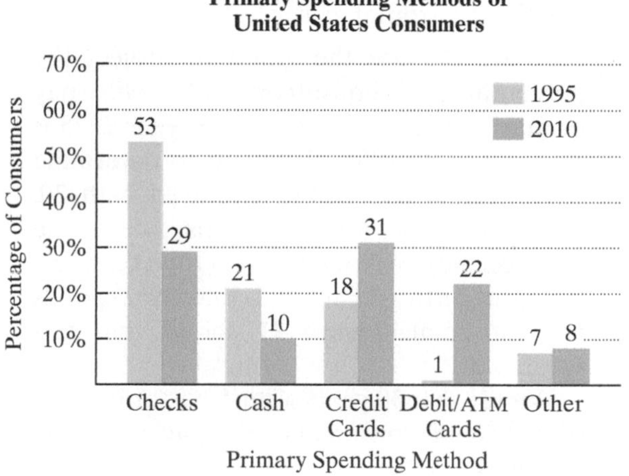

Figure 9

Source: Mintel/Visa USA Research Services

The mathematical model

$$C = -1.6n + 53$$

describes the percentage of consumers, C, who paid primarily with checks n years after 1995.

a. Let $n = 0, 5, 10, 15$, and 20. Make a table of values showing five solutions of the equation.

b. Graph the formula in a rectangular coordinate system.

c. Use the graph to estimate the percentage of consumers who will pay primarily by check in 2025.

d. Use the formula to project the percentage of consumers who will pay primarily by check in 2025.

Solution

a. The table of values shows five solutions of $C = -1.6n + 53$.

Start with these values of n. — Substitute n into $C = -1.6n + 53$ and compute C. — Form the ordered pair (n, C).

n	$C = -1.6n + 53$	(n, C)
0	$C = -1.6(0) + 53 = 0 + 53 = 53$	(0, 53)
5	$C = -1.6(5) + 53 = -8 + 53 = 45$	(5, 45)
10	$C = -1.6(10) + 53 = -16 + 53 = 37$	(10, 37)
15	$C = -1.6(15) + 53 = -24 + 53 = 29$	(15, 29)
20	$C = -1.6(20) + 53 = -32 + 53 = 21$	(20, 21)

b. Now we are ready to graph $C = -1.6n + 53$. Because of the letters used to represent the variables, we label the horizontal axis n and the vertical axis C. We plot the five ordered pairs from the table of values and connect them with a line. The graph of $C = -1.6n + 53$ is shown in **Figure 10**.

As you examine **Figure 10**, are you wondering why we did not extend the graph into the other quadrants of the rectangular coordinate system? Keep in mind that n represents the number of years after 1995 and C represents the percentage of consumers paying by check. Only nonnegative values of each variable are meaningful. Thus, when drawing the graph, we started on the positive portion of the vertical axis and ended on the positive horizontal axis.

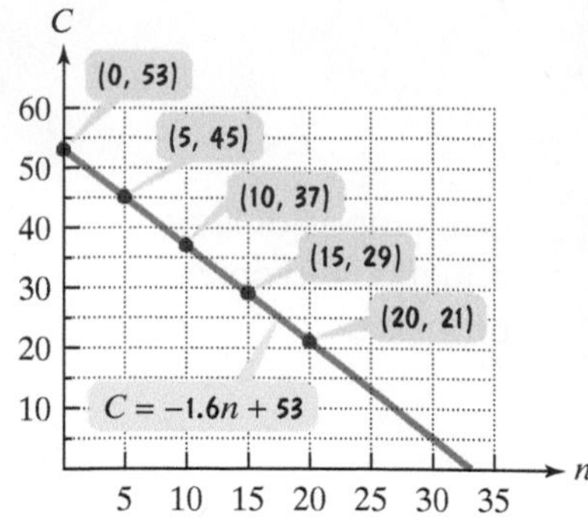

Figure 10

c. Now we can use the graph to project the percentage of consumers who will pay primarily by check in 2025. The year 2025 is 30 years after 1995. We need to determine what second coordinate is paired with 30. **Figure 11** shows how to do this. Locate the point on the line that is above 30 and then find the value on the vertical axis that corresponds to that point. **Figure 11** shows that this value is 5.

We see that 30 years after 1995, or in 2025, only 5% of consumers will pay primarily by check.

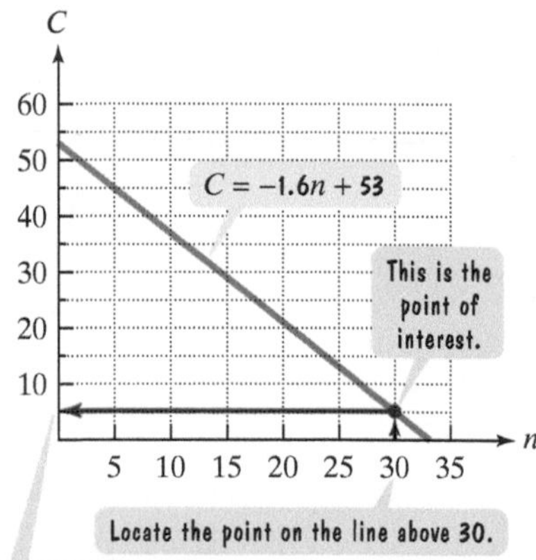

Figure 11

d. Now let's use the mathematical model to verify our graphical observation in part (c).

$C = -1.6n + 53$ This is the given mathematical model.

$C = -1.6(30) + 53$ Substitute 30 for n.

$C = -48 + 53$ Multiply: $-1.6(30) = -48$.

$C = 5$ Add.

This verifies that 30 years after 1995, in 2025, 5% of consumers will pay primarily by check. ■

✓ **CHECK POINT 8** The mathematical model

$$D = 1.4n + 1$$

describes the percentage of consumers, D, who paid primarily with debit cards n years after 1995.

a. Let $n = 0, 5, 10,$ and 15. Make a table of values showing four solutions of the equation.

b. Graph the formula in a rectangular coordinate system.

c. Use the graph to estimate the percentage of consumers who will pay primarily with debit cards in 2015.

d. Use the formula to project the percentage of consumers who will pay primarily by debit cards in 2015.

Using Technology

Graphing calculators or graphing software packages for computers are referred to as **graphing utilities** or graphers. A graphing utility is a powerful tool that quickly generates the graph of an equation in two variables. **Figure 12** shows two such graphs for the equations in Examples 5 and 6.

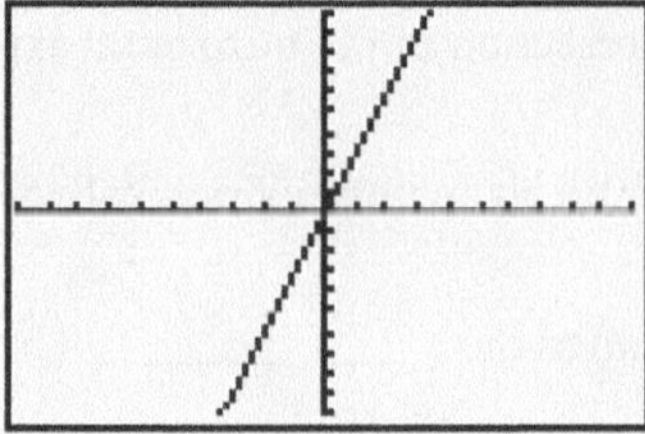

Figure 12(a) The graph of $y = 3x$

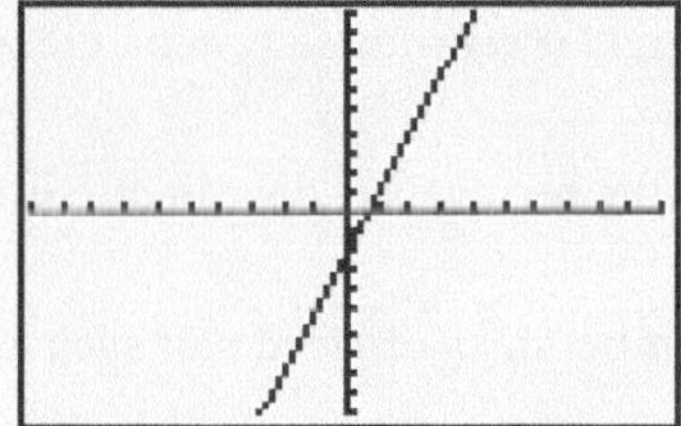

Figure 12(b) The graph of $y = 3x - 2$

What differences do you notice between these graphs and the graphs that we drew by hand? They do seem a bit "jittery." Arrows do not appear on both ends of the graphs. Furthermore, numbers are not given along the axes. For both graphs in **Figure 12**, the x-axis extends from -10 to 10 and the y-axis also extends from -10 to 10. The distance represented by each consecutive tick mark is one unit. We say that the **viewing rectangle**, or the **viewing window**, is $[-10, 10, 1]$ by $[-10, 10, 1]$.

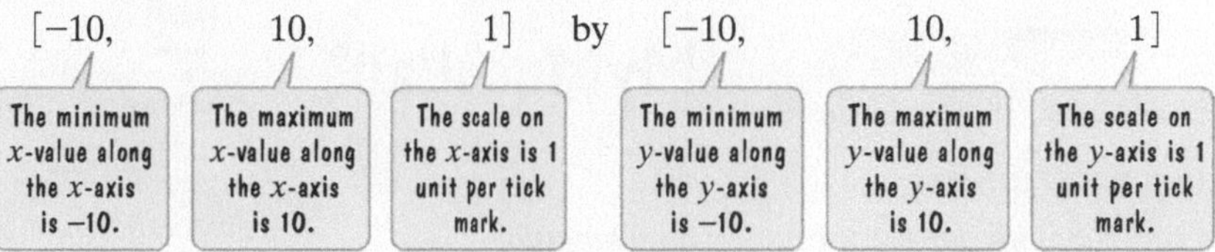

To graph an equation in x and y using a graphing utility, enter the equation and specify the size of the viewing rectangle. The size of the viewing rectangle sets minimum and maximum values for both the x- and y-axes. Enter these values, as well as the values for the distances between consecutive tick marks on the respective axes. The $[-10, 10, 1]$ by $[-10, 10, 1]$ viewing rectangle used in **Figure 12** is called the **standard viewing rectangle**.

On most graphing utilities, the display screen is two-thirds as high as it is wide. By using a square setting, you can equally space the x and y tick marks. (This does not occur in the standard viewing rectangle.) Graphing utilities can also *zoom in* and *zoom out*. When you zoom in, you see a smaller portion of the graph, but you do so in greater detail. When you zoom out, you see a larger portion of the graph. Thus, zooming out may help you to develop a better understanding of the overall character of the graph. With practice, you will become more comfortable with graphing equations in two variables using your graphing utility. You will also develop a better sense of the size of the viewing rectangle that will reveal needed information about a particular graph.

Achieving Success

An effective way to understand something is to explain it to someone else. You can do this by using the Writing in Mathematics exercises that ask you to respond with verbal or written explanations. Speaking about a new concept uses a different part of your brain than thinking about the concept. Explaining new ideas verbally will quickly reveal any gaps in your understanding. It will also help you to remember new concepts for longer periods of time.

CONCEPT AND VOCABULARY CHECK

Fill in each blank so that the resulting statement is true.

1. In the rectangular coordinate system, the horizontal number line is called the ______________.
2. In the rectangular coordinate system, the vertical number line is called the ______________.
3. In the rectangular coordinate system, the point of intersection of the horizontal axis and the vertical axis is called the ______________.
4. The axes of the rectangular coordinate system divide the plane into regions, called ______________. There are ______________ of these regions.
5. The first number in an ordered pair such as (3, 8) is called the ______________. The second number in such an ordered pair is called the ______________.
6. The ordered pair (1, 3) is a/an ______________ of the equation $y = 5x - 2$ because when 1 is substituted for x and 3 is substituted for y, we obtain a true statement. We also say that (1, 3) ______________ the equation.
7. Each ordered pair of numbers corresponds to ______________ point in the rectangular coordinate system.
8. A linear equation in two variables can be written in the form $y =$ ______________, where m and b are constants.

1 EXERCISE SET

MyMathLab®

Practice Exercises

In Exercises 1–8, plot the given point in a rectangular coordinate system. Indicate in which quadrant each point lies.

1. (3, 5)
2. (5, 3)
3. (−5, 1)
4. (1, −5)
5. (−3, −1)
6. (−1, −3)
7. (6, −3.5)
8. (−3.5, 6)

In Exercises 9–24, plot the given point in a rectangular coordinate system.

9. (−3, −3)
10. (−5, −5)
11. (−2, 0)
12. (−5, 0)
13. (0, 2)
14. (0, 5)
15. (0, −3)
16. (0, −5)
17. $\left(\frac{5}{2}, \frac{7}{2}\right)$
18. $\left(\frac{7}{2}, \frac{5}{2}\right)$
19. $\left(-5, \frac{3}{2}\right)$
20. $\left(-\frac{9}{2}, -4\right)$
21. (0, 0)
22. $\left(-\frac{5}{2}, 0\right)$
23. $\left(0, -\frac{5}{2}\right)$
24. $\left(0, \frac{7}{2}\right)$

In Exercises 25–32, give the ordered pairs that correspond to the points labeled in the figure.

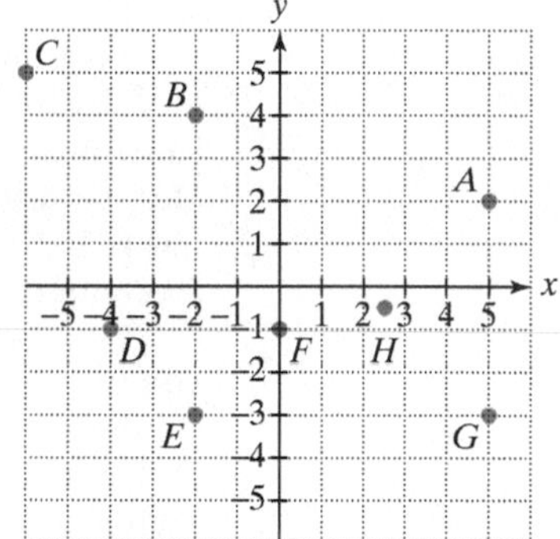

25. A
26. B
27. C
28. D
29. E
30. F
31. G
32. H
33. In which quadrants are the y-coordinates positive?
34. In which quadrants are the x-coordinates negative?
35. In which quadrants do the x-coordinates and the y-coordinates have the same sign?
36. In which quadrants do the x-coordinates and the y-coordinates have opposite signs?

In Exercises 37–48, determine whether each ordered pair is a solution of the given equation.

37. $y = 3x \quad (2, 3), (3, 2), (-4, -12)$

38. $y = 4x \quad (3, 12), (12, 3), (-5, -20)$

39. $y = -4x \quad (-5, -20), (0, 0), (9, -36)$

40. $y = -3x \quad (-5, 15), (0, 0), (7, -21)$

41. $y = 2x + 6 \quad (0, 6), (-3, 0), (2, -2)$

42. $y = 8 - 4x \quad (8, 0), (16, -2), (3, -4)$

43. $3x + 5y = 15 \quad (-5, 6), (0, 5), (10, -3)$

44. $2x - 5y = 0 \quad (-2, 0), (-10, 6), (5, 0)$

45. $x + 3y = 0 \quad (0, 0), \left(1, \frac{1}{3}\right), \left(2, -\frac{2}{3}\right)$

46. $x + 5y = 0 \quad (0, 0), \left(1, \frac{1}{5}\right), \left(2, -\frac{2}{5}\right)$

47. $x - 4 = 0 \quad (4, 7), (3, 4), (0, -4)$

48. $y + 2 = 0 \quad (0, 2), (2, 0), (0, -2)$

In Exercises 49–56, find five solutions of each equation. Select integers for x, starting with −2 and ending with 2. Organize your work in a table of values.

49. $y = 12x$

50. $y = 14x$

51. $y = -10x$

52. $y = -20x$

53. $y = 8x - 5$

54. $y = 6x - 4$

55. $y = -3x + 7$

56. $y = -5x + 9$

In Exercises 57–80, graph each linear equation in two variables. Find at least five solutions in your table of values for each equation.

57. $y = x$

58. $y = x + 1$

59. $y = x - 1$

60. $y = x - 2$

61. $y = 2x + 1$

62. $y = 2x - 1$

63. $y = -x + 2$

64. $y = -x + 3$

65. $y = -3x - 1$

66. $y = -3x - 2$

67. $y = \frac{1}{2}x$

68. $y = -\frac{1}{2}x$

69. $y = -\frac{1}{4}x$

70. $y = \frac{1}{4}x$

71. $y = \frac{1}{3}x + 1$

72. $y = \frac{1}{3}x - 1$

73. $y = -\frac{3}{2}x + 1$

74. $y = -\frac{3}{2}x + 2$

75. $y = -\frac{5}{2}x - 1$

76. $y = -\frac{5}{2}x + 1$

77. $y = x + \frac{1}{2}$

78. $y = x - \frac{1}{2}$

79. $y = 4$, or $y = 0x + 4$

80. $y = 3$, or $y = 0x + 3$

Practice PLUS

In Exercises 81–84, write each sentence as a linear equation in two variables. Then graph the equation.

81. The *y*-variable is 3 more than the *x*-variable.

82. The *y*-variable exceeds the *x*-variable by 4.

83. The *y*-variable exceeds twice the *x*-variable by 5.

84. The *y*-variable is 2 less than 3 times the *x*-variable.

85. At the beginning of a semester, a student purchased eight pens and six pads for a total cost of $14.50.

a. If *x* represents the cost of one pen and *y* represents the cost of one pad, write an equation in two variables that reflects the given conditions.

b. If pads cost $0.75 each, find the cost of one pen.

86. A nursery offers a package of three small orange trees and four small grapefruit trees for $22.

a. If *x* represents the cost of one orange tree and *y* represents the cost of one grapefruit tree, write an equation in two variables that reflects the given conditions.

b. If a grapefruit tree costs $2.50, find the cost of an orange tree.

Application Exercises

A football is thrown by a quarterback to a receiver. The points in the figure show the height of the football, in feet, above the ground in terms of its distance, in yards, from the quarterback. Use this information to solve Exercises 87–92.

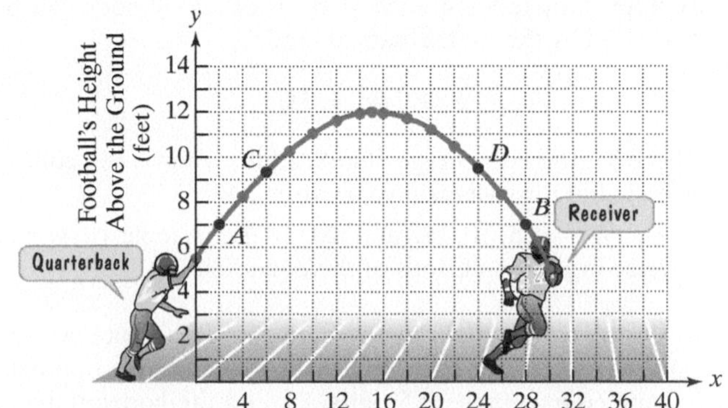

87. Find the coordinates of point *A*. Then interpret the coordinates in terms of the information given.

(In Exercises 88–92, be sure to refer to the figure at the bottom of the previous page.)

88. Find the coordinates of point B. Then interpret the coordinates in terms of the information given.

89. Estimate the coordinates of point C.

90. Estimate the coordinates of point D.

91. What is the football's maximum height? What is its distance from the quarterback when it reaches its maximum height?

92. What is the football's height when it is caught by the receiver? What is the receiver's distance from the quarterback when he catches the football?

Even as Americans increasingly view a college education as essential for success, many believe that a college education is becoming less available to qualified students. Exercises 93–94 are based on the data displayed by the graph.

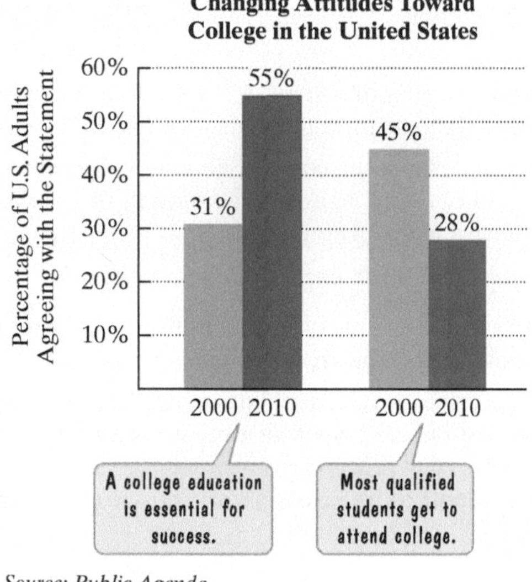

Source: Public Agenda

93. The graph shows that in 2000, 31% of U.S. adults viewed a college education as essential for success. For the period from 2000 through 2010, the percentage viewing a college education as essential for success increased on average by approximately 2.4 each year. These conditions can be described by the mathematical model

$$S = 2.4n + 31,$$

where S is the percentage of U.S. adults who viewed college as essential for success n years after 2000.

a. Let $n = 0, 5, 10, 15,$ and 20. Make a table of values showing five solutions of the equation.

b. Graph the formula in a rectangular coordinate system. Suggestion: Let each tick mark on the horizontal axis, labeled n, represent 5 units. Extend the horizontal axis to include $n = 25$. Let each tick mark on the vertical axis, labeled S, represent 10 units and extend the axis to include $S = 100$.

c. Use your graph from part (b) to estimate the percentage of U.S. adults who will view college as essential for success in 2018.

d. Use the formula to project the percentage of U.S. adults who will view college as essential for success in 2018.

94. The graph shows that in 2000, 45% of U.S. adults believed that most qualified students get to attend college. For the period from 2000 through 2010, the percentage who believed that a college education is available to most qualified students decreased by approximately 1.7 each year. These conditions can be described by the mathematical model

$$Q = -1.7n + 45,$$

where Q is the percentage believing that a college education is available to most qualified students n years after 2000.

a. Let $n = 0, 5, 10, 15,$ and 20. Make a table of values showing five solutions of the equation.

b. Graph the formula in a rectangular coordinate system. Suggestion: Let each tick mark on the horizontal axis, labeled n, represent 5 units. Extend the horizontal axis to include $n = 25$. Let each tick mark on the vertical axis, labeled Q, represent 5 units and extend the axis to include $Q = 50$.

c. Use your graph from part (b) to estimate the percentage of U.S. adults who will believe that a college education is available to most qualified students in 2018.

d. Use the formula to project the percentage of U.S. adults who will believe that a college education is available to most qualified students in 2018.

Writing in Mathematics

95. What is the rectangular coordinate system?

96. Explain how to plot a point in the rectangular coordinate system. Give an example with your explanation.

97. Explain why $(5, -2)$ and $(-2, 5)$ do not represent the same point.

98. Explain how to find the coordinates of a point in the rectangular coordinate system.

99. How do you determine whether an ordered pair is a solution of an equation in two variables, x and y?

100. Explain how to find ordered pairs that are solutions of an equation in two variables, x and y.

101. What is the graph of an equation?

102. Explain how to graph an equation in two variables in the rectangular coordinate system.

Critical Thinking Exercises

Make Sense? *In Exercises 103–106, determine whether each statement "makes sense" or "does not make sense" and explain your reasoning.*

103. When I know that an equation's graph is a straight line, I don't need to plot more than two points, although I sometimes plot three just to check that the points line up.

104. The graph that I'm looking at is U-shaped, so its equation cannot be of the form $y = mx + b$.

105. I'm working with a linear equation in two variables and found that $(-2, 2)$, $(0, 0)$, and $(2, 2)$ are solutions.

106. When a real-world situation is modeled with a linear equation in two variables, I can use its graph to predict specific information about the situation.

In Exercises 107–110, determine whether each statement is true or false. If the statement is false, make the necessary change(s) to produce a true statement.

107. The graph of $y = 3x + 1$ is the graph of $y = 2x$ shifted up 1 unit.

108. The graph of any equation in the form $y = mx + b$ passes through the point $(0, b)$.

109. The ordered pair $(3, 4)$ satisfies the equation

$$2y - 3x = -6.$$

110. If $(2, 5)$ satisfies an equation, then $(5, 2)$ also satisfies the equation.

111. a. Graph each of the following points:

$$\left(1, \frac{1}{2}\right), (2, 1), \left(3, \frac{3}{2}\right), (4, 2).$$

Parts (b)–(d) can be answered by changing the sign of one or both coordinates of the points in part (a).

b. What must be done to the coordinates so that the resulting graph is a mirror-image reflection about the y-axis of your graph in part (a)?

c. What must be done to the coordinates so that the resulting graph is a mirror-image reflection about the x-axis of your graph in part (a)?

d. What must be done to the coordinates so that the resulting graph is a straight-line extension of your graph in part (a)?

Technology Exercises

Use a graphing utility to graph each equation in Exercises 112–115 in a standard viewing rectangle, $[-10, 10, 1]$ by $[-10, 10, 1]$. Then use the TRACE *feature to trace along the line and find the coordinates of two points.*

112. $y = 2x - 1$

113. $y = -3x + 2$

114. $y = \frac{1}{2}x$

115. $y = \frac{3}{4}x - 2$

116. Use a graphing utility to verify any five of your hand-drawn graphs in Exercises 57–80. Use an appropriate viewing rectangle and the ZOOM SQUARE feature to make the graph look like the one you drew by hand.

Review Exercises

117. Solve: $3x + 5 = 4(2x - 3) + 7$.

118. Simplify: $3(1 - 2 \cdot 5) - (-28)$.

119. Solve for h: $V = \frac{1}{3}Ah$.

Preview Exercises

Exercises 120–122 will help you prepare for the material covered in the next section. Remember that a solution of an equation in two variables is an ordered pair.

120. Let $y = 0$ and find a solution of $3x - 4y = 24$.

121. Let $x = 0$ and find a solution of $3x - 4y = 24$.

122. Let $x = 0$ and find a solution of $x + 2y = 0$.

SECTION 2

Graphing Linear Equations Using Intercepts

Objectives

1. Use a graph to identify intercepts.
2. Graph a linear equation in two variables using intercepts.
3. Graph horizontal or vertical lines.

It's hard to believe that this gas-guzzler, with its huge fins and overstated design, was available in 1957 for approximately \$1800. Sadly, its elegance quickly faded, depreciating linearly by \$300 per year, often sold for scrap just six years after its glorious emergence from the dealer's showroom.

Jeff Greenberg/PhotoEdit, Inc.

From the casual observations on the previous page, we can obtain a mathematical model and its graph. The model is

$$y = -300x + 1800.$$

The car depreciated by \$300 per year for x years.

The new car was worth \$1800.

In this model, y is the car's value after x years. **Figure 13** shows the equation's graph.

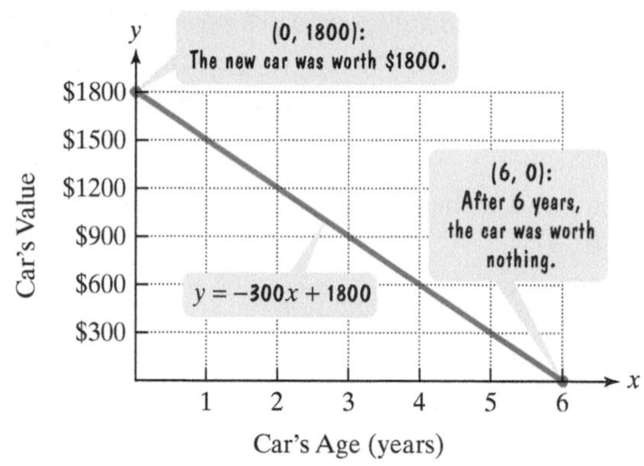

Figure 13

Here are some important observations about the model and its graph:

- The points in **Figure 13** show where the graph intersects the y-axis and where it intersects the x-axis. These important points are the topic of this section.
- We can rewrite the model, $y = -300x + 1800$, by adding $300x$ to both sides:

$$300x + y = 1800.$$

The form of this equation is $Ax + By = C$.

$$300x + y = 1800$$

A, the coefficient of x, is 300.

B, the coefficient of y, is 1.

C, the constant on the right, is 1800.

All equations of the form $Ax + By = C$ are straight lines when graphed as long as A and B are not both zero. To graph linear equations of this form, we will use the intercepts.

1 Use a graph to identify intercepts.

Intercepts

An ***x*-intercept** of a graph is the x-coordinate of a point where the graph intersects the x-axis. For example, look at the graph of $2x - 4y = 8$ in **Figure 14**. The graph crosses the x-axis at $(4, 0)$. Thus, the x-intercept is 4. **The *y*-coordinate corresponding to an *x*-intercept is always zero.**

A ***y*-intercept** of a graph is the y-coordinate of a point where the graph intersects the y-axis. The graph of $2x - 4y = 8$ in **Figure 14** shows that the graph crosses the y-axis at $(0, -2)$. Thus, the y-intercept is -2. **The *x*-coordinate corresponding to a *y*-intercept is always zero.**

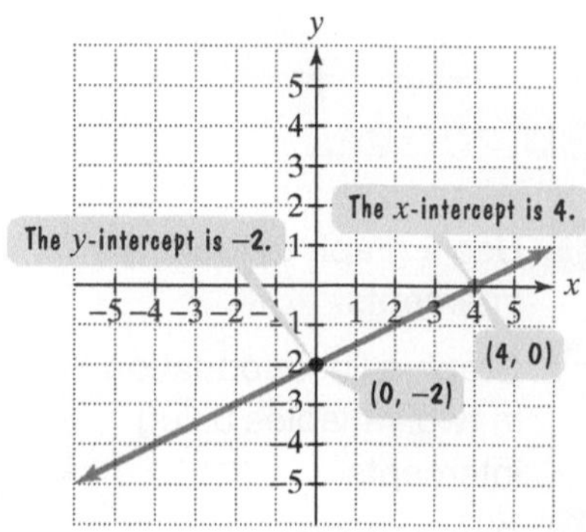

Figure 14
The graph of $2x - 4y = 8$

Great Question!

Are single numbers the only way to represent intercepts? Can ordered pairs also be used?

Mathematicians tend to use two ways to describe intercepts. Did you notice that we are using single numbers? If a graph's x-intercept is a, it passes through the point $(a, 0)$. If a graph's y-intercept is b, it passes through the point $(0, b)$.

Some books state that the x-intercept is the *point* $(a, 0)$ and the x-intercept is *at a* on the x-axis. Similarly, the y-intercept is the *point* $(0, b)$ and the y-intercept is *at b* on the y-axis. In these descriptions, the intercepts are the actual points where a graph intersects the axes.

Although we'll describe intercepts as single numbers, we'll immediately state the point on the x- or y-axis that the graph passes through. Here's the important thing to keep in mind:

x-intercept: The corresponding y is 0.
y-intercept: The corresponding x is 0.

EXAMPLE 1 Identifying Intercepts

Identify the x- and y-intercepts.

a.

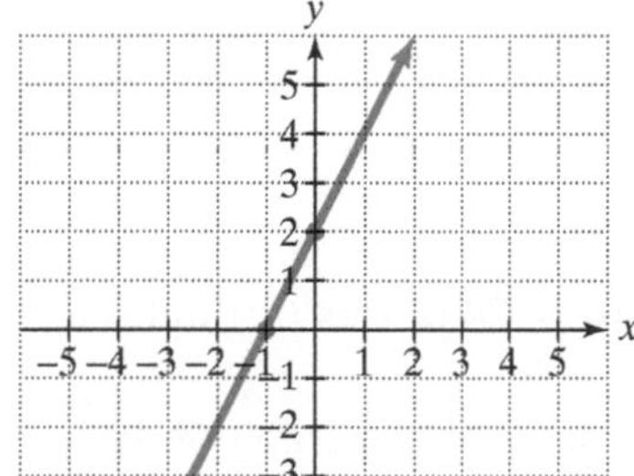

b.

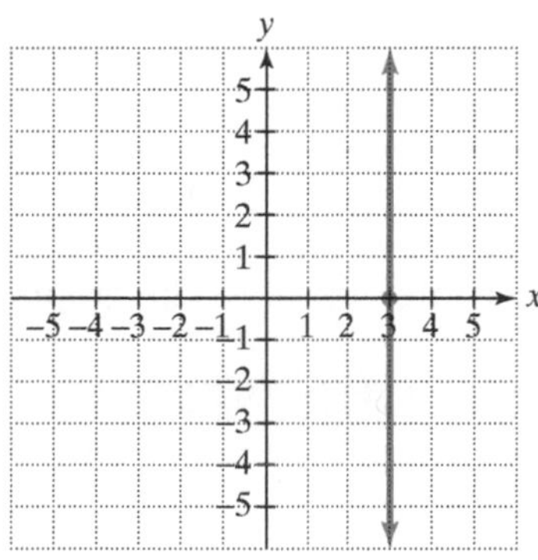

c.

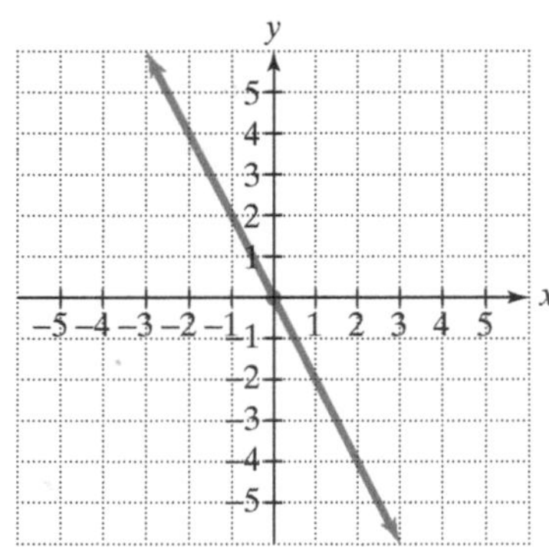

Solution

a. The graph crosses the x-axis at $(-1, 0)$. Thus, the x-intercept is -1. The graph crosses the y-axis at $(0, 2)$. Thus, the y-intercept is 2.

b. The graph crosses the x-axis at $(3, 0)$, so the x-intercept is 3. This vertical line does not cross the y-axis. Thus, there is no y-intercept.

c. This graph crosses the x- and y-axes at the same point, the origin. Because the graph crosses both axes at $(0, 0)$, the x-intercept is 0 and the y-intercept is 0. ■

✓ **CHECK POINT 1** Identify the x- and y-intercepts.

a.

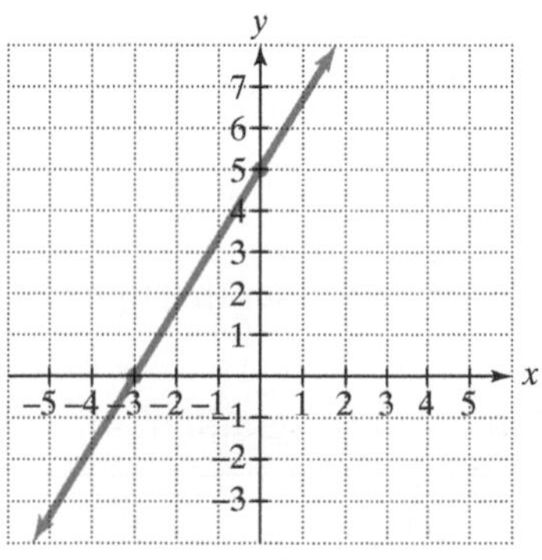

b.

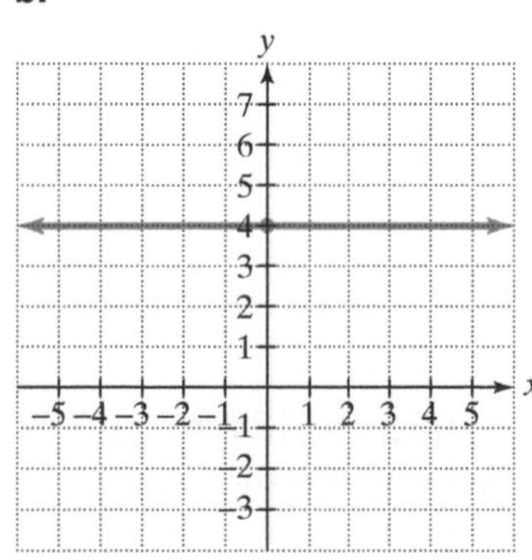

c.

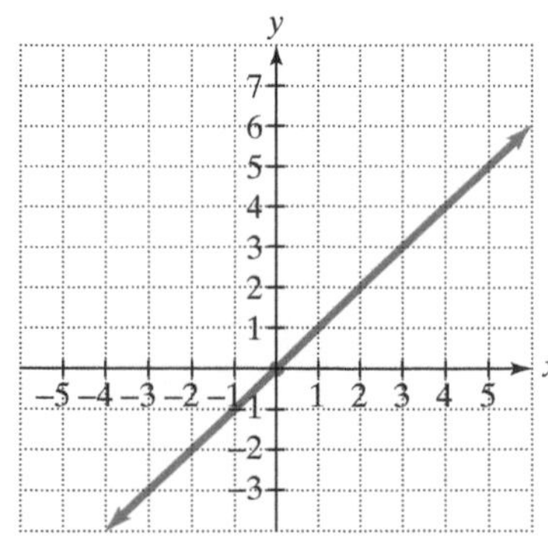

2 Graph a linear equation in two variables using intercepts.

Great Question!

Can x or y have exponents in the standard form of the equation of a line?

In the form $Ax + By = C$, the exponent that is understood on both x and y is 1. Neither x nor y can have exponents other than 1.

Forms of Equations That Do Not Represent Lines

$Ax^2 + By^2 = C \quad Ax + By^2 = C$

Exponents on x and y are not both 1.

Graphing Using Intercepts

An equation of the form $Ax + By = C$, where A, B, and C are integers, is called the **standard form** of the equation of a line. The equation can be graphed by finding the x- and y-intercepts, plotting the intercepts, and drawing a straight line through these points. How do we find the intercepts of a line, given its equation? Because the y-coordinate of the x-intercept is 0, to find the x-intercept,

- Substitute 0 for y in the equation.
- Solve for x.

EXAMPLE 2 Finding the x-Intercept

Find the x-intercept of the graph of $3x - 4y = 24$.

Solution To find the x-intercept, let $y = 0$ and solve for x.

$3x - 4y = 24$ This is the given equation.

$3x - 4 \cdot 0 = 24$ Let $y = 0$.

$3x = 24$ Simplify: $4 \cdot 0 = 0$ and $3x - 0 = 3x$.

$x = 8$ Divide both sides by 3.

The x-intercept is 8. The graph of $3x - 4y = 24$ passes through the point $(8, 0)$. ■

✓ **CHECK POINT 2** Find the x-intercept of the graph of $4x - 3y = 12$.

Because the x-coordinate of the y-intercept is 0, to find the y-intercept,

- Substitute 0 for x in the equation.
- Solve for y.

EXAMPLE 3 Finding the y-Intercept

Find the y-intercept of the graph of $3x - 4y = 24$.

Solution To find the y-intercept, let $x = 0$ and solve for y.

$3x - 4y = 24$ This is the given equation.

$3 \cdot 0 - 4y = 24$ Let $x = 0$.

$-4y = 24$ Simplify: $3 \cdot 0 = 0$ and $0 - 4y = -4y$.

$y = -6$ Divide both sides by -4.

The y-intercept is -6. The graph of $3x - 4y = 24$ passes through the point $(0, -6)$. ■

✓ **CHECK POINT 3** Find the y-intercept of the graph of $4x - 3y = 12$.

When graphing using intercepts, it is a good idea to use a third point, a checkpoint, before drawing the line. A checkpoint can be obtained by selecting a value for either variable, other than 0, and finding the corresponding value for the other variable. The checkpoint should lie on the same line as the x- and y-intercepts. If it does not, recheck your work and find the error.

Using Intercepts to Graph $Ax + By = C$

1. Find the x-intercept. Let $y = 0$ and solve for x.
2. Find the y-intercept. Let $x = 0$ and solve for y.
3. Find a checkpoint, a third ordered-pair solution.
4. Graph the equation by drawing a line through the three points.

EXAMPLE 4 Using Intercepts to Graph a Linear Equation

Graph: $3x + 2y = 6$.

Solution

Step 1. Find the x-intercept. Let $y = 0$ and solve for x.

$$3x + 2 \cdot 0 = 6 \quad \text{Replace } y \text{ with 0 in } 3x + 2y = 6.$$

$$3x = 6 \quad \text{Simplify.}$$

$$x = 2 \quad \text{Divide both sides by 3.}$$

The x-intercept is 2, so the line passes through $(2, 0)$.

Step 2. Find the y-intercept. Let $x = 0$ and solve for y.

$$3 \cdot 0 + 2y = 6 \quad \text{Replace } x \text{ with 0 in } 3x + 2y = 6.$$

$$2y = 6 \quad \text{Simplify.}$$

$$y = 3 \quad \text{Divide both sides by 2.}$$

The y-intercept is 3, so the line passes through $(0, 3)$.

Step 3. Find a checkpoint, a third ordered-pair solution. For our checkpoint, we will let $x = 1$ and find the corresponding value for y.

$$3x + 2y = 6 \quad \text{This is the given equation.}$$

$$3 \cdot 1 + 2y = 6 \quad \text{Substitute 1 for x.}$$

$$3 + 2y = 6 \quad \text{Simplify.}$$

$$2y = 3 \quad \text{Subtract 3 from both sides.}$$

$$y = \frac{3}{2} \quad \text{Divide both sides by 2.}$$

The checkpoint is the ordered pair $\left(1, \frac{3}{2}\right)$, or $(1, 1.5)$.

Step 4. Graph the equation by drawing a line through the three points. The three points in **Figure 15** lie along the same line. Drawing a line through the three points results in the graph of $3x + 2y = 6$. ■

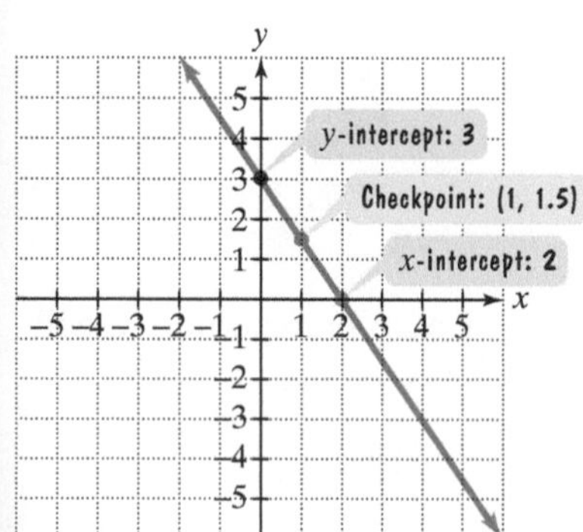

Figure 15
The graph of $3x + 2y = 6$

Using Technology

You can use a graphing utility to graph equations of the form $Ax + By = C$. Begin by solving the equation for y. For example, to graph $3x + 2y = 6$, solve the equation for y.

$$3x + 2y = 6 \quad \text{This is the equation to be graphed.}$$

$$3x - 3x + 2y = -3x + 6 \quad \text{Subtract 3x from both sides.}$$

$$2y = -3x + 6 \quad \text{Simplify.}$$

$$\frac{2y}{2} = \frac{-3x + 6}{2} \quad \text{Divide both sides by 2.}$$

$$y = -\frac{3}{2}x + 3 \quad \text{Divide each term of } -3x + 6 \text{ by 2.}$$

This is the equation to enter into your graphing utility. The graph of $y = -\frac{3}{2}x + 3$ or, equivalently, $3x + 2y = 6$, is shown below in a $[-6, 6, 1]$ by $[-6, 6, 1]$ viewing rectangle.

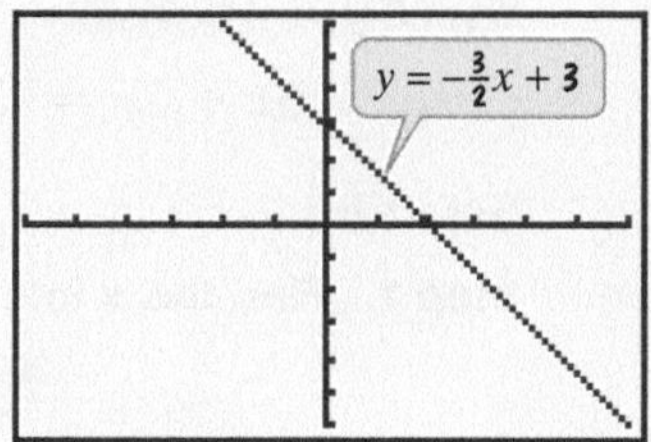

✓ **CHECK POINT 4** Graph: $2x + 3y = 6$.

EXAMPLE 5 Using Intercepts to Graph a Linear Equation

Graph: $2x - y = 4$.

Solution

Step 1. Find the x-intercept. Let $y = 0$ and solve for x.

$$2x - 0 = 4 \quad \text{Replace y with 0 in } 2x - y = 4.$$

$$2x = 4 \quad \text{Simplify.}$$

$$x = 2 \quad \text{Divide both sides by 2.}$$

The x-intercept is 2, so the line passes through $(2, 0)$.

Step 2. Find the y-intercept. Let $x = 0$ and solve for y.

$$2 \cdot 0 - y = 4 \quad \text{Replace x with 0 in } 2x - y = 4.$$

$$-y = 4 \quad \text{Simplify.}$$

$$y = -4 \quad \text{Divide (or multiply) both sides by } -1.$$

The y-intercept is -4, so the line passes through $(0, -4)$.

Step 3. Find a checkpoint, a third ordered-pair solution. For our checkpoint, we will let $x = 1$ and find the corresponding value for y.

$$2x - y = 4 \quad \text{This is the given equation.}$$

$$2 \cdot 1 - y = 4 \quad \text{Substitute 1 for x.}$$

$$2 - y = 4 \quad \text{Simplify.}$$

$$-y = 2 \quad \text{Subtract 2 from both sides.}$$

$$y = -2 \quad \text{Divide (or multiply) both sides by } -1.$$

The checkpoint is $(1, -2)$.

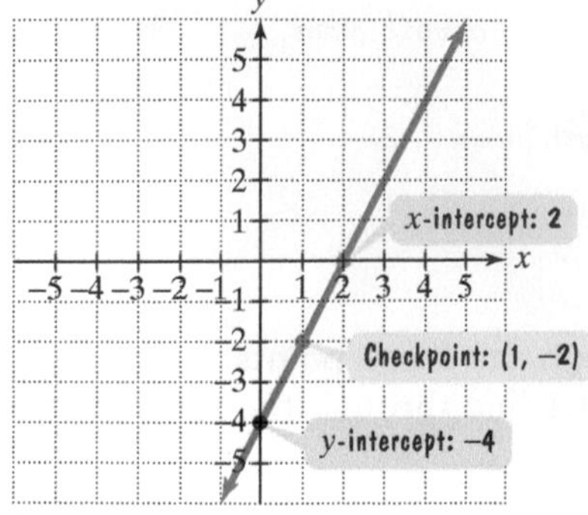

Figure 16
The graph of $2x - y = 4$

Step 4. Graph the equation by drawing a line through the three points. The three points in **Figure 16** lie along the same line. Drawing a line through the three points results in the graph of $2x - y = 4$. ■

✓ **CHECK POINT 5** Graph: $x - 2y = 4$.

We have seen that not all lines have two different intercepts. Some lines pass through the origin. Thus, they have an x-intercept of 0 and a y-intercept of 0. Is it possible to recognize these lines by their equations? Yes. **The graph of the linear equation $Ax + By = 0$ passes through the origin.** Notice that the constant on the right side of this equation is 0.

An equation of the form $Ax + By = 0$ can be graphed by using the origin as one point on the line. Find two other points by finding two other solutions of the equation. Select values for either variable, other than 0, and find the corresponding values for the other variable.

EXAMPLE 6 Graphing a Linear Equation of the Form $Ax + By = 0$

Graph: $x + 2y = 0$.

Solution Because the constant on the right is 0, the graph passes through the origin. The x- and y-intercepts are both 0. Remember that we are using two points and a checkpoint to graph a line. Thus, we still want to find two other points. Let $y = -1$ to find a second ordered-pair solution. Let $y = 1$ to find a third ordered-pair (checkpoint) solution.

$x + 2y = 0$	$x + 2y = 0$
Let $y = -1$.	Let $y = 1$.
$x + 2(-1) = 0$	$x + 2 \cdot 1 = 0$
$x + (-2) = 0$	$x + 2 = 0$
$x = 2$	$x = -2$

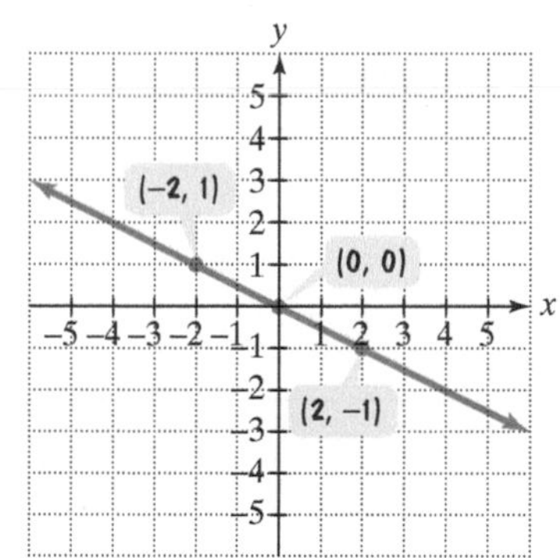

Figure 17
The graph of $x + 2y = 0$

The solutions are $(2, -1)$ and $(-2, 1)$. Plot these two points, as well as the origin—that is, $(0, 0)$. The three points in **Figure 17** lie along the same line. Drawing a line through the three points results in the graph of $x + 2y = 0$. ■

✓ **CHECK POINT 6** Graph: $x + 3y = 0$.

---

3 Graph horizontal or vertical lines.

Equations of Horizontal and Vertical Lines

We know that the graph of any equation of the form $Ax + By = C$ is a line as long as A and B are not both zero. What happens if A or B, but not both, is zero? Example 7 shows that if $A = 0$, the equation $Ax + By = C$ has no x-term and the graph is a horizontal line.

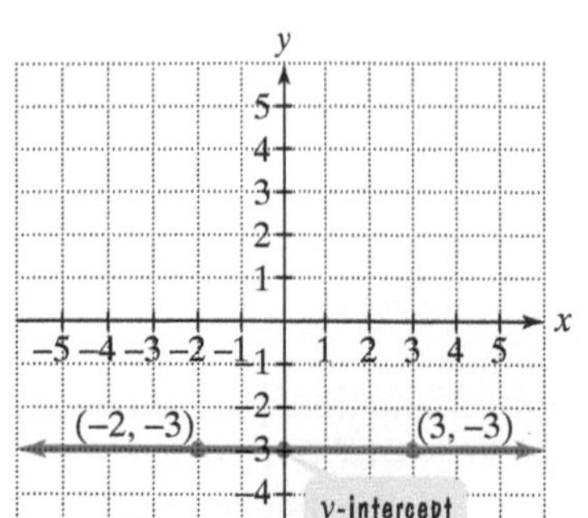

Figure 18
The graph of $y = -3$

EXAMPLE 7 Graphing a Horizontal Line

Graph: $y = -3$.

Solution All ordered pairs that are solutions of $y = -3$ have a value of y that is -3. Any value can be used for x. In the table on the right, we have selected three of the possible values for x: -2, 0, and 3. The table shows that three ordered pairs that are solutions of $y = -3$ are $(-2, -3)$, $(0, -3)$, and $(3, -3)$. Drawing a line that passes through the three points gives the horizontal line shown in **Figure 18**. ■

x	$y = -3$	(x, y)
−2	−3	(−2, −3)
0	−3	(0, −3)
3	−3	(3, −3)

For all choices of x, y is a constant -3.

✓ **CHECK POINT 7** Graph: $y = 3$.

Example 8 shows that if $B = 0$, the equation $Ax + By = C$ has no y-term and the graph is a vertical line.

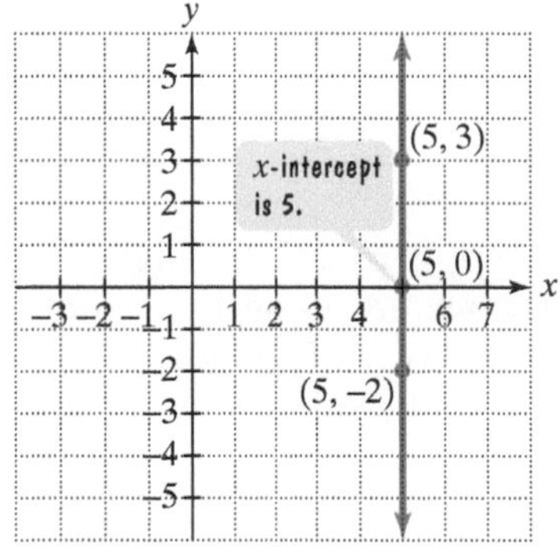

Figure 19
The graph of $x = 5$

EXAMPLE 8 Graphing a Vertical Line

Graph: $x = 5$.

Solution All ordered pairs that are solutions of $x = 5$ have a value of x that is 5. Any value can be used for y. In the table on the right, we have selected three of the possible values for y: -2, 0, and 3. The table shows that three ordered pairs that are solutions of $x = 5$ are $(5, -2)$, $(5, 0)$, and $(5, 3)$. Drawing a line that passes through the three points gives the vertical line shown in **Figure 19**. ■

For all choices of y,

$x = 5$	y	(x, y)
5	−2	(5, −2)
5	0	(5, 0)
5	3	(5, 3)

x is always 5.

Great Question!

Why isn't the graph of $x = 5$ just a single point at 5 on a number line?

Do not confuse two-dimensional graphing and one-dimensional graphing of $x = 5$. The graph of $x = 5$ in a two-dimensional rectangular coordinate system is the vertical line in **Figure 19**. By contrast, the graph of $x = 5$ on a one-dimensional number line representing values of x is a single point at 5:

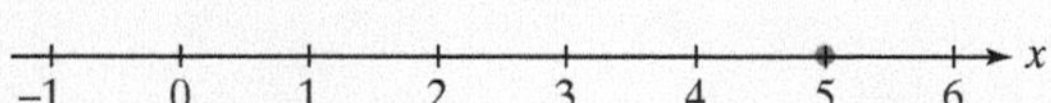

✓ **CHECK POINT 8** Graph: $x = -2$.

Horizontal and Vertical Lines

The graph of $y = b$ is a horizontal line. The y-intercept is b.

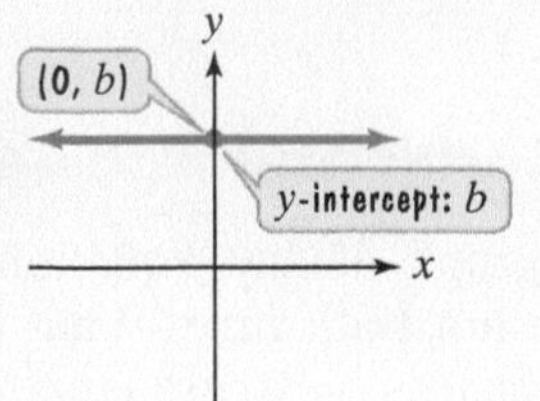

The graph of $x = a$ is a vertical line. The x-intercept is a.

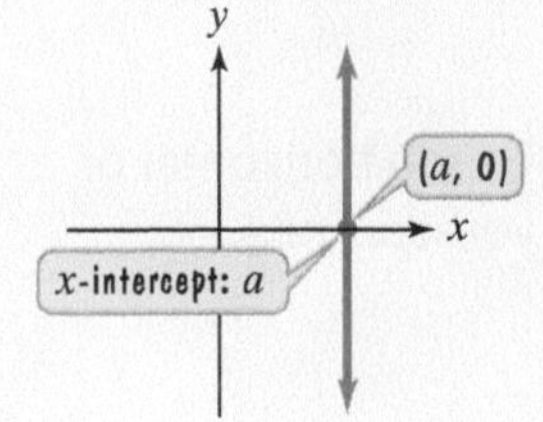

CONCEPT AND VOCABULARY CHECK

Fill in each blank so that the resulting statement is true.

1. The x-coordinate of a point where a graph crosses the x-axis is called a/an ____________.
2. The y-coordinate of a point where a graph crosses the y-axis is called a/an ____________.
3. The point (4, 0) lies along a line, so 4 is the ____________ of that line.
4. The point (0, 3) lies along a line, so 3 is the ____________ of that line.
5. An equation that can be written in the form $Ax + By = C$, where A and B are not both zero, is called the ____________ form of the equation of a line.
6. Given the equation $Ax + By = C$, to find the x-intercept (if there is one), let ____________ = 0 and solve for ____________.
7. Given the equation $Ax + By = C$, to find the y-intercept (if there is one), let ____________ = 0 and solve for ____________.
8. The graph of the equation $y = 3$ is a/an ____________ line.
9. The graph of the equation $x = -2$ is a/an ____________ line.

2 EXERCISE SET

MyMathLab®

Watch the videos in MyMathLab

Download the MyDashBoard App

Practice Exercises

In Exercises 1–8, use the graph to identify the

a. *x-intercept, or state that there is no x-intercept;*

b. *y-intercept, or state that there is no y-intercept.*

1.

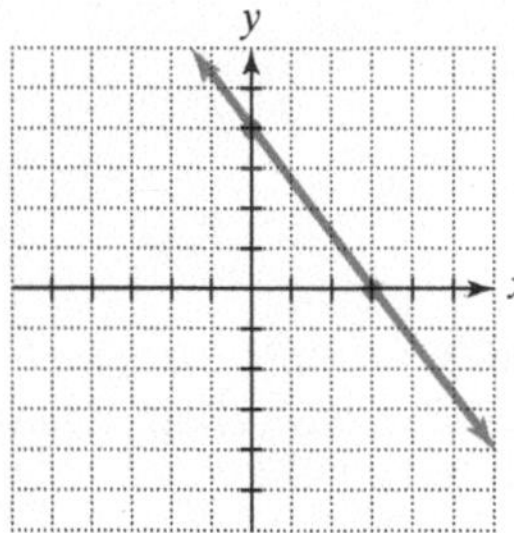

2.

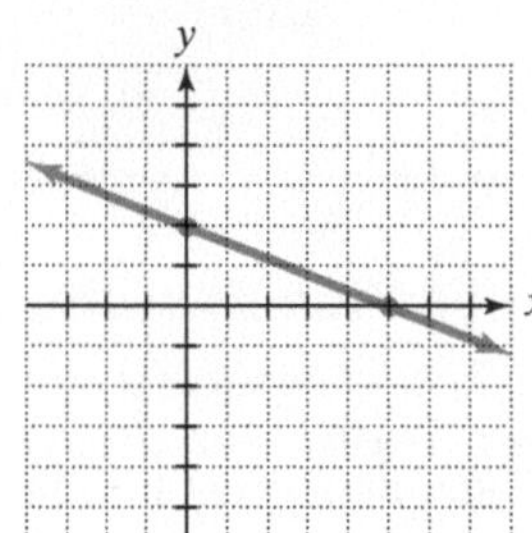

3.

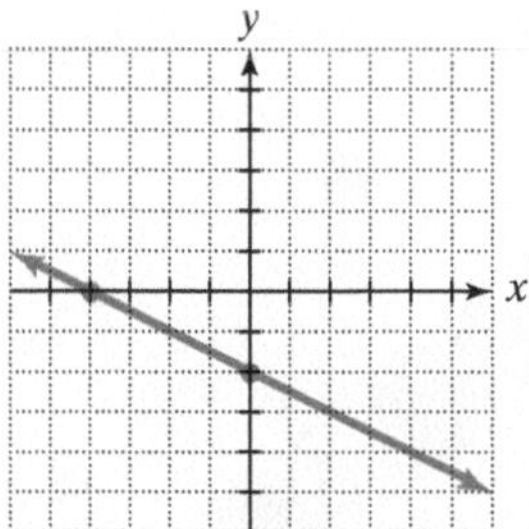

4.

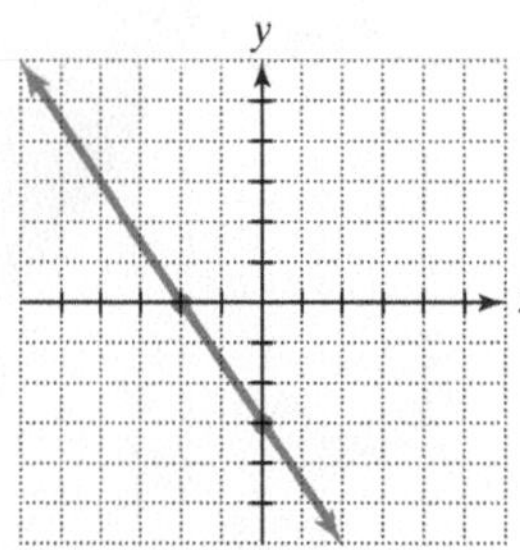

5.

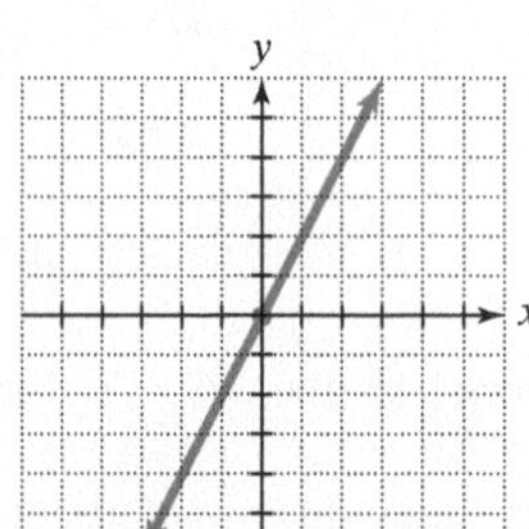

6.

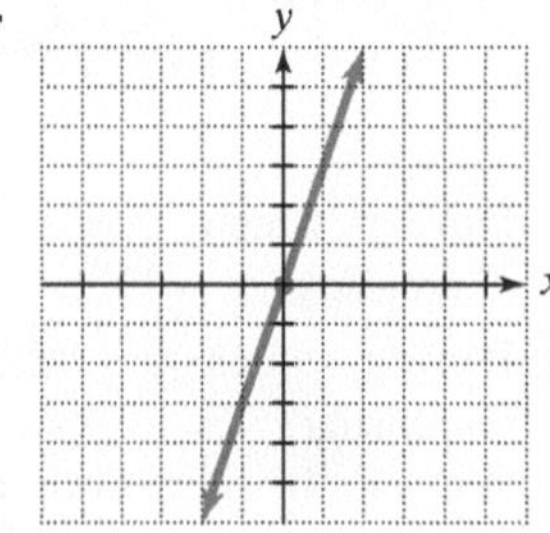

7.

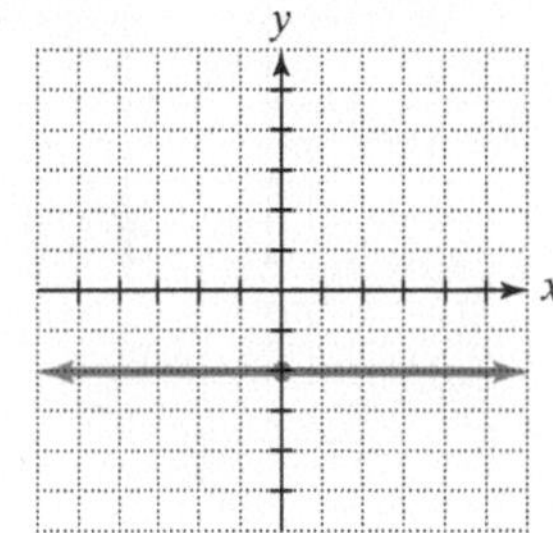

8.

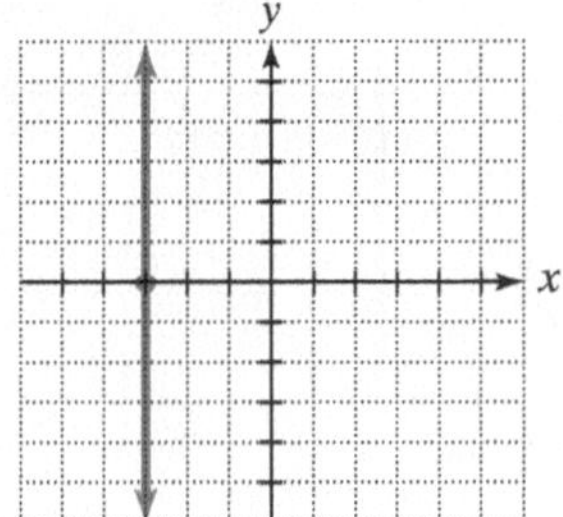

In Exercises 9–18, find the x-intercept and the y-intercept of the graph of each equation. Do not graph the equation.

9. $2x + 5y = 20$
10. $2x + 6y = 30$
11. $2x - 3y = 15$
12. $4x - 5y = 10$
13. $-x + 3y = -8$
14. $-x + 3y = -10$
15. $7x - 9y = 0$
16. $8x - 11y = 0$
17. $2x = 3y - 11$
18. $2x = 4y - 13$

In Exercises 19–40, use intercepts and a checkpoint to graph each equation.

19. $x + y = 5$
20. $x + y = 6$
21. $x + 3y = 6$
22. $2x + y = 4$
23. $6x - 9y = 18$
24. $6x - 2y = 12$
25. $-x + 4y = 6$
26. $-x + 3y = 10$
27. $2x - y = 7$
28. $2x - y = 5$

29. $3x = 5y - 15$

30. $2x = 3y + 6$

31. $25y = 100 - 50x$

32. $10y = 60 - 40x$

33. $2x - 8y = 12$

34. $3x - 6y = 15$

35. $x + 2y = 0$

36. $2x + y = 0$

37. $y - 3x = 0$

38. $y - 4x = 0$

39. $2x - 3y = -11$

40. $3x - 2y = -7$

In Exercises 41–46, write an equation for each graph.

41.

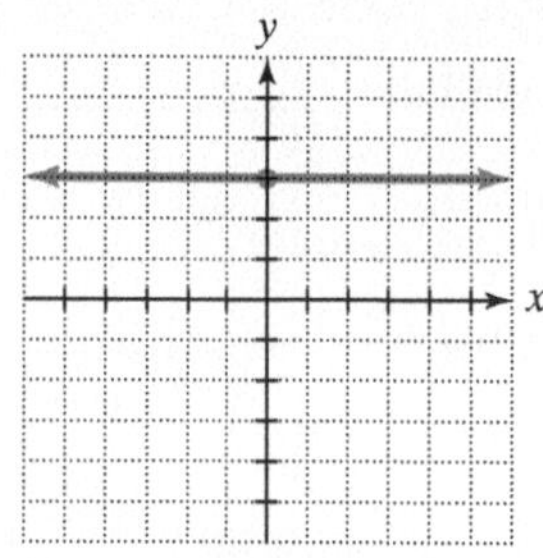

42.

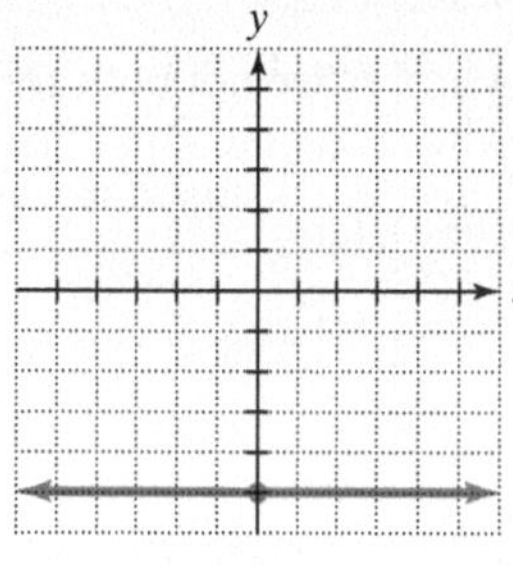

43.

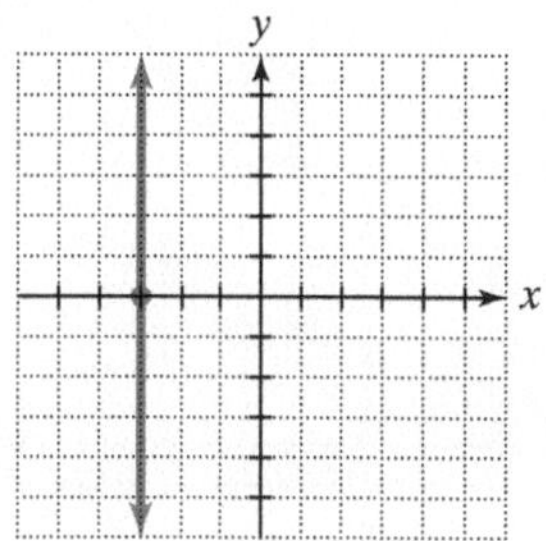

44.

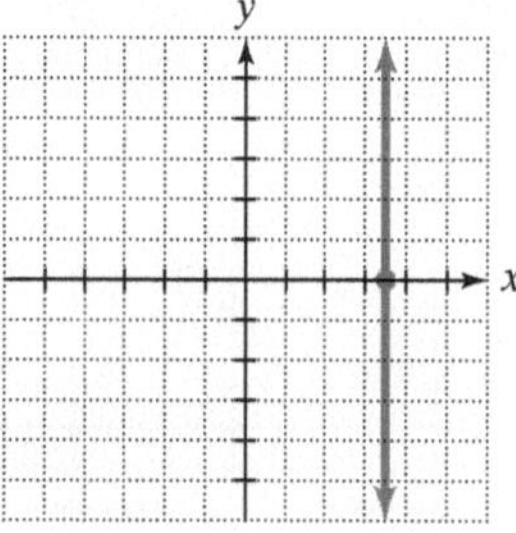

45.

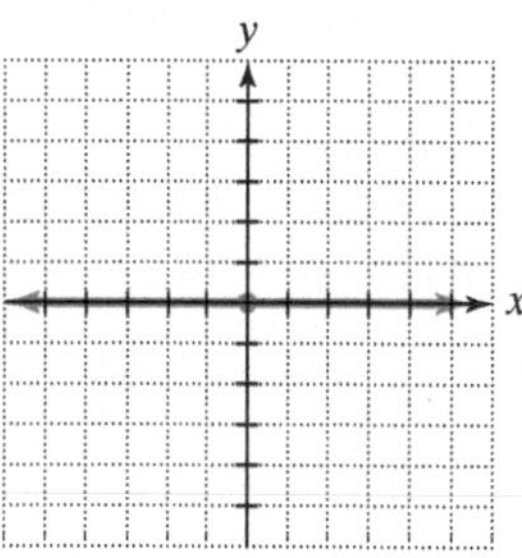

46.

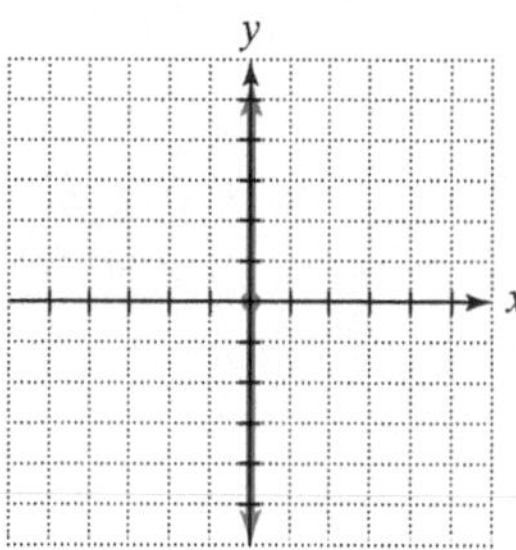

In Exercises 47–62, graph each equation.

47. $y = 4$

48. $y = 2$

49. $y = -2$

50. $y = -3$

51. $x = 2$

52. $x = 4$

53. $x + 1 = 0$

54. $x + 5 = 0$

55. $y - 3.5 = 0$

56. $y - 2.5 = 0$

57. $x = 0$

58. $y = 0$

59. $3y = 9$

60. $5y = 20$

61. $12 - 3x = 0$

62. $12 - 4x = 0$

Practice PLUS

In Exercises 63–68, match each equation with one of the graphs shown in Exercises 1–8.

63. $3x + 2y = -6$

64. $x + 2y = -4$

65. $y = -2$

66. $x = -3$

67. $4x + 3y = 12$

68. $2x + 5y = 10$

In Exercises 69–70,

a. *Write a linear equation in standard form satisfying the given condition. Assume that all measurements shown in each figure are in feet.*

b. *Graph the equation in part (a). Because x and y must be nonnegative (why?), limit your final graph to quadrant I and its boundaries.*

69. The perimeter of the larger rectangle is 58 feet.

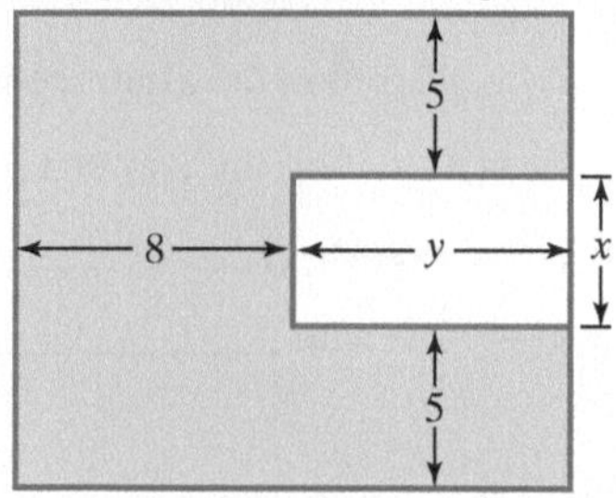

70. The perimeter of the shaded trapezoid is 84 feet.

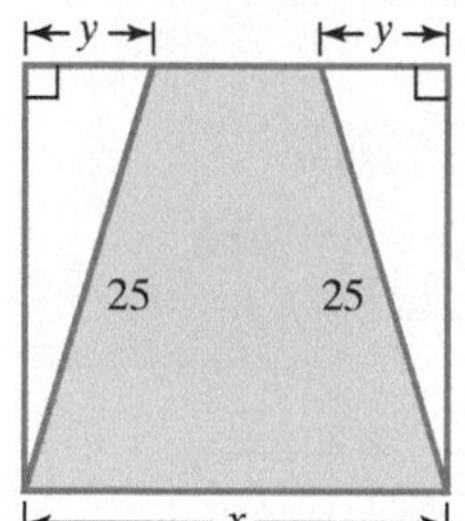

Application Exercises

The flight of an eagle is observed for 30 seconds. The graph shows the eagle's height, in meters, during this period of time. Use the graph to solve Exercises 71–75.

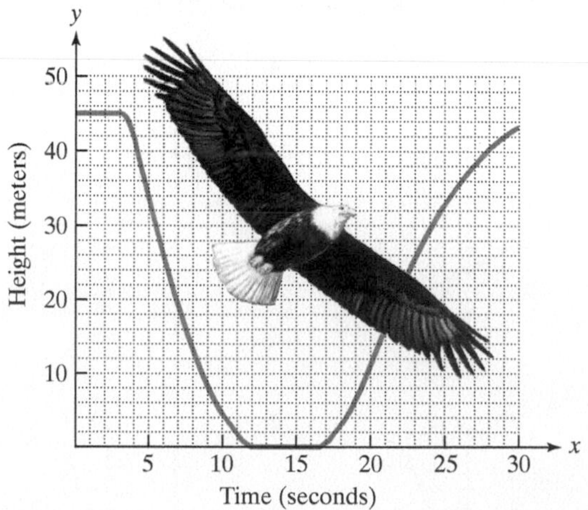

71. During which period of time is the eagle's height decreasing?

72. During which period of time is the eagle's height increasing?

73. What is the y-intercept? What does this mean about the eagle's height at the beginning of the observation?

(In Exercises 74–75, be sure to refer to the graph at the bottom of the previous page.)

74. During the first three seconds of observation, the eagle's flight is graphed as a horizontal line. Write the equation of the line. What does this mean about the eagle's flight pattern during this time?

75. Use integers to write five x-intercepts of the graph. What is the eagle doing during these times?

76. A new car worth \$24,000 is depreciating in value by \$3000 per year. The mathematical model

$$y = -3000x + 24{,}000$$

describes the car's value, y, in dollars, after x years.

a. Find the x-intercept. Describe what this means in terms of the car's value.

b. Find the y-intercept. Describe what this means in terms of the car's value.

c. Use the intercepts to graph the linear equation. Because x and y must be nonnegative (why?), limit your graph to quadrant I and its boundaries.

d. Use your graph to estimate the car's value after five years.

77. A new car worth \$45,000 is depreciating in value by \$5000 per year. The mathematical model

$$y = -5000x + 45{,}000$$

describes the car's value, y, in dollars, after x years.

a. Find the x-intercept. Describe what this means in terms of the car's value.

b. Find the y-intercept. Describe what this means in terms of the car's value.

c. Use the intercepts to graph the linear equation. Because x and y must be nonnegative (why?), limit your graph to quadrant I and its boundaries.

d. Use your graph to estimate the car's value after five years.

Writing in Mathematics

78. What is an x-intercept of a graph?

79. What is a y-intercept of a graph?

80. If you are given an equation of the form $Ax + By = C$, explain how to find the x-intercept.

81. If you are given an equation of the form $Ax + By = C$, explain how to find the y-intercept.

82. Explain how to graph $Ax + By = C$ if C is not equal to zero.

83. Explain how to graph a linear equation of the form $Ax + By = 0$.

84. How many points are needed to graph a line? How many should actually be used? Explain.

85. Describe the graph of $y = 200$.

86. Describe the graph of $x = -100$.

Critical Thinking Exercises

Make Sense? *In Exercises 87–90, determine whether each statement "makes sense" or "does not make sense" and explain your reasoning.*

87. If I could be absolutely certain that I have not made an algebraic error in obtaining intercepts, I would not need to use checkpoints.

88. I like to select a point represented by one of the intercepts as my checkpoint.

89. The graphs of $2x - 3y = -18$ and $-2x + 3y = 18$ must have the same intercepts because I can see that the equations are equivalent.

90. From 1997 through 2007, the federal minimum wage remained constant at \$5.15 per hour, so I modeled the situation with $y = 5.15$ and the graph of a vertical line.

In Exercises 91–92, find the coefficients that must be placed in each shaded area so that the equation's graph will be a line with the specified intercepts.

91. $\square\, x + \square\, y = 10$; x-intercept $= 5$; y-intercept $= 2$

92. $\square\, x + \square\, y = 12$; x-intercept $= -2$; y-intercept $= 4$

Technology Exercises

93. Use a graphing utility to verify any five of your hand-drawn graphs in Exercises 19–40. Solve the equation for y before entering it.

In Exercises 94–97, use a graphing utility to graph each equation. You will need to solve the equation for y before entering it. Use the graph displayed on the screen to identify the x-intercept and the y-intercept.

94. $2x + y = 4$

95. $3x - y = 9$

96. $2x + 3y = 30$

97. $4x - 2y = -40$

Review Exercises

98. Find the absolute value: $|-13.4|$.

99. Simplify: $7x - (3x - 5)$.

100. Solve: $8(x - 2) - 2(x - 3) \le 8x$.

Preview Exercises

Exercises 101–103 will help you prepare for the material covered in the next section. In each exercise, evaluate

$$\frac{y_2 - y_1}{x_2 - x_1}$$

for the given ordered pairs (x_1, y_1) and (x_2, y_2).

101. $(x_1, y_1) = (1, 3)$; $(x_2, y_2) = (6, 13)$

102. $(x_1, y_1) = (4, -2)$; $(x_2, y_2) = (6, -4)$

103. $(x_1, y_1) = (3, 4)$; $(x_2, y_2) = (5, 4)$

SECTION 3

Slope

Objectives

1. Compute a line's slope.
2. Use slope to show that lines are parallel.
3. Use slope to show that lines are perpendicular.
4. Calculate rate of change in applied situations.

Exactostock/SuperStock

Corbis Flirt/Alamy

A best guess at the future of our nation indicates that the numbers of men and women living alone will increase each year. **Figure 20** shows that in 2008, 14.7 million men and 18.3 million women lived alone, an increase over the numbers displayed in the graph for 1990.

By looking at **Figure 20**, can you tell that the green graph representing men is steeper than the red graph representing women? This indicates a greater rate of increase in the millions of men living alone than in the millions of women living alone over the period from 1990 through 2008. In this section, we will study the idea of a line's steepness and see what this has to do with how its variables are changing.

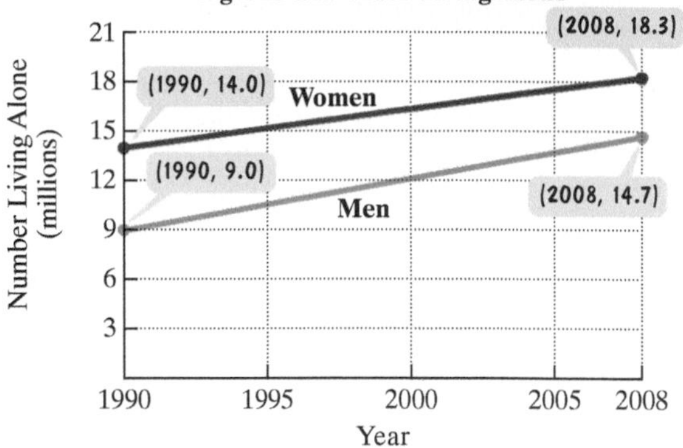

Figure 20
Source: U.S. Census Bureau

1 Compute a line's slope.

The Slope of a Line

Mathematicians have developed a useful measure of the steepness of a line, called the **slope** of the line. Slope compares the vertical change (the **rise**) to the horizontal change (the **run**) when moving from one fixed point to another along the line. To calculate the slope of a line, we use a ratio that compares the change in y (the rise) to the change in x (the run).

Definition of Slope

The **slope** of the line through the distinct points (x_1, y_1) and (x_2, y_2) is

$$\frac{\text{Change in } y}{\text{Change in } x} = \frac{\text{Rise}}{\text{Run}} = \frac{y_2 - y_1}{x_2 - x_1}$$

Rise — Vertical change
Run — Horizontal change

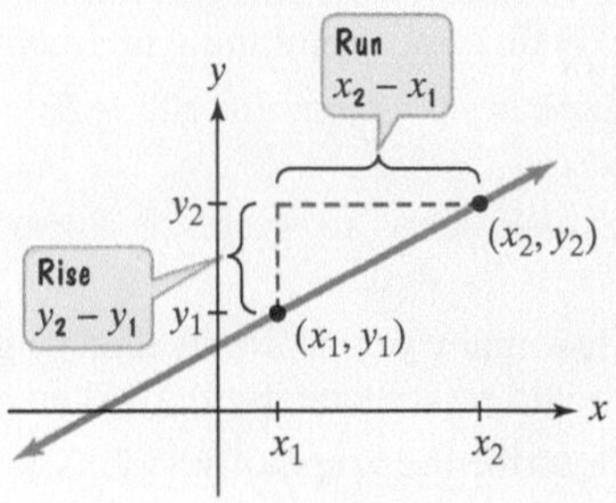

where $x_2 - x_1 \neq 0$.

It is common notation to let the letter m represent the slope of a line. The letter m is used because it is the first letter of the French verb *monter*, meaning to rise, or to ascend.

EXAMPLE 1 Using the Definition of Slope

Find the slope of the line passing through each pair of points:

a. $(-3, -1)$ and $(-2, 4)$ **b.** $(-3, 4)$ and $(2, -2)$.

Solution

a. To find the slope of the line passing through $(-3, -1)$ and $(-2, 4)$, we let $(x_1, y_1) = (-3, -1)$ and $(x_2, y_2) = (-2, 4)$. We obtain the slope as follows:

$$m = \frac{\text{Change in } y}{\text{Change in } x} = \frac{y_2 - y_1}{x_2 - x_1} = \frac{4 - (-1)}{-2 - (-3)} = \frac{5}{1} = 5.$$

The situation is illustrated in **Figure 21**. The slope of the line is 5, indicating that there is a vertical change, a rise, of 5 units for each horizontal change, a run, of 1 unit. The slope is positive and the line rises from left to right.

Great Question!

When using the definition of slope, how do I know which point to call (x_1, y_1) and which point to call (x_2, y_2)?

When computing slope, it makes no difference which point you call (x_1, y_1) and which point you call (x_2, y_2). If we let $(x_1, y_1) = (-2, 4)$ and $(x_2, y_2) = (-3, -1)$, the slope is still 5:

$$m = \frac{\text{Change in } y}{\text{Change in } x} = \frac{y_2 - y_1}{x_2 - x_1} = \frac{-1 - 4}{-3 - (-2)} = \frac{-5}{-1} = 5.$$

However, you should not subtract in one order in the numerator $(y_2 - y_1)$ and then in the opposite order in the denominator $(x_1 - x_2)$.

$$\frac{-1 - 4}{-2 - (-3)} = \frac{-5}{1} = -5$$ Incorrect! The slope is not −5.

b. To find the slope of the line passing through $(-3, 4)$ and $(2, -2)$, we can let $(x_1, y_1) = (-3, 4)$ and $(x_2, y_2) = (2, -2)$. The slope is computed as follows:

$$m = \frac{\text{Change in } y}{\text{Change in } x} = \frac{y_2 - y_1}{x_2 - x_1} = \frac{-2 - 4}{2 - (-3)} = \frac{-6}{5} = -\frac{6}{5}.$$

The situation is illustrated in **Figure 22**. The slope of the line is $-\frac{6}{5}$. For every vertical change of -6 units (6 units down), there is a corresponding horizontal change of 5 units. The slope is negative and the line falls from left to right.

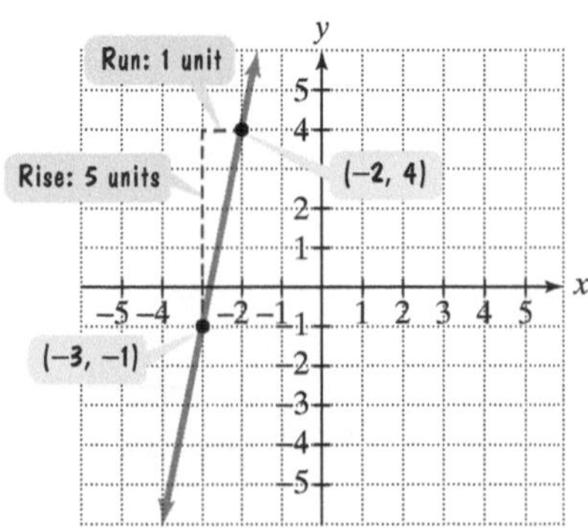

Figure 21 Visualizing a slope of 5

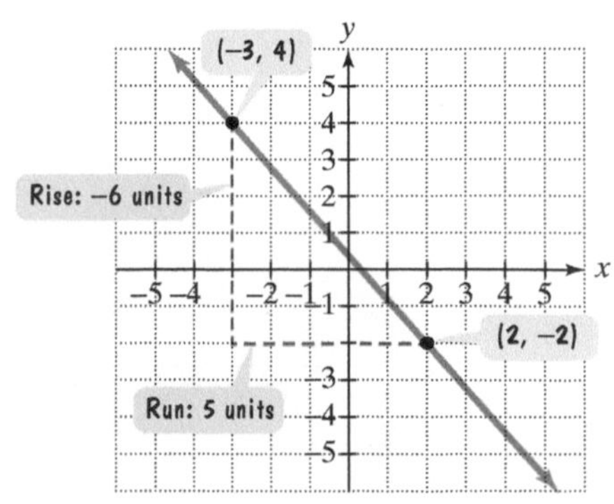

Figure 22 Visualizing a slope of $-\frac{6}{5}$ ■

✓ **CHECK POINT 1** Find the slope of the line passing through each pair of points:

a. $(-3, 4)$ and $(-4, -2)$ **b.** $(4, -2)$ and $(-1, 5)$.

EXAMPLE 2 Using the Definition of Slope for Horizontal and Vertical Lines

Find the slope of the line passing through each pair of points:

a. $(5, 4)$ and $(3, 4)$ **b.** $(2, 5)$ and $(2, 1)$.

Solution

a. Let $(x_1, y_1) = (5, 4)$ and $(x_2, y_2) = (3, 4)$. We obtain the slope as follows:

$$m = \frac{\text{Change in } y}{\text{Change in } x} = \frac{y_2 - y_1}{x_2 - x_1} = \frac{4 - 4}{3 - 5} = \frac{0}{-2} = 0.$$

The situation is illustrated in **Figure 23**. Can you see that the line is horizontal? Because any two points on a horizontal line have the same y-coordinate, these lines neither rise nor fall from left to right. The change in y, $y_2 - y_1$, is always zero. Thus, **the slope of any horizontal line is zero**.

b. We can let $(x_1, y_1) = (2, 5)$ and $(x_2, y_2) = (2, 1)$. **Figure 24** shows that these points are on a vertical line. We attempt to compute the slope as follows:

$$m = \frac{\text{Change in } y}{\text{Change in } x} = \frac{1 - 5}{2 - 2} = \frac{-4}{0}.$$

Division by zero is undefined.

Because division by zero is undefined, the slope of the vertical line in **Figure 24** is undefined. In general, **the slope of any vertical line is undefined**.

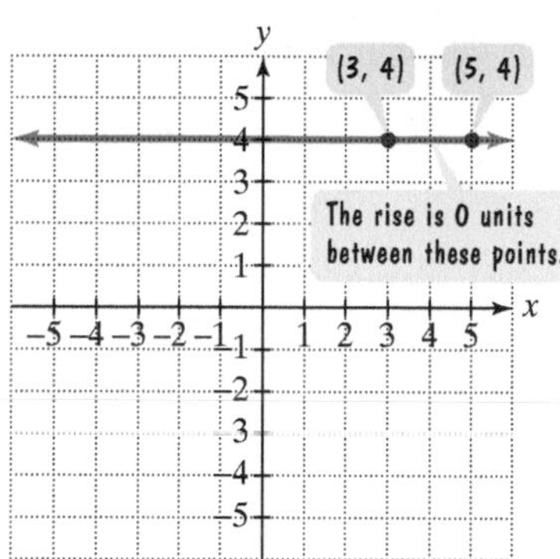

Figure 23 Horizontal lines have no vertical change.

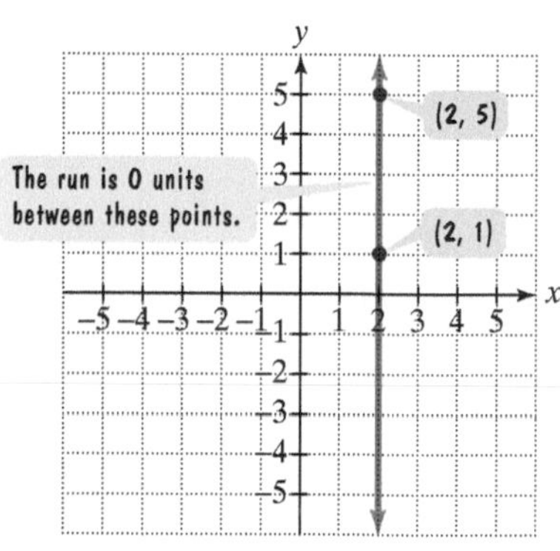

Figure 24 Vertical lines have no horizontal change. ■

Table 1 summarizes four possibilities for the slope of a line.

Table 1 Possibilities for a Line's Slope

Positive Slope	Negative Slope	Zero Slope	Undefined Slope
$m > 0$	$m < 0$	$m = 0$	m is undefined.
Line rises from left to right.	Line falls from left to right.	Line is horizontal.	Line is vertical.

✓ **CHECK POINT 2** Find the slope of the line passing through each pair of points or state that the slope is undefined:

a. (6, 5) and (2, 5) **b.** (1, 6) and (1, 4).

---

2 Use slope to show that lines are parallel.

Slope and Parallel Lines

Two nonintersecting lines that lie in the same plane are **parallel**. If two lines do not intersect, the ratio of the vertical change to the horizontal change is the same for each line. Because two parallel lines have the same "steepness," they must have the same slope.

Slope and Parallel Lines

1. If two nonvertical lines are parallel, then they have the same slope.
2. If two distinct nonvertical lines have the same slope, then they are parallel.
3. Two distinct vertical lines, each with undefined slope, are parallel.

EXAMPLE 3 Using Slope to Show That Lines Are Parallel

Show that the line passing through (1, 4) and (3, 2) is parallel to the line passing through (2, 8) and (4, 6).

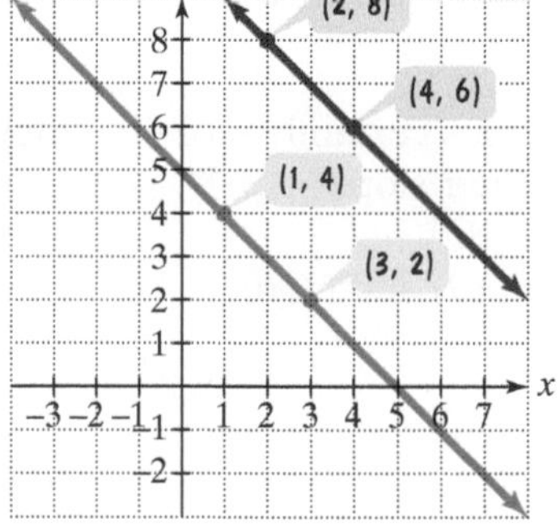

Figure 25 Using slope to show that lines are parallel

Solution The situation is illustrated in **Figure 25**. The lines certainly look like they are parallel. Let's use equal slopes to confirm this fact. For each line, we compute the ratio of the difference in y-coordinates to the difference in x-coordinates. Be sure to subtract the coordinates in the same order.

We begin with the slope of the blue line through (1, 4) and (3, 2).

Change in y is $2 - 4$.

(1, 4) (3, 2)

Change in x is $3 - 1$.

$$m = \frac{\text{Change in } y}{\text{Change in } x} = \frac{2 - 4}{3 - 1} = \frac{-2}{2} = -1$$

Now we find the slope of the red line through (2, 8) and (4, 6).

Change in y is $6 - 8$.

(2, 8) (4, 6)

Change in x is $4 - 2$.

$$m = \frac{\text{Change in } y}{\text{Change in } x} = \frac{6 - 8}{4 - 2} = \frac{-2}{2} = -1$$

Because the slopes are equal, the lines are parallel. ■

✓ **CHECK POINT 3** Show that the line passing through (4, 2) and (6, 6) is parallel to the line passing through (0, −2) and (1, 0).

3 Use slope to show that lines are perpendicular.

Slope and Perpendicular Lines

Two lines that intersect at a right angle (90°) are said to be **perpendicular**, as shown in **Figure 26**. There is a relationship between the slopes of perpendicular lines.

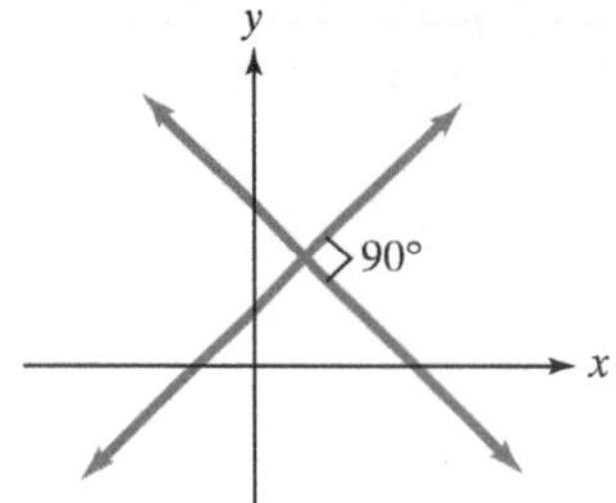

Figure 26
Perpendicular lines

Slope and Perpendicular Lines

1. If two nonvertical lines are perpendicular, then the product of their slopes is −1.
2. If the product of the slopes of two lines is −1, then the lines are perpendicular.
3. A horizontal line having zero slope is perpendicular to a vertical line having undefined slope.

EXAMPLE 4 Using Slope to Show That Lines Are Perpendicular

Show that the line passing through (−6, −9) and (3, 6) is perpendicular to the line passing through (10, −8) and (−5, 1).

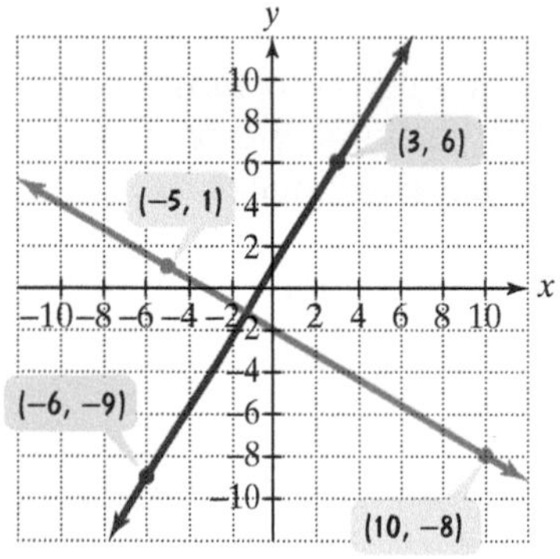

Solution The situation is illustrated in **Figure 27**. The lines certainly look like they intersect at a right angle. Let's show that the product of their slopes is −1 to confirm this fact.

We begin with the slope of the red line through (−6, −9) and (3, 6).

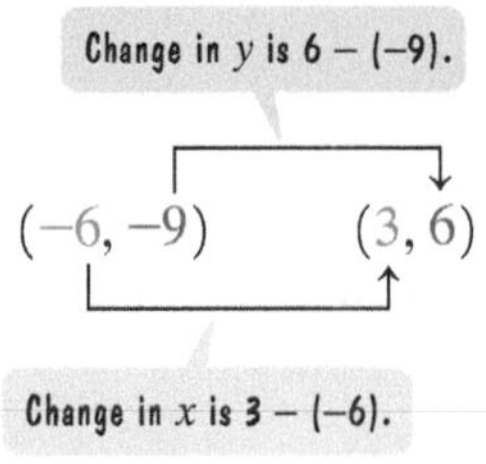

Figure 27
Using slope to show that lines are perpendicular

Change in y is $6 - (-9)$.

(−6, −9) (3, 6)

Change in x is $3 - (-6)$.

$$m = \frac{\text{Change in } y}{\text{Change in } x} = \frac{6 - (-9)}{3 - (-6)} = \frac{6 + 9}{3 + 6} = \frac{15}{9} = \frac{5}{3}$$

Now we find the slope of the blue line through (10, −8) and (−5, 1).

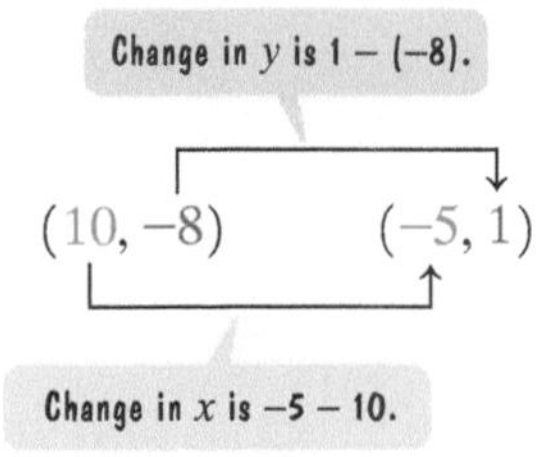

Change in y is $1 - (-8)$.

(10, −8) (−5, 1)

Change in x is $-5 - 10$.

$$m = \frac{\text{Change in } y}{\text{Change in } x} = \frac{1 - (-8)}{-5 - 10} = \frac{1 + 8}{-5 - 10} = \frac{9}{-15} = -\frac{3}{5}$$

We have determined that the slope of the red line in **Figure 27** is $\frac{5}{3}$ and the slope of the blue line is $-\frac{3}{5}$. Now we can find the product of the slopes:

$$\frac{5}{3}\left(-\frac{3}{5}\right) = -1.$$

Because the product of the slopes is -1, the lines are perpendicular. ■

In this example, the slopes of the perpendicular lines, $\frac{5}{3}$ and $-\frac{3}{5}$, are reciprocals with opposite signs, called **negative reciprocals**. This gives us an equivalent way of stating the relationship between slope and perpendicular lines:

> Two nonvertical lines are perpendicular if the slope of one is the negative reciprocal of the slope of the other.

✓ **CHECK POINT 4** Show that the line passing through $(-1, 4)$ and $(3, 2)$ is perpendicular to the line passing through $(-2, -1)$ and $(2, 7)$.

---

4 Calculate rate of change in applied situations.

Slope as Rate of Change

Slope is defined as the ratio of a change in y to a corresponding change in x. It tells how fast y is changing with respect to x. Thus, the slope of a line represents its rate of change.

Our next example shows how slope can be interpreted as a rate of change in an applied situation. When calculating slope in applied problems, keep track of the units in the numerator and the denominator.

EXAMPLE 5 Slope as a Rate of Change

The line graphs for the numbers of women and men living alone are shown again in **Figure 28**. Find the slope of the line segment for the women. Describe what this slope represents.

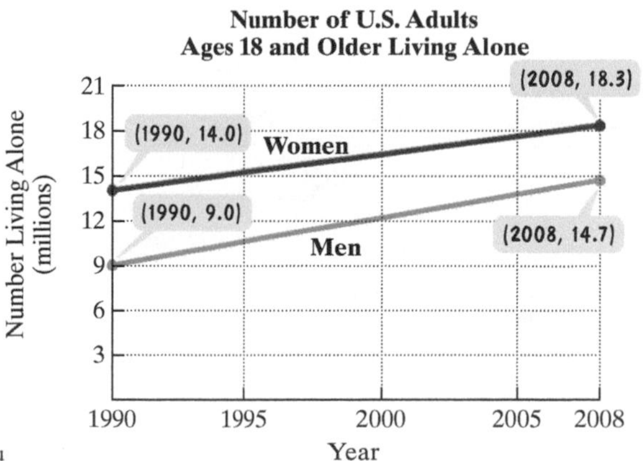

Figure 28

Source: U.S. Census Bureau

Solution We let x represent a year and y the number of women living alone in that year. Use the two points shown on the red line segment for women.

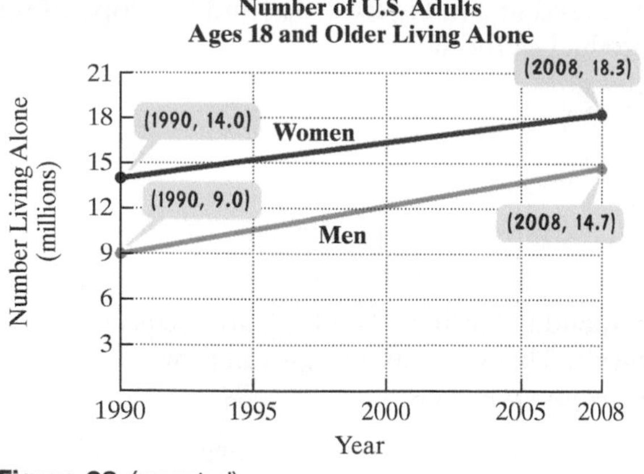

Figure 28 (repeated)

The two points shown on the line segment for women have the following coordinates:

(1990, 14.0) — In 1990, 14 million U.S. women lived alone.

(2008, 18.3). — In 2008, 18.3 million U.S. women lived alone.

Now we compute the slope:

$$m = \frac{\text{Change in } y}{\text{Change in } x} = \frac{18.3 - 14.0}{2008 - 1990}$$

The unit in the numerator is *million women*.

The unit in the denominator is *year*.

$$= \frac{4.3}{18} \approx \frac{0.24 \text{ million women}}{\text{year}}.$$

The slope indicates that the number of American women living alone increased at a rate of approximately 0.24 million each year for the period from 1990 through 2008. The rate of change is 0.24 million women per year. ■

✓ **CHECK POINT 5** Use the ordered pairs in **Figure 28** to find the slope of the green line segment for the men. Express the slope correct to two decimal places and describe what it represents.

In Check Point 5, did you find that the slope of the line segment for the men is different from that of the women? The rate of change for men living alone is greater than the rate of change for women living alone. The line segment representing men in **Figure 28** is steeper than the line segment representing women. If you extend the line segments far enough, the resulting lines will intersect. They are not parallel.

Blitzer Bonus

Railroads and Highways

The steepest part of Mt. Washington Cog Railway in New Hampshire has a 37% grade. This is equivalent to a slope of $\frac{37}{100}$. For every horizontal change of 100 feet, the railroad ascends 37 feet vertically. Engineers denote slope by grade, expressing slope as a percentage.

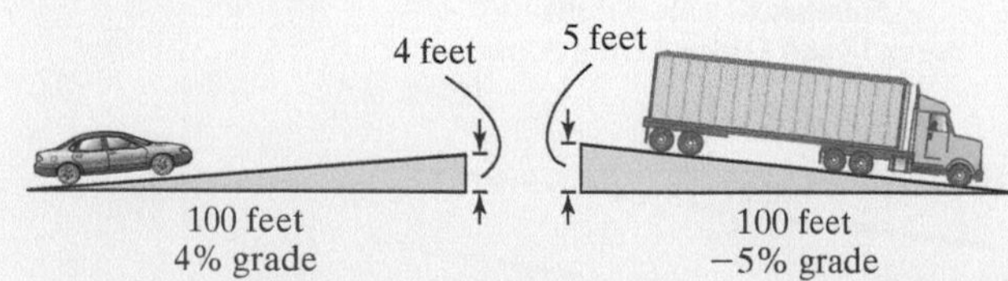

Railroad grades are usually less than 2%, although in the mountains they may go as high as 4%. The grade of the Mount Washington Cog Railway is phenomenal, making it necessary for locomotives to *push* single cars up its steepest part.

Porterfield-Chickering/Photo Researchers, Inc.

A Mount Washington Cog Railway locomotive pushing a single car up the steepest part of the railroad. The locomotive is about 120 years old.

Achieving Success

According to the Ebbinghaus retention model, you forget 50% of processed information within one hour of leaving the classroom. You lose 60% within 24 hours. After 30 days, 70% is gone. Reviewing and rewriting class notes is an effective way to counteract this phenomenon. At the very least, read your lecture notes at the end of each day. The more you engage with the material, the more you retain.

CONCEPT AND VOCABULARY CHECK

Fill in each blank so that the resulting statement is true.

1. The slope, m, of the line through the distinct points (x_1, y_1) and (x_2, y_2) is given by the formula $m =$ ______________.
2. The slope of the line through the distinct points (x_1, y_1) and (x_2, y_2) can be interpreted as the rate of change in ______________ with respect to ______________.
3. If a line rises from left to right, the line has ______________ slope.
4. If a line falls from left to right, the line has ______________ slope.
5. The slope of a horizontal line is ______________.
6. The slope of a vertical line is ______________.
7. If two distinct nonvertical lines have the same slope, then the lines are ______________.
8. If the product of the slopes of two lines is -1, then the lines are ______________.

3 EXERCISE SET

Practice Exercises

In Exercises 1–10, find the slope of the line passing through each pair of points or state that the slope is undefined. Then indicate whether the line through the points rises, falls, is horizontal, or is vertical.

1. (4, 7) and (8, 10)
2. (2, 1) and (3, 4)
3. (−2, 1) and (2, 2)
4. (−1, 3) and (2, 4)
5. (4, −2) and (3, −2)
6. (4, −1) and (3, −1)
7. (−2, 4) and (−1, −1)
8. (6, −4) and (4, −2)
9. (5, 3) and (5, −2)
10. (3, −4) and (3, 5)

In Exercises 11–22, find the slope of each line, or state that the slope is undefined.

11.

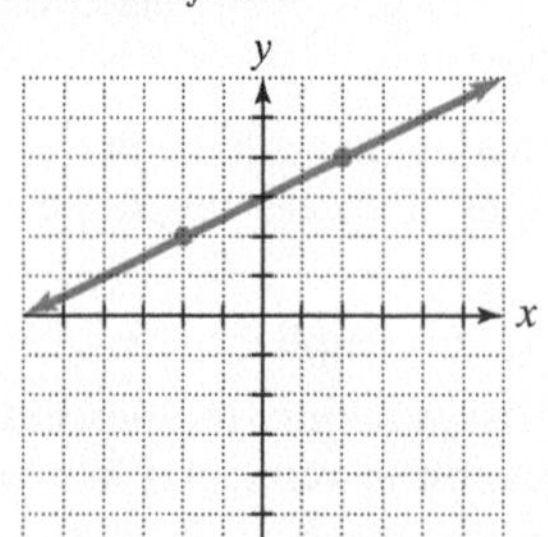

12.

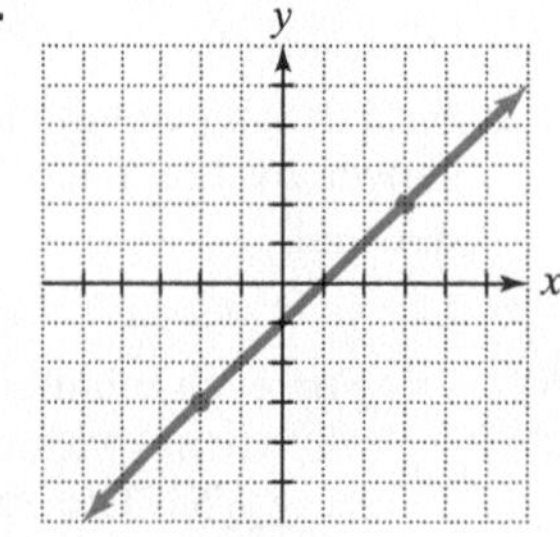

13.

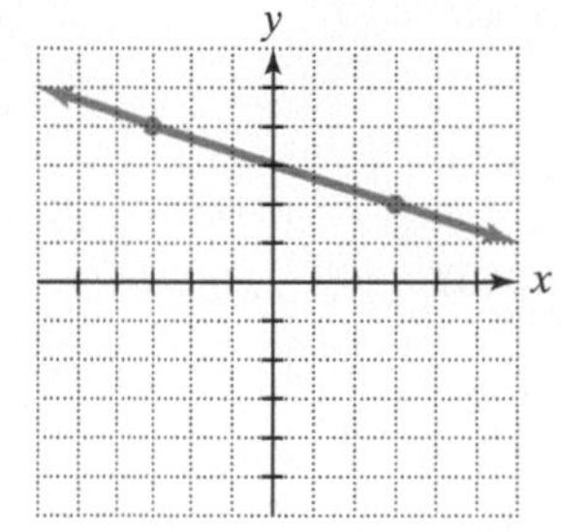

14.

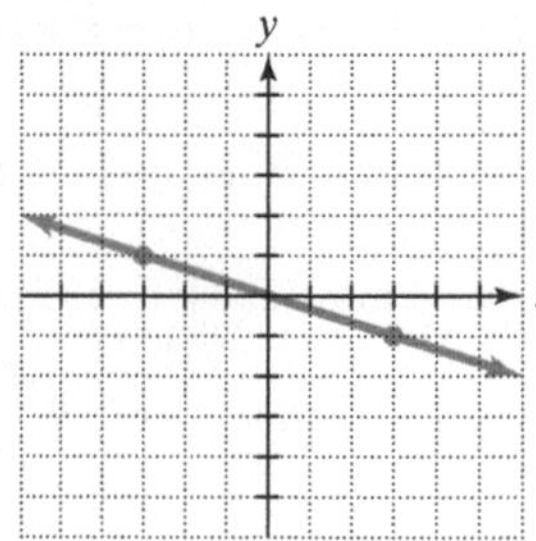

15.

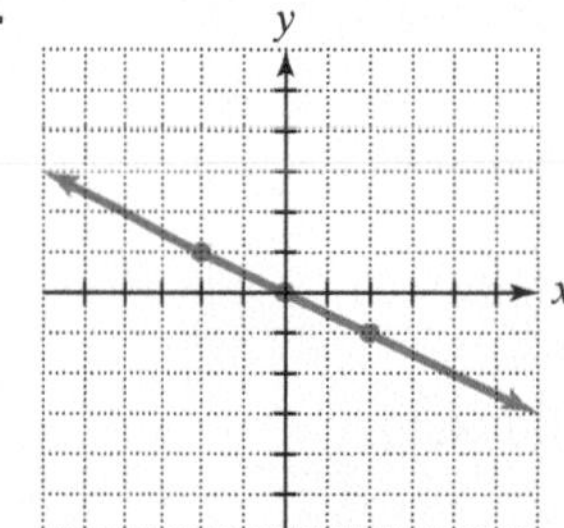

16.

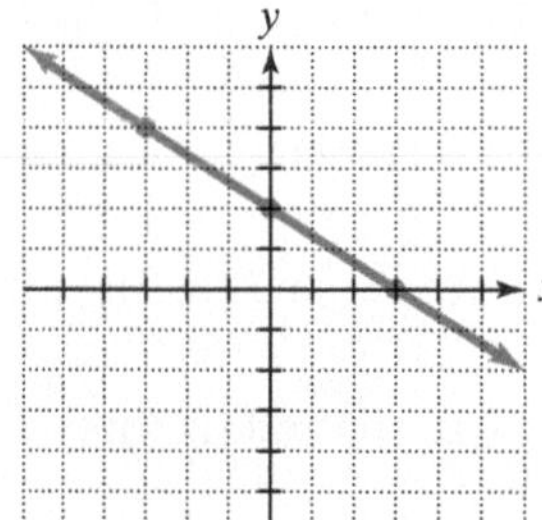

17.

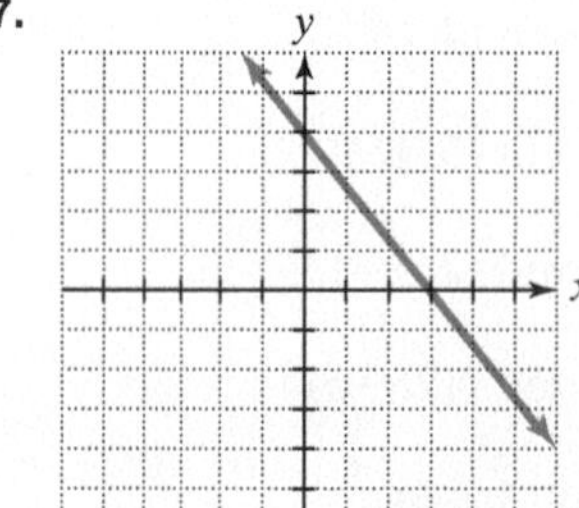

18.

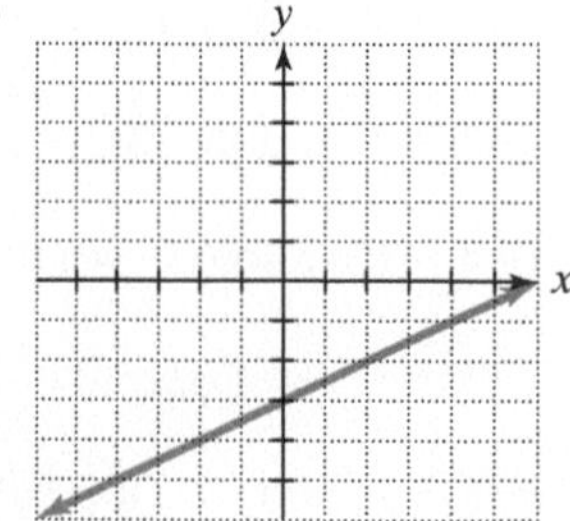

19.

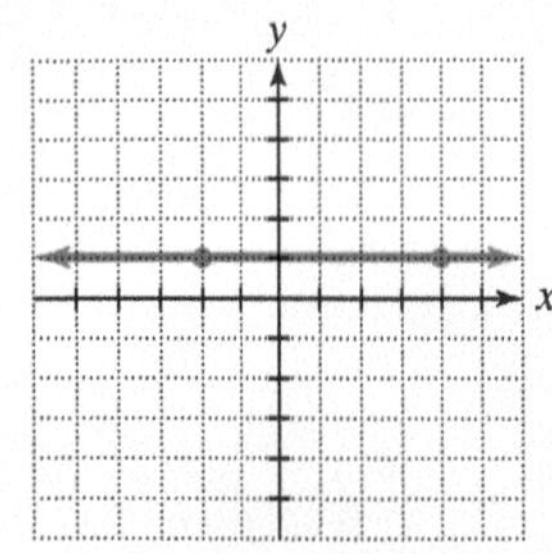

20.

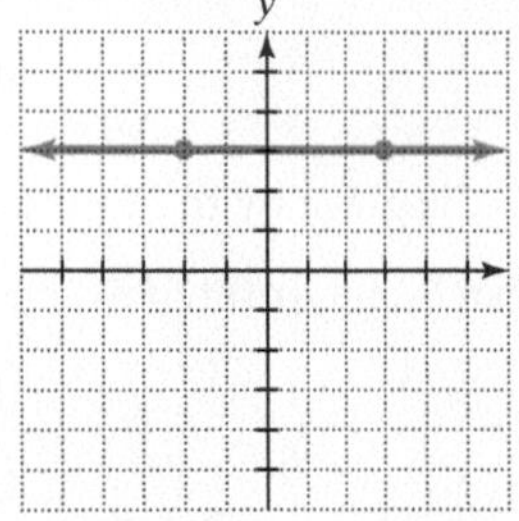

21.

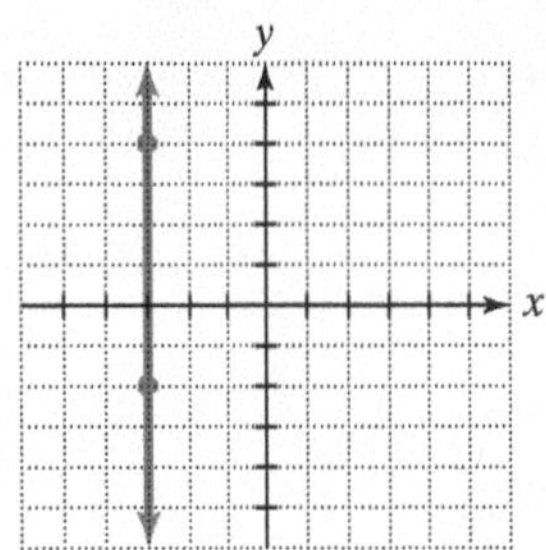

22.

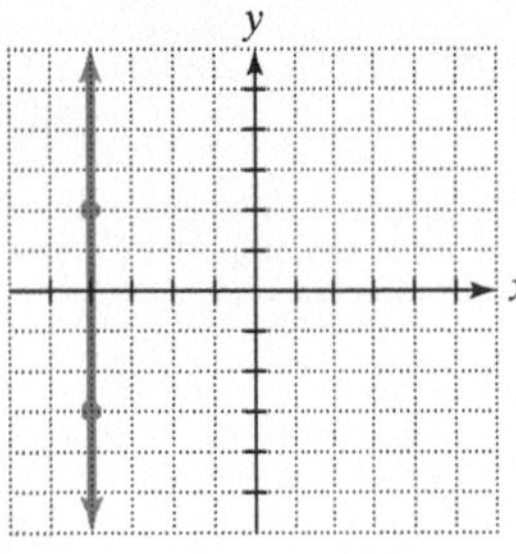

In Exercises 23–26, determine whether the distinct lines through each pair of points are parallel.

23. (−2, 0) and (0, 6); (1, 8) and (0, 5)

24. (2, 4) and (6, 1); (−3, 1) and (1, −2)

25. (0, 3) and (1, 5); (−1, 7) and (1, 10)

26. (−7, 6) and (0, 4); (−9, −3) and (1, 5)

In Exercises 27–30, determine whether the lines through each pair of points are perpendicular.

27. (1, 5) and (0, 3); (−2, 8) and (2, 6)

28. (3, 2) and (−2, −2); (3, −2) and (−1, 3)

29. (−1, −6) and (2, 9); (−15, −1) and (5, 3)

30. (−1, −6) and (2, 6); (−8, −1) and (4, 2)

In Exercises 31–36, determine whether the lines through each pair of points are parallel, perpendicular, or neither.

31. (−2, −5) and (3, 10); (−1, −9) and (4, 6)

32. (−2, −7) and (3, 13); (−1, −9) and (5, 15)

33. (−4, −12) and (0, −4); (0, −5) and (2, −4)

34. (−1, −11) and (0, −5); (0, −8) and (12, −6)

35. (−5, −1) and (0, 2); (−6, 9) and (3, −6)

36. (−2, −15) and (0, −3); (−12, 6) and (6, 3)

Practice PLUS

37. On the same set of axes, draw lines passing through the origin with slopes $-1, -\frac{1}{2}, 0, \frac{1}{3}$, and 2.

38. On the same set of axes, draw lines with y-intercept 4 and slopes $-1, -\frac{1}{2}, 0, \frac{1}{3}$, and 2.

Use slopes to solve Exercises 39–40.

39. Show that the points whose coordinates are (−3, −3), (2, −5), (5, −1), and (0, 1) are the vertices of a four-sided figure whose opposite sides are parallel. (Such a figure is called a *parallelogram.*)

40. Show that the points whose coordinates are (−3, 6), (2, −3), (11, 2), and (6, 11) are the vertices of a four-sided figure whose opposite sides are parallel.

41. The line passing through (5, y) and (1, 0) is parallel to the line joining (2, 3) and (−2, 1). Find y.

42. The line passing through (1, y) and (7, 12) is parallel to the line joining (−3, 4) and (−5, −2). Find y.

43. The line passing through (−1, y) and (1, 0) is perpendicular to the line joining (2, 3) and (−2, 1). Find y.

44. The line passing through (−2, y) and (−4, 4) is perpendicular to the line passing through (−1, −2) and (4, −1). Find y.

Application Exercises

45. Exercise is useful not only in preventing depression, but also as a treatment. The graphs show the percentage of patients with depression in remission when exercise (brisk walking) was used as a treatment. (The control group that engaged in no exercise had 11% of the patients in remission.)

Exercise and Percentage of Patients with Depression in Remission

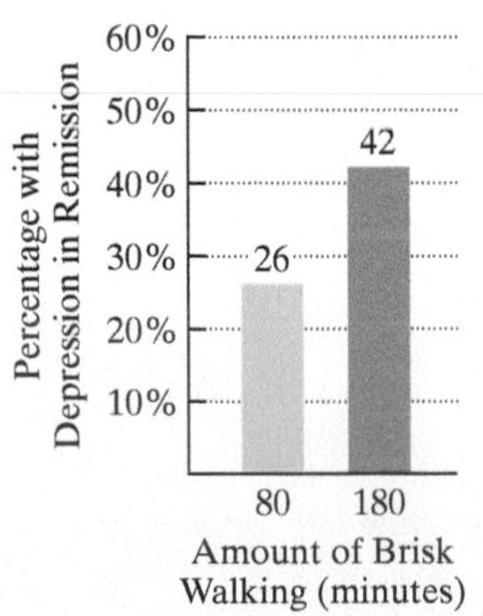

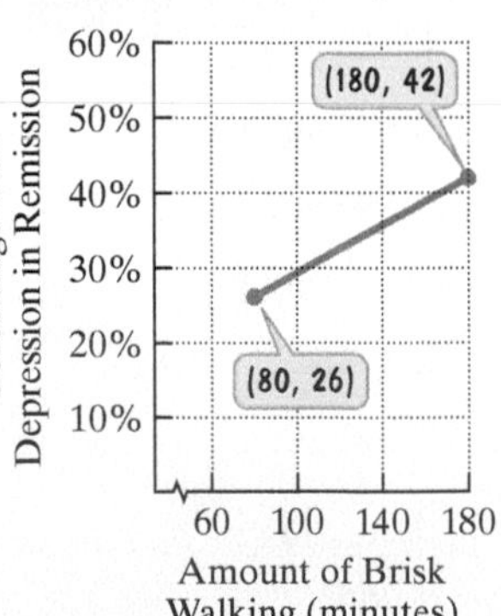

Source: Newsweek, March 26, 2007

a. Find the slope of the line passing through the two points shown by the voice balloons. Express the slope as a decimal.

b. Use your answer from part (a) to complete this statement:

For each minute of brisk walking, the percentage of patients with depression in remission increased by ___%. The rate of change is ___% per _____ __________.

46. Older, Calmer. As we age, daily stress and worry decrease and happiness increases, according to an analysis of 340,847 U.S. adults, ages 18–85, in the journal *Proceedings of the National Academy of Sciences*. The graphs show a portion of the research.

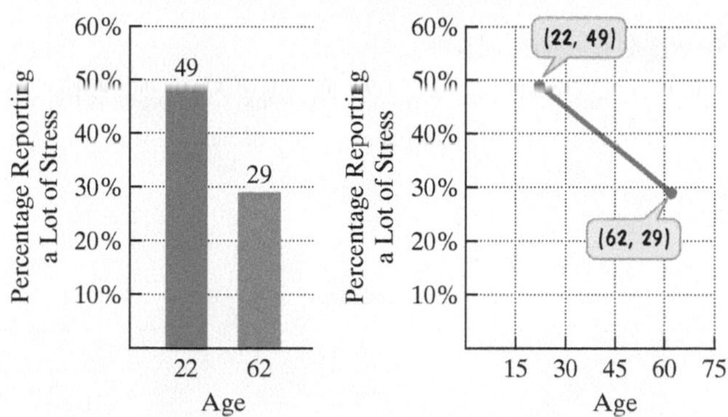

Source: National Academy of Sciences

a. Find the slope of the line passing through the two points shown by the voice balloons. Express the slope as a decimal.

b. Use your answer from part (a) to complete the statement:

For each year of aging, the percentage of Americans reporting "a lot" of stress decreases by __%. The rate of change is ___% per ________.

The pitch of a roof refers to the absolute value of its slope. In Exercises 47–48, find the pitch of each roof shown.

47.

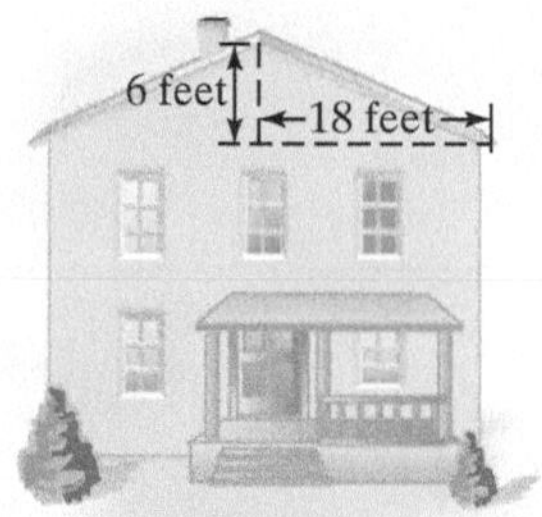

48.

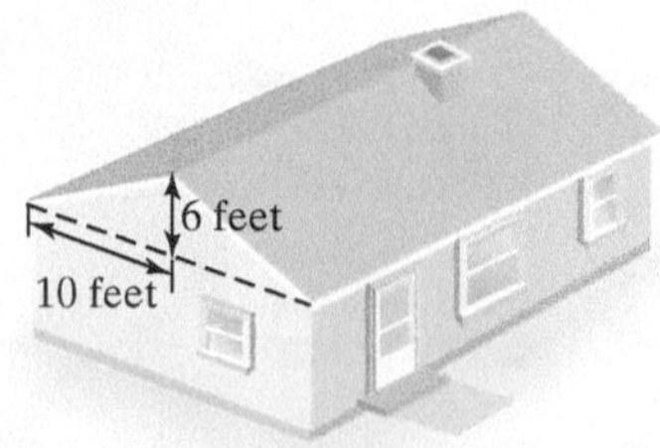

The grade of a road or ramp refers to its slope expressed as a percent. Use this information to solve Exercises 49–50.

49. Construction laws are very specific when it comes to access ramps for the disabled. Every vertical rise of 1 foot requires a horizontal run of 12 feet. What is the grade of such a ramp? Round to the nearest tenth of a percent.

50. A college campus goes beyond the standards described in Exercise 49. All wheelchair ramps on campus are designed so that every vertical rise of 1 foot is accompanied by a horizontal run of 14 feet. What is the grade of such a ramp? Round to the nearest tenth of a percent.

Writing in Mathematics

51. What is the slope of a line?

52. Describe how to calculate the slope of a line passing through two points.

53. What does it mean if the slope of a line is zero?

54. What does it mean if the slope of a line is undefined?

55. If two lines are parallel, describe the relationship between their slopes.

56. If two lines are perpendicular, describe the relationship between their slopes.

Critical Thinking Exercises

Make Sense? *In Exercises 57–60, determine whether each statement "makes sense" or "does not make sense" and explain your reasoning.*

57. When finding the slope of the line passing through $(-1, 5)$ and $(2, -3)$, I must let (x_1, y_1) be $(-1, 5)$ and (x_2, y_2) be $(2, -3)$.

58. When applying the slope formula, it is important to subtract corresponding coordinates in the same order.

59. I visualize slope as walking along a line from left to right. If I'm walking uphill, the slope is positive, and if I'm walking downhill, the slope is negative.

60. I computed the slope of one line to be $-\frac{3}{5}$ and the slope of a second line to be $-\frac{5}{3}$, so the lines must be perpendicular.

In Exercises 61–64, determine whether each statement is true or false. If the statement is false, make the necessary change(s) to produce a true statement.

61. Slope is run divided by rise.

62. The line through $(2, 2)$ and the origin has slope 1.

63. A line with slope 3 can be parallel to a line with slope -3.

64. The line through $(3, 1)$ and $(3, -5)$ has zero slope.

In Exercises 65–66, use the figure shown to make the indicated list.

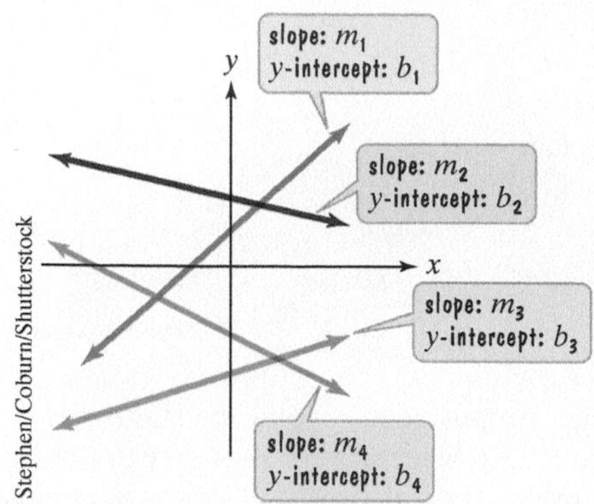

65. List the slopes m_1, m_2, m_3, and m_4 in order of decreasing size.

66. List the y-intercepts b_1, b_2, b_3, and b_4 in order of decreasing size.

Technology Exercises

Use a graphing utility to graph each equation in Exercises 67–70. Then use the TRACE *feature to trace along the line and find the coordinates of two points. Use these points to compute the line's slope.*

67. $y = 2x + 4$

68. $y = -3x + 6$

69. $y = -\frac{1}{2}x - 5$

70. $y = \frac{3}{4}x - 2$

71. In Exercises 67–70, compare the slope that you found with the line's equation. What relationship do you observe between the line's slope and one of the constants in the equation?

Review Exercises

72. A 36-inch board is cut into two pieces. One piece is twice as long as the other. How long are the pieces?

73. Simplify: $-10 + 16 \div 2(-4)$.

74. Solve and graph the solution set on a number line: $2x - 3 \leq 5$.

Preview Exercises

Exercises 75–77 will help you prepare for the material covered in the next section.

75. From $(0, -3)$, move 4 units up and 1 unit to the right. What point do you obtain?

76. From $(0, 1)$, move 2 units down and 3 units to the right. What point do you obtain?

77. Solve for y: $2x + 5y = 0$.

SECTION 4

The Slope-Intercept Form of the Equation of a Line

Objectives

1. Find a line's slope and y-intercept from its equation.
2. Graph lines in slope-intercept form.
3. Use slope and y-intercept to graph $Ax + By = C$.
4. Use slope and y-intercept to model data.

Every day in the United States, 75.2 million students gather in elementary and secondary schools, as well as in 6.6 million colleges, to learn things from 5.1 million teachers. (*Source*: Department of Education) These numbers are fueled by the reality that employers use diplomas and degrees to determine who is eligible for a job. This section contains two mathematical models based on this reality. To develop these models, we turn to a new form for a line's equation.

1 Find a line's slope and y-intercept from its equation.

The Slope-Intercept Form of the Equation of a Line

Let's begin with an example that shows how easy it is to find a line's slope and y-intercept from its equation.

Figure 29 shows the graph of $y = 2x + 4$. Verify that the x-intercept is -2 by setting y equal to 0 and solving for x. Similarly, verify that the y-intercept is 4 by setting x equal to 0 and solving for y.

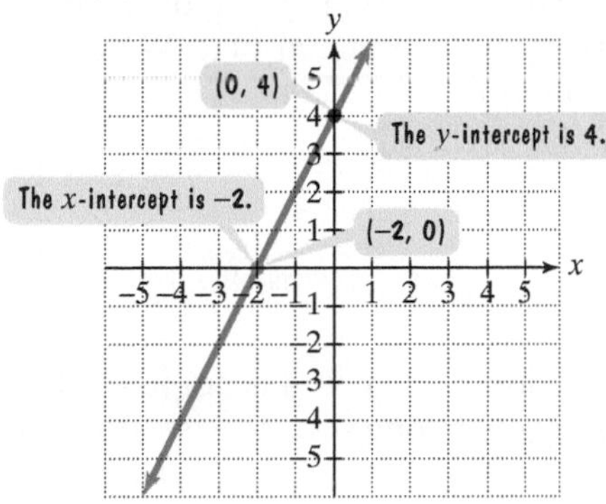

Figure 29
The graph of $y = 2x + 4$

Now that we have two points on the line, $(-2, 0)$ and $(0, 4)$, we can calculate the slope of the graph of $y = 2x + 4$.

$$\text{Slope} = \frac{\text{Change in } y}{\text{Change in } x}$$

$$= \frac{4 - 0}{0 - (-2)} = \frac{4}{2} = 2$$

We see that the slope of the line is 2, the same as the coefficient of x in the equation $y = 2x + 4$. The y-intercept is 4, the same as the constant in the equation $y = 2x + 4$.

$$y = 2x + 4$$

The slope is 2. The y-intercept is 4.

A linear equation like $y = 2x + 4$ that is solved for y is said to be in *slope-intercept form*. This is because the slope and the y-intercept can be immediately determined from the equation. The x-coefficient is the line's slope and the constant term is the y-intercept.

Slope-Intercept Form of the Equation of a Line

The **slope-intercept form of the equation** of a nonvertical line with slope m and y-intercept b is

$$y = mx + b.$$

EXAMPLE 1 Finding a Line's Slope and y-Intercept from Its Equation

Find the slope and the y-intercept of the line with the given equation:

a. $y = 2x - 4$ **b.** $y = \frac{1}{2}x + 2$ **c.** $5x + y = 4$.

Great Question!

Which are the constants and which are the variables in $y = mx + b$?

The variables in $y = mx + b$ vary in different ways. The variables for slope, m, and y-intercept, b, vary from one line's equation to another. However, they remain constant in the equation of a single line. By contrast, the variables x and y represent the infinitely many points, (x, y), on a single line. Thus, these variables vary in both the equation of a single line, as well as from one equation to another.

Solution

a. We write $y = 2x - 4$ as $y = 2x + (-4)$. The slope is the x-coefficient and the y-intercept is the constant term.

$$y = 2x + (-4)$$

The slope is 2. The y-intercept is -4.

b. The equation $y = \frac{1}{2}x + 2$ is in the form $y = mx + b$. We can find the slope, m, by identifying the coefficient of x. We can find the y-intercept, b, by identifying the constant term.

$$y = \frac{1}{2}x + 2$$

The slope is $\frac{1}{2}$. The y-intercept is 2.

c. The equation $5x + y = 4$ is not in the form $y = mx + b$. We can obtain this form by isolating y on one side. We isolate y on the left side by subtracting $5x$ from both sides.

$$5x + y = 4 \quad \text{This is the given equation.}$$
$$5x - 5x + y = -5x + 4 \quad \text{Subtract 5x from both sides.}$$
$$y = -5x + 4 \quad \text{Simplify.}$$

Now, the equation is in the form $y = mx + b$. The slope is the coefficient of x and the y-intercept is the constant term.

$$y = -5x + 4$$

The slope is -5. The y-intercept is 4. ■

✓ **CHECK POINT 1** Find the slope and the y-intercept of the line with the given equation:

a. $y = 5x - 3$

b. $y = \frac{2}{3}x + 4$

c. $7x + y = 6$.

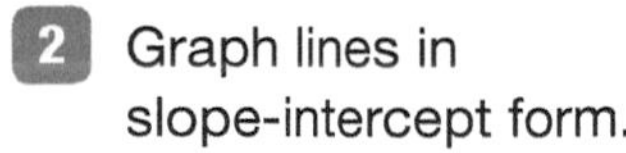
2 Graph lines in slope-intercept form.

Graphing $y = mx + b$ by Using the Slope and y-Intercept

If a line's equation is written with y isolated on one side, we can use the y-intercept and the slope to obtain its graph.

Graphing $y = mx + b$ by Using the Slope and y-Intercept

1. Plot the point containing the y-intercept on the y-axis. This is the point $(0, b)$.
2. Obtain a second point using the slope, m. Write m as a fraction, and use rise over run, starting at the point on the y-axis, to plot this point.
3. Use a straightedge to draw a line through the two points. Draw arrowheads at the ends of the line to show that the line continues indefinitely in both directions.

EXAMPLE 2 Graphing by Using the Slope and y-Intercept

Graph the line whose equation is $y = 4x - 3$.

Solution We write $y = 4x - 3$ in the form $y = mx + b$.

$$y = 4x + (-3)$$

The slope is 4. The y-intercept is -3.

Now that we have identified the slope and the y-intercept, we use the three steps in the preceding box to graph the equation.

Step 1. Plot the point containing the y-intercept on the y-axis. The y-intercept is -3. We plot the point $(0, -3)$, shown in **Figure 30(a)**.

Step 2. Obtain a second point using the slope, m. Write m as a fraction, and use rise over run, starting at the point on the y-axis, to plot this point. The slope, 4, written as a fraction is $\frac{4}{1}$.

$$m = \frac{4}{1} = \frac{\text{Rise}}{\text{Run}}$$

We plot the second point on the line by starting at $(0, -3)$, the first point. Based on the slope, we move 4 units *up* (the rise) and 1 unit to the *right* (the run). This puts us at a second point on the line, $(1, 1)$, shown in **Figure 30(b)**.

Step 3. Use a straightedge to draw a line through the two points. The graph of $y = 4x - 3$ is shown in **Figure 30(c)**.

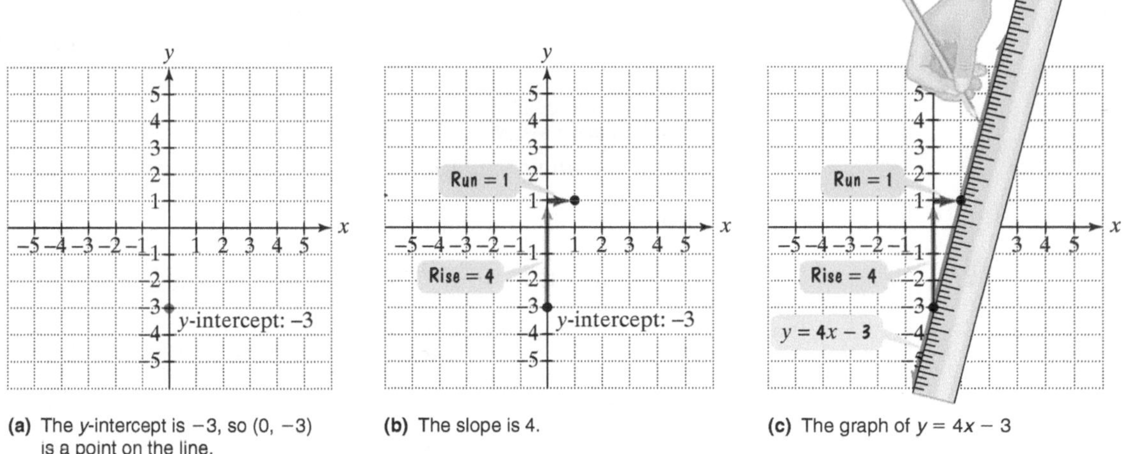

(a) The y-intercept is -3, so $(0, -3)$ is a point on the line.

(b) The slope is 4.

(c) The graph of $y = 4x - 3$

Figure 30 Graphing $y = 4x - 3$ using the y-intercept and slope ■

✓ **CHECK POINT 2** Graph the line whose equation is $y = 3x - 2$.

EXAMPLE 3 Graphing by Using the Slope and y-Intercept

Graph the line whose equation is $y = \frac{2}{3}x + 2$.

Solution The equation of the line is in the form $y = mx + b$. We can find the slope, m, by identifying the coefficient of x. We can find the y-intercept, b, by identifying the constant term.

$$y = \frac{2}{3}x + 2$$

The slope is $\frac{2}{3}$. The y-intercept is 2.

Now that we have identified the slope and the y-intercept, we use the three-step procedure to graph the equation.

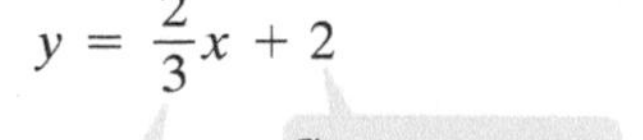

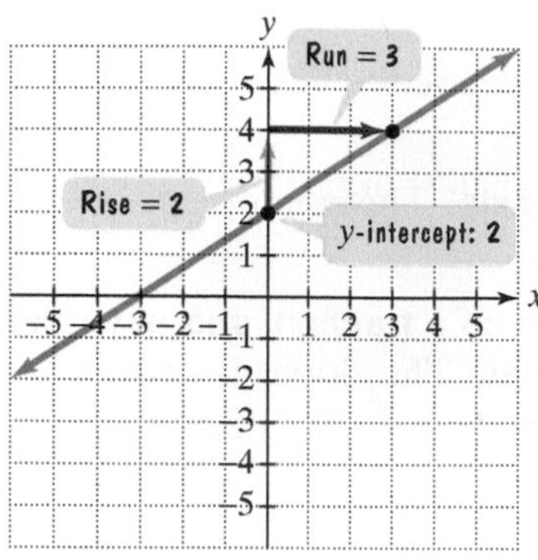

Figure 31
The graph of $y = \frac{2}{3}x + 2$

Step 1. Plot the point containing the *y*-intercept on the *y*-axis. The y-intercept is 2. We plot (0, 2), shown in **Figure 31.**

Step 2. Obtain a second point using the slope, *m*. Write *m* as a fraction, and use rise over run, starting at the point on the *y*-axis, to plot this point. The slope, $\frac{2}{3}$, is already written as a fraction.

$$m = \frac{2}{3} = \frac{\text{Rise}}{\text{Run}}$$

We plot the second point on the line by starting at (0, 2), the first point. Based on the slope, we move 2 units *up* (the rise) and 3 units to the *right* (the run). This puts us at a second point on the line, (3, 4), shown in **Figure 31.**

Step 3. Use a straightedge to draw a line through the two points. The graph of $y = \frac{2}{3}x + 2$ is shown in **Figure 31.** ■

✓ CHECK POINT 3 Graph the line whose equation is $y = \frac{3}{5}x + 1$.

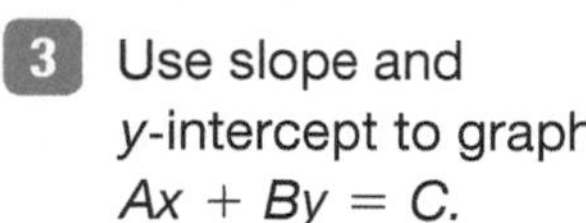

3 Use slope and y-intercept to graph $Ax + By = C$.

Graphing $Ax + By = C$ by Using the Slope and y-Intercept

Earlier in this chapter, we considered linear equations of the form $Ax + By = C$. We used x- and y-intercepts, as well as checkpoints, to graph these equations. It is also possible to obtain the graphs by using the slope and y-intercept. To do this, begin by solving $Ax + By = C$ for y. This will put the equation in slope-intercept form. Then use the three-step procedure to graph the equation. This is illustrated in Example 4.

EXAMPLE 4 Graphing by Using the Slope and y-Intercept

Graph the linear equation $2x + 5y = 0$ by using the slope and y-intercept.

Solution We put the equation in slope-intercept form by solving for y.

$$2x + 5y = 0 \quad \text{This is the given equation.}$$

$$2x - 2x + 5y = -2x + 0 \quad \text{Subtract } 2x \text{ from both sides.}$$

$$5y = -2x + 0 \quad \text{Simplify.}$$

$$\frac{5y}{5} = \frac{-2x + 0}{5} \quad \text{Divide both sides by 5.}$$

$$y = \frac{-2x}{5} + \frac{0}{5} \quad \text{Divide each term in the numerator by 5.}$$

$$y = -\frac{2}{5}x + 0 \quad \text{Simplify.}$$

Now that the equation is in slope-intercept form, we can use the slope and y-intercept to obtain its graph. Examine the slope-intercept form:

$$y = -\frac{2}{5}x + 0.$$

slope: $-\frac{2}{5}$ y-intercept: 0

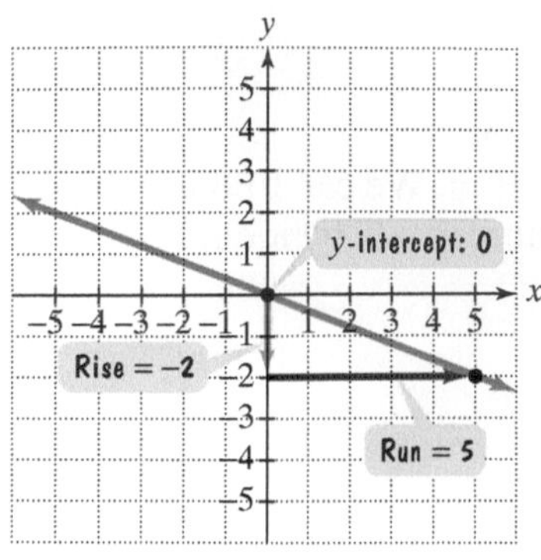

Figure 32 The graph of $2x + 5y = 0$, or $y = -\frac{2}{5}x + 0$

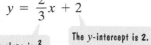

Note that the slope is $-\frac{2}{5}$ and the y-intercept is 0. Use the y-intercept to plot (0, 0) on the y-axis. Then locate a second point by using the slope.

$$m = -\frac{2}{5} = \frac{-2}{5} = \frac{\text{Rise}}{\text{Run}}$$

Because the rise is −2 and the run is 5, move *down* 2 units and to the *right* 5 units, starting at the point (0, 0). This puts us at a second point on the line, (5, −2). The graph of $2x + 5y = 0$ is the line drawn through these points, shown in **Figure 32.** ■

Discover for Yourself

You can obtain a second point in Example 4 by writing the slope as follows:

$$m = \frac{2}{-5} = \frac{\text{Rise}}{\text{Run}}.$$

$-\frac{2}{5}$ can be expressed as $\frac{-2}{5}$ or $\frac{2}{-5}$.

Now obtain this second point in **Figure 32** by moving *up* 2 units and to the *left* 5 units, starting at (0, 0). What do you observe once you graph the line?

✓ **CHECK POINT 4** Graph the linear equation $3x + 4y = 0$ by using the slope and y-intercept.

---

4 Use slope and y-intercept to model data.

Modeling with the Slope-Intercept Form of the Equation of a Line

The slope-intercept form for equations of lines is useful for obtaining mathematical models for data that fall on or near a line. For example, the bar graph in **Figure 33(a)** shows the percentage of the U.S. population who had graduated from high school and from college in 1960 and 2010. The data are displayed as points in a rectangular coordinate system in **Figure 33(b)**.

Percentage of High School Graduates and College Graduates in the U.S. Population

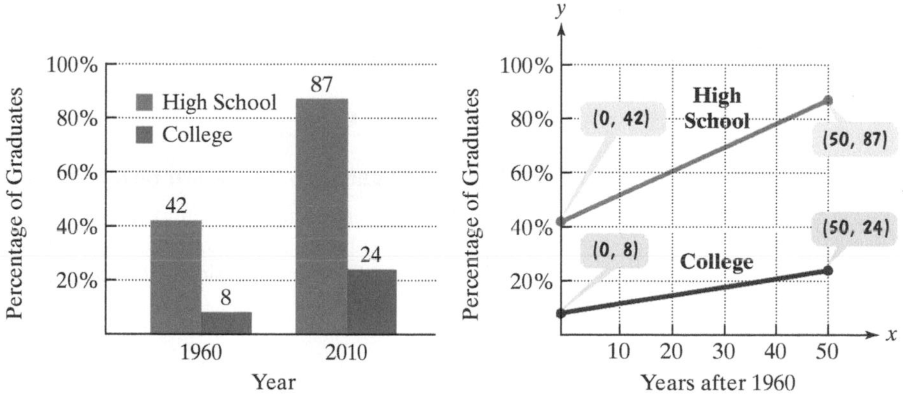

Figure 33(a) **Figure 33(b)**

Source: James M. Henslin, *Essentials of Sociology*, Ninth Edition, Pearson, 2011.

Example 5 illustrates how we can use the equation $y = mx + b$ to obtain a model for the data and make predictions about what might occur in the future.

EXAMPLE 5 Modeling with the Slope-Intercept Form of the Equation

a. Use the two points for high school in **Figure 33(b)** to find an equation in the form $y = mx + b$ that models the percentage of high school graduates in the U.S. poulation, y, x years after 1960.

b. Use the model to project the percentage of high school graduates in 2020.

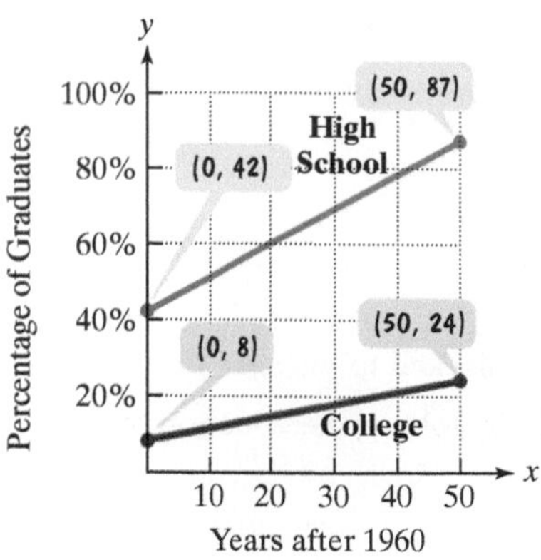

Figure 33(b) (repeated)

Solution

a. We will use the line segment for high school using the points (0, 42) and (50, 87) to obtain a model. We need values for m, the slope, and b, the y-intercept.

$$y = mx + b$$

$m = \dfrac{\text{Change in } y}{\text{Change in } x} = \dfrac{87-42}{50-0} = 0.9$

The point (0, 42) lies on the line segment, so the y-intercept is 42: $b = 42$.

The percentage of the U.S. population who graduated from high school, y, x years after 1960 can be modeled by the linear equation

$$y = 0.9x + 42.$$

The slope, 0.9, indicates an increase in the percentage of high school graduates of 0.9% per year from 1960 through 2010.

b. Now let's use this model to project the percentage of high school graduates in 2020. Because 2020 is 60 years after 1960, substitute 60 for x in $y = 0.9x + 42$ and evaluate the formula.

$$y = 0.9(60) + 42 = 54 + 42 = 96$$

Our model projects that 96% of the U.S. population will have graduated from high school in 2020. ■

✓ CHECK POINT 5

a. Use the two points for college in **Figure 33(b)** to find an equation in the form $y = mx + b$ that models the percentage of college graduates in the U.S. population, y, x years after 1960.

b. Use the model to project the percentage of college graduates in 2020.

Achieving Success

Use index cards to help learn new terms.

Many of the terms, notations, and formulas used in this text will be new to you. Buy a pack of 3 × 5 index cards. On each card, list a new vocabulary word, symbol, or title of a formula. On the other side of the card, put the definition or formula. Here are two examples:

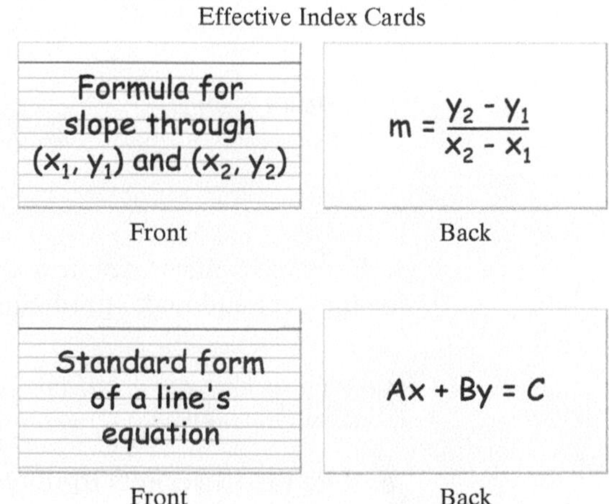

Review these cards frequently. Use the cards to quiz yourself and prepare for exams.

CONCEPT AND VOCABULARY CHECK

Fill in each blank so that the resulting statement is true.

1. The slope-intercept form of the equation of a line is ____________, where m represents the ____________ and b represents the ____________.
2. In order to graph the line whose equation is $y = \frac{2}{5}x + 3$, begin by plotting the point ____________. From this point, we move ____________ units up (the rise) and ____________ units to the right (the run).
3. In order to graph equations of the form $Ax + By = C$ using the slope and y-intercept, we begin by solving the equation for ____________.

4 EXERCISE SET

MyMathLab®

Watch the videos in MyMathLab

Download the MyDashBoard App

Practice Exercises

In Exercises 1–12, find the slope and the y-intercept of the line with the given equation.

1. $y = 3x + 2$
2. $y = 9x + 4$
3. $y = 3x - 5$
4. $y = 4x - 2$
5. $y = -\frac{1}{2}x + 5$
6. $y = -\frac{3}{4}x + 6$
7. $y = 7x$
8. $y = 10x$
9. $y = 10$
10. $y = 7$
11. $y = 4 - x$
12. $y = 5 - x$

In Exercises 13–26, begin by solving the linear equation for y. This will put the equation in slope-intercept form. Then find the slope and the y-intercept of the line with this equation.

13. $-5x + y = 7$
14. $-9x + y = 5$
15. $x + y = 6$
16. $x + y = 8$
17. $6x + y = 0$
18. $8x + y = 0$
19. $3y = 6x$
20. $3y = -9x$
21. $2x + 7y = 0$
22. $2x + 9y = 0$
23. $3x + 2y = 3$
24. $4x + 3y = 4$
25. $3x - 4y = 12$
26. $5x - 2y = 10$

In Exercises 27–38, graph each linear equation using the slope and y-intercept

27. $y = 2x + 4$
28. $y = 3x + 1$
29. $y = -3x + 5$
30. $y = -2x + 4$
31. $y = \frac{1}{2}x + 1$
32. $y = \frac{1}{3}x + 2$
33. $y = \frac{2}{3}x - 5$
34. $y = \frac{3}{4}x - 4$
35. $y = -\frac{3}{4}x + 2$
36. $y = -\frac{2}{3}x + 4$
37. $y = -\frac{5}{3}x$
38. $y = -\frac{4}{3}x$

In Exercises 39–46,

a. *Put the equation in slope-intercept form by solving for y.*
b. *Identify the slope and the y-intercept.*
c. *Use the slope and y-intercept to graph the equation.*

39. $3x + y = 0$
40. $2x + y = 0$
41. $3y = 4x$
42. $4y = 5x$
43. $2x + y = 3$
44. $3x + y = 4$
45. $7x + 2y = 14$
46. $5x + 3y = 15$

In Exercises 47–56, graph both linear equations in the same rectangular coordinate system. If the lines are parallel or perpendicular, explain why.

47. $y = 3x + 1$
    $y = 3x - 3$
48. $y = 2x + 4$
    $y = 2x - 3$
49. $y = -3x + 2$
    $y = 3x + 2$
50. $y = -2x + 1$
    $y = 2x + 1$

51. $y = x + 3$
$y = -x + 1$

52. $y = x + 2$
$y = -x - 1$

53. $x - 2y = 2$
$2x - 4y = 3$

54. $x - 3y = 9$
$3x - 9y = 18$

55. $2x - y = -1$
$x + 2y = -6$

56. $3x - y = -2$
$x + 3y = -9$

Practice PLUS

In Exercises 57–64, write an equation in the form $y = mx + b$ of the line that is described.

57. The y-intercept is 5 and the line is parallel to the line whose equation is $3x + y = 6$.

58. The y-intercept is -4 and the line is parallel to the line whose equation is $2x + y = 8$.

59. The y-intercept is 6 and the line is perpendicular to the line whose equation is $y = 5x - 1$.

60. The y-intercept is 7 and the line is perpendicular to the line whose equation is $y = 8x - 3$.

61. The line has the same y-intercept as the line whose equation is $16y = 8x + 32$ and is parallel to the line whose equation is $3x + 3y = 9$.

62. The line has the same y-intercept as the line whose equation is $2y = 6x + 8$ and is parallel to the line whose equation is $4x + 4y = 20$.

63. The line rises from left to right. It passes through the origin and a second point with equal x- and y-coordinates.

64. The line falls from left to right. It passes through the origin and a second point with opposite x- and y-coordinates.

Application Exercises

The bar graph shows the racial and ethnic composition of the United States population in 2008, with projections for 2050. Exercises 65–66 involve the graphs shown in the rectangular coordinate system for two of the racial/ethnic groups.

Racial and Ethnic Composition of the United States Population

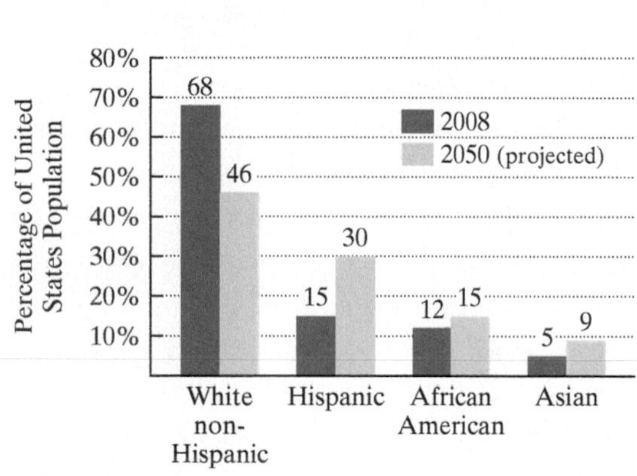

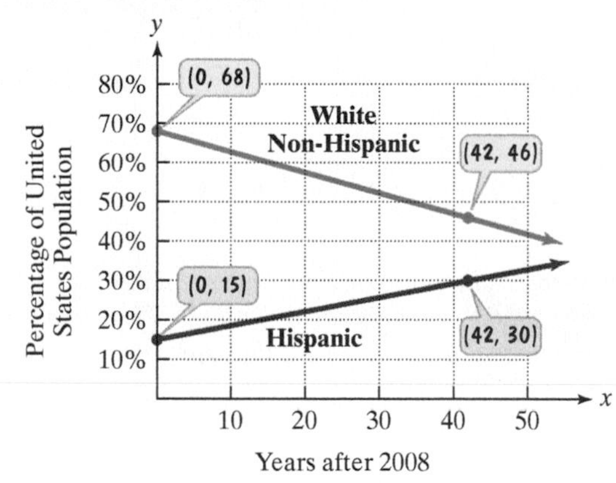

Source: Urban Institute

65. a. Use the two points for white non-Hispanics to find an equation in the form $y = mx + b$ that models the percentage of white non-Hispanics, y, in the United States population x years after 2008. Round m to two decimal places.

b. Use the model from part (a) to project the percentage of white non-Hispanics in the United States in 2108.

66. a. Use the two points for Hispanics to find an equation in the form $y = mx + b$ that models the percentage of Hispanics, y, in the United States population x years after 2008. Round m to two decimal places.

b. Use the model from part (a) to project the percentage of Hispanics in the United States in 2108.

Writing in Mathematics

67. Describe how to find the slope and the y-intercept of a line whose equation is given.

68. Describe how to graph a line using the slope and y-intercept. Provide an original example with your description.

69. A formula in the form $y = mx + b$ models the cost, y, of a four-year college x years after 2010. Would you expect m to be positive, negative, or zero? Explain your answer.

Critical Thinking Exercises

Make Sense? *In Exercises 70–73, determine whether each statement "makes sense" or "does not make sense" and explain your reasoning.*

70. The slope-intercept form of a line's equation makes it possible for me to determine immediately the slope and the y-intercept.

71. Because the variable m does not appear in $Ax + By = C$, equations in this form make it impossible to determine the line's slope.

72. If I drive m miles in a year, the formula $c = 0.25m + 3500$ models the annual cost, c, in dollars, of operating my car, so the equation shows that with no driving at all, the cost is \$3500, and the rate of increase in this cost is \$0.25 for each mile that I drive.

73. Some lines are impossible to graph because when obtaining a second point using the slope, this point lands outside the edge of my graph paper.

In Exercises 74–77, determine whether each statement is true or false. If the statement is false, make the necessary change(s) to produce a true statement.

74. The equation $y = mx + b$ shows that no line can have a y-intercept that is numerically equal to its slope.

75. Every line in the rectangular coordinate system has an equation that can be expressed in slope-intercept form.

76. The line $3x + 2y = 5$ has slope $-\frac{3}{2}$.

77. The line $2y = 3x + 7$ has a y-intercept of 7.

78. The relationship between Celsius temperature, C, and Fahrenheit temperature, F, can be described by a linear equation in the form $F = mC + b$. The graph of this equation contains the point (0, 32): Water freezes at 0°C or at 32°F. The line also contains the point (100, 212): Water boils at 100°C or at 212°F. Write the linear equation expressing Fahrenheit temperature in terms of Celsius temperature.

Review Exercises

79. Solve: $\frac{x}{2} + 7 = 13 - \frac{x}{4}$.

80. Simplify: $3(12 \div 2^2 - 3)^2$.

81. 14 is 25% of what number?

Preview Exercises

Exercises 82–84 will help you prepare for the material covered in the next section. In each exercise, solve for y and put the equation in slope-intercept form.

82. $y - 3 = 4(x + 1)$

83. $y + 3 = -\frac{3}{2}(x - 4)$

84. $y - 30.0 = 0.265(x - 10)$

MID-CHAPTER CHECK POINT Section 1–Section 4

What You Know: We learned to graph equations in two variables using point plotting, as well as a variety of other techniques. We used intercepts and a checkpoint to graph linear equations in the form $Ax + By = C$. We saw that $y = b$ graphs as a horizontal line and $x = a$ graphs as a vertical line. We determined a line's steepness, or rate of change, by computing its slope. We saw that lines with the same slope are parallel and lines with slopes that have a product of -1 are perpendicular. Finally, we learned to graph linear equations in slope-intercept form, $y = mx + b$, using the slope, m, and the y-intercept, b.

In Exercises 1–3, use each graph to determine

a. *the x-intercept, or state that there is no x-intercept.*

b. *the y-intercept, or state that there is no y-intercept.*

c. *the line's slope, or state that the slope is undefined.*

1.

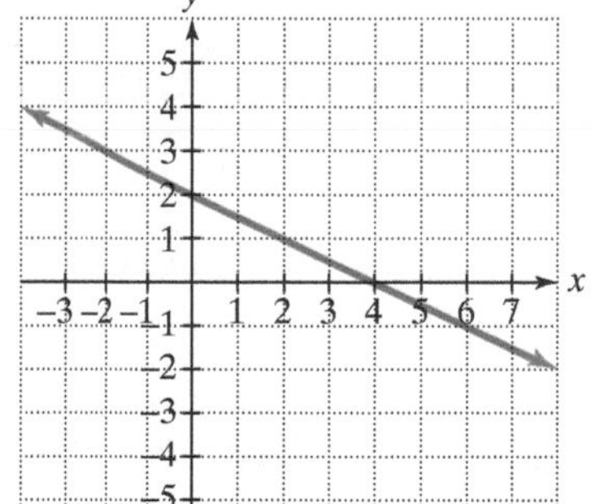

2.

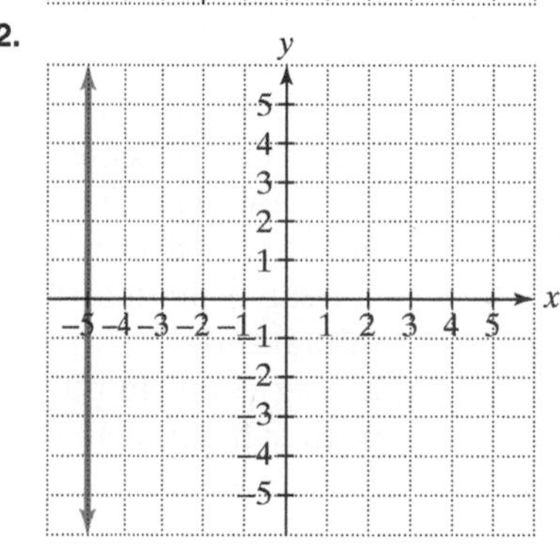

3.

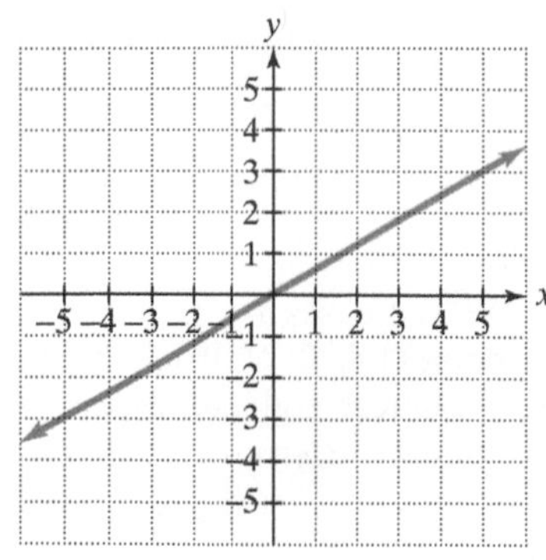

In Exercises 4–15, graph each equation in a rectangular coordinate system.

4. $y = -2x$ **5.** $y = -2$ **6.** $x + y = -2$

7. $y = \frac{1}{3}x - 2$ **8.** $x = 3.5$ **9.** $4x - 2y = 8$

10. $y = 3x + 2$ **11.** $3x + y = 0$ **12.** $y = -x + 4$

13. $y = x - 4$ **14.** $5y = -3x$ **15.** $5y = 20$

16. Find the slope and the y-intercept of the line whose equation is $5x - 2y = 10$.

In Exercises 17–19, determine whether the lines through each pair of points are parallel, perpendicular, or neither.

17. $(-5, -3)$ and $(0, -4)$; $(-2, -8)$ and $(1, 7)$

18. $(-4, 1)$ and $(2, 7)$; $(-5, 13)$ and $(4, -5)$

19. $(2, -4)$ and $(7, 0)$; $(-4, 2)$ and $(1, 6)$

20. The graphs indicate that a smaller percentage of new military recruits graduated high school in 2009 than in 1999.

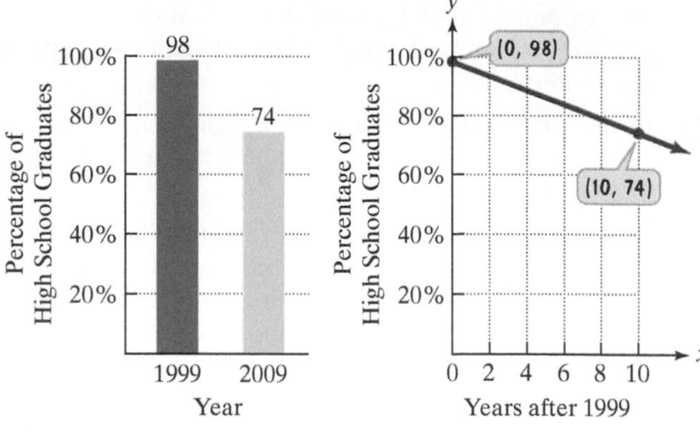

Source: Department of Defense

a. Use the two points labeled by the voice balloons to find an equation in the form $y = mx + b$ that models the percentage of new U.S. military recruits who graduated high school, y, x years after 1999.

b. If trends shown by the graphs continue, use the model in part (a) to project the percentage of new military recruits who graduated high school in 2014.

SECTION 5

The Point-Slope Form of the Equation of a Line

Objectives

1. Use the point-slope form to write equations of a line.
2. Write linear equations that model data and make predictions.

Surprised by the number of people smoking cigarettes in movies and television shows made in the 1940s and 1950s? At that time, there was little awareness of the relationship between tobacco use and numerous diseases. Cigarette smoking was seen as a healthy way to relax and help digest a hearty meal. Then, in 1964, a linear equation changed everything. To understand the mathematics behind this turning point in public health, we explore another form of a line's equation.

SuperStock/SuperStock

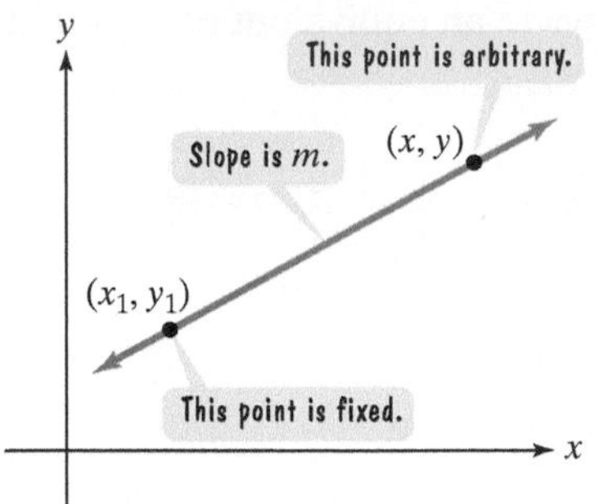

Figure 34 A line passing through (x_1, y_1) with slope m

Point-Slope Form

We can use the slope of a line to obtain another useful form of the line's equation. Consider a nonvertical line that has slope m and contains the point (x_1, y_1). Now let (x, y) represent any other point on the line, shown in **Figure 34**. Keep in mind that the point (x, y) is arbitrary and is not in one fixed position. By contrast, the point (x_1, y_1) is fixed.

Regardless of where the point (x, y) is located on the line, the steepness of the line in **Figure 34** remains the same. Thus, the ratio for slope stays a constant m. This means that for all points (x, y) along the line,

$$m = \frac{\text{Change in } y}{\text{Change in } x} = \frac{y - y_1}{x - x_1}.$$

We can clear the fraction by multiplying both sides by $x - x_1$, the least common denominator, where $x - x_1 \neq 0$.

$$m = \frac{y - y_1}{x - x_1}$$ This is the slope of the line in Figure 34.

$$m(x - x_1) = \frac{y - y_1}{x - x_1} \cdot (x - x_1)$$ Multiply both sides by $x - x_1$.

$$m(x - x_1) = y - y_1$$ Simplify: $\frac{y - y_1}{\cancel{x - x_1}} \cdot \cancel{(x - x_1)} = y - y_1$.

Now, if we reverse the two sides, we obtain the **point-slope form** of the equation of a line.

Great Question!

When using $y - y_1 = m(x - x_1)$, for which variables do I substitute numbers?

When writing the point-slope form of a line's equation, you will never substitute numbers for x and y. You will substitute values for x_1, y_1, and m.

Point-Slope Form of the Equation of a Line

The **point-slope form of the equation** of a nonvertical line with slope m that passes through the point (x_1, y_1) is

$$y - y_1 = m(x - x_1).$$

For example, the point-slope form of the equation of the line passing through (1, 4) with slope 2 $(m = 2)$ is

$$y - 4 = 2(x - 1).$$

1 Use the point-slope form to write equations of a line.

Using the Point-Slope Form to Write a Line's Equation

If we know the slope of a line and a point not containing the y-intercept through which the line passes, the point-slope form is the equation that we should use. Once we have obtained this equation, it is customary to solve for y and write the equation in slope-intercept form. Examples 1 and 2 illustrate these ideas.

EXAMPLE 1 Writing the Point-Slope Form and the Slope-Intercept Form

Write the point-slope form and the slope-intercept form of the equation of the line with slope 4 that passes through the point $(-1, 3)$.

Solution We begin with the point-slope form of the equation of a line with $m = 4$, $x_1 = -1$, and $y_1 = 3$.

$$y - y_1 = m(x - x_1)$$ This is the point-slope form of the equation.

$$y - 3 = 4[x - (-1)]$$ Substitute: $(x_1, y_1) = (-1, 3)$ and $m = 4$.

$$y - 3 = 4(x + 1)$$ We now have the point-slope form of the equation of the given line.

Now we solve the equation $y - 3 = 4(x + 1)$ for y and write an equivalent equation in slope-intercept form $(y = mx + b)$.

We need to isolate y.

$$y - 3 = 4(x + 1) \quad \text{This is the point-slope form of the equation.}$$

$$y - 3 = 4x + 4 \quad \text{Use the distributive property.}$$

$$y = 4x + 7 \quad \text{Add 3 to both sides.}$$

The slope-intercept form of the line's equation is $y = 4x + 7$. ■

✓ **CHECK POINT 1** Write the point-slope form and the slope-intercept form of the equation of the line with slope 6 that passes through the point $(2, -5)$.

EXAMPLE 2 Writing the Point-Slope Form and the Slope-Intercept Form

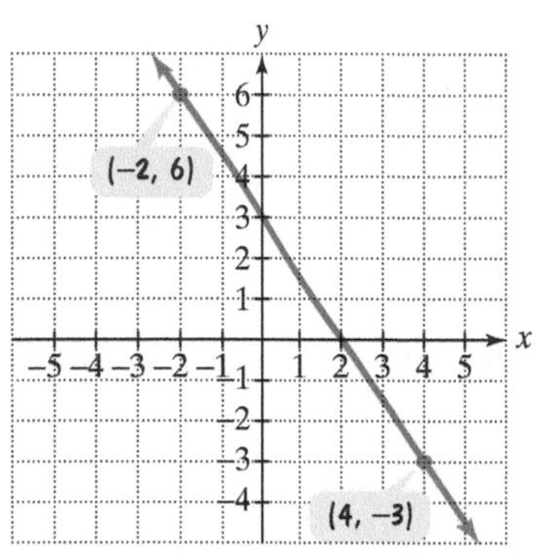

Figure 35

A line passes through the points $(4, -3)$ and $(-2, 6)$. (See **Figure 35.**) Find the equation of the line

a. in point-slope form. **b.** in slope-intercept form.

Solution

a. To use the point-slope form, we need to find the slope. The slope is the change in the y-coordinates divided by the corresponding change in the x-coordinates.

$$m = \frac{6 - (-3)}{-2 - 4} = \frac{9}{-6} = -\frac{3}{2} \quad \text{This is the definition of slope using } (4, -3) \text{ and } (-2, 6).$$

We can take either point on the line to be (x_1, y_1). Let's use $(x_1, y_1) = (4, -3)$. Now, we are ready to write the point-slope form of the equation.

$$y - y_1 = m(x - x_1) \quad \text{This is the point-slope form of the equation.}$$

$$y - (-3) = -\frac{3}{2}(x - 4) \quad \text{Substitute: } (x_1, y_1) = (4, -3) \text{ and } m = -\frac{3}{2}.$$

$$y + 3 = -\frac{3}{2}(x - 4) \quad \text{Simplify.}$$

This equation is one point-slope form of the equation of the line shown in **Figure 35.**

b. Now, we solve this equation for y and write an equivalent equation in slope-intercept form $(y = mx + b)$.

We need to isolate y.

$$y + 3 = -\frac{3}{2}(x - 4) \quad \text{This is the point-slope form of the equation.}$$

$$y + 3 = -\frac{3}{2}x + 6 \quad \text{Use the distributive property.}$$

$$y = -\frac{3}{2}x + 3 \quad \text{Subtract 3 from both sides.}$$

This equation is the slope-intercept form of the equation of the line shown in **Figure 35.** ■

Discover for Yourself

If you are given two points on a line, you can use either point for (x_1, y_1) when you write its point-slope equation. Rework Example 2 using $(-2, 6)$ for (x_1, y_1). Once you solve for y, you should obtain the same slope-intercept equation as the one shown in the last line of the solution to Example 2.

✓ **CHECK POINT 2** A line passes through the points $(-2, -1)$ and $(-1, -6)$. Find the equation of the line

a. in point-slope form.

b. in slope-intercept form.

The many forms of a line's equation can be a bit overwhelming. **Table 2** summarizes the various forms and contains the most important things you should remember about each form.

Table 2 Equations of Lines

Form	What You Should Know
Standard Form $Ax + By = C$	• Graph equations in this form using intercepts (x-intercept: set $y = 0$; y-intercept: set $x = 0$) and a checkpoint.
$y = b$	• Graph equations in this form as horizontal lines with b as the y-intercept.
$x = a$	• Graph equations in this form as vertical lines with a as the x-intercept.
Slope-Intercept Form $y = mx + b$	• Graph equations in this form using the y-intercept, b, and the slope, m. • Start with this form when writing a linear equation if you know a line's slope and y-intercept.
Point-Slope Form $y - y_1 = m(x - x_1)$	• Start with this form when writing a linear equation if you know the slope of the line and a point on the line not containing the y-intercept or two points on the line, neither of which contains the y-intercept. Calculate the slope using $m = \frac{\text{Change in } y}{\text{Change in } x} = \frac{y_2 - y_1}{x_2 - x_1}$. Although you begin with point-slope form, you usually solve for y and convert to slope-intercept form.

2 Write linear equations that model data and make predictions.

Applications

Linear equations are useful for modeling data that fall on or near a line. For example, the bar graph in **Figure 36(a)** gives the median age of the U.S. population in the indicated year. (The median age is the age in the middle when all the ages of the U.S. population are arranged from youngest to oldest.) The data are displayed as a set of five points in a rectangular coordinate system in **Figure 36(b)**.

The Graying of America: Median Age of the United States Population

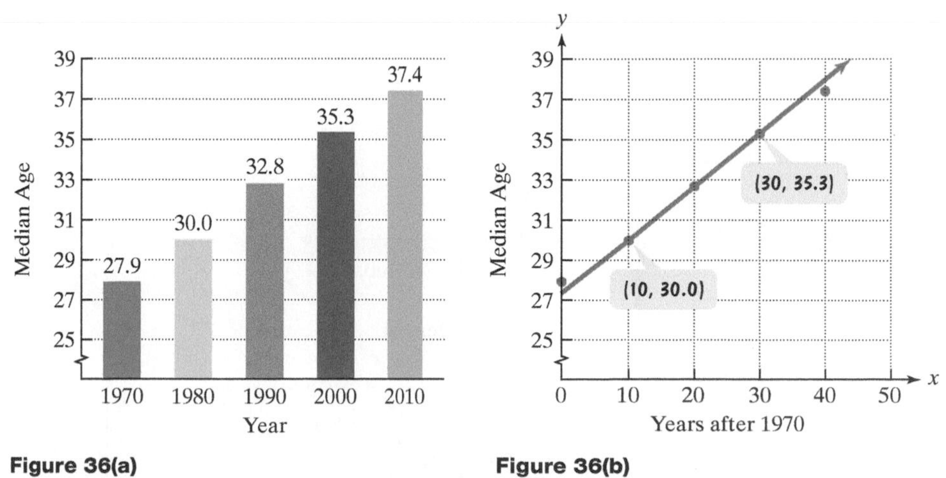

Figure 36(a)

Source: U.S. Census Bureau

Figure 36(b)

A set of points representing data is called a **scatter plot**. Also shown on the scatter plot in **Figure 36(b)** is a line that passes through or near the five points. By writing the equation of this line, we can obtain a model of the data and make predictions about the median age of the U.S. population in the future.

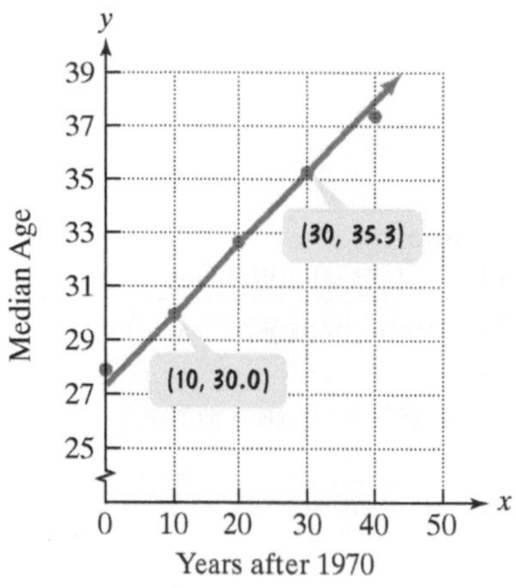

Figure 36(b) (repeated)

EXAMPLE 3 Modeling the Graying of America

Write the slope-intercept form of the equation of the line shown in Figure 36(b). Use the equation to predict the median age of the U.S. population in 2020.

Solution The line in **Figure 36(b)** passes through (10, 30.0) and (30, 35.3). We start by finding its slope.

$$m = \frac{\text{Change in } y}{\text{Change in } x} = \frac{35.3 - 30.0}{30 - 10} = \frac{5.3}{20} = 0.265$$

The slope indicates that each year the median age of the U.S. population is increasing by 0.265 year.

Now, we write the slope-intercept form of the equation for the line.

$$y - y_1 = m(x - x_1)$$ Begin with the point-slope form.

$$y - 30.0 = 0.265(x - 10)$$ Either ordered pair can be (x_1, y_1). Let $(x_1, y_1) = (10, 30.0)$. From above, $m = 0.265$.

$$y - 30.0 = 0.265x - 2.65$$ Apply the distributive property.

$$y = 0.265x + 27.35$$ Add 30 to both sides and solve for y.

A linear equation that models the median age of the U.S. population, y, x years after 1970 is

$$y = 0.265x + 27.35.$$

Now, let's use this equation to predict the median age in 2020. Because 2020 is 50 years after 1970, substitute 50 for x and compute y.

$$y = 0.265(50) + 27.35 = 40.6$$

Our model predicts that the median age of the U.S. population in 2020 will be 40.6. ■

✓ **CHECK POINT 3** Use the data points (10, 30.0) and (20, 32.8) from **Figure 36(b)** to write the slope-intercept form of an equation that models the median age of the U.S. population x years after 1970. Use this model to predict the median age in 2020.

Using Technology

You can use a graphing utility to obtain a model for a scatter plot in which the data points fall on or near a straight line. The line that best fits the data is called the **regression line**. After entering the data in **Figure 36(b)**, a graphing utility displays a scatter plot of the data and the regression line.

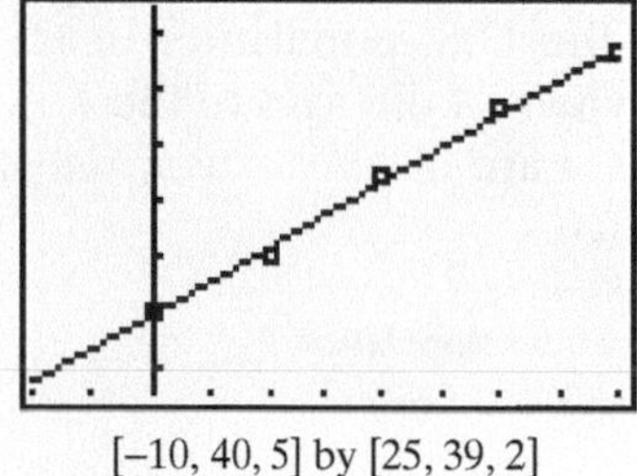

[−10, 40, 5] by [25, 39, 2]

Also displayed is the regression line's equation.

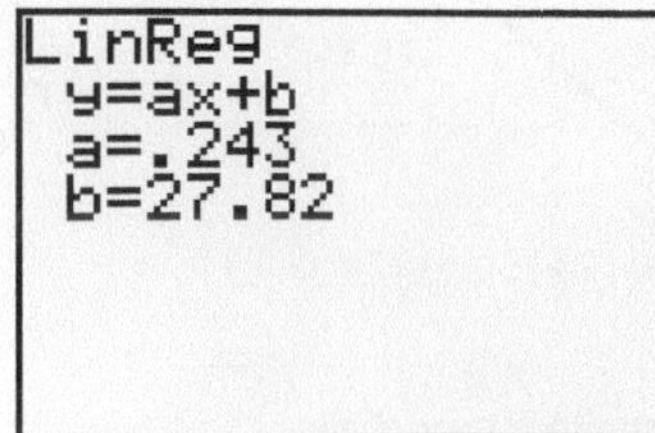

Blitzer Bonus

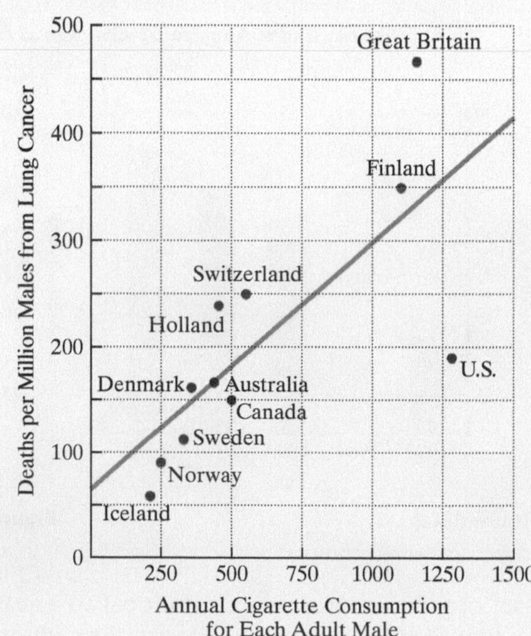

Source: Smoking and Health, Washington, D.C., 1964

Cigarettes and Lung Cancer

This scatter plot shows a relationship between cigarette consumption among males and deaths due to lung cancer per million males. The data are from 11 countries and date back to a 1964 report by the U.S. Surgeon General. The scatter plot can be modeled by a line whose slope indicates an increasing death rate from lung cancer with increased cigarette consumption. At that time, the tobacco industry argued that in spite of this regression line, tobacco use is not the cause of cancer. Recent data do, indeed, show a causal effect between tobacco use and numerous diseases.

Achieving Success

The Secret of Math Success

What's the secret of math success? The bar graph in **Figure 37** shows that Japanese teachers and students are more likely than their American counterparts to believe that the key to doing well in math is working hard. Americans tend to think that either you have mathematical intelligence or you don't. Alan Bass, author of *Math Study Skills* (Pearson Education, 2008), strongly disagrees with this American perspective:

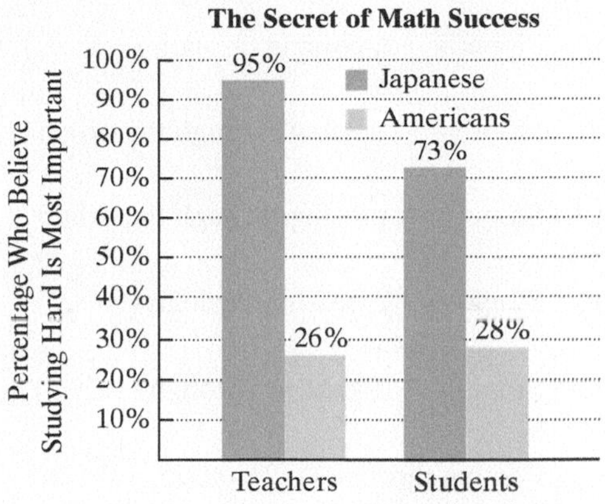

Figure 37

Source: Wade and Tavris, *Psychology*, Ninth Edition, Pearson, 2008.

> "Human beings are easily intelligent enough to understand the basic principles of math. I cannot repeat this enough, but I'll try ... **Poor performance in math is not due to a lack of intelligence!** The fact is that the key to success in math is in taking an intelligent approach. Students come up to me and say, 'I'm just not good at math.' Then I ask to see their class notebooks and they show me a chaotic mess of papers jammed into a folder. In math, that's a lot like taking apart your car's engine, dumping the heap of disconnected parts back under the hood, and then going to a mechanic to ask why it won't run. Students come to me and say, 'I'm just not good at math.' Then I ask them about their study habits and they say, 'I have to do all my studying on the weekend.' In math, that's a lot like trying to do all your eating or sleeping on the weekends and wondering why you're so tired and hungry all the time. **How you approach math is much more important than how smart you are.**"
>
> —Alan Bass

CONCEPT AND VOCABULARY CHECK

Fill in each blank so that the resulting statement is true.

1. The point-slope form of the equation of a nonvertical line with slope m that passes through the point (x_1, y_1) is ______________.
2. The equation $5x + 3y = 10$ is written in ______________ form.
3. The equation $y = 3x + 7$ is written in ______________ form.
4. The equation $y - 6 = 4(x + 1)$ is written in ______________ form.
5. The graph of $y = 3$ is a/an ______________ line.
6. The graph of $x = -1$ is a/an ______________ line.

5 EXERCISE SET

MyMathLab®

Watch the videos in MyMathLab

Download the MyDashBoard App

Practice Exercises

Write the point-slope form of the equation of the line satisfying each of the conditions in Exercises 1–28. Then use the point-slope form of the equation to write the slope-intercept form of the equation.

1. Slope $= 3$, passing through $(2, 5)$
2. Slope $= 6$, passing through $(3, 1)$
3. Slope $= 5$, passing through $(-2, 6)$
4. Slope $= 7$, passing through $(-4, 9)$
5. Slope $= -8$, passing through $(-3, -2)$
6. Slope $= -4$, passing through $(-5, -2)$
7. Slope $= -12$, passing through $(-8, 0)$
8. Slope $= -11$, passing through $(0, -3)$

9. Slope $= -1$, passing through $\left(-\frac{1}{2}, -2\right)$

10. Slope $= -1$, passing through $\left(-4, -\frac{1}{4}\right)$

11. Slope $= \frac{1}{2}$, passing through the origin

12. Slope $= \frac{1}{3}$, passing through the origin

13. Slope $= -\frac{2}{3}$, passing through $(6, -2)$

14. Slope $= -\frac{3}{5}$, passing through $(10, -4)$

15. Passing through $(1, 2)$ and $(5, 10)$

16. Passing through $(3, 5)$ and $(8, 15)$

17. Passing through $(-3, 0)$ and $(0, 3)$

18. Passing through $(-2, 0)$ and $(0, 2)$

19. Passing through $(-3, -1)$ and $(2, 4)$

20. Passing through $(-2, -4)$ and $(1, -1)$

21. Passing through $(-4, -1)$ and $(3, 4)$

22. Passing through $(-6, 1)$ and $(2, -5)$

23. Passing through $(-3, -1)$ and $(4, -1)$

24. Passing through $(-2, -5)$ and $(6, -5)$

25. Passing through $(2, 4)$ with x-intercept $= -2$

26. Passing through $(1, -3)$ with x-intercept $= -1$

27. x-intercept $= -\frac{1}{2}$ and y-intercept $= 4$

28. x-intercept $= 4$ and y-intercept $= -2$

Practice PLUS

In Exercises 29–38, write an equation in slope-intercept form of the line satisfying the given conditions.

29. The line passes through $(-3, 2)$ and is parallel to the line whose equation is $y = 4x + 1$.

30. The line passes through $(5, -3)$ and is parallel to the line whose equation is $y = 2x + 1$.

31. The line passes through $(-1, -5)$ and is parallel to the line whose equation is $3x + y = 6$.

32. The line passes through $(-4, -7)$ and is parallel to the line whose equation is $6x + y = 8$.

33. The line passes through $(4, -7)$ and is perpendicular to the line whose equation is $x - 2y = 3$.

34. The line passes through $(5, -9)$ and is perpendicular to the line whose equation is $x + 7y = 12$.

35. The line passes through $(2, 4)$ and has the same y-intercept as the line whose equation is $x - 4y = 8$.

36. The line passes through $(2, 6)$ and has the same y-intercept as the line whose equation is $x - 3y = 18$.

37. The line has an x-intercept at -4 and is parallel to the line containing $(3, 1)$ and $(2, 6)$.

38. The line has an x-intercept at -6 and is parallel to the line containing $(4, -3)$ and $(2, 2)$.

Application Exercises

39. Studies show that texting while driving is as risky as driving with a 0.08 blood alcohol level, the standard for drunk driving. The bar graph shows the number of fatalities in the United States involving distracted driving from 2004 through 2008. Although the distracted category involves such activities as talking on cellphones, conversing with passengers, and eating, experts at the National Highway Traffic Safety Administration claim that texting while driving is the clearest menace because it requires looking away from the road.

Number of Highway Fatalities in the United States Involving Distracted Driving

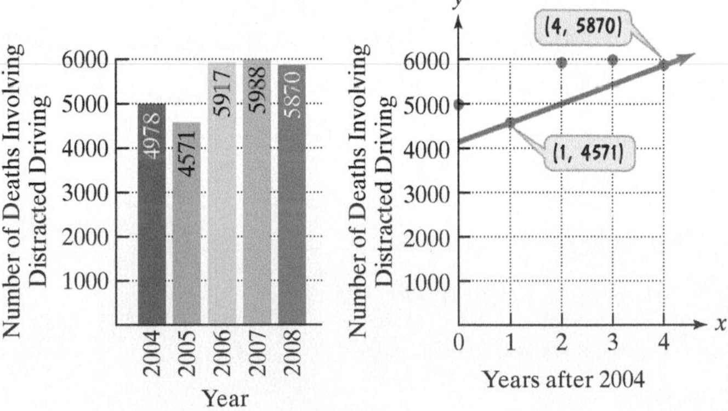

Source: National Highway Traffic Safety Administration

a. Shown to the right of the bar graph is a scatter plot with a line passing through two of the data points. Use the two points whose coordinates are shown by the voice balloons to write the slope-intercept form of an equation that models the number of highway fatalities involving distracted driving, y, in the United States x years after 2004.

b. In 2010, surveys showed overwhelming public support to ban texting while driving, although at that time only 19 states and Washington, D.C., outlawed the practice. Without additional laws that penalize texting drivers, use the model from part (a) to project the number of fatalities in the United States in 2014 involving distracted driving.

40. The bar graph shows the rise in the percentage of births to U.S. unmarried women from 1960 through 2009.

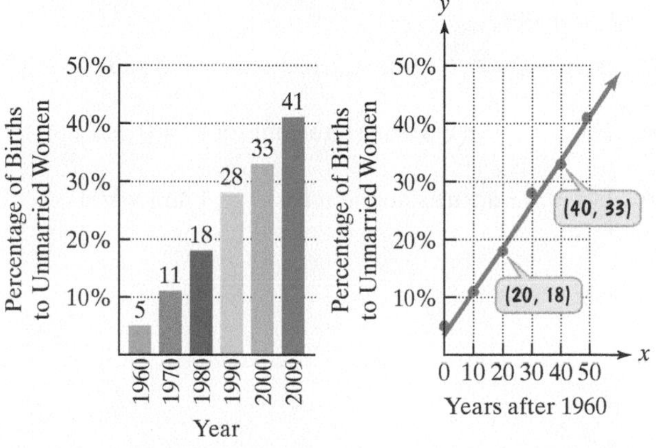

Source: National Center for Health Statistics

a. Shown to the right of the bar graph is a scatter plot with a line passing through two of the data points. Use the two points whose coordinates are shown by the voice balloons to write the slope-intercept form of an equation that models the percentage of births to unmarried women, y, in the United States x years after 1960.

b. If trends shown by the data continue, use the model from part (a) to project the percentage of births to unmarried women in the United States in 2020.

Writing in Mathematics

41. Describe how to write the equation of a line if its slope and a point on the line are known.

42. Describe how to write the equation of a line if two points on the line are known.

Critical Thinking Exercises

Make Sense? *In Exercises 43–46, determine whether each statement "makes sense" or "does not make sense" and explain your reasoning.*

43. I use $y = mx + b$ to write equations of lines passing through two points when neither contains the y-intercept.

44. In many examples, I use the slope-intercept form of a line's equation to obtain an equivalent equation in point-slope form.

45. I have linear models that describe changes for men and women over the same time period. The models have the same slope, so the graphs are parallel lines, indicating that the rate of change for men is the same as the rate of change for women.

46. The shape of this scatter plot showing per capita U.S. adult wine consumption suggests that I should not use a line or any of its equations to obtain a model.

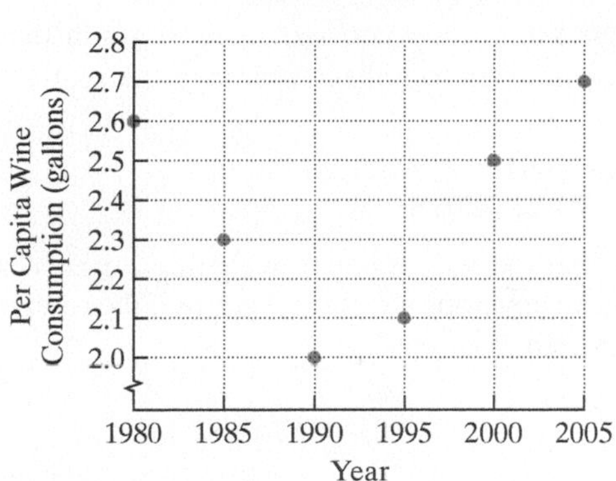

Source: Adams Business Media

In Exercises 47–50, determine whether each statement is true or false. If the statement is false, make the necessary change(s) to produce a true statement.

47. If a line has undefined slope, then it has no equation.

48. The line whose equation is $y - 3 = 7(x + 2)$ passes through $(-3, 2)$.

49. The point-slope form can be applied to obtain the equation of the line through the points $(2, -5)$ and $(2, 6)$.

50. The slope of the line whose equation is $3x + y = 7$ is 3.

51. Excited about the success of celebrity stamps, post office officials were rumored to have put forth a plan to institute two new types of thermometers. On these new scales, $°E$ represents degrees Elvis and $°M$ represents degrees Madonna. If it is known that $40°E = 25°M$, $280°E = 125°M$, and degrees Elvis is linearly related to degrees Madonna, write an equation expressing E in terms of M.

Technology Exercises

52. Use a graphing utility to graph $y = 1.75x - 2$. Select the best viewing rectangle possible by experimenting with the range settings to show that the line's slope is $\frac{7}{4}$.

53. a. Use the statistical menu of a graphing utility to enter the six data points shown in the scatter plot in Exercise 40. Refer to the bar graph to obtain coordinates of points that are not given in the scatter plot.

b. Use the DRAW menu and the scatter plot capability to draw a scatter plot of the data points like the one shown in Exercise 40.

c. Select the linear regression option. Use your utility to obtain values for a and b for the equation of the regression line, $y = ax + b$. You may also be given a *correlation coefficient*, r. Values of r close to 1 indicate that the points can be described by a linear relationship and the regression line has a positive slope. Values of r close to -1 indicate that the points can be described by a linear relationship and the regression line has a negative slope. Values of r close to 0 indicate no linear relationship between the variables.

d. Use the appropriate sequence to graph the regression equation on top of the points in the scatter plot.

Review Exercises

54. How many sheets of paper, weighing 2 grams each, can be put in an envelope weighing 4 grams if the total weight must not exceed 29 grams?

55. List all the natural numbers in this set:

$$\left\{-2, 0, \frac{1}{2}, 1, \sqrt{3}, \sqrt{4}\right\}.$$

56. Use intercepts to graph $3x - 5y = 15$. (Section 2, Example 4)

Preview Exercises

Exercises 57–59 will help you prepare for the material covered in the next section.

57. Is $2x - 3y \geq 6$ a true statement for $x = 3$ and $y = -1$?

58. Is $2x - 3y \geq 6$ a true statement for $x = 0$ and $y = 0$?

59. Is $y \leq \frac{2}{3}x$ a true statement for $x = 1$ and $y = 1$?

SECTION 6

Linear Inequalities in Two Variables

Objectives

1 Determine whether an ordered pair is a solution of an inequality.

2 Graph a linear inequality in two variables.

3 Solve applied problems involving linear inequalities in two variables.

Temperature and precipitation are two variables that affect whether regions are forests, grasslands, or deserts. In this section, you will see how linear inequalities in two variables describe some of the most magnificent places in our nation's landscape.

Robert Marmion/Alamy

Linear Inequalities in Two Variables and Their Solutions

1 Determine whether an ordered pair is a solution of an inequality.

We have seen that equations in the form $Ax + By = C$ are straight lines when graphed. If we change the $=$ sign to $>$, $<$, $\geq$, or $\leq$, we obtain a **linear inequality in two variables**. Some examples of linear inequalities in two variables are $x + y > 2$, $3x - 5y \leq 15$, and $2x - y < 4$.

A **solution of an inequality in two variables**, x and y, is an ordered pair of real numbers with the following property: When the x-coordinate is substituted for x and the y-coordinate is substituted for y in the inequality, we obtain a true statement. For example, (3, 2) is a solution of the inequality $x + y > 1$. When 3 is substituted for x and 2 is substituted for y, we obtain the true statement $3 + 2 > 1$, or $5 > 1$. Because there are infinitely many pairs of numbers that have a sum greater than 1, the inequality $x + y > 1$ has infinitely many solutions. Each ordered-pair solution is said to **satisfy** the inequality. Thus, (3, 2) satisfies the inequality $x + y > 1$.

EXAMPLE 1 Deciding Whether an Ordered Pair Satisfies an Inequality

Determine whether each ordered pair is a solution of the inequality

$$2x - 3y \geq 6:$$

a. (0, 0) **b.** (3, −1).

Solution

a. To determine whether (0, 0) is a solution of the inequality, we substitute 0 for x and 0 for y.

	$2x - 3y \geq 6$	This is the given inequality.
	$2 \cdot 0 - 3 \cdot 0 \overset{?}{\geq} 6$	Substitute 0 for x and 0 for y.
	$0 - 0 \overset{?}{\geq} 6$	Multiply: $2 \cdot 0 = 0$ and $3 \cdot 0 = 0$.
This statement is false.	$0 \geq 6$	Subtract: $0 - 0 = 0$.

Because we obtain a false statement, we conclude that (0, 0) is not a solution of $2x - 3y \geq 6$. The ordered pair (0, 0) does not satisfy the inequality.

b. To determine whether (3, −1) is a solution of the inequality, we substitute 3 for x and −1 for y.

	$2x - 3y \geq 6$	This is the given inequality.
	$2 \cdot 3 - 3(-1) \overset{?}{\geq} 6$	Substitute 3 for x and −1 for y.
	$6 - (-3) \overset{?}{\geq} 6$	Multiply: $2 \cdot 3 = 6$ and $3(-1) = -3$.
This statement is true.	$9 \geq 6$	Subtract: $6 - (-3) = 6 + 3 = 9$.

Because we obtain a true statement, we conclude that (3, −1) is a solution of $2x - 3y \geq 6$. The ordered pair (3, −1) satisfies the inequality. ■

✓ **CHECK POINT 1** Determine whether each ordered pair is a solution of the inequality $5x + 4y \leq 20$:

a. (0, 0) **b.** (6, 2).

2 Graph a linear inequality in two variables.

The Graph of a Linear Inequality in Two Variables

We know that the graph of an equation in two variables is the set of all points whose coordinates satisfy the equation. Similarly, the **graph of an inequality in two variables** is the set of all points whose coordinates satisfy the inequality.

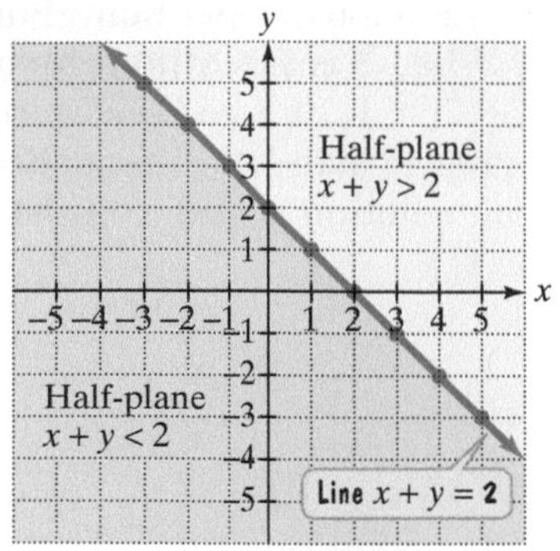

Figure 38

Let's use **Figure 38** to get an idea of what the graph of a linear inequality in two variables looks like. Part of the figure shows the graph of the linear equation $x + y = 2$. The line divides the points in the rectangular coordinate system into three sets. First, there is the set of points along the line, satisfying $x + y = 2$. Next, there is the set of points in the green region above the line. Points in the green region satisfy the linear inequality $x + y > 2$. Finally, there is the set of points in the purple region below the line. Points in the purple region satisfy the linear inequality $x + y < 2$.

A **half-plane** is the set of all the points on one side of a line. In **Figure 38**, the green region is a half-plane. The purple region is also a half-plane. A half-plane is the graph of a linear inequality that involves $>$ or $<$. The graph of an inequality that involves $\geq$ or $\leq$ is a half-plane and a line. A solid line is used to show that the line is part of the graph. A dashed line is used to show that a line is not part of a graph.

Graphing a Linear Inequality in Two Variables

1. Replace the inequality symbol with an equal sign and graph the corresponding linear equation. Draw a solid line if the original inequality contains a $\leq$ or $\geq$ symbol. Draw a dashed line if the original inequality contains a $<$ or $>$ symbol.
2. Choose a test point from one of the half-planes. (Do not choose a point that is on the line.) Substitute the coordinates of the test point into the inequality.
3. If a true statement results, shade the half-plane containing this test point. If a false statement results, shade the half-plane not containing this test point.

EXAMPLE 2 Graphing a Linear Inequality in Two Variables

Graph: $3x - 5y < 15$.

Solution

Step 1. Replace the inequality symbol with = and graph the linear equation. We need to graph $3x - 5y = 15$. We can use intercepts to graph this line.

We set $y = 0$ to find the x-intercept:	**We set $x = 0$ to find the y-intercept:**
$3x - 5y = 15$	$3x - 5y = 15$
$3x - 5 \cdot 0 = 15$	$3 \cdot 0 - 5y = 15$
$3x = 15$	$-5y = 15$
$x = 5.$	$y = -3.$

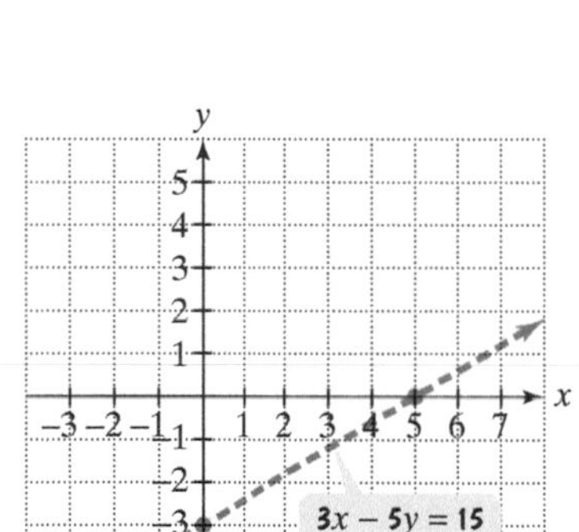

Figure 39 Preparing to graph $3x - 5y < 15$

The x-intercept is 5, so the line passes through $(5, 0)$. The y-intercept is -3, so the line passes through $(0, -3)$. The graph of the equation is indicated by a dashed line because the inequality $3x - 5y < 15$ contains a $<$ symbol, rather than $\leq$. The graph of the line is shown in **Figure 39**.

Step 2. Choose a test point from one of the half-planes and not from the line. Substitute its coordinates into the inequality. The line $3x - 5y = 15$ divides the plane into three parts—the line itself and two half-planes. The points in one half-plane satisfy $3x - 5y > 15$. The points in the other half-plane satisfy $3x - 5y < 15$. We need to find which half-plane is the solution. To do so, we test a point from either half-plane. The origin, $(0, 0)$, is the easiest point to test.

$3x - 5y < 15$ This is the given inequality.

$3 \cdot 0 - 5 \cdot 0 \stackrel{?}{<} 15$ Test (0, 0) by substituting 0 for x and 0 for y.

$0 - 0 \stackrel{?}{<} 15$ Multiply.

$0 < 15$ This statement is true.

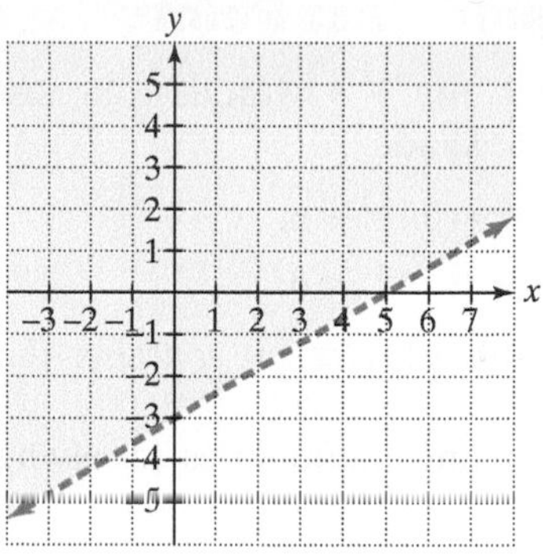

Figure 40
The graph of $3x - 5y < 15$

Step 3. If a true statement results, shade the half-plane containing the test point. Because 0 is less than 15, the test point (0, 0) is part of the solution set. All the points on the same side of the line $3x - 5y = 15$ as the point (0, 0) are members of the solution set. The solution set is the half-plane that contains the point (0, 0), indicated by shading this half-plane. The graph is shown using green shading and a dashed blue line in **Figure 40**. ■

✓ **CHECK POINT 2** Graph: $2x - 4y < 8$.

When graphing a linear inequality, test a point that lies in one of the half-planes and *not on the line dividing the half-planes*. The test point (0, 0) is convenient because it is easy to calculate when 0 is substituted for each variable. However, if (0, 0) lies on the dividing line and not in a half-plane, a different test point must be selected.

EXAMPLE 3 Graphing a Linear Inequality

Graph: $y \leq \frac{2}{3}x$.

Solution

Step 1. Replace the inequality symbol with = and graph the linear equation. Because we are interested in graphing $y \leq \frac{2}{3}x$, we begin by graphing $y = \frac{2}{3}x$. We can use the slope and the y-intercept to graph this line.

$$y = \frac{2}{3}x + 0$$

slope $= \frac{2}{3} = \frac{\text{rise}}{\text{run}}$ — y-intercept is 0.

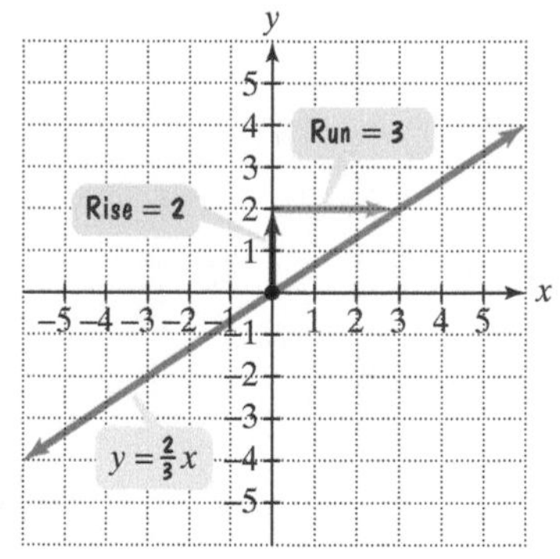

Figure 41
Preparing to graph $y \leq \frac{2}{3}x$

The y-intercept of $y = \frac{2}{3}x$ is 0, so the line passes through (0, 0). Using the y-intercept and the slope, $\frac{2}{3}$, the line is shown in **Figure 41** as a solid line. This is because the inequality $y \leq \frac{2}{3}x$ contains a $\leq$ symbol, in which equality is included.

Step 2. Choose a test point from one of the half-planes and not from the line. Substitute its coordinates into the inequality. We cannot use (0, 0) as a test point because it lies on the line and not in a half-plane. Let's use (1, 1), which lies in the half-plane above the line.

$y \leq \frac{2}{3}x$ — This is the given inequality.

$1 \stackrel{?}{\leq} \frac{2}{3} \cdot 1$ — Test (1, 1) by substituting 1 for x and 1 for y.

$1 \leq \frac{2}{3}$ — This statement is false.

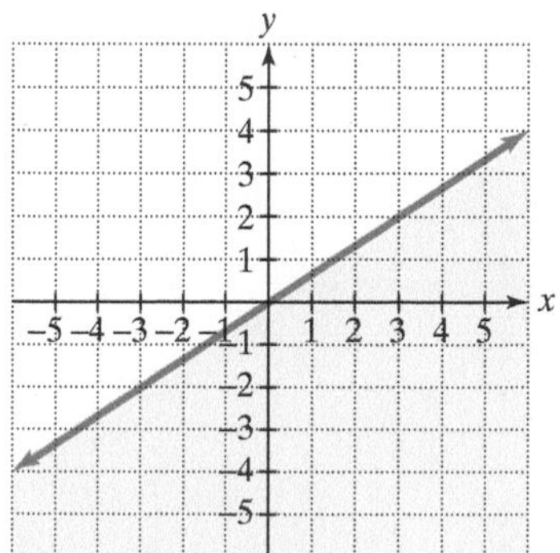

Figure 42
The graph of $y \leq \frac{2}{3}x$

Step 3. If a false statement results, shade the half-plane not containing the test point. Because 1 is not less than or equal to $\frac{2}{3}$, the test point (1, 1) is not part of the solution set. Thus, the half-plane below the solid line $y = \frac{2}{3}x$ is part of the solution set. The solution set is the line and the half-plane that does not contain the point (1, 1), indicated by shading this half-plane. The graph is shown using green shading and a blue line in **Figure 42**. ■

✓ **CHECK POINT 3** Graph: $y \geq \frac{1}{2}x$.

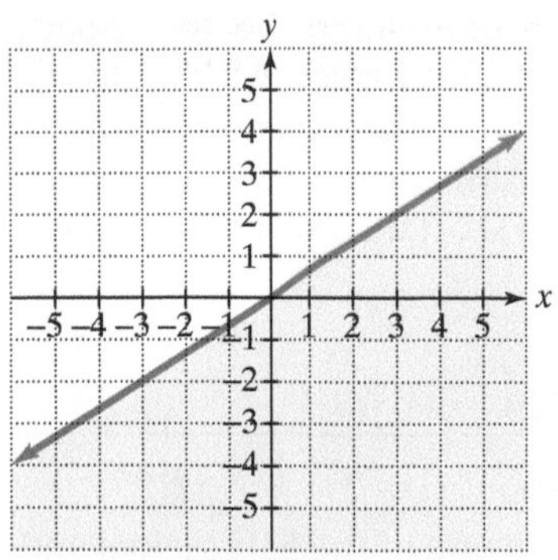

Figure 42 (repeated)
The graph of $y \leq \frac{2}{3}x$

Graphing Linear Inequalities without Using Test Points

You can graph inequalities in the form $y > mx + b$ or $y < mx + b$ without using test points. The inequality symbol indicates which half-plane to shade.

- If $y > mx + b$, shade the half-plane above the line $y = mx + b$.
- If $y < mx + b$, shade the half-plane below the line $y = mx + b$.

Observe how this is illustrated in **Figure 42**. The graph of $y \leq \frac{2}{3}x$ contains the half-plane below the line $y = \frac{2}{3}x$.

It is also not necessary to use test points when graphing inequalities involving half-planes on one side of a vertical or a horizontal line.

For the Vertical Line $x = a$:

- If $x > a$, shade the half-plane to the right of $x = a$.
- If $x < a$, shade the half-plane to the left of $x = a$.

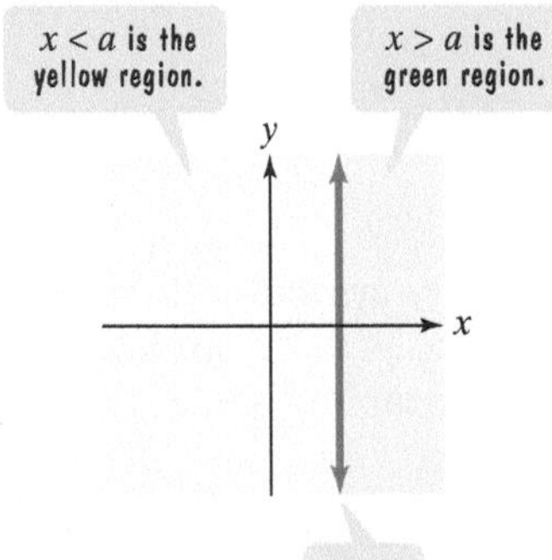

For the Horizontal Line $y = b$:

- If $y > b$, shade the half-plane above $y = b$.
- If $y < b$, shade the half-plane below $y = b$.

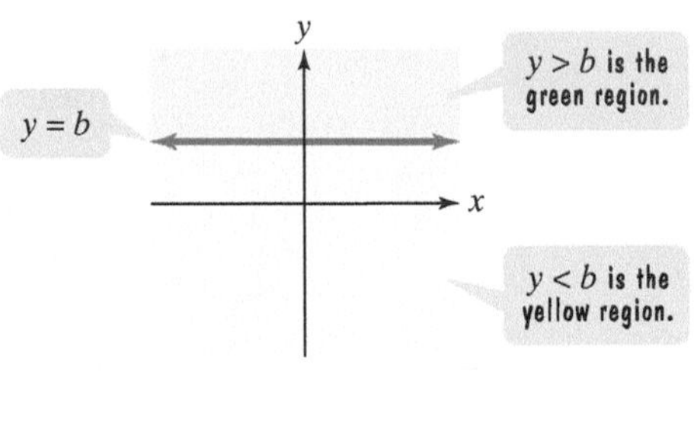

Great Question!

When is it important to use test points to graph linear inequalities?

Continue using test points to graph inequalities in the form $Ax + By > C$ or $Ax + By < C$. The graph of $Ax + By > C$ can lie above or below the line of $Ax + By = C$, depending on the value of B. The same comment applies to the graph of $Ax + By < C$.

EXAMPLE 4 Graphing Inequalities without Using Test Points

Graph each inequality in a rectangular coordinate system:

a. $y \leq -3$ **b.** $x > 2$.

Solution

a. $y \leq -3$

Graph $y = -3$, a horizontal line with y-intercept -3. The line is solid because equality is included in $y \leq -3$. Because of the less than part of $\leq$, shade the half-plane below the horizontal line.

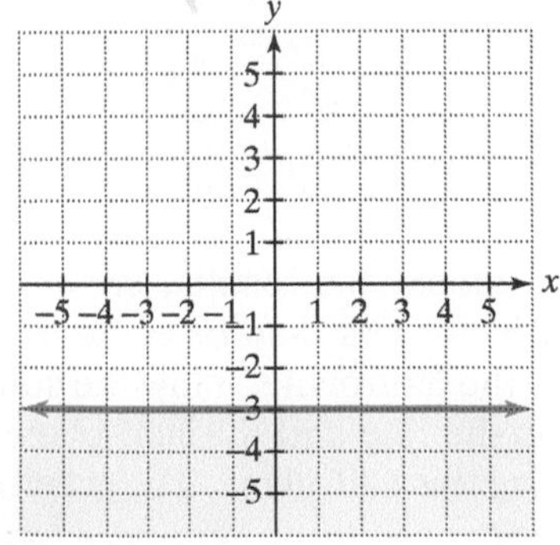

b. $x > 2$

Graph $x = 2$, a vertical line with x-intercept 2. The line is dashed because equality is not included in $x > 2$. Because of $>$, the greater than symbol, shade the half-plane to the right of the vertical line.

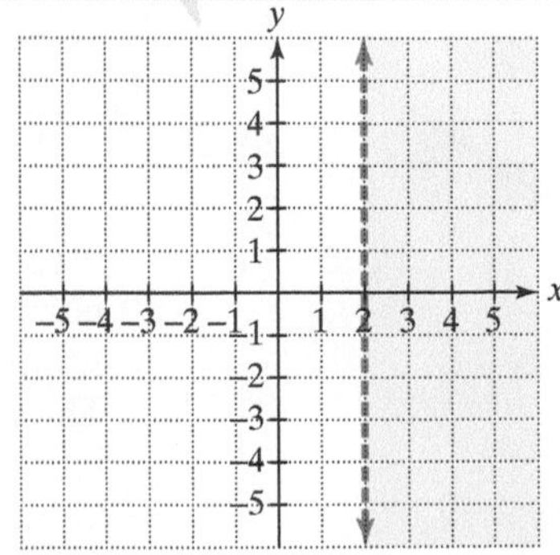

✓ **CHECK POINT 4** Graph each inequality in a rectangular coordinate system:

a. $y > 1$ **b.** $x \leq -2$.

3 Solve applied problems involving linear inequalities in two variables.

Applications

Temperature and precipitation affect whether or not trees and forests can grow. At certain levels of precipitation and temperature, only grasslands and deserts will exist. **Figure 43** shows three kinds of regions—deserts, grasslands, and forests—that result from various ranges of temperature and prccipitation. Noticc that thc horizontal axis is labeled T, for temperature, rather than x. The vertical axis is labeled P, for precipitation, rather than y. We can use inequalities in two variables, T and P, to describe the regions in the figure.

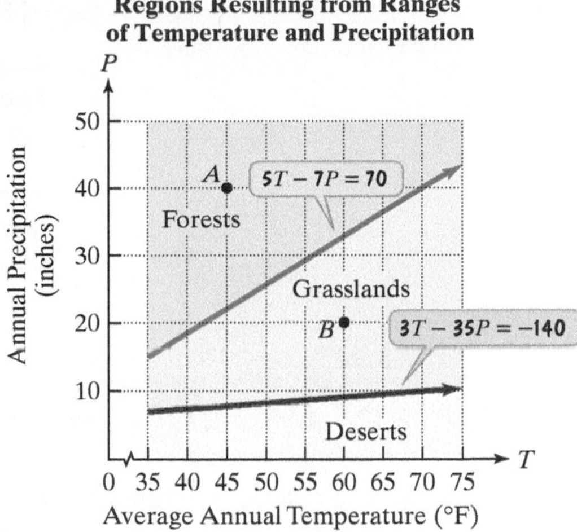

Figure 43

Source: A. Miller and J. Thompson, *Elements of Meteorology*

EXAMPLE 5 Forests and Inequalities

a. Use **Figure 43** to find the coordinates of point A. What does this mean in terms of the kind of region that occurs?

b. For average annual temperatures that exceed 35°F, the inequality

$$5T - 7P < 70$$

models where forests occur. Show that the coordinates of point A satisfy this inequality.

Solution

a. Point A has coordinates (45, 40). This means that if a region has an average annual temperature of 45°F and an average annual precipitation of 40 inches, then a forest occurs.

b. We can show that (45, 40) satisfies the inequality for forests by substituting 45 for T and 40 for P.

$$5T - 7P < 70 \quad \text{This is the given inequality.}$$

$$5 \cdot 45 - 7 \cdot 40 \stackrel{?}{<} 70 \quad \text{Substitute 45 for } T \text{ and 40 for } P.$$

$$225 - 280 \stackrel{?}{<} 70 \quad \text{Multiply: } 5 \cdot 45 = 225 \text{ and } 7 \cdot 40 = 280.$$

$$-55 < 70 \quad \text{Subtract: } 225 - 280 = -55.$$

This statement is true.

The coordinates (45, 40) make the inequality true. Thus, (45, 40) satisfies the inequality. ■

✓ CHECK POINT 5

a. Use **Figure 43** to find the coordinates of point B. What does this mean in terms of the kind of region that occurs?

b. For average annual temperatures that exceed 35°F, the inequalities $5T - 7P \geq 70$ and $3T - 35P \leq -140$ model where grasslands occur. Show that the coordinates of point B satisfy both of these inequalities.

Achieving Success

Organizing and creating your own compact chapter summaries can reinforce what you know and help with the retention of this information. Imagine that your professor will permit two index cards of notes (3 by 5; front and back) on all exams. Organize and create such a two-card summary for the test on this chapter. Begin by determining what information you would find most helpful to include on the cards. Take as long as you need to create the summary. Based on how effective you find this strategy, you may decide to use the technique to help prepare for future exams.

CONCEPT AND VOCABULARY CHECK

Fill in each blank so that the resulting statement is true.

1. The ordered pair (5, 4) is a/an ____________ of the inequality $x + y > 2$ because when 5 is substituted for ____________ and 4 is substituted for ____________, the true statement ____________ is obtained.
2. The set of all points that satisfy an inequality is called the ____________ of the inequality.
3. The set of all points on one side of a line is called a/an ____________.
4. True or false: The graph of $5x - 3y > 15$ includes the line $5x - 3y = 15$. ____________
5. True or false: The graph of the linear equation $5x - 3y = 15$ is used to graph the linear inequality $5x - 3y > 15$. ____________
6. True or false: When graphing $5x - 3y > 15$, to determine which side of the line to shade, choose a test point on $5x - 3y = 15$. ____________

6 EXERCISE SET

MyMathLab®

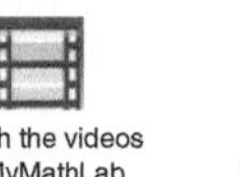
Watch the videos in MyMathLab

Download the MyDashBoard App

Practice Exercises

In Exercises 1–8, determine whether each ordered pair is a solution of the given inequality.

1. $x + y > 4$: (2, 2), (3, 2), (−3, 8)
2. $2x - y < 3$: (0, 0), (3, 0), (−4, −15)
3. $2x + y \geq 5$: (4, 0), (1, 3), (0, 0)
4. $3x - 5y \geq -12$: (2, −3), (2, 8), (0, 0)
5. $y \geq -2x + 4$: (4, 0), (1, 3), (−2, −4)
6. $y \leq -x + 5$: (5, 0), (0, 5), (8, −4)
7. $y > -2x + 1$: (2, 3), (0, 0), (0, 5)
8. $x < -y - 2$: (−1, −1), (0, 0), (4, −5)

In Exercises 9–36, graph each inequality.

9. $x + y \geq 3$
10. $x + y \geq 4$
11. $x - y < 5$
12. $x - y < 2$
13. $x + 2y > 4$
14. $2x + y > 6$
15. $3x - y \leq 6$
16. $x - 3y \leq -6$
17. $3x - 2y \leq 8$
18. $2x - 3y \geq 8$
19. $4x + 3y > 15$
20. $5x + 10y > 15$
21. $5x - y < -7$
22. $x - 5y < -7$
23. $y \leq \frac{1}{3}x$
24. $y \leq \frac{1}{4}x$
25. $y > 2x$
26. $y > 4x$
27. $y > 3x + 2$
28. $y > 2x - 1$
29. $y < \frac{3}{4}x - 3$
30. $y < \frac{2}{3}x - 1$
31. $x \leq 1$
32. $x \leq -3$
33. $y > 1$
34. $y > -3$
35. $x \geq 0$
36. $y \leq 0$

Practice PLUS

In Exercises 37–44, write each sentence as a linear inequality in two variables. Then graph the inequality.

37. The sum of the x-variable and the y-variable is at least 2.
38. The difference between the x-variable and the y-variable is at least 3.
39. The difference between 5 times the x-variable and 2 times the y-variable is at most 10.
40. The sum of 4 times the x-variable and 2 times the y-variable is at most 8.
41. The y-variable is no less than $\frac{1}{2}$ of the x-variable.
42. The y-variable is no less than $\frac{1}{4}$ of the x-variable.
43. The y-variable is no more than −1.
44. The y-variable is no more than −2.

Application Exercises

45. Bottled water and medical supplies are to be shipped to survivors of a hurricane by plane. Each plane can carry no more than 80,000 pounds. The bottled water weighs 20 pounds per container and each medical kit weighs 10 pounds. Let x represent the number of bottles of water to be shipped. Let y represent the number of medical kits. The plane's weight limitations can be described by the following inequality:

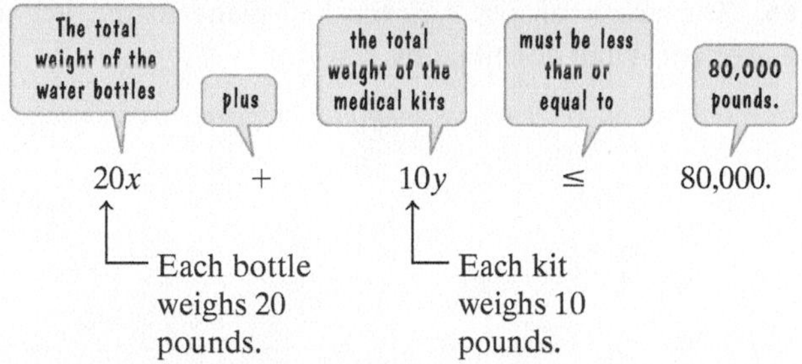

a. Graph the inequality. Because x and y must be nonnegative, limit the graph to quadrant I and its boundary only.

b. Select an ordered pair satisfying the inequality. What are its coordinates and what do they represent in this situation?

46. Bottled water and medical supplies are to be shipped to survivors of a hurricane by plane. Each plane can carry a total volume that does not exceed 6000 cubic feet. Each water bottle is 2 cubic feet and each medical kit has a volume of 1 cubic foot. Let x represent the number of bottles of water to be shipped. Let y represent the number of medical kits. The plane's volume limitations can be described by the following inequality:

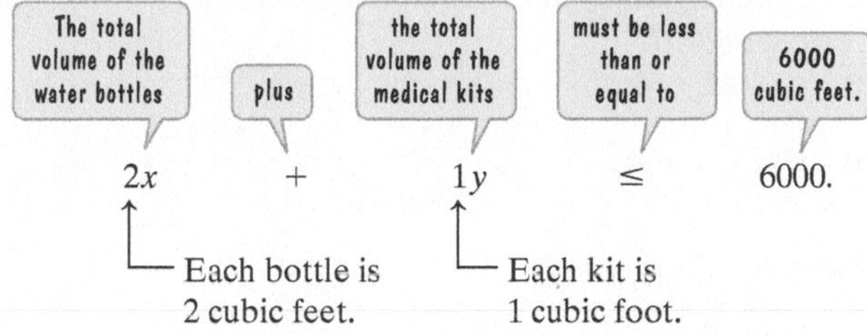

a. Graph the inequality. Because x and y must be nonnegative, limit the graph to quadrant I and its boundary only.

b. Select an ordered pair satisfying the inequality. What are its coordinates and what do they represent in this situation?

47. Many elevators have a capacity of 2000 pounds.

a. If a child averages 50 pounds and an adult 150 pounds, write an inequality that describes when x children and y adults will cause the elevator to be overloaded.

b. Graph the inequality. Because x and y must be nonnegative, limit the graph to quadrant I and its boundary only.

c. Select an ordered pair satisfying the inequality. What are its coordinates and what do they represent in this situation?

48. A patient is not allowed to have more than 330 milligrams of cholesterol per day from a diet of eggs and meat. Each egg provides 165 milligrams of cholesterol. Each ounce of meat provides 110 milligrams of cholesterol.

a. Write an inequality that describes the patient's dietary restrictions for x eggs and y ounces of meat.

b. Graph the inequality. Because x and y must be nonnegative, limit the graph to quadrant I and its boundary only.

c. Select an ordered pair satisfying the inequality. What are its coordinates and what do they represent in this situation?

Not all regions in rectangular coordinates are bounded by straight lines. Although these regions cannot be described using linear inequalities, they often have numerous applications. For example, the regions in the following two graphs indicate whether a person is obese, overweight, borderline overweight, normal weight, or underweight.

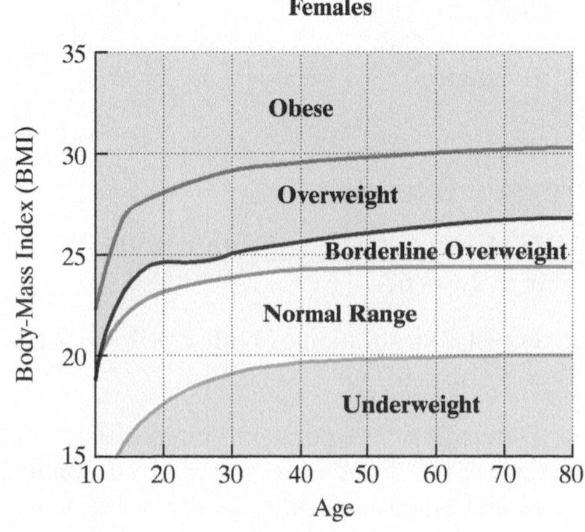

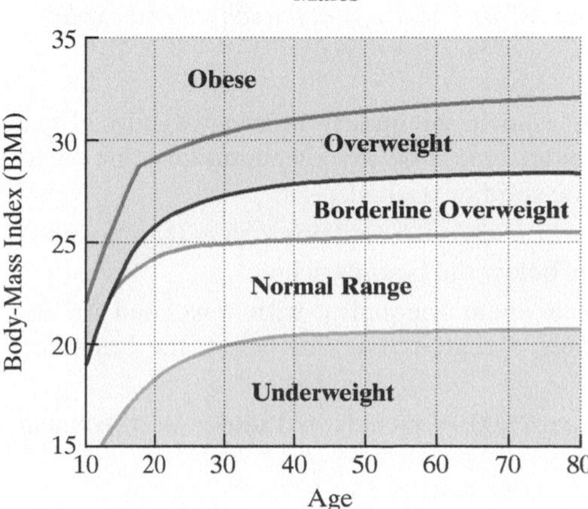

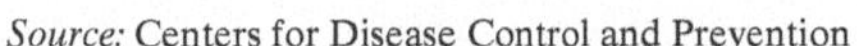

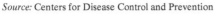

Source: Centers for Disease Control and Prevention

The horizontal axis of each graph on the previous page shows a person's age. The vertical axis shows that person's body-mass index (BMI), computed using the following formula:

$$\text{BMI} = \frac{703W}{H^2}.$$

The variable W represents weight, in pounds. The variable H represents height, in inches. Use this information to solve Exercises 49–50.

49. A man is 20 years old, 72 inches (6 feet) tall, and weighs 200 pounds.

a. Compute the man's BMI. Round to the nearest tenth.

b. Use the man's age and his BMI to locate this information as a point in the coordinate system for males shown on the previous page. Is this man obese, overweight, borderline overweight, normal weight, or underweight?

50. A woman is 25 years old, 66 inches (5 feet, 6 inches) tall, and weighs 105 pounds.

a. Compute the woman's BMI. Round to the nearest tenth.

b. Use the woman's age and her BMI to locate this information as a point in the coordinate system for females shown on the previous page. Is this woman obese, overweight, borderline overweight, normal weight, or underweight?

Writing in Mathematics

51. What is a linear inequality in two variables? Provide an example with your description.

52. How do you determine whether an ordered pair is a solution of an inequality in two variables, x and y?

53. What is a half-plane?

54. What does a solid line mean in the graph of an inequality?

55. What does a dashed line mean in the graph of an inequality?

56. Explain how to graph $2x - 3y < 6$.

57. Compare the graphs of $3x - 2y > 6$ and $3x - 2y \le 6$. Discuss similarities and differences between the graphs.

Critical Thinking Exercises

Make Sense? *In Exercises 58–61, determine whether each statement "makes sense" or "does not make sense" and explain your reasoning.*

58. By looking at a linear inequality in two variables, I can immediately determine whether the boundary line of its graph should be solid or dashed.

59. The inequality $2x - 3y < 6$ contains a "less than" symbol, so its graph lies below the boundary line.

60. When I write a linear inequality with y isolated on the left, $<$ indicates a region that lies below the boundary line.

61. I have less than $5.00 in nickels and dimes, so the linear inequality

$$0.05n + 0.10d < 5.00$$

models how many nickels, n, and how many dimes, d, that I might have.

In Exercises 62–65, determine whether each statement is true or false. If the statement is false, make the necessary change(s) to produce a true statement.

62. The ordered pair $(0, -3)$ satisfies $y > 2x - 3$.

63. The graph of $x < y + 1$ is the half-plane below the line $x = y + 1$.

64. In graphing $y \ge 4x$, a dashed line is used.

65. The graph of $x < 4$ is the half-plane to the left of the vertical line described by $x = 4$.

In Exercises 66–67, write an inequality that represents each graph.

66.

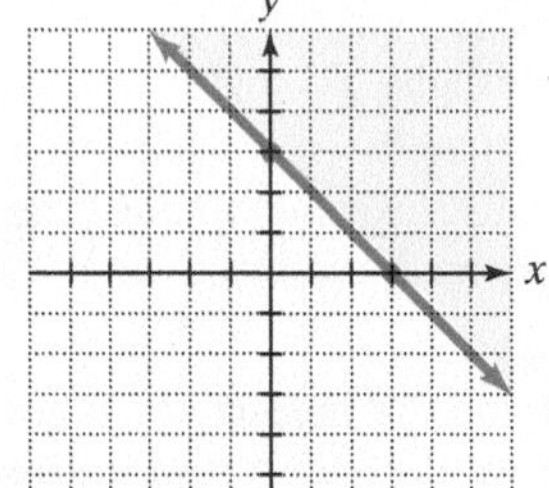

67.

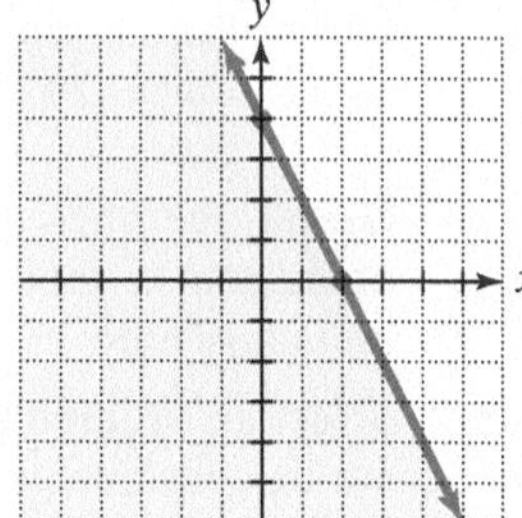

Technology Exercises

Graphing utilities can be used to shade regions in the rectangular coordinate system, thereby graphing an inequality in two variables. Read the section of the user's manual for your graphing utility that describes how to shade a region. Then use your graphing utility to graph the inequalities in Exercises 68–71.

68. $y \le 4x + 4$

69. $y \ge x - 2$

70. $y \ge \frac{1}{2}x + 4$

71. $y \le -\frac{1}{2}x + 4$

Review Exercises

72. Solve for h: $V = lwh$.

73. Find the quotient: $\frac{2}{3} \div \left(-\frac{5}{4}\right)$.

74. Evaluate $x^2 - 4$ for $x = -3$.

Preview Exercises

75. Is $(4, -1)$ a solution of both $x + 2y = 2$ and $x - 2y = 6$?

76. Is $(-4, 3)$ a solution of both $x + 2y = 2$ and $x - 2y = 6$?

77. Determine the point of intersection of the graphs of $2x + 3y = 6$ and $2x + y = -2$ by graphing both equations in the same rectangular coordinate system.

GROUP PROJECT

In Example 3 of Section 5, we used the data in **Figure 36** to develop a linear equation that modeled the graying of America. For this group exercise, you might find it helpful to pattern your work after **Figure 36** and the solution to Example 3. Group members should begin by consulting an almanac, newspaper, magazine, or the Internet to find data that lie approximately on or near a straight line. Working by hand or using a graphing utility, construct a scatter plot for the data. If working by hand, draw a line that passes through or near the data points and then write its equation. If using a graphing utility, obtain the equation of the regression line. Then use the equation of the line to make a prediction about what might happen in the future. Are there circumstances that might affect the accuracy of this prediction? List some of these circumstances.

Summary

Definitions and Concepts	Examples

Section 1 Graphing Linear Equations in Two Variables

The rectangular coordinate system consists of a horizontal number line, the x-axis, and a vertical number line, the y-axis, intersecting at their zero points, the origin. Each point in the system corresponds to an ordered pair of real numbers (x, y). The first number in the pair is the x-coordinate; the second number is the y-coordinate.

Plot: $(2, 3), (-5, 4), (-4, -3)$, and $(5, -2)$.

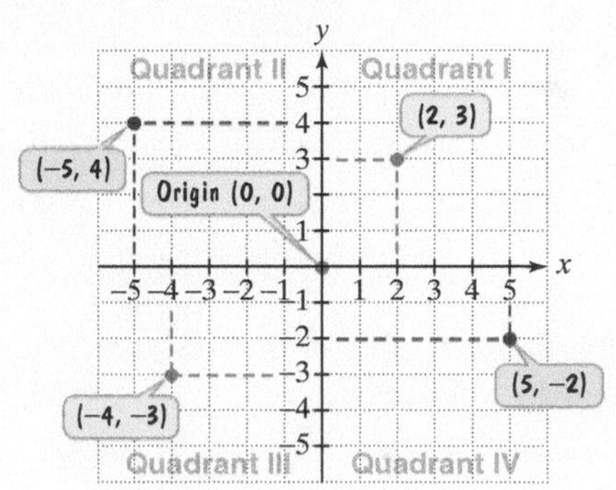

An ordered pair is a solution of an equation in two variables if replacing the variables by the coordinates of the ordered pair results in a true statement.

Is $(-1, 4)$ a solution of $2x + 5y = 18$?

$$2(-1) + 5 \cdot 4 \stackrel{?}{=} 18$$
$$-2 + 20 \stackrel{?}{=} 18$$
$$18 = 18, \text{ true}$$

Thus, $(-1, 4)$ is a solution.

One method for graphing an equation in two variables is point plotting. Find several ordered-pair solutions, plot them as points, and connect the points with a smooth curve or line.

Graph: $y = 2x + 1$.

x	$y = 2x + 1$	(x, y)
-2	$y = 2(-2) + 1 = -3$	$(-2, -3)$
-1	$y = 2(-1) + 1 = -1$	$(-1, -1)$
0	$y = 2 \cdot 0 + 1 = 1$	$(0, 1)$
1	$y = 2 \cdot 1 + 1 = 3$	$(1, 3)$
2	$y = 2 \cdot 2 + 1 = 5$	$(2, 5)$

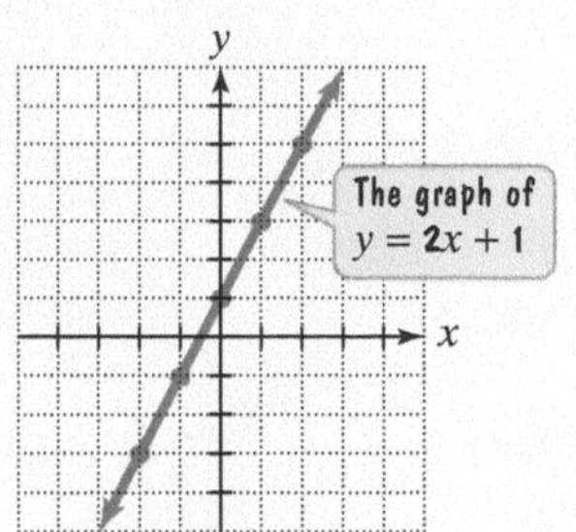

Definitions and Concepts	Examples

Section 2 Graphing Linear Equations Using Intercepts

If a graph intersects the x-axis at $(a, 0)$, then a is an x-intercept.

If a graph intersects the y-axis at $(0, b)$, then b is a y-intercept.

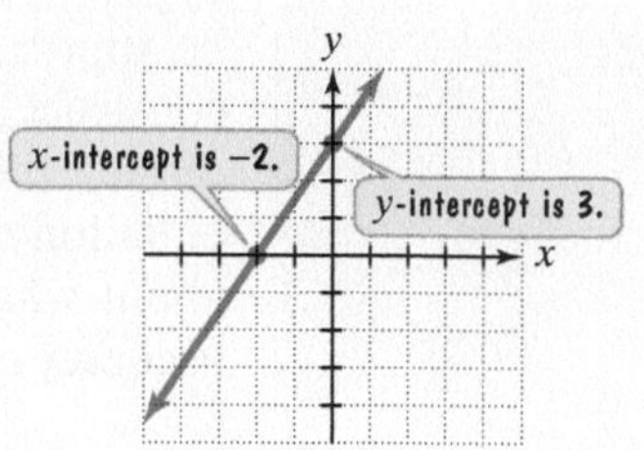

An equation of the form $Ax + By = C$, where A, B, and C are integers, is called the standard form of the equation of a line. The graph of $Ax + By = C$ is a line that can be obtained using intercepts. To find the x-intercept, let $y = 0$ and solve for x. To find the y-intercept, let $x = 0$ and solve for y. Find a checkpoint, a third ordered-pair solution. Graph the equation by drawing a line through the three points.

Graph using intercepts: $4x + 3y = 12$.

x-intercept: $4x = 12$

$x = 3$

y-intercept: $3y = 12$

$y = 4$

Checkpoint: Let $x = 2$.

$8 + 3y = 12$

$3y = 4$

$y = \frac{4}{3}$

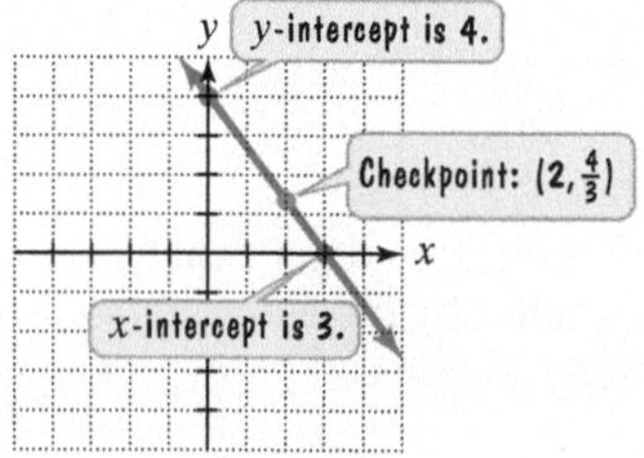

The graph of $Ax + By = 0$ is a line that passes through the origin. Find two other points by finding two other solutions of the equation. Graph the equation by drawing a line through the origin and these two points.

Graph: $x + 2y = 0$.

$x = 2$: $2 + 2y = 0$

$2y = -2$

$y = -1$

$y = 1$: $x + 2(1) = 0$

$x = -2$

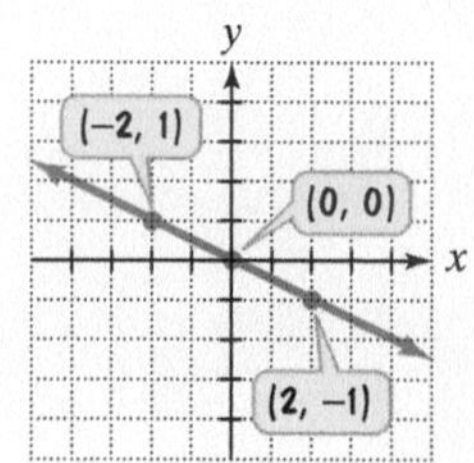

Definitions and Concepts	Examples

Section 2 Graphing Linear Equations Using Intercepts (continued)

Horizontal and Vertical Lines

The graph of $y = b$ is a horizontal line. The y-intercept is b.

The graph of $x = a$ is a vertical line. The x-intercept is a.

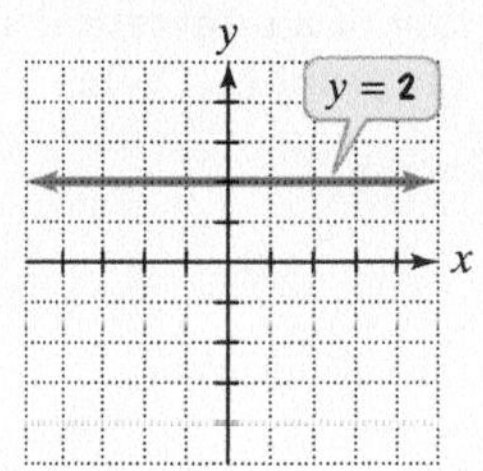

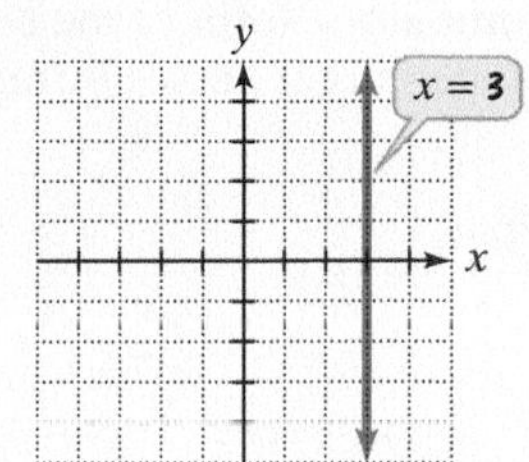

Section 3 Slope

The slope, m, of the line through the points (x_1, y_1) and (x_2, y_2) is

$$m = \frac{y_2 - y_1}{x_2 - x_1}, \quad x_2 - x_1 \neq 0.$$

If the slope is positive, the line rises from left to right. If the slope is negative, the line falls from left to right.

The slope of a horizontal line is 0. The slope of a vertical line is undefined.

If two distinct nonvertical lines have the same slope, then the lines are parallel.

If the product of the slopes of two lines is -1, then the lines are perpendicular. Equivalently, if the slopes are negative reciprocals, then the lines are perpendicular.

The slope of a line represents its rate of change.

Find the slope of the line passing through the points shown.

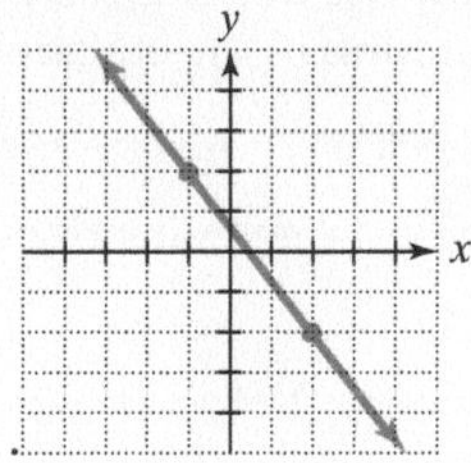

Let $(x_1, y_1) = (-1, 2)$ and $(x_2, y_2) = (2, -2)$.

$$m = \frac{y_2 - y_1}{x_2 - x_1} = \frac{-2 - 2}{2 - (-1)} = \frac{-4}{3} = -\frac{4}{3}$$

Section 4 The Slope-Intercept Form of the Equation of a Line

The slope-intercept form of the equation of a nonvertical line with slope m and y-intercept b is

$$y = mx + b.$$

Find the slope and the y-intercept of the line with the given equation.

- $y = -2x + 5$

  Slope is -2. y-intercept is 5.

- $2x + 3y = 9$ (Solve for y.)

  $3y = -2x + 9$ Subtract $2x$.

  $y = -\frac{2}{3}x + 3$ Divide by 3.

  Slope is $-\frac{2}{3}$. y-intercept is 3.

Graphing $y = mx + b$ Using the Slope and y-Intercept

1. Plot the point containing the y-intercept on the y-axis. This is the point $(0, b)$.
2. Use the slope, m, to obtain a second point. Write m as a fraction, and use rise over run, starting at the point on the y-axis, to plot this point.
3. Graph the equation by drawing a line through the two points.

Graph: $y = -\frac{3}{4}x + 1$.

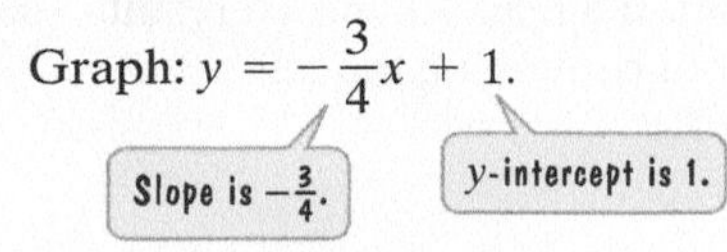

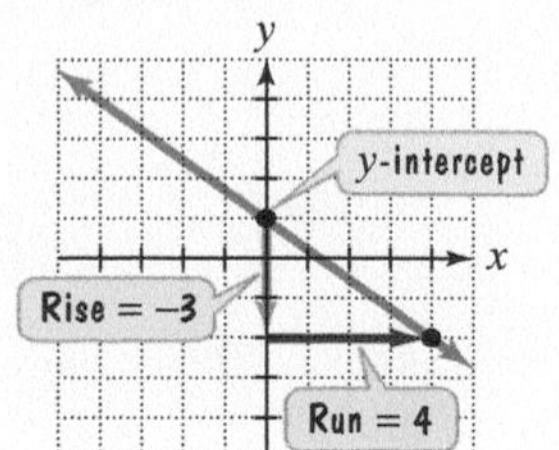

Definitions and Concepts	Examples

Section 5 The Point-Slope Form of the Equation of a Line

The point-slope form of the equation of a nonvertical line with slope m that passes through the point (x_1, y_1) is

$$y - y_1 = m(x - x_1).$$

Slope $= -3$, passing through $(-1, 5)$

$m = -3$ $x_1 = -1$ $y_1 = 5$

The point-slope form of the line's equation is

$$y - 5 = -3[x - (-1)].$$

Simplify:

$$y - 5 = -3(x + 1).$$

To write the point-slope form of the equation of a line passing through two points, begin by using the points to compute the slope, m. Use either given point as (x_1, y_1) and write the point-slope form of the equation:

$$y - y_1 = m(x - x_1).$$

Solving this equation for y gives the slope-intercept form of the line's equation.

Write an equation in point-slope form and slope-intercept form of the line passing through $(-1, -3)$ and $(4, 2)$.

$$m = \frac{2 - (-3)}{4 - (-1)} = \frac{2 + 3}{4 + 1} = \frac{5}{5} = 1$$

Using $(4, 2)$ as (x_1, y_1), the point-slope form of the equation is

$$y - 2 = 1(x - 4).$$

Solve for y to obtain the slope-intercept form.

$$y = x - 2 \quad \text{Add 2 to both sides.}$$

Section 6 Linear Inequalities in Two Variables

A linear inequality in two variables can be written in one of the following forms:

$$Ax + By < C \qquad Ax + By \le C$$

$$Ax + By > C \qquad Ax + By \ge C.$$

An ordered pair is a solution if replacing the variables by the coordinates of the ordered pair results in a true statement.

Is $(2, -6)$ a solution of $3x - 4y \le 7$?

$$3 \cdot 2 - 4(-6) \overset{?}{\le} 7$$

$$6 - (-24) \overset{?}{\le} 7$$

$$6 + 24 \overset{?}{\le} 7$$

$$30 \le 7, \text{ false}$$

Thus, $(2, -6)$ is not a solution.

Graphing a Linear Inequality in Two Variables

1. Replace the inequality symbol with an equal sign and graph the boundary line. Use a solid line for $\le$ or $\ge$ and a dashed line for $<$ or $>$.
2. Choose a test point not on the line and substitute its coordinates into the inequality.
3. If a true statement results, shade the half-plane containing the test point. If a false statement results, shade the half-plane not containing the test point.

Graph: $x - 2y \le 4$.

1. Graph $x - 2y = 4$. Use a solid line because the inequality symbol is $\le$.
2. Test $(0, 0)$.

$$0 - 2 \cdot 0 \overset{?}{\le} 4$$

$$0 \le 4, \text{ true}$$

3. The inequality is true. Shade the half-plane containing $(0, 0)$, shown in yellow below.

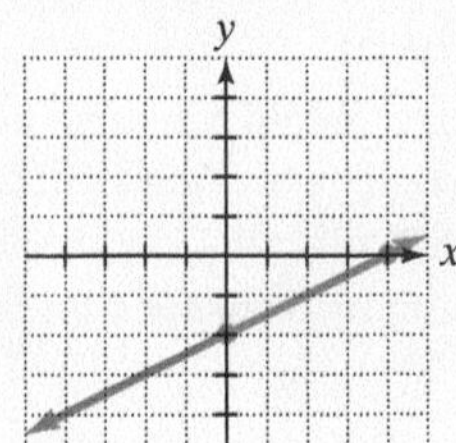

REVIEW EXERCISES

1 *In Exercises 1–4, plot the given point in a rectangular coordinate system. Indicate in which quadrant each point lies.*

1. $(1, -5)$
2. $(4, -3)$
3. $\left(\frac{7}{2}, \frac{3}{2}\right)$
4. $(-5, 2)$
5. Give the ordered pairs that correspond to the points labeled in the figure.

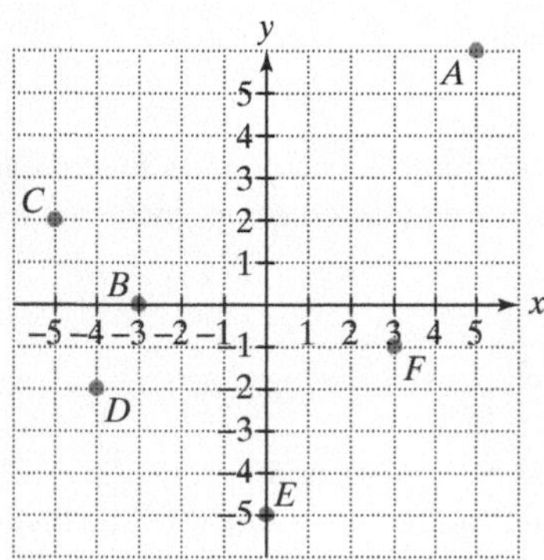

In Exercises 6–7, determine whether each ordered pair is a solution of the given equation.

6. $y = 3x + 6$ $(-3, 3), (0, 6), (1, 9)$
7. $3x - y = 12$ $(0, 4), (4, 0), (-1, 15)$

In Exercises 8–9,

a. *Find five solutions of each equation. Organize your work in a table of values.*

b. *Use the five solutions in the table to graph each equation.*

8. $y = 2x - 3$
9. $y = \frac{1}{2}x + 1$

2 *In Exercises 10–12, use the graph to identify the*

a. *x-intercept, or state that there is no x-intercept.*

b. *y-intercept, or state that there is no y-intercept.*

10.

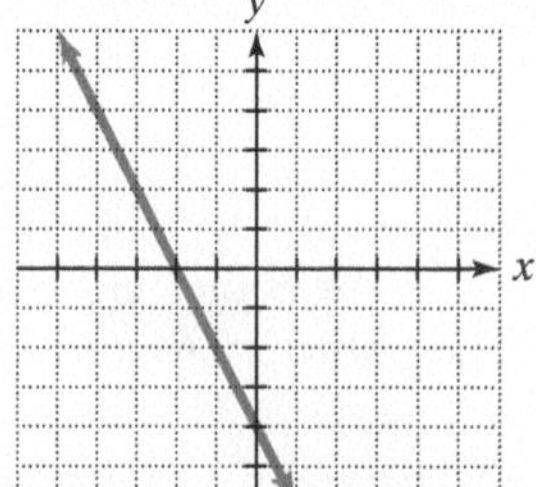

11.

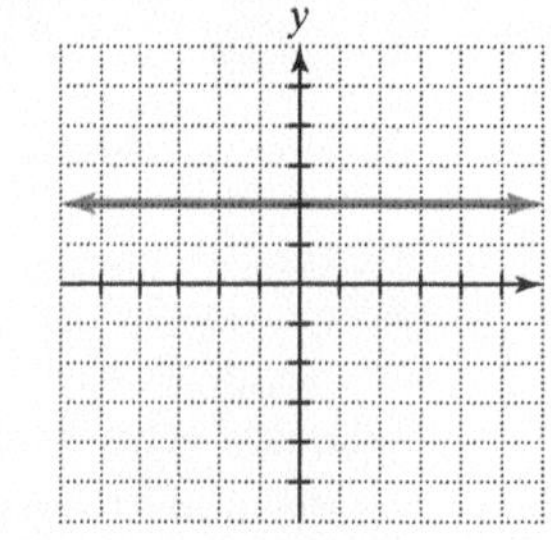

12.

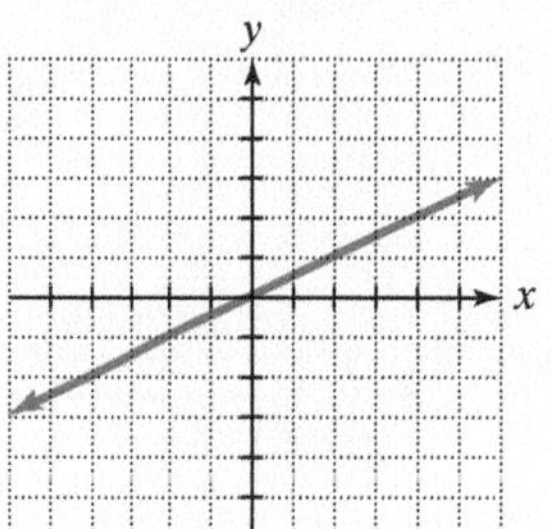

In Exercises 13–16, use intercepts to graph each equation.

13. $2x + y = 4$
14. $3x - 2y = 12$
15. $3x = 6 - 2y$
16. $3x - y = 0$

In Exercises 17–20, graph each equation.

17. $x = 3$
18. $y = -5$
19. $y + 3 = 5$
20. $2x = -8$
21. The graph shows the Fahrenheit temperature, y, x hours after noon.

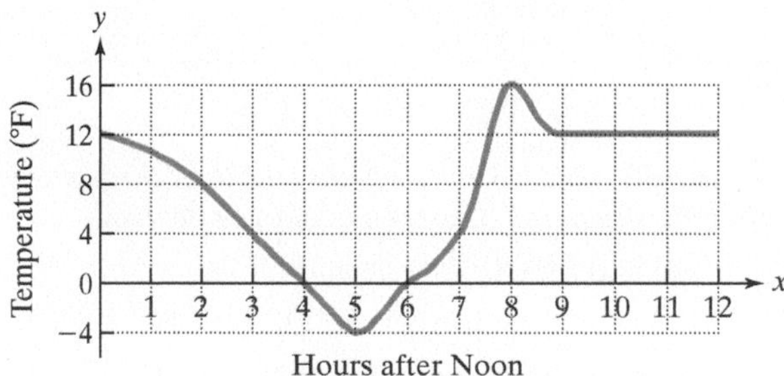

a. At what time did the minimum temperature occur? What is the minimum temperature?

b. At what time did the maximum temperature occur? What is the maximum temperature?

c. What are the x-intercepts? In terms of time and temperature, interpret the meaning of these intercepts.

d. What is the y-intercept? What does this mean in terms of time and temperature?

e. From 9 P.M. until midnight, the graph is shown as a horizontal line. What does this mean about the temperature over this period of time?

3 *In Exercises 22–25, calculate the slope of the line passing through the given points. If the slope is undefined, so state. Then indicate whether the line rises, falls, is horizontal, or is vertical.*

22. $(3, 2)$ and $(5, 1)$
23. $(-1, 2)$ and $(-3, -4)$
24. $(-3, 4)$ and $(6, 4)$
25. $(5, 3)$ and $(5, -3)$

In Exercises 26–29, find the slope of each line, or state that the slope is undefined.

26.

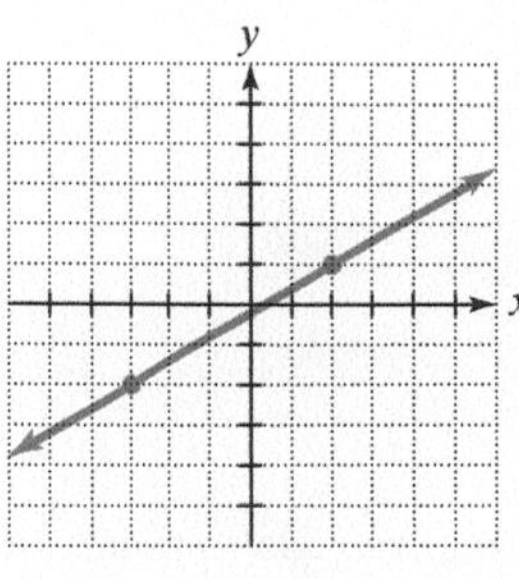

27.

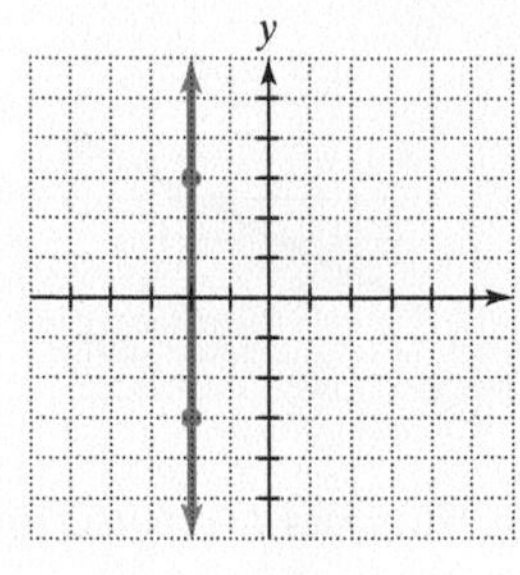
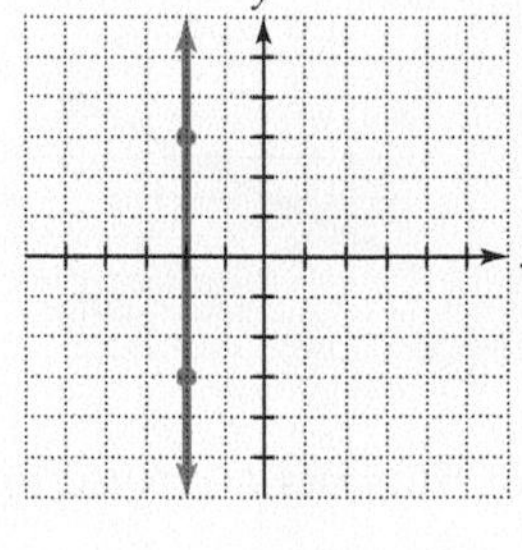

28.

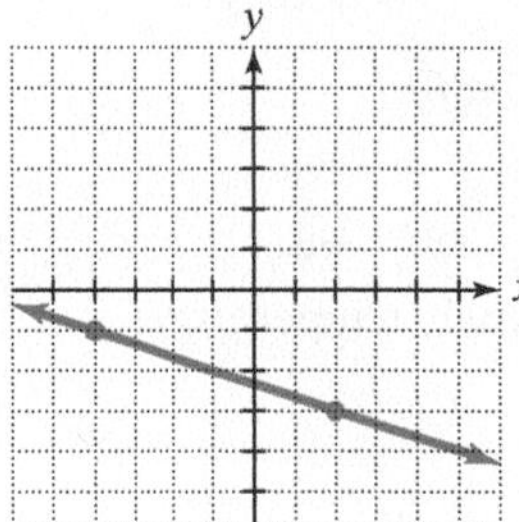

29.

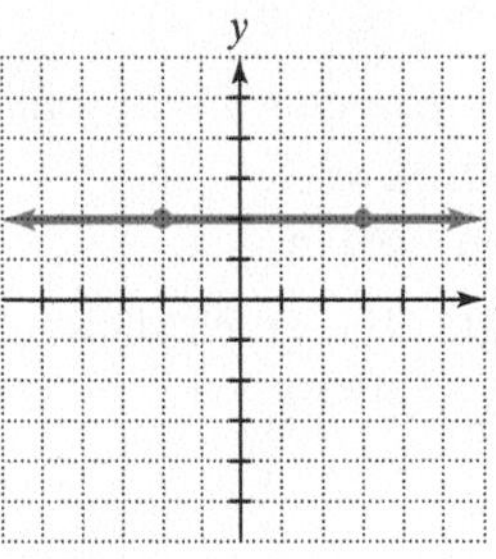

In Exercises 30–32, determine whether the lines through each pair of points are parallel, perpendicular, or neither.

30. $(-1, -3)$ and $(2, -8)$; $(8, -7)$ and $(9, 10)$

31. $(0, -4)$ and $(5, -1)$; $(-6, 8)$ and $(3, -7)$

32. $(5, 4)$ and $(9, 7)$; $(-6, 0)$ and $(-2, 3)$

33. In a 2010 survey of more than 200,000 freshmen at 279 colleges, only 52% rated their emotional health high or above average, a drop from 64% in 1985.

Percentage of U.S. College Freshmen Rating Their Emotional Health High or Above Average

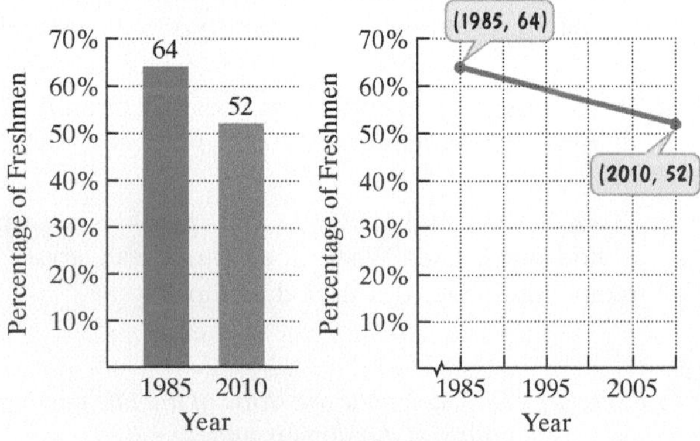

Source: UCLA Higher Education Research Institute

a. Find the slope of the line passing through the two points shown by the voice ballons.

b. Use your answer from part (a) to complete this statement:

For each year from 1985 through 2010, the percentage of U.S. college freshmen rating their emotional health high or above average decreased by ___. The rate of change was _____ per ___.

4 *In Exercises 34–37, find the slope and the y-intercept of the line with the given equation.*

34. $y = 5x - 7$

35. $y = 6 - 4x$

36. $y = 3$

37. $2x + 3y = 6$

In Exercises 38–40, graph each linear equation using the slope and y-intercept.

38. $y = 2x - 4$

39. $y = \frac{1}{2}x - 1$

40. $y = -\frac{2}{3}x + 5$

In Exercises 41–42, write each equation in slope-intercept form. Then use the slope and y-intercept to graph the equation.

41. $y - 2x = 0$

42. $\frac{1}{3}x + y = 2$

43. Graph $y = -\frac{1}{2}x + 4$ and $y = -\frac{1}{2}x - 1$ in the same rectangular coordinate system. Are the lines parallel? If so, explain why.

44. No matter who hosts, the Miss America pageant keeps losing viewers. The scatter plot shows the number of viewers of the pageant, in millions, along with some of the MCs from 1989 through 2009. Also shown is a line passing through two of the data points.

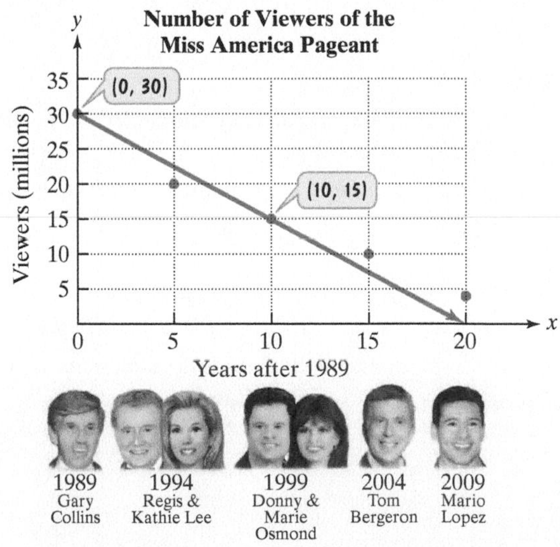

Source: Entertainment Weekly

a. Use the two points shown by the voice balloons to find an equation in the form $y = mx + b$ that models the number of viewers of the Miss America pageant, y, in millions, x years after 1989.

b. Use the model from part (a) to determine the number of viewers of the pageant in 1994. Does this underestimate or overestimate the actual number of viewers shown by the scatter plot? By how many millions of viewers?

5 *Write the point-slope form of the equation of the line satisfying the conditions in Exercises 45–46. Then use the point-slope form of the equation to write the slope-intercept form.*

45. Slope $= 6$, passing through $(-4, 7)$

46. Passing through $(3, 4)$ and $(2, 1)$

47. The bar graph shows world population, in billions, for seven selected years from 1950 through 2010. Also shown is a scatter plot with a line passing through two of the data points.

World Population, 1950–2010

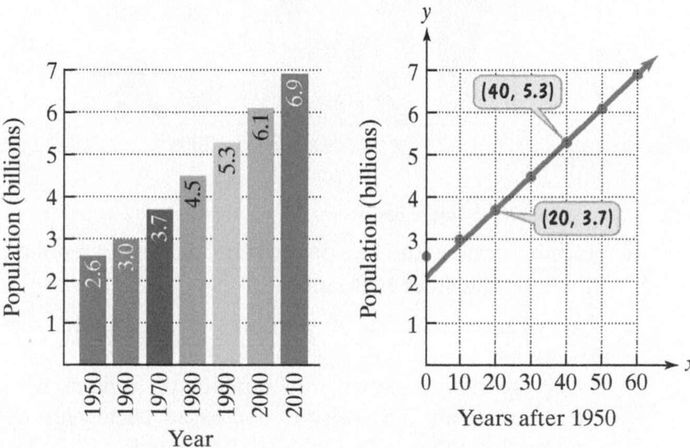

Source: U.S. Census Bureau, International Database

a. Use the two points whose coordinates are shown by the voice balloons to write the slope-intercept form of an equation that models world population, y, in billions, x years after 1950.

b. Use the model from part (a) to project world population in 2025.

6

48. Determine whether each ordered pair is a solution of $3x - 4y > 7$:

$$(0, 0),\ (3, -6),\ (-2, -5),\ (-3, 4).$$

In Exercises 49–56, graph each inequality.

49. $x - 2y > 6$

50. $4x - 6y \le 12$

51. $y > 3x + 2$

52. $y \le \frac{1}{3}x - 1$

53. $y < -\frac{1}{2}x$

54. $x < 4$

55. $y \ge -2$

56. $x + 2y \le 0$

CHAPTER TEST

Step-by-step test solutions are found on the Chapter Test Prep Videos available in MyMathLab® or on YouTube (search "BlitzerIntroAlg" and click on "Channels").

1. Determine whether each ordered pair is a solution of $4x - 2y = 10$:

$$(0, -5),\quad (-2, 1),\quad (4, 3).$$

2. Find five solutions of $y = 3x + 1$. Organize your work in a table of values. Then use the five solutions in the table to graph the equation.

3. Use the graph to identify the

a. x-intercept, or state that there is no x-intercept.

b. y-intercept, or state that there is no y-intercept.

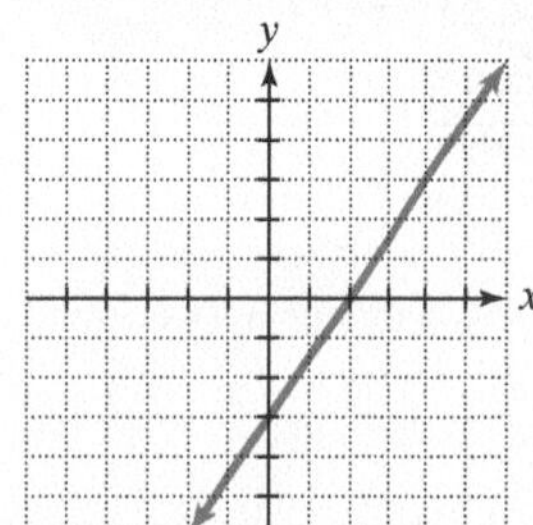

4. Use intercepts to graph $4x - 2y = -8$.

5. Graph $y = 4$ in a rectangular coordinate system.

In Exercises 6–7, calculate the slope of the line passing through the given points. If the slope is undefined, so state. Then indicate whether the line rises, falls, is horizontal, or is vertical.

6. $(-3, 4)$ and $(-5, -2)$

7. $(6, -1)$ and $(6, 3)$

8. Find the slope of the line in the figure shown or state that the slope is undefined.

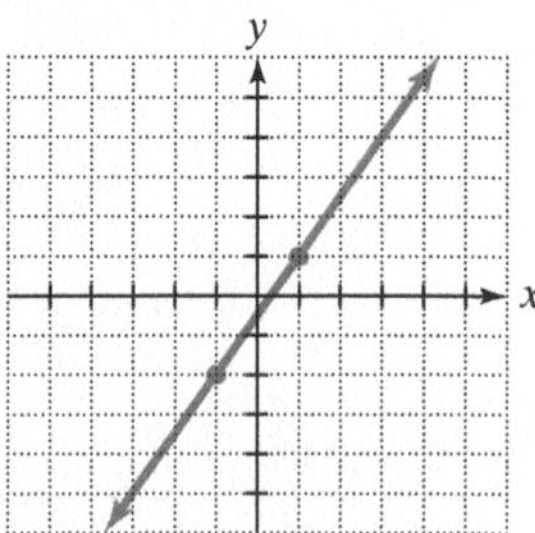

In Exercises 9–10 determine whether the lines through each pair of points are parallel, perpendicular, or neither.

9. $(-2, 10)$ and $(0, 2)$; $(-8, -7)$ and $(24, 1)$

10. $(2, 4)$ and $(6, 1)$; $(-3, 1)$ and $(1, -2)$

In Exercises 11–12, find the slope and the y-intercept of the line with the given equation.

11. $y = -x + 10$

12. $2x + y = 6$

In Exercises 13–14, graph each linear equation using the slope and y-intercept.

13. $y = \frac{2}{3}x - 1$

14. $y = -2x + 3$

In Exercises 15–16, use the given conditions to write an equation for each line in point-slope form and slope-intercept form.

15. Slope $= -2$, passing through $(-1, 4)$

16. Passing through $(2, 1)$ and $(-1, -8)$

In Exercises 17–19, graph each inequality.

17. $3x - 2y < 6$

18. $y \geq 2x - 2$

19. $x > -1$

20. Could Cool Hand Luke bust out today? Not likely. The bar graph shows the decrease in the number of inmates who escaped from U.S. prisons for selected years from 1993 through 2008.

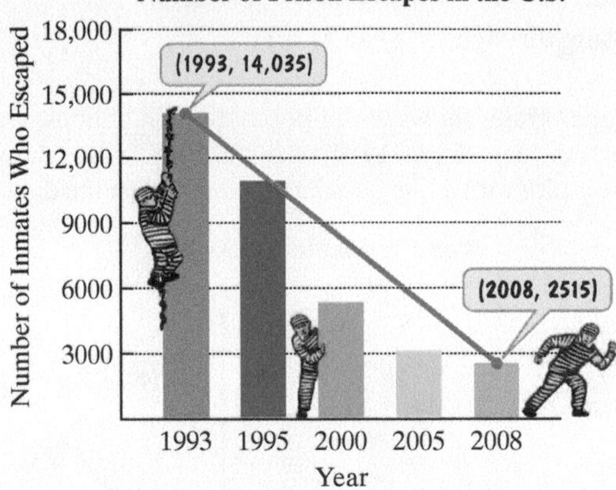

Source: Bureau of Justice Statistics

a. Find the slope of the line passing through the two points shown by the voice balloons.

b. Use your answer from part (a) to complete this statement:

For the period shown, the number of inmates who escaped from U.S. prisons decreased each year by approximately __. The rate of change was ________ per ___.

Answers to Selected Exercises

Section 1 Check Point Exercises

1.

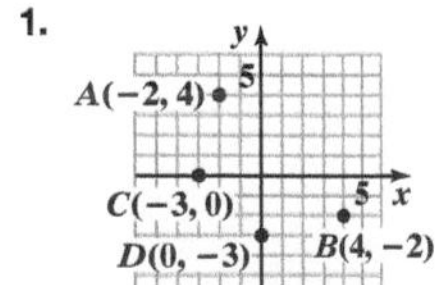

2. $E(-4, -2)$, $F(-2, 0)$, $G(6, 0)$ **3. a.** solution **b.** not a solution **4.** $(-2, -4)$, $(-1, -1)$, $(0, 2)$, $(1, 5)$, and $(2, 8)$

5.

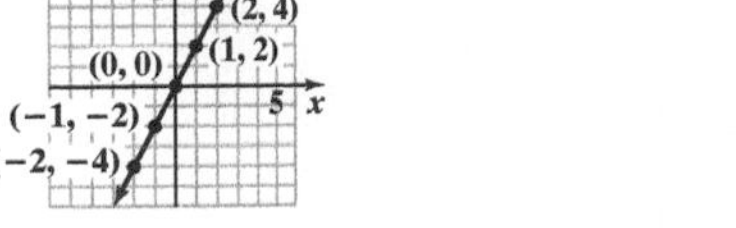

6.

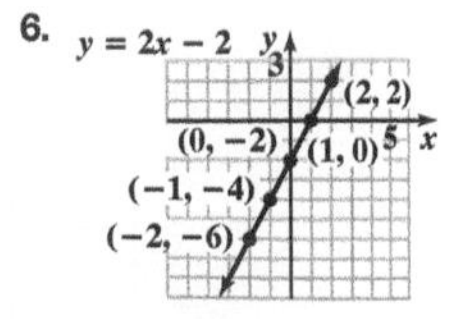

7.

8. a. $(0, 1)$, $(5, 8)$, $(10, 15)$, and $(15, 22)$ **b.**

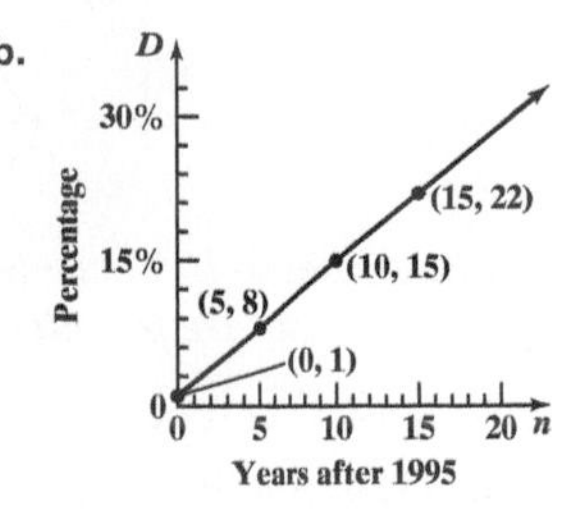

c. approximately 29%, although answers may vary by ±1% **d.** 29%

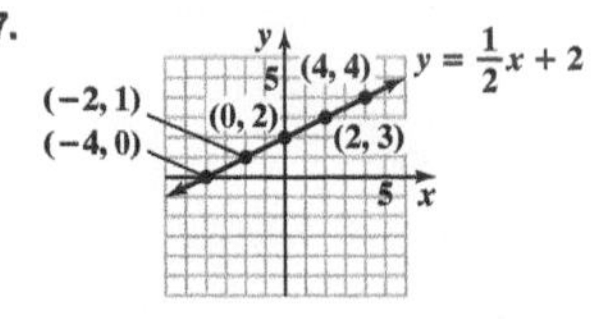

Concept and Vocabulary Check

1. x-axis **2.** y-axis **3.** origin **4.** quadrants; four **5.** x-coordinate; y-coordinate **6.** solution; satisfies **7.** a/one **8.** $mx + b$

Exercise Set 1

1. I **3.** II **5.** III **7.** IV

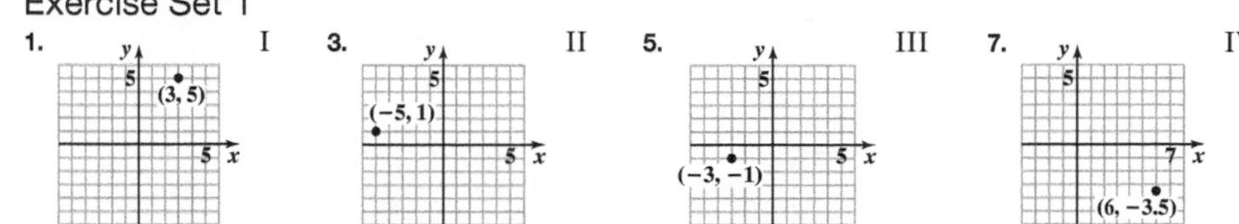

9-23.

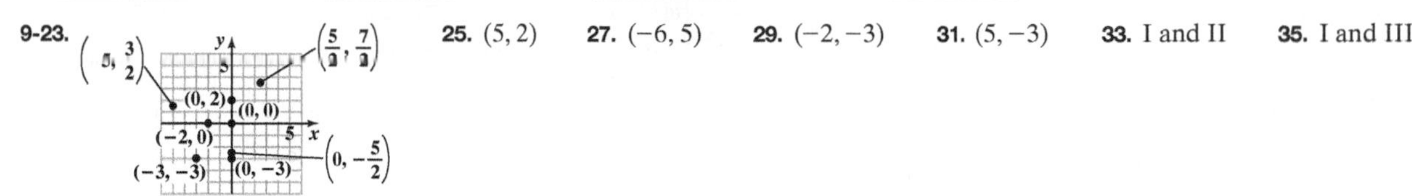

25. (5, 2) **27.** (−6, 5) **29.** (−2, −3) **31.** (5, −3) **33.** I and II **35.** I and III

37. (2, 3) and (3, 2) are not solutions; (−4, −12) is a solution. **39.** (−5, −20) is not a solution; (0, 0) and (9, −36) are solutions.
41. (2, −2) is not a solution; (0, 6) and (−3, 0) are solutions. **43.** (0, 5) is not a solution; (−5, 6) and (10, −3) are solutions.
45. $\left(1, \frac{1}{3}\right)$ is not a solution; (0, 0) and $\left(2, -\frac{2}{3}\right)$ are solutions. **47.** (3, 4) and (0, −4) are not solutions; (4, 7) is a solution.

49.

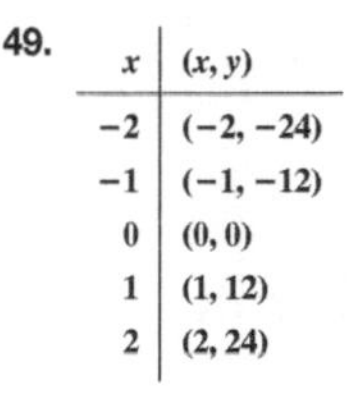

x	(x, y)
−2	(−2, −24)
−1	(−1, −12)
0	(0, 0)
1	(1, 12)
2	(2, 24)

51.

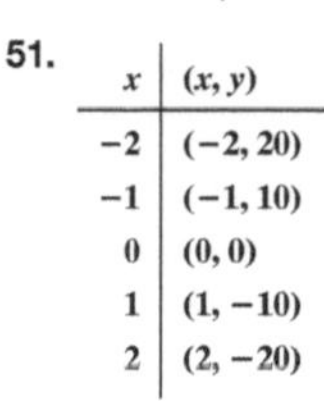

x	(x, y)
−2	(−2, 20)
−1	(−1, 10)
0	(0, 0)
1	(1, −10)
2	(2, −20)

53.

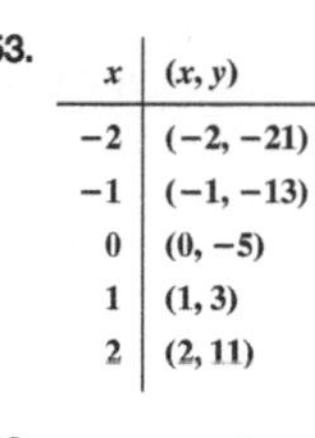

x	(x, y)
−2	(−2, −21)
−1	(−1, −13)
0	(0, −5)
1	(1, 3)
2	(2, 11)

55.

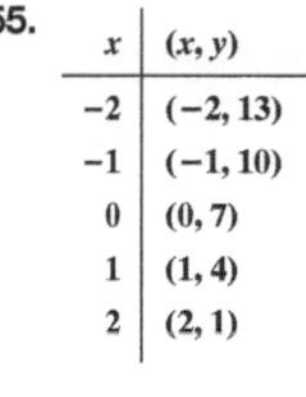

x	(x, y)
−2	(−2, 13)
−1	(−1, 10)
0	(0, 7)
1	(1, 4)
2	(2, 1)

57.

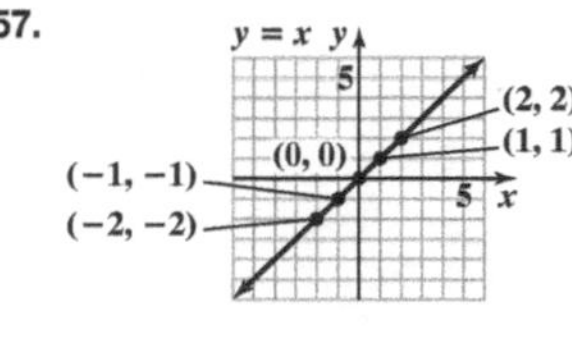

59.

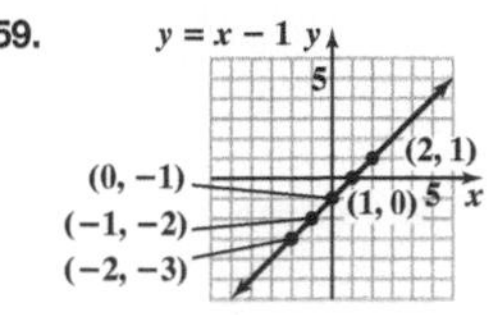

61.

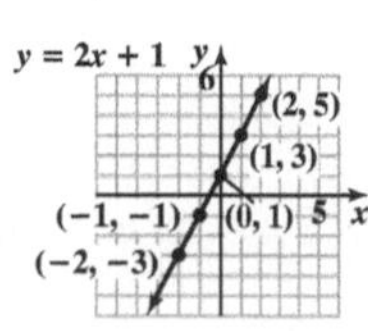

63.

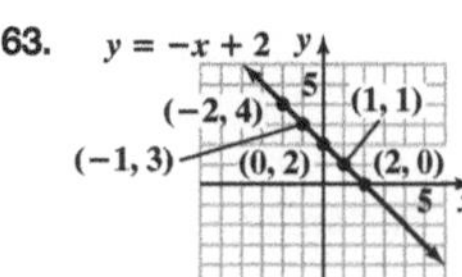

65.

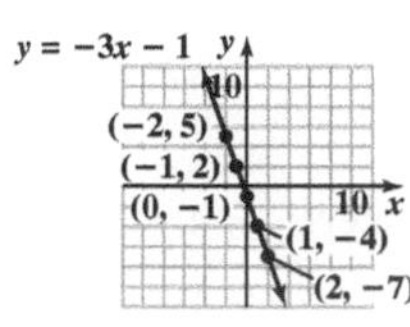

67.

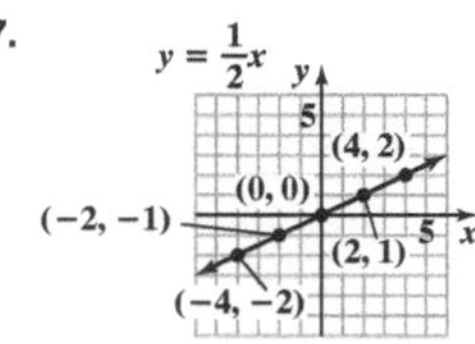

69.

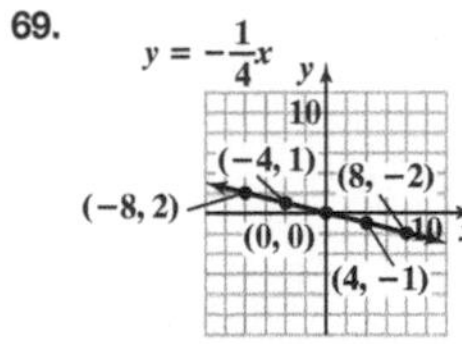

71.

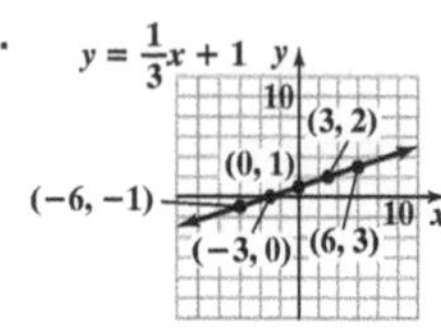

73.

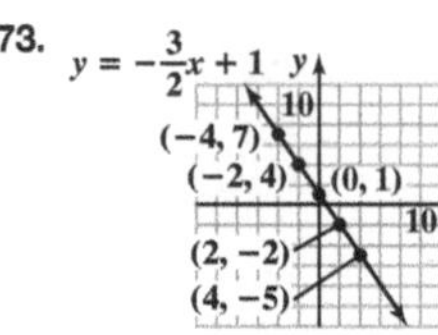

75.

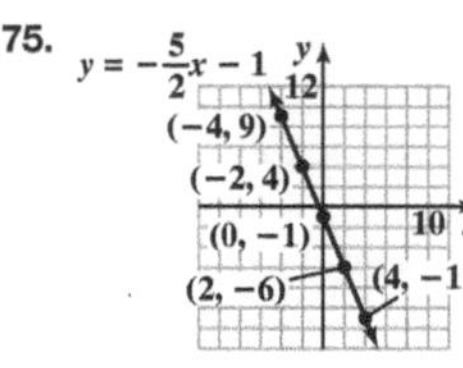

77.

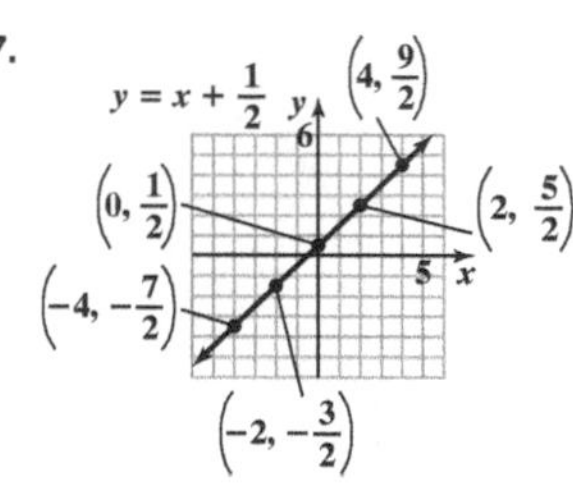

79.

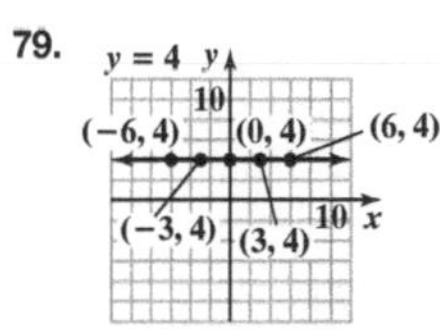

81.

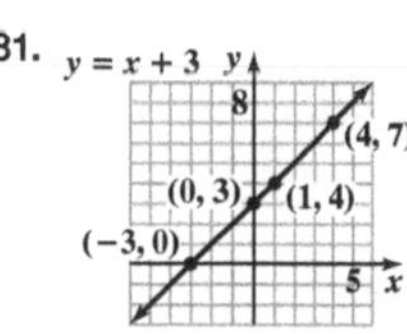

83.

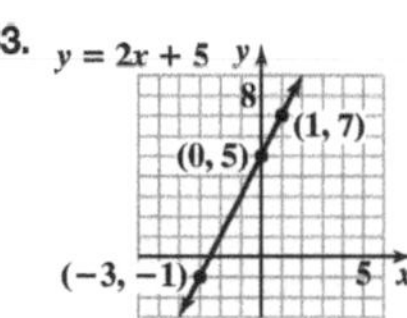

85. a. $8x + 6y = 14.50$ **b.** $1.25 **87.** (2, 7); The football is 7 ft above ground when it is 2 yd from the quarterback. **89.** (6, 9.25)

91. 12 ft; 15 yd

93. a. (0, 31), (5, 43), (10, 55), (15, 67), and (20, 79)

b.

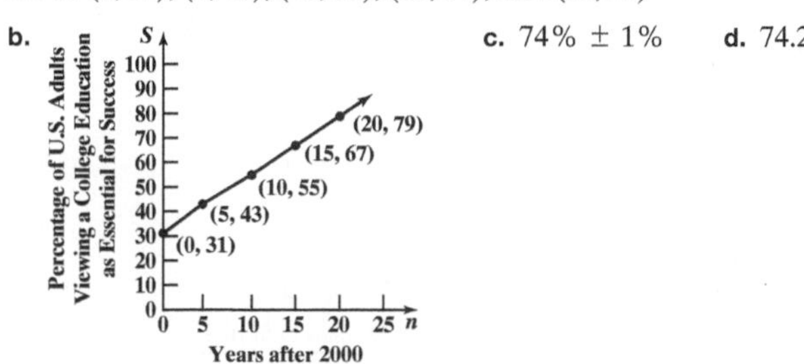

c. 74% ± 1% **d.** 74.2%

103. makes sense **105.** does not make sense **107.** false **109.** false

111. a.

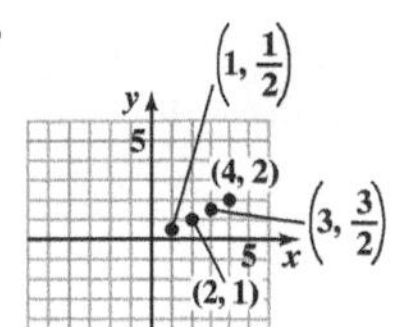

b. Change the sign of each x-coordinate. **c.** Change the sign of each y-coordinate.
d. Change the sign of both coordinates.

113.

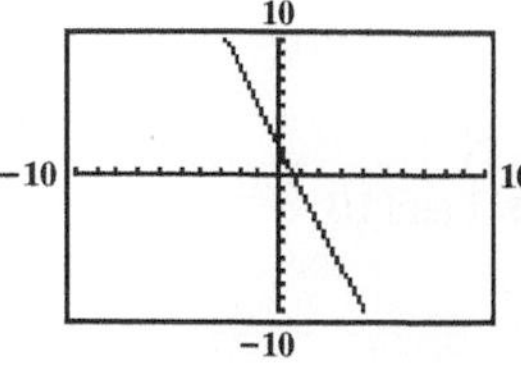

Answers will vary.

115.

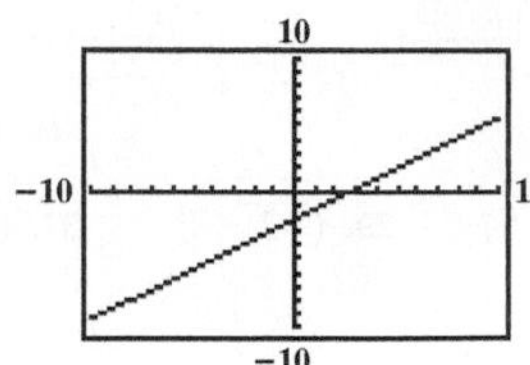

Answers will vary.

117. 2 or {2} **118.** 1 **119.** $h = \frac{3V}{A}$ **120.** (8, 0) **121.** (0, −6) **122.** (0, 0)

Section 2 Check Point Exercises

1. a. x-intercept: −3; y-intercept: 5 **b.** y-intercept: 4; no x-intercept **c.** x-intercept: 0; y-intercept: 0 **2.** 3 **3.** −4

4. 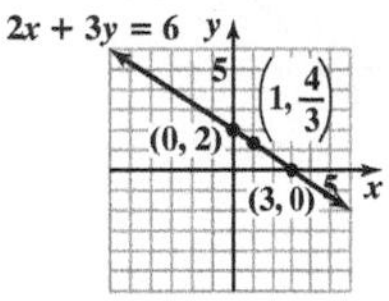 $2x + 3y = 6$

5. $x - 2y = 4$

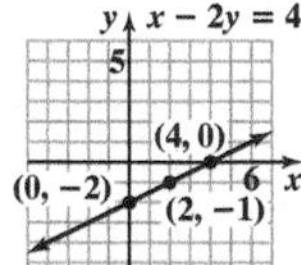

6. $x + 3y = 0$

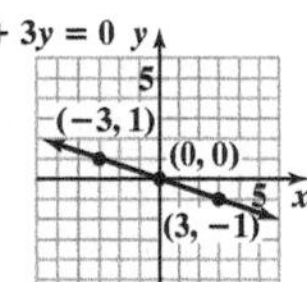

7. $y = 3$

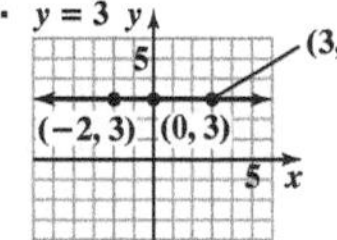

8. 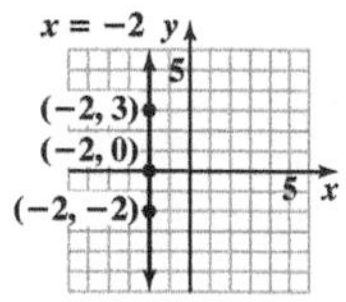 $x = -2$

Concept and Vocabulary Check

1. x-intercept **2.** y-intercept **3.** x-intercept **4.** y-intercept **5.** standard **6.** y; x **7.** x; y **8.** horizontal **9.** vertical

Exercise Set 2

1. a. 3 **b.** 4 **3. a.** −4 **b.** −2 **5. a.** 0 **b.** 0 **7. a.** no x-intercept **b.** −2 **9.** x-intercept: 10; y-intercept: 4

11. x-intercept: $\frac{15}{2}$, or $7\frac{1}{2}$; y-intercept: −5 **13.** x-intercept: 8; y-intercept: $-\frac{8}{3}$, or $-2\frac{2}{3}$ **15.** x-intercept: 0; y-intercept: 0

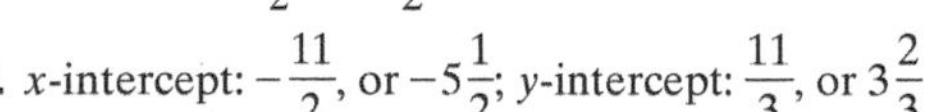

17. x-intercept: $-\frac{11}{2}$, or $-5\frac{1}{2}$; y-intercept: $\frac{11}{3}$, or $3\frac{2}{3}$

19. $x + y = 5$

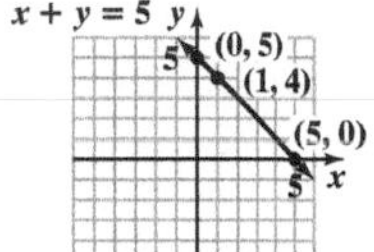

21. $x + 3y = 6$

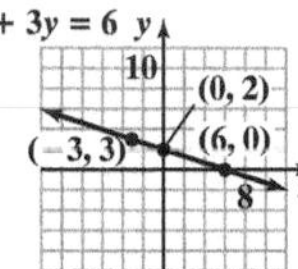

23. $6x - 9y = 18$

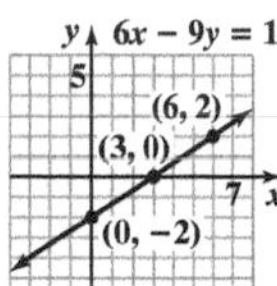

25. $-x + 4y = 6$

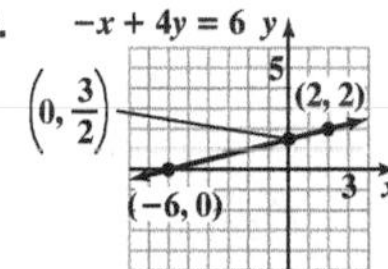

27. $2x - y = 7$

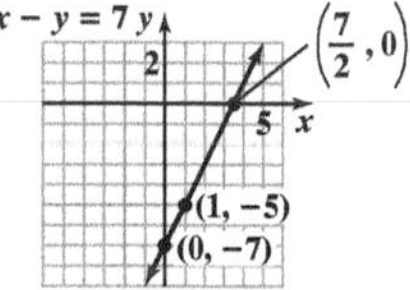

29. $3x = 5y - 15$

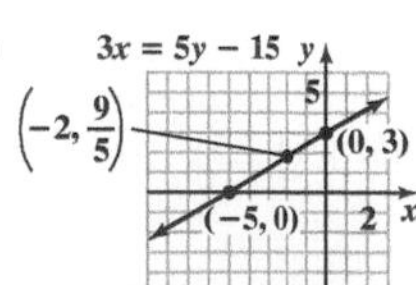

31. $25y = 100 - 50x$

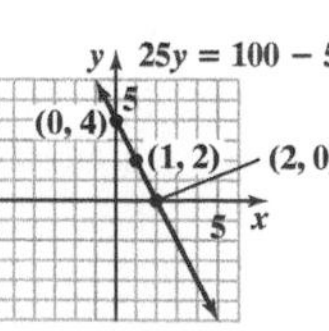

33. $2x - 8y = 12$

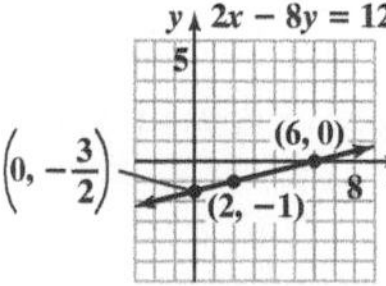

35. $x + 2y = 0$

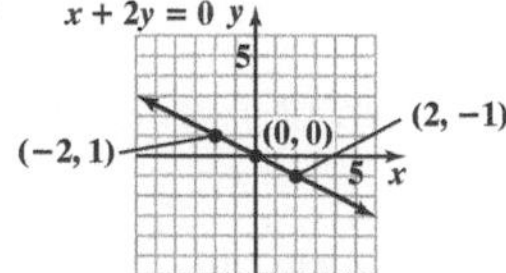

37. $y - 3x = 0$

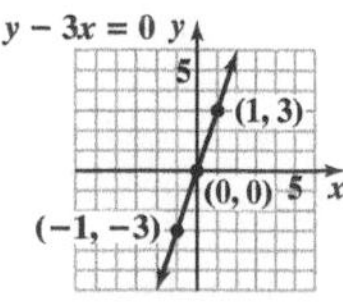

39. $2x - 3y = -11$

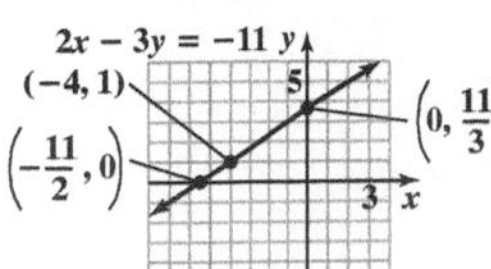

41. $y = 3$ **43.** $x = -3$ **45.** $y = 0$

47. $y = 4$

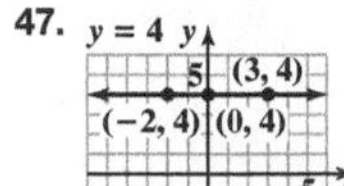

49. $y = -2$

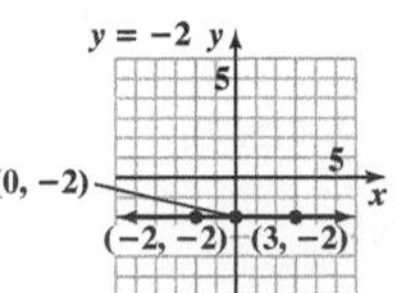

51. $x = 2$

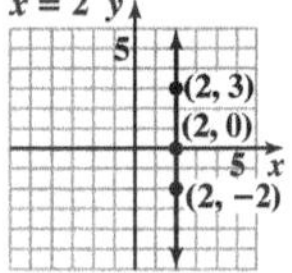

53. $x + 1 = 0$

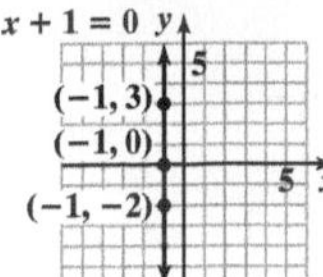

55. $y - 3.5 = 0$

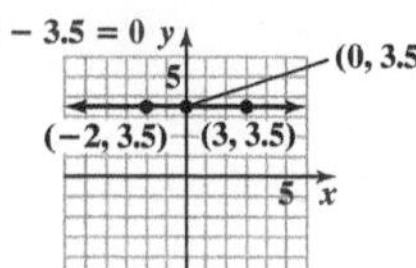

57. $x = 0$

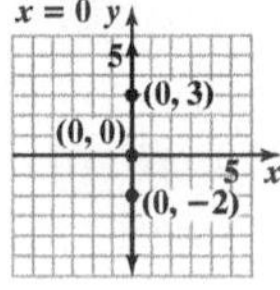

59. $3y = 9$

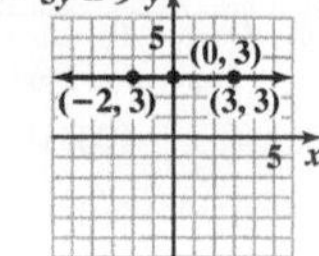

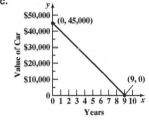

61. $12 - 3x = 0$ **63.** Exercise 4 **65.** Exercise 7 **67.** Exercise 1 **69.**

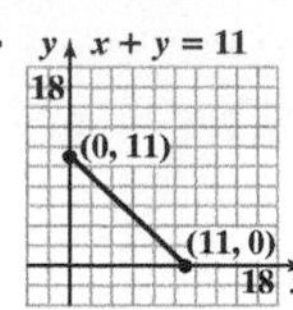

71. from 3 to 12 sec **73.** 45; The eagle was 45 m above the ground when the observation started. **75.** 12, 13, 14, 15, 16; The eagle is on the ground at this time. **77. a.** 9; After 9 years, the car is worth nothing. **b.** 45,000; The new car is worth $45,000.

c. **d.** $20,000; Estimates will vary. **87.** makes sense **89.** makes sense **91.** 2; 5

95.

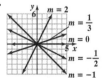

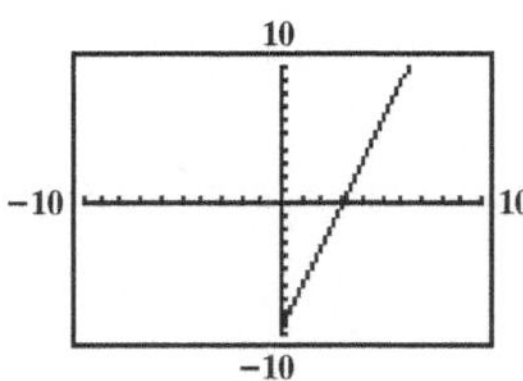

x-intercept: 3; *y*-intercept: −9

97.

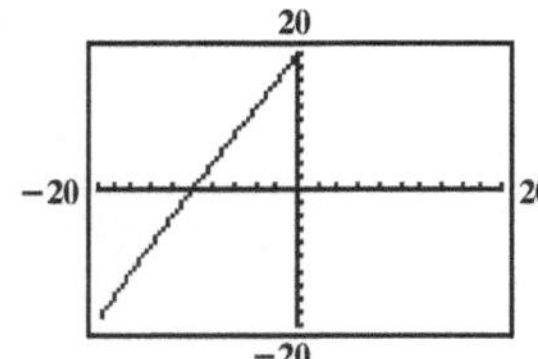

x-intercept: −10; *y*-intercept: 20

98. 13.4 **99.** $4x + 5$ **100.** $[-5, \infty)$ or $\{x|x \ge -5\}$ **101.** 2 **102.** −1 **103.** 0

Section 3 Check Point Exercises

1. a. 6 **b.** $-\frac{7}{5}$ **2. a.** 0 **b.** undefined **3.** Both slopes equal 2, so the lines are parallel. **4.** Product of slopes is $-\frac{1}{2}(2) = -1$, so the lines are perpendicular. **5.** $m \approx 0.32$; The number of men living alone increased by 0.32 million per year. The rate of change is 0.32 million men per year.

Concept and Vocabulary Check

1. $\frac{y_2 - y_1}{x_2 - x_1}$ **2.** y; x **3.** positive **4.** negative **5.** 0 **6.** undefined **7.** parallel **8.** perpendicular

Exercise Set 3

1. $\frac{3}{4}$; rises **3.** $\frac{1}{4}$; rises **5.** 0; horizontal **7.** −5; falls **9.** undefined; vertical **11.** $\frac{1}{2}$ **13.** $-\frac{1}{3}$ **15.** $-\frac{1}{2}$ **17.** $-\frac{4}{3}$ **19.** 0 **21.** undefined **23.** parallel **25.** not parallel **27.** perpendicular **29.** not perpendicular **31.** parallel **33.** neither **35.** perpendicular

37. **39.** Slopes of corresponding opposite sides are equal: $-\frac{2}{5}$ and $\frac{4}{3}$. **41.** 2 **43.** 4 **45. a.** 0.16 **b.** 0.16; 0.16; minute of brisk walking **47.** $\frac{1}{3}$ **49.** 8.3% **57.** does not make sense **59.** makes sense **61.** false **63.** false **65.** m_1, m_3, m_2, m_4 **67.** $m = 2$ **69.** $m = -\frac{1}{2}$ **71.** The line's slope is the coefficient of x.

72. 12 in. and 24 in. **73.** −42 **74.** $(-\infty, 4]$ or $\{x|x \le 4\}$

75. (1, 1) **76.** (3, −1) **77.** $y = -\frac{2}{5}x$

Section 4 Check Point Exercises

1. a. 5; −3 **b.** $\frac{2}{3}$; 4 **c.** −7; 6 **2.** $y = 3x - 2$ **3.**

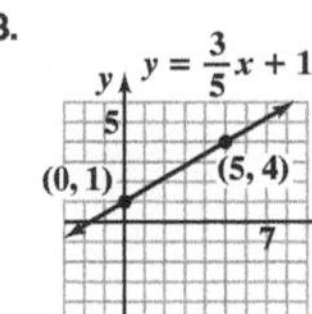

4. $3x + 4y = 0$ **5. a.** $y = 0.32x + 8$ **b.** 27.2%

Concept and Vocabulary Check

1. $y = mx + b$; slope; y-intercept **2.** $(0, 3)$; 2; 5 **3.** y

Exercise Set 4

1. 3; 2 **3.** 3; −5 **5.** $-\frac{1}{2}$; 5 **7.** 7; 0 **9.** 0; 10 **11.** −1; 4 **13.** $y = 5x + 7$; 5; 7 **15.** $y = -x + 6$; −1; 6 **17.** $y = -6x$; −6; 0

19. $y = 2x$; 2; 0 **21.** $y = -\frac{2}{7}x$; $-\frac{2}{7}$; 0 **23.** $y = -\frac{3}{2}x + \frac{3}{2}$; $-\frac{3}{2}$; $\frac{3}{2}$ **25.** $y = \frac{3}{4}x - 3$; $\frac{3}{4}$; −3

27. **29.**

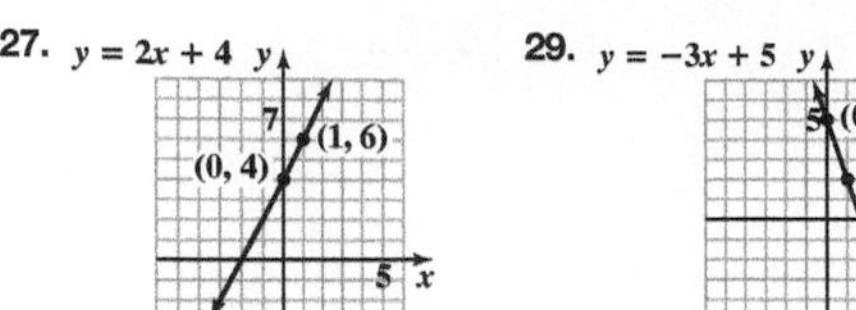

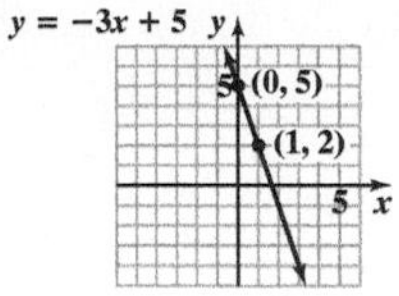

31.

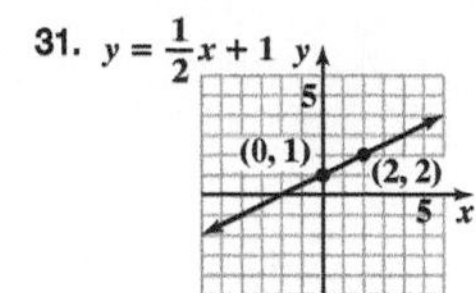

33.

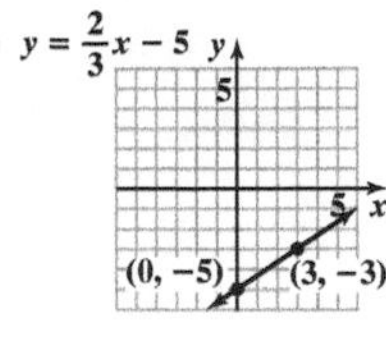

35.

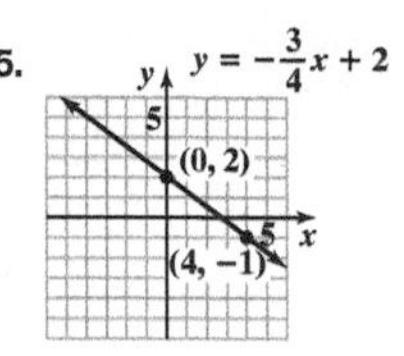

37.

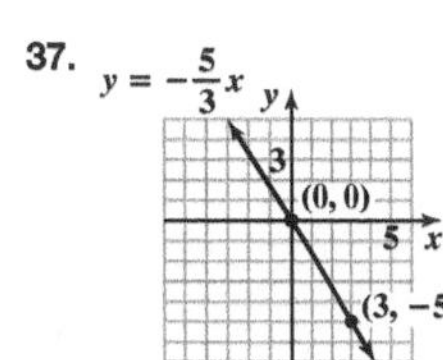

39. a. $y = -3x$ **b.** −3; 0 **c.**

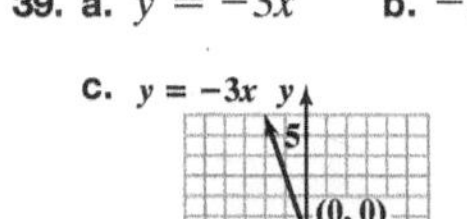

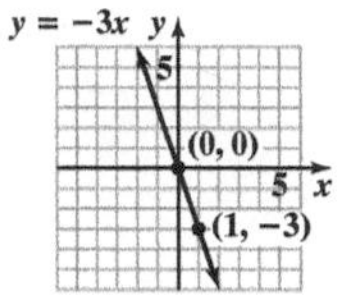

41. a. $y = \frac{4}{3}x$ **b.** $\frac{4}{3}$; 0 **c.**

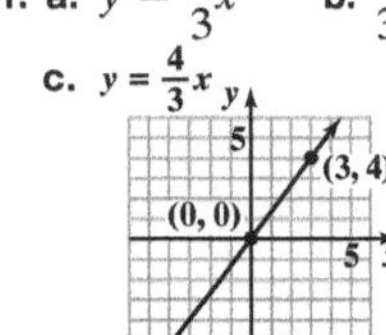

43. a. $y = -2x + 3$ **b.** −2; 3 **c.**

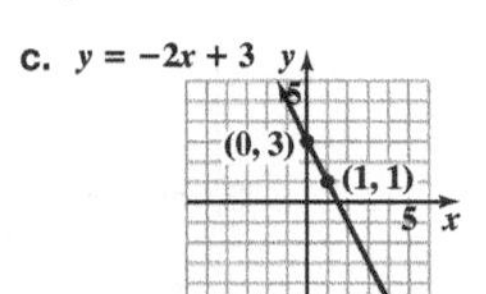

45. a. $y = -\frac{7}{2}x + 7$ **b.** $-\frac{7}{2}$; 7 **c.**

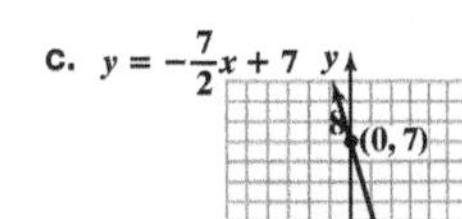

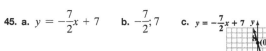

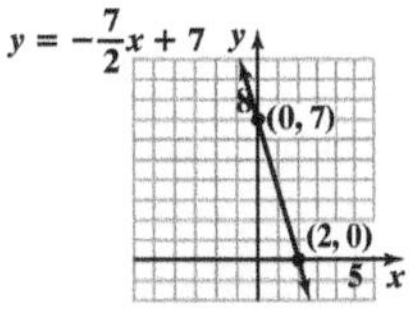

47.

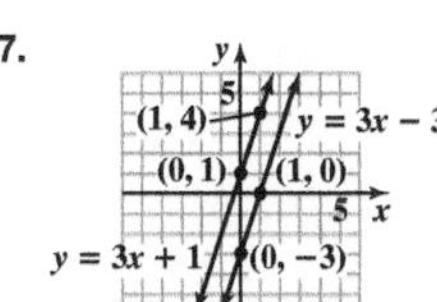

49.

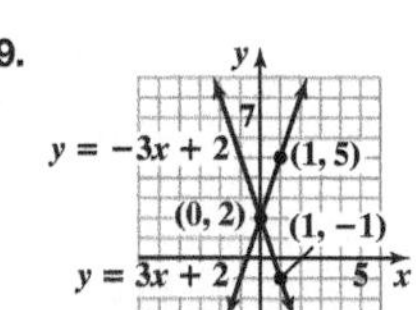

not parallel or perpendicular; $m = -3$ and $m = 3$

51.

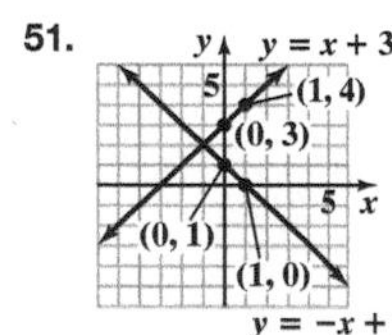

; perpendicular, $m = 1$ and $m = -1$, and $1(-1) = -1$

53.

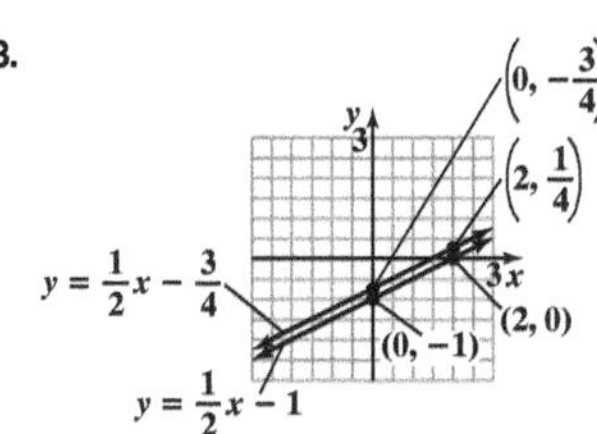

parallel; $m = \frac{1}{2}$

55.

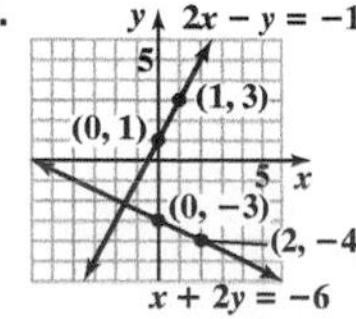

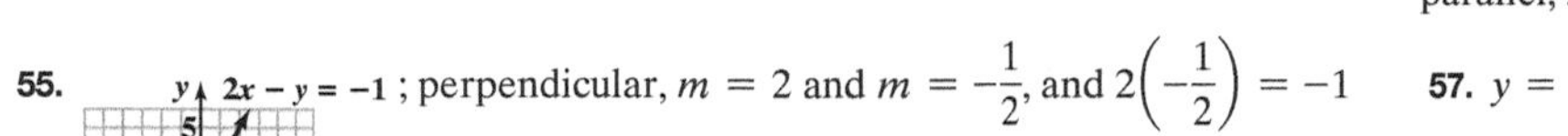

; perpendicular, $m = 2$ and $m = -\frac{1}{2}$, and $2\left(-\frac{1}{2}\right) = -1$ **57.** $y = -3x + 5$

59. $y = -\frac{1}{5}x + 6$ **61.** $y = -x + 2$ **63.** $y = x$ **65. a.** $y = -0.52x + 68$ **b.** 16% **71.** does not make sense

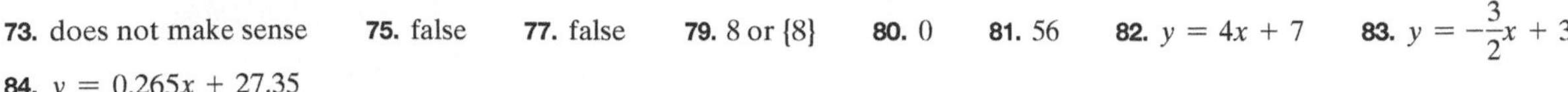

73. does not make sense **75.** false **77.** false **79.** 8 or $\{8\}$ **80.** 0 **81.** 56 **82.** $y = 4x + 7$ **83.** $y = -\frac{3}{2}x + 3$

84. $y = 0.265x + 27.35$

Mid-Chapter Check Point Exercises

1. a. 4 **b.** 2 **c.** $-\frac{1}{2}$ **2. a.** −5 **b.** no y-intercept **c.** undefined slope **3. a.** 0 **b.** 0 **c.** $\frac{3}{5}$

4. $y = -2x$

5. $y = -2$ 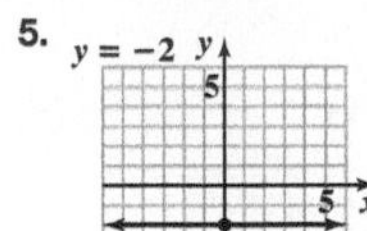

6. $x + y = -2$ 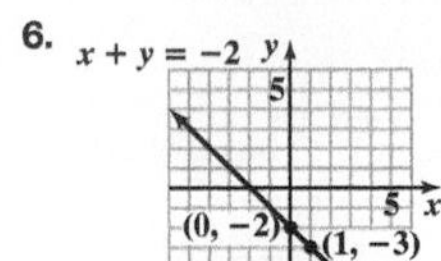

7. $y = \frac{1}{3}x - 2$ 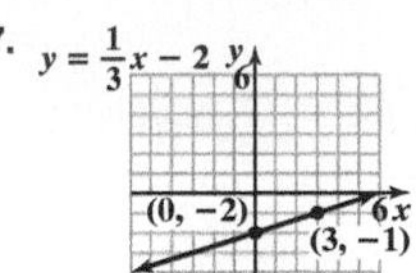

8. $x = 3.5$ 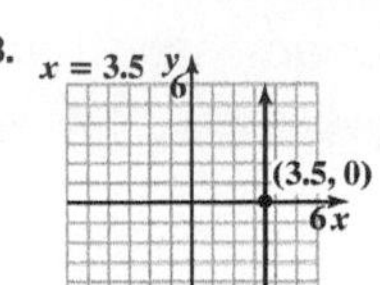

9. $4x - 2y = 8$ 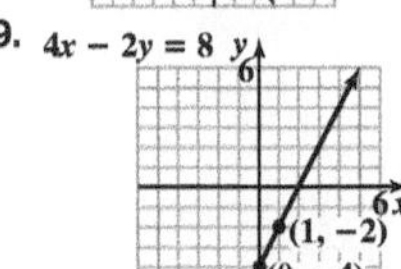

10. $y = 3x + 2$ 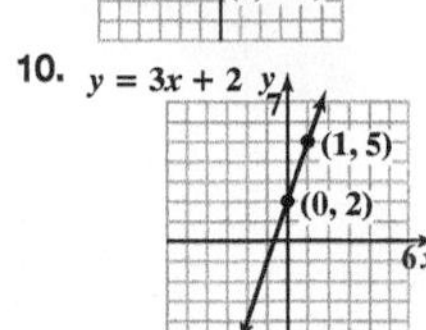

11. $3x + y = 0$ parallel; $m = -3$ 12. $y = -x + 4$ 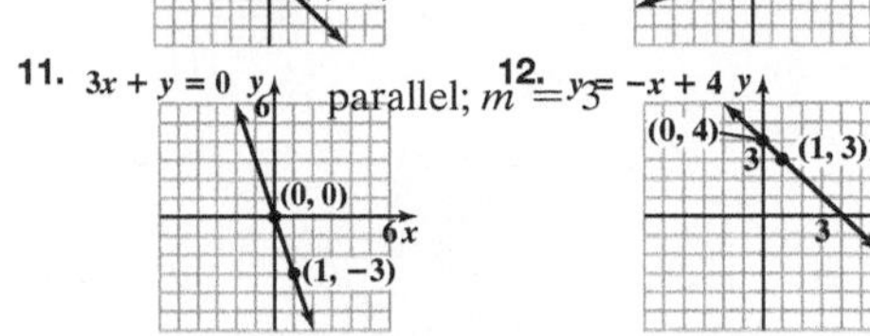

13. $y = x - 4$ 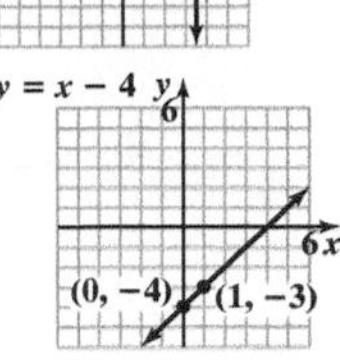

14. $5y = -3x$ 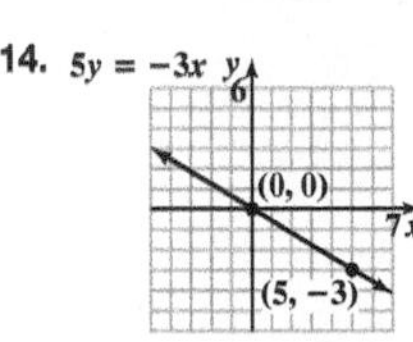

15. $5y = 20$ 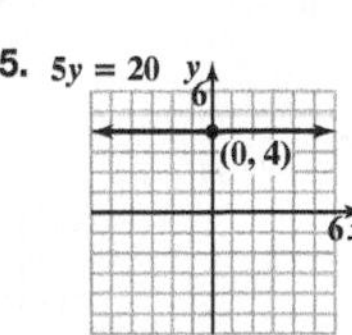

16. $\frac{5}{2}; -5$ 17. perpendicular 18. neither 19. parallel 20. a. $y = -2.4x + 98$ b. 62%

Section 5 Check Point Exercises

1. $y + 5 = 6(x - 2); y = 6x - 17$ 2. a. $y + 1 = -5(x + 2)$ or $y + 6 = -5(x + 1)$ b. $y = -5x - 11$ 3. $y = 0.28x + 27.2; 41.2$

Concept and Vocabulary Check

1. $y - y_1 = m(x - x_1)$ 2. standard 3. slope-intercept 4. point-slope 5. horizontal 6. vertical

Exercise Set 3.5

1. $y - 5 = 3(x - 2); y = 3x - 1$ 3. $y - 6 = 5(x + 2); y = 5x + 16$ 5. $y + 2 = -8(x + 3); y = -8x - 26$
7. $y - 0 = -12(x + 8); y = -12x - 96$ 9. $y + 2 = -1\left(x + \frac{1}{2}\right); y = -x - \frac{5}{2}$ 11. $y - 0 = \frac{1}{2}(x - 0); y = \frac{1}{2}x$
13. $y + 2 = -\frac{2}{3}(x - 6); y = -\frac{2}{3}x + 2$ 15. $y - 2 = 2(x - 1)$ or $y - 10 = 2(x - 5); y = 2x$
17. $y - 0 = 1(x + 3)$ or $y - 3 = 1(x - 0); y = x + 3$ 19. $y + 1 = 1(x + 3)$ or $y - 4 = 1(x - 2); y = x + 2$
21. $y + 1 = \frac{5}{7}(x + 4)$ or $y - 4 = \frac{5}{7}(x - 3); y = \frac{5}{7}x + \frac{13}{7}$ 23. $y + 1 = 0(x + 3)$ or $y + 1 = 0(x - 4); y = -1$
25. $y - 4 = 1(x - 2)$ or $y - 0 = 1(x + 2); y = x + 2$ 27. $y - 0 = 8\left(x + \frac{1}{2}\right)$ or $y - 4 = 8(x - 0); y = 8x + 4$ 29. $y = 4x + 14$
31. $y = -3x - 8$ 33. $y = -2x + 1$ 35. $y = 3x - 2$ 37. $y = -5x - 20$ 39. a. $y = 433x + 4138$ b. 8468 deaths
43. does not make sense 45. makes sense 47. false 49. false 51. $E = 2.4M - 20$ 53. b.
c. $a = 0.7417932386; b = 4.245467908; r = 0.9971076103$ d.

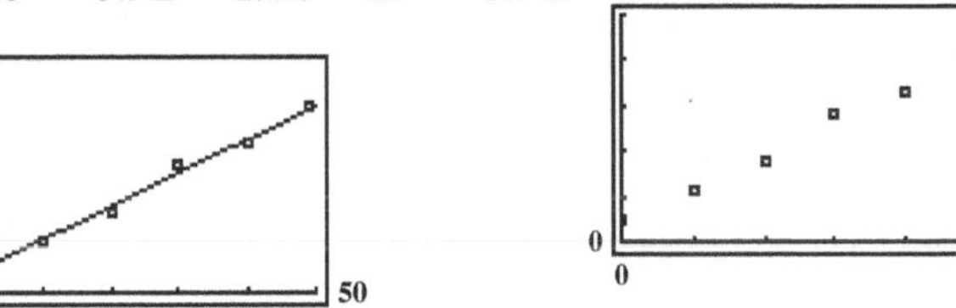

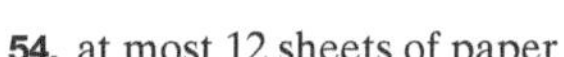

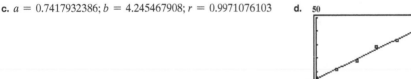

54. at most 12 sheets of paper 55. $1, \sqrt{4}$ 56. 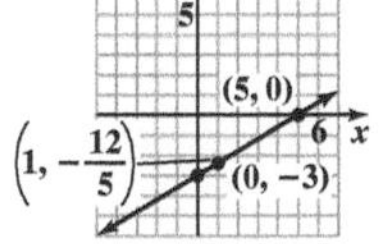 57. yes 58. no 59. no

Section 6 Check Point Exercises

1. a. solution b. not a solution 2. 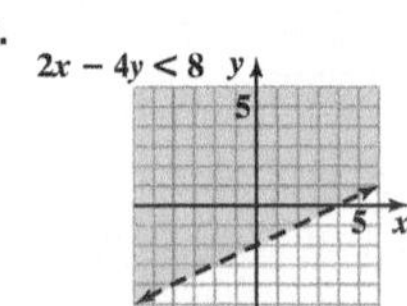 3. 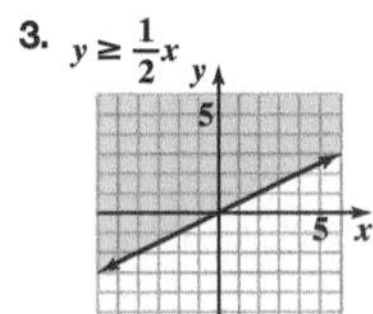 4. a. 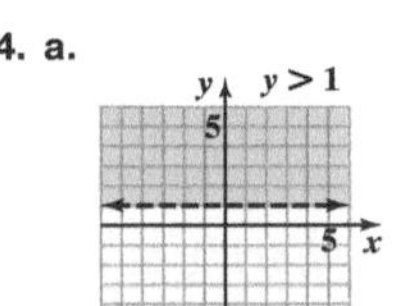 b. 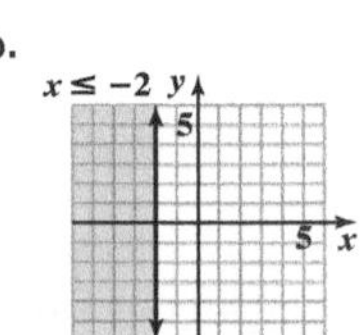

5. a. $B(60, 20)$; A region that has an average annual temperature of 60°F and an average annual precipitation of 20 inches is a grassland.
b. $5(60) - 7(20) \geq 70, 160 \geq 70$ true; $3(60) - 35(20) \leq -140, -520 \leq -140$ true

Concept and Vocabulary Check

1. solution; x; y; $9 > 2$ 2. graph 3. half-plane 4. false 5. true 6. false

Exercise Set 6

1. no; yes; yes **3.** yes; yes; no **5.** yes; yes; no **7.** yes; no; yes **9.** $x + y \geq 3$

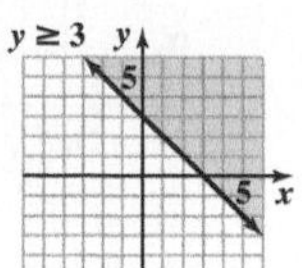

11. $x - y < 5$

13. $x + 2y > 4$

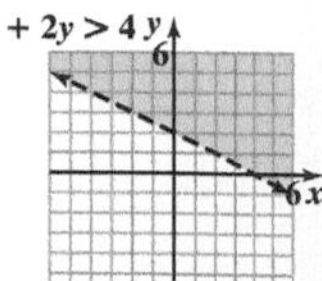

15. $3x - y \leq 6$

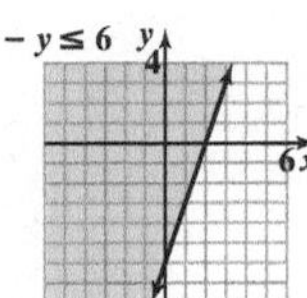

17. $3x - 2y \leq 8$

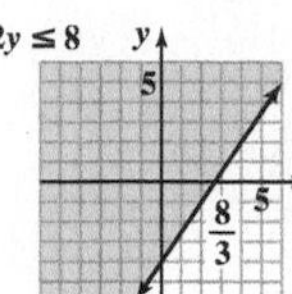

19. $4x + 3y > 15$

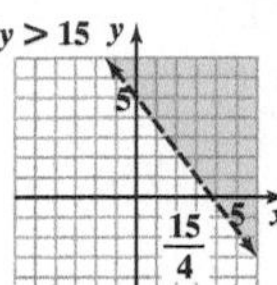

21. $5x - y < -7$

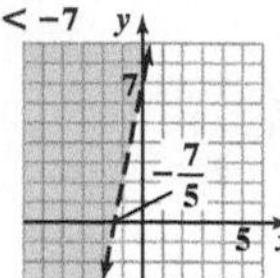

23. $y \leq \frac{1}{3}x$

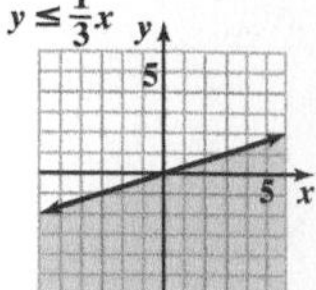

25. $y > 2x$

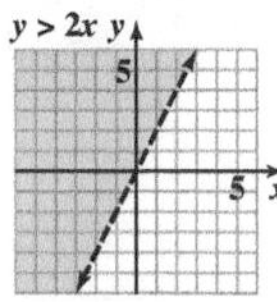

27. $y > 3x + 2$

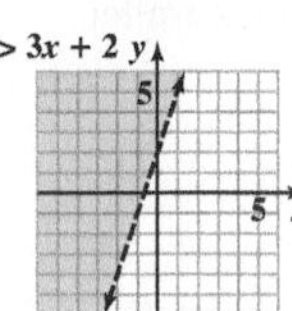

29. $y < \frac{3}{4}x - 3$

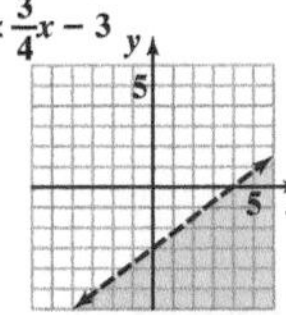

31. $x \leq 1$

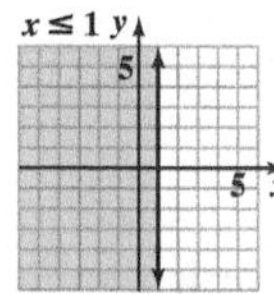

33. $y > 1$

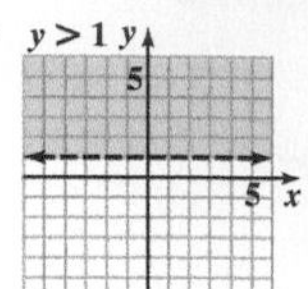

35. $x \geq 0$

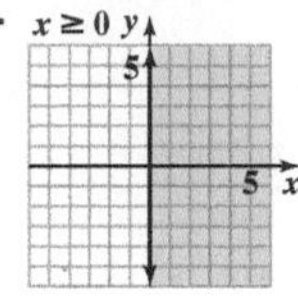

37. $x + y \geq 2$

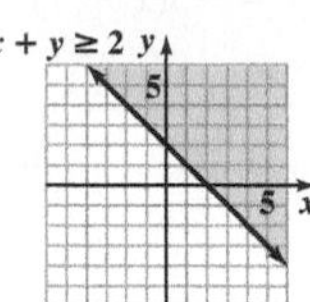

39. $5x - 2y \leq 10$

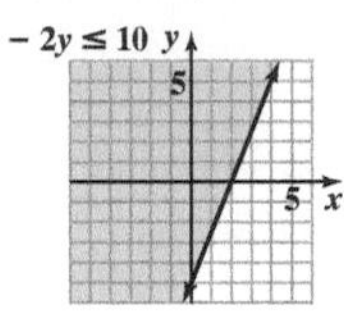

41. $y \geq \frac{1}{2}x$

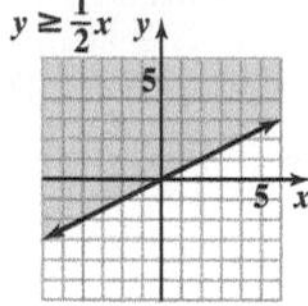

43. $y \leq -1$

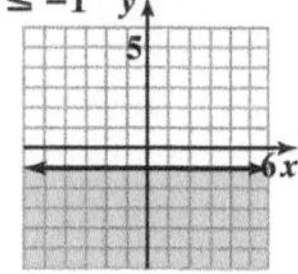

45. a. $20x + 10y \leq 80{,}000$

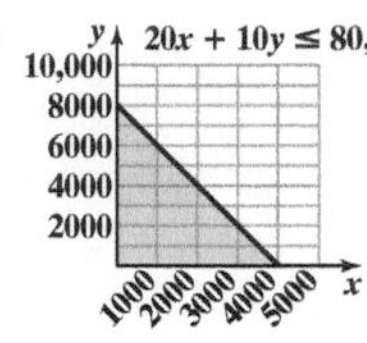

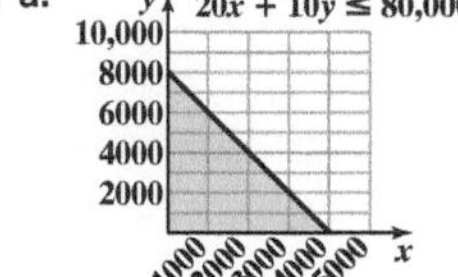

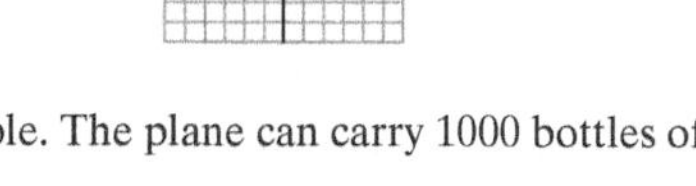

b. Answers will vary; (1000, 2000) is an example. The plane can carry 1000 bottles of water and 2000 medical kits.

47. a. $50x + 150y > 2000$ **b.** $50x + 150y > 2000$

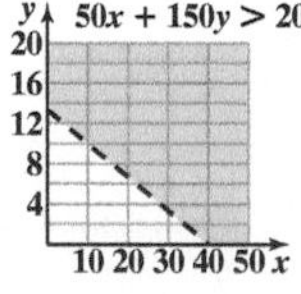

c. Answers will vary; (20, 15) is an example. The elevator cannot carry 20 children and 15 adults.

49. a. 27.1 **b.** overweight **59.** does not make sense **61.** makes sense **63.** false **65.** true **67.** $2x + y \leq 4$

69.

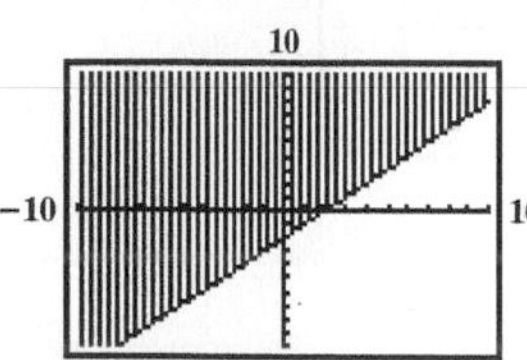

71.

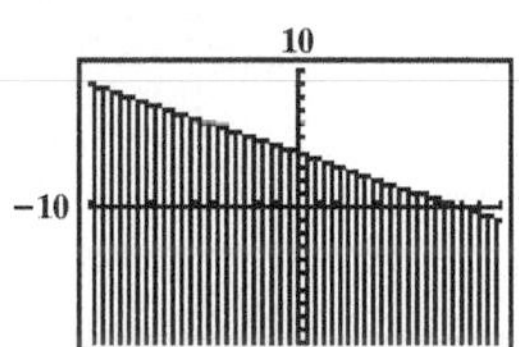

72. $h = \frac{V}{lw}$ **73.** $-\frac{8}{15}$ **74.** 5 **75.** yes **76.** no **77.** $(-3, 4)$

Review Exercises

1. IV

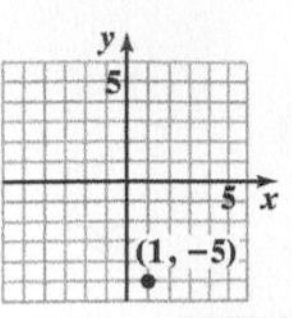

2. IV

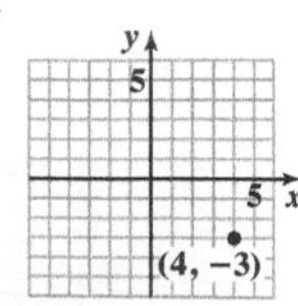

3. I

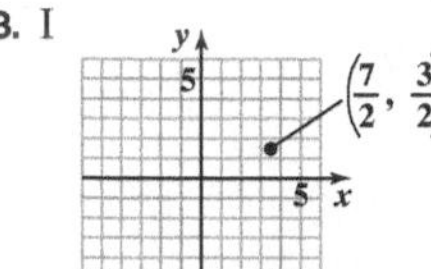

4. II

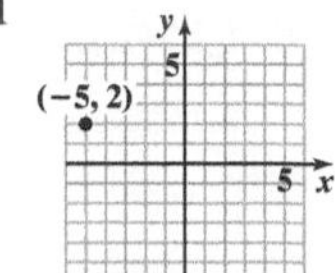

5. $A(5, 6)$; $B(-3, 0)$; $C(-5, 2)$; $D(-4, -2)$; $E(0, -5)$; $F(3, -1)$ **6.** $(-3, 3)$ is not a solution; $(0, 6)$ and $(1, 9)$ are solutions.
7. $(0, 4)$ and $(-1, 15)$ are not solutions; $(4, 0)$ is a solution.

8. a.

x	(x, y)
−2	(−2, −7)
−1	(−1, −5)
0	(0, −3)
1	(1, −1)
2	(2, 1)

b. $y = 2x - 3$

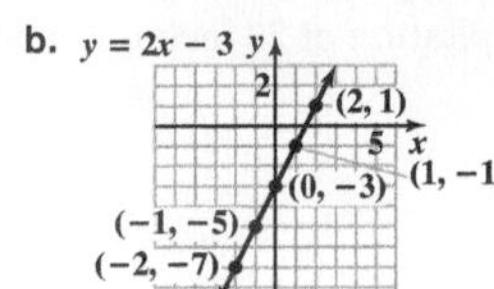

9. a.

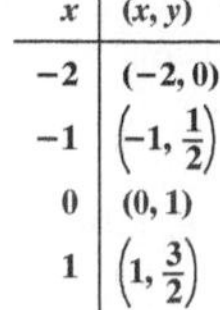

x	(x, y)
−2	(−2, 0)
−1	$\left(-1, \frac{1}{2}\right)$
0	(0, 1)
1	$\left(1, \frac{3}{2}\right)$
2	(2, 2)

b. $y = \frac{1}{2}x + 1$

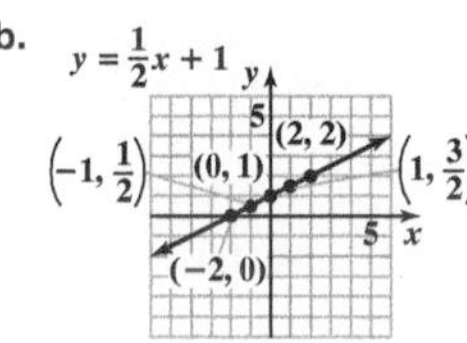

10. a. -2 **b.** -4 **11. a.** no x-intercept **b.** 2 **12. a.** 0 **b.** 0

13. $2x + y = 4$

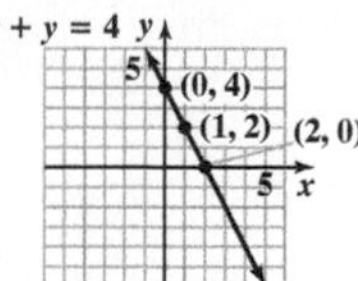

14. $3x - 2y = 12$

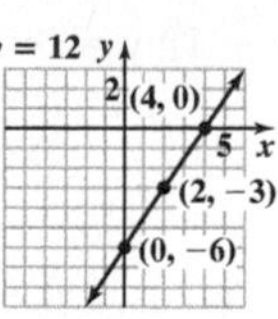

15. $3x = 6 - 2y$

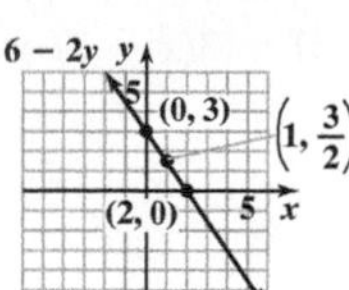

16. $3x - y = 0$

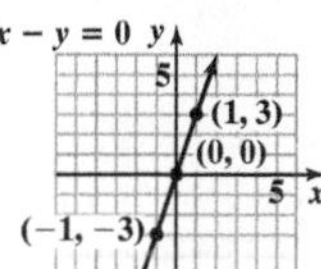

17. $x = 3$

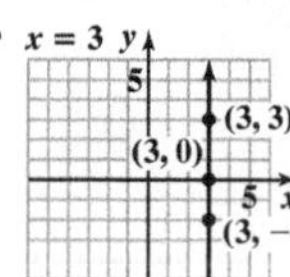

18. $y = -5$

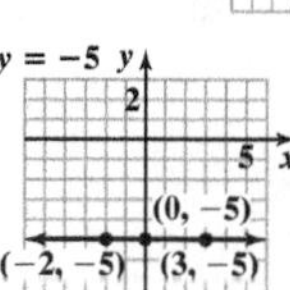

19. $y + 3 = 5$

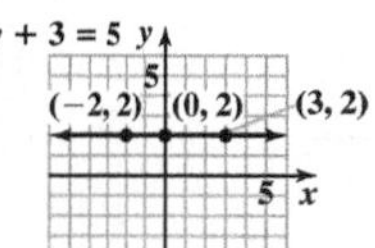

20. $2x = -8$

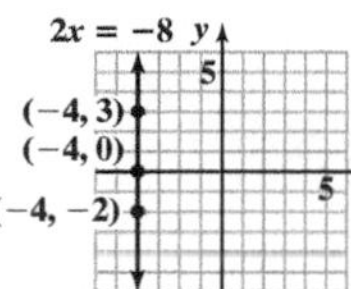

21. a. 5:00 P.M.; −4°F. **b.** 8:00 P.M.; 16°F. **c.** 4 and 6; At 4:00 P.M. and 6:00 P.M., the temperature was 0°F. **d.** 12; At noon, the temperature was 12°F. **e.** The temperature stayed the same, 12°F. **22.** $-\frac{1}{2}$; falls **23.** 3; rises **24.** 0; horizontal **25.** undefined; vertical

26. $\frac{3}{5}$ **27.** undefined **28.** $-\frac{1}{3}$ **29.** 0 **30.** neither **31.** perpendicular **32.** parallel **33. a.** -0.48 **b.** 0.48; −0.48%; year

34. 5; −7 **35.** −4; 6 **36.** 0; 3 **37.** $-\frac{2}{3}$; 2

38. $y = 2x - 4$

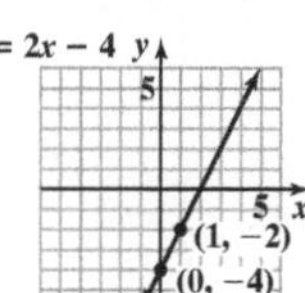

39. $y = \frac{1}{2}x - 1$

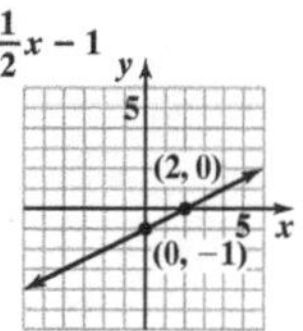

40. $y = -\frac{2}{3}x + 5$

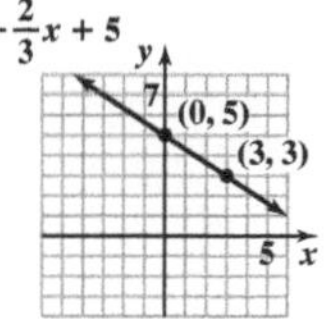

41. $y = 2x$

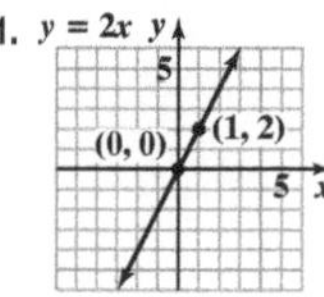

42. $y = -\frac{1}{3}x + 2$

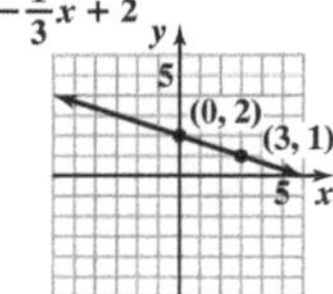

43. $y = -\frac{1}{2}x + 4$

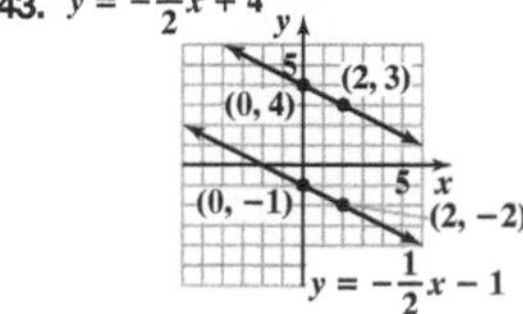

Yes, they are parallel since both have slopes of $-\frac{1}{2}$ and different y-intercepts.

44. a. $y = -1.5x + 30$ **b.** 22.5 million; overestimates by 2.5 million **45.** $y - 7 = 6(x + 4)$; $y = 6x + 31$ **46.** $y - 4 = 3(x - 3)$ or $y - 1 = 3(x - 2)$; $y = 3x - 5$ **47. a.** $y = 0.08x + 2.1$ **b.** 8.1 billion **48.** (0, 0) and (−3, 4) are not solutions; (3, −6) and (−2, −5) are solutions.

49. $x - 2y > 6$

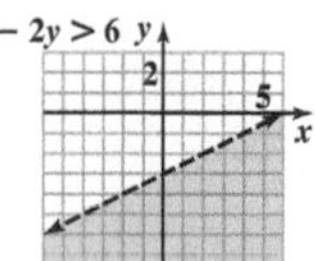

50. $4x - 6y \leq 12$

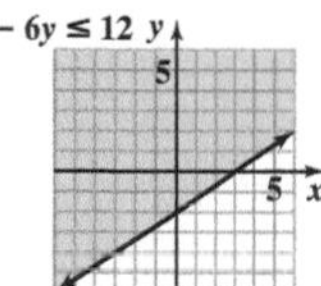

51. $y > 3x + 2$

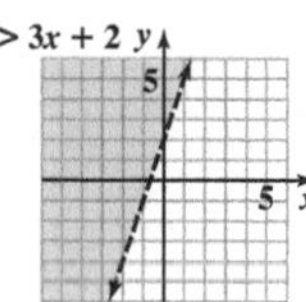

52. $y \leq \frac{1}{3}x - 1$

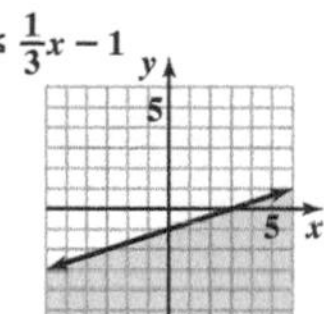

53. $y < -\frac{1}{2}x$

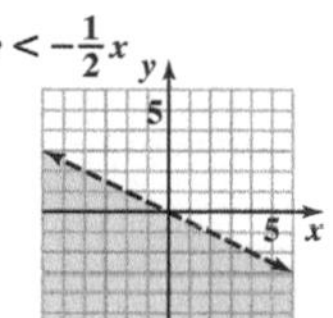

54. $x < 4$

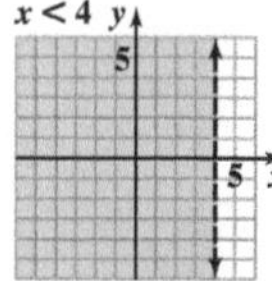

55. $y \geq -2$

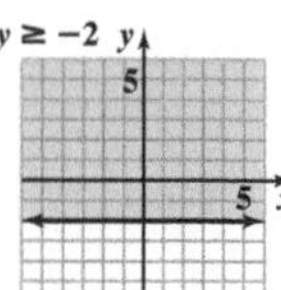

56. $x + 2y \leq 0$

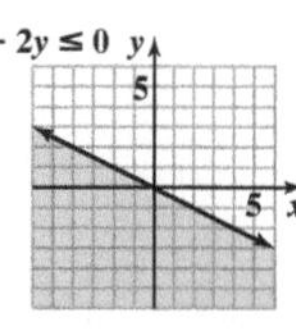

Chapter Test

1. (−2, 1) is not a solution; (0, −5) and (4, 3) are solutions.

2.

x	(x, y)
−2	(−2, −5)
−1	(−1, −2)
0	(0, 1)
1	(1, 4)
2	(2, 7)

$y = 3x + 1$

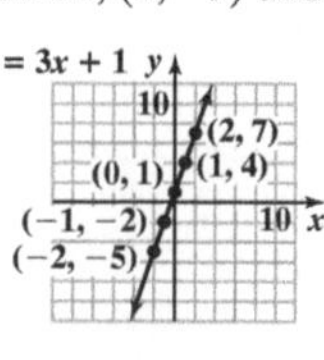

3. a. 2 **b.** −3

4. $4x - 2y = -8$

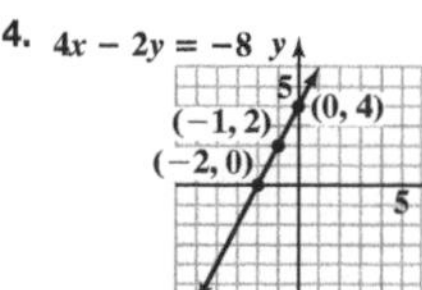

5. $y = 4$ (3, 4); (−2, 4); (0, 4)

6. 3; rises **7.** undefined; vertical **8.** $\frac{3}{2}$ **9.** perpendicular **10.** parallel **11.** −1; 10 **12.** −2; 6

13. $y = \frac{2}{3}x - 1$

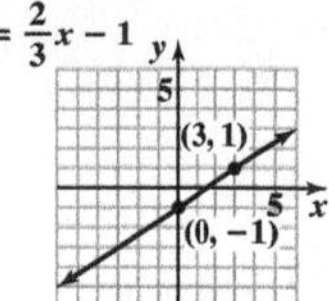

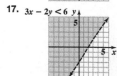

14. $y = -2x + 3$

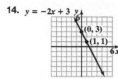

15. $y - 4 = -2(x + 1)$; $y = -2x + 2$

16. $y - 1 = 3(x - 2)$ or $y + 8 = 3(x + 1)$; $y = 3x - 5$

17. $3x - 2y < 6$

18. $y \geq 2x - 2$

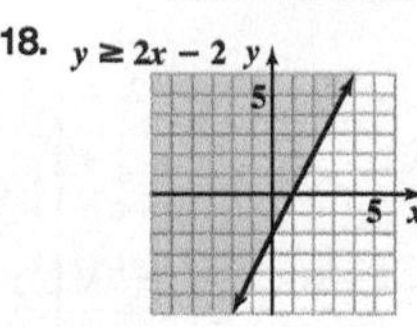

19. $x > -1$

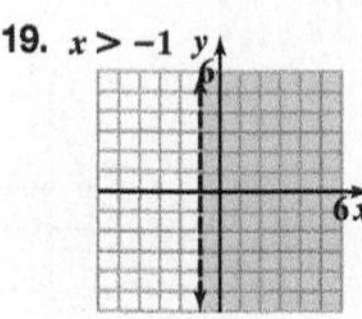

20. **a.** -768 **b.** 768; -768 inmates; year

Exponents and Polynomials

Listening to the radio on the way to campus, you hear politicians discussing the problem of the national debt that exceeds \$12 trillion. They state that it's more than the gross domestic product of China, the world's second-richest nation, and four times greater than the combined net worth of America's 691 billionaires. They make it seem like the national debt is a real problem, but later you realize that you don't really know what a number like 12 trillion means. If the national debt were evenly divided among all citizens of the country, how much would every man, woman, and child have to pay? Is economic doomsday about to arrive?

Literacy with numbers, called *numeracy*, is a prerequisite for functioning in a meaningful way personally, professionally, and as a citizen. In this chapter, you will learn to use exponents to provide a way of putting large and small numbers into perspective. The problem of the national debt appears as Example 10 in Section 7.

"Domen Colja/Alamy"

SECTION 1

Adding and Subtracting Polynomials

Objectives

1 Understand the vocabulary used to describe polynomials.
2 Add polynomials.
3 Subtract polynomials.
4 Graph equations defined by polynomials of degree 2.

More education results in a higher income. The mathematical models

$$M = -18x^3 + 923x^2 - 9603x + 48{,}446$$

$$\text{and} \quad W = 17x^3 - 450x^2 + 6392x - 14{,}764$$

describe the median, or middlemost, annual income for men, M, and women, W, who have completed x years of education. We'll be working with these models and the data upon which they are based in the exercise set.

Jan Tyler/iStockphoto

The algebraic expressions that appear on the right side of the models are examples of *polynomials*. A **polynomial** is a single term or the sum of two or more terms containing variables with whole-number exponents. These particular polynomials each contain four terms. Equations containing polynomials are used in such diverse areas as science, business, medicine, psychology, and sociology. In this section, we present basic ideas about polynomials. We then use our knowledge of combining like terms to find sums and differences of polynomials.

1 Understand the vocabulary used to describe polynomials.

Describing Polynomials

Consider the polynomial

$$7x^3 - 9x^2 + 13x - 6.$$

We can express this polynomial as

$$7x^3 + (-9x^2) + 13x + (-6).$$

The polynomial contains four terms. It is customary to write the terms in the order of descending powers of the variables. This is the **standard form** of a polynomial.

We begin this chapter by limiting our discussion to polynomials containing only one variable. Each term of such a polynomial in x is of the form ax^n. The **degree** of ax^n is n. For example, the degree of the term $7x^3$ is 3.

Great Question!

If the degree of a nonzero constant is 0, why doesn't the constant 0 also have degree 0?

We can express 0 in many ways, including $0x$, $0x^2$, and $0x^3$. It is impossible to assign a unique exponent to the variable. This is why 0 has no defined degree.

The Degree of ax^n

If $a \neq 0$ and n is a whole number, the degree of ax^n is n. The degree of a nonzero constant term is 0. The constant 0 has no defined degree.

Here is an example of a polynomial and the degree of each of its four terms:

$$6x^4 - 3x^3 - 2x - 5.$$

degree 4 | degree 3 | degree 1 | degree of nonzero constant: 0

Notice that the exponent on x for the term $-2x$, meaning $-2x^1$, is understood to be 1. For this reason, the degree of $-2x$ is 1.

A polynomial is simplified when it contains no grouping symbols and no like terms. A simplified polynomial that has exactly one term is called a **monomial.** A **binomial** is a simplified polynomial that has two terms. A **trinomial** is a simplified polynomial with three terms. Simplified polynomials with four or more terms have no special names.

The **degree of a polynomial** is the greatest degree of all the terms of the polynomial. For example, $4x^2 + 3x$ is a binomial of degree 2 because the degree of the first term is 2, and the degree of the other term is less than 2. Also, $7x^5 - 2x^2 + 4$ is a trinomial of degree 5 because the degree of the first term is 5, and the degrees of the other terms are less than 5.

We have used x to represent the variable in a polynomial. However, any letter can be used. For example,

- $7x^5 - 3x^3 + 8$ is a polynomial (in x) of degree 5. Because there are three terms, the polynomial is a trinomial.
- $6y^3 + 4y^2 - y + 3$ is a polynomial (in y) of degree 3. Because there are four terms, the polynomial has no special name.
- $z^7 + \sqrt{2}$ is a polynomial (in z) of degree 7. Because there are two terms, the polynomial is a binomial.

2 Add polynomials.

Adding Polynomials

Recall that *like terms* are terms containing exactly the same variables to the same powers. Polynomials are added by combining like terms. For example, we can add the monomials $-9x^3$ and $13x^3$ as follows:

$$-9x^3 + 13x^3 = (-9 + 13)x^3 = 4x^3.$$

These like terms both contain x to the third power.

Add coefficients and keep the same variable factor, x^3.

EXAMPLE 1 Adding Polynomials

Add: $(-9x^3 + 7x^2 - 5x + 3) + (13x^3 + 2x^2 - 8x - 6)$.

Solution The like terms are $-9x^3$ and $13x^3$, containing the same variable to the same power (x^3), as well as $7x^2$ and $2x^2$ (both containing x^2), $-5x$ and $-8x$ (both containing x), and the constant terms 3 and -6. We begin by grouping these pairs of like terms.

$$(-9x^3 + 7x^2 - 5x + 3) + (13x^3 + 2x^2 - 8x - 6)$$

$$= (-9x^3 + 13x^3) + (7x^2 + 2x^2) + (-5x - 8x) + (3 - 6) \quad \text{Group like terms.}$$

$$= 4x^3 + 9x^2 + (-13x) + (-3) \quad \text{Combine like terms.}$$

$$= 4x^3 + 9x^2 - 13x - 3 \quad \text{Express addition of opposites as subtraction.}$$

■

✓ **CHECK POINT 1** Add: $(-11x^3 + 7x^2 - 11x - 5) + (16x^3 - 3x^2 + 3x - 15)$.

Polynomials can also be added by arranging like terms in columns. Then combine like terms, column by column.

EXAMPLE 2 Adding Polynomials Vertically

Add: $(-9x^3 + 7x^2 - 5x + 3) + (13x^3 + 2x^2 - 8x - 6)$.

Solution

$$\begin{array}{r} -9x^3 + 7x^2 - 5x + 3 \\ \underline{13x^3 + 2x^2 - 8x - 6} \\ 4x^3 + 9x^2 - 13x - 3 \end{array}$$

Line up like terms vertically.

Add the like terms in each column.

This is the same answer that we found in Example 1. ■

Great Question!

What's the advantage of using a vertical format to add polynomials instead of a horizontal format?

A vertical format often makes it easier to see the like terms.

✓ **CHECK POINT 2** Add the polynomials in Check Point 1 using a vertical format. Begin by arranging like terms in columns.

3 Subtract polynomials.

Subtracting Polynomials

We subtract real numbers by adding the opposite, or additive inverse, of the number being subtracted. For example,

$$8 - 3 = 8 + (-3) = 5.$$

Subtraction of polynomials also involves opposites. If the sum of two polynomials is 0, the polynomials are **opposites**, or **additive inverses**, of each other. Here is an example:

$$(4x^2 - 6x - 7) + (-4x^2 + 6x + 7) = 0.$$

The opposite of $4x^2 - 6x - 7$ is $-4x^2 + 6x + 7$, and vice versa.

Observe that the opposite of $4x^2 - 6x - 7$ can be obtained by changing the sign of each of its coefficients:

Polynomial		**Opposite**
$4x^2 - 6x - 7$	Change 4 to −4, change −6 to 6, and change −7 to 7.	$-4x^2 + 6x + 7.$

In general, **the opposite of a polynomial is that polynomial with the sign of every coefficient changed**. Just as we did with real numbers, we subtract one polynomial from another by adding the opposite of the polynomial being subtracted.

Subtracting Polynomials

To subtract two polynomials, add the first polynomial and the opposite of the polynomial being subtracted.

EXAMPLE 3 Subtracting Polynomials

Subtract: $(7x^2 + 3x - 4) - (4x^2 - 6x - 7)$.

Solution

$$(7x^2 + 3x - 4) - (4x^2 - 6x - 7)$$

Change the sign of each coefficient.

$$= (7x^2 + 3x - 4) + (-4x^2 + 6x + 7)$$ Add the opposite of the polynomial being subtracted.

$$= (7x^2 - 4x^2) + (3x + 6x) + (-4 + 7)$$ Group like terms.

$$= 3x^2 + 9x + 3$$ Combine like terms. ■

✓ **CHECK POINT 3** Subtract: $(9x^2 + 7x - 2) - (2x^2 - 4x - 6)$.

Great Question!

I'm confused by what it means to subtract one polynomial from a second polynomial. Which polynomial should I write first?

Be careful of the order in Example 4. For example, subtracting 2 from 5 means $5 - 2$. In general, subtracting B from A means $A - B$. The order of the resulting algebraic expression is not the same as the order in English. The polynomial following the word *from* is the one to write first.

EXAMPLE 4 Subtracting Polynomials

Subtract $2x^3 - 6x^2 - 3x + 9$ from $7x^3 - 8x^2 + 9x - 6$.

Solution

$$(7x^3 - 8x^2 + 9x - 6) - (2x^3 - 6x^2 - 3x + 9)$$

Change the sign of each coefficient.

$$= (7x^3 - 8x^2 + 9x - 6) + (-2x^3 + 6x^2 + 3x - 9)$$ Add the opposite of the polynomial being subtracted.

$$= (7x^3 - 2x^3) + (-8x^2 + 6x^2) + (9x + 3x) + (-6 - 9)$$ Group like terms.

$$= 5x^3 + (-2x^2) + 12x + (-15)$$ Combine like terms.

$$= 5x^3 - 2x^2 + 12x - 15$$ Express addition of opposites as subtraction. ■

✓ **CHECK POINT 4** Subtract $3x^3 - 8x^2 - 5x + 6$ from $10x^3 - 5x^2 + 7x - 2$.

Subtraction can also be performed in columns.

EXAMPLE 5 Subtracting Polynomials Vertically

Use the method of subtracting in columns to find

$$(12y^3 - 9y^2 - 11y - 3) - (4y^3 - 5y + 8).$$

Solution Arrange like terms in columns.

$$\begin{array}{r} 12y^3 - 9y^2 - 11y - 3 \\ -(4y^3 \qquad\qquad - \ 5y + 8) \\ \hline \end{array}$$

Leave space for the missing term.

Add the opposite of the polynomial being subtracted.

$$\begin{array}{r} 12y^3 - 9y^2 - 11y - 3 \\ + -4y^3 \qquad\qquad + \ 5y - 8 \\ \hline 8y^3 - 9y^2 - 6y - 11 \end{array}$$

Change the sign of each coefficient of $4y^3 - 5y + 8$.

Combine like terms. ■

✓ **CHECK POINT 5** Use the method of subtracting in columns to find

$$(8y^3 - 10y^2 - 14y - 2) - (5y^3 - 3y + 6).$$

Pascal Rondeau/Getty Images

Graphing Equations Defined by Polynomials

Look at the picture of this gymnast. He has created a perfect balance in which the two halves of his body are mirror images of each other. Graphs of equations defined by polynomials of degree 2, such as $y = x^2 - 4$, have this mirrorlike quality. We can obtain their graphs, shaped like bowls or inverted bowls, using the point-plotting method for graphing an equation in two variables.

4 Graph equations defined by polynomials of degree 2.

EXAMPLE 6 Graphing an Equation Defined by a Polynomial of Degree 2

Graph the equation: $y = x^2 - 4$.

Solution The given equation involves two variables, x and y. However, because the variable x is squared, it is not a linear equation in two variables.

$$y = x^2 - 4$$

This is not in the form $y = mx + b$ because x is squared.

Although the graph is not a line, it is still a picture of all the ordered-pair solutions of $y = x^2 - 4$. Thus, we can use the point-plotting method to obtain the graph.

Step 1. Find several ordered pairs that are solutions of the equation. To find some solutions of $y = x^2 - 4$, we select integers for x, starting with -3 and ending with 3.

Great Question!

When I graphed lines, I used two, or possibly three, points. Why isn't this enough to use when graphing equations that are not linear?

If the graph of an equation is not a straight line, extra points are needed to get a better general idea of the graph's shape.

Start with x. Compute y. Form the ordered pair (x, y).

x	$y = x^2 - 4$	(x, y)
-3	$y = (-3)^2 - 4 = 9 - 4 = 5$	$(-3, 5)$
-2	$y = (-2)^2 - 4 = 4 - 4 = 0$	$(-2, 0)$
-1	$y = (-1)^2 - 4 = 1 - 4 = -3$	$(-1, -3)$
0	$y = 0^2 - 4 = 0 - 4 = -4$	$(0, -4)$
1	$y = 1^2 - 4 = 1 - 4 = -3$	$(1, -3)$
2	$y = 2^2 - 4 = 4 - 4 = 0$	$(2, 0)$
3	$y = 3^2 - 4 = 9 - 4 = 5$	$(3, 5)$

Step 2. Plot these ordered pairs as points in the rectangular coordinate system. The seven ordered pairs in the table of values are plotted in **Figure 1(a).**

Step 3. Connect the points with a smooth curve. The seven points are joined with a smooth curve in **Figure 1(b)**. The graph of $y = x^2 - 4$ is a curve where the part of the graph to the right of the y-axis is a reflection of the part to the left of it, and vice versa. The arrows on both ends of the curve indicate that it extends indefinitely in both directions.

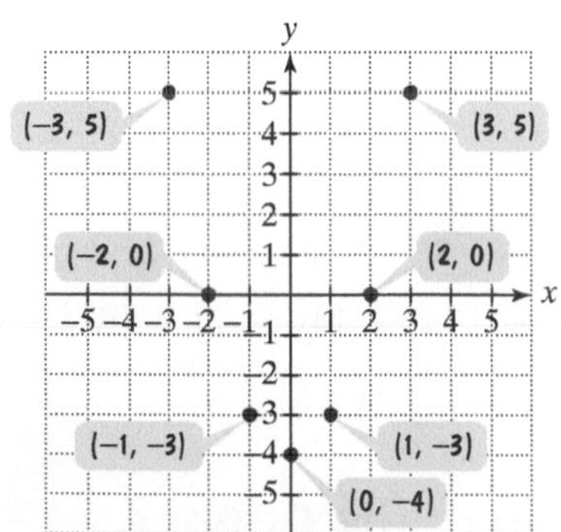

Figure 1(a) Some solutions of $y = x^2 - 4$ plotted as points

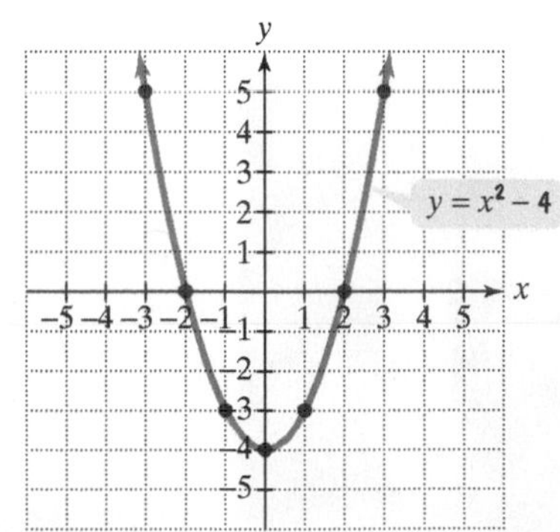

Figure 1(b)

The graph of $y = x^2 - 4$ ■

✓ CHECK POINT 6 Graph the equation: $y = x^2 - 1$. Select integers for x, starting with -3 and ending with 3.

Blitzer Bonus

Modeling *American Idol* with a Polynomial of Degree 2

The graph in **Figure 2** indicates that the ratings of *American Idol* from season 1 (2002) through season 9 (2010) have a mirrorlike quality. This suggests modeling the show's average number of viewers with a polynomial of degree 2.

Figure 2

Source: The Nielsen Company

The equation

$$y = -0.68x^2 + 7.94x + 6.78$$

models *American Idol*'s average number of viewers, y, in millions, where x is the show's season number. The graph of the model in **Figure 3** is shaped like an inverted bowl. Can you see why projections based on this graph have the show's producers looking for a shake-up?

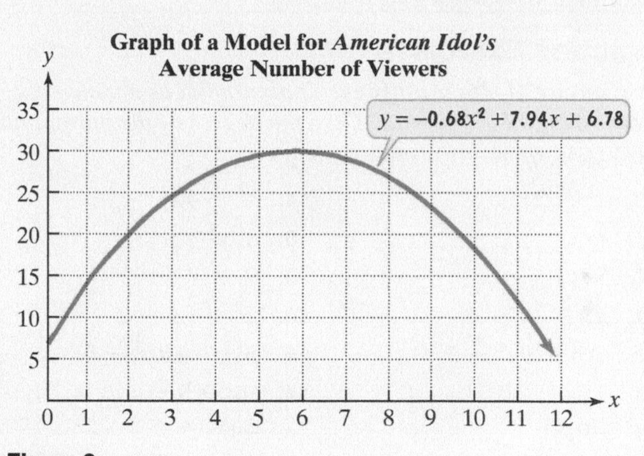

Figure 3

Achieving Success

Address your stress. Stress levels can help or hinder performance. The graph of the polynomial equation of degree 2 in **Figure 4** serves as a model that shows people under both low stress and high stress perform worse than their moderate-stress counterparts.

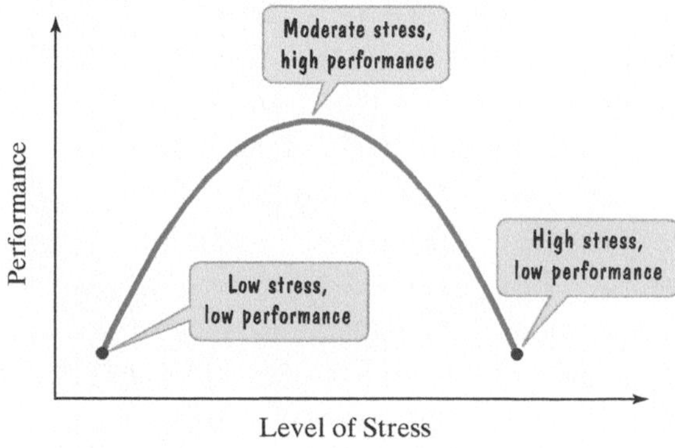

Figure 4

Source: Herbert Benson, *Your Maximum Mind*, Random House, 1987.

CONCEPT AND VOCABULARY CHECK

Fill in each blank so that the resulting statement is true.

1. A polynomial is a single term or the sum of two or more terms containing variables with exponents that are ______________ numbers.
2. It is customary to write the terms of a polynomial in the order of descending powers of the variable. This is called the ______________ form of a polynomial.
3. A simplified polynomial that has exactly one term is called a/an ______________.
4. A simplified polynomial that has two terms is called a/an ______________.
5. A simplified polynomial that has three terms is called a/an ______________.
6. The degree of ax^n is ______________, provided $a \neq 0$.
7. The degree of a polynomial is the ______________ degree of all the terms of the polynomial.
8. Polynomials are added by combining ______________ terms.
9. To subtract two polynomials, add the first polynomial and the ______________ of the polynomial being subtracted.

1 EXERCISE SET

MyMathLab®

Watch the videos in MyMathLab

Download the MyDashBoard App

Practice Exercises

In Exercises 1–16, identify each polynomial as a monomial, a binomial, or a trinomial. Give the degree of the polynomial.

1. $3x + 7$
2. $5x - 2$
3. $x^3 - 2x$
4. $x^5 - 7x$
5. $8x^2$
6. $10x^2$
7. 5
8. 9
9. $x^2 - 3x + 4$
10. $x^2 - 9x + 2$
11. $7y^2 - 9y^4 + 5$
12. $3y^2 - 14y^5 + 6$
13. $15x - 7x^3$
14. $9x - 5x^3$
15. $-9y^{23}$
16. $-11y^{26}$

In Exercises 17–38, add the polynomials.

17. $(9x + 8) + (-17x + 5)$
18. $(8x - 5) + (-13x + 9)$
19. $(4x^2 + 6x - 7) + (8x^2 + 9x - 2)$
20. $(11x^2 + 7x - 4) + (27x^2 + 10x - 20)$
21. $(7x^2 - 11x) + (3x^2 - x)$
22. $(-3x^2 + x) + (4x^2 + 8x)$
23. $(4x^2 - 6x + 12) + (x^2 + 3x + 1)$
24. $(-7x^2 + 8x + 3) + (2x^2 + x + 8)$
25. $(4y^3 + 7y - 5) + (10y^2 - 6y + 3)$
26. $(2y^3 + 3y + 10) + (3y^2 + 5y - 22)$
27. $(2x^2 - 6x + 7) + (3x^3 - 3x)$
28. $(4x^3 + 5x + 13) + (-4x^2 + 22)$
29. $(4y^2 + 8y + 11) + (-2y^3 + 5y + 2)$
30. $(7y^3 + 5y - 1) + (2y^2 - 6y + 3)$
31. $(-2y^6 + 3y^4 - y^2) + (-y^6 + 5y^4 + 2y^2)$
32. $(7r^4 + 5r^2 + 2r) + (-18r^4 - 5r^2 - r)$
33. $\left(9x^3 - x^2 - x - \frac{1}{3}\right) + \left(x^3 + x^2 + x + \frac{4}{3}\right)$
34. $\left(12x^3 - x^2 - x + \frac{4}{3}\right) + \left(x^3 + x^2 + x - \frac{1}{3}\right)$
35. $\left(\frac{1}{5}x^4 + \frac{1}{3}x^3 + \frac{3}{8}x^2 + 6\right) + \left(-\frac{3}{5}x^4 + \frac{2}{3}x^3 - \frac{1}{2}x^2 - 6\right)$
36. $\left(\frac{2}{5}x^4 + \frac{2}{3}x^3 + \frac{5}{8}x^2 + 7\right) + \left(-\frac{4}{5}x^4 + \frac{1}{3}x^3 - \frac{1}{4}x^2 - 7\right)$
37. $(0.03x^5 - 0.1x^3 + x + 0.03) + (-0.02x^5 + x^4 - 0.7x + 0.3)$
38. $(0.06x^5 - 0.2x^3 + x + 0.05) + (-0.04x^5 + 2x^4 - 0.8x + 0.5)$

In Exercises 39–54, use a vertical format to add the polynomials.

39. $\begin{array}{l} 5y^3 - 7y^2 \\ \underline{6y^3 + 4y^2} \end{array}$
40. $\begin{array}{l} 13x^4 - x^2 \\ \underline{7x^4 + 2x^2} \end{array}$
41. $\begin{array}{l} 3x^2 - 7x + 4 \\ \underline{-5x^2 + 6x - 3} \end{array}$
42. $\begin{array}{l} 7x^2 - 5x - 6 \\ \underline{-9x^2 + 4x + 6} \end{array}$
43. $\begin{array}{l} \frac{1}{4}x^4 - \frac{2}{3}x^3 - 5 \\ \underline{-\frac{1}{2}x^4 + \frac{1}{5}x^3 + 4.7} \end{array}$

44. $$\begin{array}{r} \frac{1}{3}x^9 - \frac{1}{5}x^5 - 2.7 \\ -\frac{3}{4}x^9 + \frac{2}{3}x^5 + 1 \\ \hline \end{array}$$

45. $$\begin{array}{r} y^3 + 5y^2 - 7y - 3 \\ -2y^3 + 3y^2 + 4y - 11 \\ \hline \end{array}$$

46. $$\begin{array}{r} y^3 + y^2 - 7y + 9 \\ -y^3 - 6y^2 - 8y + 11 \\ \hline \end{array}$$

47. $$\begin{array}{r} 4x^3 - 6x^2 + 5x - 7 \\ -9x^3 \qquad\qquad - 4x + 3 \\ \hline \end{array}$$

48. $$\begin{array}{r} -4y^3 + 6y^2 - 8y + 11 \\ 2y^3 \qquad\qquad + 9y - 3 \\ \hline \end{array}$$

49. $$\begin{array}{l} 7x^4 - 3x^3 + x^2 \\ \qquad\quad x^3 - x^2 + 4x - 2 \\ \hline \end{array}$$

50. $$\begin{array}{l} 7y^5 - 3y^3 + y^2 \\ \qquad\quad 2y^3 - y^2 - 4y - 3 \\ \hline \end{array}$$

51. $$\begin{array}{r} 7x^2 - 9x + 3 \\ 4x^2 + 11x - 2 \\ -3x^2 + 5x - 6 \\ \hline \end{array}$$

52. $$\begin{array}{r} 7y^2 - 11y - 6 \\ 8y^2 + 3y + 4 \\ -9y^2 - 5y + 2 \\ \hline \end{array}$$

53. $$\begin{array}{r} 1.2x^3 - 3x^2 + 9.1 \\ 7.8x^3 - 3.1x^2 + 8 \\ 1.2x^2 - 6 \\ \hline \end{array}$$

54. $$\begin{array}{r} 7.9x^3 - 6.8x^2 + 3.3 \\ 6.1x^3 - 2.2x^2 + 7 \\ 4.3x^2 - 5 \\ \hline \end{array}$$

In Exercises 55–74, subtract the polynomials.

55. $(x - 8) - (3x + 2)$

56. $(x - 2) - (7x + 9)$

57. $(x^2 - 5x - 3) - (6x^2 + 4x + 9)$

58. $(3x^2 - 8x - 2) - (11x^2 + 5x + 4)$

59. $(x^2 - 5x) - (6x^2 - 4x)$

60. $(3x^2 - 2x) - (5x^2 - 6x)$

61. $(x^2 - 8x - 9) - (5x^2 - 4x - 3)$

62. $(x^2 - 5x + 3) - (x^2 - 6x - 8)$

63. $(y - 8) - (3y - 2)$

64. $(y - 2) - (7y - 9)$

65. $(6y^3 + 2y^2 - y - 11) - (y^2 - 8y + 9)$

66. $(5y^3 + y^2 - 3y - 8) - (y^2 - 8y + 11)$

67. $(7n^3 - n^7 - 8) - (6n^3 - n^7 - 10)$

68. $(2n^2 - n^7 - 6) - (2n^3 - n^7 - 8)$

69. $(y^6 - y^3) - (y^2 - y)$

70. $(y^5 - y^3) - (y^4 - y^2)$

71. $(7x^4 + 4x^2 + 5x) - (-19x^4 - 5x^2 - x)$

72. $(-3x^6 + 3x^4 - x^2) - (-x^6 + 2x^4 + 2x^2)$

73. $\left(\frac{3}{7}x^3 - \frac{1}{5}x - \frac{1}{3}\right) - \left(-\frac{2}{7}x^3 + \frac{1}{4}x - \frac{1}{3}\right)$

74. $\left(\frac{3}{8}x^2 - \frac{1}{3}x - \frac{1}{4}\right) - \left(-\frac{1}{8}x^2 + \frac{1}{2}x - \frac{1}{4}\right)$

In Exercises 75–88, use a vertical format to subtract the polynomials.

75. $$\begin{array}{r} 7x + 1 \\ -(3x - 5) \\ \hline \end{array}$$

76. $$\begin{array}{r} 4x + 2 \\ -(3x - 5) \\ \hline \end{array}$$

77. $$\begin{array}{r} 7x^2 - 3 \\ -(-3x^2 + 4) \\ \hline \end{array}$$

78. $$\begin{array}{r} 9y^2 - 6 \\ -(-5y^2 + 2) \\ \hline \end{array}$$

79. $$\begin{array}{r} 7y^2 - 5y + 2 \\ -(11y^2 + 2y - 3) \\ \hline \end{array}$$

80. $$\begin{array}{r} 3x^5 - 5x^3 + 6 \\ -(7x^5 + 4x^3 - 2) \\ \hline \end{array}$$

81. $$\begin{array}{r} 7x^3 + 5x^2 - 3 \\ -(-2x^3 - 6x^2 + 5) \\ \hline \end{array}$$

82. $$\begin{array}{r} 3y^4 - 4y^2 + 7 \\ -(-5y^4 - 6y^2 - 13) \\ \hline \end{array}$$

83. $$\begin{array}{r} 5y^3 + 6y^2 - 3y + 10 \\ -(6y^3 - 2y^2 - 4y - 4) \\ \hline \end{array}$$

84. $$\begin{array}{r} 4y^3 + 5y^2 + 7y + 11 \\ -(-5y^3 + 6y^2 - 9y - 3) \\ \hline \end{array}$$

85. $$\begin{array}{l} 7x^4 - 3x^3 + 2x^2 \\ -(\quad - x^3 - x^2 + x - 2) \\ \hline \end{array}$$

86. $$\begin{array}{l} 5y^6 - 3y^3 + 2y^2 \\ -(\quad - y^3 - y^2 - y - 1) \\ \hline \end{array}$$

87. $$\begin{array}{l} 0.07x^3 - 0.01x^2 + 0.02x \\ -(0.02x^3 - 0.03x^2 - \quad x) \\ \hline \end{array}$$

88. $$\begin{array}{l} 0.04x^3 - 0.03x^2 + 0.05x \\ -(0.02x^3 - 0.06x^2 - \quad x) \\ \hline \end{array}$$

Graph each equation in Exercises 89–94. Find seven solutions in your table of values for each equation by using integers for x, starting with −3 and ending with 3.

89. $y = x^2$

90. $y = x^2 - 2$

91. $y = x^2 + 1$

92. $y = x^2 + 2$

93. $y = 4 - x^2$

94. $y = 9 - x^2$

Practice PLUS

In Exercises 95–98, perform the indicated operations.

95. $[(4x^2 + 7x - 5) - (2x^2 - 10x + 3)] - (x^2 + 5x - 8)$

96. $[(10x^3 - 5x^2 + 4x + 3) - (-3x^3 - 4x^2 + x)] - (7x^3 - 5x + 4)$

97. $[(4y^2 - 3y + 8) - (5y^2 + 7y - 4)] - [(8y^2 + 5y - 7) + (-10y^2 + 4y + 3)]$

98. $[(7y^2 - 4y + 2) - (12y^2 + 3y - 5)] - [(5y^2 - 2y - 8) + (-7y^2 + 10y - 13)]$

99. Subtract $x^3 - 2x^2 + 2$ from the sum of $4x^3 + x^2$ and $-x^3 + 7x - 3$.

100. Subtract $-3x^3 - 7x + 5$ from the sum of $2x^2 + 4x - 7$ and $-5x^3 - 2x - 3$.

101. Subtract $-y^2 + 7y^3$ from the difference between $-5 + y^2 + 4y^3$ and $-8 - y + 7y^3$. Express the answer in standard form.

102. Subtract $-2y^2 + 8y^3$ from the difference between $-6 + y^2 + 5y^3$ and $-12 - y + 13y^3$. Express the answer in standard form.

Application Exercises

As you complete more years of education, you can count on a greater income. The bar graph shows the median, or middlemost, annual income for Americans, by level of education, for a recent year.

Median Annual Income, by Level of Education

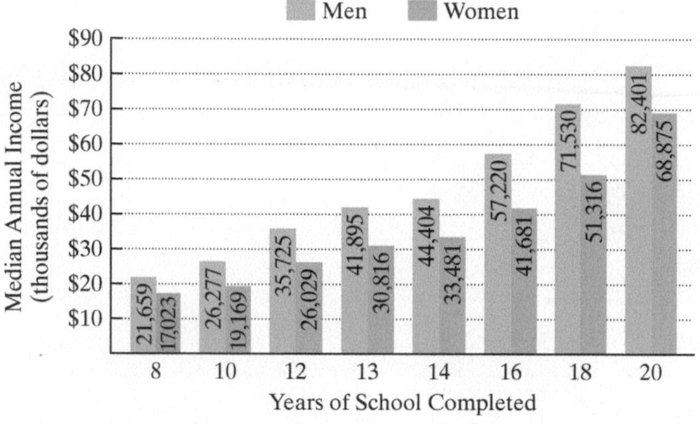

Source: Bureau of the Census

Here are polynomial models that describe the median annual income for men, M, and for women, W, who have completed x years of education:

$$M = 177x^2 + 288x + 7075$$
$$W = 255x^2 - 2956x + 24{,}336$$

$$M = -18x^3 + 923x^2 - 9603x + 48{,}446$$
$$W = 17x^3 - 450x^2 + 6392x - 14{,}764.$$

Exercises 103–106 are based on these models and the data displayed by the graph.

103. a. Use the equations defined by polynomials of degree 3 to find a mathematical model for $M - W$.

b. According to the model in part (a), what is the difference in the median annual income between men and women with 14 years of education?

c. According to the data displayed by the graph, what is the actual difference in the median annual income between men and women with 14 years of education? Did the model in part (b) underestimate or overestimate this difference? By how much?

104. a. Use the equations defined by polynomials of degree 3 to find a mathematical model for $M - W$.

b. According to the model in part (a), what is the difference in the median annual income between men and women with 16 years of education?

c. According to the data displayed by the graph, what is the actual difference in the median annual income between men and women with 16 years of education? Did the model in part (b) underestimate or overestimate this difference? By how much?

105. a. Use the equation defined by a polynomial of degree 2 to find the median annual income for a man with 16 years of education. Does this underestimate or overestimate the median income shown by the bar graph in the previous column? By how much?

b. Shown in a rectangular coordinate system are the graphs of the polynomial models of degree 2 that describe median annual income, by level of education. Identify your solution from part (a) as a point on the appropriate graph.

Graphs of Models for Median Annual Income, by Level of Education

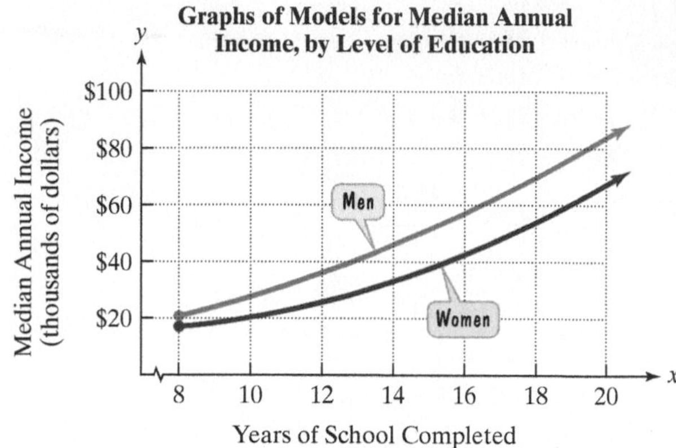

c. Use the appropriate graph in part (b) to estimate, to the nearest thousand dollars, the median annual income for a woman with 16 years of education.

106. a. Use the equation defined by a polynomial of degree 2 to find the median annual income for a woman with 18 years of education. Does this underestimate or overestimate the median income shown by the bar graph in the previous column? By how much?

b. Shown in Exercise 105(b) are rectangular coordinate graphs of the polynomial models of degree 2 that describe median annual income, by level of education. Identify your solution from part (a) as a point on the appropriate graph.

c. Use the appropriate graph in Exercise 105(b) to estimate, to the nearest thousand dollars, the median annual income for a man with 18 years of education.

Writing in Mathematics

107. What is a polynomial?

108. What is a monomial? Give an example with your explanation.

109. What is a binomial? Give an example with your explanation.

110. What is a trinomial? Give an example with your explanation.

111. What is the degree of a polynomial? Provide an example with your explanation.

112. Explain how to add polynomials.

113. Explain how to subtract polynomials.

Critical Thinking Exercises

Make Sense? *In Exercises 114–117, determine whether each statement "makes sense" or "does not make sense" and explain your reasoning.*

114. I add like monomials by adding both their coefficients and the exponents that appear on their common variable factor.

115. By looking at the first term of a polynomial, I can determine its degree.

116. As long as I understand how to add and subtract polynomials, I can select the format, horizontal or vertical, that works best for me.

117. I used two points and a checkpoint to graph $y = x^2 - 4$.

In Exercises 118–121, determine whether each statement is true or false. If the statement is false, make the necessary change(s) to produce a true statement.

118. It is not possible to write a binomial with degree 0.

119. $\frac{1}{5x^2} + \frac{1}{3x}$ is a binomial.

120. $(2x^2 - 8x + 6) - (x^2 - 3x + 5) = x^2 - 5x + 1$ for any value of x.

121. In the polynomial $3x^2 - 5x + 13$, the coefficient of x is 5.

122. What polynomial must be subtracted from $5x^2 - 2x + 1$ so that the difference is $8x^2 - x + 3$?

123. The number of people who catch a cold t weeks after January 1 is $5t - 3t^2 + t^3$. The number of people who recover t weeks after January 1 is $t - t^2 + \frac{1}{3}t^3$. Write a polynomial in standard form for the number of people who are still ill with a cold t weeks after January 1.

124. Explain why it is not possible to add two polynomials of degree 3 and get a polynomial of degree 4.

Review Exercises

125. Simplify: $(-10)(-7) \div (1 - 8)$.

126. Subtract: $-4.6 - (-10.2)$.

127. Solve: $3(x - 2) = 9(x + 2)$.

Preview Exercises

Exercises 128–130 will help you prepare for the material covered in the next section.

128. Find the missing exponent, designated by the question mark, in the final step.

$$x^3 \cdot x^4 = (x \cdot x \cdot x) \cdot (x \cdot x \cdot x \cdot x) = x^?$$

129. Use the distributive property to multiply: $3x(x + 5)$.

130. Simplify: $x(x + 2) + 3(x + 2)$.

SECTION 2

Multiplying Polynomials

Objectives

1. Use the product rule for exponents.
2. Use the power rule for exponents.
3. Use the products-to-powers rule.
4. Multiply monomials.
5. Multiply a monomial and a polynomial.
6. Multiply polynomials when neither is a monomial.

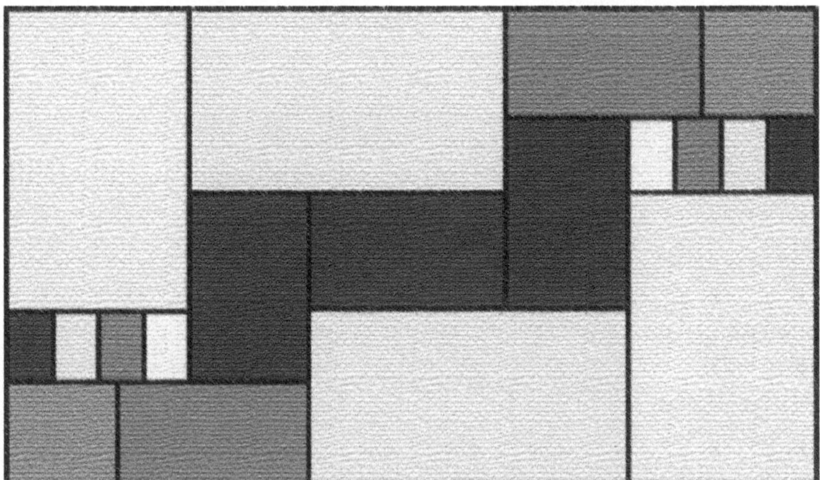

The ancient Greeks believed that the most visually pleasing rectangles have a ratio of length to width of approximately 1.618 to 1. With the exception of the squares on the lower left and the upper right, the interior of this geometric figure is filled entirely with these *golden rectangles*. Furthermore, the large rectangle is also a golden rectangle.

The total area of the large rectangle shown on the previous page can be found in many ways. This is because the area of any large rectangular region is related to the areas of the smaller rectangles that make up that region. In this section, we apply areas of rectangles as a way to picture the multiplication of polynomials. Before studying how polynomials are multiplied, we must develop some rules for working with exponents.

1 Use the product rule for exponents.

The Product Rule for Exponents

We have seen that exponents are used to indicate repeated multiplication. For example, 2^4, where 2 is the base and 4 is the exponent, indicates that 2 occurs as a factor four times:

$$2^4 = 2 \cdot 2 \cdot 2 \cdot 2.$$

Now consider the multiplication of two exponential expressions, such as $2^4 \cdot 2^3$. We are multiplying 4 factors of 2 and 3 factors of 2. We have a total of 7 factors of 2:

4 factors of 2 | 3 factors of 2

$$2^4 \cdot 2^3 = (2 \cdot 2 \cdot 2 \cdot 2) \cdot (2 \cdot 2 \cdot 2)$$

Total: 7 factors of 2

Thus,

$$2^4 \cdot 2^3 = 2^7.$$

Caution: $2^4 \cdot 2^3$ is not equal to $2^{4 \cdot 3}$, or 2^{12}, as might be expected.

We can quickly find the exponent, 7, of the product by adding 4 and 3, the original exponents:

$$2^4 \cdot 2^3 = 2^{4+3} = 2^7.$$

This suggests the following rule:

The Product Rule

$$b^m \cdot b^n = b^{m+n}$$

When multiplying exponential expressions with the same base, add the exponents. Use this sum as the exponent of the common base.

EXAMPLE 1 Using the Product Rule

Multiply each expression using the product rule:

a. $2^2 \cdot 2^3$ **b.** $x^7 \cdot x^9$ **c.** $y \cdot y^5$ **d.** $y^3 \cdot y^2 \cdot y^5$.

Solution

a. $2^2 \cdot 2^3 = 2^{2+3} = 2^5$ or 32

b. $x^7 \cdot x^9 = x^{7+9} = x^{16}$

c. $y \cdot y^5 = y^1 \cdot y^5 = y^{1+5} = y^6$

d. $y^3 \cdot y^2 \cdot y^5 = y^{3+2+5} = y^{10}$ ■

Great Question!

Can I use the product rule to multiply an expression such as $x^7 \cdot y^9$?

The product rule does not apply to exponential expressions with different bases:

$x^7 \cdot y^9$, or x^7y^9, cannot be simplified.

✓ CHECK POINT 1 Multiply each expression using the product rule:

a. $2^2 \cdot 2^4$ **b.** $x^6 \cdot x^4$ **c.** $y \cdot y^7$ **d.** $y^4 \cdot y^3 \cdot y^2$.

2 Use the power rule for exponents.

The Power Rule for Exponents

The next property of exponents applies when an exponential expression is raised to a power. Here is an example:

$$(3^2)^4.$$

The exponential expression 3^2 is raised to the fourth power.

There are 4 factors of 3^2. Thus,

$$(3^2)^4 = 3^2 \cdot 3^2 \cdot 3^2 \cdot 3^2 = 3^{2+2+2+2} = 3^8.$$

Add exponents when multiplying with the same base.

We can obtain the answer, 3^8, by multiplying the exponents:

$$(3^2)^4 = 3^{2\cdot 4} = 3^8.$$

By generalizing $(3^2)^4 = 3^{2\cdot 4} = 3^8$, we obtain the following rule:

The Power Rule (Powers to Powers)

$$(b^m)^n = b^{mn}$$

When an exponential expression is raised to a power, multiply the exponents. Place the product of the exponents on the base and remove the parentheses.

Great Question!

Can you show me examples that illustrate the difference between the product rule and the power rule?

Do not confuse the product and power rules. Note the following differences:

- $x^4 \cdot x^7 = x^{4+7} = x^{11}$
- $(x^4)^7 = x^{4\cdot 7} = x^{28}$.

EXAMPLE 2 Using the Power Rule

Simplify each expression using the power rule:

a. $(2^3)^5$ **b.** $(x^6)^4$ **c.** $[(-3)^7]^5$.

Solution

a. $(2^3)^5 = 2^{3\cdot 5} = 2^{15}$

b. $(x^6)^4 = x^{6\cdot 4} = x^{24}$

c. $[(-3)^7]^5 = (-3)^{7\cdot 5} = (-3)^{35}$ ■

✓ **CHECK POINT 2** Simplify each expression using the power rule:

a. $(3^4)^5$ **b.** $(x^9)^{10}$ **c.** $[(-5)^7]^3$.

---

3 Use the products-to-powers rule.

The Products-to-Powers Rule for Exponents

The next property of exponents applies when we are raising a product to a power. Here is an example:

$$(2x)^4.$$

The product $2x$ is raised to the fourth power.

There are four factors of $2x$. Thus,

$$(2x)^4 = 2x \cdot 2x \cdot 2x \cdot 2x = 2 \cdot 2 \cdot 2 \cdot 2 \cdot x \cdot x \cdot x \cdot x = 2^4x^4.$$

We can obtain the answer, 2^4x^4, by raising each factor within the parentheses to the fourth power:

$$(2x)^4 = 2^4x^4.$$

Generalizing from $(2x)^4 = 2^4x^4$ suggests the following rule:

Products to Powers

$$(ab)^n = a^n b^n$$

When a product is raised to a power, raise each factor to the power.

EXAMPLE 3 Using the Products-to-Powers Rule

Simplify each expression using the products-to-powers rule:

a. $(5x)^3$ **b.** $(-2y^4)^5$.

Solution

a. $(5x)^3 = 5^3x^3$ Raise each factor to the third power.

$= 125x^3$ $5^3 = 5 \cdot 5 \cdot 5 = 125$

b. $(-2y^4)^5 = (-2)^5(y^4)^5$ Raise each factor to the fifth power.

$= (-2)^5y^{4 \cdot 5}$ To raise an exponential expression to a power, multiply exponents: $(b^m)^n = b^{mn}$.

$= -32y^{20}$ $(-2)^5 = (-2)(-2)(-2)(-2)(-2) = -32$ ■

✓ **CHECK POINT 3** Simplify each expression using the products-to-powers rule:

a. $(2x)^4$ **b.** $(-4y^2)^3$.

Great Question!

What are some common errors to avoid when simplifying exponential expressions?

Here's a partial list. The first column shows the correct simplification. The second column illustrates a common error.

Correct	Incorrect	Description of Error
$b^3 \cdot b^4 = b^{3+4} = b^7$	$b^3 \cdot b^4 = b^{12}$	Exponents should be added, not multiplied.
$3^2 \cdot 3^4 = 3^{2+4} = 3^6$	$3^2 \cdot 3^4 = 9^{2+4} = 9^6$	The common base should be retained, not multiplied.
$(x^5)^3 = x^{5 \cdot 3} = x^{15}$	$(x^5)^3 = x^{5+3} = x^8$	Exponents should be multiplied, not added, when raising a power to a power.
$(4x)^3 = 4^3x^3 = 64x^3$	$(4x)^3 = 4x^3$	Both factors should be cubed.

4 Multiply monomials.

Multiplying Monomials

Now that we have developed three properties of exponents, we are ready to turn to polynomial multiplication. We begin with the product of two monomials, such as $-8x^6$ and $5x^3$. This product is obtained by multiplying the coefficients, -8 and 5, and then multiplying the variables using the product rule for exponents.

$$(-8x^6)(5x^3) = -8 \cdot 5 \cdot x^6 \cdot x^3 = -8 \cdot 5x^{6+3} = -40x^9$$

Multiply coefficients and add exponents.

Multiplying Monomials

To multiply monomials with the same variable base, multiply the coefficients and then multiply the variables. Use the product rule for exponents to multiply the variables: Keep the variable and add the exponents.

Great Question!

Because monomials with the same base and different exponents can be multiplied, can they also be added?

No. Don't confuse adding and multiplying monomials.

Addition:

$$5x^4 + 6x^4 = 11x^4$$

Multiplication:

$$(5x^4)(6x^4) = (5 \cdot 6)(x^4 \cdot x^4) = 30x^{4+4} = 30x^8$$

Only like terms can be added or subtracted, but unlike terms may be multiplied.

Addition:

$5x^4 + 3x^2$ cannot be simplified.

Multiplication:

$$(5x^4)(3x^2) = (5 \cdot 3)(x^4 \cdot x^2) = 15x^{4+2} = 15x^6$$

EXAMPLE 4 Multiplying Monomials

Multiply: **a.** $(2x)(4x^2)$ **b.** $(-10x^6)(6x^{10})$.

Solution

a. $(2x)(4x^2) = (2 \cdot 4)(x \cdot x^2)$ Multiply the coefficients and multiply the variables.

$= 8x^{1+2}$ Add exponents: $b^m \cdot b^n = b^{m+n}$.

$= 8x^3$ Simplify.

b. $(-10x^6)(6x^{10}) = (-10 \cdot 6)(x^6 \cdot x^{10})$ Multiply the coefficients and multiply the variables.

$= -60x^{6+10}$ Add exponents: $b^m \cdot b^n = b^{m+n}$.

$= -60x^{16}$ Simplify. ■

✓ **CHECK POINT 4** Multiply: **a.** $(7x^2)(10x)$ **b.** $(-5x^4)(4x^5)$.

Multiplying a Monomial and a Polynomial That Is Not a Monomial

5 Multiply a monomial and a polynomial.

We use the distributive property to multiply a monomial and a polynomial that is not a monomial. For example,

$$3x^2(2x^3 + 5x) = 3x^2 \cdot 2x^3 + 3x^2 \cdot 5x = 3 \cdot 2x^{2+3} + 3 \cdot 5x^{2+1} = 6x^5 + 15x^3.$$

Monomial ($3x^2$); Binomial ($2x^3 + 5x$); Multiply coefficients and add exponents.

Multiplying a Monomial and a Polynomial That Is Not a Monomial

To multiply a monomial and a polynomial, use the distributive property to multiply each term of the polynomial by the monomial.

EXAMPLE 5 Multiplying a Monomial and a Polynomial

Multiply: **a.** $2x(x + 4)$ **b.** $3x^2(4x^3 - 5x + 2)$.

Solution

a. $2x(x + 4) = 2x \cdot x + 2x \cdot 4$ Use the distributive property.

$= 2 \cdot 1x^{1+1} + 2 \cdot 4x$ To multiply the monomials, multiply coefficients and add exponents.

$= 2x^2 + 8x$ Simplify.

b. $3x^2(4x^3 - 5x + 2)$

$= 3x^2 \cdot 4x^3 - 3x^2 \cdot 5x + 3x^2 \cdot 2$ Use the distributive property.

$= 3 \cdot 4x^{2+3} - 3 \cdot 5x^{2+1} + 3 \cdot 2x^2$ To multiply the monomials, multiply coefficients and add exponents.

$= 12x^5 - 15x^3 + 6x^2$ Simplify. ■

Rectangles often make it possible to visualize polynomial multiplication. For example, **Figure 5** shows a rectangle with length $2x$ and width $x + 4$. The area of the large rectangle is

$$2x(x + 4).$$

The sum of the areas of the two smaller rectangles is

$$2x^2 + 8x.$$

Conclusion:

$$2x(x + 4) = 2x^2 + 8x$$

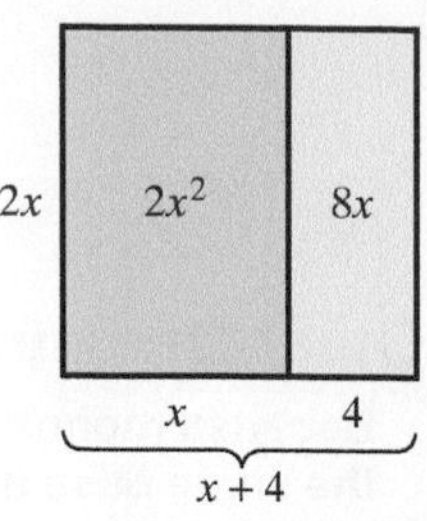

Figure 5

 **CHECK POINT 5** Multiply:

a. $3x(x + 5)$ **b.** $6x^2(5x^3 - 2x + 3)$.

6 Multiply polynomials when neither is a monomial.

Multiplying Polynomials when Neither Is a Monomial

How do we multiply two polynomials if neither is a monomial? For example, consider

$$(2x + 3)(x^2 + 4x + 5).$$

Binomial Trinomial

One way to perform this multiplication is to distribute $2x$ throughout the trinomial

$$2x(x^2 + 4x + 5)$$

and 3 throughout the trinomial

$$3(x^2 + 4x + 5).$$

Then combine the like terms that result. In general, the product of two polynomials is the polynomial obtained by multiplying each term of one polynomial by each term of the other polynomial and then combining like terms.

Multiplying Polynomials when Neither Is a Monomial

Multiply each term of one polynomial by each term of the other polynomial. Then combine like terms.

Using Technology

Graphic Connections

The graphs of

$y_1 = (x + 3)(x + 2)$

and $y_2 = x^2 + 5x + 6$

are the same.

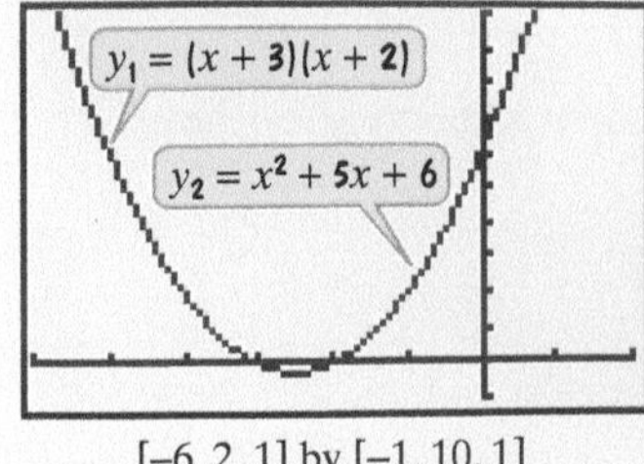

[−6, 2, 1] by [−1, 10, 1]

This verifies that

$(x + 3)(x + 2) = x^2 + 5x + 6.$

EXAMPLE 6 Multiplying Binomials

Multiply: **a.** $(x + 3)(x + 2)$ **b.** $(3x + 7)(2x - 4)$.

Solution We begin by multiplying each term of the second binomial by each term of the first binomial.

a. $(x + 3)(x + 2)$

$= x(x + 2) + 3(x + 2)$ — Multiply the second binomial by each term of the first binomial.

$= x \cdot x + x \cdot 2 + 3 \cdot x + 3 \cdot 2$ — Use the distributive property.

$= x^2 + 2x + 3x + 6$ — Multiply. Note that $x \cdot x = x^1 \cdot x^1 = x^{1+1} = x^2$.

$= x^2 + 5x + 6$ — Combine like terms.

b. $(3x + 7)(2x - 4)$

$= 3x(2x - 4) + 7(2x - 4)$ Multiply the second binomial by each term of the first binomial.

$= 3x \cdot 2x - 3x \cdot 4 + 7 \cdot 2x - 7 \cdot 4$ Use the distributive property.

$= 6x^2 - 12x + 14x - 28$ Multiply.

$= 6x^2 + 2x - 28$ Combine like terms. ■

✓ **CHECK POINT 6** Multiply:

a. $(x + 4)(x + 5)$ **b.** $(5x + 3)(2x - 7)$.

You can visualize the polynomial multiplication in Example 6(a), $(x + 3)(x + 2) = x^2 + 5x + 6$, by analyzing the areas in **Figure 6**.

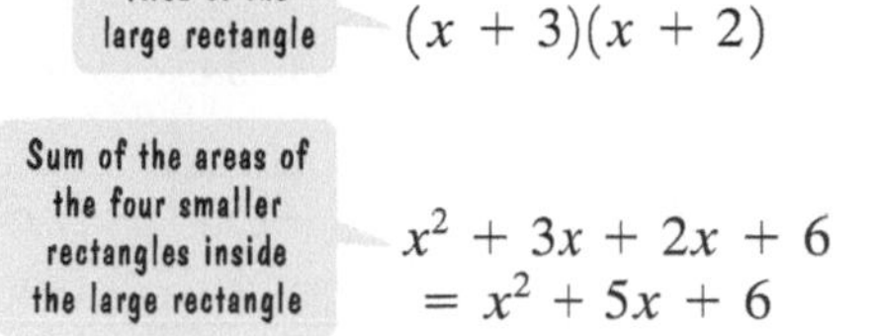

Area of the large rectangle
$(x + 3)(x + 2)$
Sum of the areas of the four smaller rectangles inside the large rectangle
$x^2 + 3x + 2x + 6$
$= x^2 + 5x + 6$

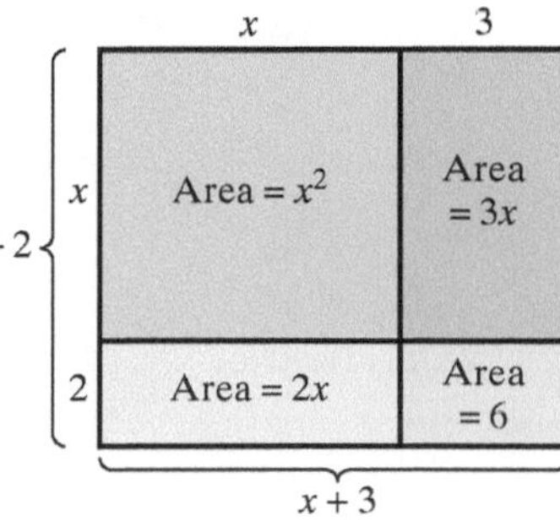

Figure 6

Conclusion:

$$(x + 3)(x + 2) = x^2 + 5x + 6$$

EXAMPLE 7 Multiplying a Binomial and a Trinomial

Multiply: $(2x + 3)(x^2 + 4x + 5)$.

Solution

$(2x + 3)(x^2 + 4x + 5)$

$= 2x(x^2 + 4x + 5) + 3(x^2 + 4x + 5)$ Multiply the trinomial by each term of the binomial.

$= 2x \cdot x^2 + 2x \cdot 4x + 2x \cdot 5 + 3x^2 + 3 \cdot 4x + 3 \cdot 5$ Use the distributive property.

$= 2x^3 + 8x^2 + 10x + 3x^2 + 12x + 15$ Multiply monomials: Multiply coefficients and add exponents.

$= 2x^3 + 11x^2 + 22x + 15$ Combine like terms: $8x^2 + 3x^2 = 11x^2$ and $10x + 12x = 22x$. ■

✓ **CHECK POINT 7** Multiply: $(5x + 2)(x^2 - 4x + 3)$.

Another method for solving Example 7 is to use a vertical format similar to that used for multiplying whole numbers.

$$\begin{array}{rrrr} & x^2 & + 4x & + 5 \\ & & 2x & + 3 \\ \hline & 3x^2 & + 12x & + 15 \\ 2x^3 + & 8x^2 & + 10x & \\ \hline 2x^3 + & 11x^2 & + 22x & + 15 \end{array}$$

Write like terms in the same column. ($3x^2 + 12x + 15$ is $3(x^2 + 4x + 5)$; $2x^3 + 8x^2 + 10x$ is $2x(x^2 + 4x + 5)$.) Combine like terms.

EXAMPLE 8 Multiplying Polynomials Using a Vertical Format

Multiply: $(2x^2 - 3x)(5x^3 - 4x^2 + 7x)$.

Solution To use the vertical format to find $(2x^2 - 3x)(5x^3 - 4x^2 + 7x)$, it is most convenient to write the polynomial with the greater number of terms in the top row.

$$\begin{array}{r} 5x^3 - 4x^2 + 7x \\ 2x^2 - 3x \\ \hline \end{array}$$

We now multiply each term in the top polynomial by the last term in the bottom polynomial.

$$\begin{array}{rrrr} & 5x^3 - & 4x^2 + & 7x \\ & & 2x^2 - & 3x \\ \hline -15x^4 + & 12x^3 - & 21x^2 & \end{array}$$

$-3x(5x^3 - 4x^2 + 7x)$

Then we multiply each term in the top polynomial by $2x^2$, the first term in the bottom polynomial. Like terms are placed in columns because the final step involves combining them.

Write like terms in the same column.

$$\begin{array}{rrrrr} & & 5x^3 - & 4x^2 + & 7x \\ & & & 2x^2 - & 3x \\ \hline & -15x^4 + & 12x^3 & - 21x^2 & \\ 10x^5 - & 8x^4 + & 14x^3 & & \\ \hline 10x^5 - & 23x^4 + & 26x^3 & - 21x^2 & \end{array}$$

$-3x(5x^3 - 4x^2 + 7x)$

$2x^2(5x^3 - 4x^2 + 7x)$

Combine like terms, which are lined up in columns. ■

✓ **CHECK POINT 8** Multiply using a vertical format: $(3x^2 - 2x)(2x^3 - 5x^2 + 4x)$.

CONCEPT AND VOCABULARY CHECK

Fill in each blank so that the resulting statement is true.

1. The product rule for exponents states that $b^m \cdot b^n =$ ____________. When multiplying exponential expressions with the same base, ____________ the exponents.
2. The power rule for exponents states that $(b^m)^n =$ ____________. When an exponential expression is raised to a power, ____________the exponents.
3. The products-to-powers rule for exponents states that $(ab)^n =$ ____________. When a product is raised to a power, raise each ____________ to the power.
4. To multiply $2x^2(x^2 + 5x + 7)$, use the ____________ property to multiply each term of the polynomial ____________ by the monomial ____________.
5. To multiply $(4x + 7)(x^2 + 8x + 3)$, begin by multiplying each term of $x^2 + 8x + 3$ by ____________. Then multiply each term of $x^2 + 8x + 3$ by ____________. Then combine ____________ terms.

2 EXERCISE SET

MyMathLab®

Watch the videos in MyMathLab

Download the MyDashBoard App

Practice Exercises

In Exercises 1–8, multiply each expression using the product rule.

1. $x^{15} \cdot x^3$
2. $x^{12} \cdot x^4$
3. $y \cdot y^{11}$
4. $y \cdot y^{19}$
5. $x^2 \cdot x^6 \cdot x^3$
6. $x^4 \cdot x^3 \cdot x^5$
7. $7^9 \cdot 7^{10}$
8. $8^7 \cdot 8^{10}$

In Exercises 9–14, simplify each expression using the power rule.

9. $(6^9)^{10}$
10. $(6^7)^{10}$
11. $(x^{15})^3$
12. $(x^{12})^4$
13. $[(-20)^3]^3$
14. $[(-50)^4]^4$

In Exercises 15–24, simplify each expression using the products-to-powers rule.

15. $(2x)^3$ **16.** $(4x)^3$

17. $(-5x)^2$ **18.** $(-6x)^2$

19. $(4x^3)^2$ **20.** $(6x^3)^2$

21. $(-2y^6)^4$ **22.** $(-2y^5)^4$

23. $(-2x^7)^5$ **24.** $(-2x^{11})^5$

In Exercises 25–34, multiply the monomials.

25. $(7x)(2x)$ **26.** $(8x)(3x)$

27. $(6x)(4x^2)$ **28.** $(10x)(3x^2)$

29. $(-5y^4)(3y^3)$ **30.** $(-6y^4)(2y^3)$

31. $\left(-\frac{1}{2}a^3\right)\left(-\frac{1}{4}a^2\right)$ **32.** $\left(-\frac{1}{3}a^4\right)\left(-\frac{1}{2}a^2\right)$

33. $(2x^2)(-3x)(8x^4)$ **34.** $(3x^3)(-2x)(5x^6)$

In Exercises 35–54, find each product of the monomial and the polynomial.

35. $4x(x + 3)$ **36.** $6x(x + 5)$

37. $x(x - 3)$ **38.** $x(x - 7)$

39. $2x(x - 6)$ **40.** $3x(x - 5)$

41. $-4y(3y + 5)$

42. $-5y(6y + 7)$

43. $4x^2(x + 2)$

44. $5x^2(x + 6)$

45. $2y^2(y^2 + 3y)$

46. $4y^2(y^2 + 2y)$

47. $2y^2(3y^2 - 4y + 7)$

48. $4y^2(5y^2 - 6y + 3)$

49. $(3x^3 + 4x^2)(2x)$

50. $(4x^3 + 5x^2)(2x)$

51. $(x^2 + 5x - 3)(-2x)$

52. $(x^3 - 2x + 2)(-4x)$

53. $-3x^2(-4x^2 + x - 5)$

54. $-6x^2(3x^2 - 2x - 7)$

In Exercises 55–78, find each product. In each case, neither factor is a monomial.

55. $(x + 3)(x + 5)$

56. $(x + 4)(x + 6)$

57. $(2x + 1)(x + 4)$

58. $(2x + 5)(x + 3)$

59. $(x + 3)(x - 5)$

60. $(x + 4)(x - 6)$

61. $(x - 11)(x + 9)$

62. $(x - 12)(x + 8)$

63. $(2x - 5)(x + 4)$

64. $(3x - 4)(x + 5)$

65. $\left(\frac{1}{4}x + 4\right)\left(\frac{3}{4}x - 1\right)$

66. $\left(\frac{1}{5}x + 5\right)\left(\frac{3}{5}x - 1\right)$

67. $(x + 1)(x^2 + 2x + 3)$

68. $(x + 2)(x^2 + x + 5)$

69. $(y - 3)(y^2 - 3y + 4)$

70. $(y - 2)(y^2 - 4y + 3)$

71. $(2a - 3)(a^2 - 3a + 5)$

72. $(2a - 1)(a^2 - 4a + 3)$

73. $(x + 1)(x^3 + 2x^2 + 3x + 4)$

74. $(x + 1)(x^3 + 4x^2 + 7x + 3)$

75. $\left(x - \frac{1}{2}\right)(4x^3 - 2x^2 + 5x - 6)$

76. $\left(x - \frac{1}{3}\right)(3x^3 - 6x^2 + 5x - 9)$

77. $(x^2 + 2x + 1)(x^2 - x + 2)$

78. $(x^2 + 3x + 1)(x^2 - 2x - 1)$

In Exercises 79–92, use a vertical format to find each product.

79. $\begin{array}{r} x^2 - 5x + 3 \\ \underline{x + 8} \end{array}$

80. $\begin{array}{r} x^2 - 7x + 9 \\ \underline{x + 4} \end{array}$

81. $\begin{array}{r} x^2 - 3x + 9 \\ \underline{2x - 3} \end{array}$

82. $\begin{array}{r} y^2 - 5y + 3 \\ \underline{4y - 5} \end{array}$

83. $\begin{array}{r} 2x^3 + x^2 + 2x + 3 \\ \underline{x + 4} \end{array}$

84. $\begin{array}{r} 3y^3 + 2y^2 + y + 4 \\ \underline{y + 3} \end{array}$

85. $\begin{array}{r} 4z^3 - 2z^2 + 5z - 4 \\ \underline{3z - 2} \end{array}$

86. $\begin{array}{r} 5z^3 - 3z^2 + 4z - 3 \\ \underline{2z - 4} \end{array}$

87. $\begin{array}{r} 7x^3 - 5x^2 + 6x \\ \underline{3x^2 - 4x} \end{array}$

88. $\begin{array}{r} 9y^3 - 7y^2 + 5y \\ \underline{3y^2 + 5y} \end{array}$

89. $\begin{array}{r} 2y^5 - 3y^3 + y^2 - 2y + 3 \\ \underline{2y - 1} \end{array}$

90. $\begin{array}{r} n^4 - n^3 + n^2 - n + 1 \\ \underline{2n + 3} \end{array}$

91. $\begin{array}{r} x^2 + 7x - 3 \\ \underline{x^2 - x - 1} \end{array}$

92. $\begin{array}{r} x^2 + 6x - 4 \\ \underline{x^2 - x - 2} \end{array}$

Practice PLUS

In Exercises 93–100, perform the indicated operations.

93. $(x + 4)(x - 5) - (x + 3)(x - 6)$
94. $(x + 5)(x - 6) - (x + 2)(x - 9)$
95. $4x^2(5x^3 + 3x - 2) - 5x^3(x^2 - 6)$
96. $3x^2(6x^3 + 2x - 3) - 4x^3(x^2 - 5)$
97. $(y + 1)(y^2 - y + 1) + (y - 1)(y^2 + y + 1)$
98. $(y + 1)(y^2 - y + 1) - (y - 1)(y^2 + y + 1)$
99. $(y + 6)^2 - (y - 2)^2$
100. $(y + 5)^2 - (y - 4)^2$

Application Exercises

101. Find a trinomial for the area of the rectangular rug shown below whose sides are $x + 5$ feet and $2x - 3$ feet.

102. The base of a triangular sail is $4x$ feet and its height is $3x + 10$ feet. Write a binomial in terms of x for the area of the sail.

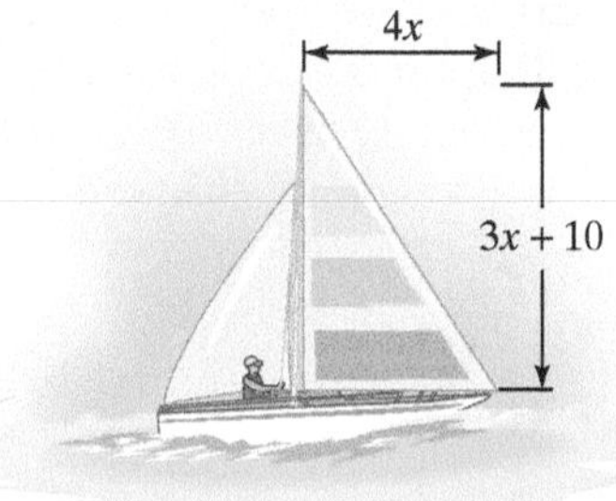

In Exercises 103–104,

a. *Express the area of the large rectangle as the product of two binomials.*
b. *Find the sum of the areas of the four smaller rectangles.*
c. *Use polynomial multiplication to show that your expressions for area in parts (a) and (b) are equal.*

103.

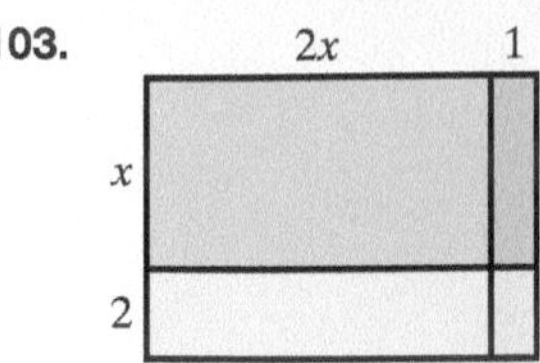

104.

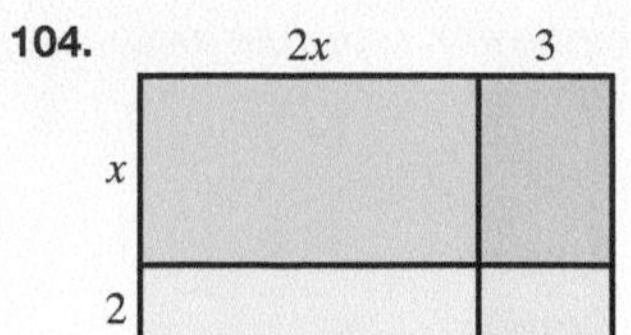

Writing in Mathematics

105. Explain the product rule for exponents. Use $2^3 \cdot 2^5$ in your explanation.
106. Explain the power rule for exponents. Use $(3^2)^4$ in your explanation.
107. Explain how to simplify an expression that involves a product raised to a power. Provide an example with your explanation.
108. Explain how to multiply monomials. Give an example.
109. Explain how to multiply a monomial and a polynomial that is not a monomial. Give an example.
110. Explain how to multiply polynomials when neither is a monomial. Give an example.
111. Explain the difference between performing these two operations:

$$2x^2 + 3x^2 \quad \text{and} \quad (2x^2)(3x^2).$$

112. Discuss situations in which a vertical format, rather than a horizontal format, is useful for multiplying polynomials.

Critical Thinking Exercises

Make Sense? *In Exercises 113–116, determine whether each statement "makes sense" or "does not make sense" and explain your reasoning.*

113. I'm working with two monomials that I cannot add, although I can multiply them.
114. I'm working with two monomials that I can add, although I cannot multiply them.
115. Other than multiplying monomials, the distributive property is used to multiply other kinds of polynomials.
116. I used the product rule for exponents to multiply x^7 and y^9.

In Exercises 117–120, determine whether each statement is true or false. If the statement is false, make the necessary change(s) to produce a true statement.

117. $4x^3 \cdot 3x^4 = 12x^{12}$
118. $5x^2 \cdot 4x^6 = 9x^8$
119. $(y - 1)(y^2 + y + 1) = y^3 - 1$
120. Some polynomial multiplications can only be performed by using a vertical format.

121. Find a polynomial in descending powers of x representing the area of the shaded region.

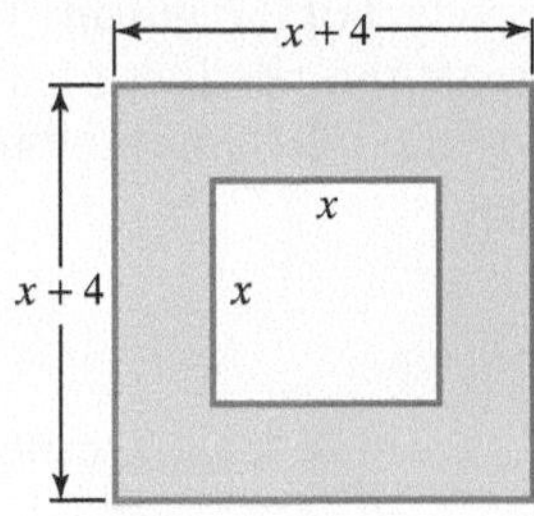

122. Find each of the products in parts (a)–(c).

a. $(x - 1)(x + 1)$

b. $(x - 1)(x^2 + x + 1)$

c. $(x - 1)(x^3 + x^2 + x + 1)$

d. Using the pattern found in parts (a)–(c), find $(x - 1)(x^4 + x^3 + x^2 + x + 1)$ without actually multiplying.

123. Find the missing factor.

$$(\_\_\_)\left(-\frac{1}{4}xy^3\right) = 2x^5y^3$$

Review Exercises

124. Solve: $4x - 7 > 9x - 2$.

125. Graph $3x - 2y = 6$ using intercepts.

126. Find the slope of the line passing through the points $(-2, 8)$ and $(1, 6)$.

Preview Exercises

Exercises 127–129 will help you prepare for the material covered in the next section. In each exercise, find the indicated products. Then, if possible, state a fast method for finding these products. (You may already be familiar with some of these methods from a high school algebra course.)

127. a. $(x + 3)(x + 4)$

b. $(x + 5)(x + 20)$

128. a. $(x + 3)(x - 3)$

b. $(x + 5)(x - 5)$

129. a. $(x + 3)^2$

b. $(x + 5)^2$

SECTION 3

Special Products

Objectives

1. Use FOIL in polynomial multiplication.
2. Multiply the sum and difference of two terms.
3. Find the square of a binomial sum.
4. Find the square of a binomial difference.

Everett Collection

Let's cut to the chase. Are there fast methods for finding products of polynomials? The answer is beepingly "yes." (Or should that be $(\text{BEEP})^2$ yes?) In this section, we'll cut to the chase by using the distributive property to develop patterns that will let you multiply certain binomials quite rapidly.

1 Use FOIL in polynomial multiplication.

The Product of Two Binomials: FOIL

Frequently, we need to find the product of two binomials. One way to perform this multiplication is to distribute each term in the first binomial through the second binomial. For example, we can find the product of the binomials $3x + 2$ and $4x + 5$ as follows:

$$\begin{aligned}(3x + 2)(4x + 5) &= 3x(4x + 5) + 2(4x + 5)\\ &= 3x(4x) + 3x(5) + 2(4x) + 2(5)\\ &= 12x^2 + 15x + 8x + 10.\end{aligned}$$

Distribute $3x$ over $4x + 5$.

Distribute 2 over $4x + 5$.

We'll combine these like terms later. For now, our interest is in how to obtain *each* of these four terms.

We can also find the product of $3x + 2$ and $4x + 5$ using a method called FOIL, which is based on our work shown on the previous page. Any two binomials can be quickly multiplied by using the FOIL method, in which **F** represents the product of the **first** terms in each binomial, **O** represents the product of the **outside** terms, **I** represents the product of the **inside** terms, and **L** represents the product of the **last**, or second, terms in each binomial. For example, we can use the FOIL method to find the product of the binomials $3x + 2$ and $4x + 5$ as follows:

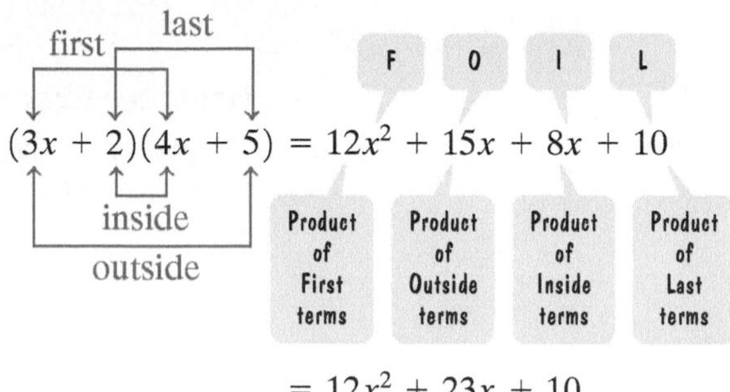

$= 12x^2 + 23x + 10$ Combine like terms.

In general, here's how to use the FOIL method to find the product of $ax + b$ and $cx + d$:

Using the FOIL Method to Multiply Binomials

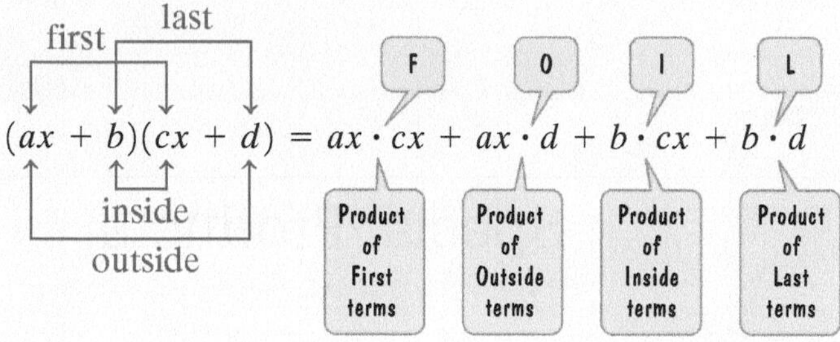

EXAMPLE 1 Using the FOIL Method

Multiply: $(x + 3)(x + 4)$.

Solution

F: First terms $= x \cdot x = x^2$ $(x + 3)(x + 4)$

O: Outside terms $= x \cdot 4 = 4x$ $(x + 3)(x + 4)$

I: Inside terms $= 3 \cdot x = 3x$ $(x + 3)(x + 4)$

L: Last terms $= 3 \cdot 4 = 12$ $(x + 3)(x + 4)$

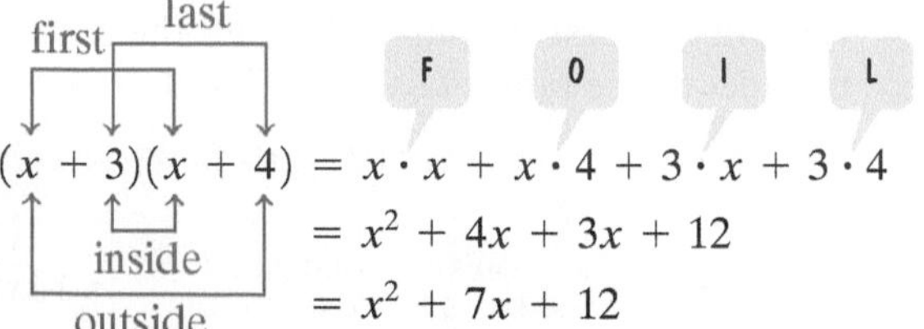

$$(x + 3)(x + 4) = x \cdot x + x \cdot 4 + 3 \cdot x + 3 \cdot 4$$
$$= x^2 + 4x + 3x + 12$$
$$= x^2 + 7x + 12$$

Combine like terms. ■

✓ **CHECK POINT 1** Multiply: $(x + 5)(x + 6)$.

EXAMPLE 2 Using the FOIL Method

Multiply: $(3x + 4)(5x - 3)$.

Solution

first, last, inside, outside; F O I L

$$(3x + 4)(5x - 3) = 3x \cdot 5x + 3x(-3) + 4 \cdot 5x + 4(-3)$$
$$= 15x^2 - 9x + 20x - 12$$
$$= 15x^2 + 11x - 12 \quad \text{Combine like terms.}$$

CHECK POINT 2 Multiply: $(7x + 5)(4x - 3)$.

EXAMPLE 3 Using the FOIL Method

Multiply: $(2 - 5x)(3 - 4x)$.

Solution

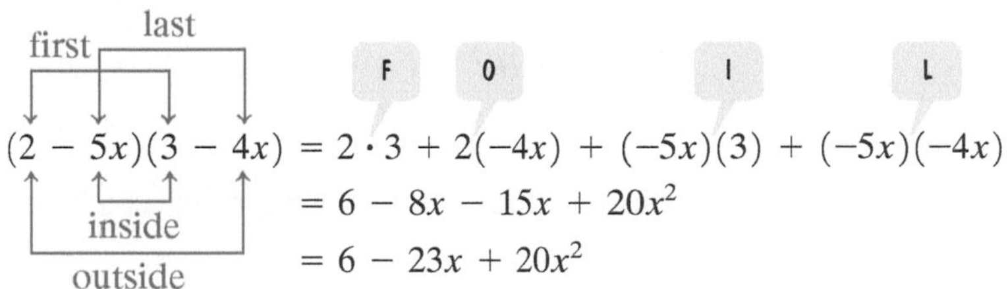

The product can also be expressed in standard form as $20x^2 - 23x + 6$. ■

CHECK POINT 3 Multiply: $(4 - 2x)(5 - 3x)$.

---

2 Multiply the sum and difference of two terms.

Multiplying the Sum and Difference of Two Terms

We can use the FOIL method to multiply $A + B$ and $A - B$ as follows:

F O I L

$$(A + B)(A - B) = A^2 - AB + AB - B^2 = A^2 - B^2.$$

Notice that the outside and inside products have a sum of 0 and the terms cancel. The FOIL multiplication provides us with a quick rule for multiplying the sum and difference of two terms, referred to as a *special-product formula.*

The Product of the Sum and Difference of Two Terms

$$(A + B)(A - B) = A^2 - B^2$$

The product of the sum and the difference of the same two terms | is | the square of the first term minus the square of the second term.

EXAMPLE 4 Finding the Product of the Sum and Difference of Two Terms

Multiply: **a.** $(4y + 3)(4y - 3)$ **b.** $(3x - 7)(3x + 7)$ **c.** $(5a^4 + 6)(5a^4 - 6)$.

Solution Use the special-product formula shown.

$$(A+B)(A-B) = A^2 - B^2$$

First term squared − Second term squared = Product

a. $(4y+3)(4y-3) = (4y)^2 - 3^2 = 16y^2 - 9$

b. $(3x-7)(3x+7) = (3x)^2 - 7^2 = 9x^2 - 49$

c. $(5a^4+6)(5a^4-6) = (5a^4)^2 - 6^2 = 25a^8 - 36$ ■

✓ **CHECK POINT 4** Multiply: **a.** $(7y+8)(7y-8)$ **b.** $(4x-5)(4x+5)$ **c.** $(2a^3+3)(2a^3-3)$.

3 Find the square of a binomial sum.

The Square of a Binomial

Let's now find $(A+B)^2$, the square of a binomial sum. To do so, we begin with the FOIL method and look for a general rule.

F O I L

$$(A+B)^2 = (A+B)(A+B) = A \cdot A + A \cdot B + A \cdot B + B \cdot B$$
$$= A^2 + 2AB + B^2$$

This result implies the following rule, which is another example of a special-product formula:

The Square of a Binomial Sum

$$(A+B)^2 = A^2 + 2AB + B^2$$

The square of a binomial sum is first term squared plus 2 times the product of the terms plus last term squared.

Great Question!

When finding $(x+3)^2$, why can't I just write $x^2 + 3^2$, or $x^2 + 9$?

Caution! The square of a sum is *not* the sum of the squares.

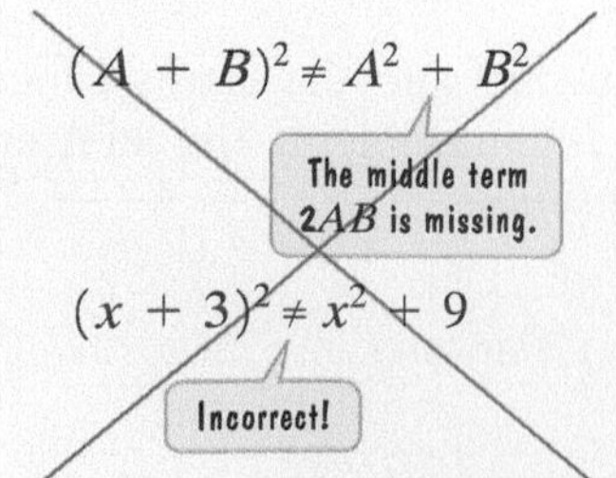

$(A+B)^2 \neq A^2 + B^2$
The middle term 2AB is missing.
$(x+3)^2 \neq x^2 + 9$
Incorrect!

Show that $(x+3)^2$ and x^2+9 are not equal by substituting 5 for x in each expression and simplifying.

EXAMPLE 5 Finding the Square of a Binomial Sum

Multiply:

a. $(x+3)^2$ **b.** $(3x+7)^2$.

Solution Use the special-product formula shown.

$$(A+B)^2 = A^2 + 2AB + B^2$$

	(First Term)^2	+	2 · Product of the Terms	+	(Last Term)^2	= Product
a. $(x+3)^2 =$	x^2	+	$2 \cdot x \cdot 3$	+	3^2	$= x^2 + 6x + 9$
b. $(3x+7)^2 =$	$(3x)^2$	+	$2(3x)(7)$	+	7^2	$= 9x^2 + 42x + 49$

■

✓ **CHECK POINT 5** Multiply:

a. $(x+10)^2$ **b.** $(5x+4)^2$.

The formula for the square of a binomial sum can be interpreted geometrically by analyzing the areas in **Figure 7**.

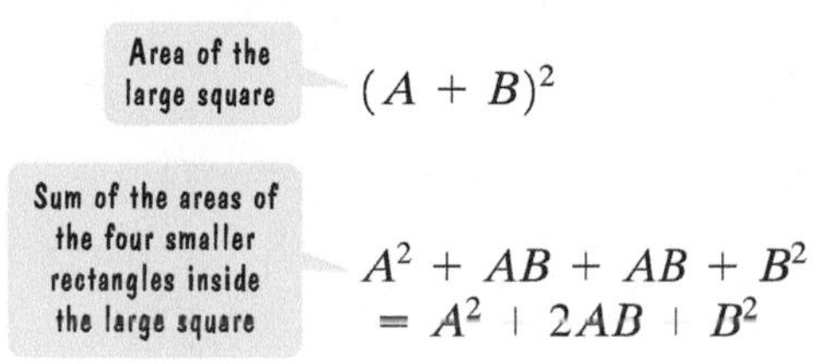

Area of the large square
$(A + B)^2$
Sum of the areas of the four smaller rectangles inside the large square
$A^2 + AB + AB + B^2$
$= A^2 + 2AB + B^2$

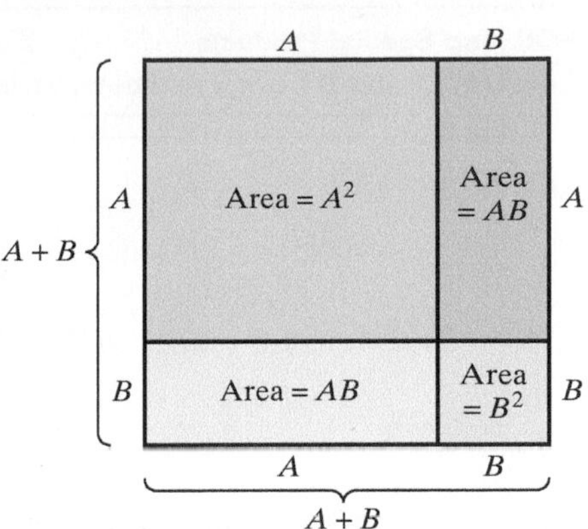

Figure 7

Conclusion:

$$(A + B)^2 = A^2 + 2AB + B^2$$

4 Find the square of a binomial difference.

A similar pattern occurs for $(A - B)^2$, the square of a binomial difference. Using the FOIL method on $(A - B)^2$, we obtain the following rule:

The Square of a Binomial Difference

$$(A - B)^2 = A^2 - 2AB + B^2$$

The square of a binomial difference is first term squared minus 2 times the product of the terms plus last term squared.

EXAMPLE 6 Finding the Square of a Binomial Difference

Multiply:

a. $(x - 4)^2$ **b.** $(5y - 6)^2$.

Solution

Use the special-product formula shown.

$(A - B)^2 =$	A^2	$-$	$2AB$	$+$	B^2	
	(First Term)^2	$-$	**2 · Product of the Terms**	$+$	**(Last Term)^2**	**= Product**
a. $(x - 4)^2 =$	x^2	$-$	$2 \cdot x \cdot 4$	$+$	4^2	$= x^2 - 8x + 16$
b. $(5y - 6)^2 =$	$(5y)^2$	$-$	$2(5y)(6)$	$+$	6^2	$= 25y^2 - 60y + 36$

✓ **CHECK POINT 6** Multiply:

a. $(x - 9)^2$ **b.** $(7x - 3)^2$.

The table at the top of the next page summarizes the FOIL method and the three special products. The special products occur so frequently in algebra that it is convenient to memorize the form or pattern of these formulas.

FOIL and Special Products
Let *A, B, C,* and *D* be real numbers, variables, or algebraic expressions.

FOIL	*Example*
F O I L $(A + B)(C + D) = AC + AD + BC + BD$	F O I L $(2x + 3)(4x + 5) = (2x)(4x) + (2x)(5) + (3)(4x) + (3)(5)$ $= 8x^2 + 10x + 12x + 15$ $= 8x^2 + 22x + 15$
Sum and Difference of Two Terms $(A + B)(A - B) = A^2 - B^2$	***Example*** $(2x + 3)(2x - 3) = (2x)^2 - 3^2$ $= 4x^2 - 9$
Square of a Binomial $(A + B)^2 = A^2 + 2AB + B^2$ $(A - B)^2 = A^2 - 2AB + B^2$	***Example*** $(2x + 3)^2 = (2x)^2 + 2(2x)(3) + 3^2$ $= 4x^2 + 12x + 9$ $(2x - 3)^2 = (2x)^2 - 2(2x)(3) + 3^2$ $= 4x^2 - 12x + 9$

Achieving Success

Manage your time. Use a day planner such as the one shown below. (Go online and search "day planner" or "day scheduler" to find a schedule grid that you can print and use.)

Sample Day Planner

	Monday	Tuesday	Wednesday	Thursday	Friday	Saturday	Sunday
5:00 A.M.							
6:00 A.M.							
7:00 A.M.							
8:00 A.M.							
9:00 A.M.							
10:00 A.M.							
11:00 A.M.							
12:00 P.M.							
1:00 P.M.							
2:00 P.M.							
3:00 P.M.							
4:00 P.M.							
5:00 P.M.							
6:00 P.M.							
7:00 P.M.							
8:00 P.M.							
9:00 P.M.							
10:00 P.M.							
11:00 P.M.							
Midnight							

- On the Sunday before the week begins, fill in the time slots with fixed items such as school, extracurricular activities, work, etc.
- Because your education should be a top priority, decide what times you would like to study and do homework. Fill in these activities on the day planner.
- Plan other flexible activities such as exercise, socializing, etc. around the times already established.
- Be flexible. Things may come up that are unavoidable or some items may take longer than planned. However, be honest with yourself: Playing video games with friends is not "unavoidable."
- Stick to your schedule. At the end of the week, you will look back and be impressed at all the things you have accomplished.

CONCEPT AND VOCABULARY CHECK

Fill in each blank so that the resulting statement is true.

1. For $(x + 5)(2x + 3)$, the product of the first terms is ______________, the product of the outside terms is ______________, the product of the inside terms is ______________, and the product of the last terms is ______________.
2. $(A + B)(A - B) =$ ______________. The product of the sum and the difference of the same two terms is the square of the first term ______________ the square of the second term.
3. $(A + B)^2 =$ ______________. The square of a binomial sum is the first term ______________ plus 2 times the ______________ plus the last term ______________.
4. $(A - B)^2 =$ ______________. The square of a binomial difference is the first term squared ______________ 2 times the ______________ plus the last term ______________.
5. True or false: $(x + 5)(x - 5) = x^2 - 25$. ______________
6. True or false: $(x + 5)^2 = x^2 + 25$. ______________

3 EXERCISE SET

MyMathLab®

Watch the videos in MyMathLab

Download the MyDashBoard App

Practice Exercises

In Exercises 1–24, use the FOIL method to find each product. Express the product in descending powers of the variable.

1. $(x + 4)(x + 6)$
2. $(x + 8)(x + 2)$
3. $(y - 7)(y + 3)$
4. $(y - 3)(y + 4)$
5. $(2x - 3)(x + 5)$
6. $(3x - 5)(x + 7)$
7. $(4y + 3)(y - 1)$
8. $(5y + 4)(y - 2)$
9. $(2x - 3)(5x + 3)$
10. $(2x - 5)(7x + 2)$
11. $(3y - 7)(4y - 5)$
12. $(4y - 5)(7y - 4)$
13. $(7 + 3x)(1 - 5x)$
14. $(2 + 5x)(1 - 4x)$
15. $(5 - 3y)(6 - 2y)$
16. $(7 - 2y)(10 - 3y)$
17. $(5x^2 - 4)(3x^2 - 7)$
18. $(7x^2 - 2)(3x^2 - 5)$
19. $(6x - 5)(2 - x)$
20. $(4x - 3)(2 - x)$
21. $(x + 5)(x^2 + 3)$
22. $(x + 4)(x^2 + 5)$
23. $(8x^3 + 3)(x^2 + 5)$
24. $(7x^3 + 5)(x^2 + 2)$

In Exercises 25–44, multiply using the rule for finding the product of the sum and difference of two terms.

25. $(x + 3)(x - 3)$
26. $(y + 5)(y - 5)$
27. $(3x + 2)(3x - 2)$
28. $(2x + 5)(2x - 5)$
29. $(3r - 4)(3r + 4)$
30. $(5z - 2)(5z + 2)$
31. $(3 + r)(3 - r)$
32. $(4 + s)(4 - s)$
33. $(5 - 7x)(5 + 7x)$
34. $(4 - 3y)(4 + 3y)$
35. $\left(2x + \frac{1}{2}\right)\left(2x - \frac{1}{2}\right)$
36. $\left(3y + \frac{1}{3}\right)\left(3y - \frac{1}{3}\right)$
37. $(y^2 + 1)(y^2 - 1)$
38. $(y^2 + 2)(y^2 - 2)$
39. $(r^3 + 2)(r^3 - 2)$
40. $(m^3 + 4)(m^3 - 4)$
41. $(1 - y^4)(1 + y^4)$
42. $(2 - s^5)(2 + s^5)$
43. $(x^{10} + 5)(x^{10} - 5)$
44. $(x^{12} + 3)(x^{12} - 3)$

In Exercises 45–62, multiply using the rules for the square of a binomial.

45. $(x + 2)^2$
46. $(x + 5)^2$
47. $(2x + 5)^2$
48. $(5x + 2)^2$

49. $(x - 3)^2$

50. $(x - 6)^2$

51. $(3y - 4)^2$

52. $(4y - 3)^2$

53. $(4x^2 - 1)^2$

54. $(5x^2 - 3)^2$

55. $(7 - 2x)^2$

56. $(9 - 5x)^2$

57. $\left(2x + \frac{1}{2}\right)^2$

58. $\left(3x + \frac{1}{3}\right)^2$

59. $\left(4y - \frac{1}{4}\right)^2$

60. $\left(2y - \frac{1}{2}\right)^2$

61. $(x^8 + 3)^2$

62. $(x^8 + 5)^2$

In Exercises 63–82, multiply using the method of your choice.

63. $(x - 1)(x^2 + x + 1)$

64. $(x + 1)(x^2 - x + 1)$

65. $(x - 1)^2$

66. $(x + 1)^2$

67. $(3y + 7)(3y - 7)$

68. $(4y + 9)(4y - 9)$

69. $3x^2(4x^2 + x + 9)$

70. $5x^2(7x^2 + x + 6)$

71. $(7y + 3)(10y - 4)$

72. $(8y + 3)(10y - 5)$

73. $(x^2 + 1)^2$

74. $(x^2 + 2)^2$

75. $(x^2 + 1)(x^2 + 2)$

76. $(x^2 + 2)(x^2 + 3)$

77. $(x^2 + 4)(x^2 - 4)$

78. $(x^2 + 5)(x^2 - 5)$

79. $(2 - 3x^5)^2$

80. $(2 - 3x^6)^2$

81. $\left(\frac{1}{4}x^2 + 12\right)\left(\frac{3}{4}x^2 - 8\right)$

82. $\left(\frac{1}{4}x^2 + 16\right)\left(\frac{3}{4}x^2 - 4\right)$

In Exercises 83–88, find the area of each shaded region. Write the answer as a polynomial in descending powers of x.

83.

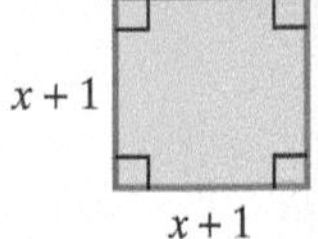

84.

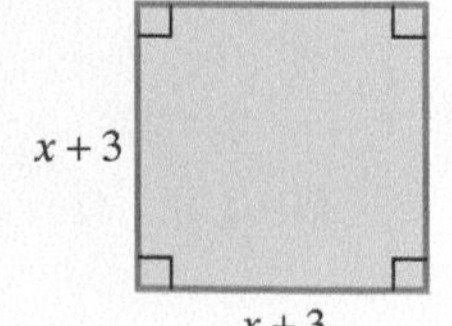

85.

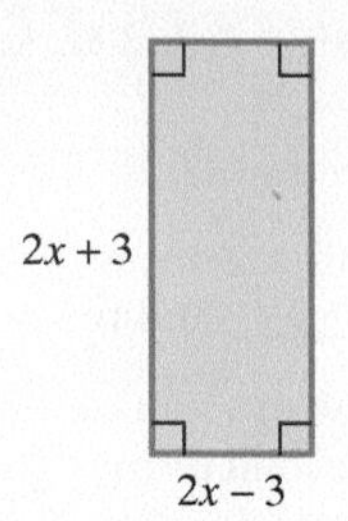

86.

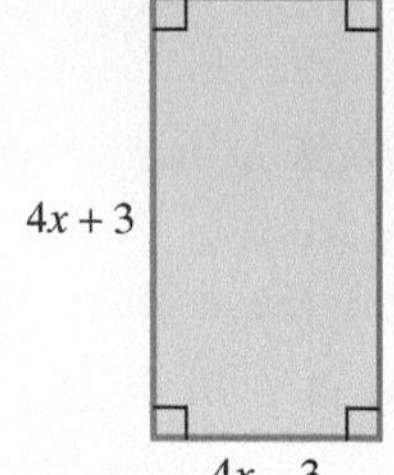

87.

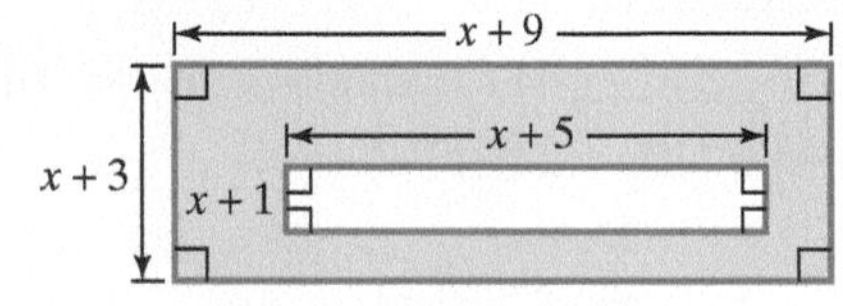

88.

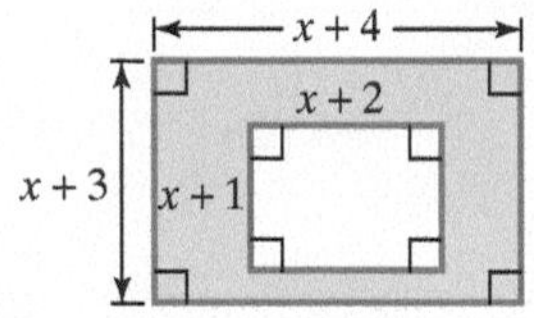

Practice PLUS

In Exercises 89–96, multiply by the method of your choice.

89. $[(2x + 3)(2x - 3)]^2$

90. $[(3x + 2)(3x - 2)]^2$

91. $(4x^2 + 1)[(2x + 1)(2x - 1)]$

92. $(9x^2 + 1)[(3x + 1)(3x - 1)]$

93. $(x + 2)^3$

94. $(x + 4)^3$

95. $[(x + 3) - y][(x + 3) + y]$

96. $[(x + 5) - y][(x + 5) + y]$

Application Exercises

The square garden shown in the figure measures x yards on each side. The garden is to be expanded so that one side is increased by 2 yards and an adjacent side is increased by 1 yard.

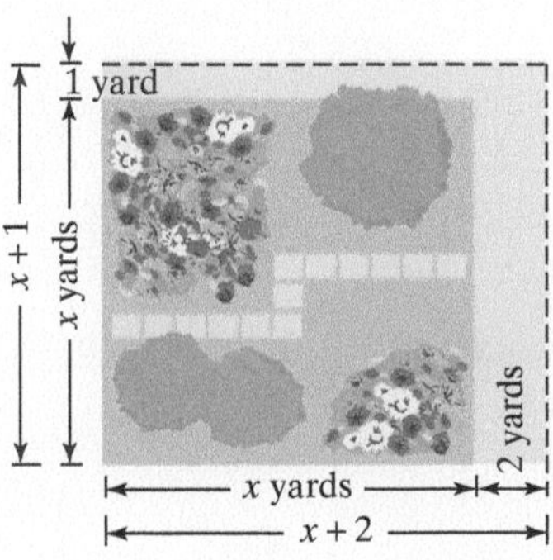

The graph shows the area of the expanded garden, y, in terms of the length of one of its original sides, x. Use this information to solve Exercises 97–100.

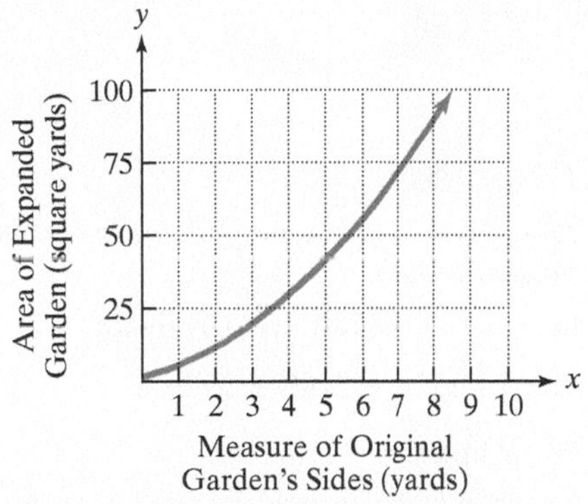

97. Use the gardens pictured at the bottom of the previous page to write a product of two binomials that expresses the area of the larger garden.

98. Use the gardens pictured at the bottom of the previous page to write a polynomial in descending powers of x that expresses the area of the larger garden.

99. If the original garden measures 6 yards on a side, use your expression from Exercise 97 to find the area of the larger garden. Then identify your solution as a point on the graph shown above.

100. If the original garden measures 8 yards on a side, use your polynomial from Exercise 98 to find the area of the larger garden. Then identify your solution as a point on the graph shown above.

The square painting in the figure measures x inches on each side. The painting is uniformly surrounded by a frame that measures 1 inch wide. Use this information to solve Exercises 101–102.

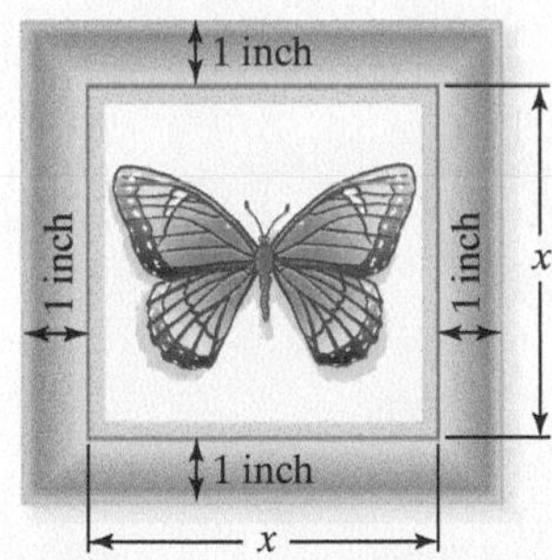

101. Write a polynomial in descending powers of x that expresses the area of the square that includes the painting and the frame.

102. Write an algebraic expression that describes the area of the frame. (*Hint*: The area of the frame is the area of the square that includes the painting and the frame minus the area of the painting.)

Writing in Mathematics

103. Explain how to multiply two binomials using the FOIL method. Give an example with your explanation.

104. Explain how to find the product of the sum and difference of two terms. Give an example with your explanation.

105. Explain how to square a binomial sum. Give an example with your explanation.

106. Explain how to square a binomial difference. Give an example with your explanation.

107. Explain why the graph for Exercises 97–100 is shown only in quadrant I.

Critical Thinking Exercises

Make Sense? *In Exercises 108–111, determine whether each statement "makes sense" or "does not make sense" and explain your reasoning.*

108. Squaring a binomial sum is as simple as squaring each of the two terms and then writing their sum.

109. I can distribute the exponent 2 on each factor of $(5x)^2$, but I cannot do the same thing on each term of $(x + 5)^2$.

110. Instead of using the formula for the square of a binomial sum, I prefer to write the binomial sum twice and then apply the FOIL method.

111. Special-product formulas for $(A + B)(A - B)$, $(A + B)^2$, and $(A - B)^2$ have patterns that make their multiplications quicker than using the FOIL method.

In Exercises 112–115, determine whether each statement is true or false. If the statement is false, make the necessary change(s) to produce a true statement.

112. $(3 + 4)^2 = 3^2 + 4^2$

113. $(2y + 7)^2 = 4y^2 + 28y + 49$

114. $(3x^2 + 2)(3x^2 - 2) = 9x^2 - 4$

115. $(x - 5)^2 = x^2 - 5x + 25$

116. What two binomials must be multiplied using the FOIL method to give a product of $x^2 - 8x - 20$?

117. Express the volume of the box as a polynomial in standard form.

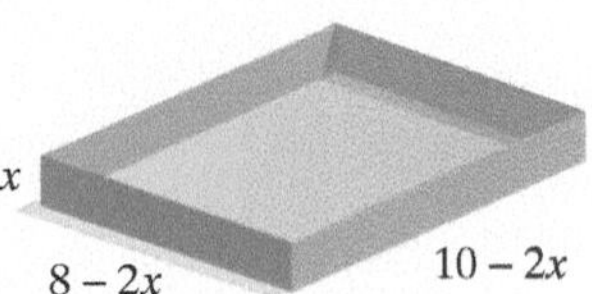

118. Express the area of the plane figure shown as a polynomial in standard form.

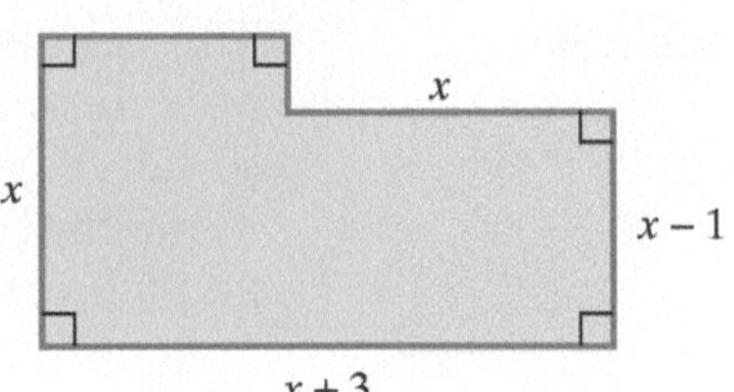

Technology Exercises

In Exercises 119–122, use a graphing utility to graph each side of the equation in the same viewing rectangle. (Call the left side y_1 and the right side y_2.) If the graphs coincide, verify that the multiplication has been performed correctly. If the graphs do not appear to coincide, this indicates that the multiplication is incorrect. In these exercises, correct the right side of the equation. Then graph the left side and the corrected right side to verify that the graphs coincide.

119. $(x + 1)^2 = x^2 + 1$; Use a $[-5, 5, 1]$ by $[0, 20, 1]$ viewing rectangle.

120. $(x + 2)^2 = x^2 + 2x + 4$; Use a $[-6, 5, 1]$ by $[0, 20, 1]$ viewing rectangle.

121. $(x + 1)(x - 1) = x^2 - 1$; Use a $[-6, 5, 1]$ by $[-2, 18, 1]$ viewing rectangle.

122. $(x - 2)(x + 2) + 4 = x^2$; Use a $[-6, 5, 1]$ by $[-2, 18, 1]$ viewing rectangle.

Review Exercises

In Exercises 123–124, solve each system by the method of your choice.

123. $\begin{cases} 2x + 3y = 1 \\ y = 3x - 7 \end{cases}$

124. $\begin{cases} 3x + 4y = 7 \\ 2x + 7y = 9 \end{cases}$

125. Graph: $y \le \frac{1}{3}x$.

Preview Exercises

Exercises 126–128 will help you prepare for the material covered in the next section.

126. Use the order of operations to evaluate

$$x^3y + 2xy^2 + 5x - 2$$

for $x = -2$ and $y = 3$.

127. Use the second step to combine the like terms.

$$5xy + 6xy = (5 + 6)xy = ?$$

128. Multiply using FOIL: $(x + 2y)(3x + 5y)$.

SECTION 4

Polynomials in Several Variables

Objectives

1. Evaluate polynomials in several variables.
2. Understand the vocabulary of polynomials in two variables.
3. Add and subtract polynomials in several variables.
4. Multiply polynomials in several variables.

Exactostock/SuperStock

The next time you visit a lumberyard and go rummaging through piles of wood, think *polynomials*, although polynomials a bit different from those we have encountered so far. The construction industry uses a polynomial in two variables to determine the number of board feet that can be manufactured from a tree with a diameter of x inches and a length of y feet. This polynomial is

$$\frac{1}{4}x^2y - 2xy + 4y.$$

We call a polynomial containing two or more variables a **polynomial in several variables**. These polynomials can be evaluated, added, subtracted, and multiplied just like polynomials that contain only one variable.

1 Evaluate polynomials in several variables.

Evaluating a Polynomial in Several Variables

Two steps can be used to evaluate a polynomial in several variables.

Evaluating a Polynomial in Several Variables

1. Substitute the given value for each variable.
2. Perform the resulting computation using the order of operations.

EXAMPLE 1 Evaluating a Polynomial in Two Variables

Evaluate $2x^3y + xy^2 + 7x - 3$ for $x = -2$ and $y = 3$.

Solution We begin by substituting -2 for x and 3 for y in the polynomial.

$2x^3y + xy^2 + 7x - 3$ This is the given polynomial.

$= 2(-2)^3 \cdot 3 + (-2) \cdot 3^2 + 7(-2) - 3$ Replace x with -2 and y with 3.

$= 2(-8) \cdot 3 + (-2) \cdot 9 + 7(-2) - 3$ Evaluate exponential expressions: $(-2)^3 = (-2)(-2)(-2) = -8$ and $3^2 = 3 \cdot 3 = 9$.

$= -48 + (-18) + (-14) - 3$ Perform the indicated multiplications.

$= -83$ Add from left to right. ■

✓ **CHECK POINT 1** Evaluate $3x^3y + xy^2 + 5y + 6$ for $x = -1$ and $y = 5$.

---

2 Understand the vocabulary of polynomials in two variables.

Describing Polynomials in Two Variables

In this section, we will limit our discussion of polynomials in several variables to two variables.

In general, a **polynomial in two variables**, x and y, contains the sum of one or more monomials in the form ax^ny^m. The constant, a, is the **coefficient**. The exponents, n and m, represent whole numbers. The **degree** of the monomial ax^ny^m is $n + m$. We'll use the polynomial from the construction industry to illustrate these ideas.

The coefficients are $\frac{1}{4}$, -2, and 4.

$$\frac{1}{4}x^2y \quad - 2xy \quad + 4y$$

Degree of monomial: $2 + 1 = 3$ | Degree of monomial: $1 + 1 = 2$ | Degree of monomial: 1

The **degree of a polynomial in two variables** is the highest degree of all its terms. For the preceding polynomial, the degree is 3.

EXAMPLE 2 Using the Vocabulary of Polynomials

Determine the coefficient of each term, the degree of each term, and the degree of the polynomial:

$$7x^2y^3 - 17x^4y^2 + xy - 6y^2 + 9.$$

Solution

Term	Coefficient	Degree (Sum of Exponents on the Variables)
$7x^2y^3$	7	$2 + 3 = 5$
$-17x^4y^2$	−17	$4 + 2 = 6$
xy	1	$1 + 1 = 2$
$-6y^2$	−6	2
9	9	0

Think of xy as $1x^1y^1$.

The degree of the polynomial is the highest degree of all its terms, which is 6. ■

✓ **CHECK POINT 2** Determine the coefficient of each term, the degree of each term, and the degree of the polynomial:

$$8x^4y^5 - 7x^3y^2 - x^2y - 5x + 11.$$

3 Add and subtract polynomials in several variables.

Adding and Subtracting Polynomials in Several Variables

Polynomials in several variables are added by combining like terms. For example, we can add the monomials $-7xy^2$ and $13xy^2$ as follows:

$$-7xy^2 + 13xy^2 = (-7 + 13)xy^2 = 6xy^2.$$

These like terms both contain the variable factors x and y^2.

Add coefficients and keep the same variable factors, xy^2.

EXAMPLE 3 Adding Polynomials in Two Variables

Add: $(6xy^2 - 5xy + 7) + (9xy^2 + 2xy - 6)$.

Solution

$(6xy^2 - 5xy + 7) + (9xy^2 + 2xy - 6)$

$= (6xy^2 + 9xy^2) + (-5xy + 2xy) + (7 - 6)$ Group like terms.

$= 15xy^2 - 3xy + 1$ Combine like terms by adding coefficients and keeping the same variable factors. ■

✓ **CHECK POINT 3** Add: $(-8x^2y - 3xy + 6) + (10x^2y + 5xy - 10)$.

We subtract polynomials in two variables just as we did when subtracting polynomials in one variable. Add the first polynomial and the opposite of the polynomial being subtracted.

EXAMPLE 4 Subtracting Polynomials in Two Variables

Subtract:

$$(5x^3 - 9x^2y + 3xy^2 - 4) - (3x^3 - 6x^2y - 2xy^2 + 3).$$

Solution

$(5x^3 - 9x^2y + 3xy^2 - 4) - (3x^3 - 6x^2y - 2xy^2 + 3)$

Change the sign of each coefficient.

$= (5x^3 - 9x^2y + 3xy^2 - 4) + (-3x^3 + 6x^2y + 2xy^2 - 3)$ Add the opposite of the polynomial being subtracted.

$= (5x^3 - 3x^3) + (-9x^2y + 6x^2y) + (3xy^2 + 2xy^2) + (-4 - 3)$ Group like terms.

$= 2x^3 - 3x^2y + 5xy^2 - 7$ Combine like terms by adding coefficients and keeping the same variable factors. ■

✓ **CHECK POINT 4** Subtract: $(7x^3 - 10x^2y + 2xy^2 - 5) - (4x^3 - 12x^2y - 3xy^2 + 5)$.

4 Multiply polynomials in several variables.

Multiplying Polynomials in Several Variables

The product of monomials forms the basis of polynomial multiplication. As with monomials in one variable, multiplication can be done mentally by multiplying coefficients and adding exponents on variables with the same base.

EXAMPLE 5 Multiplying Monomials

Multiply: $(7x^2y)(5x^3y^2)$.

Solution

$(7x^2y)(5x^3y^2)$

$= (7 \cdot 5)(x^2 \cdot x^3)(y \cdot y^2)$ This regrouping can be worked mentally.

$= 35x^{2+3}y^{1+2}$ Multiply coefficients and add exponents on variables with the same base.

$= 35x^5y^3$ Simplify. ■

✓ **CHECK POINT 5** Multiply: $(6xy^3)(10x^4y^2)$.

How do we multiply a monomial and a polynomial that is not a monomial? As we did with polynomials in one variable, multiply each term of the polynomial by the monomial.

EXAMPLE 6 Multiplying a Monomial and a Polynomial

Multiply: $3x^2y(4x^3y^2 - 6x^2y + 2)$.

Solution

$3x^2y(4x^3y^2 - 6x^2y + 2)$

$= 3x^2y \cdot 4x^3y^2 - 3x^2y \cdot 6x^2y + 3x^2y \cdot 2$ Use the distributive property.

$= 12x^{2+3}y^{1+2} - 18x^{2+2}y^{1+1} + 6x^2y$ Multiply coefficients and add exponents on variables with the same base.

$= 12x^5y^3 - 18x^4y^2 + 6x^2y$ Simplify. ■

✓ **CHECK POINT 6** Multiply: $6xy^2(10x^4y^5 - 2x^2y + 3)$.

FOIL and the special-products formulas can be used to multiply polynomials in several variables.

EXAMPLE 7 Multiplying Polynomials in Two Variables

Multiply: **a.** $(x + 4y)(3x - 5y)$ **b.** $(5x + 3y)^2$.

Solution We will perform the multiplication in part (a) using the FOIL method. We will multiply in part (b) using the formula for the square of a binomial, $(A + B)^2$.

a. $(x + 4y)(3x - 5y)$ Multiply these binomials using the FOIL method.

F O I L

$$= (x)(3x) + (x)(-5y) + (4y)(3x) + (4y)(-5y)$$
$$= 3x^2 - 5xy + 12xy - 20y^2$$
$$= 3x^2 + 7xy - 20y^2$$ Combine like terms.

$$(A + B)^2 = A^2 + 2 \cdot A \cdot B + B^2$$

b. $(5x + 3y)^2 = (5x)^2 + 2(5x)(3y) + (3y)^2$
$$= 25x^2 + 30xy + 9y^2$$ ■

✓ **CHECK POINT 7** Multiply:
a. $(7x - 6y)(3x - y)$ **b.** $(2x + 4y)^2$.

EXAMPLE 8 Multiplying Polynomials in Two Variables

Multiply: **a.** $(4x^2y + 3y)(4x^2y - 3y)$ **b.** $(x + y)(x^2 - xy + y^2)$.

Solution We perform the multiplication in part (a) using the formula for the product of the sum and difference of two terms. We perform the multiplication in part (b) by multiplying each term of the trinomial, $x^2 - xy + y^2$, by x and y, respectively, and then adding like terms.

$$(A + B) \cdot (A - B) = A^2 - B^2$$

a. $(4x^2y + 3y)(4x^2y - 3y) = (4x^2y)^2 - (3y)^2$
$$= 16x^4y^2 - 9y^2$$

b. $(x + y)(x^2 - xy + y^2)$

$$= x(x^2 - xy + y^2) + y(x^2 - xy + y^2)$$ Multiply the trinomial by each term of the binomial.

$$= x \cdot x^2 - x \cdot xy + x \cdot y^2 + y \cdot x^2 - y \cdot xy + y \cdot y^2$$ Use the distributive property.

$$= x^3 - x^2y + xy^2 + x^2y - xy^2 + y^3$$ Add exponents on variables with the same base.

$$= x^3 + y^3$$ Combine like terms: $-x^2y + x^2y = 0$ and $xy^2 - xy^2 = 0$. ■

✓ **CHECK POINT 8** Multiply:
a. $(6xy^2 + 5x)(6xy^2 - 5x)$ **b.** $(x - y)(x^2 + xy + y^2)$.

CONCEPT AND VOCABULARY CHECK

Fill in each blank so that the resulting statement is true.

1. The coefficient of the monomial $-18x^4y^2$ is ____________.
2. The degree of the monomial $-18x^4y^2$ is ____________.
3. The coefficient of the monomial ax^ny^m is ____________ and the degree is ____________.
4. The degree of x^3y^2 is ____________ and the degree of x^2y^7 is ____________, so the degree of $x^3y^2 - 8x^2y^7$ is ____________.
5. True or false: The monomials $7xy^2$ and $2x^2y$ can be added. ____________
6. True or false: The monomials $7xy^2$ and $2x^2y$ can be multiplied. ____________

4 EXERCISE SET

MyMathLab®

Watch the videos in MyMathLab

Download the MyDashBoard App

Practice Exercises

In Exercises 1–6, evaluate each polynomial for $x = 2$ and $y = -3$.

1. $x^2 + 2xy + y^2$
2. $x^2 + 3xy + y^2$
3. $xy^3 - xy + 1$
4. $x^3y - xy + 2$
5. $2x^2y - 5y + 3$
6. $3x^2y - 4y + 5$

In Exercises 7–8, determine the coefficient of each term, the degree of each term, and the degree of the polynomial.

7. $x^3y^2 - 5x^2y^7 + 6y^2 - 3$
8. $12x^4y - 5x^3y^7 - x^2 + 4$

In Exercises 9–20, add or subtract as indicated.

9. $(5x^2y - 3xy) + (2x^2y - xy)$
10. $(-2x^2y + xy) + (4x^2y + 7xy)$
11. $(4x^2y + 8xy + 11) + (-2x^2y + 5xy + 2)$
12. $(7x^2y + 5xy + 13) + (-3x^2y + 6xy + 4)$
13. $(7x^4y^2 - 5x^2y^2 + 3xy) + (-18x^4y^2 - 6x^2y^2 - xy)$
14. $(6x^4y^2 - 10x^2y^2 + 7xy) + (-12x^4y^2 - 3x^2y^2 - xy)$
15. $(x^3 + 7xy - 5y^2) - (6x^3 - xy + 4y^2)$
16. $(x^4 - 7xy - 5y^3) - (6x^4 - 3xy + 4y^3)$
17. $(3x^4y^2 + 5x^3y - 3y) - (2x^4y^2 - 3x^3y - 4y + 6x)$
18. $(5x^4y^2 + 6x^3y - 7y) - (3x^4y^2 - 5x^3y - 6y + 8x)$
19. $(x^3 - y^3) - (-4x^3 - x^2y + xy^2 + 3y^3)$
20. $(x^3 - y^3) - (-6x^3 + x^2y - xy^2 + 2y^3)$
21. Add: $\begin{array}{r} 5x^2y^2 - 4xy^2 + 6y^2 \\ \underline{-8x^2y^2 + 5xy^2 - y^2} \end{array}$
22. Add: $\begin{array}{r} 7a^2b^2 - 5ab^2 + 6b^2 \\ \underline{-10a^2b^2 + 6ab^2 + 6b^2} \end{array}$
23. Subtract: $\begin{array}{r} 3a^2b^4 - 5ab^2 + 7ab \\ \underline{-(-5a^2b^4 - 8ab^2 - ab)} \end{array}$
24. Subtract: $\begin{array}{r} 13x^2y^4 - 17xy^2 + xy \\ \underline{-(-7x^2y^4 - 8xy^2 - xy)} \end{array}$
25. Subtract $11x - 5y$ from the sum of $7x + 13y$ and $-26x + 19y$.
26. Subtract $23x - 5y$ from the sum of $6x + 15y$ and $x - 19y$.

In Exercises 27–76, find each product.

27. $(5x^2y)(8xy)$
28. $(10x^2y)(5xy)$
29. $(-8x^3y^4)(3x^2y^5)$
30. $(7x^4y^5)(-10x^7y^{11})$
31. $9xy(5x + 2y)$
32. $7xy(8x + 3y)$
33. $5xy^2(10x^2 - 3y)$
34. $6x^2y(5x^2 - 9y)$
35. $4ab^2(7a^2b^3 + 2ab)$
36. $2ab^2(20a^2b^3 + 11ab)$
37. $-b(a^2 - ab + b^2)$
38. $-b(a^3 - ab + b^3)$
39. $(x + 5y)(7x + 3y)$
40. $(x + 9y)(6x + 7y)$
41. $(x - 3y)(2x + 7y)$
42. $(3x - y)(2x + 5y)$
43. $(3xy - 1)(5xy + 2)$
44. $(7xy + 1)(2xy - 3)$
45. $(2x + 3y)^2$
46. $(2x + 5y)^2$
47. $(xy - 3)^2$

48. $(xy - 5)^2$
49. $(x^2 + y^2)^2$
50. $(2x^2 + y^2)^2$
51. $(x^2 - 2y^2)^2$
52. $(x^2 - y^2)^2$
53. $(3x + y)(3x - y)$
54. $(x + 5y)(x - 5y)$
55. $(ab + 1)(ab - 1)$
56. $(ab + 2)(ab - 2)$
57. $(x + y^2)(x - y^2)$
58. $(x^2 + y)(x^2 - y)$
59. $(3a^2b + a)(3a^2b - a)$
60. $(5a^2b + a)(5a^2b - a)$
61. $(3xy^2 - 4y)(3xy^2 + 4y)$
62. $(7xy^2 - 10y)(7xy^2 + 10y)$
63. $(a + b)(a^2 - b^2)$
64. $(a - b)(a^2 + b^2)$
65. $(x + y)(x^2 + 3xy + y^2)$
66. $(x + y)(x^2 + 5xy + y^2)$
67. $(x - y)(x^2 - 3xy + y^2)$
68. $(x - y)(x^2 - 4xy + y^2)$
69. $(xy + ab)(xy - ab)$
70. $(xy + ab^2)(xy - ab^2)$
71. $(x^2 + 1)(x^4y + x^2 + 1)$
72. $(x^2 + 1)(xy^4 + y^2 + 1)$
73. $(x^2y^2 - 3)^2$
74. $(x^2y^2 - 5)^2$
75. $(x + y + 1)(x + y - 1)$
76. $(x + y + 1)(x - y + 1)$

In Exercises 77–80, write a polynomial in two variables that describes the total area of each region shaded in blue. Express each polynomial as the sum or difference of terms.

77.

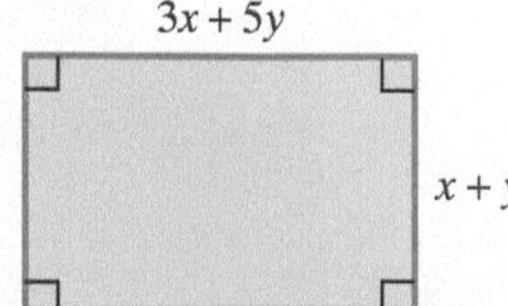

78.

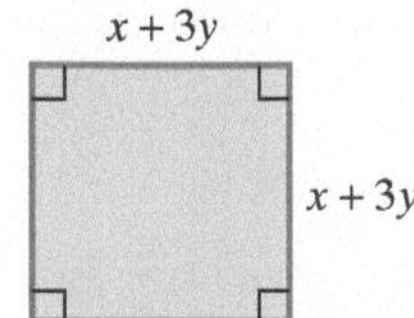

79.

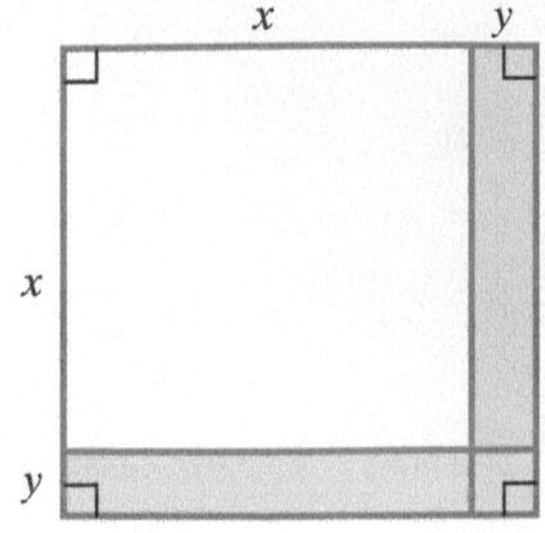

80.

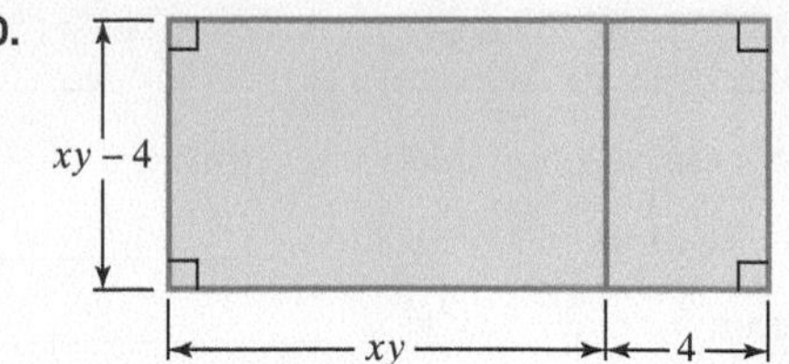

Practice PLUS

In Exercises 81–86, find each product. As we said in the Section 3 opener, cut to the chase in each part of the polynomial multiplication: Use only the special-product formula for the sum and difference of two terms or the formulas for the square of a binomial.

81. $[(x^3y^3 + 1)(x^3y^3 - 1)]^2$
82. $[(1 - a^3b^3)(1 + a^3b^3)]^2$
83. $(xy - 3)^2(xy + 3)^2$ (Do not begin by squaring a binomial.)
84. $(ab - 4)^2(ab + 4)^2$ (Do not begin by squaring a binomial.)
85. $[x + y + z][x - (y + z)]$
86. $(a - b - c)(a + b + c)$

Application Exercises

87. The number of board feet, N, that can be manufactured from a tree with a diameter of x inches and a length of y feet is modeled by the formula

$$N = \frac{1}{4}x^2y - 2xy + 4y.$$

A building contractor estimates that 3000 board feet of lumber is needed for a job. The lumber company has just milled a fresh load of timber from 20 trees that averaged 10 inches in diameter and 16 feet in length. Is this enough to complete the job? If not, how many additional board feet of lumber is needed?

88. The storage shed shown in the figure has a volume given by the polynomial

$$2x^2y + \frac{1}{2}\pi x^2y.$$

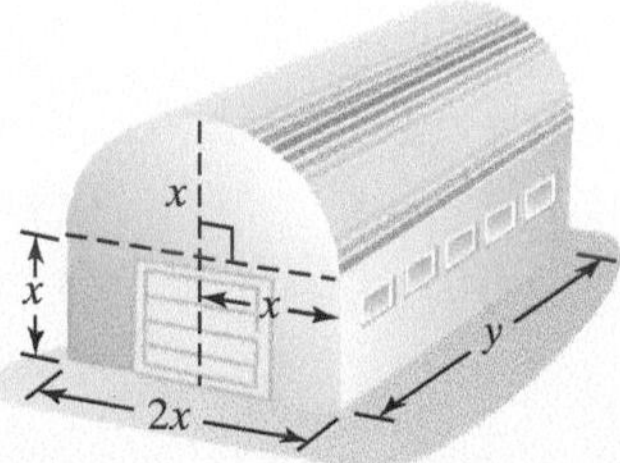

a. A small business is considering having a shed installed like the one shown in the figure. The shed's height, $2x$, is 26 feet and its length, y, is 27 feet. Using $x = 13$ and $y = 27$, find the volume of the storage shed.

b. The business requires at least 18,000 cubic feet of storage space. Should they construct the storage shed described in part (a)?

An object that is falling or vertically projected into the air has its height, in feet, above the ground given by

$$s = -16t^2 + v_0t + s_0,$$

where s is the height, in feet, v_0 is the original velocity of the object, in feet per second, t is the time the object is in motion, in seconds, and s_0 is the height, in feet, from which the object is dropped or projected. The figure shows that a ball is thrown straight up from a rooftop at an original velocity of 80 feet per second from a height of 96 feet. The ball misses the rooftop on its way down and eventually strikes the ground. Use the formula and this information to solve Exercises 89–91.

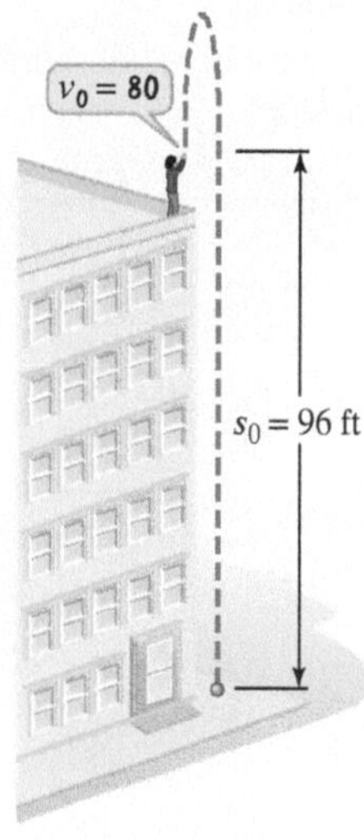

89. How high above the ground will the ball be 2 seconds after being thrown?

90. How high above the ground will the ball be 4 seconds after being thrown?

91. How high above the ground will the ball be 6 seconds after being thrown? Describe what this means in practical terms.

The graph visually displays the information about the thrown ball described in Exercises 89–91. The horizontal axis represents the ball's time in motion, in seconds. The vertical axis represents the ball's height above the ground, in feet. Use the graph to solve Exercises 92–97.

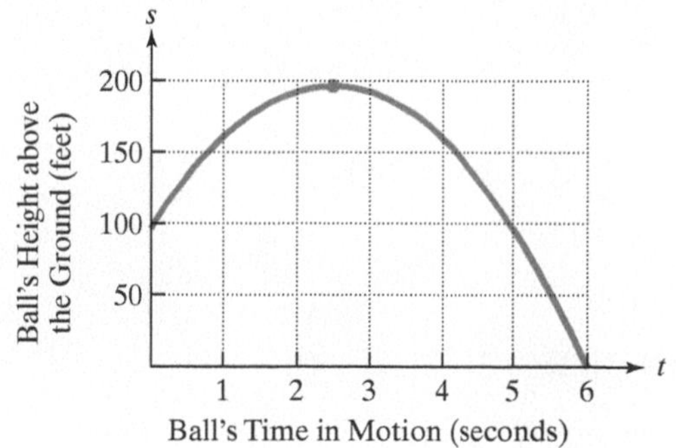

92. During which time period is the ball rising?

93. During which time period is the ball falling?

94. Identify your answer from Exercise 90 as a point on the graph.

95. Identify your answer from Exercise 89 as a point on the graph.

96. After how many seconds does the ball strike the ground?

97. After how many seconds does the ball reach its maximum height above the ground? What is a reasonable estimate of this maximum height?

Writing in Mathematics

98. What is a polynomial in two variables? Provide an example with your description.

99. Explain how to find the degree of a polynomial in two variables.

100. Suppose that you take up sky diving. Explain how to use the formula for Exercises 89–91 to determine your height above the ground at every instant of your fall.

Critical Thinking Exercises

Make Sense? *In Exercises 101–104, determine whether each statement "makes sense" or "does not make sense" and explain your reasoning.*

101. I use the same procedures for operations with polynomials in two variables as I did when performing these operations with polynomials in one variable.

102. Adding polynomials in several variables is the same as adding like terms.

103. I used FOIL to find the product of $x + y$ and $x^2 - xy + y^2$.

104. I used FOIL to multiply $5xy$ and $3xy + 4$.

In Exercises 105–108, determine whether each statement is true or false. If the statement is false, make the necessary change(s) to produce a true statement.

105. The degree of $5x^{24} - 3x^{16}y^9 - 7xy^2 + 6$ is 24.

106. In the polynomial $4x^2y + x^3y^2 + 3x^2y^3 + 7y$, the term x^3y^2 has degree 5 and no numerical coefficient.

107. $(2x + 3 - 5y)(2x + 3 + 5y) = 4x^2 + 12x + 9 - 25y^2$

108. $(6x^2y - 7xy - 4) - (6x^2y + 7xy - 4) = 0$

In Exercises 109–110, find a polynomial in two variables that describes the area of the region of each figure shaded in blue. Write the polynomial as the sum or difference of terms.

109.

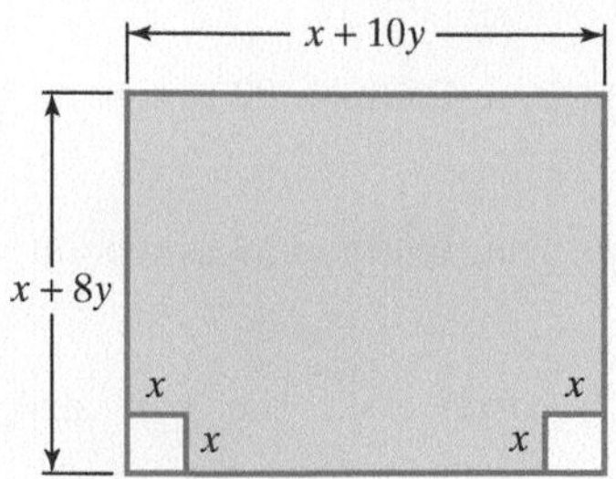

110.

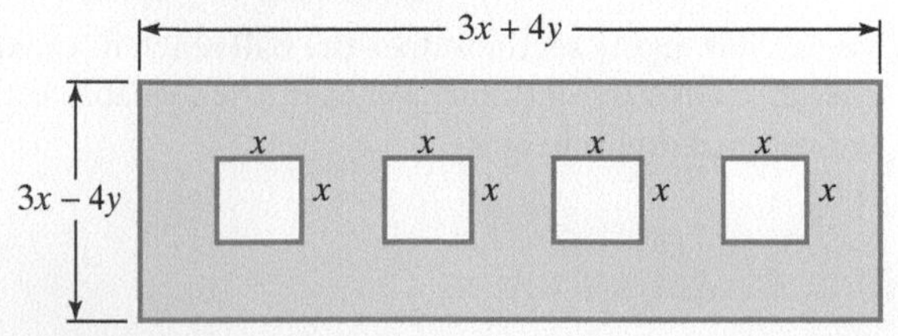

111. Use the formulas for the volume of a rectangular solid and a cylinder to derive the polynomial in Exercise 88 that describes the volume of the storage building.

Review Exercises

112. Solve for W: $R = \dfrac{L + 3W}{2}$.

113. Subtract: $-6.4 - (-10.2)$.

114. Solve: $0.02(x - 5) = 0.03 - 0.03(x + 7)$.

Preview Exercises

Exercises 115–117 will help you prepare for the material covered in the next section.

115. Find the missing exponent, designated by the question mark, in the final step.

$$\frac{x^7}{x^3} = \frac{\cancel{x}\cdot\cancel{x}\cdot\cancel{x}\cdot x\cdot x\cdot x\cdot x}{\cancel{x}\cdot\cancel{x}\cdot\cancel{x}} = x^?$$

116. Simplify: $\dfrac{(x^2)^3}{5^3}$.

117. Simplify: $\dfrac{(2a^3)^5}{(b^4)^5}$.

MID-CHAPTER CHECK POINT Section 1–Section 4

What You Know: We learned to add, subtract, and multiply polynomials. We used a number of fast methods for finding products of polynomials, including the FOIL method for multiplying binomials, a special-product formula for the product of the sum and difference of two terms $[(A + B)(A - B) = A^2 - B^2]$, and special-product formulas for squaring binomials $[(A + B)^2 = A^2 + 2AB + B^2; (A - B)^2 = A^2 - 2AB + B^2]$. Finally, we applied all of these operations to polynomials in several variables.

In Exercises 1–21, perform the indicated operations.

1. $(11x^2y^3)(-5x^2y^3)$
2. $11x^2y^3 - 5x^2y^3$
3. $(3x + 5)(4x - 7)$
4. $(3x + 5) - (4x - 7)$
5. $(2x - 5)(x^2 - 3x + 1)$
6. $(2x - 5) + (x^2 - 3x + 1)$
7. $(8x - 3)^2$
8. $(-10x^4)(-7x^5)$
9. $(x^2 + 2)(x^2 - 2)$
10. $(x^2 + 2)^2$
11. $(9a - 10b)(2a + b)$
12. $7x^2(10x^3 - 2x + 3)$
13. $(3a^2b^3 - ab + 4b^2) - (-2a^2b^3 - 3ab + 5b^2)$
14. $2(3y - 5)(3y + 5)$
15. $(-9x^3 + 5x^2 - 2x + 7) + (11x^3 - 6x^2 + 3x - 7)$
16. $10x^2 - 8xy - 3(y^2 - xy)$
17. $(-2x^5 + x^4 - 3x + 10) - (2x^5 - 6x^4 + 7x - 13)$
18. $(x + 3y)(x^2 - 3xy + 9y^2)$
19. $(5x^4 + 4)(2x^3 - 1)$
20. $(y - 6z)^2$
21. $(2x + 3)(2x - 3) - (5x + 4)(5x - 4)$
22. Graph: $y = 1 - x^2$.

SECTION 5

Dividing Polynomials

Objectives

1. Use the quotient rule for exponents.
2. Use the zero-exponent rule.
3. Use the quotients-to-powers rule.
4. Divide monomials.
5. Check polynomial division.
6. Divide a polynomial by a monomial.

In the dramatic arts, ours is the era of the movies. As individuals and as a nation, we've grown up with them. Our images of love, war, family, country—even of things that terrify us—owe much to what we've seen on screen. In this section's exercise set, we'll model our love for movies with polynomials and polynomial division. Before discussing polynomial division, we must develop some additional rules for working with exponents.

Warner Brothers/Everett Collection

1 Use the quotient rule for exponents.

The Quotient Rule for Exponents

Consider the quotient of two exponential expressions, such as the quotient of 2^7 and 2^3. We are dividing 7 factors of 2 by 3 factors of 2. We are left with 4 factors of 2:

$$\frac{2^7}{2^3} = \frac{2\cdot2\cdot2\cdot2\cdot2\cdot2\cdot2}{2\cdot2\cdot2} = \frac{\not{2}\cdot\not{2}\cdot\not{2}\cdot2\cdot2\cdot2\cdot2}{\not{2}\cdot\not{2}\cdot\not{2}} = 2\cdot2\cdot2\cdot2$$

7 factors of 2

3 factors of 2

Divide out pairs of factors: $\frac{2}{2} = 1$.

4 factors of 2

Thus,

$$\frac{2^7}{2^3} = 2^4.$$

We can quickly find the exponent, 4, on the quotient by subtracting the original exponents:

$$\frac{2^7}{2^3} = 2^{7-3}.$$

This suggests the following rule:

The Quotient Rule

$$\frac{b^m}{b^n} = b^{m-n}, \quad b \neq 0$$

When dividing exponential expressions with the same nonzero base, subtract the exponent in the denominator from the exponent in the numerator. Use this difference as the exponent of the common base.

EXAMPLE 1 Using the Quotient Rule

Divide each expression using the quotient rule:

a. $\frac{2^8}{2^4}$ **b.** $\frac{x^{13}}{x^3}$ **c.** $\frac{y^{15}}{y}$.

Solution

a. $\frac{2^8}{2^4} = 2^{8-4} = 2^4$ or 16

b. $\frac{x^{13}}{x^3} = x^{13-3} = x^{10}$

c. $\frac{y^{15}}{y} = \frac{y^{15}}{y^1} = y^{15-1} = y^{14}$ ■

✓ **CHECK POINT 1** Divide each expression using the quotient rule:

a. $\frac{5^{12}}{5^4}$ **b.** $\frac{x^9}{x^2}$ **c.** $\frac{y^{20}}{y}$.

---

2 Use the zero-exponent rule.

Zero as an Exponent

A nonzero base can be raised to the 0 power. The quotient rule can be used to help determine what zero as an exponent should mean. Consider the quotient of b^4 and b^4, where b is not zero. We can determine this quotient in two ways.

$$\frac{b^4}{b^4} = 1 \qquad \frac{b^4}{b^4} = b^{4-4} = b^0$$

Any nonzero expression divided by itself is 1.

Use the quotient rule and subtract exponents.

This means that b^0 must equal 1.

The Zero-Exponent Rule

If b is any real number other than 0,

$$b^0 = 1.$$

EXAMPLE 2 Using the Zero-Exponent Rule

Use the zero-exponent rule to simplify each expression:

a. 7^0 **b.** $(-5)^0$ **c.** -5^0 **d.** $10x^0$ **e.** $(10x)^0$.

Solution

a. $7^0 = 1$ Any nonzero number raised to the 0 power is 1.

b. $(-5)^0 = 1$ Any nonzero number raised to the 0 power is 1.

c. $-5^0 = -1$ $\quad -5^0 = -(5^0) = -1$

Only 5 is raised to the 0 power.

d. $10x^0 = 10 \cdot 1 = 10$

Only x is raised to the 0 power.

e. $(10x)^0 = 1$

The entire expression, $10x$, is raised to the 0 power. ■

✓ **CHECK POINT 2** Use the zero-exponent rule to simplify each expression:
a. 14^0 **b.** $(-10)^0$ **c.** -10^0 **d.** $20x^0$ **e.** $(20x)^0$.

3 Use the quotients-to-powers rule.

The Quotients-to-Powers Rule for Exponents

We have seen that when a product is raised to a power, we raise every factor in the product to the power:

$$(ab)^n = a^n b^n.$$

There is a similar property for raising a quotient to a power.

Quotients to Powers

If a and b are real numbers and b is nonzero, then

$$\left(\frac{a}{b}\right)^n = \frac{a^n}{b^n}.$$

When a quotient is raised to a power, raise the numerator to the power and divide by the denominator raised to the power.

EXAMPLE 3 Using the Quotients-to-Powers Rule

Simplify each expression using the quotients-to-powers rule:

a. $\left(\frac{x}{4}\right)^2$ **b.** $\left(\frac{x^2}{5}\right)^3$ **c.** $\left(\frac{2a^3}{b^4}\right)^5$.

Solution

a. $\left(\frac{x}{4}\right)^2 = \frac{x^2}{4^2} = \frac{x^2}{16}$ — Square the numerator and the denominator.

b. $\left(\frac{x^2}{5}\right)^3 = \frac{(x^2)^3}{5^3} = \frac{x^{2\cdot 3}}{5\cdot 5\cdot 5} = \frac{x^6}{125}$ — Cube the numerator and the denominator.

c. $\left(\frac{2a^3}{b^4}\right)^5 = \frac{(2a^3)^5}{(b^4)^5}$ — Raise the numerator and the denominator to the fifth power.

$= \frac{2^5(a^3)^5}{(b^4)^5}$ — Raise each factor in the numerator to the fifth power.

$= \frac{2^5 a^{3\cdot 5}}{b^{4\cdot 5}}$ — To raise exponential expressions to powers, multiply exponents: $(b^m)^n = b^{mn}$.

$= \frac{32a^{15}}{b^{20}}$ — Simplify. ■

CHECK POINT 3 Simplify each expression using the quotients-to-powers rule:

a. $\left(\frac{x}{5}\right)^2$ **b.** $\left(\frac{x^4}{2}\right)^3$ **c.** $\left(\frac{2a^{10}}{b^3}\right)^4$.

Great Question!

What are some common errors to avoid when using the quotient rule or the zero-exponent rule?

Here's a partial list. The first column shows the correct simplification. The second column illustrates a common error.

Correct	Incorrect	Description of Error
$\frac{2^{20}}{2^4} = 2^{20-4} = 2^{16}$	$\frac{2^{20}}{2^4} = 2^5$	Exponents should be subtracted, not divided.
$-8^0 = -1$	$-8^0 = 1$	Only 8 is raised to the 0 power.
$\left(\frac{x}{5}\right)^2 = \frac{x^2}{5^2} = \frac{x^2}{25}$	$\left(\frac{x}{5}\right)^2 = \frac{x^2}{5}$	The numerator and denominator must both be squared.

4 Divide monomials.

Dividing Monomials

Now that we have developed three additional properties of exponents, we are ready to turn to polynomial division. We begin with the quotient of two monomials, such as $16x^{14}$ and $8x^2$. This quotient is obtained by dividing the coefficients, 16 and 8, and then dividing the variables using the quotient rule for exponents.

$$\frac{16x^{14}}{8x^2} = \frac{16}{8}x^{14-2} = 2x^{12}$$

Divide coefficients and subtract exponents.

Dividing Monomials

To divide monomials, divide the coefficients and then divide the variables. Use the quotient rule for exponents to divide the variables: Keep the variable and subtract the exponents.

Great Question!

I notice that the exponents on x are the same in Example 4(b). Do I have to subtract exponents since I know the quotient of x^3 and x^3 is 1?

No. Rather than subtracting exponents for division that results in a 0 exponent, you might prefer to divide out x^3.

$$\frac{2x^3}{8x^3} = \frac{2}{8} = \frac{1}{4}$$

EXAMPLE 4 Dividing Monomials

Divide: **a.** $\frac{-12x^8}{4x^2}$ **b.** $\frac{2x^3}{8x^3}$ **c.** $\frac{15x^5y^4}{3x^2y}$.

Solution

a. $\frac{-12x^8}{4x^2} = \frac{-12}{4}x^{8-2} = -3x^6$

b. $\frac{2x^3}{8x^3} = \frac{2}{8}x^{3-3} = \frac{1}{4}x^0 = \frac{1}{4}\cdot 1 = \frac{1}{4}$

c. $\frac{15x^5y^4}{3x^2y} = \frac{15}{3}x^{5-2}y^{4-1} = 5x^3y^3$ ■

CHECK POINT 4 Divide:

a. $\frac{-20x^{12}}{10x^4}$ **b.** $\frac{3x^4}{15x^4}$ **c.** $\frac{9x^6y^5}{3xy^2}$.

5 Check polynomial division.

Checking Division of Polynomial Problems

The answer to a division problem can be checked. For example, consider the following problem:

$$\frac{15x^5y^4}{3x^2y} = 5x^3y^3.$$

Dividend: the polynomial you are dividing into

Divisor: the polynomial you are dividing by

Quotient: the answer to your division problem

The quotient is correct if the product of the divisor and the quotient is the dividend. Is the quotient shown in the preceding equation correct?

$$(3x^2y)(5x^3y^3) = 3 \cdot 5x^{2+3}y^{1+3} = 15x^5y^4$$

Divisor | Quotient | This is the dividend.

Because the product of the divisor and the quotient is the dividend, the answer to the division problem is correct.

Checking Division of Polynomials

To check a quotient in a division problem, multiply the divisor and the quotient. If this product is the dividend, the quotient is correct.

6 Divide a polynomial by a monomial.

Great Question!

Can I cancel identical terms in the dividend and the divisor?

No. Try to avoid this common error:

Incorrect:

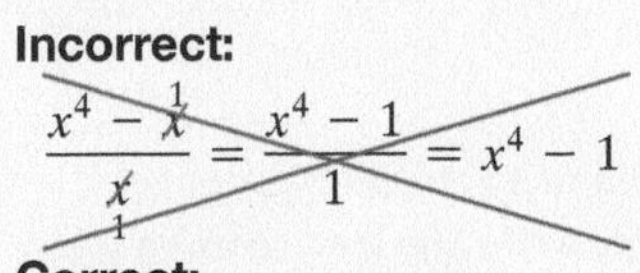

Correct:

$$\frac{x^4 - x}{x} = \frac{x^4}{x} - \frac{x}{x}$$

$$= x^{4-1} - x^{1-1}$$

$$= x^3 - x^0$$

$$= x^3 - 1$$

Don't leave out the 1.

Dividing a Polynomial That Is Not a Monomial by a Monomial

To divide a polynomial by a monomial, we divide each term of the polynomial by the monomial. For example,

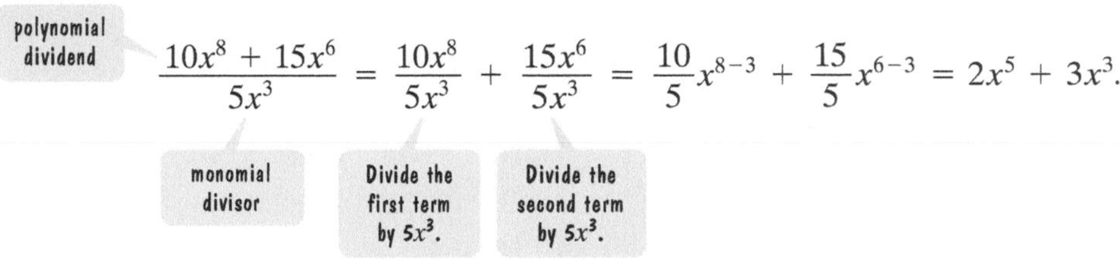

Is the quotient correct? Multiply the divisor and the quotient.

$$5x^3(2x^5 + 3x^3) = 5x^3 \cdot 2x^5 + 5x^3 \cdot 3x^3$$

$$= 5 \cdot 2x^{3+5} + 5 \cdot 3x^{3+3} = 10x^8 + 15x^6$$

Because this product gives the dividend, the quotient is correct.

Dividing a Polynomial That Is Not a Monomial by a Monomial

To divide a polynomial by a monomial, divide each term of the polynomial by the monomial.

EXAMPLE 5 Dividing a Polynomial by a Monomial

Find the quotient: $(-12x^8 + 4x^6 - 8x^3) \div 4x^2$.

Solution

$$\frac{-12x^8 + 4x^6 - 8x^3}{4x^2}$$ Rewrite the division in a vertical format.

$$= \frac{-12x^8}{4x^2} + \frac{4x^6}{4x^2} - \frac{8x^3}{4x^2}$$ Divide each term of the polynomial by the monomial.

$$= \frac{-12}{4}x^{8-2} + \frac{4}{4}x^{6-2} - \frac{8}{4}x^{3-2}$$ Divide coefficients and subtract exponents.

$$= -3x^6 + x^4 - 2x$$ Simplify.

To check the answer, multiply the divisor and the quotient.

$$4x^2(-3x^6 + x^4 - 2x) = 4x^2(-3x^6) + 4x^2 \cdot x^4 - 4x^2(2x)$$
$$= 4(-3)x^{2+6} + 4x^{2+4} - 4 \cdot 2x^{2+1}$$
$$= -12x^8 + 4x^6 - 8x^3$$

Divisor

Quotient

This is the dividend.

Because the product of the divisor and the quotient is the dividend, the answer—that is, the quotient—is correct. ■

✓ **CHECK POINT 5** Find the quotient: $(-15x^9 + 6x^5 - 9x^3) \div 3x^2$.

EXAMPLE 6 Dividing a Polynomial by a Monomial

Divide: $\dfrac{16x^5 - 9x^4 + 8x^3}{2x^3}$.

Solution

$$\frac{16x^5 - 9x^4 + 8x^3}{2x^3}$$ This is the given polynomial division.

$$= \frac{16x^5}{2x^3} - \frac{9x^4}{2x^3} + \frac{8x^3}{2x^3}$$ Divide each term by $2x^3$.

$$= \frac{16}{2}x^{5-3} - \frac{9}{2}x^{4-3} + \frac{8}{2}x^{3-3}$$ Divide coefficients and subtract exponents. Did you immediately write the last term as 4?

$$= 8x^2 - \frac{9}{2}x + 4x^0$$ Simplify.

$$= 8x^2 - \frac{9}{2}x + 4$$ $x^0 = 1$, so $4x^0 = 4 \cdot 1 = 4$.

Check the answer by showing that the product of the divisor and the quotient is the dividend. ■

✓ **CHECK POINT 6** Divide: $\dfrac{25x^9 - 7x^4 + 10x^3}{5x^3}$.

EXAMPLE 7 Dividing Polynomials in Two Variables

Divide: $(15x^5y^4 - 3x^3y^2 + 9x^2y) \div 3x^2y$.

Solution

$$\frac{15x^5y^4 - 3x^3y^2 + 9x^2y}{3x^2y}$$ Rewrite the division in a vertical format.

$$= \frac{15x^5y^4}{3x^2y} - \frac{3x^3y^2}{3x^2y} + \frac{9x^2y}{3x^2y}$$ Divide each term of the polynomial by the monomial.

$$= \frac{15}{3}x^{5-2}y^{4-1} - \frac{3}{3}x^{3-2}y^{2-1} + \frac{9}{3}x^{2-2}y^{1-1}$$ Divide coefficients and subtract exponents.

$$= 5x^3y^3 - xy + 3$$ Simplify.

Check the answer by showing that the product of the divisor and the quotient is the dividend. ■

✓ **CHECK POINT 7** Divide: $(18x^7y^6 - 6x^2y^3 + 60xy^2) \div 6xy^2$.

CONCEPT AND VOCABULARY CHECK

Fill in each blank so that the resulting statement is true.

1. The quotient rule for exponents states that $\frac{b^m}{b^n} =$ ______________, $b \neq 0$. When dividing exponential expressions with the same nonzero base, ______________ the exponents.
2. If $b \neq 0$, $b^0 =$ ______________.
3. The quotients-to-powers rule for exponents states that $\left(\frac{a}{b}\right)^n =$ ______________, $b \neq 0$. When a quotient is raised to a power, raise both the ______________ and the ______________ to the power.
4. To divide monomials, ______________ the coefficients and ______________ the exponents.
5. Consider the following division problem:

$$\frac{20x^6y^4}{10x^2y} = 2x^4y^3.$$

The polynomial in the numerator, $20x^6y^4$, is called the ______________. The polynomial in the denominator, $10x^2y$, is called the ______________. The answer to the problem, $2x^4y^3$, is called the ______________.

6. To check the answer to a division problem, multiply the ______________ and the ______________. If this product is the ______________, the answer is correct.
7. To perform the division $\frac{20x^8 - 10x^4 + 6x^3}{2x^3}$, divide each term of ______________ by ______________.

5 EXERCISE SET

MyMathLab®

Watch the videos in MyMathLab

Download the MyDashBoard App

Practice Exercises

In Exercises 1–10, divide each expression using the quotient rule. Express any numerical answers in exponential form.

1. $\frac{3^{20}}{3^5}$
2. $\frac{3^{30}}{3^{10}}$
3. $\frac{x^6}{x^2}$
4. $\frac{x^8}{x^4}$
5. $\frac{y^{13}}{y^5}$
6. $\frac{y^{19}}{y^6}$
7. $\frac{5^6 \cdot 2^8}{5^3 \cdot 2^4}$
8. $\frac{3^6 \cdot 2^8}{3^3 \cdot 2^4}$
9. $\frac{x^{100}y^{50}}{x^{25}y^{10}}$
10. $\frac{x^{200}y^{40}}{x^{25}y^{10}}$

In Exercises 11–24, use the zero-exponent rule to simplify each expression.

11. 2^0
12. 4^0
13. $(-2)^0$
14. $(-4)^0$
15. -2^0
16. -4^0
17. $100y^0$
18. $200y^0$
19. $(100y)^0$
20. $(200y)^0$
21. $-5^0 + (-5)^0$
22. $-6^0 + (-6)^0$
23. $-\pi^0 - (-\pi)^0$
24. $-\sqrt{3}^0 - (-\sqrt{3})^0$

In Exercises 25–36, simplify each expression using the quotients-to-powers rule. If possible, evaluate exponential expressions.

25. $\left(\frac{x}{3}\right)^2$

26. $\left(\frac{x}{5}\right)^2$

27. $\left(\frac{x^2}{4}\right)^3$

28. $\left(\frac{x^2}{3}\right)^3$

29. $\left(\frac{2x^3}{5}\right)^2$

30. $\left(\frac{3x^4}{7}\right)^2$

31. $\left(\frac{-4}{3a^3}\right)^3$

32. $\left(\frac{-5}{2a^3}\right)^3$

33. $\left(\frac{-2a^7}{b^4}\right)^5$

34. $\left(\frac{-2a^8}{b^3}\right)^5$

35. $\left(\frac{x^2y^3}{2z}\right)^4$

36. $\left(\frac{x^3y^2}{2z}\right)^4$

In Exercises 37–52, divide the monomials. Check each answer by showing that the product of the divisor and the quotient is the dividend.

37. $\frac{30x^{10}}{10x^5}$

38. $\frac{45x^{12}}{15x^4}$

39. $\frac{-8x^{22}}{4x^2}$

40. $\frac{-15x^{40}}{3x^4}$

41. $\frac{-9y^8}{18y^5}$

42. $\frac{-15y^{13}}{45y^9}$

43. $\frac{7y^{17}}{5y^5}$

44. $\frac{9y^{19}}{7y^{11}}$

45. $\frac{30x^7y^5}{5x^2y}$

46. $\frac{40x^9y^5}{2x^2y}$

47. $\frac{-18x^{14}y^2}{36x^2y^2}$

48. $\frac{-15x^{16}y^2}{45x^2y^2}$

49. $\frac{9x^{20}y^{20}}{7x^{20}y^{20}}$

50. $\frac{7x^{30}y^{30}}{15x^{30}y^{30}}$

51. $\frac{-5x^{10}y^{12}z^6}{50x^2y^3z^2}$

52. $\frac{-8x^{12}y^{10}z^4}{40x^2y^3z^2}$

In Exercises 53–78, divide the polynomial by the monomial. Check each answer by showing that the product of the divisor and the quotient is the dividend.

53. $\frac{10x^4 + 2x^3}{2}$

54. $\frac{20x^4 + 5x^3}{5}$

55. $\frac{14x^4 - 7x^3}{7x}$

56. $\frac{24x^4 - 8x^3}{8x}$

57. $\frac{y^7 - 9y^2 + y}{y}$

58. $\frac{y^8 - 11y^3 + y}{y}$

59. $\frac{24x^3 - 15x^2}{-3x}$

60. $\frac{10x^3 - 20x^2}{-5x}$

61. $\frac{18x^5 + 6x^4 + 9x^3}{3x^2}$

62. $\frac{18x^5 + 24x^4 + 12x^3}{6x^2}$

63. $\frac{12x^4 - 8x^3 + 40x^2}{4x}$

64. $\frac{49x^4 - 14x^3 + 70x^2}{-7x}$

65. $(4x^2 - 6x) \div x$

66. $(16y^2 - 8y) \div y$

67. $\frac{30z^3 + 10z^2}{-5z}$

68. $\frac{12y^4 - 42y^2}{-4y}$

69. $\frac{8x^3 + 6x^2 - 2x}{2x}$

70. $\frac{9x^3 + 12x^2 - 3x}{3x}$

71. $\frac{25x^7 - 15x^5 - 5x^4}{5x^3}$

72. $\frac{49x^7 - 28x^5 - 7x^4}{7x^3}$

73. $\frac{18x^7 - 9x^6 + 20x^5 - 10x^4}{-2x^4}$

74. $\frac{25x^8 - 50x^7 + 3x^6 - 40x^5}{-5x^5}$

75. $\frac{12x^2y^2 + 6x^2y - 15xy^2}{3xy}$

76. $\frac{18a^3b^2 - 9a^2b - 27ab^2}{9ab}$

77. $\frac{20x^7y^4 - 15x^3y^2 - 10x^2y}{-5x^2y}$

78. $\frac{8x^6y^3 - 12x^8y^2 - 4x^{14}y^6}{-4x^6y^2}$

Practice PLUS

In Exercises 79–82, simplify each expression.

79. $\frac{2x^3(4x + 2) - 3x^2(2x - 4)}{2x^2}$

80. $\frac{6x^3(3x - 1) + 5x^2(6x - 3)}{3x^2}$

81. $\left(\frac{18x^2y^4}{9xy^2}\right) - \left(\frac{15x^5y^6}{5x^4y^4}\right)$

82. $\left(\frac{9x^3 + 6x^2}{3x}\right) - \left(\frac{12x^2y^2 - 4xy^2}{2xy^2}\right)$

83. Divide the sum of $(y + 5)^2$ and $(y + 5)(y - 5)$ by $2y$.

84. Divide the sum of $(y + 4)^2$ and $(y + 4)(y - 4)$ by $2y$.

In Exercises 85–86, the variable n in each exponent represents a natural number. Divide the polynomial by the monomial. Then use polynomial multiplication to check the quotient.

85. $\frac{12x^{15n} - 24x^{12n} + 8x^{3n}}{4x^{3n}}$

86. $\frac{35x^{10n} - 15x^{8n} + 25x^{2n}}{5x^{2n}}$

Application Exercises

The bar graphs show U.S. film box-office receipts, in millions of dollars, and box-office admissions, in millions of tickets sold, for five selected years.

United States Film Box-Office Receipts and Admissions

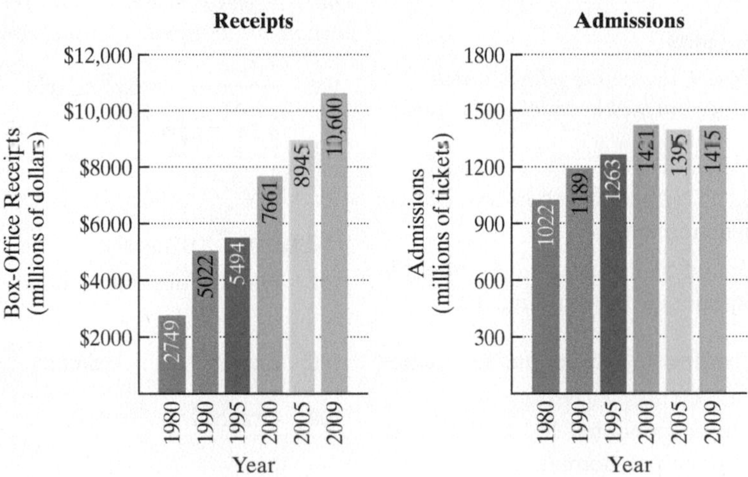

Sources: U.S. Department of Commerce, Motion Picture Association of America, National Association of Theatre Owners

The following polynomial models of degree 2 can be used to describe the data in the bar graphs:

Receipts, in millions of dollars

$$R = 3.6x^2 + 158x + 2790$$

Admissions, in millions of tickets sold

$$A = -0.2x^2 + 21x + 1015.$$

The variable x represents the number of years after 1980.

Use this information to solve Exercises 87–88.

87. **a.** Use the data displayed by the bar graphs to find the average admission charge for a film ticket in 2000. Round to two decimal places, or to the nearest cent.

b. Use the models to write an algebraic expression that describes the average admission charge for a film ticket x years after 1980.

c. Use the model from part (b) to find the average admission charge for a film ticket in 2000. Round to the nearest cent. Does the model underestimate or overestimate the actual average charge that you found in part (a)? By how much?

d. Can the polynomial division for the model in part (b) be performed using the methods that you learned in this section? Explain your answer.

88. **a.** Use the data displayed by the bar graphs to find the average admission charge for a film ticket in 2005. Round to two decimal places, or to the nearest cent.

b. Use the models to write an algebraic expression that describes the average admission charge for a film ticket x years after 1980.

c. Use the model from part (b) to find the average admission charge for a film ticket in 2005. Round to the nearest cent. Does the model underestimate or overestimate the actual average charge that you found in part (a)? By how much?

d. Can the polynomial division for the model in part (b) be performed using the methods that you learned in this section? Explain your answer.

Writing in Mathematics

89. Explain the quotient rule for exponents. Use $\frac{3^6}{3^2}$ in your explanation.

90. Explain how to find any nonzero number to the 0 power.

91. Explain the difference between $(-7)^0$ and -7^0.

92. Explain how to simplify an expression that involves a quotient raised to a power. Provide an example with your explanation.

93. Explain how to divide monomials. Give an example.

94. Explain how to divide a polynomial that is not a monomial by a monomial. Give an example.

95. Are the expressions

$$\frac{12x^2 + 6x}{3x} \quad \text{and} \quad 4x + 2$$

equal for every value of x? Explain.

Critical Thinking Exercises

Make Sense? *In Exercises 96–99, determine whether each statement "makes sense" or "does not make sense" and explain your reasoning.*

96. Because division by 0 is undefined, numbers to 0 powers should not be written in denominators.
97. The quotient rule is applied by dividing the exponent in the numerator by the exponent in the denominator.
98. I divide monomials by dividing coefficients and subtracting exponents.
99. I divide a polynomial by a monomial by dividing each term of the monomial by the polynomial.

In Exercises 100–103, determine whether each statement is true or false. If the statement is false, make the necessary change(s) to produce a true statement.

100. $x^{10} \div x^2 = x^5$ for all nonzero real numbers x.
101. $\dfrac{12x^3 - 6x}{2x} = 6x^2 - 6x$
102. $\dfrac{x^2 + x}{x} = x$
103. If a polynomial in x of degree 6 is divided by a monomial in x of degree 2, the degree of the quotient is 4.
104. What polynomial, when divided by $3x^2$, yields the trinomial $6x^6 - 9x^4 + 12x^2$ as a quotient?

In Exercises 105–106, find the missing coefficients and exponents designated by question marks.

105. $\dfrac{?x^8 - ?x^6}{3x^?} = 3x^5 - 4x^3$
106. $\dfrac{3x^{14} - 6x^{12} - ?x^7}{?x^?} = -x^7 + 2x^5 + 3$

Review Exercises

107. Find the absolute value: $|-20.3|$.
108. Express $\frac{7}{8}$ as a decimal. (
109. Graph: $y = \frac{1}{3}x + 2$.

Preview Exercises

Exercises 110–112 will help you prepare for the material covered in the next section. In each exercise, perform the long division without using a calculator, and then state the quotient and the remainder.

110. $19\overline{)494}$
111. $24\overline{)2958}$
112. $98\overline{)25{,}187}$

SECTION 6

Dividing Polynomials by Binomials

Objective

1 Divide polynomials by binomials.

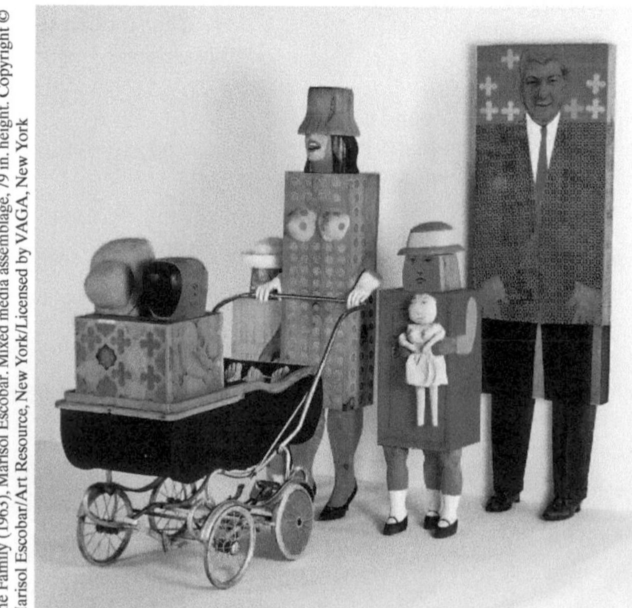

The Family (1963), Marisol Escobar. Mixed media assemblage, 79 in. height. Copyright © Marisol Escobar/Art Resource, New York/Licensed by VAGA, New York

"He was an arithmetician rather than a mathematician. None of the humor, the music, or the mysticism of higher mathematics ever entered his head."
—*John Steinbeck*

"Arithmetic has a very great and elevating effect. He who can properly divide is to be considered a god."
—*Plato*

"You cannot ask us to take sides against arithmetic."
—*Winston Churchill*

The Family (1963), Marisol Escobar. © 2011 Marisol Escobar/VAGA

So, what's the deal? Will performing the repetitive procedure of long division (don't reach for that calculator!) have an elevating effect? Or will it confine you to a computational box that allows neither humor nor music to enter? Forget the box: Mathematician Wilhelm Leibniz believed that music is nothing but unconscious arithmetic. But do think elevation, if not to the level of an ancient Greek god, then to new, algebraic highs. The bottom line: Understanding long division of whole numbers lays the foundation for performing the division of a polynomial by a binomial, such as

$$x + 3\overline{)x^2 + 10x + 21}.$$

Divisor has two terms and is a binomial.

The polynomial dividend has three terms and is a trinomial.

In this section, you will learn how to perform such divisions.

The Steps in Dividing a Polynomial by a Binomial

Dividing a polynomial by a binomial may remind you of long division. Let's review long division of whole numbers by dividing 3983 by 26.

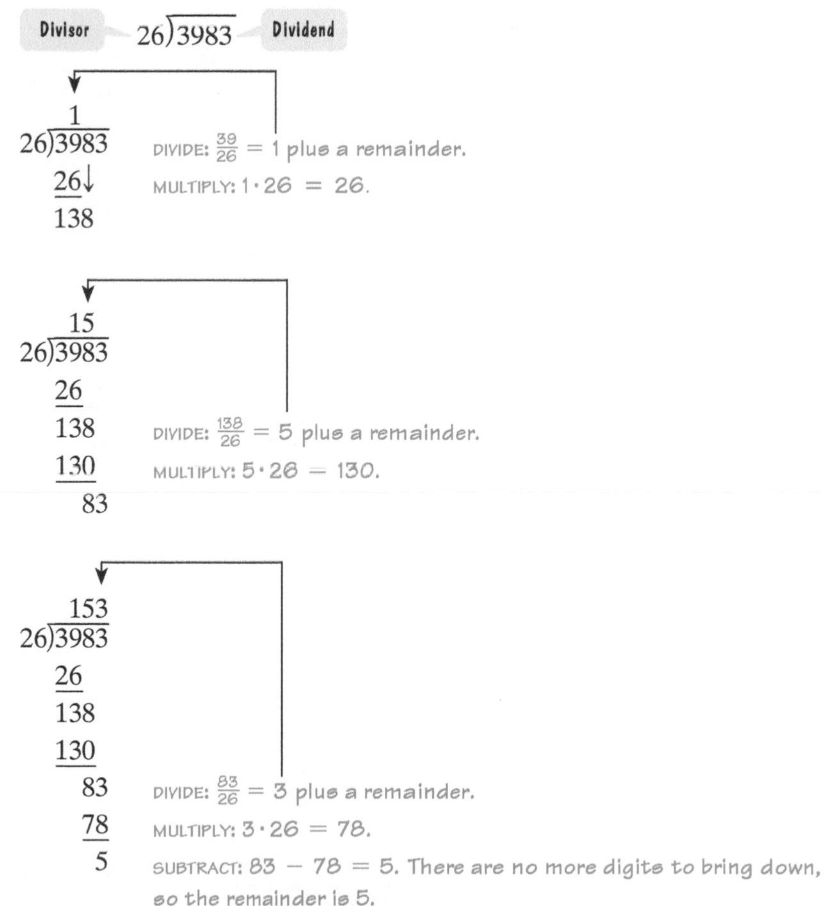

The quotient is 153 and the remainder is 5. This can be written as

$$153\frac{5}{26}.$$

Quotient

Remainder

Divisor

We see that $26\overline{)3983}$ with quotient $153\frac{5}{26}$.

This answer can be checked. Multiply the divisor and the quotient. Then add the remainder. If the result is the dividend, the answer is correct. In this case, we have

$$26(153) + 5 = 3978 + 5 = 3983.$$

Divisor | Quotient | Remainder | This is the dividend

1 Divide polynomials by binomials.

Because we obtained the dividend, the answer to the division problem, $153\frac{5}{26}$, is correct.

When a divisor is a binomial, the four steps used to divide whole numbers—**divide, multiply, subtract, bring down the next term**—form the repetitive procedure for dividing a polynomial by a binomial.

EXAMPLE 1 Dividing a Polynomial by a Binomial

Divide $x^2 + 10x + 21$ by $x + 3$.

Solution The following steps illustrate how polynomial division is very similar to numerical division.

$x + 3\overline{)x^2 + 10x + 21}$

Arrange the terms of the dividend ($x^2 + 10x + 21$) and the divisor ($x + 3$) in descending powers of x.

$x + 3\overline{)x^2 + 10x + 21}$ with quotient x

DIVIDE x^2 (the first term in the dividend) by x (the first term in the divisor): $\frac{x^2}{x} = x$. Align like terms.

$x(x + 3) = x^2 + 3x$

$x + 3\overline{)x^2 + 10x + 21}$ with quotient x; below: $x^2 + 3x$

MULTIPLY each term in the divisor ($x + 3$) by x, aligning terms of the product under like terms in

$x + 3\overline{)x^2 + 10x + 21}$ with quotient x; subtract $\ominus x^2 \ominus 3x$; result $7x$

Change signs of the polynomial being subtracted.

SUBTRACT $x^2 + 3x$ from $x^2 + 10x$ by changing the sign of each term in the lower expression and adding.

$x + 3\overline{)x^2 + 10x + 21}$ with quotient x; $x^2 + 3x$ ↓; $7x + 21$

BRING DOWN 21 from the original dividend and add algebraically to form a new dividend.

$x + 3\overline{)x^2 + 10x + 21}$ with quotient $x + 7$; $x^2 + 3x$; $7x + 21$

FIND the second term of the quotient. Divide the first term of $7x + 21$ by x, the first term of the divisor: $\frac{7x}{x} = 7$.

$7(x + 3) = 7x + 21$

$x + 3\overline{)x^2 + 10x + 21}$ with quotient $x + 7$; $x^2 + 3x$; $7x + 21$; $\ominus 7x \ominus 21$; 0

Remainder

MULTIPLY the divisor ($x + 3$) by 7, aligning under like terms in the new dividend. Then subtract to obtain the remainder of 0.

The quotient is $x + 7$ and the remainder is 0. We will not list a remainder of 0 in the answer. Thus,

$$\frac{x^2 + 10x + 21}{x + 3} = x + 7. \quad ■$$

When dividing polynomials by binomials, the answer can be checked. Find the product of the divisor and the quotient and add the remainder. If the result is the dividend, the answer to the division problem is correct. For example, let's check our work in Example 1.

$$\frac{x^2 + 10x + 21}{x + 3} = x + 7$$

Dividend

Divisor

Quotient to be checked

Multiply the divisor and the quotient and add the remainder, 0:

$$(x + 3)(x + 7) + 0 = x^2 + 7x + 3x + 21 + 0 = x^2 + 10x + 21.$$

Divisor | Quotient | Remainder | This is the dividend.

Because we obtained the dividend, the quotient is correct.

✓ **CHECK POINT 1** Divide $x^2 + 14x + 45$ by $x + 9$.

Before considering additional examples, let's summarize the general procedure for dividing a polynomial by a binomial.

Dividing a Polynomial by a Binomial

1. **Arrange the terms** of both the dividend and the divisor in descending powers of the variable.
2. **Divide** the first term in the dividend by the first term in the divisor. The result is the first term of the quotient.
3. **Multiply** every term in the divisor by the first term in the quotient. Write the resulting product beneath the dividend with like terms lined up.
4. **Subtract** the product from the dividend.
5. **Bring down** the next term in the original dividend and write it next to the remainder to form a new dividend.
6. Use this new expression as the dividend and repeat this process until the remainder can no longer be divided. This will occur when the degree of the remainder (the highest exponent on a variable in the remainder) is less than the degree of the divisor.

In our next division, we will obtain a nonzero remainder.

EXAMPLE 2 Dividing a Polynomial by a Binomial

Divide: $\dfrac{7x - 9 - 4x^2 + 4x^3}{2x - 1}$.

Solution We begin by writing the dividend, $7x - 9 - 4x^2 + 4x^3$, in descending powers of x.

$$7x - 9 - 4x^2 + 4x^3 = 4x^3 - 4x^2 + 7x - 9$$

Think of 9 as $9x^0$. The powers descend from 3 to 0.

$$2x - 1\overline{)4x^3 - 4x^2 + 7x - 9}$$

This is the problem with the dividend in descending powers of x.

$$\begin{array}{r} 2x^2 \\ 2x - 1\overline{)4x^3 - 4x^2 + 7x - 9} \end{array}$$

DIVIDE: $\frac{4x^3}{2x} = 2x^2$.

$2x^2(2x - 1) = 4x^3 - 2x^2$

$$\begin{array}{r} 2x^2 \\ 2x - 1\overline{)4x^3 - 4x^2 + 7x - 9} \\ \underline{4x^3 - 2x^2} \end{array}$$

MULTIPLY: $2x^2(2x - 1) = 4x^3 - 2x^2$.

$$\begin{array}{r} 2x^2 \\ 2x - 1\overline{)4x^3 - 4x^2 + 7x - 9} \\ \underline{\ominus 4x^3 \overset{\oplus}{-} 2x^2} \\ -2x^2 \end{array}$$

Change signs of the polynomial being subtracted.

SUBTRACT: $4x^3 - 4x^2 - (4x^3 - 2x^2)$
$= 4x^3 - 4x^2 - 4x^3 + 2x^2$
$= -2x^2$.

$$\begin{array}{r} 2x^2 \\ 2x - 1\overline{)4x^3 - 4x^2 + 7x - 9} \\ \underline{4x^3 - 2x^2} \downarrow \\ -2x^2 + 7x \end{array}$$

BRING DOWN 7x. The new dividend is $-2x^2 + 7x$.

$$\begin{array}{r} 2x^2 - x \\ 2x - 1\overline{)4x^3 - 4x^2 + 7x - 9} \\ \underline{4x^3 - 2x^2} \\ -2x^2 + 7x \end{array}$$

DIVIDE: $\frac{-2x^2}{2x} = -x$.

$-x(2x - 1) = -2x^2 + x$

$$\begin{array}{r} 2x^2 - x \\ 2x - 1\overline{)4x^3 - 4x^2 + 7x - 9} \\ \underline{4x^3 - 2x^2} \\ -2x^2 + 7x \\ \underline{-2x^2 + x} \end{array}$$

MULTIPLY: $-x(2x - 1) = -2x^2 + x$.

$$\begin{array}{r} 2x^2 - x \\ 2x - 1\overline{)4x^3 - 4x^2 + 7x - 9} \\ \underline{4x^3 - 2x^2} \\ -2x^2 + 7x \\ \underline{\overset{\oplus}{-} 2x^2 \overset{\ominus}{+} x} \\ 6x \end{array}$$

SUBTRACT: $-2x^2 + 7x - (-2x^2 + x)$
$= -2x^2 + 7x + 2x^2 - x$
$= 6x$.

$$\begin{array}{r} 2x^2 - x \\ 2x - 1\overline{)4x^3 - 4x^2 + 7x - 9} \\ \underline{4x^3 - 2x^2} \\ -2x^2 + 7x \\ \underline{-2x^2 + x} \downarrow \\ 6x - 9 \end{array}$$

BRING DOWN −9. The new dividend is $6x - 9$.

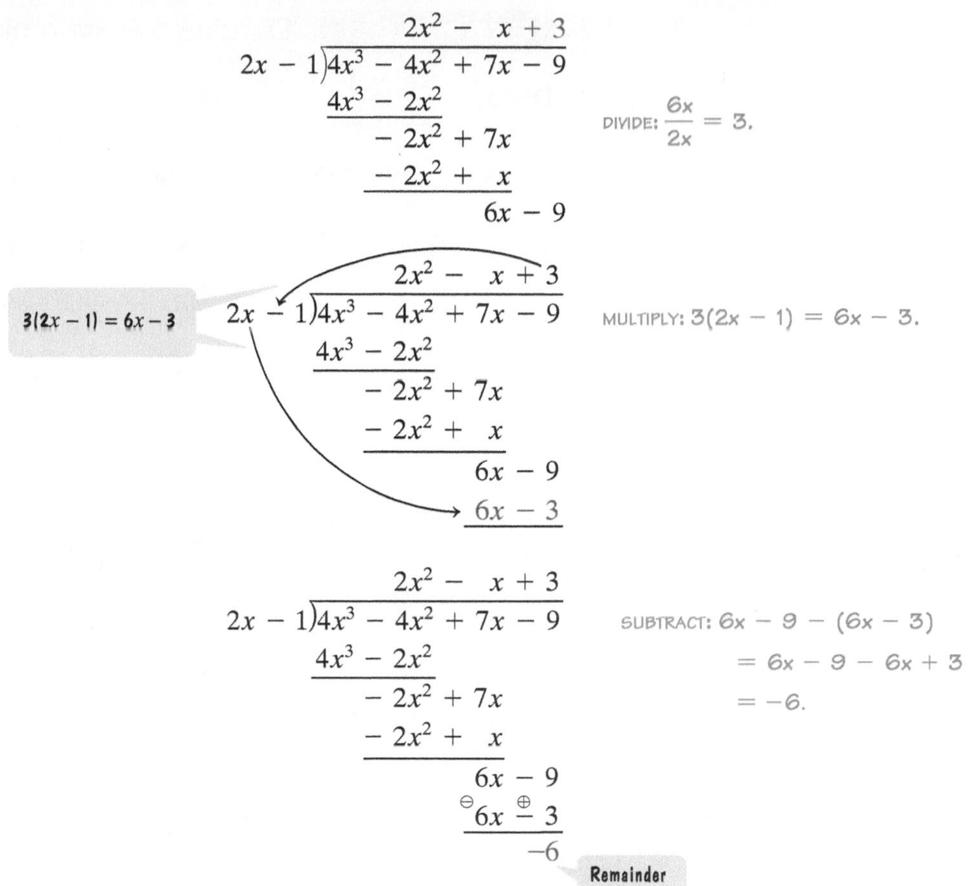

The quotient is $2x^2 - x + 3$ and the remainder is -6. When there is a nonzero remainder, as in this example, list the quotient, plus the remainder above the divisor. Thus,

$$\frac{7x - 9 - 4x^2 + 4x^3}{2x - 1} = 2x^2 - x + 3 + \frac{-6}{2x - 1}$$

Quotient

Remainder above divisor

or

$$\frac{7x - 9 - 4x^2 + 4x^3}{2x - 1} = 2x^2 - x + 3 - \frac{6}{2x - 1}.$$

Check this result by showing that the product of the divisor and the quotient,

$$(2x - 1)(2x^2 - x + 3),$$

plus the remainder, -6, is the dividend, $7x - 9 - 4x^2 + 4x^3$. ■

✓ **CHECK POINT 2** Divide: $\frac{6x + 8x^2 - 12}{2x + 3}$.

If a power of the variable is missing in a dividend, add that power of the variable with a coefficient of 0 and then divide. In this way, like terms will be aligned as you carry out the division.

EXAMPLE 3 Dividing a Polynomial with Missing Terms

Divide: $\dfrac{8x^3 - 1}{2x - 1}$.

Solution We write the dividend, $8x^3 - 1$, as

$$8x^3 + 0x^2 + 0x - 1.$$

Use a coefficient of 0 with missing terms.

By doing this, we will keep all like terms aligned.

$4x^2(2x - 1) = 8x^3 - 4x^2$

$$\begin{array}{r} 4x^2 \\ 2x - 1 \overline{)8x^3 + 0x^2 + 0x - 1} \\ \underline{8x^3 - 4x^2} \\ 4x^2 + 0x \end{array}$$

Divide $\left(\frac{8x^3}{2x} = 4x^2\right)$, multiply $[4x^2(2x - 1) = 8x^3 - 4x^2]$, subtract, and bring down the next term. The new dividend is $4x^2 + 0x$.

$2x(2x - 1) = 4x^2 - 2x$

$$\begin{array}{r} 4x^2 + 2x \\ 2x - 1 \overline{)8x^3 + 0x^2 + 0x - 1} \\ \underline{8x^3 - 4x^2} \\ 4x^2 + 0x \\ \underline{4x^2 - 2x} \\ 2x - 1 \end{array}$$

Divide $\left(\frac{4x^2}{2x} = 2x\right)$, multiply $[2x(2x - 1) = 4x^2 - 2x]$, subtract, and bring down the next term. The new dividend is $2x - 1$.

$1(2x - 1) = 2x - 1$

$$\begin{array}{r} 4x^2 + 2x + 1 \\ 2x - 1 \overline{)8x^3 + 0x^2 + 0x - 1} \\ \underline{8x^3 - 4x^2} \\ 4x^2 + 0x \\ \underline{4x^2 - 2x} \\ 2x - 1 \\ \underline{2x - 1} \\ 0 \end{array}$$

Divide $\left(\frac{2x}{2x} = 1\right)$, multiply $[1(2x - 1) = 2x - 1]$, and subtract. The remainder is 0.

Thus,

$$\frac{8x^3 - 1}{2x - 1} = 4x^2 + 2x + 1.$$

Check this result by showing that the product of the divisor and the quotient

$$(2x - 1)(4x^2 + 2x + 1)$$

plus the remainder, 0, is the dividend, $8x^3 - 1$. ■

✓ CHECK POINT 3 Divide: $\dfrac{x^3 - 1}{x - 1}$.

Using Technology

Graphic Connections

The graphs of $y_1 = \dfrac{8x^3 - 1}{2x - 1}$ and $y_2 = 4x^2 + 2x + 1$ are shown below.

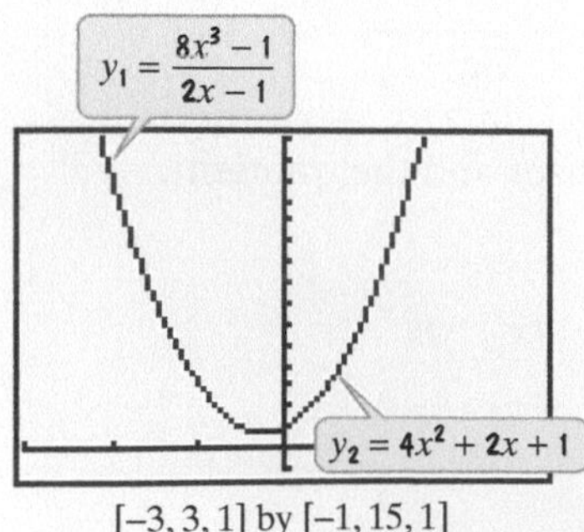

[−3, 3, 1] by [−1, 15, 1]

The graphs coincide. Thus,

$$\frac{8x^3 - 1}{2x - 1} = 4x^2 + 2x + 1.$$

CONCEPT AND VOCABULARY CHECK

Fill in each blank so that the resulting statement is true.

1. Consider the following long division problem:

$$2x + 3\overline{)4x^2 + 9 + 10x^3}.$$

We begin the division process by rewriting the dividend as ______________.

2. Consider the following long division problem:

$$2x + 1\overline{)8x^2 + 10x - 1}.$$

We begin the division process by dividing ______________ by ______________. We obtain ______________. We write this result above ______________ in the dividend.

3. In the following long division problem, the first step has been completed:

$$\begin{array}{r} 5x \\ 3x - 2\overline{)15x^2 - 22x + 19}. \end{array}$$

The next step is to multiply ______________ and ______________. We obtain ______________. We write this result below ______________.

4. In the following long division problem, the first steps have been completed:

$$\begin{array}{r} 2x \\ 3x - 5\overline{)6x^2 + 8x - 4}. \\ \underline{6x^2 - 10x} \end{array}$$

The next step is to subtract ______________ from ______________. We obtain ______________. Then we bring down ______________ and form the new dividend ______________.

5. In the following long division problem, most of the steps have been completed:

$$\begin{array}{r} x - 12 \\ x - 5\overline{)x^2 - 17x + 74}. \\ \underline{x^2 - 5x} \\ -12x + 74 \\ \underline{-12x + 60} \\ ? \end{array}$$

Completing the step designated by the question mark, we obtain ______________. Thus, the quotient is ______________ and the remainder is ______________. The answer to this long division problem is ______________.

6 EXERCISE SET

MyMathLab®

Watch the videos in MyMathLab

Download the MyDashBoard App

Practice Exercises

In Exercises 1–36, divide as indicated. Check each answer by showing that the product of the divisor and the quotient, plus the remainder, is the dividend.

1. $\dfrac{x^2 + 6x + 8}{x + 2}$

2. $\dfrac{x^2 + 7x + 10}{x + 5}$

3. $\dfrac{2x^2 + x - 10}{x - 2}$

4. $\dfrac{2x^2 + 13x + 15}{x + 5}$

5. $\dfrac{x^2 - 5x + 6}{x - 3}$

6. $\dfrac{x^2 - 2x - 24}{x + 4}$

7. $\dfrac{2y^2 + 5y + 2}{y + 2}$

8. $\dfrac{2y^2 - 13y + 21}{y - 3}$

9. $\dfrac{x^2 - 3x + 4}{x + 2}$

10. $\dfrac{x^2 - 7x + 5}{x + 3}$

11. $\dfrac{5y + 10 + y^2}{y + 2}$

12. $\dfrac{-8y + y^2 - 9}{y - 3}$

13. $\dfrac{x^3 - 6x^2 + 7x - 2}{x - 1}$

14. $\dfrac{x^3 + 3x^2 + 5x + 3}{x + 1}$

15. $\dfrac{12y^2 - 20y + 3}{2y - 3}$

16. $\dfrac{4y^2 - 8y - 5}{2y + 1}$

17. $\dfrac{4a^2 + 4a - 3}{2a - 1}$

18. $\dfrac{2b^2 - 9b - 5}{2b + 1}$

19. $\dfrac{3y - y^2 + 2y^3 + 2}{2y + 1}$

20. $\dfrac{9y + 18 - 11y^2 + 12y^3}{4y + 3}$

21. $\dfrac{6x^2 - 5x - 30}{2x - 5}$

22. $\dfrac{4y^2 + 8y + 3}{2y - 1}$

23. $\dfrac{x^3 + 4x - 3}{x - 2}$

24. $\dfrac{x^3 + 2x^2 - 3}{x - 2}$

25. $\dfrac{4y^3 + 8y^2 + 5y + 9}{2y + 3}$

26. $\dfrac{2y^3 - y^2 + 3y + 2}{2y + 1}$

27. $\dfrac{6y^3 - 5y^2 + 5}{3y + 2}$

28. $\dfrac{4y^3 + 3y + 5}{2y - 3}$

29. $\dfrac{27x^3 - 1}{3x - 1}$

30. $\dfrac{8x^3 + 27}{2x + 3}$

31. $\dfrac{81 - 12y^3 + 54y^2 + y^4 - 108y}{y - 3}$

32. $\dfrac{8y^3 + y^4 + 16 + 32y + 24y^2}{y + 2}$

33. $\dfrac{4y^2 + 6y}{2y - 1}$

34. $\dfrac{10x^2 - 3x}{x + 3}$

35. $\dfrac{y^4 - 2y^2 + 5}{y - 1}$

36. $\dfrac{y^4 - 6y^2 + 3}{y - 1}$

Practice PLUS

In Exercises 37–42, divide as indicated.

37. $\dfrac{4x^3 - 3x^2 + x + 1}{x^2 + 2}$

38. $\dfrac{3x^3 + 4x^2 + x + 7}{x^2 + 1}$

39. $\dfrac{x^3 - a^3}{x - a}$

40. $\dfrac{x^4 - a^4}{x - a}$

41. $\dfrac{6x^4 - 5x^3 - 8x^2 + 16x - 8}{3x^2 + 2x - 4}$

42. $\dfrac{2x^4 + 5x^3 - 11x^2 - 20x + 12}{x^2 + x - 6}$

43. Divide the difference between $4x^3 + x^2 - 2x + 7$ and $3x^3 - 2x^2 - 7x + 4$ by $x + 1$.

44. Divide the difference between $4x^3 + 2x^2 - x - 1$ and $2x^3 - x^2 + 2x - 5$ by $x + 2$.

Application Exercises

45. Write a simplified polynomial that represents the length of the rectangle.

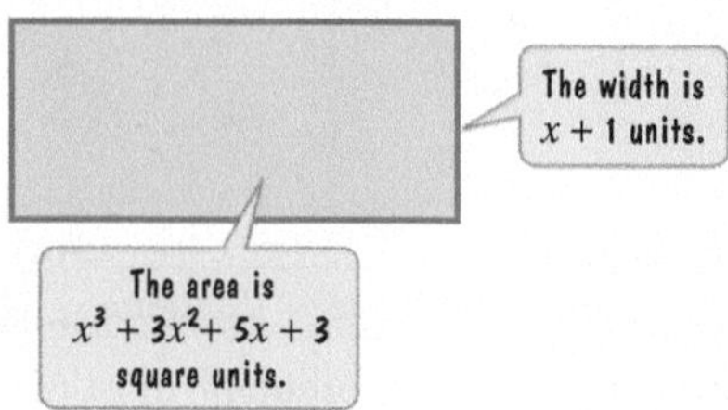
The width is
x + 1 units.
The area is
x³ + 3x² + 5x + 3
square units.

46. Write a simplified polynomial that represents the measure of the base of the parallelogram.

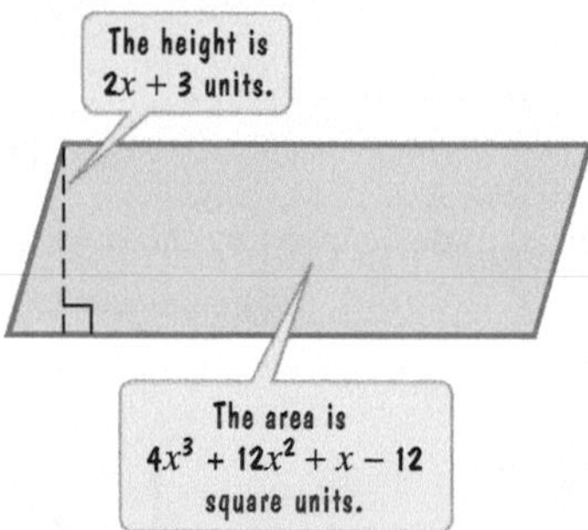
The height is
2x + 3 units.
The area is
4x³ + 12x² + x − 12
square units.

You just signed a contract for a new job. The salary for the first year is \$30,000 and there is to be a percent increase in your salary each year. The algebraic expression

$$\frac{30{,}000x^n - 30{,}000}{x - 1}$$

describes your total salary over n years, where x is the sum of 1 and the yearly percent increase, expressed as a decimal. Use this information to solve Exercises 47–48.

47. **a.** Use the given expression and write a quotient of polynomials that describes your total salary over three years.

    b. Simplify the expression in part (a) by performing the division.

c. Suppose you are to receive an increase of 5% per year. Thus, x is the sum of 1 and 0.05, or 1.05. Substitute 1.05 for x in the expression in part (a) as well as in the simplified form of the expression in part (b). Evaluate each expression. What is your total salary over the three-year period?

48. a. Use the expression given on the previous page and write a quotient of polynomials that describes your total salary over four years.

b. Simplify the expression in part (a) by performing the division.

c. Suppose you are to receive an increase of 8% per year. Thus, x is the sum of 1 and 0.08, or 1.08. Substitute 1.08 for x in the expression in part (a) as well as in the simplified form of the expression in part (b). Evaluate each expression. What is your total salary over the four-year period?

Writing in Mathematics

49. In your own words, explain how to divide a polynomial by a binomial. Use $\frac{x^2 + 4}{x + 2}$ in your explanation.

50. When dividing a polynomial by a binomial, explain when to stop dividing.

51. After dividing a polynomial by a binomial, explain how to check the answer.

52. When dividing a binomial into a polynomial with missing terms, explain the advantage of writing the missing terms with zero coefficients.

Critical Thinking Exercises

Make Sense? *In Exercises 53–56, determine whether each statement "makes sense" or "does not make sense" and explain your reasoning. Each statement applies to the division problem*

$$\frac{x^3 + 1}{x + 1}.$$

53. The purpose of writing $x^3 + 1$ as $x^3 + 0x^2 + 0x + 1$ is to keep all like terms aligned.

54. Rewriting $x^3 + 1$ as $x^3 + 0x^2 + 0x + 1$ can change the value of the variable expression for certain values of x.

55. There's no need to apply the long-division process to this problem because I can work the problem in my head and see that the quotient must be $x^2 + 1$.

56. The degree of the quotient must be $3 - 1$.

In Exercises 57–60, determine whether each statement is true or false. If the statement is false, make the necessary change(s) to produce a true statement.

57. If $4x^2 + 25x - 3$ is divided by $4x + 1$, the remainder is 9.

58. If polynomial division results in a remainder of zero, then the product of the divisor and the quotient is the dividend.

59. A nonzero remainder indicates that the answer to a polynomial long-division problem is not a polynomial.

60. When a polynomial is divided by a binomial, the division process stops when the last term of the dividend is brought down.

61. When a certain polynomial is divided by $2x + 4$, the quotient is

$$x - 3 + \frac{17}{2x + 4}.$$

What is the polynomial?

62. Find the number k such that when $16x^2 - 2x + k$ is divided by $2x - 1$, the remainder is 0.

63. Describe the pattern that you observe in the following quotients and remainders.

$$\frac{x^3 - 1}{x + 1} = x^2 - x + 1 - \frac{2}{x + 1}$$

$$\frac{x^5 - 1}{x + 1} = x^4 - x^3 + x^2 - x + 1 - \frac{2}{x + 1}$$

Use this pattern to find $\frac{x^7 - 1}{x + 1}$. Verify your result by dividing.

Technology Exercises

In Exercises 64–68, use a graphing utility to determine whether the divisions have been performed correctly. Graph each side of the given equation in the same viewing rectangle. The graphs should coincide. If they do not, correct the expression on the right side by using polynomial division. Then use your graphing utility to show that the division has been performed correctly.

64. $\frac{x^2 - 4}{x - 2} = x + 2$

65. $\frac{x^2 - 25}{x - 5} = x - 5$

66. $\frac{2x^2 + 13x + 15}{x - 5} = 2x + 3$

67. $\frac{6x^2 + 16x + 8}{3x + 2} = 2x - 4$

68. $\frac{x^3 + 3x^2 + 5x + 3}{x + 1} = x^2 - 2x + 3$

Review Exercises

69. Graph the solution set of the system:

$$\begin{cases} 2x - y \geq 4 \\ x - y \leq -1. \end{cases}$$

70. What is 6% of 20?

71. Solve: $\frac{x}{3} + \frac{2}{5} = \frac{x}{5} - \frac{2}{5}$.

Preview Exercises

Exercises 72–74 will help you prepare for the material covered in the next section.

72. **a.** Find the missing exponent, designated by the question mark, in each final step.

$$\frac{7^3}{7^5} = \frac{\cancel{7}\cdot\cancel{7}\cdot\cancel{7}}{\cancel{7}\cdot\cancel{7}\cdot\cancel{7}\cdot 7\cdot 7} = \frac{1}{7^?}$$

$$\frac{7^3}{7^5} = 7^{3-5} = 7^?$$

b. Based on your two results for $\frac{7^3}{7^5}$, what can you conclude?

73. Simplify: $\frac{(2x^3)^4}{x^{10}}$.

74. Simplify: $\left(\frac{x^5}{x^2}\right)^3$.

SECTION 7

Negative Exponents and Scientific Notation

Objectives

1. Use the negative exponent rule.
2. Simplify exponential expressions.
3. Convert from scientific notation to decimal notation.
4. Convert from decimal notation to scientific notation.
5. Compute with scientific notation.
6. Solve applied problems using scientific notation.

Bigger than the biggest thing ever and then some. Much bigger than that in fact, really amazingly immense, a totally stunning size, real 'wow, that's big', time ... Gigantic multiplied by colossal multiplied by staggeringly huge is the sort of concept we're trying to get across here.

Douglas Adams, *The Restaurant at the End of the Universe*

Although Adams's description may not quite apply to this \$12.4 trillion national debt, exponents can be used to explore the meaning of this "staggeringly huge" number. In this section, you will learn to use exponents to provide a way of putting large and small numbers in perspective.

Negative Integers as Exponents

A nonzero base can be raised to a negative power. The quotient rule can be used to help determine what a negative integer as an exponent should mean. Consider the quotient of b^3 and b^5, where b is not zero. We can determine this quotient in two ways.

$$\frac{b^3}{b^5} = \frac{1\cdot\cancel{b}\cdot\cancel{b}\cdot\cancel{b}}{\cancel{b}\cdot\cancel{b}\cdot\cancel{b}\cdot b\cdot b} = \frac{1}{b^2}$$

After dividing out pairs of factors, we have two factors of b in the denominator.

$$\frac{b^3}{b^5} = b^{3-5} = b^{-2}$$

Use the quotient rule and subtract exponents.

Notice that $\frac{b^3}{b^5}$ equals both b^{-2} and $\frac{1}{b^2}$. This means that b^{-2} must equal $\frac{1}{b^2}$. This example is a special case of the **negative exponent rule.**

1 Use the negative exponent rule.

The Negative Exponent Rule

If b is any real number other than 0 and n is a natural number, then

$$b^{-n} = \frac{1}{b^n}.$$

Great Question!

Does a negative exponent make the value of an expression negative?

No. For example,

$$7^{-2} = \frac{1}{7^2} = \frac{1}{49}$$

is positive. Avoid these common errors:

Incorrect!

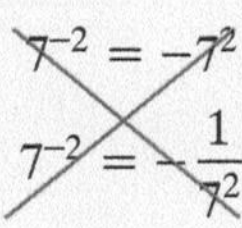

EXAMPLE 1 Using the Negative Exponent Rule

Use the negative exponent rule to write each expression with a positive exponent. Then simplify the expression.

a. 7^{-2} **b.** 4^{-3} **c.** $(-2)^{-4}$ **d.** -2^{-4} **e.** 5^{-1}

Solution

a. $7^{-2} = \frac{1}{7^2} = \frac{1}{7 \cdot 7} = \frac{1}{49}$

b. $4^{-3} = \frac{1}{4^3} = \frac{1}{4 \cdot 4 \cdot 4} = \frac{1}{64}$

c. $(-2)^{-4} = \frac{1}{(-2)^4} = \frac{1}{(-2)(-2)(-2)(-2)} = \frac{1}{16}$

d. $-2^{-4} = -\frac{1}{2^4} = -\frac{1}{2 \cdot 2 \cdot 2 \cdot 2} = -\frac{1}{16}$

The negative is not inside parentheses and is not taken to the −4 power.

e. $5^{-1} = \frac{1}{5^1} = \frac{1}{5}$ ■

✓ CHECK POINT 1 Use the negative exponent rule to write each expression with a positive exponent. Then simplify the expression.

a. 6^{-2} **b.** 5^{-3} **c.** $(-3)^{-4}$

d. -3^{-4} **e.** 8^{-1}

Negative exponents can also appear in denominators. For example,

$$\frac{1}{2^{-10}} = \frac{1}{\frac{1}{2^{10}}} = 1 \div \frac{1}{2^{10}} = 1 \cdot \frac{2^{10}}{1} = 2^{10}.$$

In general, if a negative exponent appears in a denominator, an expression can be written with a positive exponent using

$$\frac{1}{b^{-n}} = b^n.$$

For example,

$$\frac{1}{2^{-3}} = 2^3 = 8 \quad \text{and} \quad \frac{1}{(-6)^{-2}} = (-6)^2 = 36.$$

Change only the sign of the exponent and not the sign of the base, −6.

Negative Exponents in Numerators and Denominators

If b is any real number other than 0 and n is a natural number, then

$$b^{-n} = \frac{1}{b^n} \quad \text{and} \quad \frac{1}{b^{-n}} = b^n.$$

When a negative number appears as an exponent, switch the position of the base (from numerator to denominator or from denominator to numerator) and make the exponent positive. The sign of the base does not change.

EXAMPLE 2 Using Negative Exponents

Write each expression with positive exponents only. Then simplify, if possible.

a. $\frac{4^{-3}}{5^{-2}}$ **b.** $\left(\frac{3}{4}\right)^{-2}$ **c.** $\frac{1}{4x^{-3}}$ **d.** $\frac{x^{-5}}{y^{-1}}$

Solution

a. $\frac{4^{-3}}{5^{-2}} = \frac{5^2}{4^3} = \frac{5 \cdot 5}{4 \cdot 4 \cdot 4} = \frac{25}{64}$

Switch the position of the bases and make the exponents positive.

b. $\left(\frac{3}{4}\right)^{-2} = \frac{3^{-2}}{4^{-2}} = \frac{4^2}{3^2} = \frac{4 \cdot 4}{3 \cdot 3} = \frac{16}{9}$

Switch the position of the bases and make the exponents positive.

c. $\frac{1}{4x^{-3}} = \frac{x^3}{4}$

Switch the position of the base and make the exponent positive. Note that only x is raised to the -3 power.

d. $\frac{x^{-5}}{y^{-1}} = \frac{y^1}{x^5} = \frac{y}{x^5}$

✓ **CHECK POINT 2** Write each expression with positive exponents only. Then simplify, if possible.

a. $\frac{2^{-3}}{7^{-2}}$ **b.** $\left(\frac{4}{5}\right)^{-2}$ **c.** $\frac{1}{7y^{-2}}$ **d.** $\frac{x^{-1}}{y^{-8}}$

2 Simplify exponential expressions.

Simplifying Exponential Expressions

Properties of exponents are used to simplify exponential expressions. An exponential expression is **simplified** when

- Each base occurs only once.
- No parentheses appear.
- No powers are raised to powers.
- No negative or zero exponents appear.

Simplifying Exponential Expressions

	Example
1. If necessary, be sure that each base appears only once, using $b^m \cdot b^n = b^{m+n}$ or $\frac{b^m}{b^n} = b^{m-n}$.	$x^4 \cdot x^3 = x^{4+3} = x^7$
2. If necessary, remove parentheses using $(ab)^n = a^n b^n$ or $\left(\frac{a}{b}\right)^n = \frac{a^n}{b^n}$.	$(xy)^3 = x^3y^3$
3. If necessary, simplify powers to powers using $(b^m)^n = b^{mn}$.	$(x^4)^3 = x^{4\cdot 3} = x^{12}$
4. If necessary, rewrite exponential expressions with zero powers as 1 ($b^0 = 1$). Furthermore, write the answer with positive exponents using $b^{-n} = \frac{1}{b^n}$ or $\frac{1}{b^{-n}} = b^n$.	$\frac{x^5}{x^8} = x^{5-8} = x^{-3} = \frac{1}{x^3}$

The following examples show how to simplify exponential expressions. In each example, assume that any variable in a denominator is not equal to zero.

Great Question!

Is the procedure in Example 3 the only way to simplify $x^{-9} \cdot x^4$?

There is often more than one way to simplify an exponential expression. For example, you may prefer to simplify Example 3 as follows:

$$x^{-9} \cdot x^4 = \frac{x^4}{x^9} = x^{4-9} = x^{-5} = \frac{1}{x^5}.$$

EXAMPLE 3 Simplifying an Exponential Expression

Simplify: $x^{-9} \cdot x^4$.

Solution

$$x^{-9} \cdot x^4 = x^{-9+4} \qquad b^m \cdot b^n = b^{m+n}$$

$$= x^{-5} \qquad \text{The base, } x\text{, now appears only once.}$$

$$= \frac{1}{x^5} \qquad b^{-n} = \frac{1}{b^n}$$ ■

✓ **CHECK POINT 3** Simplify: $x^{-12} \cdot x^2$.

EXAMPLE 4 Simplifying Exponential Expressions

Simplify:

a. $\frac{x^4}{x^{20}}$ **b.** $\frac{25x^6}{5x^8}$ **c.** $\frac{10y^7}{-2y^{10}}$.

Solution

a. $\frac{x^4}{x^{20}} = x^{4-20} = x^{-16} = \frac{1}{x^{16}}$

b. $\frac{25x^6}{5x^8} = \frac{25}{5} \cdot \frac{x^6}{x^8} = 5x^{6-8} = 5x^{-2} = \frac{5}{x^2}$

c. $\frac{10y^7}{-2y^{10}} = \frac{10}{-2} \cdot \frac{y^7}{y^{10}} = -5y^{7-10} = -5y^{-3} = -\frac{5}{y^3}$ ■

✓ **CHECK POINT 4** Simplify:

a. $\frac{x^2}{x^{10}}$ **b.** $\frac{75x^3}{5x^9}$ **c.** $\frac{50y^8}{-25y^{14}}$.

EXAMPLE 5 Simplifying an Exponential Expression

Simplify: $\frac{(5x^3)^2}{x^{10}}$.

Solution

$$\frac{(5x^3)^2}{x^{10}} = \frac{5^2(x^3)^2}{x^{10}}$$ Raise each factor in the product to the second power using $(ab)^n = a^n b^n$.

$$= \frac{5^2 x^{3 \cdot 2}}{x^{10}}$$ Raise powers to powers using $(b^m)^n = b^{mn}$.

$$= \frac{25x^6}{x^{10}}$$ Simplify.

$$= 25x^{6-10}$$ When dividing with the same base, subtract exponents: $\frac{b^m}{b^n} = b^{m-n}$.

$$= 25x^{-4}$$ Simplify. The base, x, now appears only once.

$$= \frac{25}{x^4}$$ Rewrite with a positive exponent using $b^{-n} = \frac{1}{b^n}$. ■

 **CHECK POINT 5** Simplify: $\frac{(6x^4)^2}{x^{11}}$.

EXAMPLE 6 Simplifying an Exponential Expression

Simplify: $\left(\frac{x^5}{x^2}\right)^{-3}$.

Solution

Method 1. First perform the division within the parentheses.

$$\left(\frac{x^5}{x^2}\right)^{-3} = (x^{5-2})^{-3}$$ Within parentheses, divide by subtracting exponents: $\frac{b^m}{b^n} = b^{m-n}$.

$$= (x^3)^{-3}$$ Simplify. The base, x, now appears only once.

$$= x^{3(-3)}$$ Raise powers to powers: $(b^m)^n = b^{mn}$.

$$= x^{-9}$$ Simplify.

$$= \frac{1}{x^9}$$ Rewrite with a positive exponent using $b^{-n} = \frac{1}{b^n}$.

Method 2. Remove parentheses first by raising the numerator and the denominator to the -3 power.

$$\left(\frac{x^5}{x^2}\right)^{-3} = \frac{(x^5)^{-3}}{(x^2)^{-3}}$$ Use $\left(\frac{a}{b}\right)^n = \frac{a^n}{b^n}$ and raise the numerator and denominator to the -3 power.

$$= \frac{x^{5(-3)}}{x^{2(-3)}}$$ Raise powers to powers using $(b^m)^n = b^{mn}$.

$$= \frac{x^{-15}}{x^{-6}}$$ Simplify.

$$= x^{-15-(-6)}$$ When dividing with the same base, subtract the exponent in the denominator from the exponent in the numerator: $\frac{b^m}{b^n} = b^{m-n}$.

$$= x^{-9}$$ Subtract: $-15 - (-6) = -15 + 6 = -9$. The base, x, now appears only once.

$$= \frac{1}{x^9}$$ Rewrite with a positive exponent using $b^{-n} = \frac{1}{b^n}$.

Which method do you prefer? ■

✓ CHECK POINT 6 Simplify: $\left(\frac{x^8}{x^4}\right)^{-5}$.

Scientific Notation

Table 1	Names of Large Numbers
10^2	hundred
10^3	thousand
10^6	million
10^9	billion
10^{12}	trillion
10^{15}	quadrillion
10^{18}	quintillion
10^{21}	sextillion
10^{24}	septillion
10^{27}	octillion
10^{30}	nonillion
10^{100}	googol
10^{googol}	googolplex

In 2009, the United States government spent more than it had collected in taxes, resulting in a budget deficit of \$1.35 trillion. Put into perspective, the \$1.35 trillion could pay for 40,000 players like Alex Rodriguez, whose \$33 million salary in 2009 made him baseball's richest man. Because a trillion is 10^{12} (see **Table 1**), the 2009 budget deficit can be expressed as

$$\$1.35 \times 10^{12}.$$

The number 1.35×10^{12} is written in a form called *scientific notation*.

Scientific Notation

A positive number is written in **scientific notation** when it is expressed in the form

$$a \times 10^n,$$

where a is a number greater than or equal to 1 and less than 10 $(1 \leq a < 10)$ and n is an integer.

It is customary to use the multiplication symbol, ×, rather than a dot, when writing a number in scientific notation.

Here are two examples of numbers in scientific notation:

- In 2010, humankind generated 1.2×10^{21} bytes, or 1.2 zettabytes, of digital information. (Put into perspective, if all 6.8 billion (6.8×10^9) people on Earth joined Twitter and continuously tweeted for a century, they would crank out one zettabyte of data.) (*Source*: LiveScience.com)
- The length of the AIDS virus is 1.1×10^{-4} millimeter.

3 Convert from scientific notation to decimal notation.

We can use n, the exponent on the 10 in $a \times 10^n$, to change a number in scientific notation to decimal notation. If n is **positive**, move the decimal point in a to the **right** n places. If n is **negative**, move the decimal point in a to the **left** $|n|$ places.

EXAMPLE 7 Converting from Scientific to Decimal Notation

Write each number in decimal notation:

a. 2.6×10^7 **b.** 1.1×10^{-4}.

Solution In each case, we use the exponent on the 10 to move the decimal point. In part (a), the exponent is positive, so we move the decimal point to the right. In part (b), the exponent is negative, so we move the decimal point to the left.

a. $2.6 \times 10^7 = 26{,}000{,}000$

$n = 7$

Move the decimal point 7 places to the right.

b. $1.1 \times 10^{-4} = 0.00011$

$n = -4$

Move the decimal point $|-4|$ places, or 4 places, to the left.

✓ **CHECK POINT 7** Write each number in decimal notation:

a. 7.4×10^9 **b.** 3.017×10^{-6}.

4 Convert from decimal notation to scientific notation.

To convert a positive number from decimal notation to scientific notation, we reverse the procedure of Example 7.

Converting from Decimal to Scientific Notation

Write the number in the form $a \times 10^n$.

- Determine a, the numerical factor. Move the decimal point in the given number to obtain a number greater than or equal to 1 and less than 10.
- Determine n, the exponent on 10^n. The absolute value of n is the number of places the decimal point was moved. The exponent n is positive if the given number is greater than 10 and negative if the given number is between 0 and 1.

EXAMPLE 8 Converting from Decimal Notation to Scientific Notation

Write each number in scientific notation:

a. 4,600,000 **b.** 0.000023.

Solution

a. $4{,}600{,}000 = 4.6 \times 10^6$

This number is greater than 10, so n is positive in $a \times 10^n$.

Move the decimal point in 4,600,000 to get $1 \leq a < 10$.

The decimal point moved 6 places from 4,600,000 to 4.6.

b. $0.000023 = 2.3 \times 10^{-5}$

This number is less than 1, so n is negative in $a \times 10^n$.

Move the decimal point in 0.000023 to get $1 \leq a < 10$.

The decimal point moved 5 places from 0.000023 to 2.3. ■

Using Technology

You can use your calculator's [EE] (enter exponent) or [EXP] key to convert from decimal to scientific notation. Here is how it's done for 0.000023:

Many Scientific Calculators

Keystrokes	Display
.000023 [EE] [=]	2.3 − 05

Many Graphing Calculators

Use the mode setting for scientific notation.

Keystrokes	Display
.000023 [ENTER]	2.3E-5

✓ **CHECK POINT 8** Write each number in scientific notation:

a. 7,410,000,000 **b.** 0.000000092.

5 Compute with scientific notation.

Computations with Scientific Notation

Properties of exponents are used to perform computations with numbers that are expressed in scientific notation.

Computations with Numbers in Scientific Notation

Multiplication

$$(a \times 10^n) \times (b \times 10^m) = (a \times b) \times 10^{n+m}$$

Add the exponents on 10 and multiply the other parts of the numbers separately.

Division

$$\frac{a \times 10^n}{b \times 10^m} = \left(\frac{a}{b}\right) \times 10^{n-m}$$

Subtract the exponents on 10 and divide the other parts of the numbers separately.

Exponentiation

$$(a \times 10^n)^m = a^n \times 10^{nm}$$

Multiply exponents on 10 and raise the other part of the number to the power.

After the computation is completed, the answer may require an adjustment before it is expressed in scientific notation.

Using Technology

$(4 \times 10^5)(2 \times 10^9)$ On a Calculator:

Many Scientific Calculators

4 [EE] 5 [×] 2 [EE] 9 [=]

Display: 8. 14

Many Graphing Calculators

4 [EE] 5 [×] 2 [EE] 9 [ENTER]

Display: 8E14

EXAMPLE 9 Computations with Scientific Notation

Perform the indicated computations, writing the answers in scientific notation:

a. $(4 \times 10^5)(2 \times 10^9)$ **b.** $\dfrac{1.2 \times 10^6}{4.8 \times 10^{-3}}$ **c.** $(5 \times 10^{-4})^3$.

Solution

a. $(4 \times 10^5)(2 \times 10^9) = (4 \times 2) \times (10^5 \times 10^9)$ Regroup.

$= 8 \times 10^{5+9}$ Add the exponents on 10 and multiply the other parts.

$= 8 \times 10^{14}$ Simplify.

b. $\dfrac{1.2 \times 10^6}{4.8 \times 10^{-3}} = \left(\dfrac{1.2}{4.8}\right) \times \left(\dfrac{10^6}{10^{-3}}\right)$ Regroup.

$= 0.25 \times 10^{6-(-3)}$ Subtract the exponents on 10 and divide the other parts.

$= 0.25 \times 10^9$ Simplify. Because 0.25 is not between 1 and 10, it must be written in scientific notation.

$= 2.5 \times 10^{-1} \times 10^9$ $0.25 = 2.5 \times 10^{-1}$

$= 2.5 \times 10^{-1+9}$ Add the exponents on 10.

$= 2.5 \times 10^8$ Simplify.

c. $(5 \times 10^{-4})^3 = 5^3 \times (10^{-4})^3$ $(ab)^n = a^n b^n$. Cube each factor in parentheses.

$= 125 \times 10^{-4 \cdot 3}$ Multiply the exponents and cube the other part of the number.

$= 125 \times 10^{-12}$ Simplify. 125 must be written in scientific notation.

$= 1.25 \times 10^2 \times 10^{-12}$ $125 = 1.25 \times 10^2$

$= 1.25 \times 10^{2+(-12)}$ Add the exponents on 10.

$= 1.25 \times 10^{-10}$ Simplify. ■

✓ CHECK POINT 9 Perform the indicated computations, writing the answers in scientific notation:

a. $(3 \times 10^8)(2 \times 10^2)$

b. $\dfrac{8.4 \times 10^7}{4 \times 10^{-4}}$

c. $(4 \times 10^{-2})^3$.

---

6 Solve applied problems using scientific notation.

Applications: Putting Numbers in Perspective

Due to tax cuts and spending increases, the United States began accumulating large deficits in the 1980s. To finance the deficit, the government had borrowed \$12.3 trillion as of December 2009. The graph in **Figure 8** shows the national debt increasing over time.

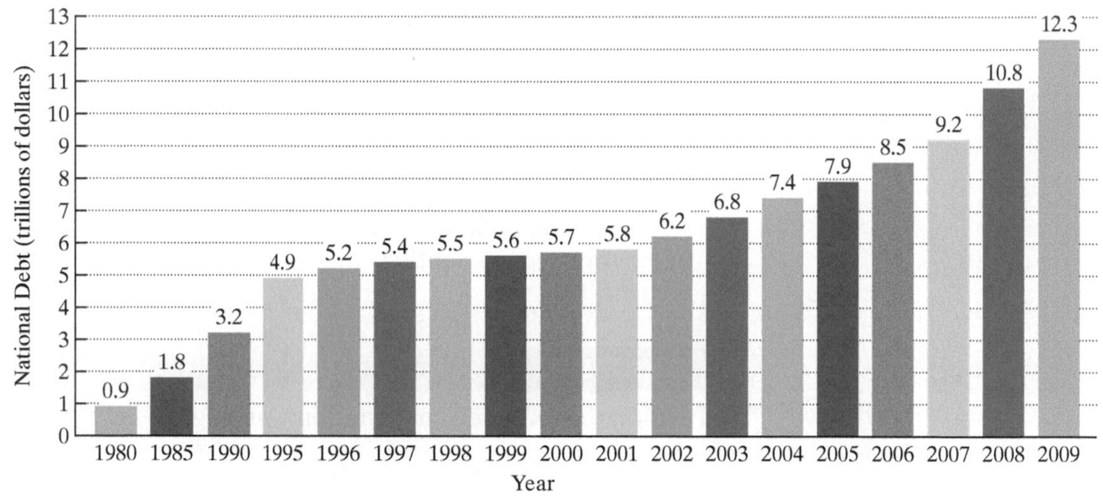

Figure 8

Source: Office of Management and Budget

Example 10 shows how we can use scientific notation to comprehend the meaning of a number such as 12.3 trillion.

EXAMPLE 10 The National Debt

As of December 2009, the national debt was \$12.3 trillion, or 12.3×10^{12} dollars. At that time, the U.S. population was approximately 307,000,000 (307 million), or 3.07×10^8. If the national debt was evenly divided among every individual in the United States, how much would each citizen have to pay?

Solution Although it is not necessary to do so, let's express the total debt, 12.3×10^{12} dollars, in scientific notation as 1.23×10^{13}. The amount each citizen must pay is the total debt, 1.23×10^{13} dollars, divided by the number of citizens, 3.07×10^8.

$$\begin{aligned} \frac{1.23 \times 10^{13}}{3.07 \times 10^8} &= \left(\frac{1.23}{3.07}\right) \times \left(\frac{10^{13}}{10^8}\right) \\ &\approx 0.401 \times 10^{13-8} \\ &= 0.401 \times 10^5 \\ &= (4.01 \times 10^{-1}) \times 10^5 \\ &= 4.01 \times 10^4 \\ &= 40{,}100 \end{aligned}$$

Every U.S. citizen would have to pay approximately \$40,100 to the federal government to pay off the national debt. ■

Using Technology

Here is the keystroke sequence for solving Example 10 using a calculator:

1.23 [EE] 13 [÷] 3.07 [EE] 8.

The quotient is displayed by pressing [=] on a scientific calculator or [ENTER] on a graphing calculator. The answer can be displayed in scientific or decimal notation. Consult your manual.

If a number is written in scientific notation, $a \times 10^n$, the digits in a are called **significant digits**.

National Debt: 1.23×10^{13} U.S. Population: 3.07×10^8

Three significant digits Three significant digits

Because these were the given numbers in Example 10, we rounded the answer, 4.01×10^4, to three significant digits. When multiplying or dividing in scientific notation where rounding is necessary and rounding instructions are not given, **round the scientific notation answer to the least number of significant digits found in any of the given numbers.**

✓ **CHECK POINT 10** The cost of President Obama's 2009 economic stimulus package was \$787 billion, or 7.87×10^{11} dollars. If this cost were evenly divided among every individual in the United States (approximately 3.07×10^8 people), how much would each citizen have to pay?

Blitzer Bonus

Seven Ways to Spend $1 Trillion

Confronting a national debt of \$12.3 trillion starts with grasping just how colossal \$1 trillion (1×10^{12}) actually is. To help you wrap your head around this mind-boggling number, and to put the national debt in further perspective, consider what \$1 trillion will buy:

- 40,816,326 new cars based on an average sticker price of \$24,500 each
- 5,574,136 homes based on the national median price of \$179,400 for existing single-family homes
- one year's salary for 14.7 million teachers based on the average teacher salary of \$68,000 in California
- the annual salaries of all 535 members of Congress for the next 10,742 years based on current salaries of \$174,000 per year
- the salary of basketball superstar LeBron James for 50,000 years based on an annual salary of \$20 million
- annual base pay for 59.5 million U.S. privates (that's 100 times the total number of active-duty soldiers in the Army) based on basic pay of \$16,794 per year
- salaries to hire all 2.8 million residents of the state of Kansas in full-time minimum-wage jobs for the next 23 years based on the federal minimum wage of \$7.25 per hour

Mike Kiev/Fotolia

Image © photobank.kiev.ua, 2009

Source: Kiplinger.com

Achieving Success

Form a study group with other students in your class. Working in small groups often serves as an excellent way to learn and reinforce new material. Set up helpful procedures and guidelines for the group. "Talk" math by discussing and explaining the concepts and exercises to one another.

CONCEPT AND VOCABULARY CHECK

Fill in each blank so that the resulting statement is true.

1. The negative exponent rule states that $b^{-n} =$ ____________, $b \neq 0$.
2. True or false: $4^{-2} = -4^2$ ____________
3. True or false: $4^{-2} = \frac{1}{4^2}$ ____________
4. Negative exponents in denominators can be evaluated using $\frac{1}{b^{-n}} =$ ____________, $b \neq 0$.
5. True or false: $\frac{1}{5^{-2}} = 5^2$ ____________
6. True or false: $\frac{1}{5^{-2}} = -5^2$ ____________
7. A positive number is written in scientific notation when it is expressed in the form $a \times 10^n$, where a is ______________________________ and n is a/an ____________.
8. True or false: 4×10^3 is written in scientific notation. ____________
9. True or false: 40×10^2 is written in scientific notation. ____________

7 EXERCISE SET

MyMathLab®

Watch the videos in MyMathLab

Download the MyDashBoard App

Practice Exercises

In Exercises 1–28, write each expression with positive exponents only. Then simplify, if possible.

1. 8^{-2}
2. 9^{-2}
3. 5^{-3}
4. 4^{-3}
5. $(-6)^{-2}$
6. $(-7)^{-2}$
7. -6^{-2}
8. -7^{-2}
9. 4^{-1}
10. 6^{-1}
11. $2^{-1} + 3^{-1}$
12. $3^{-1} - 6^{-1}$
13. $\frac{1}{3^{-2}}$
14. $\frac{1}{4^{-3}}$
15. $\frac{1}{(-3)^{-2}}$
16. $\frac{1}{(-2)^{-2}}$
17. $\frac{2^{-3}}{8^{-2}}$
18. $\frac{4^{-3}}{2^{-2}}$
19. $\left(\frac{1}{4}\right)^{-2}$
20. $\left(\frac{1}{5}\right)^{-2}$
21. $\left(\frac{3}{5}\right)^{-3}$
22. $\left(\frac{3}{4}\right)^{-3}$
23. $\frac{1}{6x^{-5}}$
24. $\frac{1}{8x^{-6}}$
25. $\frac{x^{-8}}{y^{-1}}$
26. $\frac{x^{-12}}{y^{-1}}$
27. $\frac{3}{(-5)^{-3}}$
28. $\frac{4}{(-3)^{-3}}$

In Exercises 29–78, simplify each exponential expression. Assume that variables represent nonzero real numbers.

29. $x^{-8} \cdot x^3$
30. $x^{-11} \cdot x^5$
31. $(4x^{-5})(2x^2)$
32. $(5x^{-7})(3x^3)$
33. $\frac{x^3}{x^9}$
34. $\frac{x^5}{x^{12}}$
35. $\frac{y}{y^{100}}$
36. $\frac{y}{y^{50}}$
37. $\frac{30z^5}{10z^{10}}$
38. $\frac{45z^4}{15z^{12}}$
39. $\frac{-8x^3}{2x^7}$
40. $\frac{-15x^4}{3x^9}$
41. $\frac{-9a^5}{27a^8}$
42. $\frac{-15a^8}{45a^{13}}$
43. $\frac{7w^5}{5w^{13}}$
44. $\frac{7w^8}{9w^{14}}$

45. $\dfrac{x^3}{(x^4)^2}$ **46.** $\dfrac{x^5}{(x^3)^2}$

47. $\dfrac{y^{-3}}{(y^4)^2}$ **48.** $\dfrac{y^{-5}}{(y^3)^2}$

49. $\dfrac{(4x^3)^2}{x^8}$ **50.** $\dfrac{(5x^3)^2}{x^7}$

51. $\dfrac{(6y^4)^3}{y^{-5}}$ **52.** $\dfrac{(4y^5)^3}{y^{-4}}$

50. $\left(\dfrac{x^4}{x^2}\right)^{-3}$ **54.** $\left(\dfrac{x^6}{x^2}\right)^{-3}$

55. $\left(\dfrac{4x^5}{2x^2}\right)^{-4}$ **56.** $\left(\dfrac{6x^7}{2x^2}\right)^{-4}$

57. $(3x^{-1})^{-2}$ **58.** $(4x^{-1})^{-2}$

59. $(-2y^{-1})^{-3}$ **60.** $(-3y^{-1})^{-3}$

61. $\dfrac{2x^5 \cdot 3x^7}{15x^6}$ **62.** $\dfrac{3x^3 \cdot 5x^{14}}{20x^{14}}$

63. $(x^3)^5 \cdot x^{-7}$ **64.** $(x^4)^3 \cdot x^{-5}$

65. $(2y^3)^4y^{-6}$ **66.** $(3y^4)^3y^{-7}$

67. $\dfrac{(y^3)^4}{(y^2)^7}$ **68.** $\dfrac{(y^2)^5}{(y^3)^4}$

69. $(y^{10})^{-5}$ **70.** $(y^{20})^{-5}$

71. $(a^4b^5)^{-3}$ **72.** $(a^5b^3)^{-4}$

73. $(a^{-2}b^6)^{-4}$ **74.** $(a^{-7}b^2)^{-5}$

75. $\left(\dfrac{x^2}{2}\right)^{-2}$ **76.** $\left(\dfrac{x^2}{2}\right)^{-3}$

77. $\left(\dfrac{x^2}{y^3}\right)^{-3}$ **78.** $\left(\dfrac{x^3}{y^2}\right)^{-4}$

In Exercises 79–90, write each number in decimal notation without the use of exponents.

79. 8.7×10^2 **80.** 2.75×10^3

81. 9.23×10^5 **82.** 7.24×10^4

83. 3.4×10^0 **84.** 9.115×10^0

85. 7.9×10^{-1} **86.** 8.6×10^{-1}

87. 2.15×10^{-2} **88.** 3.14×10^{-2}

89. 7.86×10^{-4} **90.** 4.63×10^{-5}

In Exercises 91–106, write each number in scientific notation.

91. 32,400 **92.** 327,000

93. 220,000,000 **94.** 370,000,000,000

95. 713 **96.** 623

97. 6751 **98.** 9832

99. 0.0027 **100.** 0.00083

101. 0.0000202 **102.** 0.00000103

103. 0.005 **104.** 0.006

105. 3.14159 **106.** 2.71828

In Exercises 107–126, perform the indicated computations. Write the answers in scientific notation.

107. $(2 \times 10^3)(3 \times 10^2)$

108. $(3 \times 10^4)(3 \times 10^2)$

109. $(2 \times 10^5)(8 \times 10^3)$

110. $(4 \times 10^3)(5 \times 10^4)$

111. $\dfrac{12 \times 10^6}{4 \times 10^2}$ **112.** $\dfrac{20 \times 10^{20}}{10 \times 10^{10}}$

113. $\dfrac{15 \times 10^4}{5 \times 10^{-2}}$ **114.** $\dfrac{18 \times 10^2}{9 \times 10^{-3}}$

115. $\dfrac{15 \times 10^{-4}}{5 \times 10^2}$ **116.** $\dfrac{18 \times 10^{-2}}{9 \times 10^3}$

117. $\dfrac{180 \times 10^6}{2 \times 10^3}$ **118.** $\dfrac{180 \times 10^8}{2 \times 10^4}$

119. $\dfrac{3 \times 10^4}{12 \times 10^{-3}}$ **120.** $\dfrac{5 \times 10^2}{20 \times 10^{-3}}$

121. $(5 \times 10^2)^3$ **122.** $(4 \times 10^3)^2$

123. $(3 \times 10^{-2})^4$

124. $(2 \times 10^{-3})^5$

125. $(4 \times 10^6)^{-1}$ **126.** $(5 \times 10^4)^{-1}$

Practice PLUS

In Exercises 127–134, simplify each exponential expression. Assume that variables represent nonzero real numbers.

127. $\dfrac{(x^{-2}y)^{-3}}{(x^2y^{-1})^3}$

128. $\dfrac{(xy^{-2})^{-2}}{(x^{-2}y)^{-3}}$

129. $(2x^{-3}yz^{-6})(2x)^{-5}$

130. $(3x^{-4}yz^{-7})(3x)^{-3}$

131. $\left(\dfrac{x^3y^4z^5}{x^{-3}y^{-4}z^{-5}}\right)^{-2}$

132. $\left(\dfrac{x^4y^5z^6}{x^{-4}y^{-5}z^{-6}}\right)^{-4}$

133. $\dfrac{(2^{-1}x^{-2}y^{-1})^{-2}(2x^{-4}y^3)^{-2}(16x^{-3}y^3)^0}{(2x^{-3}y^{-5})^2}$

134. $\dfrac{(2^{-1}x^{-3}y^{-1})^{-2}(2x^{-6}y^4)^{-2}(9x^3y^{-3})^0}{(2x^{-4}y^{-6})^2}$

In Exercises 135–138, perform the indicated computations. Express answers in scientific notation.

135. $(5 \times 10^3)(1.2 \times 10^{-4}) \div (2.4 \times 10^2)$

136. $(2 \times 10^2)(2.6 \times 10^{-3}) \div (4 \times 10^3)$

137. $\dfrac{(1.6 \times 10^4)(7.2 \times 10^{-3})}{(3.6 \times 10^8)(4 \times 10^{-3})}$

138. $\dfrac{(1.2 \times 10^6)(8.7 \times 10^{-2})}{(2.9 \times 10^6)(3 \times 10^{-3})}$

Application Exercises

We have seen that in 2009, the United States government spent more than it had collected in taxes, resulting in a budget deficit of \$1.35 trillion. In Exercises 139–142, you will use scientific notation to put a number like 1.35 trillion in perspective.

139. **a.** Express 1.35 trillion in scientific notation.

b. Express the 2009 U.S. population, 307 million, in scientific notation.

c. Use your scientific notation answers from parts (a) and (b) to answer this question: If the 2009 budget deficit was evenly divided among every individual in the United States, how much would each citizen have to pay? Express the answer in scientific and decimal notations.

140. **a.** Express 1.35 trillion in scientific notation.

b. A trip around the world at the Equator is approximately 25,000 miles. Express this number in scientific notation.

c. Use your scientific notation answers from parts (a) and (b) to answer this question: How many times can you circle the world at the Equator by traveling 1.35 trillion miles?

141. If there are approximately 3.2×10^7 seconds in a year, approximately how many years is 1.35 trillion seconds? (*Note:* 1.35 trillion seconds would take us back in time to a period when Neanderthals were using stones to make tools.)

142. The Washington Monument, overlooking the U.S. Capitol, stands about 555 feet tall. Stacked end to end, how many monuments would it take to reach 1.35 trillion feet? (*Note:* That's more than twice the distance from Earth to the sun.)

Use the motion formula $d = rt$, distance equals rate times time, and the fact that light travels at the rate of 1.86×10^5 miles per second, to solve Exercises 143–144.

143. If the moon is approximately 2.325×10^5 miles from Earth, how many seconds does it take moonlight to reach Earth?

144. If the sun is approximately 9.14×10^7 miles from Earth, how many seconds, to the nearest tenth of a second, does it take sunlight to reach Earth?

145. Refer to the Blitzer Bonus. Use scientific notation to verify any three of the bulleted items on ways to spend \$1 trillion.

Writing in Mathematics

146. Explain the negative exponent rule and give an example.

147. How do you know if an exponential expression is simplified?

148. How do you know if a number is written in scientific notation?

149. Explain how to convert from scientific to decimal notation and give an example.

150. Explain how to convert from decimal to scientific notation and give an example.

151. Describe one advantage of expressing a number in scientific notation over decimal notation.

Critical Thinking Exercises

Make Sense? *In Exercises 152–155, determine whether each statement "makes sense" or "does not make sense" and explain your reasoning.*

152. There are many exponential expressions that are equal to $36x^{12}$, such as $(6x^6)^2$, $(6x^3)(6x^9)$, $36(x^3)^9$, and $6^2(x^2)^6$.

153. If 5^{-2} is raised to the third power, the result is a number between 0 and 1.

154. The population of Colorado is approximately 4.6×10^{12}.

155. I wrote a number where there is no advantage to using scientific notation instead of decimal notation.

In Exercises 156–163, determine whether each statement is true or false. If the statement is false, make the necessary change(s) to produce a true statement.

156. $4^{-2} < 4^{-3}$

157. $5^{-2} > 2^{-5}$

158. $(-2)^4 = 2^{-4}$

159. $5^2 \cdot 5^{-2} > 2^5 \cdot 2^{-5}$

160. $534.7 = 5.347 \times 10^3$

161. $\dfrac{8 \times 10^{30}}{4 \times 10^{-5}} = 2 \times 10^{25}$

162. $(7 \times 10^5) + (2 \times 10^{-3}) = 9 \times 10^2$

163. $(4 \times 10^3) + (3 \times 10^2) = 4.3 \times 10^3$

164. The mad Dr. Frankenstein has gathered enough bits and pieces (so to speak) for $2^{-1} + 2^{-2}$ of his creature-to-be. Write a fraction that represents the amount of his creature that must still be obtained.

Technology Exercises

165. Use a calculator in a fraction mode to check any five of your answers in Exercises 1–22.

166. Use a calculator to check any three of your answers in Exercises 79–90.

167. Use a calculator to check any three of your answers in Exercises 91–106.

168. Use a calculator with an EE or EXP key to check any four of your computations in Exercises 107–126. Display the result of the computation in scientific notation.

Review Exercises

169. Solve: $8 - 6x > 4x - 12$.

170. Simplify: $24 \div 8 \cdot 3 + 28 \div (-7)$.

171. List the whole numbers in this set:

$$\left\{-4, -\frac{1}{5}, 0, \pi, \sqrt{16}, \sqrt{17}\right\}.$$

Preview Exercises

In each exercise, find the product.

172. $4x^3(4x^2 - 3x + 1)$

173. $9xy(3xy^2 - y + 9)$

174. $(x + 3)(x^2 + 5)$

GROUP PROJECT

A large number can be put into perspective by comparing it with another number. For example, we put the \$12.3 trillion national debt (Example 10) into perspective by comparing this number to the number of U.S. citizens. In Exercises 139–142, we put the \$1.35 trillion budget deficit into perspective by comparing 1.35 trillion to the number of U.S. citizens, the distance around the world, the number of seconds in a year, and the height of the Washington Monument.

For this project, each group member should consult an almanac, a newspaper, or the Internet to find a number greater than one million. Explain to other members of the group the context in which the large number is used. Express the number in scientific notation. Then put the number into perspective by comparing it with another number.

Summary

Definitions and Concepts	Examples
Section 1 Adding and Subtracting Polynomials	
A polynomial is a single term or the sum of two or more terms containing variables with whole number exponents. A monomial is a polynomial with exactly one term; a binomial has exactly two terms; a trinomial has exactly three terms. The degree of a polynomial is the highest power of all the terms. The standard form of a polynomial is written in descending powers of the variable.	Polynomials Monomial: $2x^5$ (Degree is 5.) Binomial: $6x^3 + 5x$ (Degree is 3.) Trinomial: $7x + 4x^2 - 5$ (Degree is 2.)
To add polynomials, add like terms.	$(6x^3 + 5x^2 - 7x) + (-9x^3 + x^2 + 6x)$ $= (6x^3 - 9x^3) + (5x^2 + x^2) + (-7x + 6x)$ $= -3x^3 + 6x^2 - x$
The opposite, or additive inverse, of a polynomial is that polynomial with the sign of every coefficient changed. To subtract two polynomials, add the first polynomial and the opposite of the polynomial being subtracted.	$(5y^3 - 9y^2 - 4) - (3y^3 - 12y^2 - 5)$ $= (5y^3 - 9y^2 - 4) + (-3y^3 + 12y^2 + 5)$ $= (5y^3 - 3y^3) + (-9y^2 + 12y^2) + (-4 + 5)$ $= 2y^3 + 3y^2 + 1$

Definitions and Concepts	Examples

Section 1 Adding and Subtracting Polynomials (continued)

The graphs of equations defined by polynomials of degree 2, shaped like bowls or inverted bowls, can be obtained using the point-plotting method.

Graph: $y = x^2 - 1$.

x	$y = x^2 - 1$
-2	$(-2)^2 - 1 = 3$
-1	$(-1)^2 - 1 = 0$
0	$0^2 - 1 = -1$
1	$1^2 - 1 = 0$
2	$2^2 - 1 = 3$

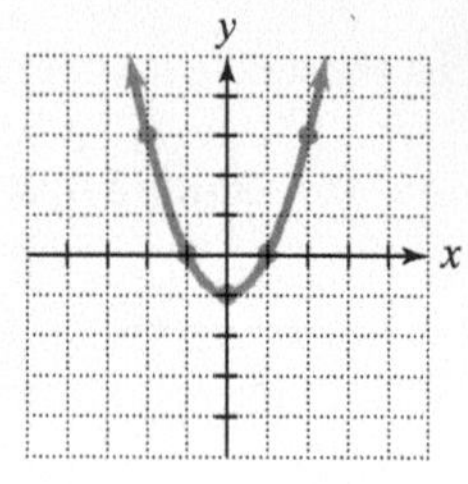

Section 2 Multiplying Polynomials

Properties of Exponents

Product Rule: $b^m \cdot b^n = b^{m+n}$

Power Rule: $(b^m)^n = b^{mn}$

Products to Powers: $(ab)^n = a^n b^n$

$$x^3 \cdot x^8 = x^{3+8} = x^{11}$$

$$(x^3)^8 = x^{3\cdot 8} = x^{24}$$

$$(-5x^2)^3 = (-5)^3(x^2)^3 = -125x^6$$

To multiply monomials, multiply coefficients and add exponents.

$$(-6x^4)(3x^{10}) = -6 \cdot 3x^{4+10} = -18x^{14}$$

To multiply a monomial and a polynomial, multiply each term of the polynomial by the monomial.

$$2x^4(3x^2 - 6x + 5)$$
$$= 2x^4 \cdot 3x^2 - 2x^4 \cdot 6x + 2x^4 \cdot 5$$
$$= 6x^6 - 12x^5 + 10x^4$$

To multiply polynomials when neither is a monomial, multiply each term of one polynomial by each term of the other polynomial. Then combine like terms.

$$(2x + 3)(5x^2 - 4x + 2)$$
$$= 2x(5x^2 - 4x + 2) + 3(5x^2 - 4x + 2)$$
$$= 10x^3 - 8x^2 + 4x + 15x^2 - 12x + 6$$
$$= 10x^3 + 7x^2 - 8x + 6$$

Section 3 Special Products

The FOIL method may be used when multiplying two binomials: First terms multiplied. Outside terms multiplied. Inside terms multiplied. Last terms multiplied.

F O I L

$$(3x + 7)(2x - 5) = 3x \cdot 2x + 3x(-5) + 7 \cdot 2x + 7(-5)$$
$$= 6x^2 - 15x + 14x - 35$$
$$= 6x^2 - x - 35$$

The Product of the Sum and Difference of Two Terms

$$(A + B)(A - B) = A^2 - B^2$$

$$(4x + 7)(4x - 7) = (4x)^2 - 7^2$$
$$= 16x^2 - 49$$

Definitions and Concepts	Examples

Section 3 Special Products (continued)

Definitions and Concepts	Examples
The Square of a Binomial Sum $(A + B)^2 = A^2 + 2AB + B^2$	$(x^2 + 6)^2 = (x^2)^2 + 2 \cdot x^2 \cdot 6 + 6^2$ $= x^4 + 12x^2 + 36$
The Square of a Binomial Difference $(A - B)^2 = A^2 - 2AB + B^2$	$(9x - 3)^2 = (9x)^2 - 2 \cdot 9x \cdot 3 + 3^2$ $= 81x^2 - 54x + 9$

Section 4 Polynomials in Several Variables

To evaluate a polynomial in several variables, substitute the given value for each variable and perform the resulting computation.

Evaluate $4x^2y + 3xy - 2x$ for $x = -1$ and $y = -3$.

$$\begin{aligned} &4x^2y + 3xy - 2x \\ &= 4(-1)^2(-3) + 3(-1)(-3) - 2(-1) \\ &= 4(1)(-3) + 3(-1)(-3) - 2(-1) \\ &= -12 + 9 + 2 = -1 \end{aligned}$$

For a polynomial in two variables, the degree of a term is the sum of the exponents on its variables. The degree of the polynomial is the highest degree of all its terms.

$$7x^2y + 12x^4y^3 - 17x^5 + 6$$

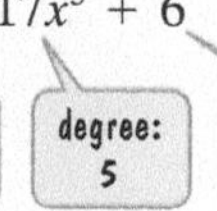

Degree of polynomial $= 7$

Polynomials in several variables are added, subtracted, and multiplied using the same rules for polynomials in one variable.

$$\begin{aligned} &(5x^2y^3 - xy + 4y^2) - (8x^2y^3 - 6xy - 2y^2) \\ &= (5x^2y^3 - xy + 4y^2) + (-8x^2y^3 + 6xy + 2y^2) \\ &= (5x^2y^3 - 8x^2y^3) + (-xy + 6xy) + (4y^2 + 2y^2) \\ &= -3x^2y^3 + 5xy + 6y^2 \end{aligned}$$

F O I L

$$\begin{aligned} (3x - 2y)(x - y) &= 3x \cdot x + 3x(-y) + (-2y)x + (-2y)(-y) \\ &= 3x^2 - 3xy - 2xy + 2y^2 \\ &= 3x^2 - 5xy + 2y^2 \end{aligned}$$

Section 5 Dividing Polynomials

Definitions and Concepts	Examples
Additional Properties of Exponents	
Quotient Rule: $\frac{b^m}{b^n} = b^{m-n}, \quad b \neq 0$	$\frac{x^{12}}{x^4} = x^{12-4} = x^8$
Zero-Exponent Rule: $b^0 = 1, \quad b \neq 0$	$(-3)^0 = 1 \qquad -3^0 = -(3^0) = -1$
Quotients to Powers: $\left(\frac{a}{b}\right)^n = \frac{a^n}{b^n}, \quad b \neq 0$	$\left(\frac{y^2}{4}\right)^3 = \frac{(y^2)^3}{4^3} = \frac{y^{2 \cdot 3}}{4 \cdot 4 \cdot 4} = \frac{y^6}{64}$
To divide monomials, divide coefficients and subtract exponents.	$\frac{-40x^{40}}{20x^{20}} = \frac{-40}{20}x^{40-20} = -2x^{20}$

Definitions and Concepts	Examples

Section 5 Dividing Polynomials (continued)

To divide a polynomial by a monomial, divide each term of the polynomial by the monomial.

$$\frac{8x^6 - 4x^3 + 10x}{2x}$$
$$= \frac{8x^6}{2x} - \frac{4x^3}{2x} + \frac{10x}{2x}$$
$$= 4x^{6-1} - 2x^{3-1} + 5x^{1-1} = 4x^5 - 2x^2 + 5$$

Section 6 Dividing Polynomials by Binomials

To divide a polynomial by a binomial, begin by arranging the polynomial in descending powers of the variable. If a power of a variable is missing, add that power with a coefficient of 0. Repeat the four steps—divide, multiply, subtract, bring down the next term—until the degree of the remainder is less than the degree of the divisor.

Divide: $\frac{10x^2 + 13x + 8}{2x + 3}$.

$$\begin{array}{r} 5x - 1 + \frac{11}{2x+3} \\ 2x + 3\overline{)10x^2 + 13x + 8} \\ \underline{10x^2 + 15x} \\ -2x + 8 \\ \underline{-2x - 3} \\ 11 \end{array}$$

Section 7 Negative Exponents and Scientific Notation

Negative Exponents in Numerators and Denominators

If $b \neq 0$, $b^{-n} = \frac{1}{b^n}$ and $\frac{1}{b^{-n}} = b^n$.

$$6^{-2} = \frac{1}{6^2} = \frac{1}{36}$$
$$\frac{1}{(-2)^{-4}} = (-2)^4 = 16$$
$$\left(\frac{2}{3}\right)^{-3} = \frac{2^{-3}}{3^{-3}} = \frac{3^3}{2^3} = \frac{27}{8}$$

An exponential expression is simplified when

- Each base occurs only once.
- No parentheses appear.
- No powers are raised to powers.
- No negative or zero exponents appear.

Simplify: $\frac{(2x^4)^3}{x^{18}}$.

$$\frac{(2x^4)^3}{x^{18}} = \frac{2^3(x^4)^3}{x^{18}} = \frac{8x^{4\cdot 3}}{x^{18}} = \frac{8x^{12}}{x^{18}} = 8x^{12-18} = 8x^{-6} = \frac{8}{x^6}$$

A positive number in scientific notation is expressed as $a \times 10^n$, where $1 \leq a < 10$ and n is an integer.

Write 2.9×10^{-3} in decimal notation.

$$2.9 \times 10^{-3} = .0029 = 0.0029$$

Write 16,000 in scientific notation.

$$16{,}000 = 1.6 \times 10^4$$

Use properties of exponents with base 10

$$10^m \cdot 10^n = 10^{m+n}, \quad \frac{10^m}{10^n} = 10^{m-n}, \quad \text{and} \quad (10^m)^n = 10^{mn}$$

to perform computations with scientific notation.

$$(5 \times 10^3)(4 \times 10^{-8})$$
$$= 5 \cdot 4 \times 10^{3-8}$$
$$= 20 \times 10^{-5}$$
$$= 2 \times 10^1 \times 10^{-5} = 2 \times 10^{-4}$$

REVIEW EXERCISES

1 *In Exercises 1–3, identify each polynomial as a monomial, binomial, or trinomial. Give the degree of the polynomial.*

1. $7x^4 + 9x$
2. $3x + 5x^2 - 2$
3. $16x$

In Exercises 4–8, add or subtract as indicated.

4. $(-6x^3 + 7x^2 - 9x + 3) + (14x^3 + 3x^2 - 11x - 7)$
5. $(9y^3 - 7y^2 + 5) + (4y^3 - y^2 + 7y - 10)$
6. $(5y^2 - y - 8) - (-6y^2 + 3y - 4)$
7. $(13x^4 - 8x^3 + 2x^2) - (5x^4 - 3x^3 + 2x^2 - 6)$
8. Subtract $x^4 + 7x^2 - 11x$ from $-13x^4 - 6x^2 + 5x$.

In Exercises 9–11, add or subtract as indicated.

9. Add. $\begin{array}{r} 7y^4 - 6y^3 + 4y^2 - 4y \\ \underline{y^3 - y^2 + 3y - 4} \end{array}$
10. Subtract. $\begin{array}{r} 7x^2 - 9x + 2 \\ \underline{-(4x^2 - 2x - 7)} \end{array}$
11. Subtract. $\begin{array}{r} 5x^3 - 6x^2 - 9x + 14 \\ \underline{-(-5x^3 + 3x^2 - 11x + 3)} \end{array}$

In Exercises 12–13, graph each equation.

12. $y = x^2 + 3$
13. $y = 1 - x^2$

2 *In Exercises 14–18, simplify each expression.*

14. $x^{20} \cdot x^3$
15. $y \cdot y^5 \cdot y^8$
16. $(x^{20})^5$
17. $(10y)^2$
18. $(-4x^{10})^3$

In Exercises 19–27, find each product.

19. $(5x)(10x^3)$
20. $(-12y^7)(3y^4)$
21. $(-2x^5)(-3x^4)(5x^3)$
22. $7x(3x^2 + 9)$
23. $5x^3(4x^2 - 11x)$
24. $3y^2(-7y^2 + 3y - 6)$
25. $2y^5(8y^3 - 10y^2 + 1)$
26. $(x + 3)(x^2 - 5x + 2)$
27. $(3y - 2)(4y^2 + 3y - 5)$

In Exercises 28–29, use a vertical format to find each product.

28. $\begin{array}{r} y^2 - 4y + 7 \\ \underline{3y - 5} \end{array}$
29. $\begin{array}{r} 4x^3 - 2x^2 - 6x - 1 \\ \underline{2x + 3} \end{array}$

3 *In Exercises 30–42, find each product.*

30. $(x + 6)(x + 2)$
31. $(3y - 5)(2y + 1)$
32. $(4x^2 - 2)(x^2 - 3)$
33. $(5x + 4)(5x - 4)$
34. $(7 - 2y)(7 + 2y)$
35. $(y^2 + 1)(y^2 - 1)$
36. $(x + 3)^2$
37. $(3y + 4)^2$
38. $(y - 1)^2$
39. $(5y - 2)^2$
40. $(x^2 + 4)^2$
41. $(x^2 + 4)(x^2 - 4)$
42. $(x^2 + 4)(x^2 - 5)$
43. Write a polynomial in descending powers of x that represents the area of the shaded region.

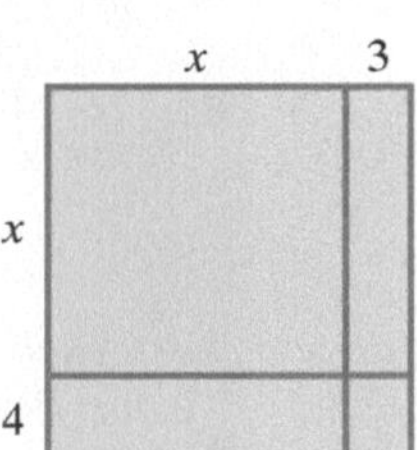

44. The parking garage shown in the figure measures 30 yards by 20 yards. The length and the width are each increased by a fixed amount, x yards. Write a trinomial that describes the area of the expanded garage.

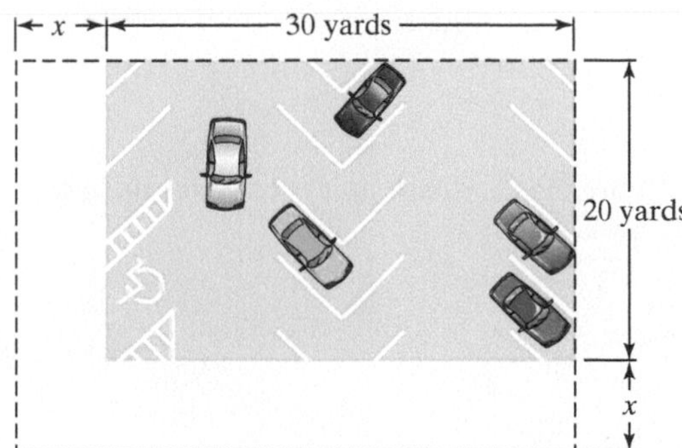

4

45. Evaluate $2x^3y - 4xy^2 + 5y + 6$ for $x = -1$ and $y = 2$.
46. Determine the coefficient of each term, the degree of each term, and the degree of the polynomial:

$$4x^2y + 9x^3y^2 - 17x^4 - 12.$$

In Exercises 47–56, perform the indicated operations.

47. $(7x^2 - 8xy + y^2) + (-8x^2 - 9xy + 4y^2)$

48. $(13x^3y^2 - 5x^2y - 9x^2) - (11x^3y^2 - 6x^2y - 3x^2 + 4)$

49. $(-7x^2y^3)(5x^4y^6)$

50. $5ab^2(3a^2b^3 - 4ab)$

51. $(x + 7y)(3x - 5y)$

52. $(4xy - 3)(9xy - 1)$

53. $(3x + 5y)^2$

54. $(xy - 7)^2$

55. $(7x + 4y)(7x - 4y)$

56. $(a - b)(a^2 + ab + b^2)$

5 *In Exercises 57–63, simplify each expression.*

57. $\frac{6^{40}}{6^{10}}$

58. $\frac{x^{18}}{x^3}$

59. $(-10)^0$

60. -10^0

61. $400x^0$

62. $\left(\frac{x^4}{2}\right)^3$

63. $\left(\frac{-3}{2y^6}\right)^4$

In Exercises 64–68, divide and check each answer.

64. $\frac{-15y^8}{3y^2}$

65. $\frac{40x^8y^6}{5xy^3}$

66. $\frac{18x^4 - 12x^2 + 36x}{6x}$

67. $\frac{30x^8 - 25x^7 - 40x^5}{-5x^3}$

68. $\frac{27x^3y^2 - 9x^2y - 18xy^2}{3xy}$

6 *In Exercises 69–72, divide and check each answer.*

69. $\frac{2x^2 + 3x - 14}{x - 2}$

70. $\frac{2x^3 - 5x^2 + 7x + 5}{2x + 1}$

71. $\frac{x^3 - 2x^2 - 33x - 7}{x - 7}$

72. $\frac{y^3 - 27}{y - 3}$

7 *In Exercises 73–77, write each expression with positive exponents only and then simplify.*

73. 7^{-2}

74. $(-4)^{-3}$

75. $2^{-1} + 4^{-1}$

76. $\frac{1}{5^{-2}}$

77. $\left(\frac{2}{5}\right)^{-3}$

In Exercises 78–86, simplify each exponential expression. Assume that variables in denominators do not equal zero.

78. $\frac{x^3}{x^9}$

79. $\frac{30y^6}{5y^8}$

80. $(5x^{-7})(6x^2)$

81. $\frac{x^4 \cdot x^{-2}}{x^{-6}}$

82. $\frac{(3y^3)^4}{y^{10}}$

83. $\frac{y^{-7}}{(y^4)^3}$

84. $(2x^{-1})^{-3}$

85. $\left(\frac{x^7}{x^4}\right)^{-2}$

86. $\frac{(y^3)^4}{(y^{-2})^4}$

In Exercises 87–89, write each number in decimal notation without the use of exponents.

87. 2.3×10^4

88. 1.76×10^{-3}

89. 9×10^{-1}

In Exercises 90–93, write each number in scientific notation.

90. 73,900,000

91. 0.00062

92. 0.38

93. 3.8

In Exercises 94–96, perform the indicated computation. Write the answers in scientific notation.

94. $(6 \times 10^{-3})(1.5 \times 10^6)$

95. $\frac{2 \times 10^2}{4 \times 10^{-3}}$

96. $(4 \times 10^{-2})^2$

In Exercises 97–98, use 10^6 for one million and 10^9 for one billion to rewrite the number in each statement in scientific notation.

97. The 2009 economic stimulus package allocated \$53.6 billion for grants to states for education.

98. The population of the United States at the time the economic stimulus package was voted into law was approximately 307 million.

99. Use your scientific notation answers from Exercises 97 and 98 to answer this question:

If the cost for grants to states for education was evenly divided among every individual in the United States, how much would each citizen have to pay?

CHAPTER TEST

Step-by-step test solutions are found on the Chapter Test Prep Videos available in MyMathLab® or on YouTube (search "BlitzerIntroAlg" and click on "Channels").

1. Identify $9x + 6x^2 - 4$ as a monomial, binomial, or trinomial. Give the degree of the polynomial.

In Exercises 2–3, add or subtract as indicated.

2. $(7x^3 + 3x^2 - 5x - 11) + (6x^3 - 2x^2 + 4x - 13)$

3. $(9x^3 - 6x^2 - 11x - 4) - (4x^3 - 8x^2 - 13x + 5)$

4. Graph the equation: $y = x^2 - 3$. Select integers for x, starting with -3 and ending with 3.

In Exercises 5–11, find each product.

5. $(-7x^3)(5x^8)$

6. $6x^2(8x^3 - 5x - 2)$

7. $(3x + 2)(x^2 - 4x - 3)$

8. $(3y + 7)(2y - 9)$

9. $(7x + 5)(7x - 5)$

10. $(x^2 + 3)^2$

11. $(5x - 3)^2$

12. Evaluate $4x^2y + 5xy - 6x$ for $x = -2$ and $y = 3$.

In Exercises 13–15, perform the indicated operations.

13. $(8x^2y^3 - xy + 2y^2) - (6x^2y^3 - 4xy - 10y^2)$

14. $(3a - 7b)(4a + 5b)$

15. $(2x + 3y)^2$

In Exercises 16–18, divide and check each answer.

16. $\dfrac{-25x^{16}}{5x^4}$

17. $\dfrac{15x^4 - 10x^3 + 25x^2}{5x}$

18. $\dfrac{2x^3 - 3x^2 + 4x + 4}{2x + 1}$

In Exercises 19–20, write each expression with positive exponents only and then simplify.

19. 10^{-2}

20. $\dfrac{1}{4^{-3}}$

In Exercises 21–26, simplify each expression.

21. $(-3x^2)^3$

22. $\dfrac{20x^3}{5x^8}$

23. $(-7x^{-8})(3x^2)$

24. $\dfrac{(2y^3)^4}{y^8}$

25. $(5x^{-4})^{-2}$

26. $\left(\dfrac{x^{10}}{x^5}\right)^{-3}$

27. Write 3.7×10^{-4} in decimal notation.

28. Write 7,600,000 in scientific notation.

In Exercises 29–30, perform the indicated computation. Write the answers in scientific notation.

29. $(4.1 \times 10^2)(3 \times 10^{-5})$

30. $\dfrac{8.4 \times 10^6}{4 \times 10^{-2}}$

31. Write a polynomial in descending powers of x that represents the area of the figure.

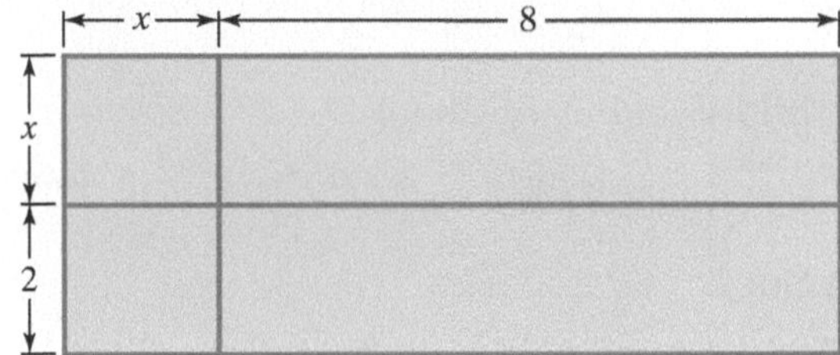

Answers to Selected Exercises

Section 1 Check Point Exercises

1. $5x^3 + 4x^2 - 8x - 20$ **2.** $5x^3 + 4x^2 - 8x - 20$ **3.** $7x^2 + 11x + 4$ **4.** $7x^3 + 3x^2 + 12x - 8$ **5.** $3y^3 - 10y^2 - 11y - 8$

6. $y = x^2 - 1$

(−3, 8) (3, 8) (−2, 3) (2, 3) (−1, 0) (1, 0) (0, −1)

Concept and Vocabulary Check

1. whole **2.** standard **3.** monomial **4.** binomial **5.** trinomial **6.** n **7.** greatest **8.** like **9.** opposite

Exercise Set 1

1. binomial, 1 **3.** binomial, 3 **5.** monomial, 2 **7.** monomial, 0 **9.** trinomial, 2 **11.** trinomial, 4 **13.** binomial, 3 **15.** monomial, 23 **17.** $-8x + 13$ **19.** $12x^2 + 15x - 9$ **21.** $10x^2 - 12x$ **23.** $5x^2 - 3x + 13$ **25.** $4y^3 + 10y^2 + y - 2$ **27.** $3x^3 + 2x^2 - 9x + 7$ **29.** $-2y^3 + 4y^2 + 13y + 13$ **31.** $-3y^6 + 8y^4 + y^2$ **33.** $10x^3 + 1$ **35.** $-\frac{2}{5}x^4 + x^3 - \frac{1}{8}x^2$ **37.** $0.01x^5 + x^4 - 0.1x^3 + 0.3x + 0.33$ **39.** $11y^3 - 3y^2$ **41.** $-2x^2 - x + 1$ **43.** $-\frac{1}{4}x^4 - \frac{7}{15}x^3 - 0.3$ **45.** $-y^3 + 8y^2 - 3y - 14$ **47.** $-5x^3 - 6x^2 + x - 4$ **49.** $7x^4 - 2x^3 + 4x - 2$ **51.** $8x^2 + 7x - 5$ **53.** $9x^3 - 4.9x^2 + 11.1$ **55.** $-2x - 10$ **57.** $-5x^2 - 9x - 12$ **59.** $-5x^2 - x$ **61.** $-4x^2 - 4x - 6$ **63.** $-2y - 6$ **65.** $6y^3 + y^2 + 7y - 20$ **67.** $n^3 + 2$ **69.** $y^6 - y^3 - y^2 + y$ **71.** $26x^4 + 9x^2 + 6x$ **73.** $\frac{5}{7}x^3 - \frac{9}{20}x$ **75.** $4x + 6$ **77.** $10x^2 - 7$ **79.** $-4y^2 - 7y + 5$ **81.** $9x^3 + 11x^2 - 8$ **83.** $-y^3 + 8y^2 + y + 14$ **85.** $7x^4 - 2x^3 + 3x^2 - x + 2$ **87.** $0.05x^3 + 0.02x^2 + 1.02x$

89.
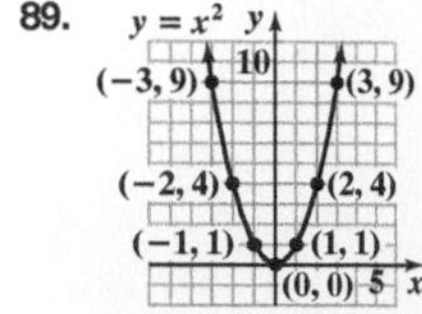

91.
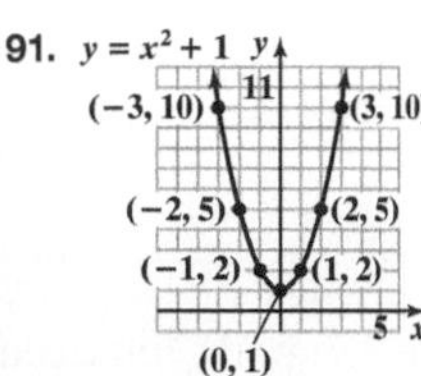

93.
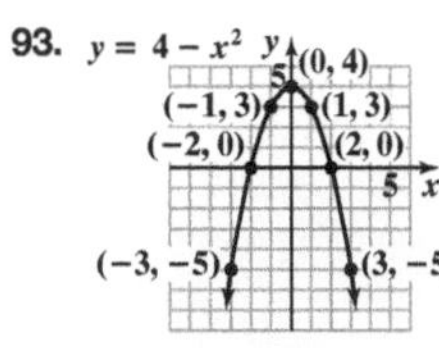

95. $x^2 + 12x$ **97.** $y^2 - 19y + 16$ **99.** $2x^3 + 3x^2 + 7x - 5$ **101.** $-10y^3 + 2y^2 + y + 3$ **103. a.** $M - W = -35x^3 + 1373x^2 - 15{,}995x + 63{,}210$ **b.** \$12,348 **c.** \$10,923; overestimates by \$1425 **105. a.** \$56,995; underestimates by \$225 **b.** (16, 56,995) on the graph for men **c.** \$42,000, although estimates may vary by $\pm$\$1000 **115.** does not make sense **117.** does not make sense **119.** false **121.** false **123.** $\frac{2}{3}t^3 - 2t^2 + 4t$ **125.** -10 **126.** 5.6 **127.** -4 or $\{-4\}$ **128.** 7 **129.** $3x^2 + 15x$ **130.** $x^2 + 5x + 6$

Section 2 Check Point Exercises

1. a. 2^6 or 64 **b.** x^{10} **c.** y^8 **d.** y^9 **2. a.** 3^{20} **b.** x^{90} **c.** $(-5)^{21}$ **3. a.** $16x^4$ **b.** $-64y^6$ **4. a.** $70x^3$ **b.** $-20x^9$ **5. a.** $3x^2 + 15x$ **b.** $30x^5 - 12x^3 + 18x^2$ **6. a.** $x^2 + 9x + 20$ **b.** $10x^2 - 29x - 21$ **7.** $5x^3 - 18x^2 + 7x + 6$ **8.** $6x^5 - 19x^4 + 22x^3 - 8x^2$

Concept and Vocabulary Check

1. b^{m+n}; add **2.** b^{mn}; multiply **3.** a^nb^n; factor **4.** distributive; $x^2 + 5x + 7$; $2x^2$ **5.** $4x$; 7; like

Exercise Set 2

1. x^{18} **3.** y^{12} **5.** x^{11} **7.** 7^{19} **9.** 6^{90} **11.** x^{45} **13.** $(-20)^9$ **15.** $8x^3$ **17.** $25x^2$ **19.** $16x^6$ **21.** $16y^{24}$ **23.** $-32x^{35}$ **25.** $14x^2$ **27.** $24x^3$ **29.** $-15y^7$ **31.** $\frac{1}{8}a^5$ **33.** $-48x^7$ **35.** $4x^2 + 12x$ **37.** $x^2 - 3x$ **39.** $2x^2 - 12x$ **41.** $-12y^2 - 20y$ **43.** $4x^3 + 8x^2$ **45.** $2y^4 + 6y^3$ **47.** $6y^4 - 8y^3 + 14y^2$ **49.** $6x^4 + 8x^3$ **51.** $-2x^3 - 10x^2 + 6x$ **53.** $12x^4 - 3x^3 + 15x^2$ **55.** $x^2 + 8x + 15$ **57.** $2x^2 + 9x + 4$ **59.** $x^2 - 2x - 15$ **61.** $x^2 - 2x - 99$ **63.** $2x^2 + 3x - 20$ **65.** $\frac{3}{16}x^2 + \frac{11}{4}x - 4$ **67.** $x^3 + 3x^2 + 5x + 3$ **69.** $y^3 - 6y^2 + 13y - 12$ **71.** $2a^3 - 9a^2 + 19a - 15$ **73.** $x^4 + 3x^3 + 5x^2 + 7x + 4$ **75.** $4x^4 - 4x^3 + 6x^2 - \frac{17}{2}x + 3$ **77.** $x^4 + x^3 + x^2 + 3x + 2$ **79.** $x^3 + 3x^2 - 37x + 24$ **81.** $2x^3 - 9x^2 + 27x - 27$ **83.** $2x^4 + 9x^3 + 6x^2 + 11x + 12$ **85.** $12z^4 - 14z^3 + 19z^2 - 22z + 8$ **87.** $21x^5 - 43x^4 + 38x^3 - 24x^2$ **89.** $4y^6 - 2y^5 - 6y^4 + 5y^3 - 5y^2 + 8y - 3$ **91.** $x^4 + 6x^3 - 11x^2 - 4x + 3$ **93.** $2x - 2$ **95.** $15x^5 + 42x^3 - 8x^2$ **97.** $2y^3$ **99.** $16y + 32$ **101.** $2x^2 + 7x - 15$ ft^2 **103. a.** $(2x + 1)(x + 2)$ **b.** $2x^2 + 5x + 2$ **c.** $(2x + 1)(x + 2) = 2x^2 + 5x + 2$ **113.** makes sense **115.** makes sense **117.** false **119.** true **121.** $8x + 16$ **123.** $-8x^4$ **124.** $(-\infty, -1)$ or $\{x | x < -1\}$

125.
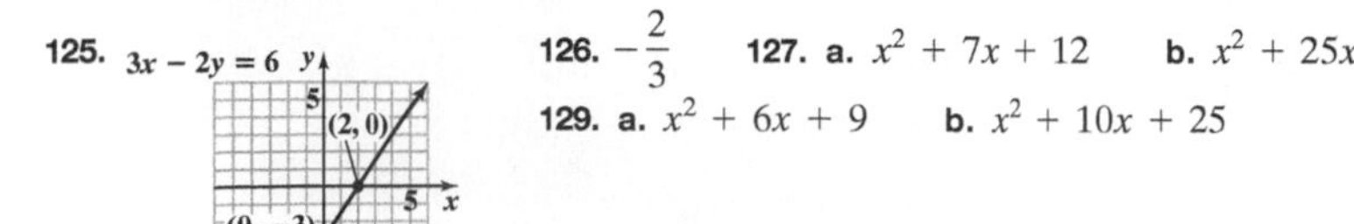

126. $-\frac{2}{3}$ **127. a.** $x^2 + 7x + 12$ **b.** $x^2 + 25x + 100$ **128. a.** $x^2 - 9$ **b.** $x^2 - 25$ **129. a.** $x^2 + 6x + 9$ **b.** $x^2 + 10x + 25$

Section 3 Check Point Exercises

1. $x^2 + 11x + 30$ **2.** $28x^2 - x - 15$ **3.** $6x^2 - 22x + 20$ **4. a.** $49y^2 - 64$ **b.** $16x^2 - 25$ **c.** $4a^6 - 9$ **5. a.** $x^2 + 20x + 100$ **b.** $25x^2 + 40x + 16$ **6. a.** $x^2 - 18x + 81$ **b.** $49x^2 - 42x + 9$

Concept and Vocabulary Check

1. $2x^2$; $3x$; $10x$; 15 **2.** $A^2 - B^2$; minus **3.** $A^2 + 2AB + B^2$; squared; product of the terms; squared
4. $A^2 - 2AB + B^2$; minus; product of the terms; squared **5.** true **6.** false

Exercise Set 3

1. $x^2 + 10x + 24$ **3.** $y^2 - 4y - 21$ **5.** $2x^2 + 7x - 15$ **7.** $4y^2 - y - 3$ **9.** $10x^2 - 9x - 9$ **11.** $12y^2 - 43y + 35$
13. $-15x^2 - 32x + 7$ **15.** $6y^2 - 28y + 30$ **17.** $15x^4 - 47x^2 + 28$ **19.** $-6x^2 + 17x - 10$ **21.** $x^3 + 5x^2 + 3x + 15$
23. $8x^5 + 40x^3 + 3x^2 + 15$ **25.** $x^2 - 9$ **27.** $9x^2 - 4$ **29.** $9r^2 - 16$ **31.** $9 - r^2$ **33.** $25 - 49x^2$ **35.** $4x^2 - \frac{1}{4}$ **37.** $y^4 - 1$
39. $r^6 - 4$ **41.** $1 - y^8$ **43.** $x^{20} - 25$ **45.** $x^2 + 4x + 4$ **47.** $4x^2 + 20x + 25$ **49.** $x^2 - 6x + 9$ **51.** $9y^2 - 24y + 16$
53. $16x^4 - 8x^2 + 1$ **55.** $49 - 28x + 4x^2$ **57.** $4x^2 + 2x + \frac{1}{4}$ **59.** $16y^2 - 2y + \frac{1}{16}$ **61.** $x^{16} + 6x^8 + 9$ **63.** $x^3 - 1$
65. $x^2 - 2x + 1$ **67.** $9y^2 - 49$ **69.** $12x^4 + 3x^3 + 27x^2$ **71.** $70y^2 + 2y - 12$ **73.** $x^4 + 2x^2 + 1$ **75.** $x^4 + 3x^2 + 2$
77. $x^4 - 16$ **79.** $4 - 12x^5 + 9x^{10}$ **81.** $\frac{3}{16}x^4 + 7x^2 - 96$ **83.** $x^2 + 2x + 1$ **85.** $4x^2 - 9$ **87.** $6x + 22$
89. $16x^4 - 72x^2 + 81$ **91.** $16x^4 - 1$ **93.** $x^3 + 6x^2 + 12x + 8$ **95.** $x^2 + 6x + 9 - y^2$ **97.** $(x + 1)(x + 2)$ yd^2 **99.** 56 yd^2; (6, 56)
101. $(x^2 + 4x + 4)$ in^2 **109.** makes sense **111.** makes sense, although answers may vary **113.** true **115.** false **117.** $4x^3 - 36x^2 + 80x$
119. Change $x^2 + 1$ to $x^2 + 2x + 1$. **121.** Graphs coincide. **123.** $(2, -1)$ or $\{(2, -1)\}$ **124.** $(1, 1)$ or $\{(1, 1)\}$

125. 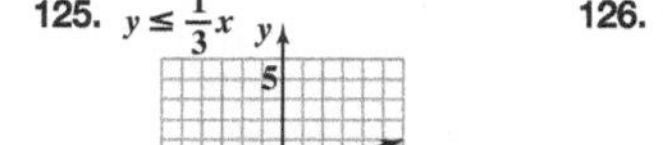

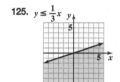

126. -72 **127.** $11xy$ **128.** $3x^2 + 11xy + 10y^2$

Section 4 Check Point Exercises

1. -9 **2.** polynomial degree: 9;

Term	Coefficient	Degree
$8x^4y^5$	8	9
$-7x^3y^2$	-7	5
$-x^2y$	-1	3
$-5x$	-5	1
11	11	0

$2x^2y + 2xy - 4$ **4.** $3x^3 + 2x^2y + 5xy^2 - 10$ **5.** $60x^5y^5$ **6.** $60x^5y^7 - 12x^3y^3 + 18xy^2$
7. a. $21x^2 - 25xy + 6y^2$ **b.** $4x^2 + 16xy + 16y^2$ **8. a.** $36x^2y^4 - 25x^2$ **b.** $x^3 - y^3$

Concept and Vocabulary Check

1. -18 **2.** 6 **3.** a; $n + m$ **4.** 5; 9; 9 **5.** false **6.** true

Exercise Set 4

1. 1 **3.** -47 **5.** -6 **7.** polynomial degree: 9;

Term	Coefficient	Degree
x^3y^2	1	5
$-5x^2y^7$	-5	9
$6y^2$	6	2
-3	-3	0

9. $7x^2y - 4xy$ **11.** $2x^2y + 13xy + 13$ **13.** $-11x^4y^2 - 11x^2y^2 + 2xy$ **15.** $-5x^3 + 8xy - 9y^2$ **17.** $x^4y^2 + 8x^3y + y - 6x$
19. $5x^3 + x^2y - xy^2 - 4y^3$ **21.** $-3x^2y^2 + xy^2 + 5y^2$ **23.** $8a^2b^4 + 3ab^2 + 8ab$ **25.** $-30x + 37y$ **27.** $40x^3y^2$ **29.** $-24x^5y^9$
31. $45x^2y + 18xy^2$ **33.** $50x^3y^2 - 15xy^3$ **35.** $28a^3b^5 + 8a^2b^3$ **37.** $-a^2b + ab^2 - b^3$ **39.** $7x^2 + 38xy + 15y^2$ **41.** $2x^2 + xy - 21y^2$
43. $15x^2y^2 + xy - 2$ **45.** $4x^2 + 12xy + 9y^2$ **47.** $x^2y^2 - 6xy + 9$ **49.** $x^4 + 2x^2y^2 + y^4$ **51.** $x^4 - 4x^2y^2 + 4y^4$ **53.** $9x^2 - y^2$
55. $a^2b^2 - 1$ **57.** $x^2 - y^4$ **59.** $9a^4b^2 - a^2$ **61.** $9x^2y^4 - 16y^2$ **63.** $a^3 - ab^2 + a^2b - b^3$ **65.** $x^3 + 4x^2y + 4xy^2 + y^3$
67. $x^3 - 4x^2y + 4xy^2 - y^3$ **69.** $x^2y^2 - a^2b^2$ **71.** $x^6y + x^4y + x^4 + 2x^2 + 1$ **73.** $x^4y^4 - 6x^2y^2 + 9$ **75.** $x^2 + 2xy + y^2 - 1$
77. $3x^2 + 8xy + 5y^2$ **79.** $2xy + y^2$ **81.** $x^{12}y^{12} - 2x^6y^6 + 1$ **83.** $x^4y^4 - 18x^2y^2 + 81$ **85.** $x^2 - y^2 - 2yz - z^2$
87. no; need 120 more board feet **89.** 192 ft **91.** 0 ft; The ball hits the ground. **93.** 2.5 to 6 sec **95.** (2, 192)
97. 2.5 sec; 196 ft **101.** makes sense **103.** does not make sense **105.** false **107.** true **109.** $-x^2 + 18xy + 80y^2$
112. $W = \frac{2R - L}{3}$ **113.** 3.8 **114.** -1.6 or $\{-1.6\}$ **115.** 4 **116.** $\frac{x^6}{125}$ **117.** $\frac{32a^{15}}{b^{20}}$

Mid-Chapter Check Point Exercises

1. $-55x^4y^6$ **2.** $6x^2y^3$ **3.** $12x^2 - x - 35$ **4.** $-x + 12$ **5.** $2x^3 - 11x^2 + 17x - 5$ **6.** $x^2 - x - 4$ **7.** $64x^2 - 48x + 9$ **8.** $70x^9$ **9.** $x^4 - 4$ **10.** $x^4 + 4x^2 + 4$ **11.** $18a^2 - 11ab - 10b^2$ **12.** $70x^5 - 14x^3 + 21x^2$ **13.** $5a^2b^3 + 2ab - b^2$ **14.** $18y^2 - 50$ **15.** $2x^3 - x^2 + x$ **16.** $10x^2 - 5xy - 3y^2$ **17.** $-4x^5 + 7x^4 - 10x + 23$ **18.** $x^3 + 27y^3$ **19.** $10x^7 - 5x^4 + 8x^3 - 4$ **20.** $y^2 - 12yz + 36z^2$ **21.** $-21x^2 + 7$

22.

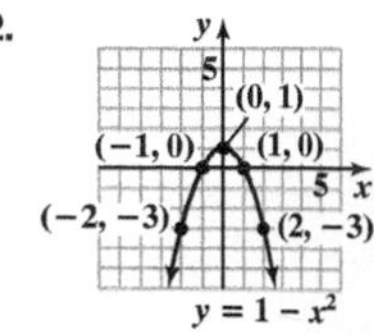

Section 5 Check Point Exercises

1. a. 5^8 **b.** x^7 **c.** y^{19} **2. a.** 1 **b.** 1 **c.** −1 **d.** 20 **e.** 1 **3. a.** $\frac{x^2}{25}$ **b.** $\frac{x^{12}}{8}$ **c.** $\frac{16a^{40}}{b^{12}}$

4. a. $-2x^8$ **b.** $\frac{1}{5}$ **c.** $3x^5y^3$ **5.** $-5x^7 + 2x^3 - 3x$ **6.** $5x^6 - \frac{7}{5}x + 2$ **7.** $3x^6y^4 - xy + 10$

Concept and Vocabulary Check

1. b^{m-n}; subtract **2.** 1 **3.** $\frac{a^n}{b^n}$; numerator; denominator **4.** divide; subtract **5.** dividend; divisor; quotient **6.** divisor; quotient; dividend **7.** $20x^8 - 10x^4 + 6x^3$; $2x^3$

Exercise Set 5

1. 3^{15} **3.** x^4 **5.** y^8 **7.** $5^3 \cdot 2^4$ **9.** $x^{75}y^{40}$ **11.** 1 **13.** 1 **15.** −1 **17.** 100 **19.** 1 **21.** 0 **23.** −2 **25.** $\frac{x^2}{9}$ **27.** $\frac{x^6}{64}$ **29.** $\frac{4x^6}{25}$ **31.** $-\frac{64}{27a^9}$ **33.** $-\frac{32a^{35}}{b^{20}}$ **35.** $\frac{x^8y^{12}}{16z^4}$ **37.** $3x^5$ **39.** $-2x^{20}$ **41.** $-\frac{1}{2}y^3$ **43.** $\frac{7}{5}y^{12}$ **45.** $6x^5y^4$ **47.** $-\frac{1}{2}x^{12}$ **49.** $\frac{9}{7}$ **51.** $-\frac{1}{10}x^8y^9z^4$ **53.** $5x^4 + x^3$ **55.** $2x^3 - x^2$ **57.** $y^6 - 9y + 1$ **59.** $-8x^2 + 5x$ **61.** $6x^3 + 2x^2 + 3x$ **63.** $3x^3 - 2x^2 + 10x$ **65.** $4x - 6$ **67.** $-6z^2 - 2z$ **69.** $4x^2 + 3x - 1$ **71.** $5x^4 - 3x^2 - x$ **73.** $-9x^3 + \frac{9}{2}x^2 - 10x + 5$ **75.** $4xy + 2x - 5y$ **77.** $-4x^5y^3 + 3xy + 2$ **79.** $4x^2 - x + 6$ **81.** $-xy^2$ **83.** $y + 5$ **85.** $3x^{12n} - 6x^{9n} + 2$ **87. a.** \$5.39 **b.** $\frac{3.6x^2 + 158x + 2790}{-0.2x^2 + 21x + 1015}$ **c.** \$5.45; overestimates by \$0.06 **d.** no; The divisor is not a monomial. **97.** does not make sense **99.** does not make sense **101.** false **103.** true **105.** $\frac{9x^8 - 12x^6}{3x^3}$ **107.** 20.3 **108.** 0.875

109.

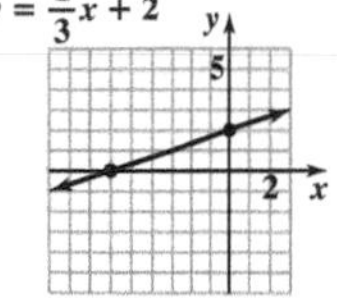

110. quotient: 26; remainder: 0 **111.** quotient: 123; remainder: 6 **112.** quotient: 257; remainder: 1

Section 6 Check Point Exercises

1. $x + 5$ **2.** $4x - 3 - \frac{3}{2x + 3}$ **3.** $x^2 + x + 1$

Concept and Vocabulary Check

1. $10x^3 + 4x^2 + 0x + 9$ **2.** $8x^2$; $2x$; $4x$; $10x$ **3.** $5x$; $3x - 2$; $15x^2 - 10x$; $15x^2 - 22x$ **4.** $6x^2 - 10x$; $6x^2 + 8x$; $18x$; -4; $18x - 4$ **5.** 14; $x - 12$; 14; $x - 12 + \frac{14}{x - 5}$

Exercise Set 6

1. $x + 4$ **3.** $2x + 5$ **5.** $x - 2$ **7.** $2y + 1$ **9.** $x - 5 + \frac{14}{x + 2}$ **11.** $y + 3 + \frac{4}{y + 2}$ **13.** $x^2 - 5x + 2$ **15.** $6y - 1$

17. $2a + 3$ **19.** $y^2 - y + 2$ **21.** $3x + 5 - \frac{5}{2x - 5}$ **23.** $x^2 + 2x + 8 + \frac{13}{x - 2}$ **25.** $2y^2 + y + 1 + \frac{6}{2y + 3}$
27. $2y^2 - 3y + 2 + \frac{1}{3y + 2}$ **29.** $9x^2 + 3x + 1$ **31.** $y^3 - 9y^2 + 27y - 27$ **33.** $2y + 4 + \frac{4}{2y - 1}$ **35.** $y^3 + y^2 - y - 1 + \frac{4}{y - 1}$
37. $4x - 3 + \frac{-7x + 7}{x^2 + 2}$ **39.** $x^2 + ax + a^2$ **41.** $2x^2 - 3x + 2$ **43.** $x^2 + 2x + 3$ **45.** $x^2 + 2x + 3$ units **47. a.** $\frac{30{,}000x^3 - 30{,}000}{x - 1}$
b. $30{,}000x^2 + 30{,}000x + 30{,}000$ **c.** \$94,575 **53.** makes sense **55.** does not make sense **57.** false **59.** true **61.** $2x^2 - 2x + 5$
63. Answers will vary; $x^6 - x^5 + x^4 - x^3 + x^2 - x + 1 - \frac{2}{x + 1}$ **65.** $x - 5$ should be $x + 5$. **67.** $2x - 4$ should be $2x + 4$.

69.
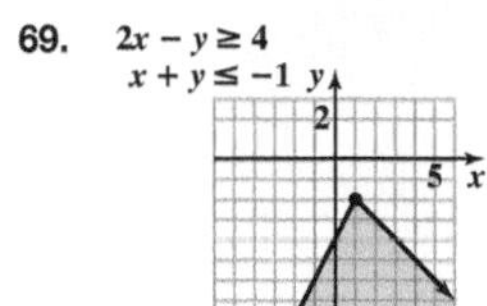

70. 1.2 **71.** -6 or $\{-6\}$ **72. a.** $2; -2$ **b.** $\frac{1}{7^2} = 7^{-2}$ **73.** $16x^2$ **74.** x^9

Section 7 Check Point Exercises

1. a. $\frac{1}{6^2} = \frac{1}{36}$ **b.** $\frac{1}{5^3} = \frac{1}{125}$ **c.** $\frac{1}{(-3)^4} = \frac{1}{81}$ **d.** $-\frac{1}{3^4} = -\frac{1}{81}$ **e.** $\frac{1}{8^1} = \frac{1}{8}$ **2. a.** $\frac{7^2}{2^3} = \frac{49}{8}$ **b.** $\frac{5^2}{4^2} = \frac{25}{16}$ **c.** $\frac{y^2}{7}$ **d.** $\frac{y^8}{x^1} = \frac{y^8}{x}$
3. $\frac{1}{x^{10}}$ **4. a.** $\frac{1}{x^8}$ **b.** $\frac{15}{x^6}$ **c.** $-\frac{2}{y^6}$ **5.** $\frac{36}{x^3}$ **6.** $\frac{1}{x^{20}}$ **7. a.** 7,400,000,000 **b.** 0.000003017 **8. a.** 7.41×10^9 **b.** 9.2×10^{-8}
9. a. 6×10^{10} **b.** 2.1×10^{11} **c.** 6.4×10^{-5} **10.** \$2560

Concept and Vocabulary Check

1. $\frac{1}{b^n}$ **2.** false **3.** true **4.** b^n **5.** true **6.** false **7.** a number greater than or equal to 1 and less than 10; integer **8.** true **9.** false

Exercise Set 7

1. $\frac{1}{8^2} = \frac{1}{64}$ **3.** $\frac{1}{5^3} = \frac{1}{125}$ **5.** $\frac{1}{(-6)^2} = \frac{1}{36}$ **7.** $-\frac{1}{6^2} = -\frac{1}{36}$ **9.** $\frac{1}{4^1} = \frac{1}{4}$ **11.** $\frac{1}{2^1} + \frac{1}{3^1} = \frac{1}{2} + \frac{1}{3} = \frac{5}{6}$ **13.** $3^2 = 9$ **15.** $(-3)^2 = 9$
17. $\frac{8^2}{2^3} = 8$ **19.** $\frac{4^2}{1^2} = 16$ **21.** $\frac{5^3}{3^3} = \frac{125}{27}$ **23.** $\frac{x^5}{6}$ **25.** $\frac{y^1}{x^8} = \frac{y}{x^8}$ **27.** $3 \cdot (-5)^3 = -375$ **29.** $\frac{1}{x^5}$ **31.** $\frac{8}{x^3}$ **33.** $\frac{1}{x^6}$ **35.** $\frac{1}{y^{99}}$
37. $\frac{3}{z^5}$ **39.** $-\frac{4}{x^4}$ **41.** $-\frac{1}{3a^3}$ **43.** $\frac{7}{5w^8}$ **45.** $\frac{1}{x^5}$ **47.** $\frac{1}{y^{11}}$ **49.** $\frac{16}{x^2}$ **51.** $216y^{17}$ **53.** $\frac{1}{x^6}$ **55.** $\frac{1}{16x^{12}}$ **57.** $\frac{x^2}{9}$ **59.** $-\frac{y^3}{8}$
61. $\frac{2x^6}{5}$ **63.** x^8 **65.** $16y^6$ **67.** $\frac{1}{y^2}$ **69.** $\frac{1}{y^{50}}$ **71.** $\frac{1}{a^{12}b^{15}}$ **73.** $\frac{a^8}{b^{24}}$ **75.** $\frac{4}{x^4}$ **77.** $\frac{y^9}{x^6}$ **79.** 870 **81.** 923,000 **83.** 3.4
85. 0.79 **87.** 0.0215 **89.** 0.000786 **91.** 3.24×10^4 **93.** 2.2×10^8 **95.** 7.13×10^2 **97.** 6.751×10^3 **99.** 2.7×10^{-3}
101. 2.02×10^{-5} **103.** 5×10^{-3} **105.** 3.14159×10^0 **107.** 6×10^5 **109.** 1.6×10^9 **111.** 3×10^4 **113.** 3×10^6 **115.** 3×10^{-6}
117. 9×10^4 **119.** 2.5×10^6 **121.** 1.25×10^8 **123.** 8.1×10^{-7} **125.** 2.5×10^{-7} **127.** 1 **129.** $\frac{y}{16x^8z^6}$ **131.** $\frac{1}{x^{12}y^{16}z^{20}}$
133. $\frac{x^{18}y^6}{4}$ **135.** 2.5×10^{-3} **137.** 8×10^{-5} **139. a.** 1.35×10^{12} **b.** 3.07×10^8 **c.** $\$4.40 \times 10^3$; \$4400 **141.** 42,000 years
143. 1.25 sec **153.** makes sense **155.** makes sense **157.** true **159.** false **161.** false **163.** true **169.** $(-\infty, 2)$ or $\{x \mid x < 2\}$
170. 5 **171.** $0, \sqrt{16}$ **172.** $16x^5 - 12x^4 + 4x^3$ **173.** $27x^2y^3 - 9xy^2 + 81xy$ **174.** $x^3 + 3x^2 + 5x + 15$

Review Exercises

1. binomial, 4 **2.** trinomial, 2 **3.** monomial, 1 **4.** $8x^3 + 10x^2 - 20x - 4$ **5.** $13y^3 - 8y^2 + 7y - 5$ **6.** $11y^2 - 4y - 4$
7. $8x^4 - 5x^3 + 6$ **8.** $-14x^4 - 13x^2 + 16x$ **9.** $7y^4 - 5y^3 + 3y^2 - y - 4$ **10.** $3x^2 - 7x + 9$ **11.** $10x^3 - 9x^2 + 2x + 11$

12. **13.**
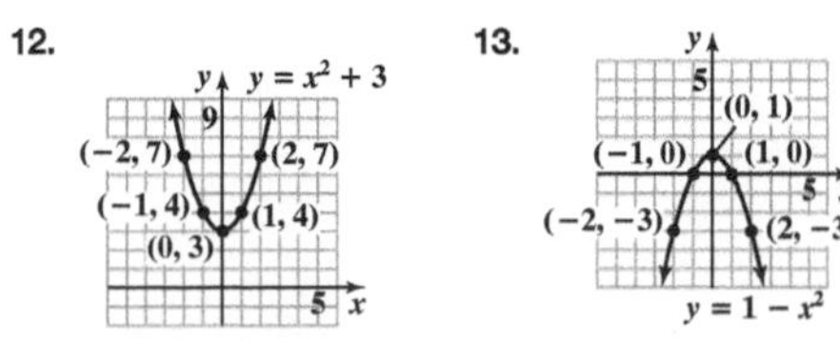

14. x^{23} **15.** y^{14} **16.** x^{100} **17.** $100y^2$ **18.** $-64x^{30}$ **19.** $50x^4$ **20.** $-36y^{11}$ **21.** $30x^{12}$ **22.** $21x^3 + 63x$ **23.** $20x^5 - 55x^4$
24. $-21y^4 + 9y^3 - 18y^2$ **25.** $16y^8 - 20y^7 + 2y^5$ **26.** $x^3 - 2x^2 - 13x + 6$ **27.** $12y^3 + y^2 - 21y + 10$ **28.** $3y^3 - 17y^2 + 41y - 35$
29. $8x^4 + 8x^3 - 18x^2 - 20x - 3$ **30.** $x^2 + 8x + 12$ **31.** $6y^2 - 7y - 5$ **32.** $4x^4 - 14x^2 + 6$ **33.** $25x^2 - 16$ **34.** $49 - 4y^2$
35. $y^4 - 1$ **36.** $x^2 + 6x + 9$ **37.** $9y^2 + 24y + 16$ **38.** $y^2 - 2y + 1$ **39.** $25y^2 - 20y + 4$ **40.** $x^4 + 8x^2 + 16$ **41.** $x^4 - 16$
42. $x^4 - x^2 - 20$ **43.** $x^2 + 7x + 12$ **44.** $x^2 + 50x + 600$ yd^2 **45.** 28

46. polynomial degree: 5;

Term	Coefficient	Degree
$4x^2y$	4	3
$9x^3y^2$	9	5
$-17x^4$	-17	4
-12	-12	0

47. $-x^2 - 17xy + 5y^2$ **48.** $2x^3y^2 + x^2y - 6x^2 - 4$ **49.** $-35x^6y^9$ **50.** $15a^3b^5 - 20a^2b^3$ **51.** $3x^2 + 16xy - 35y^2$ **52.** $36x^2y^2 - 31xy + 3$ **53.** $9x^2 + 30xy + 25y^2$ **54.** $x^2y^2 - 14xy + 49$ **55.** $49x^2 - 16y^2$ **56.** $a^3 - b^3$ **57.** 6^{30} **58.** x^{15} **59.** 1 **60.** -1 **61.** 400 **62.** $\frac{x^{12}}{8}$ **63.** $\frac{81}{16y^{24}}$ **64.** $-5y^6$ **65.** $8x^7y^3$ **66.** $3x^3 - 2x + 6$ **67.** $-6x^5 + 5x^4 + 8x^2$ **68.** $9x^2y - 3x - 6y$ **69.** $2x + 7$ **70.** $x^2 - 3x + 5$ **71.** $x^2 + 5x + 2 + \frac{7}{x - 7}$ **72.** $y^2 + 3y + 9$ **73.** $\frac{1}{7^2} = \frac{1}{49}$ **74.** $\frac{1}{(-4)^3} = -\frac{1}{64}$ **75.** $\frac{1}{2^1} + \frac{1}{4^1} = \frac{1}{2} + \frac{1}{4} = \frac{3}{4}$ **76.** $5^2 = 25$ **77.** $\frac{5^3}{2^3} = \frac{125}{8}$ **78.** $\frac{1}{x^6}$ **79.** $\frac{6}{y^2}$ **80.** $\frac{30}{x^5}$ **81.** x^8 **82.** $81y^2$ **83.** $\frac{1}{y^{19}}$ **84.** $\frac{x^3}{8}$ **85.** $\frac{1}{x^6}$ **86.** y^{20} **87.** 23,000 **88.** 0.00176 **89.** 0.9 **90.** 7.39×10^7 **91.** 6.2×10^{-4} **92.** 3.8×10^{-1} **93.** 3.8×10^0 **94.** 9×10^3 **95.** 5×10^4 **96.** 1.6×10^{-3} **97.** $\$5.36 \times 10^{10}$ **98.** 3.07×10^8 **99.** $\approx \$175$

Chapter Test

1. trinomial, 2 **2.** $13x^3 + x^2 - x - 24$ **3.** $5x^3 + 2x^2 + 2x - 9$ **4.**

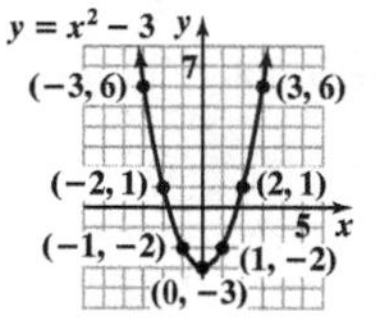

5. $-35x^{11}$ **6.** $48x^5 - 30x^3 - 12x^2$ **7.** $3x^3 - 10x^2 - 17x - 6$ **8.** $6y^2 - 13y - 63$ **9.** $49x^2 - 25$ **10.** $x^4 + 6x^2 + 9$ **11.** $25x^2 - 30x + 9$ **12.** 30 **13.** $2x^2y^3 + 3xy + 12y^2$ **14.** $12a^2 - 13ab - 35b^2$ **15.** $4x^2 + 12xy + 9y^2$ **16.** $-5x^{12}$ **17.** $3x^3 - 2x^2 + 5x$ **18.** $x^2 - 2x + 3 + \frac{1}{2x + 1}$ **19.** $\frac{1}{10^2} = \frac{1}{100}$ **20.** $4^3 = 64$ **21.** $-27x^6$ **22.** $\frac{4}{x^5}$ **23.** $-\frac{21}{x^6}$ **24.** $16y^4$ **25.** $\frac{x^8}{25}$ **26.** $\frac{1}{x^{15}}$ **27.** 0.00037 **28.** 7.6×10^6 **29.** 1.23×10^{-2} **30.** 2.1×10^8 **31.** $x^2 + 10x + 16$

Factoring Polynomials

Motion and change are the very essence of life. Moving air brushes against our faces; rain falls on our heads; birds fly past us; plants spring from the earth, grow, and then die; and rocks thrown upward reach a maximum height before falling to the ground. In this chapter, we analyze the where and when of moving objects by writing polynomials as products and using equations in which the highest exponent on the variable is 2.

Motion is modeled in Example 7 of Section 6, as well as in the visual discussion that follows the example.

Amana Images Inc/Alamy

SECTION 1

The Greatest Common Factor and Factoring by Grouping

Objectives

1. Find the greatest common factor.
2. Factor out the greatest common factor of a polynomial.
3. Factor out the negative of the greatest common factor of a polynomial.
4. Factor by grouping.

A two-year-old boy is asked, "Do you have a brother?" He answers, "Yes." "What is your brother's name?" "Tom." Asked if Tom has a brother, the two-year-old replies, "No." The child can go in the direction from self to brother, but he cannot reverse this direction and move from brother back to self.

As our intellects develop, we learn to reverse the direction of our thinking. Reversibility of thought is found throughout algebra. For example, we can multiply polynomials and show that

$$5x(2x + 3) = 10x^2 + 15x.$$

We can also reverse this process and express the resulting polynomial as

$$10x^2 + 15x = 5x(2x + 3).$$

Steve Shott/Dorling Kindersley, Ltd.

Factoring a polynomial containing the sum of monomials means finding an equivalent expression that is a product.

Factoring $10x^2 + 15x$

Sum of monomials

Equivalent expression that is a product

$$10x^2 + 15x = 5x(2x + 3)$$

The factors of $10x^2 + 15x$ are $5x$ and $2x + 3$.

In this chapter, we will be factoring over the set of integers, meaning that the coefficients in the factors are integers. Polynomials that cannot be factored using integer coefficients are called **prime polynomials** over the set of integers.

Factoring Out the Greatest Common Factor

We use the distributive property to multiply a monomial and a polynomial of two or more terms. When we factor, we reverse this process, expressing the polynomial as a product.

Multiplication	Factoring
$a(b + c) = ab + ac$	$ab + ac = a(b + c)$

Here is a specific example:

Multiplication	Factoring
$5x(2x + 3)$	$10x^2 + 15x$
$= 5x \cdot 2x + 5x \cdot 3$	$= 5x \cdot 2x + 5x \cdot 3$
$= 10x^2 + 15x$	$= 5x(2x + 3).$

In the process of finding an equivalent expression for $10x^2 + 15x$ that is a product, we used the fact that $5x$ is a factor of the monomials $10x^2$ and $15x$. The factoring on the right shows that $5x$ is a *common factor* for both terms of the binomial $10x^2 + 15x$.

1 Find the greatest common factor.

In any factoring problem, the first step is to look for the *greatest common factor*. The **greatest common factor**, abbreviated GCF, is an expression of the highest degree that divides each term of the polynomial. Can you see that $5x$ is the greatest common factor of $10x^2 + 15x$? 5 is the greatest integer that divides both 10 and 15. Furthermore, x is the greatest expression that divides both x^2 and x.

The variable part of the greatest common factor always contains the smallest power of a variable that appears in all terms of the polynomial. For example, consider the polynomial

$$10x^2 + 15x.$$

x^1, or x, is the variable raised to the smaller exponent.

We see that x is the variable part of the greatest common factor, $5x$.

EXAMPLE 1 Finding the Greatest Common Factor

Find the greatest common factor of each list of monomials:

a. $6x^3$ and $10x^2$ **b.** $15y^5, -9y^4$, and $27y^3$ **c.** x^5y^3, x^4y^4, and x^3y^2.

Solution Use numerical coefficients to determine the coefficient of the GCF. Use variable factors to determine the variable factor of the GCF.

2 is the greatest integer that divides 6 and 10.

a. $6x^3$ and $10x^2$

x^2 is the variable raised to the smaller exponent.

We see that 2 is the coefficient of the GCF and x^2 is the variable factor of the GCF. Thus, the GCF of $6x^3$ and $10x^2$ is $2x^2$.

3 is the greatest integer that divides 15, −9, and 27.

b. $15y^5$, $-9y^4$, and $27y^3$

y^3 is the variable raised to the smallest exponent.

We see that 3 is the coefficient of the GCF and y^3 is the variable factor of the GCF. Thus, the GCF of $15y^5, -9y^4$, and $27y^3$ is $3y^3$.

x^3 is the variable, x, raised to the smallest exponent.

c. x^5y^3, x^4y^4, and x^3y^2

y^2 is the variable, y, raised to the smallest exponent.

Because all terms have coefficients of 1, 1 is the greatest integer that divides these coefficients. Thus, 1 is the coefficient of the GCF. The voice balloons show that x^3 and y^2 are the variable factors of the GCF. Thus, the GCF of x^5y^3, x^4y^4, and x^3y^2 is x^3y^2. ■

✓ **CHECK POINT 1** Find the greatest common factor of each list of monomials:

a. $18x^3$ and $15x^2$ **b.** $-20x^2, 12x^4$, and $40x^3$

c. x^4y, x^3y^2, and x^2y.

2 Factor out the greatest common factor of a polynomial.

When we factor a monomial from a polynomial, we determine the greatest common factor of all terms in the polynomial. Sometimes there may not be a GCF other than 1. When a GCF other than 1 exists, we use the following procedure:

Factoring a Monomial From a Polynomial

1. Determine the greatest common factor of all terms in the polynomial.
2. Express each term as the product of the GCF and its other factor.
3. Use the distributive property to factor out the GCF.

Great Question!

Is $5 \cdot x^2 + 5 \cdot 6$ a factorization of $5x^2 + 30$?

No. When we express $5x^2 + 30$ as $5 \cdot x^2 + 5 \cdot 6$, we have factored the *terms* of the binomial, but not the binomial itself. The factorization of the binomial is not complete until we write

$$5(x^2 + 6).$$

Now we have expressed the binomial *as a product.*

EXAMPLE 2 Factoring Out the Greatest Common Factor

Factor: $5x^2 + 30$.

Solution The GCF of $5x^2$ and 30 is 5.

$$5x^2 + 30$$

$$= 5 \cdot x^2 + 5 \cdot 6 \quad \text{Express each term as the product of the GCF and its other factor.}$$

$$= 5(x^2 + 6) \quad \text{Factor out the GCF.}$$

Because factoring reverses the process of multiplication, all factorizations can be checked by multiplying.

$$5(x^2 + 6) = 5 \cdot x^2 + 5 \cdot 6 = 5x^2 + 30$$

The factorization is correct because multiplication gives us the original polynomial. ■

✓ **CHECK POINT 2** Factor: $6x^2 + 18$.

EXAMPLE 3 Factoring Out the Greatest Common Factor

Factor: $18x^3 + 27x^2$.

Solution We begin by determining the greatest common factor.

9 is the greatest integer that divides 18 and 27.

$18x^3$ and $27x^2$

x^2 is the variable raised to the smaller exponent.

The GCF of the two terms in the polynomial is $9x^2$.

$$18x^3 + 27x^2$$

$$= 9x^2 \cdot 2x + 9x^2 \cdot 3 \quad \text{Express each term as the product of the GCF and its other factor.}$$

$$= 9x^2(2x + 3) \quad \text{Factor out the GCF.}$$

We can check this factorization by multiplying $9x^2$ and $2x + 3$, obtaining the original polynomial as the answer. ■

Discover for Yourself

What happens if you factor out $3x^2$ rather than $9x^2$ from $18x^3 + 27x^2$? Although $3x^2$ is a common factor of the two terms, it is not the *greatest* common factor. Factor out $3x^2$ from $18x^3 + 27x^2$ and describe what happens with the second factor. Now factor again. Make the final result look like the factorization in Example 3. What is the advantage of factoring out the greatest common factor rather than just a common factor?

✓ **CHECK POINT 3** Factor: $25x^2 + 35x^3$.

EXAMPLE 4 Factoring Out the Greatest Common Factor

Factor: $16x^5 - 12x^4 + 4x^3$.

Solution First, determine the greatest common factor.

4 is the greatest integer that divides 16, −12, and 4.

$$16x^5, \quad -12x^4, \quad \text{and} \quad 4x^3$$

x^3 is the variable raised to the smallest exponent.

The GCF of the three terms of the polynomial is $4x^3$.

$$16x^5 - 12x^4 + 4x^3$$

$$= 4x^3 \cdot 4x^2 - 4x^3 \cdot 3x + 4x^3 \cdot 1$$

Express each term as the product of the GCF and its other factor.

You can obtain the factors shown in black by dividing each term of the given polynomial by $4x^3$, the GCF: $\frac{16x^5}{4x^3} = 4x^2$ $\frac{12x^4}{4x^3} = 3x$ $\frac{4x^3}{4x^3} = 1$.

$$= 4x^3(4x^2 - 3x + 1)$$

Factor out the GCF. ■

Don't leave out the 1.

✓ **CHECK POINT 4** Factor: $15x^5 + 12x^4 - 27x^3$.

EXAMPLE 5 Factoring Out the Greatest Common Factor

Factor: $27x^2y^3 - 9xy^2 + 81xy$.

Solution First, determine the greatest common factor.

9 is the greatest integer that divides 27, −9, and 81.

$$27x^2y^3, \quad -9xy^2, \quad \text{and} \quad 81xy$$

The variables raised to the smallest exponents are x and y.

The GCF of the three terms of the polynomial is $9xy$.

$$27x^2y^3 - 9xy^2 + 81xy$$

$$= 9xy \cdot 3xy^2 - 9xy \cdot y + 9xy \cdot 9$$

Express each term as the product of the GCF and its other factor.

You can obtain the factors shown in black by dividing each term of the given polynomial by $9xy$, the GCF: $\frac{27x^2y^3}{9xy} = 3xy^2$ $\frac{9xy^2}{9xy} = y$ $\frac{81xy}{9xy} = 9$.

$$= 9xy(3xy^2 - y + 9)$$

Factor out the GCF. ■

✓ **CHECK POINT 5** Factor: $8x^3y^2 - 14x^2y + 2xy$.

3 Factor out the negative of the greatest common factor of a polynomial.

Factoring with a Negative Coefficient in the First Term

Suppose we are interested in factoring

$$-5x^2 + 30.$$

The first term has a negative coefficient.

When factoring polynomials, it is preferable to have a first term with a positive coefficient inside parentheses. We can do this with $-5x^2 + 30$ by factoring out -5, the negative of the GCF.

$$-5x^2 + 30$$

$= -5 \cdot x^2 - 5(-6)$ Express each term as the product of the negative of the GCF and its other factor.

$= -5(x^2 - 6)$ Factor out the negative of the GCF.

Factoring with a Negative Coefficient in the First Term

Express each term as the product of the negative of the GCF and its other factor. Then use the distributive property to factor out the negative of the GCF.

EXAMPLE 6 Factoring Out the Negative of the GCF

Factor: $-18a^4b^3 + 6a^2b^2 - 15a^3b$.

Solution First, determine the greatest common factor.

3 is the greatest integer that divides −18, 6, and −15.

$-18a^4b^3$, $6a^2b^2$, and $-15a^3b$

The variables raised to the smallest exponents are a^2 and b.

The GCF of the three terms of the polynomial is $3a^2b$. Because the polynomial has a negative coefficient in the first term, −18, we will factor out the negative of the GCF. Thus, we will factor out $-3a^2b$.

$$-18a^4b^3 + 6a^2b^2 - 15a^3b$$

$= -3a^2b \cdot 6a^2b^2 - 3a^2b(-2b) - 3a^2b \cdot 5a$ Express each term as the product of the negative of the GCF and its other factor.

$= -3a^2b(6a^2b^2 - 2b + 5a)$ Factor out the negative of the GCF. ■

✓ **CHECK POINT 6** Factor: $-16a^4b^5 + 24a^3b^4 - 20ab^2$.

4 Factor by grouping.

Factoring by Grouping

Up to now, we have factored a monomial from a polynomial. By contrast, in our next example, the greatest common factor of the polynomial is a binomial.

EXAMPLE 7 Factoring Out the Greatest Common Binomial Factor

Factor:

a. $x^2(x + 3) + 5(x + 3)$ **b.** $x(y + 1) - 2(y + 1)$.

Solution Let's identify the common binomial factor in each part of the problem.

$x^2(x + 3)$ and $5(x + 3)$ — The GCF, a binomial, is $x + 3$.

$x(y + 1)$ and $-2(y + 1)$ — The GCF, a binomial, is $y + 1$.

We factor out these common binomial factors as follows.

a. $x^2(x + 3) + 5(x + 3)$

$= (x + 3)x^2 + (x + 3)5$ — Express each term as the product of the GCF and its other factor, in that order. Hereafter, we omit this step.

$= (x + 3)(x^2 + 5)$ — Factor out the GCF, $x + 3$.

b. $x(y + 1) - 2(y + 1)$ — The GCF is $y + 1$.

$= (y + 1)(x - 2)$ — Factor out the GCF. ■

✓ **CHECK POINT 7** Factor:

a. $x^2(x + 1) + 7(x + 1)$ **b.** $x(y + 4) - 7(y + 4)$.

Some polynomials have only a greatest common factor of 1. However, by a suitable grouping of the terms, it still may be possible to factor. This process, called **factoring by grouping**, is illustrated in Example 8.

EXAMPLE 8 Factoring by Grouping

Factor: $x^3 + 4x^2 + 3x + 12$.

Solution There is no factor other than 1 common to all four terms. However, we can group terms that have a common factor:

$$\boxed{x^3 + 4x^2} + \boxed{3x + 12}.$$

Common factor is x^2. Common factor is 3.

Discover for Yourself

In Example 8, group the terms as follows:

$$(x^3 + 3x) + (4x^2 + 12).$$

Factor out the greatest common factor from each group and complete the factoring process. Describe what happens. What can you conclude?

We now factor the given polynomial as follows:

$x^3 + 4x^2 + 3x + 12$

$= (x^3 + 4x^2) + (3x + 12)$ — Group terms with common factors.

$= x^2(x + 4) + 3(x + 4)$ — Factor out the greatest common factor from the grouped terms. The remaining two terms have $x + 4$ as a common binomial factor.

$= (x + 4)(x^2 + 3)$. — Factor out the GCF, $x + 4$.

Thus, $x^3 + 4x^2 + 3x + 12 = (x + 4)(x^2 + 3)$. Check the factorization by multiplying the right side of the equation using the FOIL method. Because the factorization is correct, you should obtain the original polynomial. ■

✓ **CHECK POINT 8** Factor: $x^3 + 5x^2 + 2x + 10$.

Factoring by Grouping

1. Group terms that have a common monomial factor. There will usually be two groups. Sometimes the terms must be rearranged.
2. Factor out the common monomial factor from each group.
3. Factor out the remaining common binomial factor (if one exists).

EXAMPLE 9 Factoring by Grouping

Factor: $xy + 5x - 4y - 20$.

Solution There is no factor other than 1 common to all four terms. However, we can group terms that have a common factor:

$$\boxed{xy + 5x} + \boxed{-4y - 20}.$$

Common factor is x: $xy + 5x = x(y + 5)$.

Use -4, rather than 4, as the common factor: $-4y - 20 = -4(y + 5)$. In this way, the common binomial factor, $y + 5$, appears.

The voice balloons illustrate that it is sometimes necessary to factor out a negative number from a grouping to obtain a common binomial factor for the two groupings. We now factor the given polynomial as follows:

$$xy + 5x - 4y - 20$$

$$= x(y + 5) - 4(y + 5) \quad \text{Factor } x \text{ and } -4\text{, respectively, from each grouping.}$$

$$= (y + 5)(x - 4). \quad \text{Factor out the GCF, } y + 5.$$

Thus, $xy + 5x - 4y - 20 = (y + 5)(x - 4)$. Using the commutative property of multiplication, the factorization can also be expressed as $(x - 4)(y + 5)$. Multiply these factors using the FOIL method to verify that, regardless of the order, these are the correct factors. ■

✓ **CHECK POINT 9** Factor: $xy + 3x - 5y - 15$.

Achieving Success

When using your professor's office hours, show up prepared. If you are having difficulty with a concept or problem, bring your work so that your instructor can determine where you are having trouble. If you miss a lecture, read the appropriate section in the text, borrow class notes, and attempt the assigned homework before your office visit. It is not realistic to expect your professor to rehash all or part of a class lecture during office hours.

CONCEPT AND VOCABULARY CHECK

Fill in each blank so that the resulting statement is true.

1. The process of writing a polynomial containing the sum of monomials as a product is called ______________.
2. An expression of the highest degree that divides each term of a polynomial is called the ______________. The variable part of this expression contains the ______________ power of a variable that appears in all terms of the polynomial.
3. True or false: The factorization of $15x + 20$ is $5 \cdot 3x + 5 \cdot 4$.______________
4. True or false: The factorization of $x^2 + 3x + 5x + 15$ is $x(x + 3) + 5(x + 3)$.______________

1 EXERCISE SET

MyMathLab®

Watch the videos in MyMathLab

Download the MyDashBoard App

Practice Exercises

In Exercises 1–12, find the greatest common factor of each list of monomials.

1. 4 and $8x$
2. 5 and $15x$
3. $12x^2$ and $8x$
4. $20x^2$ and $15x$
5. $-2x^4$ and $6x^3$
6. $-3x^4$ and $6x^3$
7. $9y^5$, $18y^2$, and $-3y$
8. $10y^5$, $20y^2$, and $-5y$
9. xy, xy^2, and xy^3
10. x^2y, $3x^3y$, and $6x^2$
11. $16x^5y^4$, $8x^6y^3$, and $20x^4y^5$
12. $18x^5y^4$, $6x^6y^3$, and $12x^4y^5$

In Exercises 13–48, factor each polynomial using the greatest common factor. If there is no common factor other than 1 and the polynomial cannot be factored, so state.

13. $8x + 8$
14. $9x + 9$
15. $4y - 4$
16. $5y - 5$
17. $5x + 30$
18. $10x + 30$
19. $30x - 12$
20. $32x - 24$
21. $x^2 + 5x$
22. $x^2 + 6x$
23. $18y^2 + 12$
24. $20y^2 + 15$
25. $14x^3 + 21x^2$
26. $6x^3 + 15x^2$
27. $13y^2 - 25y$
28. $11y^2 - 30y$
29. $9y^4 + 27y^6$
30. $10y^4 + 15y^6$
31. $8x^2 - 4x^4$
32. $12x^2 - 4x^4$
33. $12y^2 + 16y - 8$
34. $15y^2 - 3y + 9$
35. $9x^4 + 18x^3 + 6x^2$
36. $32x^4 + 2x^3 + 8x^2$
37. $100y^5 - 50y^3 + 100y^2$
38. $26y^5 - 13y^3 + 39y^2$
39. $10x - 20x^2 + 5x^3$
40. $6x - 4x^2 + 2x^3$
41. $11x^2 - 23$
42. $12x^2 - 25$
43. $6x^3y^2 + 9xy$
44. $4x^2y^3 + 6xy$
45. $30x^2y^3 - 10xy^2 + 20xy$
46. $27x^2y^3 - 18xy^2 + 45x^2y$
47. $32x^3y^2 - 24x^3y - 16x^2y$
48. $18x^3y^2 - 12x^3y - 24x^2y$

In Exercises 49–56, factor each polynomial using the negative of the greatest common factor.

49. $-12x^2 + 18$
50. $-15x^2 + 20$
51. $-8x^4 + 32x^3 + 16x^2$
52. $-18x^4 + 9x^3 + 6x^2$
53. $-4a^3b^2 + 6ab$
54. $-9a^2b^3 + 12ab$
55. $-12x^3y^2 - 18x^3y + 24x^2y$
56. $-24x^3y^2 - 32x^3y + 16x^2y$

In Exercises 57–68, factor each polynomial using the greatest common binomial factor.

57. $x(x + 5) + 3(x + 5)$
58. $x(x + 7) + 10(x + 7)$
59. $x(x + 2) - 4(x + 2)$
60. $x(x + 3) - 8(x + 3)$
61. $x(y + 6) - 7(y + 6)$
62. $x(y + 9) - 11(y + 9)$
63. $3x(x + y) - (x + y)$
64. $7x(x + y) - (x + y)$
65. $4x(3x + 1) + 3x + 1$
66. $5x(2x + 1) + 2x + 1$
67. $7x^2(5x + 4) + 5x + 4$
68. $9x^2(7x + 2) + 7x + 2$

In Exercises 69–86, factor by grouping.

69. $x^2 + 2x + 4x + 8$
70. $x^2 + 3x + 5x + 15$
71. $x^2 + 3x - 5x - 15$
72. $x^2 + 7x - 4x - 28$
73. $x^3 - 2x^2 + 5x - 10$
74. $x^3 - 3x^2 + 4x - 12$
75. $x^3 - x^2 + 2x - 2$
76. $x^3 + 6x^2 - 2x - 12$
77. $xy + 5x + 9y + 45$
78. $xy + 6x + 2y + 12$
79. $xy - x + 5y - 5$
80. $xy - x + 7y - 7$
81. $3x^2 - 6xy + 5xy - 10y^2$
82. $10x^2 - 12xy + 35xy - 42y^2$
83. $3x^3 - 2x^2 - 6x + 4$
84. $4x^3 - x^2 - 12x + 3$
85. $x^2 - ax - bx + ab$
86. $x^2 + ax + bx + ab$

Practice PLUS

In Exercises 87–94, factor each polynomial.

87. $24x^3y^3z^3 + 30x^2y^2z + 18x^2yz^2$
88. $16x^2y^2z^2 + 32x^2yz^2 + 24x^2yz$
89. $x^3 - 4 + 3x^3y - 12y$
90. $x^3 - 5 + 2x^3y - 10y$
91. $4x^5(x + 1) - 6x^3(x + 1) - 8x^2(x + 1)$

92. $8x^5(x + 2) - 10x^3(x + 2) - 2x^2(x + 2)$

93. $3x^5 - 3x^4 + x^3 - x^2 + 5x - 5$

94. $7x^5 - 7x^4 + x^3 - x^2 + 3x - 3$

The figures for Exercises 95–96 show one or more circles drawn inside a square. Write a polynomial that represents the shaded blue area in each figure. Then factor the polynomial.

95.

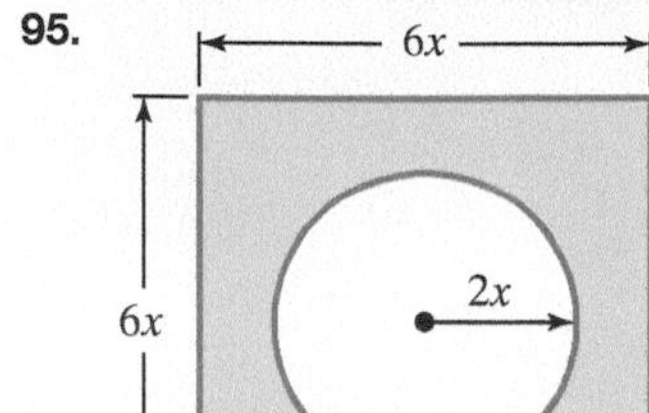

96.

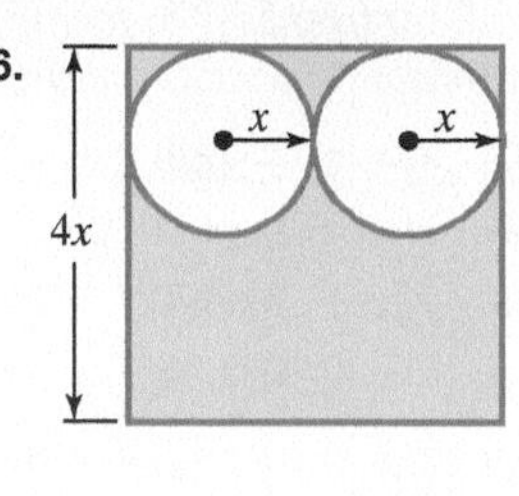

Application Exercises

97. An explosion causes debris to rise vertically with an initial velocity of 64 feet per second. The polynomial $64x - 16x^2$ describes the height of the debris above the ground, in feet, after x seconds.

a. Find the height of the debris after 3 seconds.

b. Factor the polynomial.

c. Use the factored form of the polynomial in part (b) to find the height of the debris after 3 seconds. Do you get the same answer as you did in part (a)? If so, does this prove that your factorization is correct? Explain.

98. An explosion causes debris to rise vertically with an initial velocity of 72 feet per second. The polynomial $72x - 16x^2$ describes the height of the debris above the ground, in feet, after x seconds.

a. Find the height of the debris after 4 seconds.

b. Factor the polynomial.

c. Use the factored form of the polynomial in part (b) to find the height of the debris after 4 seconds. Do you get the same answer as you did in part (a)? If so, does this prove that your factorization is correct? Explain

In Exercises 99–100, write a polynomial for the length of each rectangle.

99.

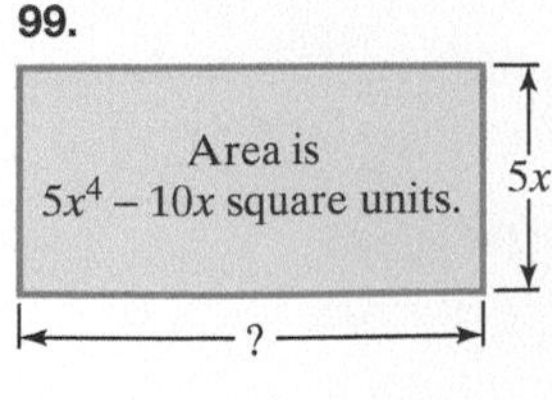

100.

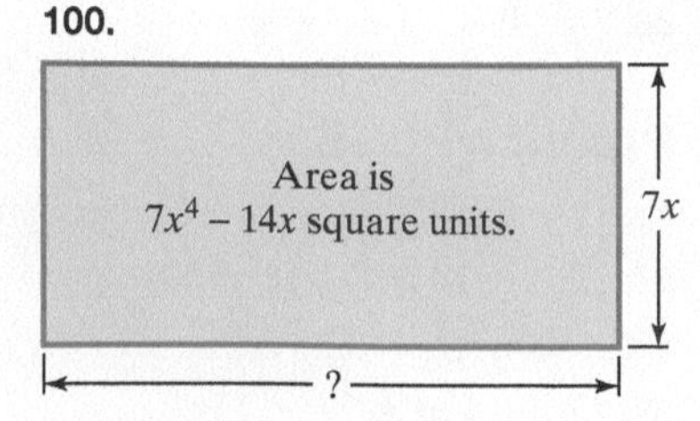

Writing in Mathematics

101. What is factoring?

102. What is a prime polynomial?

103. Explain how to find the greatest common factor of a list of terms. Give an example with your explanation.

104. Use an example and explain how to factor out the greatest common factor of a polynomial.

105. Suppose that a polynomial contains four terms and can be factored by grouping. Explain how to obtain the factorization.

106. Write a sentence that uses the word "factor" as a noun. Then write a sentence that uses the word "factor" as a verb.

Critical Thinking Exercises

Make Sense? *In Exercises 107–110, determine whether each statement "makes sense" or "does not make sense" and explain your reasoning.*

107. After factoring $20x^3 + 8x^2$ and $20x^3 + 10x$, I noticed that I factored the monomial $20x^3$ in two different ways.

108. After I've factored a polynomial, my answer cannot always be checked by multiplication.

109. The word *greatest* in greatest common factor is helpful because it tells me to look for the greatest power of a variable appearing in all terms.

110. You grouped the polynomial's terms using different groupings than I did, yet we both obtained the same factorization.

In Exercises 111–114, determine whether each statement is true or false. If the statement is false, make the necessary change(s) to produce a true statement.

111. Since the GCF of $9x^3 + 6x^2 + 3x$ is $3x$, it is not necessary to write the 1 when $3x$ is factored from the last term.

112.
$$\begin{aligned} a(x - 7) + b(7 - x) &= a(x - 7) + b(-1)(x - 7) \\ &= a(x - 7) - b(x - 7) \\ &= (x - 7)(a - b) \end{aligned}$$

113.
$$\begin{aligned} a^2 + b^2 &= a^2 + ab - ab + b^2 \\ &= a(a + b) - b(a + b) \\ &= (a + b)(a - b) \end{aligned}$$

114. $-4x^2 + 12x$ can be factored as $-4x(x - 3)$ or $4x(-x + 3)$.

115. Suppose you receive x dollars in January. Each month thereafter, you receive \$100 more than you received the month before. Write a factored polynomial that describes the total dollar amount you receive from January through April.

In Exercises 116–117, write a polynomial that fits the given description. Do not use a polynomial that appears in this section or in the Exercise Set.

116. The polynomial has four terms and can be factored using a greatest common factor that has both a coefficient and a variable.

117. The polynomial has four terms and can be factored by grouping.

Technology Exercises

In Exercises 118–120, use a graphing utility to graph each side of the equation in the same viewing rectangle. Do the graphs coincide? If so, this means that the polynomial on the left side has been factored correctly. If not, factor the polynomial correctly and then use your graphing utility to verify the factorization.

118. $-3x - 6 = -3(x - 2)$

119. $x^2 - 2x + 5x - 10 = (x - 2)(x - 5)$

120. $x^2 + 2x + x + 2 = x(x + 2) + 1$

Review Exercises

121. Multiply: $(x + 7)(x + 10)$.

122. Solve the system by graphing:

$$\begin{cases} 2x - y = -4 \\ x - 3y = 3. \end{cases}$$

123. Write the point-slope form of the equation of the line passing through $(-7, 2)$ and $(-4, 5)$. Then use the point-slope form of the equation to write the slope-intercept form of the equation.

Preview Exercises

Exercises 124–126 will help you prepare for the material covered in the next section.

124. Find two factors of 8 whose sum is 6.

125. Find two factors of 6 whose sum is -5.

126. Find two factors of -35 whose sum is 2.

SECTION 2

Factoring Trinomials Whose Leading Coefficient Is 1

Objective

1. Factor trinomials of the form $x^2 + bx + c$.

Exactostock/SuperStock

Not afraid of heights and cutting-edge excitement? How about sky diving? Behind your exhilarating experience is the world of algebra. After you jump from the airplane, your height above the ground at every instant of your fall can be described by a formula involving a variable that is squared. At a height of approximately 2000 feet, you'll need to open your parachute. How can you determine when you must do so?

The answer to this critical question involves using the factoring technique presented in this section. In Section 6, in which applications are discussed, this technique is applied to models involving the height of any free-falling object—in this case, you.

1 Factor trinomials of the form $x^2 + bx + c$.

A Strategy for Factoring $x^2 + bx + c$

We use the FOIL method to multiply two binomials. The product is often a trinomial. The following are some examples:

Factored Form	F O I L	Trinomial Form
$(x + 3)(x + 4)$	$= x^2 + 4x + 3x + 12$	$= x^2 + 7x + 12$
$(x - 3)(x - 4)$	$= x^2 - 4x - 3x + 12$	$= x^2 - 7x + 12$
$(x + 3)(x - 5)$	$= x^2 - 5x + 3x - 15$	$= x^2 - 2x - 15.$

Observe that each trinomial is of the form $x^2 + bx + c$, where the coefficient of the squared term, called the **leading coefficient**, is 1. Our goal in this section is to start with the trinomial form and, assuming that it is factorable, return to the factored form.

The first FOIL multiplication shown above indicates that $(x + 3)(x + 4) = x^2 + 7x + 12$. Let's reverse the sides of this equation:

$$x^2 + 7x + 12 = (x + 3)(x + 4).$$

We can make several important observations about the factors on the right side.

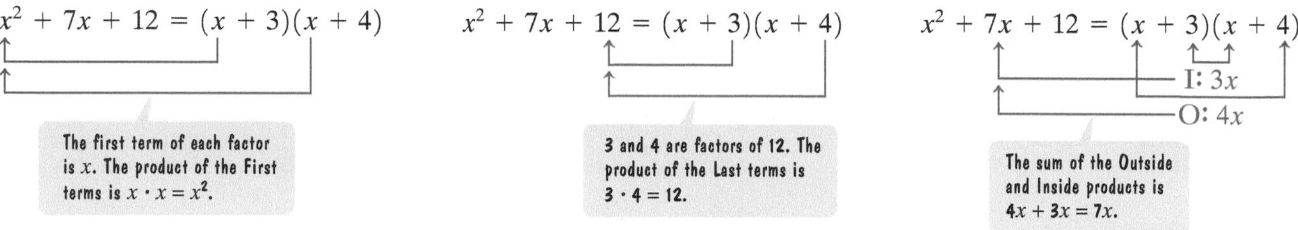

$x^2 + 7x + 12 = (x + 3)(x + 4)$
The first term of each factor is x. The product of the First terms is $x \cdot x = x^2$.
$x^2 + 7x + 12 = (x + 3)(x + 4)$
3 and 4 are factors of 12. The product of the Last terms is $3 \cdot 4 = 12$.
$x^2 + 7x + 12 = (x + 3)(x + 4)$
I: $3x$
O: $4x$
The sum of the Outside and Inside products is $4x + 3x = 7x$.

These observations provide us with a procedure for factoring $x^2 + bx + c$.

A Strategy for Factoring $x^2 + bx + c$

1. Enter x as the first term of each factor.

$$(x \quad)(x \quad) = x^2 + bx + c$$

2. List pairs of factors of the constant c.
3. Try various combinations of these factors as the second term in each set of parentheses. Select the combination in which the sum of the Outside and Inside products is equal to bx.

$$(x + \square)(x + \square) = x^2 + bx + c$$

I

O

Sum of O + I

4. Check your work by multiplying the factors using the FOIL method. You should obtain the original trinomial.

If none of the possible combinations yield an Outside product and an Inside product whose sum is equal to bx, the trinomial cannot be factored using integers and is called **prime** over the set of integers.

EXAMPLE 1 Factoring a Trinomial in $x^2 + bx + c$ Form

Factor: $x^2 + 6x + 8$.

Solution

Step 1. Enter x as the first term of each factor.

$$x^2 + 6x + 8 = (x \quad)(x \quad)$$

Step 2. List pairs of factors of the constant, 8.

Factors of 8	8, 1	4, 2	−8, −1	−4, −2

Step 3. Try various combinations of these factors. The correct factorization of $x^2 + 6x + 8$ is the one in which the sum of the Outside and Inside products is equal to $6x$. Here is a list of the possible factorizations:

Possible Factorizations of $x^2 + 6x + 8$	Sum of Outside and Inside Products (Should Equal $6x$)
$(x + 8)(x + 1)$	$x + 8x = 9x$
$(x + 4)(x + 2)$	$2x + 4x = 6x$
$(x - 8)(x - 1)$	$-x - 8x = -9x$
$(x - 4)(x - 2)$	$-2x - 4x = -6x$

This is the required middle term.

Thus, $x^2 + 6x + 8 = (x + 4)(x + 2)$.

Step 4. Check this result by multiplying the right side using the FOIL method. You should obtain the original trinomial. Because of the commutative property, the factorization can also be expressed as

$$x^2 + 6x + 8 = (x + 2)(x + 4). \quad ■$$

Using Technology

Graphic and Numeric Connections

If a polynomial contains one variable, a graphing utility can be used to check its factorization. For example, the factorization in Example 1,

$$x^2 + 6x + 8 = (x + 4)(x + 2),$$

can be checked graphically or numerically.

Graphic Check

Use the [GRAPH] feature. Graph $y_1 = x^2 + 6x + 8$ and $y_2 = (x + 4)(x + 2)$ on the same screen. Because the graphs are identical, the factorization appears to be correct.

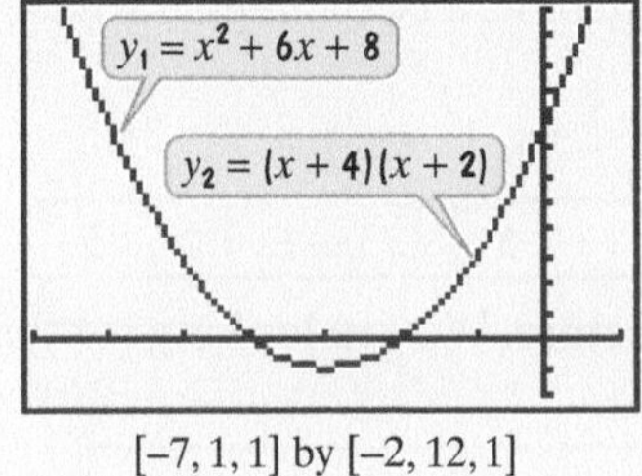

[−7, 1, 1] by [−2, 12, 1]

Numeric Check

Use the [TABLE] feature. Enter $y_1 = x^2 + 6x + 8$ and $y_2 = (x + 4)(x + 2)$ and press [TABLE]. Two columns of values are shown, one for y_1 and one for y_2. Because the corresponding values are equal regardless of how far up or down we scroll, the factorization is correct.

X	Y1	Y2
-3	-1	-1
-2	0	0
-1	3	3
0	8	8
1	15	15
2	24	24
3	35	35

X= -3

✓ **CHECK POINT 1** Factor: $x^2 + 5x + 6$.

EXAMPLE 2 Factoring a Trinomial in $x^2 + bx + c$ Form

Factor: $x^2 - 5x + 6$.

Solution

Step 1. Enter x as the first term of each factor.

$$x^2 - 5x + 6 = (x \quad)(x \quad)$$

Step 2. List pairs of factors of the constant, 6.

Factors of 6	6, 1	3, 2	−6, −1	−3, −2

Step 3. Try various combinations of these factors. The correct factorization of $x^2 - 5x + 6$ is the one in which the sum of the Outside and Inside products is equal to $-5x$. Here is a list of the possible factorizations:

Possible Factorizations of $x^2 - 5x + 6$	Sum of Outside and Inside Products (Should Equal $-5x$)
$(x + 6)(x + 1)$	$x + 6x = 7x$
$(x + 3)(x + 2)$	$2x + 3x = 5x$
$(x - 6)(x - 1)$	$-x - 6x = -7x$
$(x - 3)(x - 2)$	$-2x - 3x = -5x$

This is the required middle term.

Thus, $x^2 - 5x + 6 = (x - 3)(x - 2)$. Verify this result using the FOIL method. ■

Great Question!

Is there a way to eliminate some of the combinations of factors for $x^2 + bx + c$ when c is positive?

Yes. To factor $x^2 + bx + c$ when c is positive, find two numbers with the same sign as the middle term.

$$x^2 + 6x + 8 = (x + 2)(x + 4)$$

Same signs

$$x^2 - 5x + 6 = (x - 3)(x - 2)$$

Same signs

In factoring a trinomial of the form $x^2 + bx + c$, you can speed things up by listing the factors of c and then finding their sums. We are interested in a sum of b. For example, in factoring $x^2 - 5x + 6$, we are interested in the factors of 6 whose sum is -5.

Factors of 6	6, 1	3, 2	−6, −1	−3, −2
Sum of Factors	7	5	−7	−5

This is the desired sum.

Thus, $x^2 - 5x + 6 = (x - 3)(x - 2)$.

✓ CHECK POINT 2 Factor: $x^2 - 6x + 8$.

EXAMPLE 3 Factoring a Trinomial in $x^2 + bx + c$ Form

Factor: $x^2 + 2x - 35$.

Solution

Step 1. Enter x as the first term of each factor.

$$x^2 + 2x - 35 = (x \quad)(x \quad)$$

To find the second term of each factor, we must find two integers whose product is -35 and whose sum is 2.

Step 2. List pairs of factors of the constant, −35.

Factors of −35	−35, 1	−7, 5	35, −1	7, −5

Step 3. Try various combinations of these factors. We are looking for the pair of factors whose sum is 2.

Factors of −35	−35, 1	−7, 5	35, −1	7, −5
Sum of Factors	−34	−2	34	2

This is the desired sum.

Thus, $x^2 + 2x - 35 = (x + 7)(x - 5)$.

Step 4. Verify the factorization using the FOIL method.

$$(x + 7)(x - 5) = x^2 - 5x + 7x - 35 = x^2 + 2x - 35$$

Because the product of the factors is the original polynomial, the factorization is correct. ■

✓ **CHECK POINT 3** Factor: $x^2 + 3x - 10$.

EXAMPLE 4 Factoring a Trinomial Whose Leading Coefficient Is 1

Factor: $y^2 - 2y - 99$.

Solution

Step 1. Enter y as the first term of each factor.

$$y^2 - 2y - 99 = (y \quad)(y \quad)$$

To find the second term of each factor, we must find two integers whose product is -99 and whose sum is -2.

Step 2. List pairs of factors of the constant, -99.

Factors of -99	$-99, 1$	$-11, 9$	$-33, 3$	$99, -1$	$11, -9$	$33, -3$

Step 3. Try various combinations of these factors. In order to factor $y^2 - 2y - 99$, we are interested in the pair of factors of -99 whose sum is -2.

Factors of −99	$-99, 1$	$-11, 9$	$-33, 3$	$99, -1$	$11, -9$	$33, -3$
Sum of Factors	-98	-2	-30	98	2	30

This is the desired sum.

Thus, $y^2 - 2y - 99 = (y - 11)(y + 9)$. Verify this result using the FOIL method. ■

Great Question!

Is there a way to eliminate some of the combinations of factors for $x^2 + bx + c$ when c is negative?

Yes. To factor $x^2 + bx + c$ when c is negative, find two numbers with opposite signs whose sum is the coefficient of the middle term.

$$x^2 + 2x - 35 = (x + 7)(x - 5)$$

Negative — Opposite signs

$$y^2 - 2y - 99 = (y - 11)(y + 9)$$

Negative — Opposite signs

✓ **CHECK POINT 4** Factor: $y^2 - 6y - 27$.

EXAMPLE 5 Trying to Factor a Trinomial in $x^2 + bx + c$ Form

Factor: $x^2 + x - 5$.

Solution

Step 1. Enter x as the first term of each factor.

$$x^2 + x - 5 = (x \quad)(x \quad)$$

To find the second term of each factor, we must find two integers whose product is -5 and whose sum is 1.

Steps 2 and 3. List pairs of factors of the constant, -5, and try various combinations of these factors. We are interested in a pair of factors whose sum is 1.

Factors of −5	$-5, 1$	$5, -1$
Sum of Factors	-4	4

No pair gives the desired sum, 1.

Because neither pair has a sum of 1, $x^2 + x - 5$ cannot be factored using integers. This trinomial is prime. ■

✓ **CHECK POINT 5** Factor: $x^2 + x - 7$.

EXAMPLE 6 Factoring a Trinomial in Two Variables

Factor: $x^2 - 5xy + 6y^2$.

Solution

Step 1. Enter *x* as the first term of each factor. Because the last term of the trinomial contains y^2, the second term of each factor must contain y.

$$x^2 - 5xy + 6y^2 = (x \quad ?y)(x \quad ?y)$$

The question marks indicate that we are looking for the coefficients of y in each factor. To find these coefficients, we must find two integers whose product is 6 and whose sum is -5.

Steps 2 and 3. List pairs of factors of the coefficient of the last term, 6, and try various combinations of these factors. We are interested in the pair of factors whose sum is -5.

Factors of 6	6, 1	3, 2	−6, −1	−3, −2
Sum of Factors	7	5	−7	−5

This is the desired sum.

Thus, $x^2 - 5xy + 6y^2 = (x - 3y)(x - 2y)$.

Step 4. Verify the factorization using the FOIL method.

$$(x - 3y)(x - 2y) = x^2 - 2xy - 3xy + 6y^2 = x^2 - 5xy + 6y^2$$

Because the product of the factors is the original polynomial, the factorization is correct. ■

✓ **CHECK POINT 6** Factor: $x^2 - 4xy + 3y^2$.

Some polynomials can be factored using more than one technique. **Always begin by looking for a greatest common factor** and, if there is one, factor it out. A polynomial is **factored completely** when it is written as the product of prime polynomials.

EXAMPLE 7 Factoring Completely

Factor: $3x^3 - 15x^2 - 42x$.

Solution The GCF of the three terms of the polynomial is $3x$. We begin by factoring out $3x$. Then we factor the remaining trinomial by the methods of this section.

$3x^3 - 15x^2 - 42x$

$= 3x(x^2 - 5x - 14)$ Factor out the GCF.

$= 3x(x \quad)(x \quad)$ Begin factoring $x^2 - 5x - 14$. Find two integers whose product is −14 and whose sum is −5.

$= 3x(x - 7)(x + 2)$ The integers are −7 and 2.

Thus,

$$3x^3 - 15x^2 - 42x = 3x(x - 7)(x + 2).$$

Be sure to include the GCF in the factorization.

How can we check this factorization? We will multiply the binomials using the FOIL method. Then use the distributive property and multiply each term of this product by $3x$. If the factorization is correct, we should obtain the original polynomial.

$$3x(x-7)(x+2) = 3x(x^2+2x-7x-14) = 3x(x^2-5x-14) = 3x^3-15x^2-42x$$

Use the FOIL method on $(x-7)(x+2)$.

This is the original polynomial.

The factorization is correct. ■

✓ **CHECK POINT 7** Factor: $2x^3 + 6x^2 - 56x$.

EXAMPLE 8 Factoring Completely by Factoring Out the Negative of the GCF

Factor: $-16t^2 + 16t + 96$.

Solution The GCF of the three terms of the polynomial is 16. Because the polynomial has a negative coefficient in the first term, we will factor out the negative of the GCF. Thus, we will factor out -16.

$$-16t^2 + 16t + 96$$

$$= -16(t^2 - t - 6)$$ Factor out the negative of the GCF.

$$= -16(t \quad)(t \quad)$$ Begin factoring $t^2 - t - 6$. Find two integers whose product is -6 and whose sum is -1.

$$= -16(t-3)(t+2)$$ The integers are -3 and 2.

Thus,

$$-16t^2 + 16t + 96 = -16(t-3)(t+2).$$

Verify this factorization using the FOIL method to multiply $t - 3$ and $t + 2$. Then use the distributive property and multiply each term of this product by -16. You should obtain the original polynomial. ■

✓ **CHECK POINT 8** Factor: $-2y^2 - 10y + 28$.

CONCEPT AND VOCABULARY CHECK

Fill in each blank so that the resulting statement is true.

1. To factor $x^2 - 12x + 20$, we must find two integers whose product is ______________ and whose sum is ______________.
2. A polynomial is factored ______________ when it is written as a product of prime polynomials.
3. $x^2 + 13x + 30 = (x + 3)(x \_\_\_)$
4. $x^2 - 9x + 18 = (x - 3)(x \_\_\_)$
5. $x^2 - x - 30 = (x - 6)(x \_\_\_)$
6. $x^2 - 5x - 14 = (x + 2)(x \_\_\_)$
7. $x^2 - 10xy + 16y^2 = (x - 8y)(x \_\_\_)$

2 EXERCISE SET

MyMathLab®

Watch the videos in MyMathLab

Download the MyDashBoard App

Practice Exercises

In Exercises 1–42, factor each trinomial, or state that the trinomial is prime. Check each factorization using FOIL multiplication.

1. $x^2 + 7x + 6$
2. $x^2 + 9x + 8$
3. $x^2 + 7x + 10$
4. $x^2 + 9x + 14$
5. $x^2 + 11x + 10$
6. $x^2 + 13x + 12$
7. $x^2 - 7x + 12$
8. $x^2 - 13x + 40$
9. $x^2 - 12x + 36$
10. $x^2 - 8x + 16$
11. $y^2 - 8y + 15$
12. $y^2 - 8y + 7$
13. $x^2 + 3x - 10$
14. $x^2 + 3x - 28$
15. $y^2 + 10y - 39$
16. $y^2 + 5y - 24$
17. $x^2 - 2x - 15$
18. $x^2 - 4x - 5$
19. $x^2 - 2x - 8$
20. $x^2 - 5x - 6$
21. $x^2 + 4x + 12$
22. $x^2 + 4x + 5$
23. $y^2 - 16y + 48$
24. $y^2 - 10y + 21$
25. $x^2 - 3x + 6$
26. $x^2 + 4x - 10$
27. $w^2 - 30w - 64$
28. $w^2 + 12w - 64$
29. $y^2 - 18y + 65$
30. $y^2 - 22y + 72$
31. $r^2 + 12r + 27$
32. $r^2 - 15r - 16$
33. $y^2 - 7y + 5$
34. $y^2 - 15y + 5$
35. $x^2 + 7xy + 6y^2$
36. $x^2 + 6xy + 8y^2$
37. $x^2 - 8xy + 15y^2$
38. $x^2 - 9xy + 14y^2$
39. $x^2 - 3xy - 18y^2$
40. $x^2 - xy - 30y^2$
41. $a^2 - 18ab + 45b^2$
42. $a^2 - 18ab + 80b^2$

In Exercises 43–66, factor completely.

43. $3x^2 + 15x + 18$
44. $3x^2 + 21x + 36$
45. $4y^2 - 4y - 8$
46. $3y^2 + 3y - 18$
47. $10x^2 - 40x - 600$
48. $2x^2 + 10x - 48$
49. $3x^2 - 33x + 54$
50. $2x^2 - 14x + 24$
51. $2r^3 + 6r^2 + 4r$
52. $2r^3 + 8r^2 + 6r$
53. $4x^3 + 12x^2 - 72x$
54. $3x^3 - 15x^2 + 18x$
55. $2r^3 + 8r^2 - 64r$
56. $3r^3 - 9r^2 - 54r$
57. $y^4 + 2y^3 - 80y^2$
58. $y^4 - 12y^3 + 35y^2$
59. $x^4 - 3x^3 - 10x^2$
60. $x^4 - 22x^3 + 120x^2$
61. $2w^4 - 26w^3 - 96w^2$
62. $3w^4 + 54w^3 + 135w^2$
63. $15xy^2 + 45xy - 60x$
64. $20x^2y - 100xy + 120y$
65. $x^5 + 3x^4y - 4x^3y^2$
66. $x^3y - 2x^2y^2 - 3xy^3$

In Exercises 67–74, use the negative of the greatest common factor to factor completely.

67. $-16t^2 + 64t + 80$
68. $-16t^2 + 80t + 96$
69. $-5x^2 + 50x - 45$
70. $-3x^2 + 36x - 33$
71. $-x^2 - 3x + 40$
72. $-x^2 - 4x + 45$
73. $-2x^3 - 6x^2 + 8x$
74. $-3x^3 + 6x^2 + 24x$

Practice PLUS

In Exercises 75–82, factor completely.

75. $2x^2y^2 - 32x^2yz + 30x^2z^2$
76. $2x^2y^2 - 30x^2yz + 28x^2z^2$
77. $(a + b)x^2 + (a + b)x - 20(a + b)$
78. $(a + b)x^2 - 13(a + b)x + 36(a + b)$

(Hint on Exercises 79–82: Factors contain rational numbers.)

79. $x^2 + 0.5x + 0.06$
80. $x^2 - 0.5x - 0.06$
81. $x^2 - \frac{2}{5}x + \frac{1}{25}$
82. $x^2 + \frac{2}{3}x + \frac{1}{9}$

Application Exercises

83. You dive directly upward from a board that is 32 feet high. After t seconds, your height above the water is described by the polynomial

$$-16t^2 + 16t + 32.$$

a. Factor the polynomial completely.

b. Evaluate both the original polynomial and its factored form for $t = 2$. Do you get the same answer for each evaluation? Describe what this answer means.

84. You dive directly upward from a board that is 48 feet high. After t seconds, your height above the water is described by the polynomial

$$-16t^2 + 32t + 48.$$

a. Factor the polynomial completely.

b. Evaluate both the original polynomial and its factored form for $t = 3$. Do you get the same answer for each evaluation? Describe what this answer means.

Writing in Mathematics

85. Explain how to factor $x^2 + 8x + 15$.

86. Give two helpful suggestions for factoring $x^2 - 5x + 6$.

87. In factoring $x^2 + bx + c$, describe how the last terms in each factor are related to b and c.

88. Without actually factoring and without multiplying the given factors, explain why the following factorization is not correct:

$$x^2 + 46x + 513 = (x - 27)(x - 19).$$

Critical Thinking Exercises

Make Sense? *In Exercises 89–92, determine whether each statement "makes sense" or "does not make sense" and explain your reasoning.*

89. If I have a correct factorization, switching the order of the factors can give me an incorrect factorization.

90. I began factoring $x^2 - 17x + 72$ by finding all number pairs with a sum of -17.

91. It's easy to factor $x^2 + x + 1$ because of the relatively small numbers for the constant term and the coefficient of x.

92. I factor $x^2 + bx + c$ by finding two numbers that have a product of c and a sum of b.

In Exercises 93–96, determine whether each statement is true or false. If the statement is false, make the necessary change(s) to produce a true statement.

93. One factor of $x^2 + x + 20$ is $x + 5$.

94. A trinomial can never have two identical factors.

95. One factor of $y^2 + 5y - 24$ is $y - 3$.

96. $x^2 + 4 = (x + 2)(x + 2)$

In Exercises 97–98, find all positive integers b so that the trinomial can be factored.

97. $x^2 + bx + 15$

98. $x^2 + 4x + b$

99. Write a trinomial of the form $x^2 + bx + c$ that is prime.

100. Factor: $x^{2n} + 20x^n + 99$.

101. Factor $x^3 + 3x^2 + 2x$. If x represents an integer, use the factorization to describe what the trinomial represents.

102. A box with no top is to be made from an 8-inch by 6-inch piece of metal by cutting identical squares from each corner and turning up the sides (see the figure). The volume of the box is modeled by the polynomial $4x^3 - 28x^2 + 48x$. Factor the polynomial completely. Then use the dimensions given on the box and show that its volume is equivalent to the factorization that you obtain.

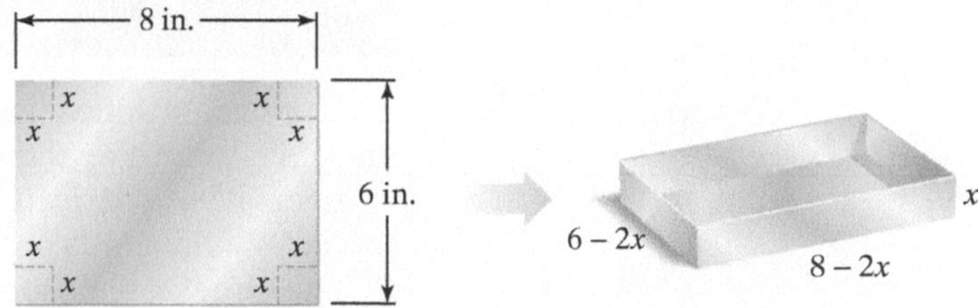

Technology Exercises

In Exercises 103–106, use the GRAPH *or* TABLE *feature of a graphing utility to determine if the polynomial on the left side of each equation has been correctly factored. If the graphs of y_1 and y_2 coincide, or if their corresponding table values are equal, this means that the polynomial on the left side has been correctly factored. If not, factor the trinomial correctly and then use your graphing utility to verify the factorization.*

103. $x^2 - 5x + 6 = (x - 2)(x - 3)$

104. $2x^2 + 2x - 12 = 2(x - 3)(x + 2)$

105. $x^2 - 2x + 1 = (x + 1)(x - 1)$

106. $2x^2 + 8x + 6 = (x + 3)(x + 1)$

Review Exercises

107. Solve: $4(x - 2) = 3x + 5$.

108. Graph: $6x - 5y \leq 30$.

109. Graph: $y = -\frac{1}{3}x + 2$.

Preview Exercises

Exercises 110–112 will help you prepare for the material covered in the next section.

110. Multiply: $(2x + 3)(x - 2)$.

111. Multiply: $(3x + 4)(3x + 1)$.

112. Factor by grouping: $8x^2 - 2x - 20x + 5$.

SECTION

3

Factoring Trinomials Whose Leading Coefficient Is Not 1

Objectives

1 Factor trinomials by trial and error.

2 Factor trinomials by grouping.

The False Mirror (Le Faux Miroir), 1928, René Magritte. Oil on canvas, 21 1/4 x 31 7/8 in. (54 x 80.9 cm). Digital Image copyright © The Museum of Modern Art/Licensed by SCALA/Art Resource, New York. Copyright © 2011 C. Herscovici, London/Artists Rights Society (ARS), New York

The False Mirror (*Le Faux Miroir*) (1928), René Magritte. © 2011 MoMA/Herscovici/ARS.

The special significance of the number 1 is reflected in our language. "One," "an," and "a" mean the same thing. The words "unit," "unity," "union," "unique," and "universal" are derived from the Latin word for "one." For the ancient Greeks, 1 was the indivisible unit from which all other numbers arose.

The Greeks' philosophy of 1 applies to our work in this section. Factoring trinomials whose leading coefficient is 1 is the basic technique from which other methods of factoring $ax^2 + bx + c$, where the leading coefficient a is not equal to 1, follow.

1 Factor trinomials by trial and error.

Factoring by the Trial-and-Error Method

How do we factor a trinomial such as $3x^2 - 20x + 28$? Notice that the leading coefficient is 3. We must find two binomials whose product is $3x^2 - 20x + 28$. The product of the First terms must be $3x^2$:

$$(3x \quad)(x \quad).$$

From this point on, the factoring strategy is exactly the same as the one we use to factor trinomials whose leading coefficient is 1.

A Strategy for Factoring $ax^2 + bx + c$

Assume, for the moment, that there is no greatest common factor other than 1.

1. Find two First terms whose product is ax^2:

$$(\square x + \quad)(\square x + \quad) = ax^2 + bx + c.$$

2. Find two Last terms whose product is c:

$$(\square x + \square)(\square x + \square) = ax^2 + bx + c.$$

3. By trial and error, perform steps 1 and 2 until the sum of the Outside product and the Inside product is bx:

$$(\square x + \square)(\square x + \square) = ax^2 + bx + c.$$

I

O

Sum of O + I

If no such combinations exist, the polynomial is prime.

Great Question!

Should I feel discouraged if it takes me a while to get the correct factorization?

The *error* part of the factoring strategy plays an important role in the process. If you do not get the correct factorization the first time, this is not a bad thing. This error is often helpful in leading you to the correct factorization.

EXAMPLE 1 Factoring a Trinomial Whose Leading Coefficient Is Not 1

Factor: $3x^2 - 20x + 28$.

Solution

Step 1. Find two First terms whose product is $3x^2$.

$$3x^2 - 20x + 28 = (3x \quad)(x \quad)$$

Step 2. Find two Last terms whose product is 28. The number 28 has pairs of factors that are either both positive or both negative. Because the middle term, $-20x$, is negative, both factors must be negative. The negative factorizations of 28 are $-1(-28)$, $-2(-14)$, and $-4(-7)$.

Step 3. Try various combinations of these factors. The correct factorization of $3x^2 - 20x + 28$ is the one in which the sum of the Outside and Inside products is equal to $-20x$. Here is a list of the possible factorizations:

Great Question!

When factoring trinomials, must I list every possible factorization before getting the correct one?

With practice, you will find that it is not necessary to list every possible factorization of the trinomial. As you practice factoring, you will be able to narrow down the list of possible factors to just a few. When it comes to factoring, practice makes perfect.

Possible Factorizations of $3x^2 - 20x + 28$	Sum of Outside and Inside Products (Should Equal $-20x$)
$(3x - 1)(x - 28)$	$-84x - x = -85x$
$(3x - 28)(x - 1)$	$-3x - 28x = -31x$
$(3x - 2)(x - 14)$	$-42x - 2x = -44x$
$(3x - 14)(x - 2)$	$-6x - 14x = -20x$ (This is the required middle term.)
$(3x - 4)(x - 7)$	$-21x - 4x = -25x$
$(3x - 7)(x - 4)$	$-12x - 7x = -19x$

Thus,

$$3x^2 - 20x + 28 = (3x - 14)(x - 2) \quad \text{or} \quad (x - 2)(3x - 14).$$

Show that this factorization is correct by multiplying the factors using the FOIL method. You should obtain the original trinomial. ■

✓ **CHECK POINT 1** Factor: $5x^2 - 14x + 8$.

EXAMPLE 2 Factoring a Trinomial Whose Leading Coefficient Is Not 1

Factor: $8x^2 - 10x - 3$.

Solution

Step 1. Find two First terms whose product is $8x^2$.

$$8x^2 - 10x - 3 \stackrel{?}{=} (8x \quad)(x \quad)$$
$$8x^2 - 10x - 3 \stackrel{?}{=} (4x \quad)(2x \quad)$$

Step 2. Find two Last terms whose product is -3. The possible factorizations are $1(-3)$ and $-1(3)$.

Step 3. Try various combinations of these factors. The correct factorization of $8x^2 - 10x - 3$ is the one in which the sum of the Outside and Inside products is equal to $-10x$. Here is a list of the possible factorizations:

These four factorizations use $(8x \quad)(x \quad)$ with $1(-3)$ and $-1(3)$ as factorizations of -3.

These four factorizations use $(4x \quad)(2x \quad)$ with $1(-3)$ and $-1(3)$ as factorizations of -3.

Possible Factorizations of $8x^2 - 10x - 3$	Sum of Outside and Inside Products (Should Equal $-10x$)
$(8x + 1)(x - 3)$	$-24x + x = -23x$
$(8x - 3)(x + 1)$	$8x - 3x = 5x$
$(8x - 1)(x + 3)$	$24x - x = 23x$
$(8x + 3)(x - 1)$	$-8x + 3x = -5x$
$(4x + 1)(2x - 3)$	$-12x + 2x = -10x$
$(4x - 3)(2x + 1)$	$4x - 6x = -2x$
$(4x - 1)(2x + 3)$	$12x - 2x = 10x$
$(4x + 3)(2x - 1)$	$-4x + 6x = 2x$

This is the required middle term.

Thus,

$$8x^2 - 10x - 3 = (4x + 1)(2x - 3) \quad \text{or} \quad (2x - 3)(4x + 1).$$

Use FOIL multiplication to check either of these factorizations. ■

✓ **CHECK POINT 2** Factor: $6x^2 + 19x - 7$.

Great Question!

I zone out reading your long lists of possible factorizations. Are there any rules for shortening these lists?

Here are some suggestions for reducing the list of possible factorizations for $ax^2 + bx + c$:

1. If b is relatively small, avoid the larger factors of a.
2. If c is positive, the signs in both binomial factors must match the sign of b.
3. If the trinomial has no common factor, no binomial factor can have a common factor.
4. Reversing the signs in the binomial factors changes the sign of bx, the middle term.

EXAMPLE 3 Factoring a Trinomial in Two Variables

Factor: $2x^2 - 7xy + 3y^2$.

Solution

Step 1. Find two First terms whose product is $2x^2$.

$$2x^2 - 7xy + 3y^2 = (2x \qquad)(x \qquad)$$

Step 2. Find two Last terms whose product is $3y^2$. The possible factorizations are $(y)(3y)$ and $(-y)(-3y)$.

Step 3. Try various combinations of these factors. The correct factorization of $2x^2 - 7xy + 3y^2$ is the one in which the sum of the Outside and Inside products is equal to $-7xy$. Here is a list of possible factorizations:

Possible Factorizations of $2x^2 - 7xy + 3y^2$	Sum of Outside and Inside Products (Should Equal $-7xy$)
$(2x + 3y)(x + y)$	$2xy + 3xy = 5xy$
$(2x + y)(x + 3y)$	$6xy + xy = 7xy$
$(2x - 3y)(x - y)$	$-2xy - 3xy = -5xy$
$(2x - y)(x - 3y)$	$-6xy - xy = -7xy$

This is the required middle term.

Thus,

$$2x^2 - 7xy + 3y^2 = (2x - y)(x - 3y) \quad \text{or} \quad (x - 3y)(2x - y).$$

Use FOIL multiplication to check either of these factorizations. ■

✓ **CHECK POINT 3** Factor: $3x^2 - 13xy + 4y^2$.

2 Factor trinomials by grouping.

Factoring by the Grouping Method

A second method for factoring $ax^2 + bx + c, a \neq 0$, is called the **grouping method**. The method involves both trial and error, as well as grouping. The trial and error in factoring $ax^2 + bx + c$ depends on finding two numbers, p and q, for which $p + q = b$. Then we factor $ax^2 + px + qx + c$ using grouping.

Let's see how this works by looking at our factorization in Example 2:

$$8x^2 - 10x - 3 = (2x - 3)(4x + 1).$$

If we multiply using FOIL on the right, we obtain:

$$(2x - 3)(4x + 1) = 8x^2 + 2x - 12x - 3.$$

In this case, the desired numbers, p and q, are $p = 2$ and $q = -12$. Compare these numbers to ac and b in the given polynomial:

$a = 8$ $\quad b = -10$ $\quad c = -3$

$$8x^2 - 10x - 3.$$

$ac = 8(-3) = -24$

Can you see that p and q, 2 and -12, are factors of ac, or -24? Furthermore, p and q have a sum of b, namely -10. By expressing the middle term, $-10x$, in terms of p and q, we can factor by grouping as follows:

$8x^2 - 10x - 3$

$= 8x^2 + (2x - 12x) - 3$ — Rewrite $-10x$ as $2x - 12x$.

$= (8x^2 + 2x) + (-12x - 3)$ — Group terms.

$= 2x(4x + 1) - 3(4x + 1)$ — Factor from each group.

$= (4x + 1)(2x - 3)$ — Factor out the common binomial factor.

As we obtained in Example 2,

$$8x^2 - 10x - 3 = (4x + 1)(2x - 3).$$

Generalizing from this example, here's how to factor a trinomial by grouping:

Factoring $ax^2 + bx + c$ Using Grouping ($a \neq 1$)

1. Multiply the leading coefficient, a, and the constant, c.
2. Find the factors of ac whose sum is b.
3. Rewrite the middle term, bx, as a sum or difference using the factors from step 2.
4. Factor by grouping.

EXAMPLE 4 Factoring by Grouping

Factor by grouping: $2x^2 - x - 6$.

Solution The trinomial is of the form $ax^2 + bx + c$.

$$2x^2 - x - 6$$

$a = 2$ $\quad b = -1$ $\quad c = -6$

Step 1. Multiply the leading coefficient, *a*, and the constant, *c*. Using $a = 2$ and $c = -6$,

$$ac = 2(-6) = -12.$$

Step 2. Find the factors of *ac* whose sum is *b*. We want the factors of -12 whose sum is b, or -1. The factors of -12 whose sum is -1 are -4 and 3.

Discover for Yourself

In step 2, we discovered that the desired numbers were -4 and 3, and in step 3 we wrote $-x$ as $-4x + 3x$. What happens if we write $-x$ as $3x - 4x$? Use factoring by grouping on

$$2x^2 - x - 6$$
$$= 2x^2 + 3x - 4x - 6.$$

Describe what happens.

Step 3. Rewrite the middle term, $-x$, as a sum or difference using the factors from step 2, -4 and 3.

$$2x^2 - x - 6 = 2x^2 - 4x + 3x - 6$$

Step 4. Factor by grouping.

$$= (2x^2 - 4x) + (3x - 6) \quad \text{Group terms.}$$
$$= 2x(x - 2) + 3(x - 2) \quad \text{Factor from each group.}$$
$$= (x - 2)(2x + 3) \quad \text{Factor out the common binomial factor.}$$

Thus,

$$2x^2 - x - 6 = (x - 2)(2x + 3) \quad \text{or} \quad (2x + 3)(x - 2). \; ■$$

✓ **CHECK POINT 4** Factor by grouping: $3x^2 - x - 10$.

EXAMPLE 5 Factoring by Grouping

Factor by grouping: $8x^2 - 22x + 5$.

Solution The trinomial is of the form $ax^2 + bx + c$.

$$8x^2 - 22x + 5$$

$a = 8$ $b = -22$ $c = 5$

Step 1. Multiply the leading coefficient, *a*, and the constant, *c*. Using $a = 8$ and $c = 5$, $ac = 8 \cdot 5 = 40$.

Step 2. Find the factors of *ac* whose sum is *b*. We want the factors of 40 whose sum is b, or -22. The factors of 40 whose sum is -22 are -2 and -20.

Step 3. Rewrite the middle term, $-22x$, as a sum or difference using the factors from step 2, -2 and -20.

$$8x^2 - 22x + 5 = 8x^2 - 2x - 20x + 5$$

Step 4. Factor by grouping.

$$= (8x^2 - 2x) + (-20x + 5) \quad \text{Group terms.}$$
$$= 2x(4x - 1) - 5(4x - 1) \quad \text{Factor from each group.}$$
$$= (4x - 1)(2x - 5) \quad \text{Factor out the common binomial factor.}$$

Thus,

$$8x^2 - 22x + 5 = (4x - 1)(2x - 5) \quad \text{or} \quad (2x - 5)(4x - 1). \; ■$$

✓ **CHECK POINT 5** Factor by grouping: $8x^2 - 10x + 3$.

Factoring Completely

Always begin the process of factoring a polynomial by looking for a greatest common factor other than 1. If there is one, **factor out the GCF first**. After doing this, you should attempt to factor the remaining polynomial, using one of the methods presented in this section, if appropriate.

EXAMPLE 6 Factoring Completely

Factor completely: $15y^4 + 26y^3 + 7y^2$.

Solution We will first factor out a common monomial factor from the polynomial and then factor the resulting trinomial by the methods of this section. The GCF of the three terms is y^2.

$$15y^4 + 26y^3 + 7y^2 = y^2(15y^2 + 26y + 7) \quad \text{Factor out the GCF.}$$
$$= y^2(5y + 7)(3y + 1) \quad \text{Factor } 15y^2 + 26y + 7 \text{ using trial and error or grouping.}$$

Thus,

$$15y^4 + 26y^3 + 7y^2 = y^2(5y + 7)(3y + 1) \quad \text{or} \quad y^2(3y + 1)(5y + 7).$$

Be sure to include the GCF, y^2, in the factorization.

■

✓ CHECK POINT 6 Factor completely: $5y^4 + 13y^3 + 6y^2$.

Great Question!

As I approach the next Exercise Set (it looks long!), can you give me any other hints for shortening those oppressive lists of possible factorizations?

Here is an observation that sometimes helps narrow down the list of possible factorizations. If a polynomial does not have a GCF other than 1 or if you have factored out the GCF, there will be no common factor within any of its binomial factors. Here is an example:

$$6x^2 - 17x + 12.$$ There is no GCF other than 1.

$$(2x - 4)(3x - 3)$$ This is not a possible factorization.

This binomial has a common factor of 2. This binomial has a common factor of 3.

CONCEPT AND VOCABULARY CHECK

Fill in each blank so that the resulting statement is true.

1. We begin the process of factoring a polynomial by first factoring out the ________________, assuming that there is one other than 1.
2. $8x^2 - 10x - 3 = (4x + 1)(2x$ ____$)$
3. $12x^2 - x - 20 = (4x + 5)(3x$ ____$)$
4. $2x^2 - 5x + 3 = (x - 1)($______$)$
5. $6x^2 + 17x + 12 = (2x + 3)($______$)$
6. $5x^2 - 8xy - 4y^2 = (5x + 2y)($______$)$

3 EXERCISE SET

MyMathLab®

Watch the videos in MyMathLab

Download the MyDashBoard App

Practice Exercises

In Exercises 1–58, use the method of your choice to factor each trinomial, or state that the trinomial is prime. Check each factorization using FOIL multiplication.

1. $2x^2 + 5x + 3$
2. $3x^2 + 5x + 2$
3. $3x^2 + 13x + 4$
4. $2x^2 + 7x + 3$
5. $2x^2 + 11x + 12$
6. $2x^2 + 19x + 35$
7. $5y^2 - 16y + 3$
8. $5y^2 - 17y + 6$
9. $3y^2 + y - 4$
10. $3y^2 - y - 4$
11. $3x^2 + 13x - 10$
12. $3x^2 + 14x - 5$
13. $3x^2 - 22x + 7$
14. $3x^2 - 10x + 7$
15. $5y^2 - 16y + 3$
16. $5y^2 - 8y + 3$
17. $3x^2 - 17x + 10$
18. $3x^2 - 25x - 28$
19. $6w^2 - 11w + 4$
20. $6w^2 - 17w + 12$

21. $8x^2 + 33x + 4$

22. $7x^2 + 43x + 6$

23. $5x^2 + 33x - 14$

24. $3x^2 + 22x - 16$

25. $14y^2 + 15y - 9$

26. $6y^2 + 7y - 24$

27. $6x^2 - 7x + 3$

28. $9x^2 + 3x + 2$

29. $25z^2 - 30z + 9$

30. $9z^2 + 12z + 4$

31. $15y^2 - y - 2$

32. $15y^2 + 13y - 2$

33. $5x^2 + 2x + 9$

34. $3x^2 - 5x + 1$

35. $10y^2 + 43y - 9$

36. $16y^2 - 46y + 15$

37. $8x^2 - 2x - 1$

38. $8x^2 - 22x + 5$

39. $9y^2 - 9y + 2$

40. $9y^2 + 5y - 4$

41. $20x^2 + 27x - 8$

42. $15x^2 - 19x + 6$

43. $2x^2 + 3xy + y^2$

44. $3x^2 + 4xy + y^2$

45. $3x^2 + 5xy + 2y^2$

46. $3x^2 + 11xy + 6y^2$

47. $2x^2 - 9xy + 9y^2$

48. $3x^2 + 5xy - 2y^2$

49. $6x^2 - 5xy - 6y^2$

50. $6x^2 - 7xy - 5y^2$

51. $15x^2 + 11xy - 14y^2$

52. $15x^2 - 31xy + 10y^2$

53. $2a^2 + 7ab + 5b^2$

54. $2a^2 + 5ab + 2b^2$

55. $15a^2 - ab - 6b^2$

56. $3a^2 - ab - 14b^2$

57. $12x^2 - 25xy + 12y^2$

58. $12x^2 + 7xy - 12y^2$

In Exercises 59–88, factor completely.

59. $4x^2 + 26x + 30$

60. $4x^2 - 18x - 10$

61. $9x^2 - 6x - 24$

62. $12x^2 - 33x + 21$

63. $4y^2 + 2y - 30$

64. $36y^2 + 6y - 12$

65. $9y^2 + 33y - 60$

66. $16y^2 - 16y - 12$

67. $3x^3 + 4x^2 + x$

68. $3x^3 + 14x^2 + 8x$

69. $2x^3 - 3x^2 - 5x$

70. $6x^3 + 4x^2 - 10x$

71. $9y^3 - 39y^2 + 12y$

72. $10y^3 + 12y^2 + 2y$

73. $60z^3 + 40z^2 + 5z$

74. $80z^3 + 80z^2 - 60z$

75. $15x^4 - 39x^3 + 18x^2$

76. $24x^4 + 10x^3 - 4x^2$

77. $10x^5 - 17x^4 + 3x^3$

78. $15x^5 - 2x^4 - x^3$

79. $6x^2 - 3xy - 18y^2$

80. $4x^2 + 14xy + 10y^2$

81. $12x^2 + 10xy - 8y^2$

82. $24x^2 + 3xy - 27y^2$

83. $8x^2y + 34xy - 84y$

84. $6x^2y - 2xy - 60y$

85. $12a^2b - 46ab^2 + 14b^3$

86. $12a^2b - 34ab^2 + 14b^3$

87. $-32x^2y^4 + 20xy^4 + 12y^4$

88. $-10x^2y^4 + 14xy^4 + 12y^4$

Practice PLUS

In Exercises 89–90, factor completely.

89. $30(y + 1)x^2 + 10(y + 1)x - 20(y + 1)$

90. $6(y + 1)x^2 + 33(y + 1)x + 15(y + 1)$

91. **a.** Factor $2x^2 - 5x - 3$.

b. Use the factorization in part (a) to factor

$$2(y + 1)^2 - 5(y + 1) - 3.$$

Then simplify each factor.

92. **a.** Factor $3x^2 + 5x - 2$.

b. Use the factorization in part (a) to factor

$$3(y + 1)^2 + 5(y + 1) - 2.$$

Then simplify each factor.

93. Divide $3x^3 - 11x^2 + 12x - 4$ by $x - 2$. Use the quotient to factor $3x^3 - 11x^2 + 12x - 4$ completely.

94. Divide $2x^3 + x^2 - 13x + 6$ by $x - 2$. Use the quotient to factor $2x^3 + x^2 - 13x + 6$ completely.

Application Exercises

It is possible to construct geometric models for factorizations so that you can see the factoring. This idea is developed in Exercises 95–96.

95. Consider the following figure.

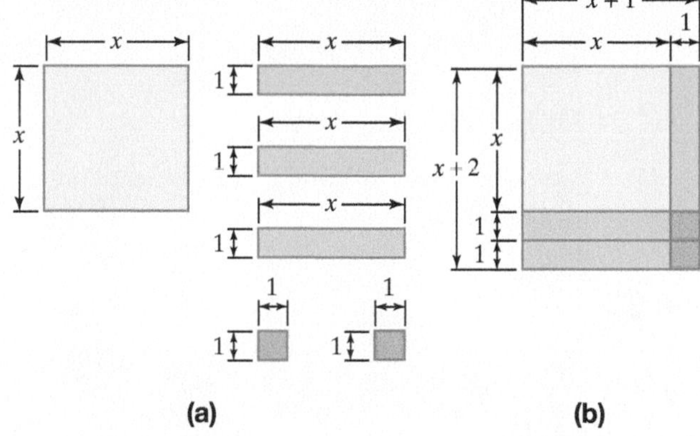

a. Write a trinomial that expresses the sum of the areas of the six rectangular pieces shown in figure (a).

b. Express the area of the large rectangle in figure (b) as the product of two binomials.

c. Are the pieces in figures (a) and (b) the same? Set the expressions that you wrote in parts (a) and (b) equal to each other. What factorization is illustrated?

96. Copy the figure and cut out the six pieces. Use the pieces to create a geometric model for the factorization

$$2x^2 + 3x + 1 = (2x + 1)(x + 1)$$

by forming a large rectangle using all the pieces.

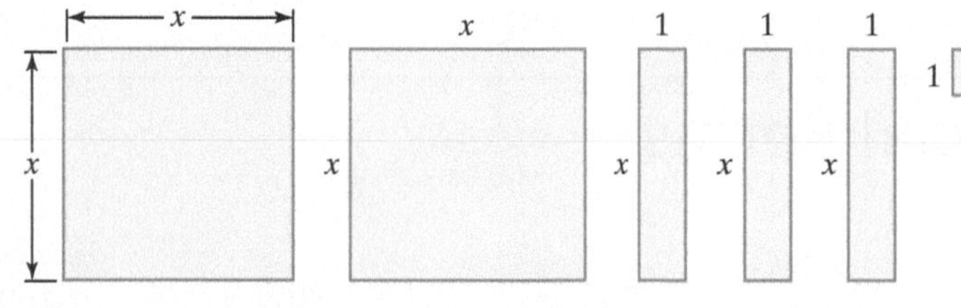

Writing in Mathematics

97. Explain how to factor $2x^2 - x - 1$.

98. Why is it a good idea to factor out the GCF first and then use other methods of factoring? Use $3x^2 - 18x + 15$ as an example. Discuss what happens if one first uses trial and error to factor as two binomials rather than first factoring out the GCF.

99. In factoring $3x^2 - 10x - 8$, a student lists $(3x - 2)(x + 4)$ as a possible factorization. Use FOIL multiplication to determine if this factorization is correct. If it is not correct, describe how the correct factorization can quickly be obtained using these factors.

100. Explain why $2x - 10$ cannot be one of the factors in the correct factorization of $6x^2 - 19x + 10$.

Critical Thinking Exercises

Make Sense? *In Exercises 101–104, determine whether each statement "makes sense" or "does not make sense" and explain your reasoning.*

101. I'm often able to use an incorrect factorization to lead me to the correct factorization.

102. First factoring out the GCF makes it easier for me to determine how to factor the remaining factor, assuming it is not prime.

103. I'm working with a polynomial that has a GCF other than 1, but then it doesn't factor further, so the polynomial that I'm working with is prime.

104. My graphing calculator showed the same graphs for $y_1 = 4x^2 - 20x + 24$ and $y_2 = 4(x^2 - 5x + 6)$, so I can conclude that the complete factorization of $4x^2 - 20x + 24$ is $4(x^2 - 5x + 6)$.

In Exercises 105–108, determine whether each statement is true or false. If the statement is false, make the necessary change(s) to produce a true statement.

105. Once the GCF is factored from $18y^2 - 6y + 6$, the remaining trinomial factor is prime.

106. One factor of $12x^2 - 13x + 3$ is $4x + 3$.

107. One factor of $4y^2 - 11y - 3$ is $y + 3$.

108. The trinomial $3x^2 + 2x + 1$ has relatively small coefficients and therefore can be factored.

In Exercises 109–110, find all integers b so that the trinomial can be factored.

109. $3x^2 + bx + 2$

110. $2x^2 + bx + 3$

111. Factor: $3x^{10} - 4x^5 - 15$.

112. Factor: $2x^{2n} - 7x^n - 4$.

Review Exercises

113. Solve the system:

$$\begin{cases} 4x - y = 105 \\ x + 7y = -10. \end{cases}$$

114. Write 0.00086 in scientific notation.

115. Solve: $8x - \frac{x}{6} = \frac{1}{6} - 8$.

Preview Exercises

Exercises 116–118 will help you prepare for the material covered in the next section. In each exercise, perform the indicated operation.

116. $(9x + 10)(9x - 10)$

117. $(4x + 5y)^2$

118. $(x + 2)(x^2 - 2x + 4)$

Achieving Success

Success in mathematics cannot be achieved without a complete understanding of factoring. Be sure to work all the exercises in the Mid-Chapter Check Point so that you can apply each of the factoring techniques discussed in the first half of the chapter. The more deeply you force your brain to think about factoring by working many exercises, the better will be your chances of achieving success in future algebra courses.

MID-CHAPTER CHECK POINT Section 1–Section 3

What You Know: We learned to factor out a polynomial's greatest common factor and to use grouping to factor polynomials with four terms. We factored polynomials with three terms, beginning with trinomials with leading coefficient 1 and moving on to $ax^2 + bx + c$, with $a \neq 1$. We saw that the factoring process should begin by looking for a GCF other than 1 and, if there is one, factoring it out first.

In Exercises 1–13, factor completely, or state that the polynomial is prime.

1. $x^5 + x^4$
2. $x^2 + 7x - 18$
3. $x^2y^3 - x^2y^2 + x^2y$
4. $x^2 - 2x + 4$
5. $7x^2 - 22x + 3$
6. $x^3 + 5x^2 + 3x + 15$
7. $2x^3 - 11x^2 + 5x$
8. $xy - 7x - 4y + 28$
9. $x^2 - 17xy + 30y^2$
10. $25x^2 - 25x - 14$
11. $16x^2 - 70x + 24$
12. $3x^2 + 10xy + 7y^2$
13. $-6x^3 + 8x^2 + 30x$

SECTION 4

Factoring Special Forms

Objectives

1. Factor the difference of two squares.
2. Factor perfect square trinomials.
3. Factor the sum or difference of two cubes.

Blackred/iStockphoto

Do you enjoy solving puzzles? The process is a natural way to develop problem-solving skills that are important to every area of our lives. Engaging in problem solving for sheer pleasure releases chemicals in the brain that enhance our feeling of well-being. Perhaps this is why puzzles date back 12,000 years.

In this section, we develop factoring techniques by reversing the formulas for special products. These factorizations can be visualized by fitting pieces of a puzzle together to form rectangles.

1 Factor the difference of two squares.

Factoring the Difference of Two Squares

A method for factoring the difference of two squares is obtained by reversing the special product for the sum and difference of two terms.

The Difference of Two Squares

If A and B are real numbers, variables, or algebraic expressions, then

$$A^2 - B^2 = (A + B)(A - B).$$

In words: The difference of the squares of two terms factors as the product of a sum and a difference of those terms.

EXAMPLE 1 Factoring the Difference of Two Squares

Factor:

a. $x^2 - 4$ **b.** $81x^2 - 49$.

Solution We must express each term as the square of some monomial. Then we use the formula for factoring $A^2 - B^2$.

a. $x^2 - 4 = x^2 - 2^2 = (x + 2)(x - 2)$

$A^2 - B^2 = (A + B)(A - B)$

b. $81x^2 - 49 = (9x)^2 - 7^2 = (9x + 7)(9x - 7)$ ■

In order to apply the factoring formula for $A^2 - B^2$, each term must be the square of an integer or a polynomial.

- A number that is the square of an integer is called a **perfect square**. For example, 100 is a perfect square because $100 = 10^2$.
- Any monomial involving a perfect-square coefficient and variables to even powers is a perfect square. For example, $16x^{10}$ is a perfect square because $16x^{10} = (4x^5)^2$.

Great Question!

You mentioned that because $100 = 10^2$, 100 is a perfect square. What are some other perfect squares that I should recognize?

It's helpful to identify perfect squares. Here are 16 perfect squares, printed in boldface.

$\mathbf{1} = 1^2$	$\mathbf{25} = 5^2$	$\mathbf{81} = 9^2$	$\mathbf{169} = 13^2$
$\mathbf{4} = 2^2$	$\mathbf{36} = 6^2$	$\mathbf{100} = 10^2$	$\mathbf{196} = 14^2$
$\mathbf{9} = 3^2$	$\mathbf{49} = 7^2$	$\mathbf{121} = 11^2$	$\mathbf{225} = 15^2$
$\mathbf{16} = 4^2$	$\mathbf{64} = 8^2$	$\mathbf{144} = 12^2$	$\mathbf{256} = 16^2$

✓ **CHECK POINT 1** Factor:

a. $x^2 - 81$ **b.** $36x^2 - 25$.

Be careful when determining whether or not to apply the factoring formula for the difference of two squares.

Prime Over the Integers		**Factorable**
• $x^2 - 5$	• $x^7 - 25$	• $9 - 16x^{10}$
5 is not a perfect square.	7 is an odd power. x^7 is not the square of any integer power of x.	Perfect square: $9 = 3^2$; Perfect square: $16x^{10} = (4x^5)^2$

EXAMPLE 2 Factoring the Difference of Two Squares

Factor:

a. $9 - 16x^{10}$ **b.** $25x^2 - 4y^2$.

Solution Begin by expressing each term as the square of some monomial. Then use the formula for factoring $A^2 - B^2$.

a. $9 - 16x^{10} = 3^2 - (4x^5)^2 = (3 + 4x^5)(3 - 4x^5)$

$A^2 - B^2 = (A + B)(A - B)$

b. $25x^2 - 4y^2 = (5x)^2 - (2y)^2 = (5x + 2y)(5x - 2y)$ ■

✓ **CHECK POINT 2** Factor:

a. $25 - 4x^{10}$ **b.** $100x^2 - 9y^2$.

When factoring, always check first for common factors. If there are common factors other than 1, factor out the GCF and then factor the resulting polynomial.

EXAMPLE 3 Factoring Out the GCF and Then Factoring the Difference of Two Squares

Factor:

a. $12x^3 - 3x$ **b.** $80 - 125x^2$.

Solution

a. $12x^3 - 3x = 3x(4x^2 - 1) = 3x[(2x)^2 - 1^2] = 3x(2x + 1)(2x - 1)$

Factor out the GCF. $A^2 - B^2 = (A + B)(A - B)$

b. $80 - 125x^2 = 5(16 - 25x^2) = 5[4^2 - (5x)^2] = 5(4 + 5x)(4 - 5x)$ ■

Great Question!

If I rewrite $80 - 125x^2$ as $-125x^2 + 80$, will I still get the same factorization?

Yes. Because the coefficient of $-125x^2$ is negative, factor out -5, the negative of the GCF.

$$-125x^2 + 80 = -5(25x^2 - 16) = -5[(5x)^2 - 4^2] = -5(5x + 4)(5x - 4)$$

Factor out the negative of the GCF.

To show that this is the same factorization as the one in the solution to part (b), factor -1 from $(5x - 4)$.

✓ CHECK POINT 3 Factor:

a. $18x^3 - 2x$

b. $72 - 18x^2$.

A polynomial is factored completely when it is written as the product of prime polynomials. To be sure that you have factored completely, check to see whether any factors with more than one term in the factored polynomial can be factored further. If so, continue factoring.

EXAMPLE 4 A Repeated Factorization

Factor completely: $x^4 - 81$.

Solution

$x^4 - 81 = (x^2)^2 - 9^2$ — Express as the difference of two squares.

$= (x^2 + 9)(x^2 - 9)$ — The factors are the sum and the difference of the expressions being squared.

$= (x^2 + 9)(x^2 - 3^2)$ — The factor $x^2 - 9$ is the difference of two squares and can be factored.

$= (x^2 + 9)(x + 3)(x - 3)$ — The factors of $x^2 - 9$ are the sum and the difference of the expressions being squared. ■

Great Question!

Why isn't factoring $x^4 - 81$ as $(x^2 + 9)(x^2 - 9)$ a complete factorization?

The second factor, $x^2 - 9$, is itself a difference of two squares and can be factored.

Are you tempted to factor $x^2 + 9$ further, the sum of two squares, in Example 4? Resist the temptation! **The sum of two squares, $A^2 + B^2$, with no common factor other than 1 is a prime polynomial over the integers.**

✓ CHECK POINT 4 Factor completely: $81x^4 - 16$.

In Examples 1–4, we used the formula for factoring the difference of two squares. Although we obtained the formula by reversing the special product for the sum and difference of two terms, it can also be obtained geometrically.

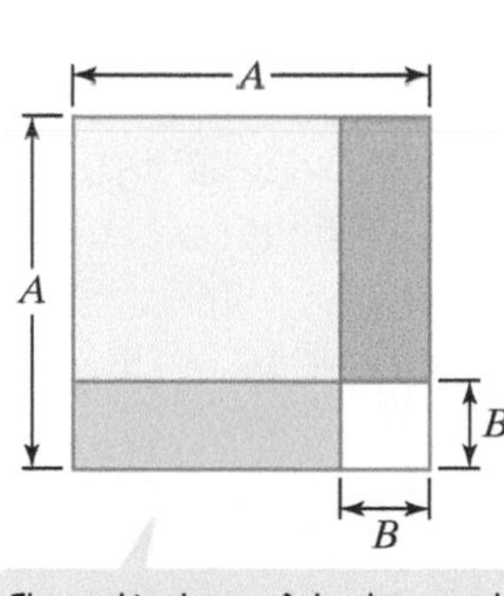

The combined area of the three purple rectangles is $A^2 - B^2$.

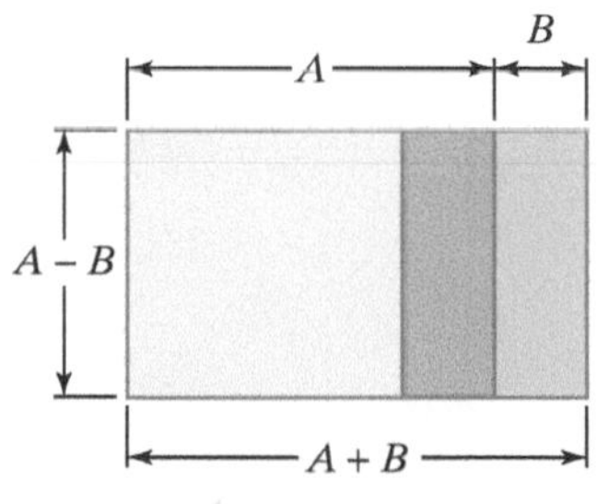

We've rearranged the three purple rectangles. Their combined area is $(A + B)(A - B)$.

Because the three purple rectangles make up the same combined area in both figures,

$$A^2 - B^2 = (A + B)(A - B).$$

2 Factor perfect square trinomials.

Factoring Perfect Square Trinomials

Our next factoring technique is obtained by reversing the special products for squaring binomials. The trinomials that are factored using this technique are called **perfect square trinomials**.

Factoring Perfect Square Trinomials

Let A and B be real numbers, variables, or algebraic expressions.

1. $A^2 + 2AB + B^2 = (A + B)^2$

   Same sign

2. $A^2 - 2AB + B^2 = (A - B)^2$

   Same sign

The two formulas in the box show that perfect square trinomials, $A^2 + 2AB + B^2$ and $A^2 - 2AB + B^2$, come in two forms: one in which the coefficient of the middle term is positive and one in which the coefficient of the middle term is negative. Here's how to recognize a perfect square trinomial:

1. The first and last terms are squares of monomials or integers.
2. The middle term is twice the product of the expressions being squared in the first and last terms.

EXAMPLE 5 Factoring Perfect Square Trinomials

Factor:

a. $x^2 + 6x + 9$ **b.** $x^2 - 16x + 64$ **c.** $25x^2 - 60x + 36$.

Solution

a. $x^2 + 6x + 9 = x^2 + 2 \cdot x \cdot 3 + 3^2 = (x + 3)^2$

$A^2 + 2AB + B^2 = (A + B)^2$

The middle term has a positive sign.

b. $x^2 - 16x + 64 = x^2 - 2 \cdot x \cdot 8 + 8^2 = (x - 8)^2$

$A^2 - 2AB + B^2 = (A - B)^2$

The middle term has a negative sign.

c. We suspect that $25x^2 - 60x + 36$ is a perfect square trinomial because $25x^2 = (5x)^2$ and $36 = 6^2$. The middle term can be expressed as twice the product of $5x$ and 6.

$$25x^2 - 60x + 36 = (5x)^2 - 2 \cdot 5x \cdot 6 + 6^2 = (5x - 6)^2$$

$A^2 - 2AB + B^2 = (A - B)^2$ ■

✓ CHECK POINT 5 Factor:

a. $x^2 + 14x + 49$ **b.** $x^2 - 6x + 9$

c. $16x^2 - 56x + 49$.

EXAMPLE 6 Factoring a Perfect Square Trinomial in Two Variables

Factor: $16x^2 + 40xy + 25y^2$.

Solution Observe that $16x^2 = (4x)^2$, $25y^2 = (5y)^2$, and $40xy$ is twice the product of $4x$ and $5y$. Thus, we have a perfect square trinomial.

$$16x^2 + 40xy + 25y^2 = (4x)^2 + 2 \cdot 4x \cdot 5y + (5y)^2 = (4x + 5y)^2$$

$$A^2 + 2AB + B^2 = (A + B)^2$$

■

✓ CHECK POINT 6 Factor: $4x^2 + 12xy + 9y^2$.

In Examples 5 and 6, we factored perfect square trinomials using $A^2 + 2AB + B^2 = (A + B)^2$. Although we obtained the formula by reversing the special product for $(A + B)^2$, it can also be obtained geometrically.

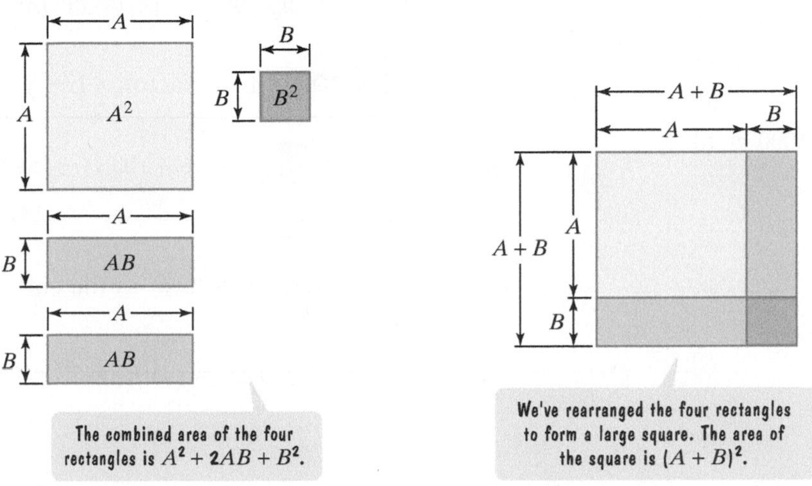

A
B
A²
B²
A
B
AB
AB
A + B
A
B
The combined area of the four rectangles is A² + 2AB + B².
We've rearranged the four rectangles to form a large square. The area of the square is (A + B)².

Because the four rectangles make up the same combined area in both figures,

$$A^2 + 2AB + B^2 = (A + B)^2.$$

3 Factor the sum or difference of two cubes.

Factoring the Sum or Difference of Two Cubes

We can use the following formulas to factor the sum or the difference of two cubes:

Factoring the Sum or Difference of Two Cubes

1. Factoring the Sum of Two Cubes

$$A^3 + B^3 = (A + B)(A^2 - AB + B^2)$$

Same signs Opposite signs

2. Factoring the Difference of Two Cubes

$$A^3 - B^3 = (A - B)(A^2 + AB + B^2)$$

Same signs Opposite signs

EXAMPLE 7 Factoring the Sum of Two Cubes

Factor: $x^3 + 8$.

Solution We must express each term as the cube of some monomial. Then we use the formula for factoring $A^3 + B^3$.

$$x^3 + 8 = x^3 + 2^3 = (x + 2)(x^2 - x \cdot 2 + 2^2) = (x + 2)(x^2 - 2x + 4)$$

$$A^3 + B^3 = (A + B)(A^2 - AB + B^2)$$

■

Great Question!

What are some cubes that I should be able to identify?

When factoring the sum or difference of cubes, it is helpful to recognize the following cubes:

$$1 = 1^3$$
$$8 = 2^3$$
$$27 = 3^3$$
$$64 = 4^3$$
$$125 = 5^3$$
$$216 = 6^3$$
$$1000 = 10^3.$$

✓ **CHECK POINT 7** Factor: $x^3 + 27$.

EXAMPLE 8 Factoring the Difference of Two Cubes

Factor: $27 - y^3$.

Solution Express each term as the cube of some monomial. Then use the formula for factoring $A^3 - B^3$.

$$27 - y^3 = 3^3 - y^3 = (3 - y)(3^2 + 3y + y^2) = (3 - y)(9 + 3y + y^2)$$

$$A^3 - B^3 = (A - B)(A^2 + AB + B^2)$$

■

✓ **CHECK POINT 8** Factor: $1 - y^3$.

EXAMPLE 9 Factoring the Sum of Two Cubes

Factor: $64x^3 + 125$.

Solution Express each term as the cube of some monomial. Then use the formula for factoring $A^3 + B^3$.

$$64x^3 + 125 = (4x)^3 + 5^3 = (4x + 5)[(4x)^2 - (4x)(5) + 5^2]$$

$$A^3 + B^3 = (A + B)(A^2 - AB + B^2)$$

$$= (4x + 5)(16x^2 - 20x + 25)$$

■

✓ **CHECK POINT 9** Factor: $125x^3 + 8$.

Great Question!

A Cube of SOAP

The formulas for factoring $A^3 + B^3$ and $A^3 - B^3$ are difficult to remember and easy to confuse. Can you help me out?

When factoring sums or differences of cubes, observe the sign patterns.

Same signs

$$A^3 + B^3 = (A + B)(A^2 - AB + B^2)$$

Opposite signs — Always positive

Same signs

$$A^3 - B^3 = (A - B)(A^2 + AB + B^2)$$

Opposite signs — Always positive

The word *SOAP* is a way to remember these patterns:

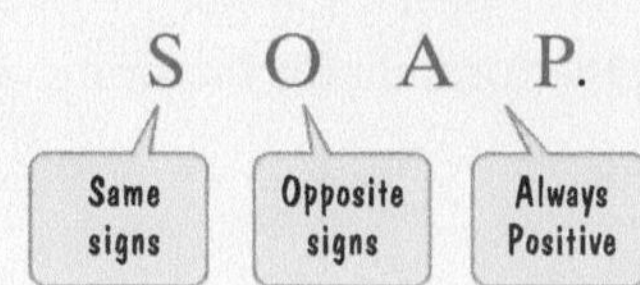

CONCEPT AND VOCABULARY CHECK

Fill in each blank so that the resulting statement is true.

1. The formula for factoring the difference of two squares is $A^2 - B^2 =$ ________________.
2. A formula for factoring a perfect square trinomial is $A^2 + 2AB + B^2 =$ ________________.
3. A formula for factoring a perfect square trinomial is $A^2 - 2AB + B^2 =$ ________________.
4. The formula for factoring the sum of two cubes is $A^3 + B^3 =$ ________________.
5. The formula for factoring the difference of two cubes is $A^3 - B^3 =$ ________________.
6. $36x^2 - 49 = ($________ $+ 7)($________ $- 7)$
7. $x^2 - 12x + 36 = (x$________$)^2$
8. $16x^2 - 24x + 9 = ($________ $- 3)^2$
9. $x^3 + 8 = (x$________$)(x^2 - 2x + 4)$
10. $x^3 - 27 = (x$ ________$)(x^2 + 3x$ ________$)$
11. True or false: $x^2 - 8$ is the difference of two perfect squares. ____________
12. True or false: $x^2 + 8x + 16$ is a perfect square trinomial. ____________
13. True or false: $x^2 - 5x + 25$ is a perfect square trinomial. ____________
14. True or false: $x^3 + 1000$ is the sum of two cubes. ____________
15. True or false: $x^3 - 100$ is the difference of two cubes. ____________

4 EXERCISE SET

MyMathLab®

Watch the videos in MyMathLab

Download the MyDashBoard App

Practice Exercises

In Exercises 1–26, factor each difference of two squares.

1. $x^2 - 25$
2. $x^2 - 16$
3. $y^2 - 1$
4. $y^2 - 9$
5. $4x^2 - 9$
6. $9x^2 - 25$
7. $25 - x^2$
8. $16 - x^2$
9. $1 - 49x^2$
10. $1 - 64x^2$
11. $9 - 25y^2$
12. $16 - 49y^2$
13. $x^4 - 9$
14. $x^4 - 25$
15. $49y^4 - 16$
16. $49y^4 - 25$
17. $x^{10} - 9$
18. $x^{10} - 1$
19. $25x^2 - 16y^2$
20. $9x^2 - 25y^2$
21. $x^4 - y^{10}$
22. $x^{14} - y^4$
23. $x^4 - 16$
24. $x^4 - 1$
25. $16x^4 - 81$
26. $81x^4 - 1$

In Exercises 27–44, factor completely, or state that the polynomial is prime.

27. $2x^2 - 18$
28. $5x^2 - 45$
29. $2x^3 - 72x$
30. $2x^3 - 8x$
31. $x^2 + 36$
32. $x^2 + 4$
33. $3x^3 + 27x$
34. $3x^3 + 15x$
35. $18 - 2y^2$
36. $32 - 2y^2$
37. $3y^3 - 48y$
38. $3y^3 - 75y$
39. $18x^3 - 2x$
40. $20x^3 - 5x$
41. $-3x^2 + 75$
42. $-4x^2 + 4$
43. $-5y^3 + 20y$
44. $-54y^3 + 6y$

In Exercises 45–66, factor any perfect square trinomials, or state that the polynomial is prime.

45. $x^2 + 2x + 1$
46. $x^2 + 4x + 4$
47. $x^2 - 14x + 49$
48. $x^2 - 10x + 25$
49. $x^2 - 2x + 1$
50. $x^2 - 4x + 4$

51. $x^2 + 22x + 121$
52. $x^2 + 24x + 144$
53. $4x^2 + 4x + 1$
54. $9x^2 + 6x + 1$
55. $25y^2 - 10y + 1$
56. $64y^2 - 16y + 1$
57. $x^2 - 10x + 100$
58. $x^2 - 7x + 49$
59. $x^2 + 14xy + 49y^2$
60. $x^2 + 16xy + 64y^2$
61. $x^2 - 12xy + 36y^2$
62. $x^2 - 18xy + 81y^2$
63. $x^2 - 8xy + 64y^2$
64. $x^2 + 9xy + 16y^2$
65. $16x^2 - 40xy + 25y^2$
66. $9x^2 + 48xy + 64y^2$

In Exercises 67–78, factor completely.

67. $12x^2 - 12x + 3$
68. $18x^2 + 24x + 8$
69. $9x^3 + 6x^2 + x$
70. $25x^3 - 10x^2 + x$
71. $2y^2 - 4y + 2$
72. $2y^2 - 40y + 200$
73. $2y^3 + 28y^2 + 98y$
74. $50y^3 + 20y^2 + 2y$
75. $-6x^2 + 24x - 24$
76. $-5x^2 + 30x - 45$
77. $-16y^3 - 16y^2 - 4y$
78. $-45y^3 - 30y^2 - 5y$

In Exercises 79–96, factor using the formula for the sum or difference of two cubes.

79. $x^3 + 1$
80. $x^3 + 64$
81. $x^3 - 27$
82. $x^3 - 64$
83. $8y^3 - 1$
84. $27y^3 - 1$
85. $27x^3 + 8$
86. $125x^3 + 8$
87. $x^3y^3 - 64$
88. $x^3y^3 - 27$
89. $27y^4 + 8y$
90. $64y - y^4$
91. $54 - 16y^3$
92. $128 - 250y^3$
93. $64x^3 + 27y^3$
94. $8x^3 + 27y^3$
95. $125x^3 - 64y^3$
96. $125x^3 - y^3$

Practice PLUS

In Exercises 97–104, factor completely. (Hint on Exercises 97–102: Factors contain rational numbers.)

97. $25x^2 - \dfrac{4}{49}$
98. $16x^2 - \dfrac{9}{25}$
99. $y^4 - \dfrac{y}{1000}$
100. $y^4 - \dfrac{y}{8}$
101. $0.25x - x^3$
102. $0.64x - x^3$
103. $(x + 1)^2 - 25$
104. $(x + 2)^2 - 49$
105. Divide $x^3 - x^2 - 5x - 3$ by $x - 3$. Use the quotient to factor $x^3 - x^2 - 5x - 3$ completely.
106. Divide $x^3 + 4x^2 - 3x - 18$ by $x - 2$. Use the quotient to factor $x^3 + 4x^2 - 3x - 18$ completely.

Application Exercises

In Exercises 107–110, find the formula for the area of the shaded blue region and express it in factored form.

107.

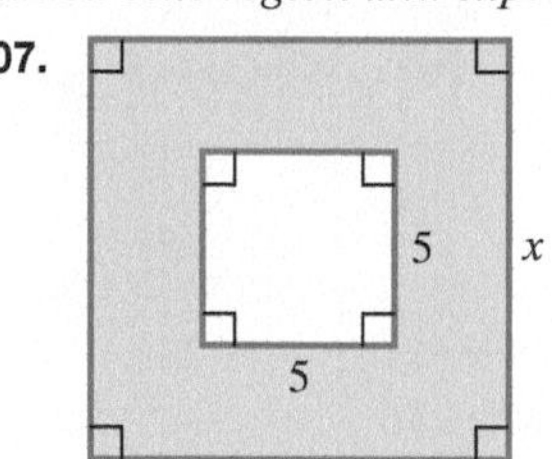

108.

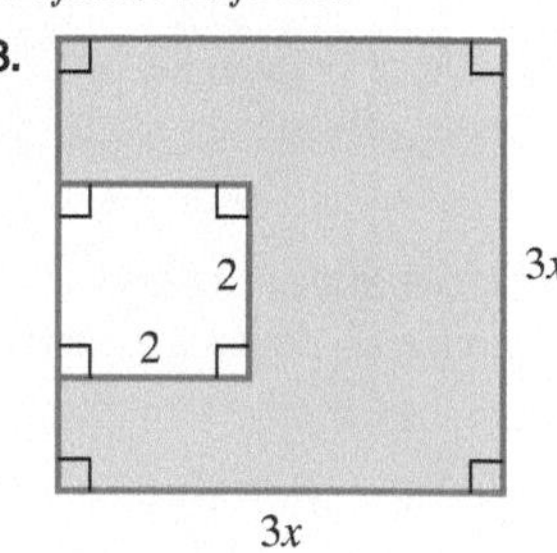

109.

110.

Writing in Mathematics

111. Explain how to factor the difference of two squares. Provide an example with your explanation.
112. What is a perfect square trinomial and how is it factored?
113. Explain why $x^2 - 1$ is factorable, but $x^2 + 1$ is not.
114. Explain how to factor $x^3 + 1$.

Critical Thinking Exercises

Make Sense? *In Exercises 115–118, determine whether each statement "makes sense" or "does not make sense" and explain your reasoning.*

115. I factored $9x^2 - 36$ completely and obtained

$$(3x + 6)(3x - 6).$$

116. Although I can factor the difference of squares and perfect square trinomials using trial and error, recognizing these special forms shortens the process.

117. I factored $9 - 25x^2$ as $(3 + 5x)(3 - 5x)$ and then applied the commutative property to rewrite the factorization as $(5x + 3)(5x - 3)$.

118. I compared the factorization for the sum of cubes with the factorization for the difference of cubes and noticed that the only difference between them is the positive and negative signs.

In Exercises 119–122, determine whether each statement is true or false. If the statement is false, make the necessary change(s) to produce a true statement.

119. Because $x^2 - 25 = (x + 5)(x - 5)$, then $x^2 + 25 = (x - 5)(x + 5)$.

120. All perfect square trinomials are squares of binomials.

121. Any polynomial that is the sum of two squares is prime.

122. The polynomial $16x^2 + 20x + 25$ is a perfect square trinomial.

123. Where is the error in this "proof" that $2 = 0$?

$a = b$	Suppose that a and b are any equal real numbers.
$a^2 = b^2$	Square both sides of the equation.
$a^2 - b^2 = 0$	Subtract b^2 from both sides.
$2(a^2 - b^2) = 2 \cdot 0$	Multiply both sides by 2.
$2(a^2 - b^2) = 0$	On the right side, $2 \cdot 0 = 0$.
$2(a + b)(a - b) = 0$	Factor $a^2 - b^2$.
$2(a + b) = 0$	Divide both sides by $a - b$.
$2 = 0$	Divide both sides by $a + b$.

In Exercises 124–127, factor each polynomial.

124. $x^2 - y^2 + 3x + 3y$

125. $x^{2n} - 25y^{2n}$

126. $4x^{2n} + 12x^n + 9$

127. $(x + 3)^2 - 2(x + 3) + 1$

In Exercises 128–129, find all integers k so that the trinomial is a perfect square trinomial.

128. $9x^2 + kx + 1$

129. $64x^2 - 16x + k$

Technology Exercises

In Exercises 130–133, use the GRAPH *or* TABLE *feature of a graphing utility to determine if the polynomial on the left side of each equation has been correctly factored. If the graphs of y_1 and y_2 coincide, or if their corresponding table values are equal, this means that the polynomial on the left side has been correctly factored. If not, factor the polynomial correctly and then use your graphing utility to verify the factorization.*

130. $4x^2 - 9 = (4x + 3)(4x - 3)$

131. $x^2 - 6x + 9 = (x - 3)^2$

132. $4x^2 - 4x + 1 = (4x - 1)^2$

133. $x^3 - 1 = (x - 1)(x^2 - x + 1)$

Review Exercises

134. Simplify: $(2x^2y^3)^4(5xy^2)$.

135. Subtract: $(10x^2 - 5x + 2) - (14x^2 - 5x - 1)$.

136. Divide: $\dfrac{6x^2 + 11x - 10}{3x - 2}$.

Preview Exercises

Exercises 137–139 will help you prepare for the material covered in the next section. In each exercise, factor completely.

137. $3x^3 - 75x$

138. $2x^2 - 20x + 50$

139. $x^3 - 2x^2 - x + 2$

SECTION 5

A General Factoring Strategy

Objectives

1. Recognize the appropriate method for factoring a polynomial.
2. Use a general strategy for factoring polynomials.

Yogi Berra, catcher and renowned hitter for the New York Yankees (1946–1963), said it best: "If you don't know where you're going, you'll probably end up someplace else." When it comes to factoring, it's easy to know where you're going. Why? In this section, you will learn a step-by-step strategy that provides a plan and direction for solving factoring problems.

Man with a Bowler Hat (1964), René Magritte. © 2011 Herscovici/ARS

1 Recognize the appropriate method for factoring a polynomial.

A Strategy for Factoring Polynomials

It is important to practice factoring a wide variety of polynomials so that you can quickly select the appropriate technique. The polynomial is factored completely when all its polynomial factors, except possibly the monomial factor, are prime. Because of the commutative property, the order of the factors does not matter.

Here is a general strategy for factoring polynomials:

A Strategy for Factoring a Polynomial

1. If there is a common factor other than 1, factor out the GCF.
2. Determine the number of terms in the polynomial and try factoring as follows:
   a. If there are two terms, can the binomial be factored by one of the following special forms?

      Difference of two squares: $A^2 - B^2 = (A + B)(A - B)$
      Sum of two cubes: $A^3 + B^3 = (A + B)(A^2 - AB + B^2)$
      Difference of two cubes: $A^3 - B^3 = (A - B)(A^2 + AB + B^2)$

   b. If there are three terms, is the trinomial a perfect square trinomial? If so, factor by one of the following special forms:

      $$A^2 + 2AB + B^2 = (A + B)^2$$
      $$A^2 - 2AB + B^2 = (A - B)^2.$$

      If the trinomial is not a perfect square trinomial, try factoring by trial and error or grouping.
   c. If there are four or more terms, try factoring by grouping.
3. Check to see if any factors with more than one term in the factored polynomial can be factored further. If so, factor completely.
4. Check by multiplying.

2 Use a general strategy for factoring polynomials.

The following examples and those in the exercise set are similar to the previous factoring problems. One difference is that although these polynomials may be factored using the techniques we have studied in this chapter, most must be factored using at least two techniques. Also different is that these factorizations are not all of the same type. They are intentionally mixed to promote the development of a general factoring strategy.

EXAMPLE 1 Factoring a Polynomial

Factor: $4x^4 - 16x^2$.

Solution

Step 1. If there is a common factor, factor out the GCF. Because $4x^2$ is common to both terms, we factor it out.

$$4x^4 - 16x^2 = 4x^2(x^2 - 4) \quad \text{Factor out the GCF.}$$

Step 2. Determine the number of terms and factor accordingly. The factor $x^2 - 4$ has two terms. It is the difference of two squares: $x^2 - 2^2$. We factor using the special form for the difference of two squares and rewrite the GCF.

$$4x^4 - 16x^2 = 4x^2(x + 2)(x - 2)$$

Use $A^2 - B^2 = (A + B)(A - B)$ on $x^2 - 4$: $A = x$ and $B = 2$.

Step 3. Check to see if any factors with more than one term can be factored further. No factor with more than one term can be factored further, so we have factored completely.

Step 4. Check by multiplying.

$$4x^2(x + 2)(x - 2) = 4x^2(x^2 - 4) = 4x^4 - 16x^2$$

This is the original polynomial, so the factorization is correct. ■

✓ **CHECK POINT 1** Factor: $5x^4 - 45x^2$.

EXAMPLE 2 Factoring a Polynomial

Factor: $3x^2 - 6x - 45$.

Solution

Step 1. If there is a common factor, factor out the GCF. Because 3 is common to all terms, we factor it out.

$$3x^2 - 6x - 45 = 3(x^2 - 2x - 15) \quad \text{Factor out the GCF.}$$

Step 2. Determine the number of terms and factor accordingly. The factor $x^2 - 2x - 15$ has three terms, but it is not a perfect square trinomial. We factor it using trial and error.

$$3x^2 - 6x - 45 = 3(x^2 - 2x - 15) = 3(x - 5)(x + 3)$$

Step 3. Check to see if factors can be factored further. In this case, they cannot, so we have factored completely.

Step 4. Check by multiplying.

$$3(x - 5)(x + 3) = 3(x^2 - 2x - 15) = 3x^2 - 6x - 45$$

FOIL

This is the original polynomial, so the factorization is correct. ■

✓ **CHECK POINT 2** Factor: $4x^2 - 16x - 48$.

EXAMPLE 3 Factoring a Polynomial

Factor: $7x^5 - 7x$.

Solution

Step 1. If there is a common factor, factor out the GCF. Because $7x$ is common to both terms, we factor it out.

$$7x^5 - 7x = 7x(x^4 - 1) \quad \text{Factor out the GCF.}$$

Step 2. Determine the number of terms and factor accordingly. The factor $x^4 - 1$ has two terms. This binomial can be expressed as $(x^2)^2 - 1^2$, so it can be factored as the difference of two squares.

$$7x^5 - 7x = 7x(x^4 - 1) = 7x(x^2 + 1)(x^2 - 1)$$

Use $A^2 - B^2 = (A + B)(A - B)$ on $x^4 - 1$: $A = x^2$ and $B = 1$.

Step 3. Check to see if factors can be factored further. We note that $(x^2 - 1)$ is also the difference of two squares, $x^2 - 1^2$, so we continue factoring.

$$7x^5 - 7x = 7x(x^2 + 1)(x + 1)(x - 1)$$

Factor $x^2 - 1$ as the difference of two squares.

Step 4. Check by multiplying.

$$7x(x^2 + 1)(x + 1)(x - 1) = 7x(x^2 + 1)(x^2 - 1) = 7x(x^4 - 1) = 7x^5 - 7x$$

We obtain the original polynomial, so the factorization is correct. ■

✓ **CHECK POINT 3** Factor: $4x^5 - 64x$.

EXAMPLE 4 Factoring a Polynomial

Factor: $x^3 - 5x^2 - 4x + 20$.

Solution

Step 1. If there is a common factor, factor out the GCF. Other than 1, there is no common factor.

Step 2. Determine the number of terms and factor accordingly. There are four terms. We try factoring by grouping.

$$x^3 - 5x^2 - 4x + 20$$

$= (x^3 - 5x^2) + (-4x + 20)$ Group terms with common factors.

$= x^2(x - 5) - 4(x - 5)$ Factor from each group.

$= (x - 5)(x^2 - 4)$ Factor out the common binomial factor, $x - 5$.

Step 3. Check to see if factors can be factored further. We note that $(x^2 - 4)$ is the difference of two squares, $x^2 - 2^2$, so we continue factoring.

$$x^3 - 5x^2 - 4x + 20 = (x - 5)(x + 2)(x - 2)$$

Factor $x^2 - 4$ as the difference of two squares.

We have factored completely because no factor with more than one term can be factored further.

Step 4. Check by multiplying.

F O I L

$$(x-5)(x+2)(x-2) = (x-5)(x^2-4) = x^3 - 4x - 5x^2 + 20$$
$$= x^3 - 5x^2 - 4x + 20$$

We obtain the original polynomial, so the factorization is correct. ■

✓ **CHECK POINT 4** Factor: $x^3 - 4x^2 - 9x + 36$.

EXAMPLE 5 Factoring a Polynomial

Factor: $2x^3 - 24x^2 + 72x$.

Solution

Step 1. If there is a common factor, factor out the GCF. Because $2x$ is common to all terms, we factor it out.

$$2x^3 - 24x^2 + 72x = 2x(x^2 - 12x + 36) \quad \text{Factor out the GCF.}$$

Step 2. Determine the number of terms and factor accordingly. The factor $x^2 - 12x + 36$ has three terms. Is it a perfect square trinomial? Yes. The first term, x^2, is the square of a monomial. The last term, 36 or 6^2, is the square of an integer. The middle term involves twice the product of x and 6. We factor using $A^2 - 2AB + B^2 = (A - B)^2$.

$$2x^3 - 24x^2 + 72x = 2x(x^2 - 12x + 36)$$
$$= 2x(x^2 - 2 \cdot x \cdot 6 + 6^2) \quad \text{The second factor is a perfect square trinomial.}$$

$A^2 - 2\,A\,B + B^2$

$$= 2x(x-6)^2 \quad A^2 - 2AB + B^2 = (A - B)^2$$

Step 3. Check to see if factors can be factored further. In this problem, they cannot, so we have factored completely.

Step 4. Check by multiplying. Let's verify that $2x^3 - 24x^2 + 72x = 2x(x - 6)^2$.

$$2x(x-6)^2 = 2x(x^2 - 12x + 36) = 2x^3 - 24x^2 + 72x$$ ■

We obtain the original polynomial, so the factorization is correct.

✓ **CHECK POINT 5** Factor: $3x^3 - 30x^2 + 75x$.

EXAMPLE 6 Factoring a Polynomial

Factor: $3x^5 + 24x^2$.

Solution

Step 1. If there is a common factor, factor out the GCF. Because $3x^2$ is common to both terms, we factor it out.

$$3x^5 + 24x^2 = 3x^2(x^3 + 8) \quad \text{Factor out the GCF.}$$

Step 2. Determine the number of terms and factor accordingly. Our factorization up to this point, $3x^5 + 24x^2 = 3x^2(x^3 + 8)$, is not complete. The factor $x^3 + 8$ has two terms. This binomial can be expressed as $x^3 + 2^3$, so it can be factored as the sum of two cubes.

$$3x^5 + 24x^2 = 3x^2(\underbrace{x^3 + 2^3}_{A^3 + B^3})$$ Express $x^3 + 8$ as the sum of two cubes.

$$= 3x^2\underbrace{(x + 2)(x^2 - 2x + 4)}_{(A + B)(A^2 - AB + B^2)}$$ Factor the sum of two cubes.

Step 3. Check to see if factors can be factored further. In this problem, they cannot, so we have factored completely.

Step 4. Check by multiplying.

$$\begin{aligned} 3x^2(x + 2)(x^2 - 2x + 4) &= 3x^2[x(x^2 - 2x + 4) + 2(x^2 - 2x + 4)] \\ &= 3x^2(x^3 - 2x^2 + 4x + 2x^2 - 4x + 8) \\ &= 3x^2(x^3 + 8) = 3x^5 + 24x^2 \end{aligned}$$

We obtain the original polynomial, so the factorization is correct. ■

Discover for Yourself

In Examples 1–6, substitute 1 for the variable in both the given polynomial and in its factored form. Evaluate each expression. What do you observe? Do this for a second value of the variable. Is this a complete check or only a partial check of the factorization? Explain.

✓ **CHECK POINT 6** Factor: $2x^5 + 54x^2$.

EXAMPLE 7 Factoring a Polynomial in Two Variables

Factor: $32x^4y - 2y^5$.

Solution

Step 1. If there is a common factor, factor out the GCF. Because $2y$ is common to both terms, we factor it out.

$$32x^4y - 2y^5 = 2y(16x^4 - y^4)$$ Factor out the GCF.

Step 2. Determine the number of terms and factor accordingly. The factor $16x^4 - y^4$ has two terms. It is the difference of two squares: $(4x^2)^2 - (y^2)^2$. We factor using the special form for the difference of two squares.

$$32x^4y - 2y^5 = 2y[\underbrace{(4x^2)^2 - (y^2)^2}_{A^2 - B^2}]$$ Express $16x^4 - y^4$ as the difference of two squares.

$$= 2y\underbrace{(4x^2 + y^2)}_{(A + B)}\underbrace{(4x^2 - y^2)}_{(A - B)}$$ $A^2 - B^2 = (A + B)(A - B)$

Step 3. Check to see if factors can be factored further. We note that the last factor, $4x^2 - y^2$, is also the difference of two squares, $(2x)^2 - y^2$, so we continue factoring.

$$32x^4y - 2y^5 = 2y(4x^2 + y^2)(2x + y)(2x - y)$$

Step 4. Check by multiplying. Multiply the factors in the factorization and verify that you obtain the original polynomial. ■

✓ **CHECK POINT 7** Factor: $3x^4y - 48y^5$.

EXAMPLE 8 Factoring a Polynomial in Two Variables

Factor: $18x^3 + 48x^2y + 32xy^2$.

Solution

Step 1. If there is a common factor, factor out the GCF. Because $2x$ is common to all terms, we factor it out.

$$18x^3 + 48x^2y + 32xy^2 = 2x(9x^2 + 24xy + 16y^2)$$

Step 2. Determine the number of terms and factor accordingly. The factor $9x^2 + 24xy + 16y^2$ has three terms. Is it a perfect square trinomial? Yes. The first term, $9x^2$ or $(3x)^2$, and the last term, $16y^2$ or $(4y)^2$, are squares of monomials. The middle term, $24xy$, is twice the product of $3x$ and $4y$. We factor using $A^2 + 2AB + B^2 = (A + B)^2$.

$$18x^3 + 48x^2y + 32xy^2 = 2x(9x^2 + 24xy + 16y^2)$$

$$= 2x[(3x)^2 + 2 \cdot 3x \cdot 4y + (4y)^2]$$

The second factor is a perfect square trinomial.

$$= 2x(3x + 4y)^2$$

$A^2 + 2AB + B^2 = (A + B)^2$

Step 3. Check to see if factors can be factored further. In this problem, they cannot, so we have factored completely.

Step 4. Check by multiplication. Multiply the factors in the factorization and verify that you obtain the original polynomial. ■

✓ **CHECK POINT 8** Factor: $12x^3 + 36x^2y + 27xy^2$.

CONCEPT AND VOCABULARY CHECK

Here is a list of the factoring techniques that we have discussed.

a. Factoring out the GCF

b. Factoring out the negative of the GCF

c. Factoring by grouping

d. Factoring trinomials by trial and error or grouping

e. Factoring the difference of two squares
$A^2 - B^2 = (A + B)(A - B)$

f. Factoring perfect square trinomials
$A^2 + 2AB + B^2 = (A + B)^2$
$A^2 - 2AB + B^2 = (A - B)^2$

g. Factoring the sum of two cubes
$A^3 + B^3 = (A + B)(A^2 - AB + B^2)$

h. Factoring the difference of two cubes
$A^3 - B^3 = (A - B)(A^2 + AB + B^2)$

Fill in each blank by writing the letter of the technique (a through h) for factoring the polynomial.

1. $-3x^2 + 21x$ ____________

2. $16x^2 - 25$ ____________

3. $27x^3 - 1$ ____________

4. $x^2 + 7x + xy + 7y$ ____________

5. $4x^2 + 8x + 3$ ____________

6. $9x^2 + 24x + 16$ ____________

7. $5x^2 + 10x$ ____________

8. $x^3 + 1000$ ____________

5 EXERCISE SET

MyMathLab®

Watch the videos in MyMathLab

Download the MyDashBoard App

Practice Exercises

Before getting to multiple-step factorizations, let's be sure that you are comfortable with exercises requiring only one of the factoring techniques. In Exercises 1–16, factor each polynomial.

1. $-7x^2 + 35x$ **2.** $-6x^2 + 24x$

3. $25x^2 - 49$

4. $100x^2 - 81$

5. $27x^3 - 1$

6. $64x^3 - 1$

7. $5x + 5y + x^2 + xy$

8. $7x + 7y + x^2 + xy$

9. $14x^2 - 9x + 1$

10. $3x^2 + 2x - 5$

11. $x^2 - 2x + 1$ **12.** $x^2 - 4x + 4$

13. $27x^3y^3 + 8$

14. $216x^3y^3 + 125$

15. $6x^2 + x - 15$

16. $4x^2 - x - 5$

Now let's move on to factorizations that may require two or more techniques. In Exercises 17–80, factor completely, or state that the polynomial is prime. Check factorizations using multiplication or a graphing utility.

17. $5x^3 - 20x$

18. $4x^3 - 100x$

19. $7x^3 + 7x$ **20.** $6x^3 + 24x$

21. $5x^2 - 5x - 30$

22. $5x^2 - 15x - 50$

23. $2x^4 - 162$

24. $7x^4 - 7$

25. $x^3 + 2x^2 - 9x - 18$

26. $x^3 + 3x^2 - 25x - 75$

27. $3x^3 - 24x^2 + 48x$

28. $5x^3 - 20x^2 + 20x$

29. $2x^5 + 2x^2$

30. $2x^5 + 128x^2$

31. $6x^2 + 8x$ **32.** $21x^2 - 35x$

33. $-2y^2 + 2y + 112$

34. $-6x^2 + 6x + 12$

35. $7y^4 + 14y^3 + 7y^2$

36. $2y^4 + 28y^3 + 98y^2$

37. $y^2 + 8y - 16$ **38.** $y^2 - 18y - 81$

39. $16y^2 - 4y - 2$

40. $32y^2 + 4y - 6$

41. $r^2 - 25r$ **42.** $3r^2 - 27r$

43. $4w^2 + 8w - 5$

44. $35w^2 - 2w - 1$

45. $x^3 - 4x$ **46.** $9x^3 - 9x$

47. $x^2 + 64$ **48.** $y^2 + 36$

49. $9y^2 + 13y + 4$

50. $20y^2 + 12y + 1$

51. $y^3 + 2y^2 - 4y - 8$

52. $y^3 + 2y^2 - y - 2$

53. $16y^2 + 24y + 9$

54. $25y^2 + 20y + 4$

55. $-4y^3 + 28y^2 - 40y$

56. $-7y^3 + 21y^2 - 14y$

57. $y^5 - 81y$

58. $y^5 - 16y$

59. $20a^4 - 45a^2$

60. $48a^4 - 3a^2$

61. $9x^4 + 18x^3 + 6x^2$

62. $10x^4 + 20x^3 + 15x^2$

63. $12y^2 - 11y + 2$

64. $21x^2 - 25x - 4$

65. $9y^2 - 64$

66. $100y^2 - 49$

67. $9y^2 + 64$ **68.** $100y^2 + 49$

69. $2y^3 + 3y^2 - 50y - 75$

70. $12y^3 + 16y^2 - 3y - 4$

71. $2r^3 + 30r^2 - 68r$

72. $3r^3 - 27r^2 - 210r$

73. $8x^5 - 2x^3$

74. $y^9 - y^5$

75. $3x^2 + 243$ **76.** $27x^2 + 75$

77. $x^4 + 8x$

78. $x^4 + 27x$

79. $2y^5 - 2y^2$

80. $2y^5 - 128y^2$

Exercises 81–112 contain polynomials in several variables. Factor each polynomial completely and check using multiplication.

81. $6x^2 + 8xy$ **82.** $21x^2 - 35xy$

83. $xy - 7x + 3y - 21$

84. $xy - 5x + 2y - 10$

85. $x^2 - 3xy - 4y^2$

86. $x^2 - 4xy - 12y^2$

87. $72a^3b^2 + 12a^2 - 24a^4b^2$

88. $24a^4b + 60a^3b^2 + 150a^2b^3$

89. $3a^2 + 27ab + 54b^2$

90. $3a^2 + 15ab + 18b^2$

91. $48x^4y - 3x^2y$

92. $16a^3b^2 - 4ab^2$

93. $6a^2b + ab - 2b$

94. $16a^2 - 32ab + 12b^2$
95. $7x^5y - 7xy^5$
96. $3x^4y^2 - 3x^2y^2$
97. $10x^3y - 14x^2y^2 + 4xy^3$
98. $18x^3y + 57x^2y^2 + 30xy^3$
99. $2bx^2 + 44bx + 242b$
100. $3xz^2 - 72xz + 432x$
101. $15a^2 + 11ab - 14b^2$
102. $25a^2 + 25ab + 6b^2$
103. $-36x^3y + 62x^2y^2 - 12xy^3$
104. $-10a^4b^2 + 15a^3b^3 + 25a^2b^4$
105. $a^2y - b^2y - a^2x + b^2x$
106. $bx^2 - 4b + ax^2 - 4a$
107. $9ax^3 + 15ax^2 - 14ax$
108. $4ay^3 - 12ay^2 + 9ay$
109. $2x^4 + 6x^3y + 2x^2y^2$
110. $3x^4 - 9x^3y + 3x^2y^2$
111. $81x^4y - y^5$
112. $16x^4y - y^5$

Practice PLUS

In Exercises 113–122, factor completely.

113. $10x^2(x + 1) - 7x(x + 1) - 6(x + 1)$
114. $12x^2(x - 1) - 4x(x - 1) - 5(x - 1)$
115. $6x^4 + 35x^2 - 6$
116. $7x^4 + 34x^2 - 5$
117. $(x - 7)^2 - 4a^2$
118. $(x - 6)^2 - 9a^2$
119. $x^2 + 8x + 16 - 25a^2$
120. $x^2 + 14x + 49 - 16a^2$
121. $y^7 + y$
122. $(y + 1)^3 + 1$

Application Exercises

123. A rock is dropped from the top of a 256-foot cliff. The height, in feet, of the rock above the water after t seconds is modeled by the polynomial $256 - 16t^2$. Factor this expression completely.

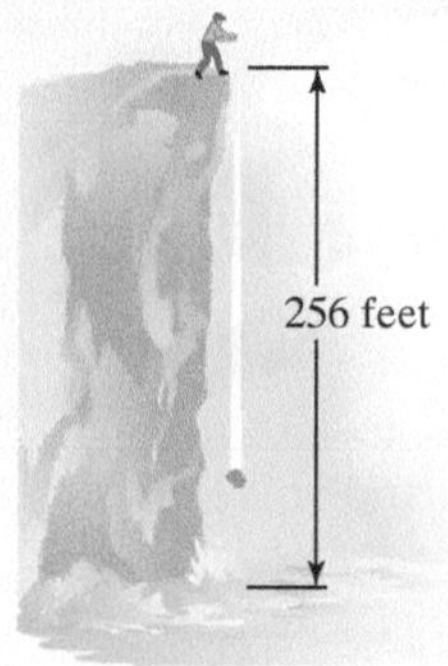

124. The building shown in the figure has a height represented by x feet. The building's base is a square and the building's volume is $x^3 - 60x^2 + 900x$ cubic feet. Express the building's dimensions in terms of x.

125. Express the area of the blue shaded ring shown in the figure in terms of π. Then factor this expression completely.

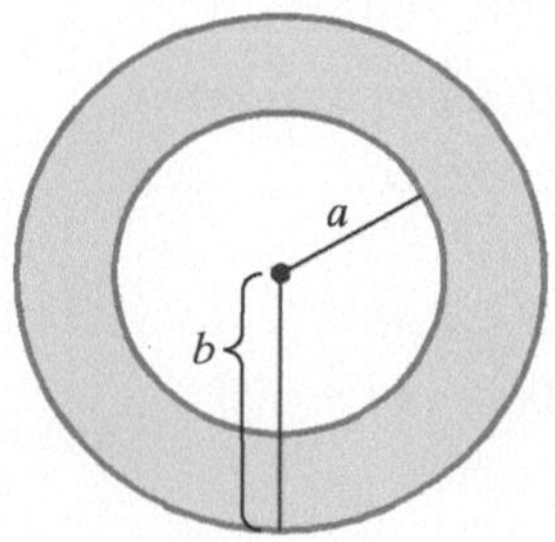

Writing in Mathematics

126. Describe a strategy that can be used to factor polynomials.

127. Describe some of the difficulties in factoring polynomials. What suggestions can you offer to overcome these difficulties?

128. You are about to take a great picture of fog rolling into San Francisco from the middle of the Golden Gate Bridge, 400 feet above the water. Whoops! You accidently lean too far over the safety rail and drop your camera. The height, in feet, of the camera after t seconds is modeled by the polynomial $400 - 16t^2$. The factored form of the polynomial is $16(5 + t)(5 - t)$. Describe something about your falling camera that is easier to see from the factored form, $16(5 + t)(5 - t)$, than from the form $400 - 16t^2$.

Critical Thinking Exercises

Make Sense? *In Exercises 129–132, determine whether each statement "makes sense" or "does not make sense" and explain your reasoning.*

129. It takes a great deal of practice to get good at factoring a wide variety of polynomials.

130. Multiplying polynomials is relatively mechanical, but factoring often requires a great deal of thought.

131. The factorable trinomial $4x^2 + 8x + 3$ and the prime trinomial $4x^2 + 8x + 1$ are in the form $ax^2 + bx + c$, but $b^2 - 4ac$ is a perfect square only in the case of the factorable trinomial.

132. When a factorization requires two factoring techniques, I'm less likely to make errors if I show one technique at a time rather than combining the two factorizations into one step.

In Exercises 133–136, determine whether each statement is true or false. If the statement is false, make the necessary change(s) to produce a true statement.

133. $x^2 - 9 = (x - 3)^2$ for any real number x.

134. The polynomial $4x^2 + 100$ is the sum of two squares and therefore cannot be factored.

135. If the general factoring strategy is used to factor a polynomial, at least two factorizations are necessary before the given polynomial is factored completely.

136. Once a common monomial factor is removed from $3xy^3 + 9xy^2 + 21xy$, the remaining trinomial factor cannot be factored further.

In Exercises 137–141, factor completely.

137. $3x^5 - 21x^3 - 54x$

138. $5y^5 - 5y^4 - 20y^3 + 20y^2$

139. $4x^4 - 9x^2 + 5$

140. $(x + 5)^2 - 20(x + 5) + 100$

141. $3x^{2n} - 27y^{2n}$

Technology Exercises

In Exercises 142–146, use the GRAPH *or* TABLE *feature of a graphing utility to determine if the polynomial on the left side of each equation has been correctly factored. If not, factor the polynomial correctly and then use your graphing utility to verify the factorization.*

142. $4x^2 - 12x + 9 = (4x - 3)^2$; $[-5, 5, 1]$ by $[0, 20, 1]$

143. $3x^3 - 12x^2 - 15x = 3x(x + 5)(x - 1)$; $[-5, 7, 1]$ by $[-80, 80, 10]$

144. $6x^2 + 10x - 4 = 2(3x - 1)(x + 2)$; $[-5, 5, 1]$ by $[-20, 20, 2]$

145. $x^4 - 16 = (x^2 + 4)(x + 2)(x - 2)$; $[-5, 5, 1]$ by $[-20, 20, 2]$

146. $2x^3 + 10x^2 - 2x - 10 = 2(x + 5)(x^2 + 1)$; $[-8, 4, 1]$ by $[-100, 100, 10]$

Review Exercises

147. Factor: $9x^2 - 16$. (Section 4, Example 1)

148. Graph using intercepts: $5x - 2y = 10$.

149. The second angle of a triangle measures three times that of the first angle's measure. The third angle measures 80° more than the first. Find the measure of each angle.

Preview Exercises

Exercises 150–152 will help you prepare for the material covered in the next section.

150. Evaluate $(3x - 1)(x + 2)$ for $x = \frac{1}{3}$.

151. Evaluate $2x^2 + 7x - 4$ for $x = \frac{1}{2}$.

152. Factor: $(x - 2)(x + 3) - 6$.

SECTION 6

Solving Quadratic Equations by Factoring

Objectives

1. Use the zero-product principle.
2. Solve quadratic equations by factoring.
3. Solve problems using quadratic equations.

The alligator, at one time an endangered species, was the subject of a protection program at Florida's Everglades National Park. Park rangers used the formula

$$P = -10x^2 + 475x + 3500$$

to estimate the alligator population, P, after x years of the protection program. Their goal was to bring the population up to 7250. To find out how long the program had to be continued for this to happen, we substitute 7250 for P in the formula and solve for x:

$$7250 = -10x^2 + 475x + 3500.$$

Do you see how this equation differs from a linear equation? The highest exponent on x is 2. Solving such an equation involves finding the numbers that will make the equation a true statement. In this section, we use factoring to solve equations in the form $ax^2 + bx + c = 0$. We also look at applications of these equations.

The Standard Form of a Quadratic Equation

We begin by defining a quadratic equation.

Definition of a Quadratic Equation

A **quadratic equation** in x is an equation that can be written in the **standard form**

$$ax^2 + bx + c = 0,$$

where a, b, and c are real numbers, with $a \neq 0$. A quadratic equation in x is also called a **second-degree polynomial equation** in x.

Here is an example of a quadratic equation in standard form:

$$x^2 - 7x + 10 = 0.$$

$a = 1$ $b = -7$ $c = 10$

1 Use the zero-product principle.

Solving Quadratic Equations by Factoring

We can factor the left side of the quadratic equation $x^2 - 7x + 10 = 0$. We obtain $(x - 5)(x - 2) = 0$. If a quadratic equation has zero on one side and a factored expression on the other side, it can be solved using the **zero-product principle**.

The Zero-Product Principle

If the product of two algebraic expressions is zero, then at least one of the factors is equal to zero.

$$\text{If } AB = 0, \text{ then } A = 0 \text{ or } B = 0.$$

For example, consider the equation $(x - 5)(x - 2) = 0$. According to the zero-product principle, this product can be zero only if at least one of the factors is zero. We set each individual factor equal to zero and solve each resulting equation for x.

$$(x - 5)(x - 2) = 0$$

$$x - 5 = 0 \quad \text{or} \quad x - 2 = 0$$

$$x = 5 \qquad\qquad x = 2$$

We can check each of the proposed solutions, 5 and 2, in the original quadratic equation, $x^2 - 7x + 10 = 0$. Substitute each one separately for x in the equation.

Check 5:

$$x^2 - 7x + 10 = 0$$

$$5^2 - 7 \cdot 5 + 10 \stackrel{?}{=} 0$$

$$25 - 35 + 10 \stackrel{?}{=} 0$$

$$0 = 0, \quad \text{true}$$

Check 2:

$$x^2 - 7x + 10 = 0$$

$$2^2 - 7 \cdot 2 + 10 \stackrel{?}{=} 0$$

$$4 - 14 + 10 \stackrel{?}{=} 0$$

$$0 = 0, \quad \text{true}$$

The resulting true statements indicate that the solutions are 5 and 2. Note that with a quadratic equation, we can have two solutions, compared to the linear equation that usually had one.

EXAMPLE 1 Using the Zero-Product Principle

Solve the equation: $(3x - 1)(x + 2) = 0$.

Solution The product $(3x - 1)(x + 2)$ is equal to zero. By the zero-product principle, the only way that this product can be zero is if at least one of the factors is zero. Thus,

$$3x - 1 = 0 \quad \text{or} \quad x + 2 = 0.$$

$$3x = 1 \qquad\qquad x = -2 \quad \text{Solve each equation for } x.$$

$$x = \frac{1}{3}$$

Because each linear equation has a solution, the original equation, $(3x - 1)(x + 2) = 0$, has two solutions, $\frac{1}{3}$ and -2. Check these solutions by substituting each one separately into the given equation. The equation's solution set is $\left\{-2, \frac{1}{3}\right\}$. ■

✓ **CHECK POINT 1** Solve the equation: $(2x + 1)(x - 4) = 0$.

2 Solve quadratic equations by factoring.

In Example 1 and Check Point 1, the given equations were in factored form. Here is a procedure for solving a quadratic equation when we must first do the factoring.

Solving a Quadratic Equation by Factoring

1. If necessary, rewrite the equation in the standard form $ax^2 + bx + c = 0$, moving all terms to one side, thereby obtaining zero on the other side.
2. Factor.
3. Apply the zero-product principle, setting each factor equal to zero.
4. Solve the equations formed in step 3.
5. Check the solutions in the original equation.

EXAMPLE 2 Solving a Quadratic Equation by Factoring

Solve: $2x^2 + 7x - 4 = 0$.

Solution

Step 1. Move all terms to one side and obtain zero on the other side. All terms are already on the left and zero is on the other side, so we can skip this step.

Step 2. Factor.

$$2x^2 + 7x - 4 = 0$$

$$(2x - 1)(x + 4) = 0$$

Steps 3 and 4. Set each factor equal to zero and solve each resulting equation.

$$2x - 1 = 0 \quad \text{or} \quad x + 4 = 0$$

$$2x = 1 \qquad\qquad x = -4$$

$$x = \frac{1}{2}$$

Step 5. Check the solutions in the original equation.

Check $\frac{1}{2}$:

$$2x^2 + 7x - 4 = 0$$
$$2\left(\frac{1}{2}\right)^2 + 7\left(\frac{1}{2}\right) - 4 \stackrel{?}{=} 0$$
$$2\left(\frac{1}{4}\right) + 7\left(\frac{1}{2}\right) - 4 \stackrel{?}{=} 0$$
$$\frac{1}{2} + \frac{7}{2} - 4 \stackrel{?}{=} 0$$
$$4 - 4 \stackrel{?}{=} 0$$
$$0 = 0, \quad \text{true}$$

Check -4:

$$2x^2 + 7x - 4 = 0$$
$$2(-4)^2 + 7(-4) - 4 \stackrel{?}{=} 0$$
$$2(16) + 7(-4) - 4 \stackrel{?}{=} 0$$
$$32 + (-28) - 4 \stackrel{?}{=} 0$$
$$4 - 4 \stackrel{?}{=} 0$$
$$0 = 0, \quad \text{true}$$

The solutions are -4 and $\frac{1}{2}$, and the solution set is $\left\{-4, \frac{1}{2}\right\}$. ■

✓ CHECK POINT 2 Solve: $x^2 - 6x + 5 = 0$.

Great Question!

After factoring a polynomial, should I set each factor equal to zero?

No. Do not confuse factoring a polynomial with solving a quadratic equation by factoring.

Factoring a Polynomial	**Solving a Quadratic Equation**
Factor: $2x^2 + 7x - 4$.	Solve: $2x^2 + 7x - 4 = 0$.
Solution $(2x - 1)(x + 4)$	Solution $(2x - 1)(x + 4) = 0$
	$2x - 1 = 0$ or $x + 4 = 0$
	$x = \frac{1}{2}$ $\quad$ $x = -4$
	The solution set is $\left\{-4, \frac{1}{2}\right\}$.

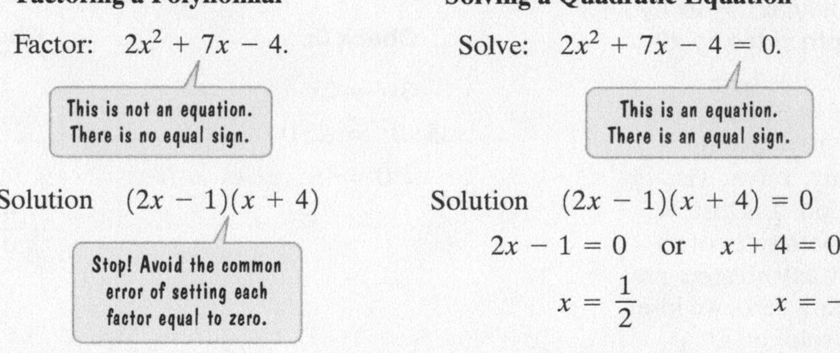

This is not an equation. There is no equal sign.
This is an equation. There is an equal sign.
Stop! Avoid the common error of setting each factor equal to zero.

Using Technology

Graphic Connections

You can use a graphing utility to check the real number solutions of a quadratic equation. **The solutions of $ax^2 + bx + c = 0$ correspond to the x-intercepts for the graph of $y = ax^2 + bx + c$.** For example, to check the solutions of $2x^2 + 7x - 4 = 0$, graph $y = 2x^2 + 7x - 4$. The U-shaped, bowl-like, graph is shown below. The x-intercepts are -4 and $\frac{1}{2}$, verifying -4 and $\frac{1}{2}$ as the solutions.

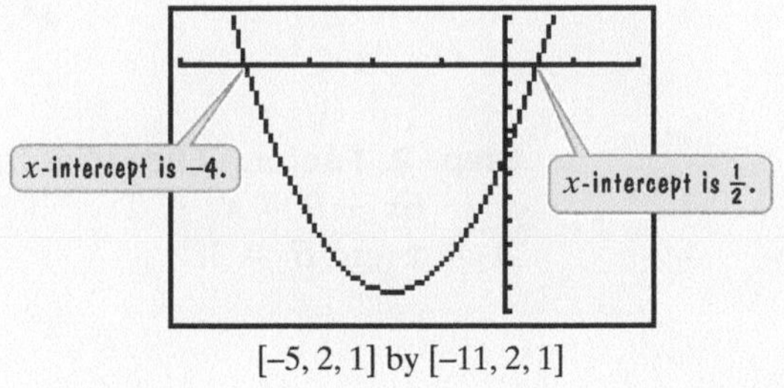

[−5, 2, 1] by [−11, 2, 1]

EXAMPLE 3 Solving a Quadratic Equation by Factoring

Solve: $3x^2 = 2x$.

Solution

Step 1. Move all terms to one side and obtain zero on the other side. Subtract $2x$ from both sides and write the equation in standard form.

$$3x^2 - 2x = 2x - 2x$$
$$3x^2 - 2x = 0$$

Step 2. Factor. We factor out x from the two terms on the left side.

$$3x^2 - 2x = 0$$
$$x(3x - 2) = 0$$

Steps 3 and 4. Set each factor equal to zero and solve the resulting equations.

$$x = 0 \quad \text{or} \quad 3x - 2 = 0$$
$$3x = 2$$
$$x = \frac{2}{3}$$

Step 5. Check the solutions in the original equation.

Check 0:

$$3x^2 = 2x$$
$$3 \cdot 0^2 \stackrel{?}{=} 2 \cdot 0$$
$$0 = 0, \quad \text{true}$$

Check $\frac{2}{3}$:

$$3x^2 = 2x$$
$$3\left(\frac{2}{3}\right)^2 \stackrel{?}{=} 2\left(\frac{2}{3}\right)$$
$$3\left(\frac{4}{9}\right) \stackrel{?}{=} 2\left(\frac{2}{3}\right)$$
$$\frac{4}{3} = \frac{4}{3}, \quad \text{true}$$

The solutions are 0 and $\frac{2}{3}$, and the solution set is $\{0, \frac{2}{3}\}$. ■

Great Question!

Can I simplify $3x^2 = 2x$ by dividing both sides by x?

No. If you divide both sides of $3x^2 = 2x$ by x, you will obtain $3x = 2$ and, consequently, $x = \frac{2}{3}$. The other solution, 0, is lost. We can divide both sides of an equation by any *nonzero* real number. If x is zero, we lose the second solution.

✓ **CHECK POINT 3** Solve: $4x^2 = 2x$.

EXAMPLE 4 Solving a Quadratic Equation by Factoring

Solve: $x^2 = 6x - 9$.

Solution

Step 1. Move all terms to one side and obtain zero on the other side. To obtain zero on the right, we subtract $6x$ and add 9 on both sides.

$$x^2 - 6x + 9 = 6x - 6x - 9 + 9$$
$$x^2 - 6x + 9 = 0$$

Step 2. Factor. The trinomial on the left side is a perfect square trinomial: $x^2 - 6x + 9 = x^2 - 2 \cdot x \cdot 3 + 3^2$. We factor using $A^2 - 2AB + B^2 = (A - B)^2$: $A = x$ and $B = 3$.

$$x^2 - 6x + 9 = 0$$
$$(x - 3)^2 = 0$$

Using Technology

Graphic Connections

The graph of $y = x^2 - 6x + 9$ is shown below. Notice that there is only one x-intercept, namely 3, verifying that the solution of

$$x^2 - 6x + 9 = 0$$

is 3.

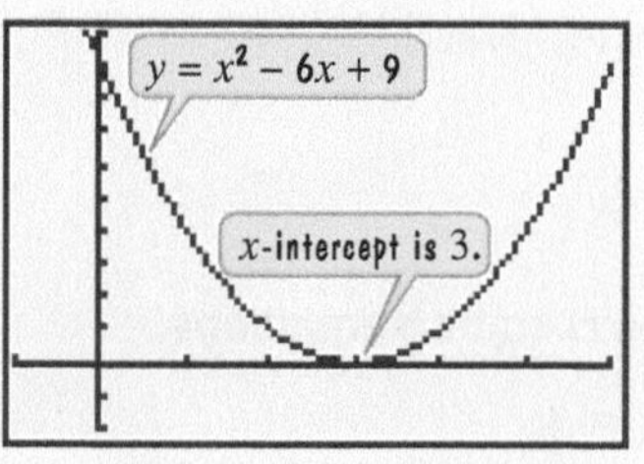

[-1, 6, 1] by [-2, 10, 1]

Steps 3 and 4. Set each factor equal to zero and solve the resulting equations. Because both factors are the same, it is only necessary to set one of them equal to zero.

$$x - 3 = 0$$
$$x = 3$$

Step 5. Check the solution in the original equation.

Check 3:

$$x^2 = 6x - 9$$
$$3^2 \stackrel{?}{=} 6 \cdot 3 - 9$$
$$9 \stackrel{?}{=} 18 - 9$$
$$9 = 9, \quad \text{true}$$

The solution is 3 and the solution set is $\{3\}$. ■

✓ **CHECK POINT 4** Solve: $x^2 = 10x - 25$.

EXAMPLE 5 Solving a Quadratic Equation by Factoring

Solve: $9x^2 = 16$.

Solution

Step 1. Move all terms to one side and obtain zero on the other side. Subtract 16 from both sides and write the equation in standard form.

$$9x^2 - 16 = 16 - 16$$
$$9x^2 - 16 = 0$$

Step 2. Factor. The binomial on the left side is the difference of two squares: $9x^2 - 16 = (3x)^2 - 4^2$. We factor using $A^2 - B^2 = (A + B)(A - B)$: $A = 3x$ and $B = 4$.

$$9x^2 - 16 = 0$$
$$(3x + 4)(3x - 4) = 0$$

Steps 3 and 4. Set each factor equal to zero and solve the resulting equations. We use the zero-product principle to solve $(3x + 4)(3x - 4) = 0$.

$$3x + 4 = 0 \quad \text{or} \quad 3x - 4 = 0$$
$$3x = -4 \qquad\qquad 3x = 4$$
$$x = -\frac{4}{3} \qquad\qquad x = \frac{4}{3}$$

Step 5. Check the solutions in the original equation. Do this now and verify that the solutions of $9x^2 = 16$ are $-\frac{4}{3}$ and $\frac{4}{3}$. The equation's solution set is $\left\{-\frac{4}{3}, \frac{4}{3}\right\}$. ■

✓ **CHECK POINT 5** Solve: $16x^2 = 25$.

EXAMPLE 6 Solving a Quadratic Equation by Factoring

Solve: $(x - 2)(x + 3) = 6$.

Solution

Step 1. Move all terms to one side and obtain zero on the other side. We write $(x - 2)(x + 3) = 6$ in standard form by multiplying out the product on the left side and then subtracting 6 from both sides.

$(x - 2)(x + 3) = 6$	This is the given equation.
$x^2 + 3x - 2x - 6 = 6$	Use the FOIL method.
$x^2 + x - 6 = 6$	Simplify.
$x^2 + x - 6 - 6 = 6 - 6$	Subtract 6 from both sides.
$x^2 + x - 12 = 0$	Simplify.

Step 2. Factor.

$$x^2 + x - 12 = 0$$
$$(x + 4)(x - 3) = 0$$

Steps 3 and 4. Set each factor equal to zero and solve the resulting equations.

$$x + 4 = 0 \quad \text{or} \quad x - 3 = 0$$
$$x = -4 \qquad\qquad x = 3$$

Step 5. Check the solutions in the original equation. Do this now and verify that the solutions are −4 and 3. The equation's solution set is $\{-4, 3\}$. ■

✓ **CHECK POINT 6** Solve: $(x - 5)(x - 2) = 28$.

3 Solve problems using quadratic equations.

Applications of Quadratic Equations

Solving quadratic equations by factoring can be used to answer questions about variables contained in mathematical models.

EXAMPLE 7 Modeling Motion

You throw a ball straight up from a rooftop 160 feet high with an initial speed of 48 feet per second. The formula

$$h = -16t^2 + 48t + 160$$

describes the ball's height above the ground, h, in feet, t seconds after you throw it. The ball misses the rooftop on its way down and eventually strikes the ground. The situation is illustrated in **Figure 1**. How long will it take for the ball to hit the ground?

Figure 1

Solution The ball hits the ground when h, its height above the ground, is 0 feet. Thus, we substitute 0 for h in the given formula and solve for t.

$h = -16t^2 + 48t + 160$	This is the formula that models the ball's height.
$0 = -16t^2 + 48t + 160$	Substitute 0 for h.
$0 = -16(t^2 - 3t - 10)$	Factor out the negative of the GCF.
$0 = -16(t - 5)(t + 2)$	Factor the trinomial.

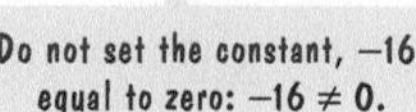
Do not set the constant, −16,
equal to zero: −16 ≠ 0.

$t - 5 = 0$ or $t + 2 = 0$	Set each variable factor equal to 0.
$t = 5 \qquad t = -2$	Solve for t.

Because we begin describing the ball's height at $t = 0$, we discard the solution $t = -2$. The ball hits the ground after 5 seconds. ■

Great Question!

You began solving $0 = -16t^2 + 48t + 160$ by factoring out -16, the negative of the GCF. What happens if I begin by multiplying both sides of the equation by -1?

You will still get the same solutions, 5 and -2. Here's how it works:

$-1 \cdot 0 = -1(-16t^2 + 48t + 160)$	Multiply both sides of $0 = -16t^2 + 48t + 160$ by -1.
$0 = 16t^2 - 48t - 160$	Multiply each term on the right side by -1.
$0 = 16(t^2 - 3t - 10)$	Factor out the GCF, 16.
$0 = 16(t - 5)(t + 2)$	Factor the trinomial.
$t - 5 = 0$ or $t + 2 = 0$	Set each variable factor equal to 0.
$t = 5 \qquad t = -2.$	Solve for t.

Figure 2 shows the graph of the formula $h = -16t^2 + 48t + 160$. The horizontal axis is labeled t, for the ball's time in motion. The vertical axis is labeled h, for the ball's height above the ground. Because time and height are both positive, the model is graphed in quadrant I and its boundaries only.

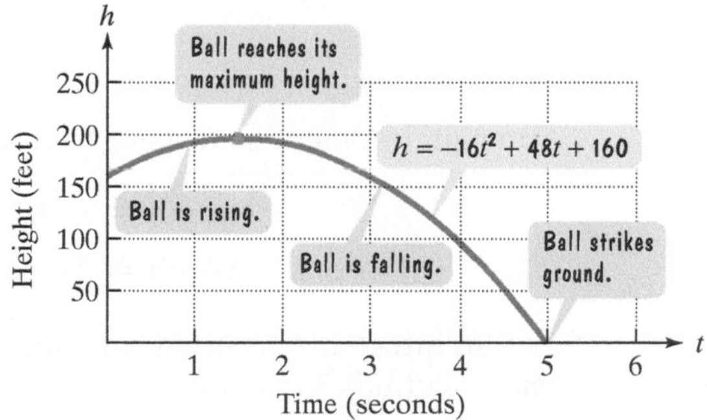

Figure 2

The graph visually shows what we discovered algebraically: The ball hits the ground after 5 seconds. The graph also reveals that the ball reaches its maximum height, nearly 200 feet, after 1.5 seconds. Then the ball begins to fall.

✓ **CHECK POINT 7** Use the formula $h = -16t^2 + 48t + 160$ to determine when the ball's height is 192 feet. Identify your solutions as points on the graph in **Figure 2**.

In our next example, we use our five-step strategy for solving word problems.

EXAMPLE 8 Solving a Problem About a Rectangle's Area

An architect is allowed no more than 15 square meters to add a small bedroom to a house. Because of the room's design in relationship to the existing structure, the width of its rectangular floor must be 7 meters less than two times the length. Find the precise length and width of the rectangular floor of maximum area that the architect is permitted.

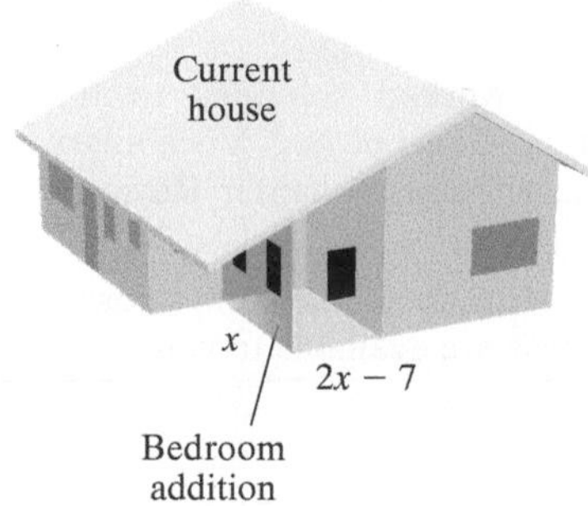

Figure 3

Solution

Step 1. Let x represent one of the quantities. We know something about the width: It must be 7 meters less than two times the length. We will let

$$x = \text{the length of the floor.}$$

Step 2. Represent other unknown quantities in terms of x. Because the width must be 7 meters less than two times the length, let

$$2x - 7 = \text{the width of the floor.}$$

The problem is illustrated in **Figure 3**.

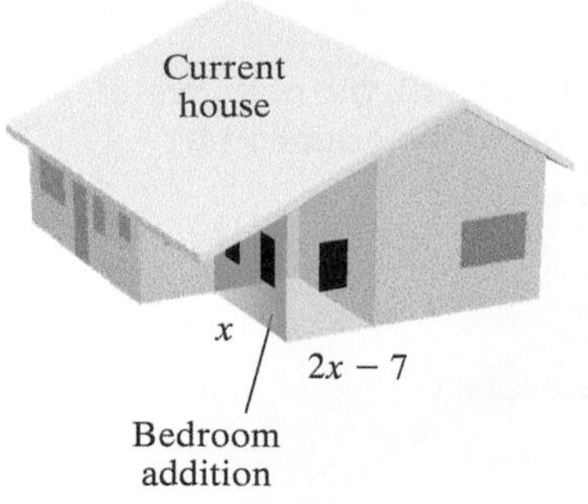

Figure 3 (repeated)

Step 3. Write an equation that models the conditions. Because the architect is allowed no more than 15 square meters, an area of 15 square meters is the maximum area permitted. The area of a rectangle is the product of its length and its width.

Length of the floor	times	Width of the floor	is	the area.
x	$\cdot$	$(2x - 7)$	$=$	15

Step 4. Solve the equation and answer the question.

$$x(2x - 7) = 15 \quad \text{This is the equation that models the problem's conditions.}$$

$$2x^2 - 7x = 15 \quad \text{Use the distributive property.}$$

$$2x^2 - 7x - 15 = 0 \quad \text{Subtract 15 from both sides.}$$

$$(2x + 3)(x - 5) = 0 \quad \text{Factor.}$$

$$2x + 3 = 0 \quad \text{or} \quad x - 5 = 0 \quad \text{Set each factor equal to zero.}$$

$$2x = -3 \qquad x = 5 \quad \text{Solve the resulting equations.}$$

$$x = -\frac{3}{2}$$

A rectangle cannot have a negative length. Thus,

$$\text{Length} = x = 5$$

$$\text{Width} = 2x - 7 = 2 \cdot 5 - 7 = 10 - 7 = 3.$$

The architect is permitted a room of maximum area whose length is 5 meters and whose width is 3 meters.

Step 5. Check the proposed solution in the original wording of the problem. The area of the floor using the dimensions that we found is

$$A = lw = (5 \text{ meters})(3 \text{ meters}) = 15 \text{ square meters}.$$

Because the problem's wording tells us that the maximum area permitted is 15 square meters, our dimensions are correct. ■

✓ **CHECK POINT 8** The length of a rectangular sign is 3 feet longer than the width. If the sign's area is 54 square feet, find its length and width.

Achieving Success

Be sure to use the Chapter Test Prep on YouTube for each chapter test. The Chapter Test Prep videos provide step-by-step solutions to every exercise in the test and let you review any exercises you miss.

Are you using any of the other textbook supplements for help and additional study? These include:

- The Student Solutions Manual. This contains fully worked solutions to the odd-numbered section exercises plus all Check Points, Concept and Vocabulary Checks, Review/Preview Exercises, Mid-Chapter Check Points, Chapter Reviews, Chapter Tests, and Cumulative Reviews.
- MyMathLab is a text-specific online course. Math XL is an online homework, tutorial, and assessment system. Ask your instructor whether these are available to you.

CONCEPT AND VOCABULARY CHECK

Fill in each blank so that the resulting statement is true.

1. An equation that can be written in the standard form $ax^2 + bx + c = 0, a \neq 0$, is called a/an ________________.
2. The zero-product principle states that if $AB = 0$, then ____________.
3. The solutions of $ax^2 + bx + c = 0$ correspond to the ____________ for the graph of $y = ax^2 + bx + c$.
4. The equation $3x^2 = 5x$ can be written in standard form by ____________ on both sides.
5. The equation $9x^2 = 30x - 25$ can be written in standard form by ____________ and ____________ on both sides.

6 EXERCISE SET

MyMathLab®

Watch the videos in MyMathLab

Download the MyDashBoard App

Practice Exercises

In Exercises 1–8, solve each equation using the zero-product principle.

1. $x(x + 7) = 0$
2. $x(x - 3) = 0$
3. $(x - 6)(x + 4) = 0$
4. $(x - 3)(x + 8) = 0$
5. $(x - 9)(5x + 4) = 0$
6. $(x + 7)(3x - 2) = 0$
7. $10(x - 4)(2x + 9) = 0$
8. $8(x - 5)(3x + 11) = 0$

In Exercises 9–56, use factoring to solve each quadratic equation. Check by substitution or by using a graphing utility and identifying x-intercepts.

9. $x^2 + 8x + 15 = 0$
10. $x^2 + 5x + 6 = 0$
11. $x^2 - 2x - 15 = 0$
12. $x^2 + x - 42 = 0$
13. $x^2 - 4x = 21$
14. $x^2 + 7x = 18$
15. $x^2 + 9x = -8$
16. $x^2 - 11x = -10$
17. $x^2 + 4x = 0$
18. $x^2 - 6x = 0$
19. $x^2 - 5x = 0$
20. $x^2 + 3x = 0$
21. $x^2 = 4x$
22. $x^2 = 8x$
23. $2x^2 = 5x$
24. $3x^2 = 5x$
25. $3x^2 = -5x$
26. $2x^2 = -3x$
27. $x^2 + 4x + 4 = 0$
28. $x^2 + 6x + 9 = 0$
29. $x^2 = 12x - 36$
30. $x^2 = 14x - 49$
31. $4x^2 = 12x - 9$
32. $9x^2 = 30x - 25$
33. $2x^2 = 7x + 4$
34. $3x^2 = x + 4$
35. $5x^2 = 18 - x$
36. $3x^2 = 15 + 4x$
37. $x^2 - 49 = 0$
38. $x^2 - 25 = 0$
39. $4x^2 - 25 = 0$
40. $9x^2 - 100 = 0$
41. $81x^2 = 25$
42. $25x^2 = 49$
43. $x(x - 4) = 21$
44. $x(x - 3) = 18$
45. $4x(x + 1) = 15$
46. $x(3x + 8) = -5$
47. $(x - 1)(x + 4) = 14$
48. $(x - 3)(x + 8) = -30$
49. $(x + 1)(2x + 5) = -1$
50. $(x + 3)(3x + 5) = 7$
51. $y(y + 8) = 16(y - 1)$
52. $y(y + 9) = 4(2y + 5)$
53. $4y^2 + 20y + 25 = 0$
54. $4y^2 + 44y + 121 = 0$
55. $64w^2 = 48w - 9$
56. $25w^2 = 80w - 64$

Practice PLUS

In Exercises 57–66, solve each equation and check your solutions.

57. $(x - 4)(x^2 + 5x + 6) = 0$
58. $(x - 5)(x^2 - 3x + 2) = 0$
59. $x^3 - 36x = 0$
60. $x^3 - 4x = 0$
61. $y^3 + 3y^2 + 2y = 0$
62. $y^3 + 2y^2 - 3y = 0$
63. $2(x - 4)^2 + x^2 = x(x + 50) - 46x$
64. $(x - 4)(x - 5) + (2x + 3)(x - 1) = x(2x - 25) - 13$
65. $(x - 2)^2 - 5(x - 2) + 6 = 0$
66. $(x - 3)^2 + 2(x - 3) - 8 = 0$

Application Exercises

A ball is thrown straight up from a rooftop 300 feet high. The formula

$$h = -16t^2 + 20t + 300$$

describes the ball's height above the ground, h, in feet, t seconds after it was thrown. The ball misses the rooftop on its way down and eventually strikes the ground. The graph of the formula is shown, with tick marks omitted along the horizontal axis. Use the formula to solve Exercises 67–69.

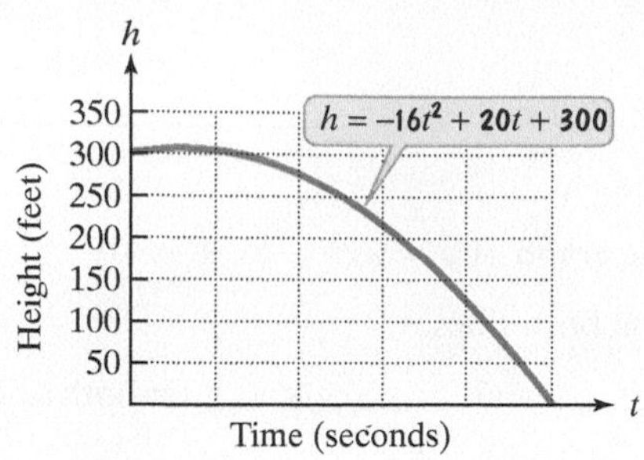

67. How long will it take for the ball to hit the ground? Use this information to provide tick marks with appropriate numbers along the horizontal axis in the figure shown.

68. When will the ball's height be 304 feet? Identify the solution as a point on the graph.

69. When will the ball's height be 276 feet? Identify the solution as a point on the graph.

An explosion causes debris to rise vertically with an initial speed of 72 feet per second. The formula

$$h = -16t^2 + 72t$$

describes the height of the debris above the ground, h, in feet, t seconds after the explosion. Use this information to solve Exercises 70–71.

70. How long will it take for the debris to hit the ground?

71. When will the debris be 32 feet above the ground?

The formula

$$S = 2x^2 - 12x + 82$$

models spending by international travelers to the United States, S, in billions of dollars, x years after 2000. Use this formula to solve Exercises 72–73.

72. In which years did international travelers spend \$72 billion?

73. In which years did international travelers spend \$66 billion?

The graph of the formula modeling spending by international travelers is shown below. Use the graph to solve Exercises 74–75.

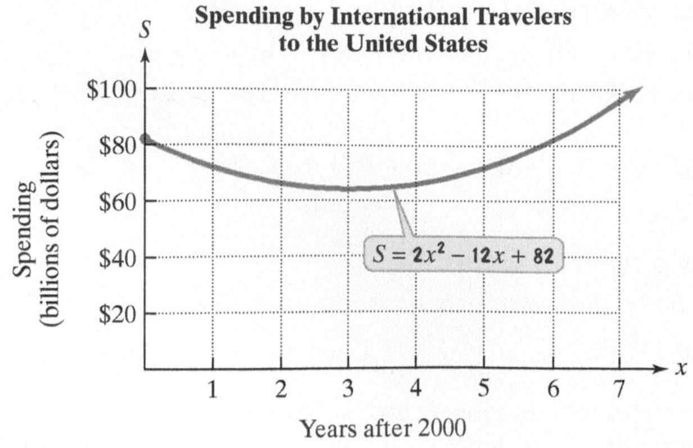

Source: Travel Industry Association of America

74. Identify your solutions from Exercise 72 as points on the graph.

75. Identify your solutions from Exercise 73 as points on the graph.

The alligator, at one time an endangered species, is the subject of a protection program. The formula

$$P = -10x^2 + 475x + 3500$$

models the alligator population, P, after x years of the protection program, where $0 \le x \le 12$. Use the formula to solve Exercises 76–77.

76. After how long is the population up to 5990?

77. After how long is the population up to 7250?

The graph of the alligator population is shown over time. Use the graph to solve Exercises 78–79.

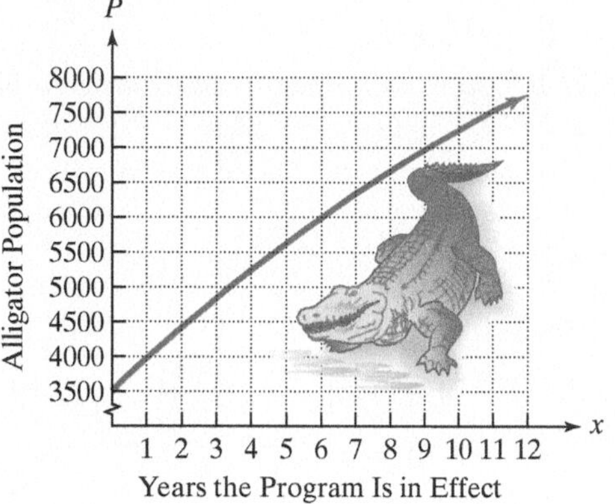

78. Identify your solution from Exercise 76 as a point on the graph.

79. Identify your solution from Exercise 77 as a point on the graph.

The formula

$$N = \frac{t^2 - t}{2}$$

describes the number of football games, N, that must be played in a league with t teams if each team is to play every other team once. Use this information to solve Exercises 80–81.

80. If a league has 36 games scheduled, how many teams belong to the league, assuming that each team plays every other team once?

81. If a league has 45 games scheduled, how many teams belong to the league, assuming that each team plays every other team once?

82. The length of a rectangular garden is 5 feet greater than the width. The area of the rectangle is 300 square feet. Find the length and the width.

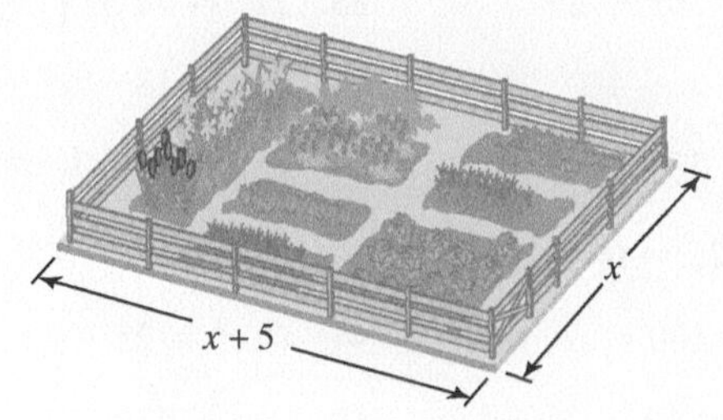

83. A rectangular parking lot has a length that is 3 yards greater than the width. The area of the parking lot is 180 square yards. Find the length and the width.

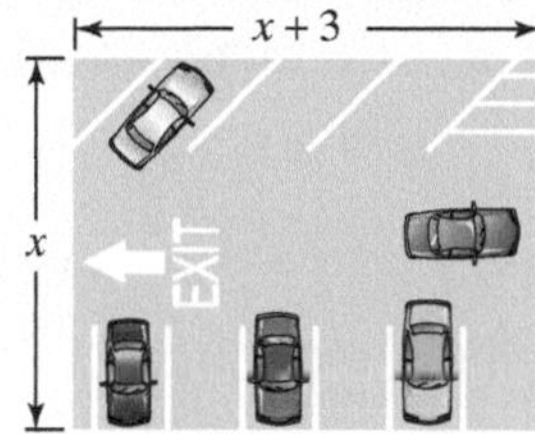

84. Each end of a glass prism is a triangle with a height that is 1 inch shorter than twice the base. If the area of the triangle is 60 square inches, how long are the base and height?

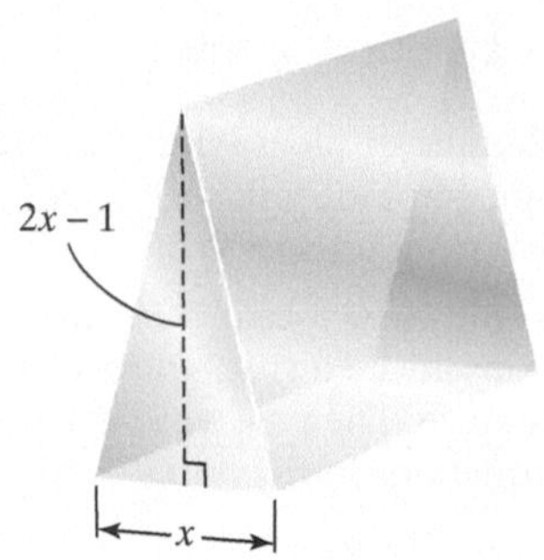

85. Great white sharks have triangular teeth with a height that is 1 centimeter longer than the base. If the area of one tooth is 15 square centimeters, find its base and height.

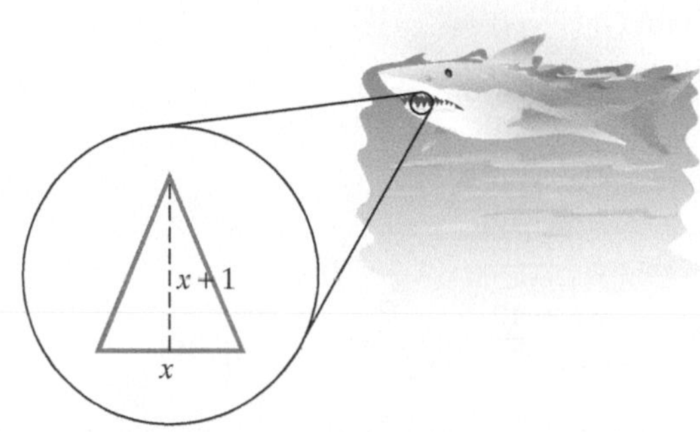

86. A vacant rectangular lot is being turned into a community vegetable garden measuring 15 meters by 12 meters. A path of uniform width is to surround the garden. If the area of the lot is 378 square meters, find the width of the path surrounding the garden.

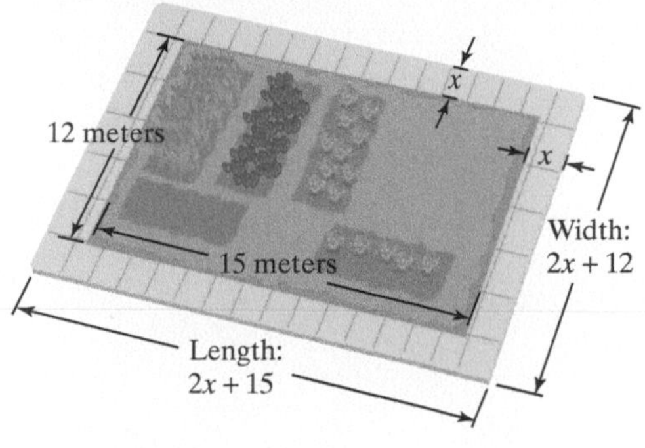

87. As part of a landscaping project, you put in a flower bed measuring 10 feet by 12 feet. You plan to surround the bed with a uniform border of low-growing plants.

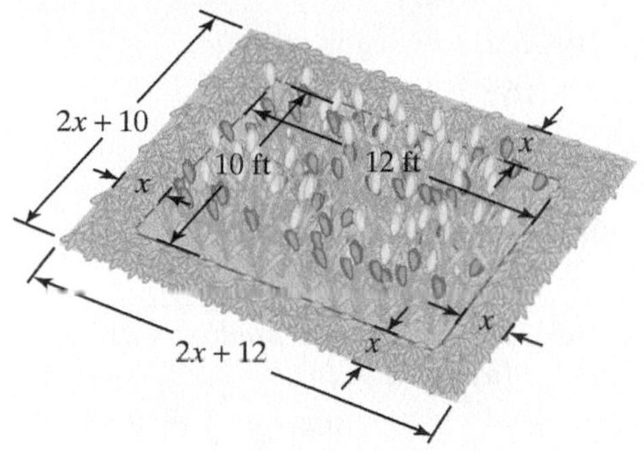

a. Write a polynomial that describes the area of the uniform border that surrounds your flower bed. (*Hint*: The area of the border is the area of the large rectangle shown in the figure minus the area of the flower bed.)

b. The low-growing plants surrounding the flower bed require 1 square foot each when mature. If you have 168 of these plants, how wide a strip around the flower bed should you prepare for the border?

Writing in Mathematics

88. What is a quadratic equation?

89. Explain how to solve $x^2 + 6x + 8 = 0$ using factoring and the zero-product principle.

90. If $(x + 2)(x - 4) = 0$ indicates that $x + 2 = 0$ or $x - 4 = 0$, explain why $(x + 2)(x - 4) = 6$ does not mean $x + 2 = 6$ or $x - 4 = 6$. Could we solve the equation using $x + 2 = 3$ and $x - 4 = 2$ because $3 \cdot 2 = 6$?

Critical Thinking Exercises

Make Sense? *In Exercises 91–94, determine whether each statement "makes sense" or "does not make sense" and explain your reasoning.*

91. When solving $4(x - 3)(x + 2) = 0$ and $4x(x + 2) = 0$, I can ignore the monomial factors.

92. I set the quadratic equation $2x^2 - 5x = 12$ equal to zero and obtained $2x^2 - 5x = 0$.

93. Because some trinomials are prime, some quadratic equations cannot be solved by factoring.

94. I'm looking at a graph with one x-intercept, so it must be the graph of a linear equation.

In Exercises 95–98, determine whether each statement is true or false. If the statement is false, make the necessary change(s) to produce a true statement.

95. If $(x + 3)(x - 4) = 2$, then $x + 3 = 0$ or $x - 4 = 0$.

96. The solutions of the equation $4(x - 5)(x + 3) = 0$ are 4, 5, and -3.

97. Equations solved by factoring always have two different solutions.

98. Both 0 and $-\pi$ are solutions of the equation $x(x + \pi) = 0$.

99. Write a quadratic equation in standard form whose solutions are -3 and 5.

In Exercises 100–102, solve each equation.

100. $x^3 - x^2 - 16x + 16 = 0$

101. $3^{x^2-9x+20} = 1$

102. $(x^2 - 5x + 5)^3 = 1$

In Exercises 103–106, match each equation with its graph. The graphs are labeled (a) through (d).

103. $y = x^2 - x - 2$ **104.** $y = x^2 + x - 2$

105. $y = x^2 - 4$ **106.** $y = x^2 - 4x$

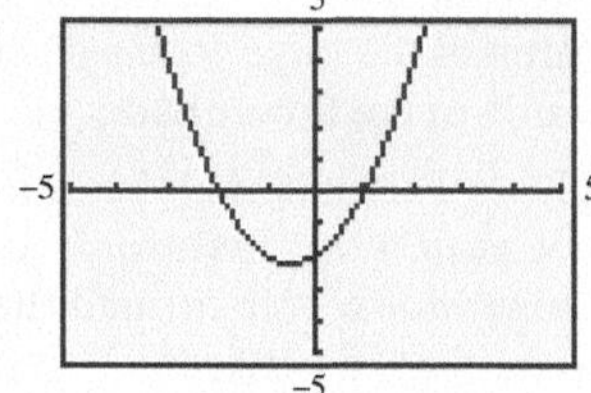

b.

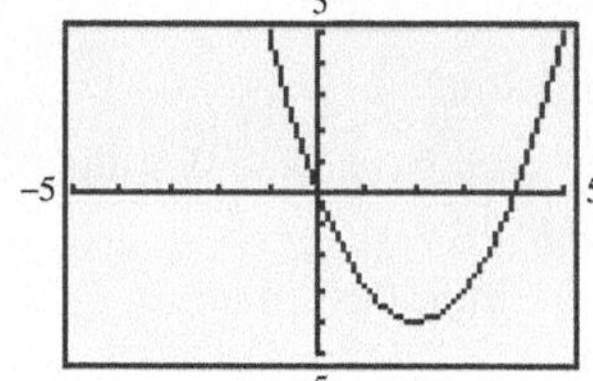

c.

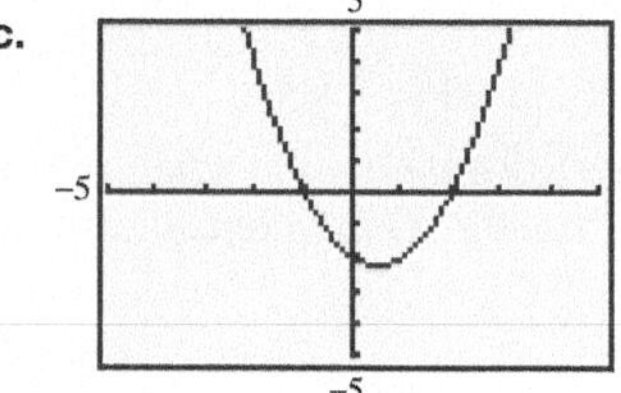

d.

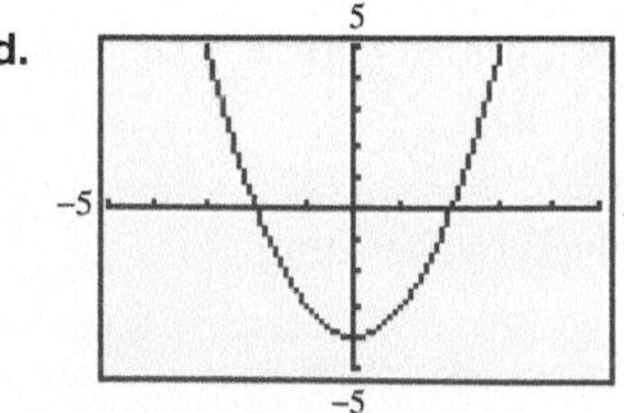

Technology Exercises

In Exercises 107–110, use the x-intercepts for the graph in a $[-10, 10, 1]$ by $[-13, 10, 1]$ viewing rectangle to solve the quadratic equation. Check by substitution.

107. Use the graph of $y = x^2 + 3x - 4$ to solve

$$x^2 + 3x - 4 = 0.$$

108. Use the graph of $y = x^2 + x - 6$ to solve

$$x^2 + x - 6 = 0.$$

109. Use the graph of $y = (x - 2)(x + 3) - 6$ to solve

$$(x - 2)(x + 3) - 6 = 0.$$

110. Use the graph of $y = x^2 - 2x + 1$ to solve

$$x^2 - 2x + 1 = 0.$$

111. Use the technique of identifying x-intercepts on a graph generated by a graphing utility to check any five equations that you solved in Exercises 9–56.

112. If you have access to a calculator that solves quadratic equations, consult the owner's manual to determine how to use this feature. Then use your calculator to solve any five of the equations in Exercises 9–56.

Review Exercises

113. Graph: $y > -\frac{2}{3}x + 1$.

114. Simplify: $\left(\frac{8x^4}{4x^7}\right)^2$.

115. Solve: $5x + 28 = 6 - 6x$.

Preview Exercises

116. Evaluate $\frac{250x}{100 - x}$ for $x = 60$.

117. Why is $\frac{6x + 12}{7x - 28}$ undefined for $x = 4$?

118. Factor the numerator and the denominator. Then simplify by dividing out the common factor in the numerator and the denominator.

$$\frac{x^2 + 6x + 5}{x^2 - 25}$$

GROUP PROJECT

Group members are on the board of a condominium association. The condominium has just installed a 35-foot-by-30-foot pool. Your job is to choose a material to surround the pool to create a border of uniform width.

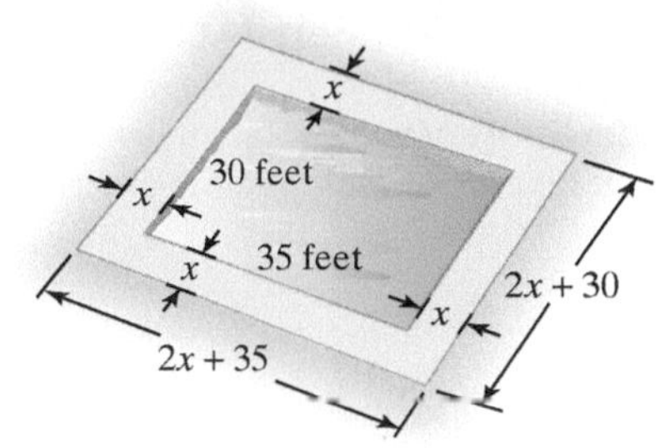

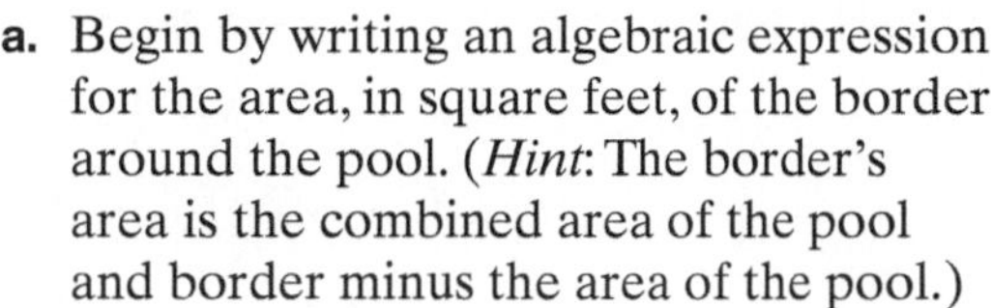

a. Begin by writing an algebraic expression for the area, in square feet, of the border around the pool. (*Hint*: The border's area is the combined area of the pool and border minus the area of the pool.)

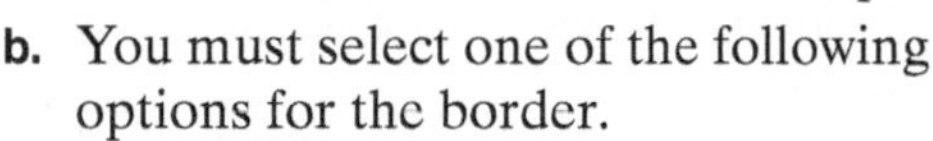

b. You must select one of the following options for the border.

Options for the Border	Price
Cement	\$6 per square foot
Outdoor carpeting	\$5 per square foot plus \$10 per foot to install edging around the rectangular border
Brick	\$8 per square foot plus a \$60 charge for delivering the bricks

Write an algebraic expression for the cost of installing the border for each of these options.

c. You would like the border to be 5 feet wide. Use the algebraic expressions in part (b) to find the cost of the border for each of the three options.

d. You would prefer not to use cement. However, the condominium association is limited by a \$5000 budget. Given this limitation, approximately how wide can the border be using outdoor carpeting or brick? Which option should you select and why?

Summary

Definitions and Concepts	Examples
Section 1 The Greatest Common Factor and Factoring by Grouping	
Factoring a polynomial containing the sum of monomials means finding an equivalent expression that is a product. The greatest common factor, GCF, is an expression that divides every term of the polynomial. The variable part of the GCF contains the smallest power of a variable that appears in all terms of the polynomial.	Find the GCF of $16x^2y$, $20x^3y^2$, and $8x^2y^3$. The GCF of 16, 20, and 8 is 4. The GCF of x^2, x^3, and x^2 is x^2. The GCF of y, y^2, and y^3 is y. $\text{GCF} = 4 \cdot x^2 \cdot y = 4x^2y$
To factor a monomial from a polynomial, express each term as the product of the GCF and its other factor. Then use the distributive property to factor out the GCF.	$16x^2y + 20x^3y^2 + 8x^2y^3$ $= 4x^2y \cdot 4 + 4x^2y \cdot 5xy + 4x^2y \cdot 2y^2$ $= 4x^2y(4 + 5xy + 2y^2)$
To factor a monomial from a polynomial with a negative coefficient in the first term, express each term as the product of the negative of the GCF and its other factor. Then use the distributive property to factor out the negative of the GCF.	$-20x^4y^3 + 10x^2y^2 - 15x^3y$ $= -5x^2y \cdot 4x^2y^2 - 5x^2y(-2y) - 5x^2y \cdot 3x$ The negative of the GCF is $-5x^2y$. $= -5x^2y(4x^2y^2 - 2y + 3x)$

Definitions and Concepts	Examples

Section 1 The Greatest Common Factor and Factoring by Grouping (continued)

To factor by grouping, factor out the GCF from each group. Then factor out the remaining common factor.	$xy + 5x - 3y - 15$ $= x(y + 5) - 3(y + 5)$ $= (y + 5)(x - 3)$

Section 2 Factoring Trinomials Whose Leading Coefficient Is 1

To factor a trinomial of the form $x^2 + bx + c$, find two numbers whose product is c and whose sum is b. The factorization is $(x + \text{one number})(x + \text{other number})$.	Factor: $x^2 + 9x + 20$. Find two numbers whose product is 20 and whose sum is 9. The numbers are 4 and 5. $x^2 + 9x + 20 = (x + 4)(x + 5)$

Section 3 Factoring Trinomials Whose Leading Coefficient Is Not 1

To factor $ax^2 + bx + c$ by trial and error, try various combinations of factors of ax^2 and c until a middle term of bx is obtained for the sum of outside and inside products.	Factor: $3x^2 + 7x - 6$. Factors of $3x^2$: $3x, x$ Factors of -6: 1 and -6, -1 and 6, 2 and -3, -2 and 3 A possible combination of these factors is $(3x - 2)(x + 3)$. Sum of outside and inside products should equal $7x$. $9x - 2x = 7x$ Thus, $3x^2 + 7x - 6 = (3x - 2)(x + 3)$.
To factor $ax^2 + bx + c$ by grouping, find the factors of ac whose sum is b. Write bx using these factors. Then factor by grouping.	Factor: $3x^2 + 7x - 6$. Find the factors of $3(-6)$, or -18, whose sum is 7. They are 9 and -2. $3x^2 + 7x - 6$ $= 3x^2 + 9x - 2x - 6$ $= 3x(x + 3) - 2(x + 3) = (x + 3)(3x - 2)$

Section 4 Factoring Special Forms

The Difference of Two Squares $A^2 - B^2 = (A + B)(A - B)$	$9x^2 - 25y^2$ $= (3x)^2 - (5y)^2 = (3x + 5y)(3x - 5y)$
Perfect Square Trinomials $A^2 + 2AB + B^2 = (A + B)^2$ $A^2 - 2AB + B^2 = (A - B)^2$	$x^2 + 16x + 64 = x^2 + 2 \cdot x \cdot 8 + 8^2 = (x + 8)^2$ $25x^2 - 30x + 9 = (5x)^2 - 2 \cdot 5x \cdot 3 + 3^2 = (5x - 3)^2$
Sum or Difference of Cubes $A^3 + B^3 = (A + B)(A^2 - AB + B^2)$ $A^3 - B^3 = (A - B)(A^2 + AB + B^2)$	$8x^3 - 125 = (2x)^3 - 5^3$ $= (2x - 5)[(2x)^2 + 2x \cdot 5 + 5^2]$ $= (2x - 5)(4x^2 + 10x + 25)$

Definitions and Concepts	Examples

Section 5 A General Factoring Strategy

A Factoring Strategy

1. Factor out the GCF.
2. a. If two terms, try
   $$A^2 - B^2 = (A + B)(A - B)$$
   $$A^3 + B^3 = (A + B)(A^2 - AB + B^2)$$
   $$A^3 - B^3 = (A - B)(A^2 + AB + B^2).$$
   b. If three terms, try
   $$A^2 + 2AB + B^2 = (A + B)^2$$
   $$A^2 - 2AB + B^2 = (A - B)^2.$$
   If not a perfect square trinomial, try trial and error or grouping.
   c. If four terms, try factoring by grouping.
3. See if any factors can be factored further.
4. Check by multiplying.

Factor: $2x^4 + 10x^3 - 8x^2 - 40x$.

The GCF is $2x$.

$$2x^4 + 10x^3 - 8x^2 - 40x$$
$$= 2x(x^3 + 5x^2 - 4x - 20)$$

Four terms: Try grouping.

$$= 2x[x^2(x + 5) - 4(x + 5)]$$
$$= 2x(x + 5)(x^2 - 4)$$

This can be factored further.

$$= 2x(x + 5)(x + 2)(x - 2)$$

Section 6 Solving Quadratic Equations by Factoring

The Zero-Product Principle

If $AB = 0$, then $A = 0$ or $B = 0$.

Solve: $(x - 6)(x + 10) = 0$.

$$x - 6 = 0 \quad \text{or} \quad x + 10 = 0$$
$$x = 6 \qquad\qquad x = -10$$

The solutions are -10 and 6, and the solution set is $\{-10, 6\}$.

A quadratic equation in x is an equation that can be written in the standard form

$$ax^2 + bx + c = 0, \quad a \neq 0.$$

To solve by factoring, write the equation in standard form, factor, set each factor equal to zero, and solve each resulting equation. Check proposed solutions in the original equation.

Solve: $4x^2 + 9x = 9$.

$$4x^2 + 9x - 9 = 0$$
$$(4x - 3)(x + 3) = 0$$
$$4x - 3 = 0 \quad \text{or} \quad x + 3 = 0$$
$$x = \frac{3}{4} \qquad\qquad x = -3$$

The solutions are -3 and $\frac{3}{4}$, and the solution set is $\left\{-3, \frac{3}{4}\right\}$.

REVIEW EXERCISES

1 *In Exercises 1–5, factor each polynomial using the greatest common factor. If there is no common factor other than 1 and the polynomial cannot be factored, so state.*

1. $30x - 45$
2. $-12x^3 - 16x^2 + 400x$
3. $30x^4y + 15x^3y + 5x^2y$
4. $7(x + 3) - 2(x + 3)$
5. $7x^2(x + y) - (x + y)$

In Exercises 6–9, factor by grouping.

6. $x^3 + 3x^2 + 2x + 6$
7. $xy + y + 4x + 4$
8. $x^3 + 5x + x^2 + 5$
9. $xy + 4x - 2y - 8$

2 *In Exercises 10–17, factor completely, or state that the trinomial is prime.*

10. $x^2 - 3x + 2$
11. $x^2 - x - 20$
12. $x^2 + 19x + 48$
13. $x^2 - 6xy + 8y^2$
14. $x^2 + 5x - 9$
15. $x^2 + 16xy - 17y^2$

16. $3x^2 + 6x - 24$

17. $3x^3 - 36x^2 + 33x$

3 *In Exercises 18–26, factor completely, or state that the trinomial is prime.*

18. $3x^2 + 17x + 10$

19. $5y^2 - 17y + 6$

20. $4x^2 + 4x - 15$

21. $5y^2 + 11y + 4$

22. $-8x^2 - 8x + 6$

23. $2x^3 + 7x^2 - 72x$

24. $12y^3 + 28y^2 + 8y$

25. $2x^2 - 7xy + 3y^2$

26. $5x^2 - 6xy - 8y^2$

4 *In Exercises 27–30, factor each difference of two squares completely.*

27. $4x^2 - 1$

28. $81 - 100y^2$

29. $25a^2 - 49b^2$

30. $z^4 - 16$

In Exercises 31–34, factor completely, or state that the polynomial is prime.

31. $2x^2 - 18$

32. $x^2 + 1$

33. $9x^3 - x$

34. $18xy^2 - 8x$

In Exercises 35–41, factor any perfect square trinomials, or state that the polynomial is prime.

35. $x^2 + 22x + 121$

36. $x^2 - 16x + 64$

37. $9y^2 + 48y + 64$

38. $16x^2 - 40x + 25$

39. $25x^2 + 15x + 9$

40. $36x^2 + 60xy + 25y^2$

41. $25x^2 - 40xy + 16y^2$

In Exercises 42–45, factor using the formula for the sum or difference of two cubes.

42. $x^3 - 27$

43. $64x^3 + 1$

44. $54x^3 - 16y^3$

45. $27x^3y + 8y$

In Exercises 46–47, find the formula for the area of the blue shaded region and express it in factored form.

46.

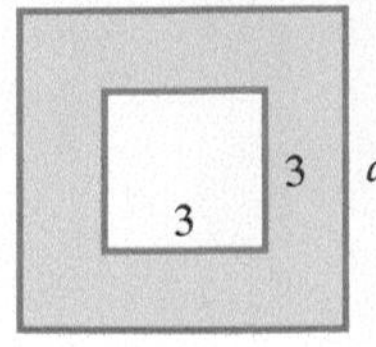

47.

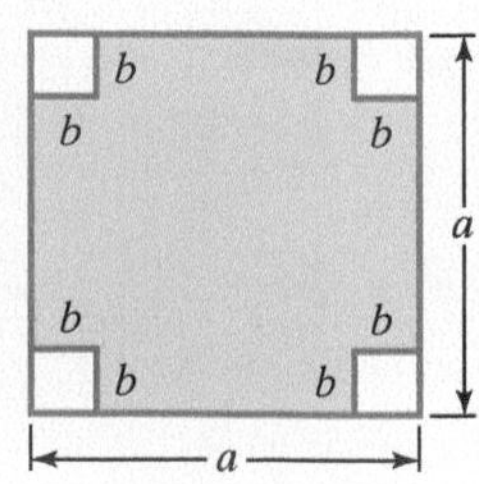

48. The figure shows a geometric interpretation of a factorization. Use the sum of the areas of the four pieces on the left and the area of the square on the right to write the factorization that is illustrated.

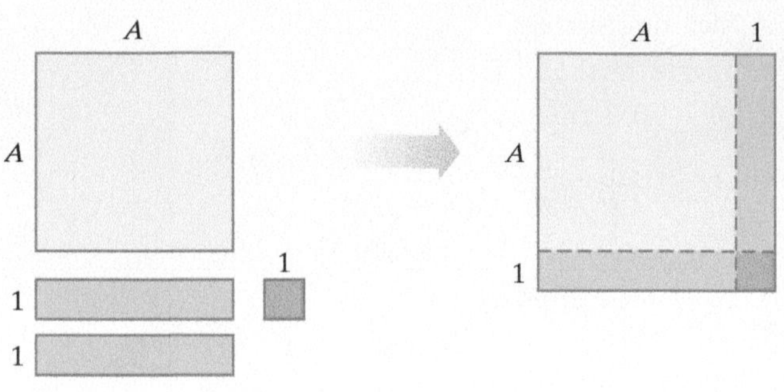

5 *In Exercises 49–81, factor completely, or state that the polynomial is prime.*

49. $x^3 - 8x^2 + 7x$

50. $10y^2 + 9y + 2$

51. $128 - 2y^2$

52. $9x^2 + 6x + 1$

53. $-20x^7 + 36x^3$

54. $x^3 - 3x^2 - 9x + 27$

55. $y^2 + 16$

56. $2x^3 + 19x^2 + 35x$

57. $3x^3 - 30x^2 + 75x$

58. $3x^5 - 24x^2$

59. $4y^4 - 36y^2$

60. $5x^2 + 20x - 105$

61. $9x^2 + 8x - 3$

62. $-10x^5 + 44x^4 - 16x^3$

63. $100y^2 - 49$

64. $9x^5 - 18x^4$

65. $x^4 - 1$

66. $2y^3 - 16$

67. $x^3 + 64$

68. $6x^2 + 11x - 10$

69. $3x^4 - 12x^2$

70. $x^2 - x - 90$

71. $25x^2 + 25xy + 6y^2$

72. $x^4 + 125x$

73. $32y^3 + 32y^2 + 6y$

74. $-2y^2 + 16y - 32$

75. $x^2 - 2xy - 35y^2$

76. $x^2 + 7x + xy + 7y$

77. $9x^2 + 24xy + 16y^2$

78. $2x^4y - 2x^2y$

79. $100y^2 - 49z^2$

80. $x^2 + xy + y^2$

81. $3x^4y^2 - 12x^2y^4$

6 *In Exercises 82–83, solve each equation using the zero-product principle.*

82. $x(x - 12) = 0$

83. $3(x - 7)(4x + 9) = 0$

In Exercises 84–92, use factoring to solve each quadratic equation.

84. $x^2 + 5x - 14 = 0$

85. $5x^2 + 20x = 0$

86. $2x^2 + 15x = 8$

87. $x(x - 4) = 32$

88. $(x + 3)(x - 2) = 50$

89. $x^2 = 14x - 49$

90. $9x^2 = 100$

91. $3x^2 + 21x + 30 = 0$

92. $3x^2 = 22x - 7$

93. You dive from a board that is 32 feet above the water. The formula

$$h = -16t^2 + 16t + 32$$

describes your height above the water, h, in feet, t seconds after you dive. How long will it take you to hit the water?

94. The length of a rectangular sign is 3 feet longer than the width. If the sign has space for 40 square feet of advertising, find its length and its width.

95. The square lot shown here is being turned into a garden with a 3-meter path at one end. If the area of the garden is 88 square meters, find the dimensions of the square lot.

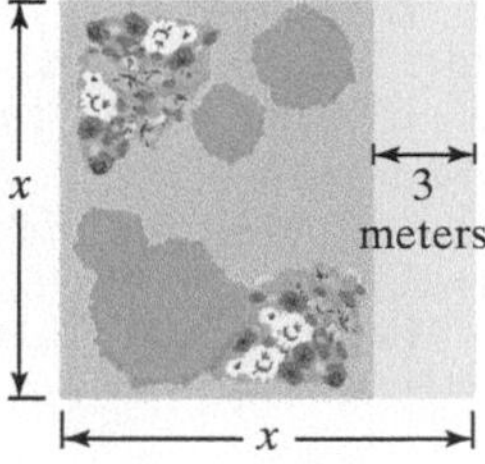

CHAPTER TEST

Step-by-step test solutions are found on the Chapter Test Prep Videos available in MyMathLab® or on YouTube® (search "BlitzerIntroAlg" and click on "Channels").

In Exercises 1–21, factor completely, or state that the polynomial is prime.

1. $x^2 - 9x + 18$

2. $x^2 - 14x + 49$

3. $15y^4 - 35y^3 + 10y^2$

4. $x^3 + 2x^2 + 3x + 6$

5. $x^2 - 9x$

6. $x^3 + 6x^2 - 7x$

7. $14x^2 + 64x - 30$

8. $25x^2 - 9$

9. $x^3 + 8$

10. $x^2 - 4x - 21$

11. $x^2 + 4$

12. $6y^3 + 9y^2 + 3y$

13. $4y^2 - 36$

14. $16x^2 + 48x + 36$

15. $2x^4 - 32$

16. $36x^2 - 84x + 49$

17. $7x^2 - 50x + 7$

18. $x^3 + 2x^2 - 5x - 10$

19. $-12y^3 + 12y^2 + 45y$

20. $y^3 - 125$

21. $5x^2 - 5xy - 30y^2$

In Exercises 22–27, solve each quadratic equation.

22. $x^2 + 2x - 24 = 0$

23. $3x^2 - 5x = 2$

24. $x(x - 6) = 16$

25. $6x^2 = 21x$

26. $16x^2 = 81$

27. $(5x + 4)(x - 1) = 2$

28. Find a formula for the area of the shaded blue region and express it in factored form.

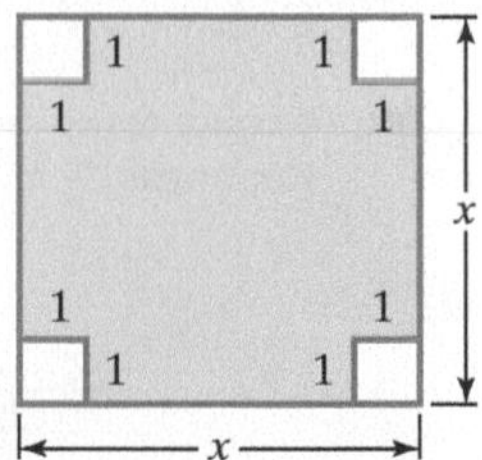

29. A model rocket is launched from a height of 96 feet. The formula

$$h = -16t^2 + 80t + 96$$

describes the rocket's height, h, in feet, t seconds after it was launched. How long will it take the rocket to reach the ground?

30. The length of a rectangular garden is 6 feet longer than its width. If the area of the garden is 55 square feet, find its length and its width.

Answers to Selected Exercises

Section 1 Check Point Exercises

1. a. $3x^2$ **b.** $4x^2$ **c.** x^2y **2.** $6(x^2 + 3)$ **3.** $5x^2(5 + 7x)$ **4.** $3x^3(5x^2 + 4x - 9)$ **5.** $2xy(4x^2y - 7x + 1)$ **6.** $-4ab^2(4a^3b^3 - 6a^2b^2 + 5)$ **7. a.** $(x + 1)(x^2 + 7)$ **b.** $(y + 4)(x - 7)$ **8.** $(x + 5)(x^2 + 2)$ **9.** $(y + 3)(x - 5)$

Concept and Vocabulary Check

1. factoring **2.** greatest common factor; smallest/least **3.** false **4.** false

Exercise Set 1

1. 4 **3.** $4x$ **5.** $2x^3$ **7.** $3y$ **9.** xy **11.** $4x^4y^3$ **13.** $8(x + 1)$ **15.** $4(y - 1)$ **17.** $5(x + 6)$ **19.** $6(5x - 2)$ **21.** $x(x + 5)$ **23.** $6(3y^2 + 2)$ **25.** $7x^2(2x + 3)$ **27.** $y(13y - 25)$ **29.** $9y^4(1 + 3y^2)$ **31.** $4x^2(2 - x^2)$ **33.** $4(3y^2 + 4y - 2)$ **35.** $3x^2(3x^2 + 6x + 2)$ **37.** $50y^2(2y^3 - y + 2)$ **39.** $5x(2 - 4x + x^2)$ **41.** cannot be factored **43.** $3xy(2x^2y + 3)$ **45.** $10xy(3xy^2 - y + 2)$ **47.** $8x^2y(4xy - 3x - 2)$ **49.** $-6(2x^2 - 3)$ **51.** $-8x^2(x^2 - 4x - 2)$ **53.** $-2ab(2a^2b - 3)$ **55.** $-6x^2y(2xy + 3x - 4)$ **57.** $(x + 5)(x + 3)$ **59.** $(x + 2)(x - 4)$ **61.** $(y + 6)(x - 7)$ **63.** $(x + y)(3x - 1)$ **65.** $(3x + 1)(4x + 1)$ **67.** $(5x + 4)(7x^2 + 1)$ **69.** $(x + 2)(x + 4)$ **71.** $(x - 5)(x + 3)$ **73.** $(x^2 + 5)(x - 2)$ **75.** $(x^2 + 2)(x - 1)$ **77.** $(y + 5)(x + 9)$ **79.** $(y - 1)(x + 5)$ **81.** $(x - 2y)(3x + 5y)$ **83.** $(3x - 2)(x^2 - 2)$ **85.** $(x - a)(x - b)$ **87.** $6x^2yz(4xy^2z^2 + 5y + 3z)$ **89.** $(x^3 - 4)(1 + 3y)$ **91.** $2x^2(x + 1)(2x^3 - 3x - 4)$ **93.** $(x - 1)(3x^4 + x^2 + 5)$ **95.** $36x^2 - 4\pi x^2$; $4x^2(9 - \pi)$ **97. a.** 48 ft **b.** $16x(4 - x)$ **c.** 48 ft; yes; no; Answers will vary. **99.** $x^3 - 2$ **107.** makes sense **109.** does not make sense **111.** false **113.** false **115.** $4(x + 150)$ **119.** $(x - 2)(x - 5)$ should be $(x - 2)(x + 5)$ **121.** $x^2 + 17x + 70$ **122.** $(-3, -2)$ or $\{(-3, -2)\}$ **123.** $y - 2 = 1(x + 7)$ or $y - 5 = 1(x + 4)$; $y = x + 9$ **124.** 2 and 4 **125.** -3 and -2 **126.** -5 and 7

Section 2 Check Point Exercises

1. $(x + 2)(x + 3)$ **2.** $(x - 2)(x - 4)$ **3.** $(x + 5)(x - 2)$ **4.** $(y - 9)(y + 3)$ **5.** cannot factor over the integers; prime **6.** $(x - 3y)(x - y)$ **7.** $2x(x - 4)(x + 7)$ **8.** $-2(y - 2)(y + 7)$

Concept and Vocabulary Check

1. $20; -12$ **2.** completely **3.** $+ 10$ **4.** $- 6$ **5.** $+ 5$ **6.** $- 7$ **7.** $- 2y$

Exercise Set 2

1. $(x + 6)(x + 1)$ **3.** $(x + 2)(x + 5)$ **5.** $(x + 1)(x + 10)$ **7.** $(x - 4)(x - 3)$ **9.** $(x - 6)(x - 6)$ **11.** $(y - 3)(y - 5)$ **13.** $(x + 5)(x - 2)$ **15.** $(y + 13)(y - 3)$ **17.** $(x - 5)(x + 3)$ **19.** $(x - 4)(x + 2)$ **21.** prime **23.** $(y - 4)(y - 12)$ **25.** prime **27.** $(w - 32)(w + 2)$ **29.** $(y - 5)(y - 13)$ **31.** $(r + 3)(r + 9)$ **33.** prime **35.** $(x + 6y)(x + y)$ **37.** $(x - 3y)(x - 5y)$ **39.** $(x - 6y)(x + 3y)$ **41.** $(a - 15b)(a - 3b)$ **43.** $3(x + 2)(x + 3)$ **45.** $4(y - 2)(y + 1)$ **47.** $10(x - 10)(x + 6)$ **49.** $3(x - 2)(x - 9)$ **51.** $2r(r + 2)(r + 1)$ **53.** $4x(x + 6)(x - 3)$ **55.** $2r(r + 8)(r - 4)$ **57.** $y^2(y + 10)(y - 8)$ **59.** $x^2(x - 5)(x + 2)$ **61.** $2w^2(w - 16)(w + 3)$ **63.** $15x(y - 1)(y + 4)$ **65.** $x^3(x - y)(x + 4y)$ **67.** $-16(t - 5)(t + 1)$ **69.** $-5(x - 9)(x - 1)$ **71.** $-(x + 8)(x - 5)$ **73.** $-2x(x + 4)(x - 1)$ **75.** $2x^2(y - 15z)(y - z)$ **77.** $(a + b)(x + 5)(x - 4)$ **79.** $(x + 0.3)(x + 0.2)$ **81.** $\left(x - \frac{1}{5}\right)\left(x - \frac{1}{5}\right)$ **83. a.** $-16(t - 2)(t + 1)$ **b.** 0; yes; After 2 seconds, you hit the water. **89.** does not make sense **91.** does not make sense **93.** false **95.** true **97.** 8, 16 **101.** $x(x + 1)(x + 2)$; the product of three consecutive integers **103.** correctly factored **105.** $(x + 1)(x - 1)$ should be $(x - 1)(x - 1)$. **107.** 13 or $\{13\}$

108.

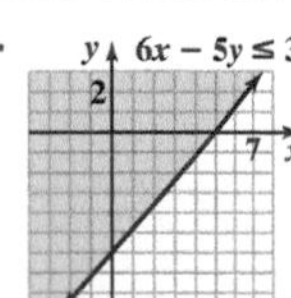

109.

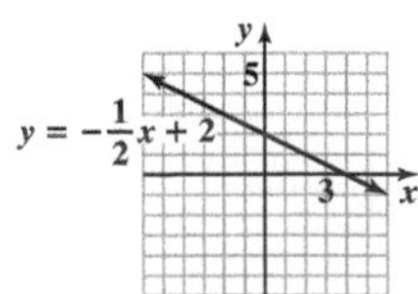

110. $2x^2 - x - 6$ **111.** $9x^2 + 15x + 4$ **112.** $(4x - 1)(2x - 5)$

Section 3 Check Point Exercises

1. $(5x - 4)(x - 2)$ **2.** $(3x - 1)(2x + 7)$ **3.** $(3x - y)(x - 4y)$ **4.** $(3x + 5)(x - 2)$ **5.** $(2x - 1)(4x - 3)$ **6.** $y^2(5y + 3)(y + 2)$

Concept and Vocabulary Check

1. greatest common factor **2.** $- 3$ **3.** $- 4$ **4.** $2x - 3$ **5.** $3x + 4$ **6.** $x - 2y$

Exercise Set 3

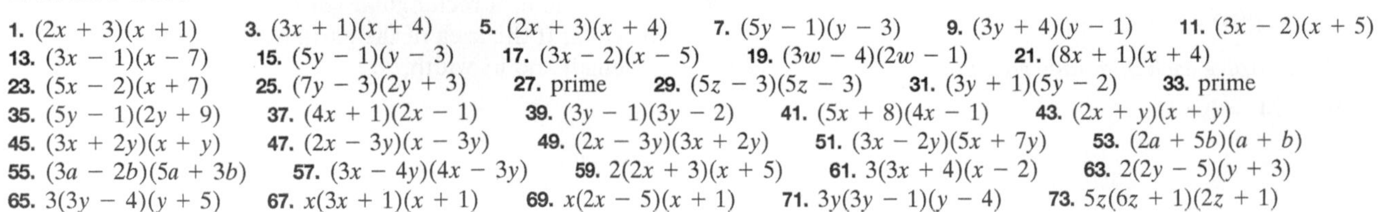

1. $(2x + 3)(x + 1)$ **3.** $(3x + 1)(x + 4)$ **5.** $(2x + 3)(x + 4)$ **7.** $(5y - 1)(y - 3)$ **9.** $(3y + 4)(y - 1)$ **11.** $(3x - 2)(x + 5)$ **13.** $(3x - 1)(x - 7)$ **15.** $(5y - 1)(y - 3)$ **17.** $(3x - 2)(x - 5)$ **19.** $(3w - 4)(2w - 1)$ **21.** $(8x + 1)(x + 4)$ **23.** $(5x - 2)(x + 7)$ **25.** $(7y - 3)(2y + 3)$ **27.** prime **29.** $(5z - 3)(5z - 3)$ **31.** $(3y + 1)(5y - 2)$ **33.** prime **35.** $(5y - 1)(2y + 9)$ **37.** $(4x + 1)(2x - 1)$ **39.** $(3y - 1)(3y - 2)$ **41.** $(5x + 8)(4x - 1)$ **43.** $(2x + y)(x + y)$ **45.** $(3x + 2y)(x + y)$ **47.** $(2x - 3y)(x - 3y)$ **49.** $(2x - 3y)(3x + 2y)$ **51.** $(3x - 2y)(5x + 7y)$ **53.** $(2a + 5b)(a + b)$ **55.** $(3a - 2b)(5a + 3b)$ **57.** $(3x - 4y)(4x - 3y)$ **59.** $2(2x + 3)(x + 5)$ **61.** $3(3x + 4)(x - 2)$ **63.** $2(2y - 5)(y + 3)$ **65.** $3(3y - 4)(y + 5)$ **67.** $x(3x + 1)(x + 1)$ **69.** $x(2x - 5)(x + 1)$ **71.** $3y(3y - 1)(y - 4)$ **73.** $5z(6z + 1)(2z + 1)$

75. $3x^2(5x - 3)(x - 2)$ **77.** $x^3(2x - 3)(5x - 1)$ **79.** $3(2x + 3y)(x - 2y)$ **81.** $2(2x - y)(3x + 4y)$ **83.** $2y(4x - 7)(x + 6)$
85. $2b(2a - 7b)(3a - b)$ **87.** $-4y^4(8x + 3)(x - 1)$ **89.** $10(y + 1)(x + 1)(3x - 2)$ **91. a.** $(2x + 1)(x - 3)$ **b.** $(2y + 3)(y - 2)$
93. $(x - 2)(3x - 2)(x - 1)$ **95. a.** $x^2 + 3x + 2$ **b.** $(x + 2)(x + 1)$ **c.** $x^2 + 3x + 2 = (x + 2)(x + 1)$ **101.** makes sense
103. does not make sense **105.** true **107.** false **109.** $5, 7, -5, -7$ **111.** $(3x^5 + 5)(x^5 - 3)$ **113.** $(25, -5)$ or $\{(25, -5)\}$
114. 8.6×10^{-4} **115.** -1 or $\{-1\}$ **116.** $81x^2 - 100$ **117.** $16x^2 + 40xy + 25y^2$ **118.** $x^3 + 8$

Mid-Chapter Check Point Exercises

1. $x^4(x + 1)$ **2.** $(x + 9)(x - 2)$ **3.** $x^2y(y^2 - y + 1)$ **4.** prime **5.** $(7x - 1)(x - 3)$ **6.** $(x^2 + 3)(x + 5)$ **7.** $x(2x - 1)(x - 5)$
8. $(x - 4)(y - 7)$ **9.** $(x - 15y)(x - 2y)$ **10.** $(5x + 2)(5x - 7)$ **11.** $2(8x - 3)(x - 4)$ **12.** $(3x + 7y)(x + y)$ **13.** $-2x(3x + 5)(x - 3)$

Section 4 Check Point Exercises

1. a. $(x + 9)(x - 9)$ **b.** $(6x + 5)(6x - 5)$ **2. a.** $(5 + 2x^5)(5 - 2x^5)$ **b.** $(10x + 3y)(10x - 3y)$ **3. a.** $2x(3x + 1)(3x - 1)$
b. $18(2 + x)(2 - x)$ or $-18(x + 2)(x - 2)$ **4.** $(9x^2 + 4)(3x + 2)(3x - 2)$ **5. a.** $(x + 7)^2$ **b.** $(x - 3)^2$ **c.** $(4x - 7)^2$ **6.** $(2x + 3y)^2$
7. $(x + 3)(x^2 - 3x + 9)$ **8.** $(1 - y)(1 + y + y^2)$ **9.** $(5x + 2)(25x^2 - 10x + 4)$

Concept and Vocabulary Check

1. $(A + B)(A - B)$ **2.** $(A + B)^2$ **3.** $(A - B)^2$ **4.** $(A + B)(A^2 - AB + B^2)$ **5.** $(A - B)(A^2 + AB + B^2)$
6. $6x$; $6x$ **7.** -6 **8.** $4x$ **9.** $+2$ **10.** -3; $+9$ **11.** false **12.** true **13.** false **14.** true **15.** false

Exercise Set 4

1. $(x + 5)(x - 5)$ **3.** $(y + 1)(y - 1)$ **5.** $(2x + 3)(2x - 3)$ **7.** $(5 + x)(5 - x)$ **9.** $(1 + 7x)(1 - 7x)$ **11.** $(3 + 5y)(3 - 5y)$
13. $(x^2 + 3)(x^2 - 3)$ **15.** $(7y^2 + 4)(7y^2 - 4)$ **17.** $(x^5 + 3)(x^5 - 3)$ **19.** $(5x + 4y)(5x - 4y)$ **21.** $(x^2 + y^5)(x^2 - y^5)$
23. $(x^2 + 4)(x + 2)(x - 2)$ **25.** $(4x^2 + 9)(2x + 3)(2x - 3)$ **27.** $2(x + 3)(x - 3)$ **29.** $2x(x + 6)(x - 6)$ **31.** prime **33.** $3x(x^2 + 9)$
35. $2(3 + y)(3 - y)$ **37.** $3y(y + 4)(y - 4)$ **39.** $2x(3x + 1)(3x - 1)$ **41.** $-3(x + 5)(x - 5)$ **43.** $-5y(y + 2)(y - 2)$
45. $(x + 1)^2$ **47.** $(x - 7)^2$ **49.** $(x - 1)^2$ **51.** $(x + 11)^2$ **53.** $(2x + 1)^2$ **55.** $(5y - 1)^2$ **57.** prime **59.** $(x + 7y)^2$ **61.** $(x - 6y)^2$
63. prime **65.** $(4x - 5y)^2$ **67.** $3(2x - 1)^2$ **69.** $x(3x + 1)^2$ **71.** $2(y - 1)^2$ **73.** $2y(y + 7)^2$ **75.** $-6(x - 2)^2$ **77.** $-4y(2y + 1)^2$
79. $(x + 1)(x^2 - x + 1)$ **81.** $(x - 3)(x^2 + 3x + 9)$ **83.** $(2y - 1)(4y^2 + 2y + 1)$ **85.** $(3x + 2)(9x^2 - 6x + 4)$
87. $(xy - 4)(x^2y^2 + 4xy + 16)$ **89.** $y(3y + 2)(9y^2 - 6y + 4)$ **91.** $2(3 - 2y)(9 + 6y + 4y^2)$ **93.** $(4x + 3y)(16x^2 - 12xy + 9y^2)$
95. $(5x - 4y)(25x^2 + 20xy + 16y^2)$ **97.** $\left(5x + \frac{2}{7}\right)\left(5x - \frac{2}{7}\right)$ **99.** $y\left(y - \frac{1}{10}\right)\left(y^2 + \frac{y}{10} + \frac{1}{100}\right)$ **101.** $x(0.5 + x)(0.5 - x)$
103. $(x + 6)(x - 4)$ **105.** $(x - 3)(x + 1)^2$ **107.** $x^2 - 25 = (x + 5)(x - 5)$ **109.** $x^2 - 16 = (x + 4)(x - 4)$
115. does not make sense **117.** does not make sense **119.** false **121.** false **123.** $a - b = 0$ and division by 0 is not permitted.
125. $(x^n + 5y^n)(x^n - 5y^n)$ **127.** $[(x + 3) - 1]^2$ or $(x + 2)^2$ **129.** 1 **131.** correctly factored
133. $(x - 1)(x^2 - x + 1)$ should be $(x - 1)(x^2 + x + 1)$. **134.** $80x^9y^{14}$ **135.** $-4x^2 + 3$
136. $2x + 5$ **137.** $3x(x + 5)(x - 5)$ **138.** $2(x - 5)^2$ **139.** $(x - 2)(x + 1)(x - 1)$

Section 5 Check Point Exercises

1. $5x^2(x + 3)(x - 3)$ **2.** $4(x - 6)(x + 2)$ **3.** $4x(x^2 + 4)(x + 2)(x - 2)$ **4.** $(x - 4)(x + 3)(x - 3)$ **5.** $3x(x - 5)^2$
6. $2x^2(x + 3)(x^2 - 3x + 9)$ **7.** $3y(x^2 + 4y^2)(x + 2y)(x - 2y)$ **8.** $3x(2x + 3y)^2$

Concept and Vocabulary Check

1. b **2.** e **3.** h **4.** c **5.** d **6.** f **7.** a **8.** g

Exercise Set 5

1. $-7x(x - 5)$ **3.** $(5x + 7)(5x - 7)$ **5.** $(3x - 1)(9x^2 + 3x + 1)$ **7.** $(5 + x)(x + y)$ **9.** $(7x - 1)(2x - 1)$ **11.** $(x - 1)^2$
13. $(3xy + 2)(9x^2y^2 - 6xy + 4)$ **15.** $(3x + 5)(2x - 3)$ **17.** $5x(x + 2)(x - 2)$ **19.** $7x(x^2 + 1)$ **21.** $5(x - 3)(x + 2)$
23. $2(x^2 + 9)(x + 3)(x - 3)$ **25.** $(x + 2)(x + 3)(x - 3)$ **27.** $3x(x - 4)^2$ **29.** $2x^2(x + 1)(x^2 - x + 1)$ **31.** $2x(3x + 4)$
33. $-2(y - 8)(y + 7)$ **35.** $7y^2(y + 1)^2$ **37.** prime **39.** $2(4y + 1)(2y - 1)$ **41.** $r(r - 25)$ **43.** $(2w + 5)(2w - 1)$
45. $x(x + 2)(x - 2)$ **47.** prime **49.** $(9y + 4)(y + 1)$ **51.** $(y + 2)(y + 2)(y - 2)$ **53.** $(4y + 3)^2$ **55.** $-4y(y - 5)(y - 2)$
57. $y(y^2 + 9)(y + 3)(y - 3)$ **59.** $5a^2(2a + 3)(2a - 3)$ **61.** $3x^2(3x^2 + 6x + 2)$ **63.** $(4y - 1)(3y - 2)$ **65.** $(3y + 8)(3y - 8)$ **67.** prime
69. $(2y + 3)(y + 5)(y - 5)$ **71.** $2r(r + 17)(r - 2)$ **73.** $2x^3(2x + 1)(2x - 1)$ **75.** $3(x^2 + 81)$ **77.** $x(x + 2)(x^2 - 2x + 4)$
79. $2y^2(y - 1)(y^2 + y + 1)$ **81.** $2x(3x + 4y)$ **83.** $(y - 7)(x + 3)$ **85.** $(x - 4y)(x + y)$ **87.** $12a^2(6ab^2 + 1 - 2a^2b^2)$
89. $3(a + 6b)(a + 3b)$ **91.** $3x^2y(4x + 1)(4x - 1)$ **93.** $b(3a + 2)(2a - 1)$ **95.** $7xy(x^2 + y^2)(x + y)(x - y)$ **97.** $2xy(5x - 2y)(x - y)$
99. $2b(x + 11)^2$ **101.** $(5a + 7b)(3a - 2b)$ **103.** $-2xy(9x - 2y)(2x - 3y)$ **105.** $(y - x)(a + b)(a - b)$ **107.** $ax(3x + 7)(3x - 2)$
109. $2x^2(x^2 + 3xy + y^2)$ **111.** $y(9x^2 + y^2)(3x + y)(3x - y)$ **113.** $(x + 1)(5x - 6)(2x + 1)$ **115.** $(x^2 + 6)(6x^2 - 1)$
117. $(x - 7 + 2a)(x - 7 - 2a)$ **119.** $(x + 4 + 5a)(x + 4 - 5a)$ **121.** $y(y^2 + 1)(y^4 - y^2 + 1)$ **123.** $16(4 + t)(4 - t)$
125. $\pi b^2 - \pi a^2$; $\pi(b + a)(b - a)$ **129.** makes sense **131.** makes sense **133.** false **135.** false **137.** $3x(x^2 + 2)(x + 3)(x - 3)$
139. $(4x^2 - 5)(x + 1)(x - 1)$ **141.** $3(x^n + 3y^n)(x^n - 3y^n)$ **143.** $3x(x + 5)(x - 1)$ should be $3x(x - 5)(x + 1)$.
145. correctly factored **147.** $(3x + 4)(3x - 4)$ **148.** $5x - 2y = 10$ (2, 0) (0, −5) **149.** 20°, 60°, 100° **150.** 0 **151.** 0 **152.** $(x + 4)(x - 3)$

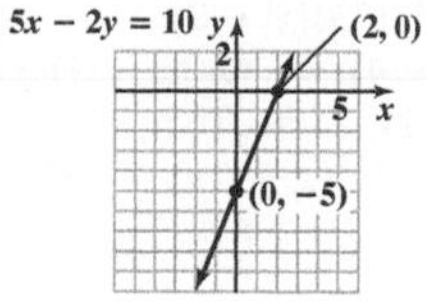

Section 6 Check Point Exercises

1. $-\frac{1}{2}$ and 4, or $\left\{-\frac{1}{2}, 4\right\}$ **2.** 1 and 5, or $\{1, 5\}$ **3.** 0 and $\frac{1}{2}$, or $\left\{0, \frac{1}{2}\right\}$ **4.** 5 or $\{5\}$ **5.** $-\frac{5}{4}$ and $\frac{5}{4}$, or $\left\{-\frac{5}{4}, \frac{5}{4}\right\}$ **6.** -2 and 9, or $\{-2, 9\}$
7. 1 sec and 2 sec; (1, 192) and (2, 192) **8.** length: 9ft; width: 6ft

Concept and Vocabulary Check

1. quadratic equation **2.** $A = 0$ or $B = 0$ **3.** x-intercepts **4.** subtracting 5x **5.** subtracting 30x; adding 25

Exercise Set 6

1. -7 and 0, or $\{-7, 0\}$ **3.** -4 and 6, or $\{-4, 6\}$ **5.** $-\frac{4}{5}$ and 9, or $\left\{-\frac{4}{5}, 9\right\}$ **7.** $-\frac{9}{2}$ and 4, or $\left\{-\frac{9}{2}, 4\right\}$ **9.** -5 and -3, or $\{-5, -3\}$
11. -3 and 5, or $\{-3, 5\}$ **13.** -3 and 7, or $\{-3, 7\}$ **15.** -8 and -1, or $\{-8, -1\}$ **17.** -4 and 0, or $\{-4, 0\}$ **19.** 0 and 5, or $\{0, 5\}$
21. 0 and 4, or $\{0, 4\}$ **23.** 0 and $\frac{5}{2}$, or $\left\{0, \frac{5}{2}\right\}$ **25.** $-\frac{5}{3}$ and 0, or $\left\{-\frac{5}{3}, 0\right\}$ **27.** -2 or $\{-2\}$ **29.** 6 or $\{6\}$ **31.** $\frac{3}{2}$ or $\left\{\frac{3}{2}\right\}$
33. $-\frac{1}{2}$ and 4, or $\left\{-\frac{1}{2}, 4\right\}$ **35.** -2 and $\frac{9}{5}$, or $\left\{-2, \frac{9}{5}\right\}$ **37.** -7 and 7, or $\{-7, 7\}$ **39.** $-\frac{5}{2}$ and $\frac{5}{2}$, or $\left\{-\frac{5}{2}, \frac{5}{2}\right\}$ **41.** $-\frac{5}{9}$ and $\frac{5}{9}$, or $\left\{-\frac{5}{9}, \frac{5}{9}\right\}$
43. -3 and 7, or $\{-3, 7\}$ **45.** $-\frac{5}{2}$ and $\frac{3}{2}$, or $\left\{-\frac{5}{2}, \frac{3}{2}\right\}$ **47.** -6 and 3, or $\{-6, 3\}$ **49.** -2 and $-\frac{3}{2}$, or $\left\{-2, -\frac{3}{2}\right\}$ **51.** 4 or $\{4\}$
53. $-\frac{5}{2}$ or $\left\{-\frac{5}{2}\right\}$ **55.** $\frac{3}{8}$ or $\left\{\frac{3}{8}\right\}$ **57.** $-3, -2$, and 4, or $\{-3, -2, 4\}$ **59.** -6, 0, and 6, or $\{-6, 0, 6\}$ **61.** $-2, -1$, and 0, or $\{-2, -1, 0\}$
63. 2 and 8, or $\{2, 8\}$ **65.** 4 and 5, or $\{4, 5\}$ **67.** 5 sec; Each tick represents one second. **69.** 2 sec; (2, 276) **71.** $\frac{1}{2}$ sec and 4 sec
73. 2002 and 2004 **75.** (2, 66) and (4, 66) **77.** 10 yr **79.** (10, 7250) **81.** 10 teams **83.** length: 15 yd; width: 12 yd
85. base: 5 cm; height: 6 cm **87. a.** $4x^2 + 44x$ **b.** 3 ft **91.** does not make sense **93.** makes sense **95.** false **97.** false
99. $x^2 - 2x - 15 = 0$ **101.** 4 and 5, or $\{4, 5\}$ **103.** c **105.** d **107.** -4 and 1, or $\{-4, 1\}$ **109.** -4 and 3, or $\{-4, 3\}$

113. $y > -\frac{2}{3}x + 1$ **114.** $\frac{4}{x^6}$ **115.** -2 or $\{-2\}$ **116.** 375 **117.** When x is replaced with 4, the denominator is 0.
118. $\frac{(x + 5)(x + 1)}{(x + 5)(x - 5)}; \frac{x + 1}{x - 5}$

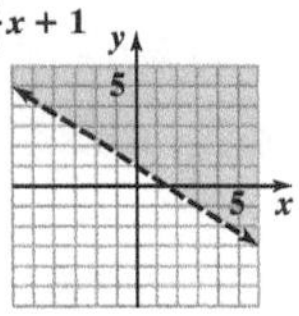

Review Exercises

1. $15(2x - 3)$ **2.** $-4x(3x^2 + 4x - 100)$ **3.** $5x^2y(6x^2 + 3x + 1)$ **4.** $5(x + 3)$ **5.** $(7x^2 - 1)(x + y)$ **6.** $(x^2 + 2)(x + 3)$
7. $(x + 1)(y + 4)$ **8.** $(x^2 + 5)(x + 1)$ **9.** $(x - 2)(y + 4)$ **10.** $(x - 2)(x - 1)$ **11.** $(x - 5)(x + 4)$ **12.** $(x + 3)(x + 16)$
13. $(x - 4y)(x - 2y)$ **14.** prime **15.** $(x + 17y)(x - y)$ **16.** $3(x + 4)(x - 2)$ **17.** $3x(x - 11)(x - 1)$ **18.** $(x + 5)(3x + 2)$
19. $(y - 3)(5y - 2)$ **20.** $(2x + 5)(2x - 3)$ **21.** prime **22.** $-2(2x + 3)(2x - 1)$ **23.** $x(2x - 9)(x + 8)$ **24.** $4y(3y + 1)(y + 2)$
25. $(2x - y)(x - 3y)$ **26.** $(5x + 4y)(x - 2y)$ **27.** $(2x + 1)(2x - 1)$ **28.** $(9 + 10y)(9 - 10y)$ **29.** $(5a + 7b)(5a - 7b)$
30. $(z^2 + 4)(z + 2)(z - 2)$ **31.** $2(x + 3)(x - 3)$ **32.** prime **33.** $x(3x + 1)(3x - 1)$ **34.** $2x(3y + 2)(3y - 2)$ **35.** $(x + 11)^2$
36. $(x - 8)^2$ **37.** $(3y + 8)^2$ **38.** $(4x - 5)^2$ **39.** prime **40.** $(6x + 5y)^2$ **41.** $(5x - 4y)^2$ **42.** $(x - 3)(x^2 + 3x + 9)$
43. $(4x + 1)(16x^2 - 4x + 1)$ **44.** $2(3x - 2y)(9x^2 + 6xy + 4y^2)$ **45.** $y(3x + 2)(9x^2 - 6x + 4)$ **46.** $(a + 3)(a - 3)$
47. $(a + 2b)(a - 2b)$ **48.** $A^2 + 2A + 1 = (A + 1)^2$ **49.** $x(x - 7)(x - 1)$ **50.** $(5y + 2)(2y + 1)$ **51.** $2(8 + y)(8 - y)$
52. $(3x + 1)^2$ **53.** $-4x^3(5x^4 - 9)$ **54.** $(x - 3)^2(x + 3)$ **55.** prime **56.** $x(2x + 5)(x + 7)$ **57.** $3x(x - 5)^2$
58. $3x^2(x - 2)(x^2 + 2x + 4)$ **59.** $4y^2(y + 3)(y - 3)$ **60.** $5(x + 7)(x - 3)$ **61.** prime **62.** $-2x^3(5x - 2)(x - 4)$
63. $(10y + 7)(10y - 7)$ **64.** $9x^4(x - 2)$ **65.** $(x^2 + 1)(x + 1)(x - 1)$ **66.** $2(y - 2)(y^2 + 2y + 4)$ **67.** $(x + 4)(x^2 - 4x + 16)$
68. $(3x - 2)(2x + 5)$ **69.** $3x^2(x + 2)(x - 2)$ **70.** $(x - 10)(x + 9)$ **71.** $(5x + 2y)(5x + 3y)$ **72.** $x(x + 5)(x^2 - 5x + 25)$
73. $2y(4y + 3)(4y + 1)$ **74.** $-2(y - 4)^2$ **75.** $(x + 5y)(x - 7y)$ **76.** $(x + y)(x + 7)$ **77.** $(3x + 4y)^2$ **78.** $2x^2y(x + 1)(x - 1)$
79. $(10y + 7z)(10y - 7z)$ **80.** prime **81.** $3x^2y^2(x + 2y)(x - 2y)$ **82.** 0 and 12, or $\{0, 12\}$ **83.** $-\frac{9}{4}$ and 7, or $\left\{-\frac{9}{4}, 7\right\}$
84. -7 and 2, or $\{-7, 2\}$ **85.** -4 and 0, or $\{-4, 0\}$ **86.** -8 and $\frac{1}{2}$, or $\left\{-8, \frac{1}{2}\right\}$ **87.** -4 and 8, or $\{-4, 8\}$ **88.** -8 and 7, or $\{-8, 7\}$
89. 7 or $\{7\}$ **90.** $-\frac{10}{3}$ and $\frac{10}{3}$, or $\left\{-\frac{10}{3}, \frac{10}{3}\right\}$ **91.** -5 and -2, or $\{-5, -2\}$ **92.** $\frac{1}{3}$ and 7, or $\left\{\frac{1}{3}, 7\right\}$
93. 2 sec **94.** width: 5 ft; length: 8 ft **95.** 11 m by 11 m

Chapter Test

1. $(x - 3)(x - 6)$ **2.** $(x - 7)^2$ **3.** $5y^2(3y - 1)(y - 2)$ **4.** $(x^2 + 3)(x + 2)$ **5.** $x(x - 9)$ **6.** $x(x + 7)(x - 1)$
7. $2(7x - 3)(x + 5)$ **8.** $(5x + 3)(5x - 3)$ **9.** $(x + 2)(x^2 - 2x + 4)$ **10.** $(x + 3)(x - 7)$ **11.** prime **12.** $3y(2y + 1)(y + 1)$
13. $4(y + 3)(y - 3)$ **14.** $4(2x + 3)^2$ **15.** $2(x^2 + 4)(x + 2)(x - 2)$ **16.** $(6x - 7)^2$ **17.** $(7x - 1)(x - 7)$ **18.** $(x^2 - 5)(x + 2)$
19. $-3y(2y + 3)(2y - 5)$ **20.** $(y - 5)(y^2 + 5y + 25)$ **21.** $5(x - 3y)(x + 2y)$ **22.** -6 and 4, or $\{-6, 4\}$
23. $-\frac{1}{3}$ and 2, or $\left\{-\frac{1}{3}, 2\right\}$ **24.** -2 and 8, or $\{-2, 8\}$ **25.** 0 and $\frac{7}{2}$, or $\left\{0, \frac{7}{2}\right\}$ **26.** $-\frac{9}{4}$ and $\frac{9}{4}$, or $\left\{-\frac{9}{4}, \frac{9}{4}\right\}$
27. -1 and $\frac{6}{5}$, or $\left\{-1, \frac{6}{5}\right\}$ **28.** $x^2 - 4 = (x + 2)(x - 2)$ **29.** 6 sec **30.** width: 5 ft; length: 11 ft

Quadratic Equations and Introduction to Functions

America is a nation of immigrants. Since 1820, more than 40 million people have immigrated to the United States from all over the world. They chose to come for various reasons, such as to live in freedom, to practice religion without persecution, to escape poverty or oppression, and to make better lives for themselves and their children. As a result, in 2008, 12.5% of the United States population was foreign-born. How can we use mathematical models to project when this percentage might grow to one in every five Americans, or even more?

MistikaS/iStockphoto

In this chapter, you will learn techniques for solving quadratic equations,

$$ax^2 + bx + c = 0,$$

that will give you new ways of exploring mathematical models. The United States foreign-born model appears as Example 3 in Section 3.

Mark Harmel FAP/Alamy

SECTION 1

Solving Quadratic Equations by the Square Root Property

Objectives

1. Solve quadratic equations using the square root property.
2. Solve problems using the Pythagorean Theorem.
3. Find the distance between two points.

School of Athens (Detail) (1511), Rapahel. Stanza della Segnatura, Vatican Palace/Scala/Art Resource, New York

Shown here is Renaissance artist Raphael Sanzio's (1483–1520) image of Pythagoras from The School of Athens *mural. Detail of left side.*

Raphael (1483–1520) "School of Athens" detail of left side. Stanza della Segnatura, Vatican Palace, Vatican State. Scala/Art

For the followers of the Greek mathematician Pythagoras in the sixth century B.C., numbers took on a life-and-death importance. The "Pythagorean Brotherhood" was a secret group whose members were convinced that properties of whole numbers were the key to understanding the universe. Members of the Brotherhood (which admitted women) thought that all numbers that were not whole numbers could be represented as the ratio of whole numbers. A crisis occurred for the Pythagoreans when they discovered the existence of a number that was not rational. Because the Pythagoreans viewed numbers with reverence and awe, the punishment for speaking about this irrational number was death. However, a member of the Brotherhood revealed the secret of the irrational number's existence. When he later died in a shipwreck, his death was viewed as punishment from the gods.

In this section, you will work with the triangle that led the Pythagoreans to the discovery of irrational numbers. You will find the lengths of one of the triangle's sides using a property other than factoring that can be used to solve quadratic equations.

1 Solve quadratic equations using the square root property.

The Square Root Property

Let's begin with a relatively simple quadratic equation:

$$x^2 = 9.$$

The value of x must be a number whose square is 9. There are two numbers whose square is 9:

$$x = \sqrt{9} = 3 \quad \text{or} \quad x = -\sqrt{9} = -3.$$

Thus, the solutions of $x^2 = 9$ are 3 and -3. This is an example of the **square root property**.

The Square Root Property

If u is an algebraic expression and d is a positive real number, then $u^2 = d$ has exactly two solutions:

$$\text{If } u^2 = d, \quad \text{then } u = \sqrt{d} \text{ or } u = -\sqrt{d}.$$

Equivalently,

$$\text{If } u^2 = d, \quad \text{then } u = \pm\sqrt{d}.$$

Notice that $u = \pm\sqrt{d}$ is a shorthand notation to indicate that $u = \sqrt{d}$ or $u = -\sqrt{d}$. Although we usually read $u = \pm\sqrt{d}$ as "u equals plus or minus the square root of d," we actually mean that u is the positive square root of d or the negative square root of d.

EXAMPLE 1 Solving Quadratic Equations by the Square Root Property

Solve by the square root property:

a. $x^2 = 49$ **b.** $4x^2 = 20$ **c.** $2x^2 - 5 = 0$.

Solution

a.

$x^2 = 49$ — This is the original equation.

$x = \sqrt{49}$ or $x = -\sqrt{49}$ — Apply the square root property. You can also write $x = \pm\sqrt{49}$.

$x = 7$ or $x = -7$ — In abbreviated notation, $x = \pm 7$.

Substitute both values into the original equation and confirm that the solutions are 7 and -7. The solution set is $\{\pm 7\}$.

b. To apply the square root property, we need a squared expression by itself on one side of the equation.

$$4x^2 = 20$$

We want x^2 by itself.

We can get x^2 by itself if we divide both sides by 4.

$4x^2 = 20$ — This is the original equation.

$\frac{4x^2}{4} = \frac{20}{4}$ — Divide both sides by 4.

$x^2 = 5$ — Simplify.

$x = \sqrt{5}$ or $x = -\sqrt{5}$ — Apply the square root property.

Now let's check these proposed solutions in the original equation. Because the equation has an x^2-term and no x-term, we can check both values, $\pm\sqrt{5}$, at once.

Check $\sqrt{5}$ and $-\sqrt{5}$:

$4x^2 = 20$ — This is the original equation.

$4(\pm\sqrt{5})^2 \stackrel{?}{=} 20$ — Substitute the proposed solutions.

$4 \cdot 5 \stackrel{?}{=} 20$ — $(\pm\sqrt{5})^2 = 5$

$20 = 20,$ — true

The solutions are $-\sqrt{5}$ and $\sqrt{5}$. The solution set is $\{-\sqrt{5}, \sqrt{5}\}$ or $\{\pm\sqrt{5}\}$.

c. To solve $2x^2 - 5 = 0$ by the square root property, we must isolate the squared expression by itself on one side of the equation.

$$2x^2 - 5 = 0$$

We want x^2 by itself.

$$2x^2 - 5 = 0 \quad \text{This is the original equation.}$$

$$2x^2 = 5 \quad \text{Add 5 to both sides.}$$

$$x^2 = \frac{5}{2} \quad \text{Divide both sides by 2.}$$

$$x = \sqrt{\frac{5}{2}} \text{ or } x = -\sqrt{\frac{5}{2}} \quad \text{Apply the square root property.}$$

In this section, we will express irrational solutions in simplified radical form, rationalizing denominators when possible. Because the proposed solutions are opposites, we can rationalize both denominators at once:

$$\pm\sqrt{\frac{5}{2}} = \pm\frac{\sqrt{5}}{\sqrt{2}} = \pm\frac{\sqrt{5}}{\sqrt{2}}\cdot\frac{\sqrt{2}}{\sqrt{2}} = \pm\frac{\sqrt{10}}{2}.$$

Substitute these values into the original equation and verify that the solutions are $-\frac{\sqrt{10}}{2}$ and $\frac{\sqrt{10}}{2}$. The solution set is $\left\{-\frac{\sqrt{10}}{2}, \frac{\sqrt{10}}{2}\right\}$ or $\left\{\pm\frac{\sqrt{10}}{2}\right\}$. ■

✓ **CHECK POINT 1** Solve by the square root property:

a. $x^2 = 36$ **b.** $5x^2 = 15$

c. $2x^2 - 7 = 0$.

Can we solve an equation such as $(x - 5)^2 = 16$ using the square root property? Yes. The equation is in the form $u^2 = d$, where u^2, the squared expression, is by itself on the left side.

$$(x - 5)^2 = 16$$

This is u^2 in $u^2 = d$ with $u = x - 5$.

This is d in $u^2 = d$ with $d = 16$.

EXAMPLE 2 Solving a Quadratic Equation by the Square Root Property

Solve by the square root property: $(x - 5)^2 = 16$.

Solution

$$(x - 5)^2 = 16 \quad \text{This is the original equation.}$$

$$x - 5 = \sqrt{16} \text{ or } x - 5 = -\sqrt{16} \quad \text{Apply the square root property.}$$

$$x - 5 = 4 \text{ or } x - 5 = -4 \quad \text{Simplify.}$$

$$x = 9 \qquad x = 1 \quad \text{Add 5 to both sides in each equation.}$$

Substitute both values into the original equation and confirm that the solutions are 9 and 1. The solutions are visually confirmed in the Using Technology box on the next page. The solution set is $\{1, 9\}$. ■

Using Technology

Graphic Connections

We can use graphs to confirm that the solution set of $(x - 5)^2 = 16$ is $\{1, 9\}$.

The graph of $y = (x - 5)^2 - 16$ has x-intercepts at 1 and 9. The solutions of $(x - 5)^2 - 16 = 0$, or $(x - 5)^2 = 16$, are 1 and 9.

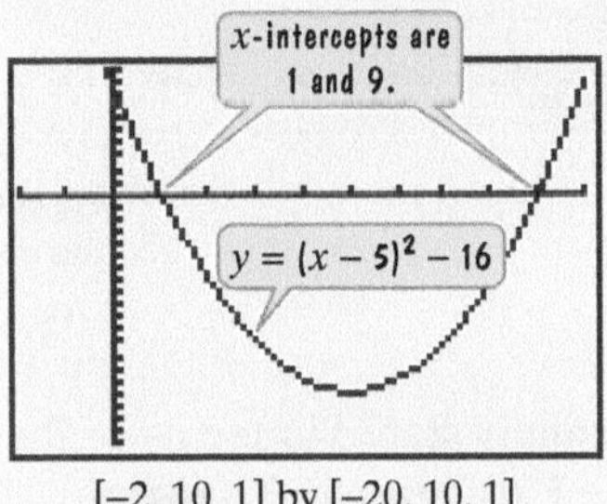

[−2, 10, 1] by [−20, 10, 1]

Another option is to graph each side of the equation and find the x-coordinates of the intersection points. Graphing

$$y_1 = (x - 5)^2$$

and

$$y_2 = 16,$$

the x-coordinates of the intersection points are 1 and 9.

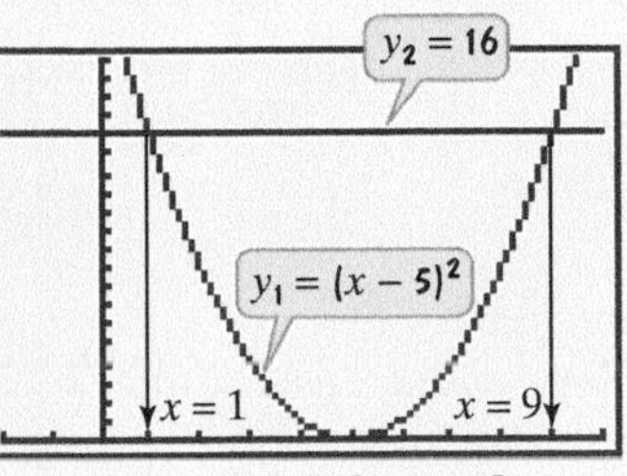

[−2, 10, 1] by [0, 20, 1]

✓ **CHECK POINT 2** Solve by the square root property: $(x - 3)^2 = 25$.

EXAMPLE 3 Solving a Quadratic Equation by the Square Root Property

Solve by the square root property: $(x - 1)^2 = 5$.

Solution

$$(x - 1)^2 = 5 \quad \text{This is the original equation.}$$

$$x - 1 = \sqrt{5} \quad \text{or} \quad x - 1 = -\sqrt{5} \quad \text{Apply the square root property.}$$

$$x = 1 + \sqrt{5} \qquad x = 1 - \sqrt{5} \quad \text{Add 1 to both sides in each equation.}$$

Check $1 + \sqrt{5}$:

$$(x - 1)^2 = 5$$
$$(1 + \sqrt{5} - 1)^2 \stackrel{?}{=} 5$$
$$(\sqrt{5})^2 \stackrel{?}{=} 5$$
$$5 = 5, \text{ true}$$

Check $1 - \sqrt{5}$:

$$(x - 1)^2 = 5$$
$$(1 - \sqrt{5} - 1)^2 \stackrel{?}{=} 5$$
$$(-\sqrt{5})^2 \stackrel{?}{=} 5$$
$$5 = 5, \text{ true}$$

The solutions are $1 + \sqrt{5}$ and $1 - \sqrt{5}$, expressed in abbreviated notation as $1 \pm \sqrt{5}$. The solution set is $\{1 \pm \sqrt{5}\}$. ■

✓ **CHECK POINT 3** Solve by the square root property: $(x - 2)^2 = 7$.

---

2 Solve problems using the Pythagorean Theorem.

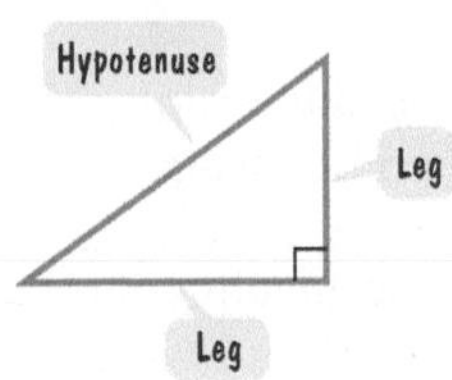

The Pythagorean Theorem and the Square Root Property

The ancient Greek philosopher and mathematician Pythagoras (approximately 582–500 B.C.) founded a school whose motto was "All is number." Pythagoras is best remembered for his work with the **right triangle**, a triangle with one angle measuring 90°. The side opposite the 90° angle is called the **hypotenuse**. The other sides are called **legs**.

Pythagoras found that if he constructed squares on each of the legs, as well as a larger square on the hypotenuse, the sum of the areas of the smaller squares is equal to the area of the larger square. This is illustrated in **Figure 1**.

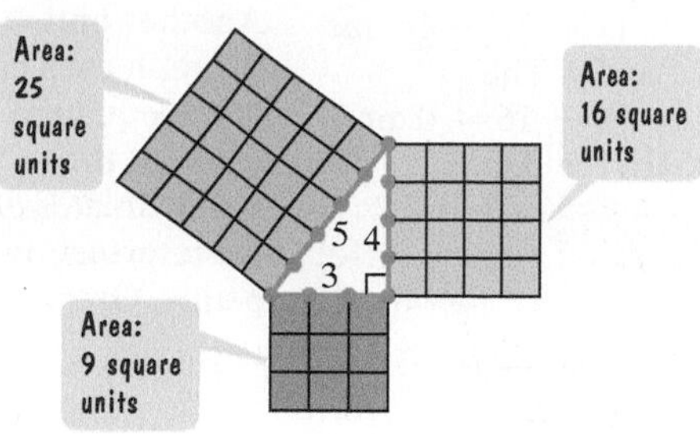

Figure 1 The area of the large square equals the sum of the areas of the smaller squares.

This relationship is usually stated in terms of the lengths of the three sides of a right triangle and is called the **Pythagorean Theorem**.

The Pythagorean Theorem

The sum of the squares of the lengths of the legs of a right triangle equals the square of the length of the hypotenuse.

If the legs have lengths a and b, and the hypotenuse has length c, then

$$a^2 + b^2 = c^2.$$

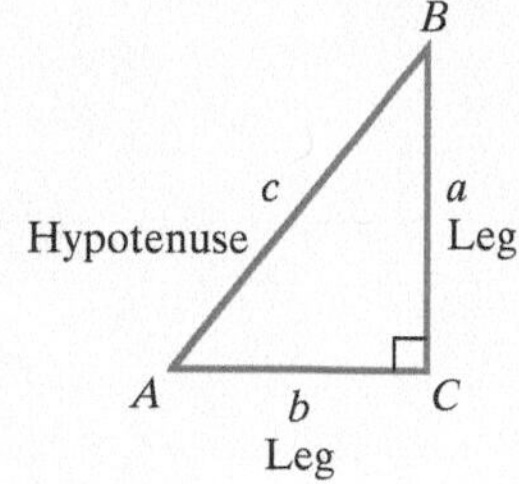

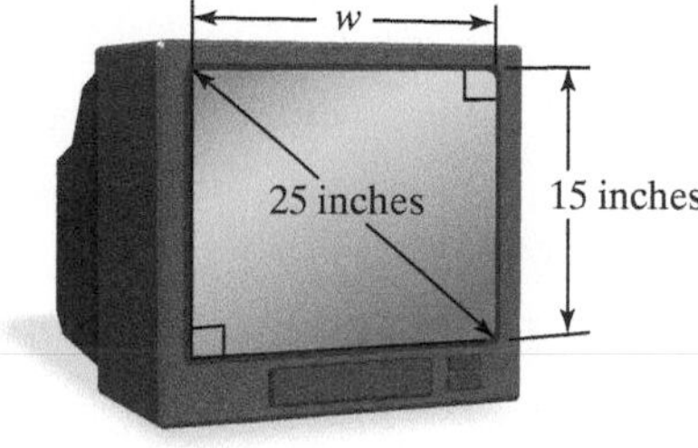

Figure 2 A right triangle is formed by the television screen's height, width, and diagonal.

EXAMPLE 4 Using the Pythagorean Theorem

In a 25-inch television set, the length of the screen's diagonal is 25 inches. If the screen's height is 15 inches, what is its width?

Solution **Figure 2** shows a right triangle that is formed by the height, width, and diagonal. We can find w, the screen's width, using the Pythagorean Theorem.

(leg)^2	plus	(leg)^2	equals	(hypotenuse)^2.
w^2	$+$	15^2	$=$	25^2

This is the equation resulting from the Pythagorean Theorem.

The equation $w^2 + 15^2 = 25^2$ can be solved by the square root property.

$w^2 + 15^2 = 25^2$ This is the equation that models the verbal conditions.

$w^2 + 225 = 625$ Square 15 and 25.

$w^2 = 400$ Isolate w^2 by subtracting 225 from both sides.

$w = \sqrt{400}$ or $w = -\sqrt{400}$ Apply the square root property.

$w = 20$ $\quad w = -20$ Simplify.

Because w represents the width of the television's screen, this dimension must be positive. We reject -20. Thus, the width of the television screen is 20 inches. ■

✓ CHECK POINT 4 What is the width of a rectangle whose height is 20 inches and whose diagonal measures 50 inches? Express the answer in simplified radical form. Then find an approximation correct to the nearest tenth of an inch.

3 Find the distance between two points.

The Distance Formula

Using the Pythagorean Theorem, we can find the distance between the two points $P_1(x_1, y_1)$ and $P_2(x_2, y_2)$ in the rectangular coordinate system. The two points are illustrated in **Figure 3**.

The distance that we need to find is represented by d and shown in blue. Notice that the distance between two points on the dashed horizontal line is the absolute value of the difference between the x-coordinates of the two points. This distance, $|x_2 - x_1|$, is shown in pink. Similarly, the distance between two points on the dashed vertical line is the absolute value of the difference between the y-coordinates of the two points. This distance, $|y_2 - y_1|$, is also shown in pink.

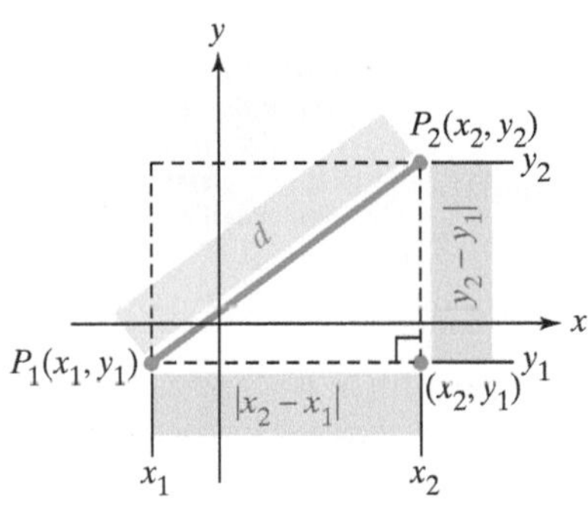

Figure 3

Because the dashed lines are horizontal and vertical, a right triangle is formed. Thus, we can use the Pythagorean Theorem to find the distance d. Squaring the lengths of the triangle's sides results in positive numbers, so absolute value notation is not necessary.

$$d^2 = (x_2 - x_1)^2 + (y_2 - y_1)^2$$ Apply the Pythagorean Theorem to the right triangle in Figure 3.

$$d = \pm\sqrt{(x_2 - x_1)^2 + (y_2 - y_1)^2}$$ Apply the square root property.

$$d = \sqrt{(x_2 - x_1)^2 + (y_2 - y_1)^2}$$ Because distance is nonnegative, write only the principal square root.

This result is called the **distance formula**.

The Distance Formula

The distance, d, between the points (x_1, y_1) and (x_2, y_2) in the rectangular coordinate system is

$$d = \sqrt{(x_2 - x_1)^2 + (y_2 - y_1)^2}.$$

To compute the distance between two points, find the square of the difference between the x-coordinates plus the square of the difference between the y-coordinates. The principal square root of this sum is the distance.

When using the distance formula, it does not matter which point you call (x_1, y_1) and which you call (x_2, y_2).

EXAMPLE 5 Using the Distance Formula

Find the distance between $(-4, -3)$ and $(6, 2)$.

Solution We will let $(x_1, y_1) = (-4, -3)$ and $(x_2, y_2) = (6, 2)$.

$$d = \sqrt{(x_2 - x_1)^2 + (y_2 - y_1)^2}$$ Use the distance formula.

$$= \sqrt{[6 - (-4)]^2 + [2 - (-3)]^2}$$ Substitute the given values.

$$= \sqrt{10^2 + 5^2}$$ Perform operations within grouping symbols: $6 - (-4) = 6 + 4 = 10$ and $2 - (-3) = 2 + 3 = 5$.

$$= \sqrt{100 + 25}$$ Square 10 and 5.

Caution! This is not equal to $\sqrt{100} + \sqrt{25}$.

$$= \sqrt{125}$$ Add.

$$= 5\sqrt{5} \approx 11.18$$ $\sqrt{125} = \sqrt{25 \cdot 5} = \sqrt{25}\sqrt{5} = 5\sqrt{5}$

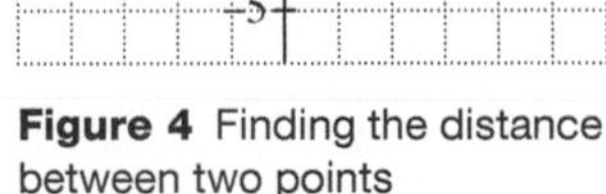

Figure 4 Finding the distance between two points

The distance between the given points is $5\sqrt{5}$ units, or approximately 11.18 units. The situation is illustrated in **Figure 4**. ■

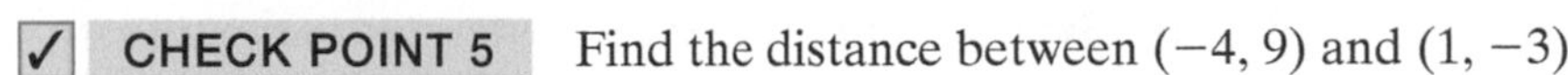

✓ **CHECK POINT 5** Find the distance between $(-4, 9)$ and $(1, -3)$.

Achieving Success

Here are some suggestions from other students for improving your success in college. Which of these suggestions do you find most relevant for achieving success in this course? What helpful suggestions would you add to this list?

- Recognize that to start studying earlier is better.
  —*Azusa Uchiada, Yokkaichi, Japan*
- Do your work—get it over! There's no magic secret behind it.
  —*James Arnold, Layton, Utah*
- Have smart friends.
  —*Janet, Long Beach, California*
- Have an open mind about all points of view.
  —*Solongo, Ulan Bator, Mongolia*
- Work hard to get better knowledge even if your results are not the highest.
  —*Daniel Tilahun Mezegebu, Addis Ababa, Ethiopia*
- Review your test papers after the tests.
  —*Jim Iantao, Taipei, Taiwan*
- Don't watch TV while you're studying.
  —*Cammy Le, Long Beach, California*

This includes preparing for your final exam. We'll give you some strategies to prepare for a final in Section 3.

Source: Sean Covey, *The 6 Most Important Decisions You'll Ever Make: A Guide for Teens*, Fireside Press, 2006.

CONCEPT AND VOCABULARY CHECK

Fill in each blank so that the resulting statement is true.

1. The square root property states that if $u^2 = d$, then $u =$ ____________, $d > 0$.
2. A triangle with one angle measuring 90° is called a/an ____________ triangle. The side opposite the 90° angle is called the ____________. The other sides are called ____________.
3. The Pythagorean Theorem states that in any ____________ triangle, the sum of the squares of the lengths of the ____________ equals ____________.
4. The distance, d, between the points (x_1, y_1) and (x_2, y_2) in the rectangular coordinate system is given by the formula $d =$ ________________.

1 EXERCISE SET

MyMathLab®

Watch the videos in MyMathLab

Download the MyDashBoard App

Practice Exercises

In Exercises 1–30, solve each quadratic equation by the square root property. If possible, simplify radicals or rationalize denominators.

1. $x^2 = 16$
2. $x^2 = 100$
3. $y^2 = 81$
4. $y^2 = 144$
5. $x^2 = 7$
6. $x^2 = 13$
7. $x^2 = 50$
8. $x^2 = 27$
9. $5x^2 = 20$
10. $3x^2 = 75$
11. $4y^2 = 49$
12. $16y^2 = 25$
13. $2x^2 + 1 = 51$
14. $3x^2 - 1 = 47$
15. $3x^2 - 2 = 0$
16. $3x^2 - 5 = 0$
17. $5z^2 - 7 = 0$
18. $5z^2 - 2 = 0$
19. $(x - 3)^2 = 16$
20. $(x - 2)^2 = 25$
21. $(x + 5)^2 = 121$
22. $(x + 6)^2 = 144$

23. $(3x + 2)^2 = 9$

24. $(2x + 1)^2 = 49$

25. $(x - 5)^2 = 3$

26. $(x - 3)^2 = 15$

27. $(y + 8)^2 = 11$

28. $(y + 7)^2 = 5$

29. $(z - 4)^2 = 18$

30. $(z - 6)^2 = 12$

In Exercises 31–40, solve each quadratic equation by first factoring the perfect square trinomial on the left side. Then apply the square root property. Simplify radicals, if possible.

31. $x^2 + 4x + 4 = 16$

32. $x^2 + 4x + 4 = 25$

33. $x^2 - 6x + 9 = 36$

34. $x^2 - 6x + 9 = 49$

35. $x^2 - 10x + 25 = 2$

36. $x^2 - 10x + 25 = 3$

37. $x^2 + 2x + 1 = 5$

38. $x^2 + 2x + 1 = 7$

39. $y^2 - 14y + 49 = 12$

40. $y^2 - 14y + 49 = 18$

In Exercises 41–48, use the Pythagorean Theorem to find the missing length in each right triangle. Express the answer in radical form and simplify, if possible.

41.

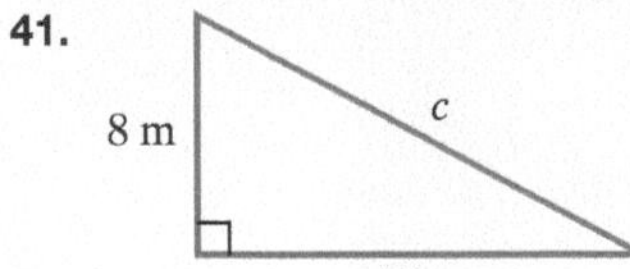

42.

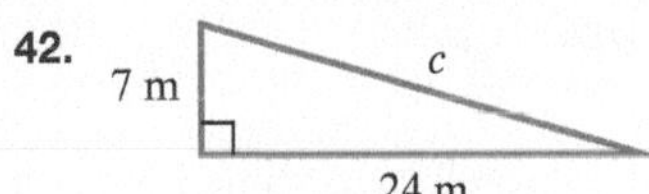

43.

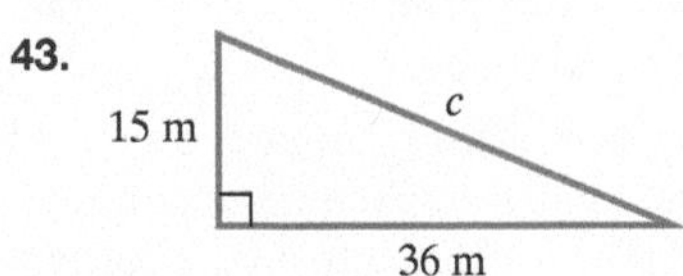

44. **45.**

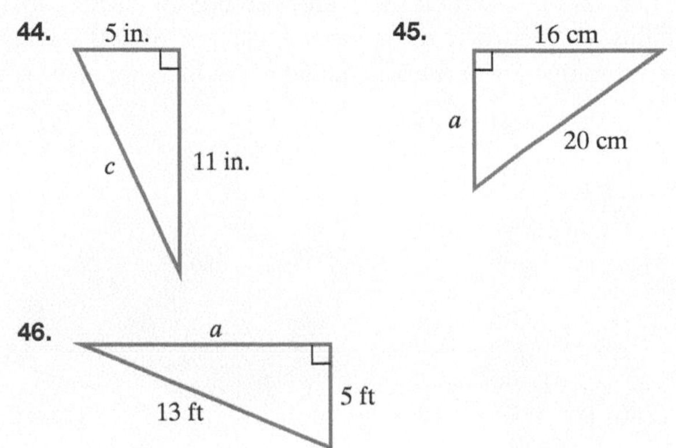

46.

a
13 ft
5 ft

47.

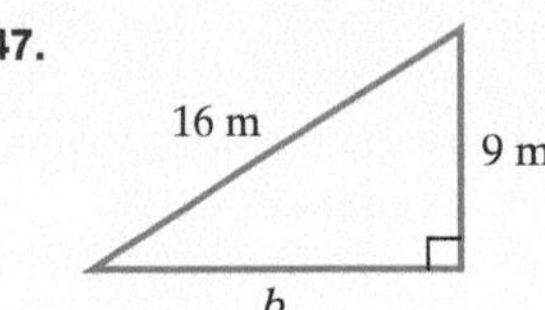

48.

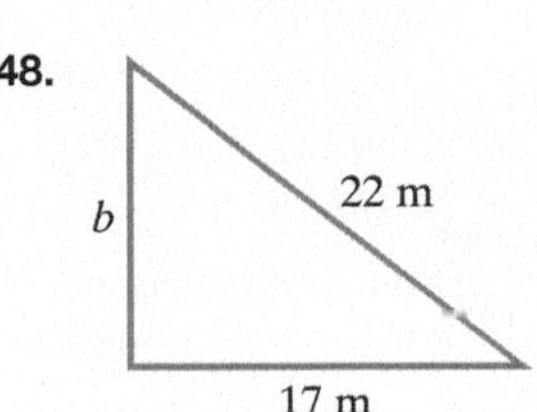

In Exercises 49–58, find the distance between each pair of points. Express answers in simplified radical form and, if necessary, round to two decimal places.

49. $(3, 5)$ and $(4, 1)$

50. $(1, 5)$ and $(6, 2)$

51. $(-4, 2)$ and $(4, 17)$

52. $(2, -2)$ and $(5, 2)$

53. $(6, -1)$ and $(9, 5)$

54. $(-4, -1)$ and $(2, -3)$

55. $(-7, -5)$ and $(-2, -1)$

56. $(-8, -4)$ and $(-3, -8)$

57. $(-2\sqrt{7}, 10)$ and $(4\sqrt{7}, 8)$

58. $(-\sqrt{3}, 4\sqrt{6})$ and $(2\sqrt{3}, \sqrt{6})$

Practice PLUS

59. The square of the difference between a number and 3 is 25. Find the number(s).

60. The square of the difference between a number and 7 is 16. Find the number(s).

61. If 3 times a number is increased by 2 and this sum is squared, the result is 49. Find the number(s).

62. If 4 times a number is decreased by 3 and this difference is squared, the result is 9. Find the number(s).

In Exercises 63–66, solve the formula for the specified variable. Because each variable is nonnegative, list only the principal square root. If possible, simplify radicals or eliminate radicals from denominators.

63. $A = \pi r^2$ for r

64. $ax^2 - b = 0$ for x

65. $I = \dfrac{k}{d^2}$ for d

66. $A = p(1 + r)^2$ for r

Application Exercises

Use the Pythagorean Theorem to solve Exercises 67–72. Express the answer in radical form and simplify, if possible.

67. Find the length of the ladder.

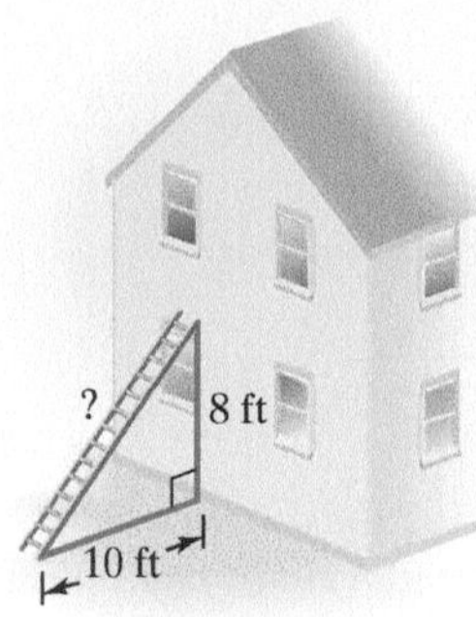

68. How high is the airplane above the ground?

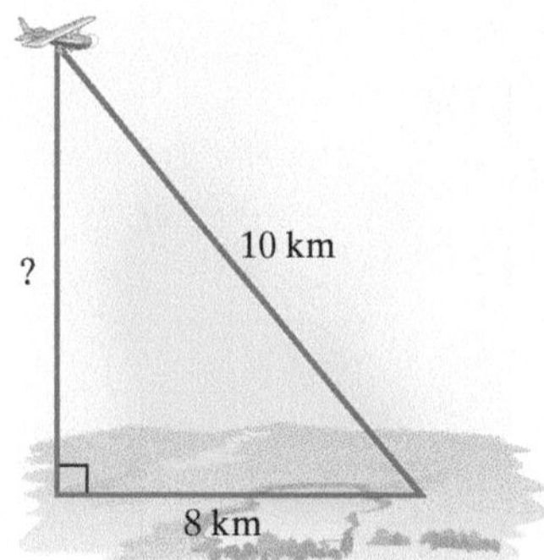

69. A baseball diamond is actually a square with 90-foot sides. What is the distance from home plate to second base?

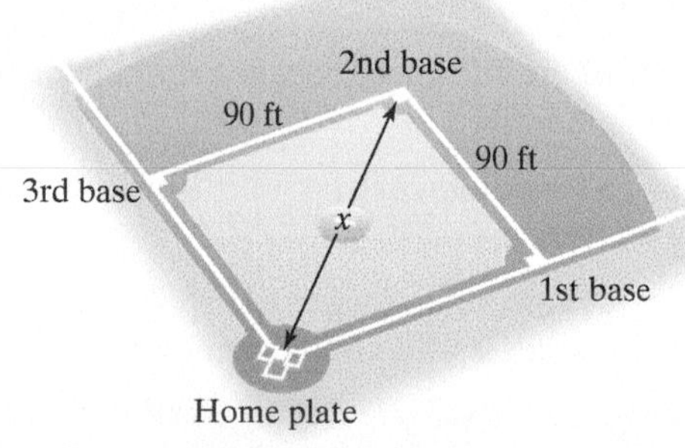

70. The base of a 20-foot ladder is 15 feet from the house. How far up the house does the ladder reach?

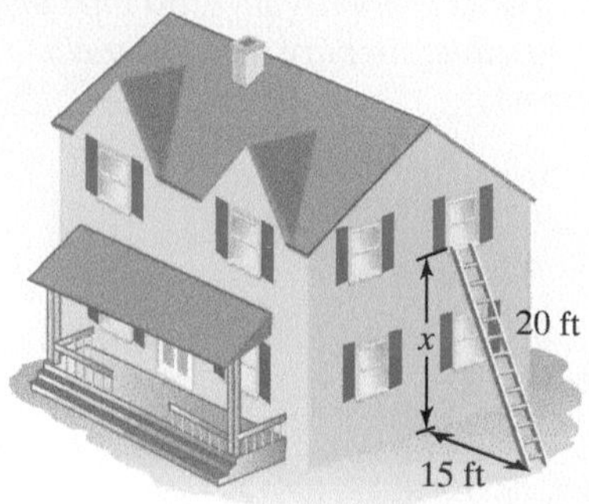

Use the formula for the area of a circle, $A = \pi r^2$, to solve Exercises 71–72.

71. If the area of a circle is 36π square inches, find its radius.

72. If the area of a circle is 49π square inches, find its radius.

The weight of a human fetus is modeled by the formula $W = 3t^2$, where W is the weight, in grams, and t is the time, in weeks, with $0 \le t \le 39$. Use this formula to solve Exercises 73–74.

73. After how many weeks does the fetus weigh 108 grams?

74. After how many weeks does the fetus weigh 192 grams?

The distance, d, in feet, that an object falls in t seconds is modeled by the formula $d = 16t^2$. Use this formula to solve Exercises 75–76.

75. If you drop a rock from a cliff 400 feet above the water how long will it take for the rock to hit the water?

76. If you drop a rock from a cliff 576 feet above the water, how long will it take for the rock to hit the water?

77. A square flower bed is to be enlarged by adding 2 meters on each side. If the larger square has an area of 144 square meters, what is the length of the original square?

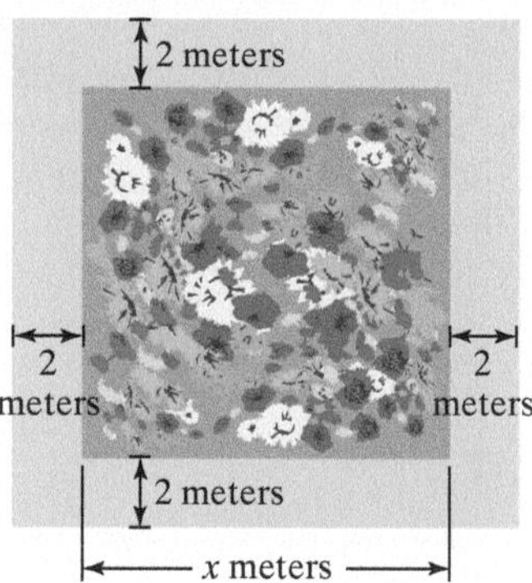

78. A square flower bed is to be enlarged by adding 3 feet on each side. If the larger square has an area of 169 square feet, what is the length of the original square?

79. A machine produces open boxes using square sheets of metal. The figure illustrates that the machine cuts equal-sized squares measuring 2 inches on a side from the corners and then shapes the metal into an open box by turning up the sides. If each box must have a volume of 200 cubic inches, find the size of the length and width of the open box.

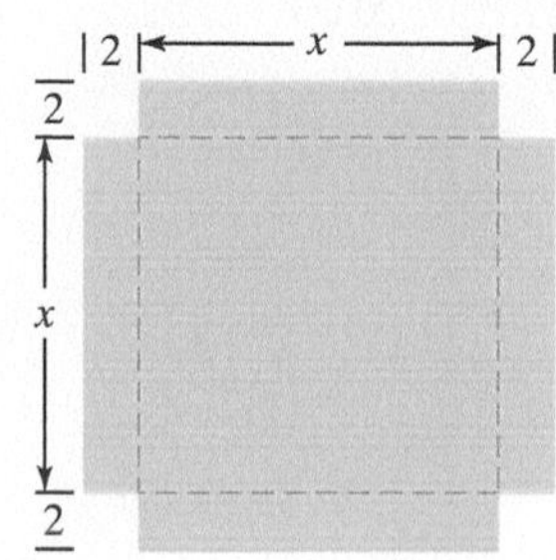

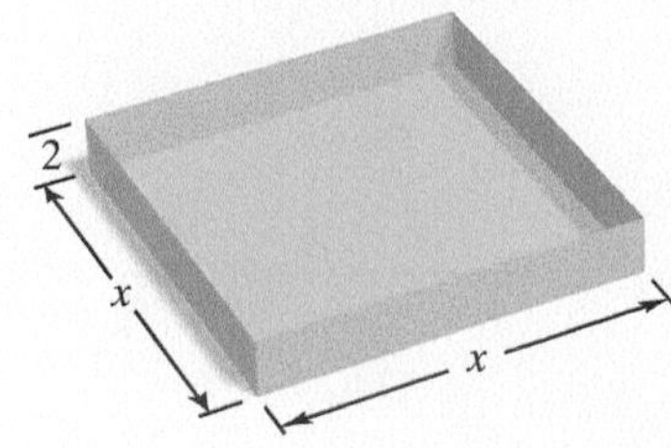

80. A machine produces open boxes using square sheets of metal. The machine cuts equal-sized squares measuring 3 inches on a side from the corners and then shapes the metal into an open box by turning up the sides. If each box must have a volume of 75 cubic inches, find the size of the length and width of the open box.

Writing in Mathematics

81. What is the square root property?

82. Explain how to solve $(x - 1)^2 = 16$ using the square root property.

83. In your own words, state the Pythagorean Theorem.

84. In the 1939 movie *The Wizard of Oz,* upon being presented with a Th.D. (Doctor of Thinkology), the Scarecrow proudly exclaims, "The sum of the square roots of any two sides of an isosceles triangle is equal to the square root of the remaining side." Did the Scarecrow get the Pythagorean Theorem right? In particular, describe four errors in the Scarecrow's statement.

Everett Collection, Inc.,

Critical Thinking Exercises

Make Sense? *In Exercises 85–88, determine whether each statement "makes sense" or "does not make sense" and explain your reasoning.*

85. I have a graphing calculator, so I used the x-coordinates of the intersection points of the graphs of $y_1 = (x - 2)^2$ and $y_2 = 25$ to verify the solution set for $(x - 2)^2 = 25$.

86. When I'm given the picture of a right triangle, the hypotenuse is always the side on top.

87. I've noticed that in mathematics there is a connection between topics, such as using the Pythagorean Theorem to derive the distance formula.

88. When I use the square root property to determine the length of a right triangle's side, I don't even bother to list the negative square root.

In Exercises 89–92, determine whether each statement is true or false. If the statement is false, make the necessary change(s) to produce a true statement.

89. The equation $(x + 5)^2 = 8$ is equivalent to $x + 5 = 2\sqrt{2}$.

90. The equation $x^2 = 0$ has no solution.

91. The equation $x^2 = -1$ has no solutions that are real numbers.

92. The solutions of $3x^2 - 5 = 0$ are $\frac{\sqrt{5}}{3}$ and $-\frac{\sqrt{5}}{3}$.

93. Find the value(s) of x if the distance between $(-3, -2)$ and $(x, -5)$ is 5 units.

Technology Exercises

94. Use a graphing utility to solve $4 - (x + 1)^2 = 0$. Graph $y = 4 - (x + 1)^2$ in a $[-5, 5, 1]$ by $[-5, 5, 1]$ viewing rectangle. The equation's solutions are the graph's x-intercepts. Check by substitution in the given equation.

95. Use a graphing utility to solve $(x - 1)^2 - 9 = 0$. Graph $y = (x - 1)^2 - 9$ in a $[-5, 5, 1]$ by $[-9, 3, 1]$ viewing rectangle. The equation's solutions are the graph's x-intercepts. Check by substitution in the given equation.

Review Exercises

96. Factor completely: $12x^2 + 14x - 6$.

97. Divide: $\frac{x^2 - x - 6}{3x - 3} \div \frac{x^2 - 4}{x - 1}$.

98. Solve: $4(x - 5) = 22 + 2(6x + 3)$.

Preview Exercises

Exercises 99–101 will help you prepare for the material covered in the next section.

99. Factor: $x^2 + 8x + 16$.

100. Factor: $x^2 - 14x + 49$.

101. Factor: $x^2 + 5x + \frac{25}{4}$.

SECTION 2

Solving Quadratic Equations by Completing the Square

Objectives

1. Complete the square of a binomial.
2. Solve quadratic equations by completing the square.

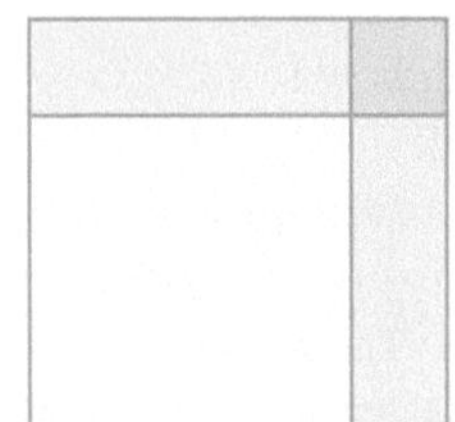

Rind (1955), M. C. Escher © 2011 M. C. Escher Company, Holland.

There is a lack of completion in both the Escher image and the unfinished square on the left. Completion for the geometric figure can be obtained by adding a small square to its upper-right-hand corner. Understanding this process algebraically will give you a new method, appropriately called *completing the square*, for solving quadratic equations.

1 Complete the square a binomial.

Completing the Square

How do we solve a quadratic equation, $ax^2 + bx + c = 0$, if the trinomial $ax^2 + bx + c$ cannot be factored? We can convert the equation into an equivalent equation that can be solved using the square root property. This is accomplished by **completing the square**.

Completing the Square

If $x^2 + bx$ is a binomial, then by adding $\left(\frac{b}{2}\right)^2$, which is the square of half the coefficient of x, a perfect square trinomial will result. That is,

The coefficient of x^2 must be 1 to complete the square.

$$x^2 + bx + \left(\frac{b}{2}\right)^2 = \left(x + \frac{b}{2}\right)^2.$$

EXAMPLE 1 Completing the Square

Complete the square for each binomial. Then factor the resulting perfect square trinomial:

a. $x^2 + 8x$ **b.** $x^2 - 14x$ **c.** $x^2 + 5x$.

Solution To complete the square, we must add a term to each binomial. The term that should be added is the square of half the coefficient of x.

$x^2 + 8x$	$x^2 - 14x$	$x^2 + 5x$
Add $\left(\frac{8}{2}\right)^2 = 4^2$. Add 16 to complete the square.	Add $\left(\frac{-14}{2}\right)^2 = (-7)^2$. Add 49 to complete the square.	Add $\left(\frac{5}{2}\right)^2$, or $\frac{25}{4}$, to complete the square.

a. The coefficient of the x-term of $x^2 + 8x$ is 8. Half of 8 is 4, and $4^2 = 16$. Add 16.

$$x^2 + 8x + 16 = (x + 4)^2$$

b. The coefficient of the x-term of $x^2 - 14x$ is -14. Half of -14 is -7, and $(-7)^2 = 49$. Add 49.

$$x^2 - 14x + 49 = (x - 7)^2$$

c. The coefficient of the x-term of $x^2 + 5x$ is 5. Half of 5 is $\frac{5}{2}$, and $\left(\frac{5}{2}\right)^2 = \frac{25}{4}$. Add $\frac{25}{4}$.

$$x^2 + 5x + \frac{25}{4} = \left(x + \frac{5}{2}\right)^2$$ ■

Geometric figures make it possible to visualize completing the square.

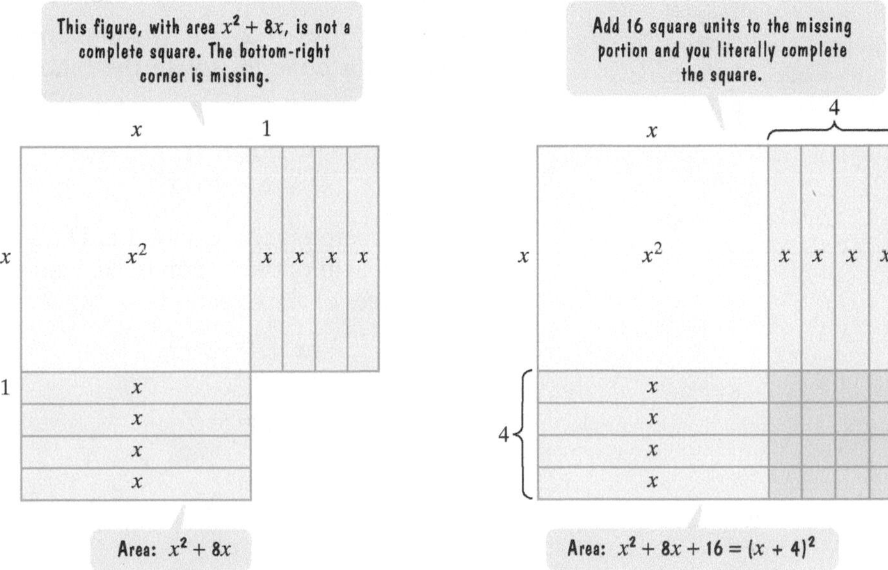

✓ **CHECK POINT 1** Complete the square for each binomial. Then factor the resulting perfect square trinomial:

a. $x^2 + 10x$ **b.** $x^2 - 6x$

c. $x^2 + 3x$.

---

2 Solve quadratic equations by completing the square.

Solving Quadratic Equations by Completing the Square

We can solve *any* quadratic equation by completing the square. If the coefficient of the x^2-term is one, we add the square of half the coefficient of x to both sides of the equation. **When you add a constant term to one side of the equation to complete the square, be certain to add the same constant to the other side of the equation.** These ideas are illustrated in Example 2.

EXAMPLE 2 Solving Quadratic Equations by Completing the Square

Solve by completing the square:

a. $x^2 + 8x = -15$ **b.** $x^2 - 6x + 2 = 0$.

Great Question!

When I solve a quadratic equation by completing the square, does this result in a new equation? Why are the solutions of this new equation the same as those of the given equation?

When you complete the square for the binomial expression $x^2 + bx$, you obtain a different polynomial. When you solve a quadratic equation by completing the square, you obtain an equation with the same solution set because the constant needed to complete the square is added to *both sides*.

Solution

a. Our first equation is $x^2 + 8x = -15$. To complete the square on the binomial $x^2 + 8x$, we take half of 8, which is 4, and square 4, giving 16. We add 16 to both sides of the equation. This makes the left side a perfect square trinomial.

$x^2 + 8x = -15$	This is the given equation.
$x^2 + 8x + 16 = -15 + 16$	Add 16 to both sides to complete the square.
$(x + 4)^2 = 1$	Factor and simplify.
$x + 4 = \sqrt{1}$ or $x + 4 = -\sqrt{1}$	Apply the square root property.
$x + 4 = 1$ $x + 4 = -1$	Simplify.
$x = -3$ $x = -5$	Subtract 4 from both sides in each equation.

The solutions are -5 and -3. The solution set is $\{-5, -3\}$.

b. To solve $x^2 - 6x + 2 = 0$ by completing the square, we first subtract 2 from both sides. This is done to isolate the binomial $x^2 - 6x$ so that we can complete the square.

$x^2 - 6x + 2 = 0$	This is the original equation.
$x^2 - 6x = -2$	Subtract 2 from both sides.

Next, we complete the square. Find half the coefficient of the x-term and square it. The coefficient of the x-term is -6. Half of -6 is -3, and $(-3)^2 = 9$. Thus, we add 9 to both sides of the equation.

$x^2 - 6x + 9 = -2 + 9$	Add 9 to both sides to complete the square.
$(x - 3)^2 = 7$	Factor and simplify.
$x - 3 = \sqrt{7}$ or $x - 3 = -\sqrt{7}$	Apply the square root property.
$x = 3 + \sqrt{7}$ $x = 3 - \sqrt{7}$	Add 3 to both sides in each equation.

The solutions are $3 + \sqrt{7}$ and $3 - \sqrt{7}$, expressed in abbreviated notation as $3 \pm \sqrt{7}$. The solution set is $\{3 \pm \sqrt{7}\}$. ■

If you solve a quadratic equation by completing the square and the solutions are rational numbers, the equation can also be solved by factoring. By contrast, quadratic equations with irrational solutions cannot be solved by factoring. However, all quadratic equations can be solved by completing the square.

✓ **CHECK POINT 2** Solve by completing the square:

a. $x^2 + 6x = 7$ **b.** $x^2 - 10x + 18 = 0$.

The leading coefficient must be 1 in order to complete the square. If the coefficient of the x^2-term in a quadratic equation is not 1, you must divide each side of the equation by this coefficient before completing the square. For example, to solve $2x^2 + 5x - 4 = 0$ by completing the square, first divide every term by 2:

$$\frac{2x^2}{2} + \frac{5x}{2} - \frac{4}{2} = \frac{0}{2}$$

$$x^2 + \frac{5}{2}x - 2 = 0.$$

Now that the coefficient of the x^2-term is 1, we can solve by completing the square.

EXAMPLE 3 Solving a Quadratic Equation by Completing the Square

Solve by completing the square: $2x^2 + 5x - 4 = 0$.

Solution

$2x^2 + 5x - 4 = 0$	This is the original equation.
$x^2 + \frac{5}{2}x - 2 = 0$	Divide both sides by 2.
$x^2 + \frac{5}{2}x = 2$	Add 2 to both sides and isolate the binomial.
$x^2 + \frac{5}{2}x + \frac{25}{16} = 2 + \frac{25}{16}$	Complete the square: Half of $\frac{5}{2}$ is $\frac{5}{4}$ and $\left(\frac{5}{4}\right)^2 = \frac{25}{16}$.
$\left(x + \frac{5}{4}\right)^2 = \frac{57}{16}$	Factor and simplify. On the right: $2 + \frac{25}{16} = \frac{32}{16} + \frac{25}{16} = \frac{57}{16}$.
$x + \frac{5}{4} = \sqrt{\frac{57}{16}}$ or $x + \frac{5}{4} = -\sqrt{\frac{57}{16}}$	Apply the square root property.
$x + \frac{5}{4} = \frac{\sqrt{57}}{4}$ $\quad$ $x + \frac{5}{4} = -\frac{\sqrt{57}}{4}$	$\sqrt{\frac{57}{16}} = \frac{\sqrt{57}}{\sqrt{16}} = \frac{\sqrt{57}}{4}$
$x = -\frac{5}{4} + \frac{\sqrt{57}}{4}$ $\quad$ $x = -\frac{5}{4} - \frac{\sqrt{57}}{4}$	Solve the equations, subtracting $\frac{5}{4}$ from both sides.
$x = \frac{-5 + \sqrt{57}}{4}$ $\quad$ $x = \frac{-5 - \sqrt{57}}{4}$	Express solutions with a common denominator.

The solutions are $\frac{-5 \pm \sqrt{57}}{4}$ and the solution set is $\left\{\frac{-5 \pm \sqrt{57}}{4}\right\}$. ■

Using Technology

Graphic Connections

Obtain a decimal approximation for each solution of $2x^2 + 5x - 4 = 0$, the equation in Example 3:

$$\frac{-5 + \sqrt{57}}{4} \approx 0.6$$

$$\frac{-5 - \sqrt{57}}{4} \approx -3.1.$$

The x-intercepts of $y = 2x^2 + 5x - 4$ verify these solutions.

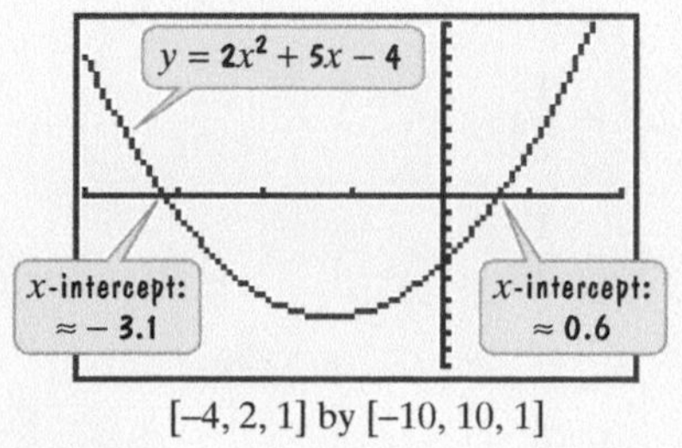

[−4, 2, 1] by [−10, 10, 1]

✓ **CHECK POINT 3** Solve by completing the square: $2x^2 - 10x - 1 = 0$.

CONCEPT AND VOCABULARY CHECK

Fill in each blank so that the resulting statement is true.

1. To complete the square on $x^2 + 18x$, add ____________.
2. To complete the square on $x^2 - 6x$, add ____________.
3. To complete the square on $x^2 + 7x$, add ____________.
4. To complete the square on $x^2 - \frac{5}{2}x$, add ____________.
5. To complete the square on $x^2 + bx$, add ____________.

Fill in each blank with the number needed to make each binomial a perfect square trinomial.

6. $x^2 + 20x +$ ____________
7. $x^2 - 2x +$ ____________
8. $x^2 + x +$ ____________

2 EXERCISE SET

MyMathLab®

Watch the videos in MyMathLab

Download the MyDashBoard App

Practice Exercises

In Exercises 1–12, complete the square for each binomial. Then factor the resulting perfect square trinomial.

1. $x^2 + 10x$
2. $x^2 + 12x$
3. $x^2 - 2x$
4. $x^2 - 4x$
5. $x^2 + 5x$
6. $x^2 + 3x$
7. $x^2 - 7x$
8. $x^2 - x$
9. $x^2 + \frac{1}{2}x$
10. $x^2 + \frac{1}{3}x$
11. $x^2 - \frac{4}{3}x$
12. $x^2 - \frac{4}{5}x$

In Exercises 13–34, solve each quadratic equation by completing the square.

13. $x^2 + 4x = 5$
14. $x^2 + 6x = -8$
15. $x^2 - 10x = -24$
16. $x^2 - 2x = 8$
17. $x^2 - 2x = 5$
18. $x^2 - 4x = -2$
19. $x^2 + 4x + 1 = 0$
20. $x^2 + 6x - 5 = 0$
21. $x^2 - 3x = 28$
22. $x^2 - 5x = -6$
23. $x^2 + 3x - 1 = 0$
24. $x^2 - 3x - 5 = 0$
25. $x^2 = 7x - 3$
26. $x^2 = 5x - 3$
27. $2x^2 - 2x - 6 = 0$
28. $2x^2 - 4x - 2 = 0$
29. $2x^2 - 3x + 1 = 0$

30. $2x^2 - x - 1 = 0$

31. $2x^2 + 10x + 11 = 0$

32. $2x^2 + 8x + 5 = 0$

33. $4x^2 - 2x - 3 = 0$

34. $3x^2 - 2x - 4 = 0$

Practice PLUS

In Exercises 35–40, solve each quadratic equation by completing the square.

35. $\frac{x^2}{6} - \frac{x}{3} - 1 = 0$

36. $\frac{x^2}{6} + x - \frac{3}{2} = 0$

37. $(x + 2)(x - 3) = 1$

38. $(x - 5)(x - 3) = 1$

39. $x^2 + 4bx = 5b^2$

40. $x^2 + 6bx = 7b^2$

Writing in Mathematics

41. Explain how to complete the square for a binomial. Use $x^2 + 6x$ to illustrate your explanation.

42. Explain how to solve $x^2 + 6x + 8 = 0$ by completing the square.

Critical Thinking Exercises

Make Sense? *In Exercises 43–46, determine whether each statement "makes sense" or "does not make sense" and explain your reasoning.*

43. When I complete the square, I convert a quadratic equation into an equivalent equation that can be solved by the square root property.

44. When the coefficient of the x-term in a quadratic equation is negative and I'm solving by completing the square, I add a negative constant to each side of the equation.

45. When I complete the square for the binomial $x^2 + bx$, I obtain a different polynomial, but when I solve a quadratic equation by completing the square, I obtain an equation with the same solution set.

46. I solved $4x^2 + 10x = 0$ by completing the square and added 25 to both sides of the equation.

In Exercises 47–50, determine whether each statement is true or false. If the statement is false, make the necessary change(s) to produce a true statement.

47. Completing the square is a method for finding the area and perimeter of a square.

48. The trinomial $x^2 - 3x + 9$ is a perfect square trinomial.

49. Although not every quadratic equation can be solved by completing the square, they can all be solved using factoring.

50. In completing the square for $x^2 - 7x = 5$, we should add $\frac{49}{4}$ to both sides.

51. Write a perfect square trinomial whose x-term is $-20x$.

52. Solve by completing the square: $x^2 + x + c = 0$.

53. Solve by completing the square: $x^2 + bx + c = 0$.

Technology Exercises

54. Use the technique shown in the Using Technology box to verify the solutions of any two quadratic equations in Exercises 17–20.

Review Exercises

In Exercises 55–56, perform the indicated operations. If possible, simplify the answer.

55. $\frac{2x + 3}{x^2 - 7x + 12} - \frac{2}{x - 3}$

56. $\frac{x - \frac{1}{3}}{3 - \frac{1}{x}}$

57. Solve: $\sqrt{2x + 3} = 2x - 3$.

Preview Exercises

Exercises 58–60 will help you prepare for the material covered in the next section. In each exercise, evaluate

$$\frac{-b \pm \sqrt{b^2 - 4ac}}{2a}$$

for the given values of a, b, and c. Where necessary, express answers in simplified radical form.

58. $a = 2, b = 9, c = -5$

59. $a = 9, b = -12, c = 4$

60. $a = 1, b = -2, c = -6$

SECTION

3

The Quadratic Formula

Objectives

1 Solve quadratic equations using the quadratic formula.

2 Determine the most efficient method to use when solving a quadratic equation.

3 Solve problems using quadratic equations.

In the chapter opener, we observed that a substantial percentage of the United States population is foreign-born. In this section, we will explore the foreign-born model using a formula that will enable you to solve quadratic equations more quickly than using the method of completing the square. We begin by deriving this formula.

Momentimages/Photolibrary New York

Solving Quadratic Equations Using the Quadratic Formula

We can apply the method of completing the square to derive a formula that can be used to solve all quadratic equations. The derivation given here also shows a particular quadratic equation, $3x^2 - 2x - 4 = 0$, to specifically illustrate each of the steps.

Deriving the Quadratic Formula

Standard Form of a Quadratic Equation	Comment	A Specific Example
$ax^2 + bx + c = 0, a > 0$	This is the given equation.	$3x^2 - 2x - 4 = 0$
$x^2 + \frac{b}{a}x + \frac{c}{a} = 0$	Divide both sides by a so that the coefficient of x^2 is 1.	$x^2 - \frac{2}{3}x - \frac{4}{3} = 0$
$x^2 + \frac{b}{a}x = -\frac{c}{a}$	Isolate the binomial by adding $-\frac{c}{a}$ on both sides of the equation.	$x^2 - \frac{2}{3}x = \frac{4}{3}$
$x^2 + \frac{b}{a}x + \left(\frac{b}{2a}\right)^2 = -\frac{c}{a} + \left(\frac{b}{2a}\right)^2$ (half)^2 $x^2 + \frac{b}{a}x + \frac{b^2}{4a^2} = -\frac{c}{a} + \frac{b^2}{4a^2}$	Complete the square. Add the square of half the coefficient of x to both sides.	$x^2 - \frac{2}{3}x + \left(-\frac{1}{3}\right)^2 = \frac{4}{3} + \left(-\frac{1}{3}\right)^2$ (half)^2 $x^2 - \frac{2}{3}x + \frac{1}{9} = \frac{4}{3} + \frac{1}{9}$
$\left(x + \frac{b}{2a}\right)^2 = -\frac{c}{a} \cdot \frac{4a}{4a} + \frac{b^2}{4a^2}$	Factor on the left side and obtain a common denominator on the right side.	$\left(x - \frac{1}{3}\right)^2 = \frac{4}{3} \cdot \frac{3}{3} + \frac{1}{9}$
$\left(x + \frac{b}{2a}\right)^2 = \frac{-4ac + b^2}{4a^2}$ $\left(x + \frac{b}{2a}\right)^2 = \frac{b^2 - 4ac}{4a^2}$	Add fractions on the right side.	$\left(x - \frac{1}{3}\right)^2 = \frac{12 + 1}{9}$ $\left(x - \frac{1}{3}\right)^2 = \frac{13}{9}$
$x + \frac{b}{2a} = \pm\sqrt{\frac{b^2 - 4ac}{4a^2}}$	Apply the square root property.	$x - \frac{1}{3} = \pm\sqrt{\frac{13}{9}}$
$x + \frac{b}{2a} = \pm\frac{\sqrt{b^2 - 4ac}}{2a}$	Take the square root of the quotient, simplifying the denominator.	$x - \frac{1}{3} = \pm\frac{\sqrt{13}}{3}$
$x = \frac{-b}{2a} \pm \frac{\sqrt{b^2 - 4ac}}{2a}$	Solve for x by subtracting $\frac{b}{2a}$ from both sides.	$x = \frac{1}{3} \pm \frac{\sqrt{13}}{3}$
$x = \frac{-b \pm \sqrt{b^2 - 4ac}}{2a}$	Combine fractions on the right side.	$x = \frac{1 \pm \sqrt{13}}{3}$

The formula shown at the bottom of the left column on the previous page is called the *quadratic formula*. A similar proof shows that the same formula can be used to solve quadratic equations if a, the coefficient of the x^2-term, is negative.

1 Solve quadratic equations using the quadratic formula.

The Quadratic Formula

The solutions of a quadratic equation in standard form $ax^2 + bx + c = 0$, with $a \neq 0$, are given by the **quadratic formula**

$$x = \frac{-b \pm \sqrt{b^2 - 4ac}}{2a}.$$

x equals negative b plus or minus the square root of $b^2 - 4ac$, all divided by $2a$.

To use the quadratic formula, begin by writing the quadratic equation in standard form, if necessary. Then determine the numerical values for a (the coefficient of the x^2-term), b (the coefficient of the x-term), and c (the constant term). Substitute the values of a, b, and c into the quadratic formula and evaluate the expression. The $\pm$ sign indicates that if $b^2 - 4ac$ is not zero, there are two solutions of the equation.

EXAMPLE 1 Solving a Quadratic Equation Using the Quadratic Formula

Solve using the quadratic formula: $2x^2 + 9x - 5 = 0$.

Solution The given equation is in standard form. Begin by identifying the values for a, b, and c.

$$2x^2 + 9x - 5 = 0$$

$a = 2$ $b = 9$ $c = -5$

Substituting these values into the quadratic formula and simplifying gives the equation's solutions.

$$x = \frac{-b \pm \sqrt{b^2 - 4ac}}{2a}$$ Use the quadratic formula.

$$x = \frac{-9 \pm \sqrt{9^2 - 4(2)(-5)}}{2(2)}$$ Substitute the values for a, b, and c: $a = 2$, $b = 9$, and $c = -5$.

$$= \frac{-9 \pm \sqrt{81 + 40}}{4}$$ $9^2 - 4(2)(-5) = 81 - (-40) = 81 + 40$

$$= \frac{-9 \pm \sqrt{121}}{4}$$ Add under the radical sign.

$$= \frac{-9 \pm 11}{4}$$ $\sqrt{121} = 11$

Now we will evaluate this expression in two different ways to obtain the two solutions. At the left, we will *add* 11 to -9. At the right, we will *subtract* 11 from -9.

$$x = \frac{-9 + 11}{4} \quad \text{or} \quad x = \frac{-9 - 11}{4}$$

$$= \frac{2}{4} = \frac{1}{2} \qquad\qquad = \frac{-20}{4} = -5$$

The solutions are -5 and $\frac{1}{2}$, and the solution set is $\left\{-5, \frac{1}{2}\right\}$. ■

Using Technology

Graphic Connections

The graph of $y = 2x^2 + 9x - 5$ has x-intercepts at -5 and $\frac{1}{2}$. This verifies that -5 and $\frac{1}{2}$ are the solutions of

$$2x^2 + 9x - 5 = 0.$$

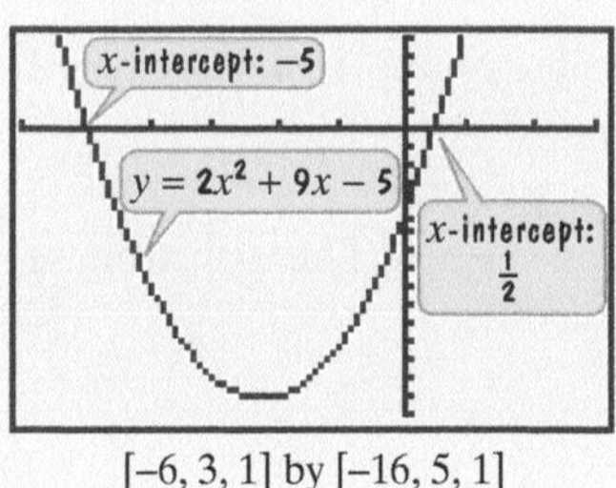

[−6, 3, 1] by [−16, 5, 1]

In Example 1, the solutions of $2x^2 + 9x - 5 = 0$ are rational numbers. This means that the equation can also be solved using factoring. The reason that the solutions are rational numbers is that $b^2 - 4ac$, the radicand in the quadratic formula, is 121, which is a perfect square.

✓ **CHECK POINT 1** Solve using the quadratic formula: $8x^2 + 2x - 1 = 0$.

EXAMPLE 2 Solving a Quadratic Equation Using the Quadratic Formula

Solve using the quadratic formula: $2x^2 = 6x - 1$.

Solution The quadratic equation must be in standard form to identify the values for a, b, and c. We need to move all terms to one side and obtain zero on the other side. To obtain zero on the right, we subtract $6x$ and add 1 on both sides. Then we can identify the values for a, b, and c.

$$2x^2 = 6x - 1$$
$$2x^2 - 6x + 1 = 6x - 6x - 1 + 1$$
$$2x^2 - 6x + 1 = 0$$

$a = 2 \quad b = -6 \quad c = 1$

Identify a, the x^2-coefficient, b, the x-coefficient, and c, the constant.

Substituting these values into the quadratic formula and simplifying gives the equation's solutions.

$$x = \frac{-b \pm \sqrt{b^2 - 4ac}}{2a}$$ Use the quadratic formula.

$$x = \frac{-(-6) \pm \sqrt{(-6)^2 - 4(2)(1)}}{2 \cdot 2}$$ Substitute the values for a, b, and c: $a = 2$, $b = -6$, and $c = 1$.

$$= \frac{6 \pm \sqrt{36 - 8}}{4}$$ $-(-6) = 6$ and $(-6)^2 = (-6)(-6) = 36$.

$$= \frac{6 \pm \sqrt{28}}{4}$$ Complete the subtraction under the radical.

$$= \frac{6 \pm 2\sqrt{7}}{4}$$ $\sqrt{28} = \sqrt{4 \cdot 7} = \sqrt{4}\sqrt{7} = 2\sqrt{7}$

$$= \frac{2(3 \pm \sqrt{7})}{4}$$ Factor out 2 from the numerator.

$$= \frac{3 \pm \sqrt{7}}{2}$$ Divide the numerator and denominator by 2.

The solutions are $\frac{3 + \sqrt{7}}{2}$ and $\frac{3 - \sqrt{7}}{2}$, abbreviated $\frac{3 \pm \sqrt{7}}{2}$. The solution set is $\left\{\frac{3 \pm \sqrt{7}}{2}\right\}$. ■

In Example 2, the solutions of $2x^2 = 6x - 1$ are irrational numbers. This means that the equation cannot be solved using factoring. The reason that the solutions are irrational numbers is that $b^2 - 4ac$, the radicand in the quadratic formula, is 28, which is not a perfect square.

Great Question!

The simplification of the irrational solutions in Example 2 was kind of tricky. Any suggestions to guide the process?

Many students use the quadratic formula correctly until the last step, where they make an error in simplifying the solutions. Be sure to factor the numerator before dividing the numerator and denominator by the greatest common factor:

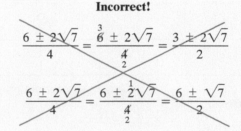

$$\frac{6 \pm 2\sqrt{7}}{4} = \frac{2(3 \pm \sqrt{7})}{4} = \frac{\overset{1}{\cancel{2}}(3 \pm \sqrt{7})}{\underset{2}{\cancel{4}}} = \frac{3 \pm \sqrt{7}}{2}.$$

Factor first.

Then divide by the GCF.

You cannot divide just one term in the numerator and the denominator by their greatest common factor.

Incorrect!

$$\frac{6 \pm 2\sqrt{7}}{4} = \frac{\overset{3}{\cancel{6}} \pm 2\sqrt{7}}{\underset{2}{\cancel{4}}} = \frac{3 \pm 2\sqrt{7}}{2}$$

$$\frac{6 \pm 2\sqrt{7}}{4} = \frac{6 \pm \overset{1}{\cancel{2}}\sqrt{7}}{\underset{2}{\cancel{4}}} = \frac{6 \pm \sqrt{7}}{2}$$

Great Question!

Can all irrational solutions of quadratic equations be simplified?

No. The following solutions cannot be simplified.

$$\frac{5 \pm 2\sqrt{7}}{2} \qquad \frac{-4 \pm 3\sqrt{7}}{2}$$

Other than 1, terms in each numerator have no common factor.

✓ **CHECK POINT 2** Solve using the quadratic formula: $x^2 = 6x - 4$.

---

2 Determine the most efficient method to use when solving a quadratic equation.

Determining Which Method to Use

All quadratic equations can be solved by the quadratic formula. However, if an equation is in the form $u^2 = d$, such as $x^2 = 5$ or $(2x + 3)^2 = 8$, it is faster to use the square root property, taking the square root of both sides. If the equation is not in the form $u^2 = d$, write the quadratic equation in standard form ($ax^2 + bx + c = 0$). Try to solve the equation by factoring. If $ax^2 + bx + c$ cannot be factored, then solve the quadratic equation by the quadratic formula.

Because we used the method of completing the square to derive the quadratic formula, we no longer need it for solving quadratic equations. However, you will use completing the square in more advanced algebra courses to help graph certain kinds of equations.

Table 1 summarizes our observations about which technique to use when solving a quadratic equation.

Table 1 Determining the Most Efficient Technique to Use When Solving a Quadratic Equation

Description and Form of the Quadratic Equation	Most Efficient Solution Method	Example
$ax^2 + bx + c = 0$ and $ax^2 + bx + c$ can be factored easily.	Factor and use the zero-product principle.	$3x^2 + 5x - 2 = 0$ $(3x - 1)(x + 2) = 0$ $3x - 1 = 0$ or $x + 2 = 0$ $x = \frac{1}{3}$ $\quad x = -2$
$ax^2 + c = 0$ The quadratic equation has no x-term. $(b = 0)$	Solve for x^2 and apply the square root property.	$4x^2 - 7 = 0$ $4x^2 = 7$ $x^2 = \frac{7}{4}$ $x = \pm\frac{\sqrt{7}}{2}$
$u^2 = d$; u is a first-degree polynomial.	Use the square root property.	$(x + 4)^2 = 5$ $x + 4 = \pm\sqrt{5}$ $x = -4 \pm \sqrt{5}$
$ax^2 + bx + c = 0$ and $ax^2 + bx + c$ cannot be factored or the factoring is too difficult.	Use the quadratic formula: $x = \frac{-b \pm \sqrt{b^2 - 4ac}}{2a}$.	$x^2 - 2x - 6 = 0$ $a = 1$ $\quad b = -2$ $\quad c = -6$ $x = \frac{-(-2) \pm \sqrt{(-2)^2 - 4(1)(-6)}}{2(1)}$ $= \frac{2 \pm \sqrt{4 + 24}}{2(1)}$ $= \frac{2 \pm \sqrt{28}}{2} = \frac{2 \pm \sqrt{4}\sqrt{7}}{2}$ $= \frac{2 \pm 2\sqrt{7}}{2} = \frac{2(1 \pm \sqrt{7})}{2}$ $= 1 \pm \sqrt{7}$

3 Solve problems using quadratic equations.

Application

Quadratic equations can be solved by any efficient method to answer questions about variables contained in mathematical models.

EXAMPLE 3 Making Predictions About the U.S. Foreign-Born Population

A substantial percentage of the United States population is foreign-born. The graph in **Figure 5** shows the percentage of foreign-born Americans for selected years from 1920 through 2008.

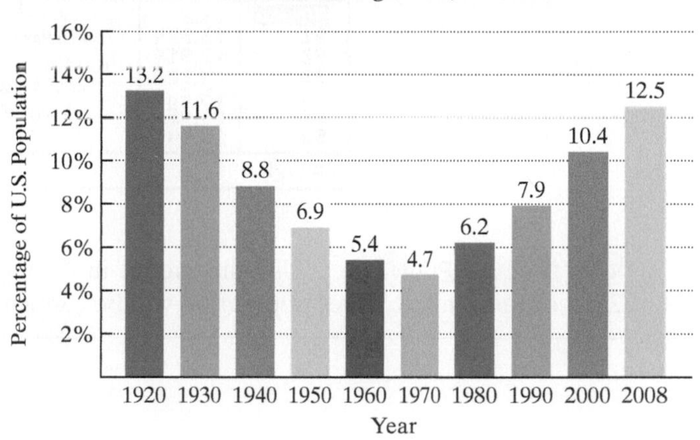

Figure 5

Source: U.S. Census Bureau

The percentage, p, of the United States population that was foreign-born x years after 1920 can be modeled by the formula

$$p = 0.004x^2 - 0.37x + 14.1.$$

According to this model, in which year will 15% of the United States population be foreign-born?

Solution Because we are interested in when the foreign-born percentage will reach 15%, we substitute 15 for p in the given formula. Then we solve for x, the number of years after 1920.

$$p = 0.004x^2 - 0.37x + 14.1$$ This is the given formula.

$$15 = 0.004x^2 - 0.37x + 14.1$$ Substitute 15 for p.

$$0 = 0.004x^2 - 0.37x - 0.9$$ Subtract 15 from both sides and write the quadratic equation in standard form.

$a = 0.004$ $b = -0.37$ $c = -0.9$

Because the trinomial on the right side of the equation, $0.004x^2 - 0.37x - 0.9$, is not easily factored, if it can be factored at all, we solve using the quadratic formula.

$$x = \frac{-b \pm \sqrt{b^2 - 4ac}}{2a}$$ Use the quadratic formula.

$$x = \frac{-(-0.37) \pm \sqrt{(-0.37)^2 - 4(0.004)(-0.9)}}{2(0.004)}$$ Substitute the values for a, b, and c: $a = 0.004$, $b = -0.37$, and $c = -0.9$.

$$= \frac{0.37 \pm \sqrt{0.1513}}{0.008}$$ Perform the indicated computations. Use a calculator to simplify the radicand.

$$x = \frac{0.37 + \sqrt{0.1513}}{0.008} \quad \text{or} \quad x = \frac{0.37 - \sqrt{0.1513}}{0.008}$$

$$x \approx 95 \qquad x \approx -2$$ Use a calculator and round to the nearest whole number.

Reject this solution. The model applies to years *after*, not *before*, 1920.

According to the model, approximately 95 years after 1920, or in 2015, 15% of the United States population will be foreign-born. ■

Using Technology

Numeric Connections

A graphing utility's TABLE feature can be used to verify the solution to Example 3.

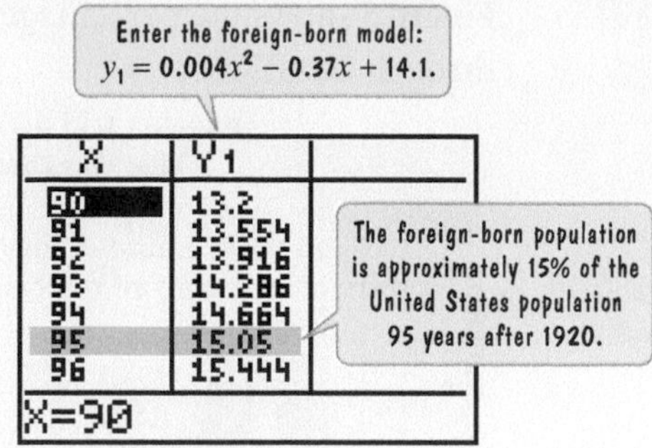

Enter the foreign-born model:
$y_1 = 0.004x^2 - 0.37x + 14.1.$
X | Y1
90 | 13.2
91 | 13.554
92 | 13.916
93 | 14.286
94 | 14.664
95 | 15.05
96 | 15.444
X=90
The foreign-born population is approximately 15% of the United States population 95 years after 1920.

✓ **CHECK POINT 3** Use the model in Example 3 to determine in which year 25% of the United States population will be foreign-born.

Blitzer Bonus

Art, Nature, and Quadratic Equations

A **golden rectangle** can be a rectangle of any size, but its long side must be Φ times as long as its short side, where $\Phi \approx 1.6$. Artists often use golden rectangles in their work because they are considered to be more visually pleasing than other rectangles.

If a golden rectangle is divided into a square and a rectangle, as in **Figure 6(a)**, the smaller rectangle is a golden rectangle. If the smaller golden rectangle is divided again, the same is true of the yet smaller rectangle, and so on. The process of repeatedly dividing each golden rectangle in this manner is illustrated in **Figure 6(b)**. We've also created a spiral by connecting the opposite corners of all the squares with a smooth curve. This spiral matches the spiral shape of the chambered nautilus shell shown in **Figure 6(c)**. The shell spirals out at an ever-increasing rate that is governed by this geometry.

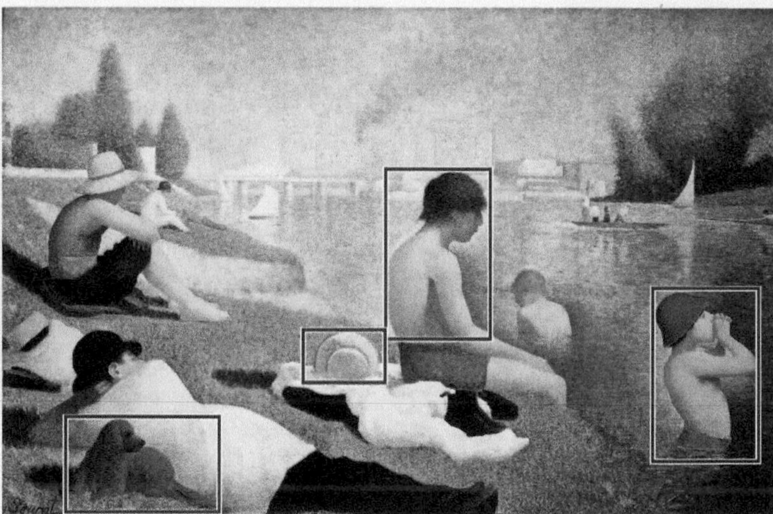

Bathers at Asnières (1884), Georges Seurat. Oil on canvas, 79 1/2 x 118 1/2 in. (201 x 300 cm.). National Gallery, London/Art Resource, New York

In *Bathers at Asnières*, by the French impressionist Georges Seurat (1859–1891), the artist positions parts of the painting as though they were inside golden rectangles.

Bathers at Asnières (1884), George Seurat Art Resource

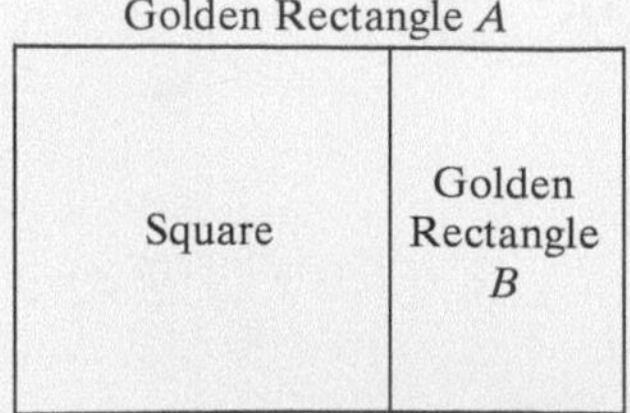

Figure 6(a)

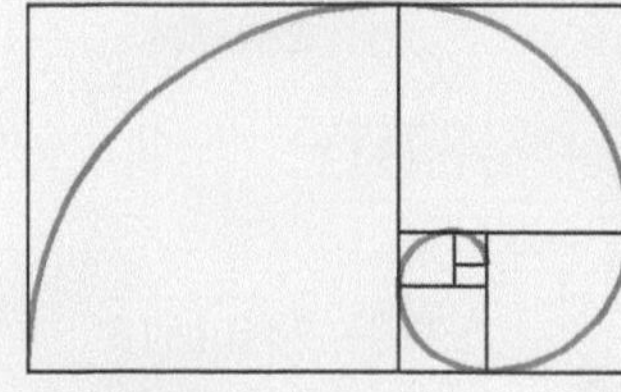

Figure 6(b)

Figure 6(c)

In the Exercise Set that follows, you will use the golden rectangles in **Figure 6(a)** to obtain an exact value of Φ, the ratio of the long side to the short side in a golden rectangle of any size. Your model will involve a quadratic equation that can be solved by the quadratic formula. (See Exercise 63.)

Achieving Success

Here are some strategies to help you prepare for your final exam:

- Review your previous exams. Be sure you understand any errors that you made. Seek help with any concepts that are still unclear.
- Ask your professor if there are additional materials to help students review for the final. This includes review sheets and final exams from previous semesters.
- Attend any review sessions conducted by your professor or by the math department.
- Imagine that your professor will permit two 3 by 5 index cards of notes on the final. Organize and create such a two-card summary for the most vital information in the course, including all important formulas.
- For further review, work the relevant exercises in the Review at the end of this chapter.
- Write your own final exam with detailed solutions for each item. You can use test questions from previous exams in mixed order, worked examples from the chapter summary, exercises in the Reviews, and problems from course handouts. Use your test as a practice final exam.

CONCEPT AND VOCABULARY CHECK

Fill in each blank so that the resulting statement is true.

1. The solutions of a quadratic equation in standard form $ax^2 + bx + c = 0, a \neq 0$, are given by the quadratic formula $x =$ ____________.
2. In order to solve $3x^2 + 10x - 8 = 0$ by the quadratic formula, we use $a =$ ____________, $b =$ ____________, and $c =$ ____________.
3. In order to solve $x^2 + 8x - 15 = 14$ by the quadratic formula, we use $a =$ ____________, $b =$ ____________, and $c =$ ____________.
4. In order to solve $6x^2 = 3x + 4$ by the quadratic formula, we use $a =$ ____________, $b =$ ____________, and $c =$ ____________.
5. $x = \dfrac{-(-5) \pm \sqrt{(-5)^2 - 4(3)(-2)}}{2(3)}$ simplifies to $x =$ ____________ and $x =$ ____________.
6. $x = \dfrac{-8 \pm \sqrt{8^2 - 4(1)(-29)}}{2(1)}$ simplifies to $x =$ ____________.
7. The most efficient technique for solving $(x + 3)^2 = 7$ is by using ____________.
8. The most efficient technique for solving $x^2 - 2x - 3 = 0$ is by using ____________.
9. The most efficient technique for solving $x^2 - 5x - 10 = 0$ is by using ____________.

3 EXERCISE SET

MyMathLab®

Watch the videos in MyMathLab

Download the MyDashBoard App

Practice Exercises

In Exercises 1–22, solve each equation using the quadratic formula. Simplify irrational solutions, if possible.

1. $x^2 + 5x + 6 = 0$
2. $x^2 + 7x + 10 = 0$
3. $x^2 + 5x + 3 = 0$
4. $x^2 + 5x + 2 = 0$
5. $x^2 + 4x - 6 = 0$
6. $x^2 + 2x - 4 = 0$
7. $x^2 + 4x - 7 = 0$
8. $x^2 + 4x + 1 = 0$
9. $x^2 - 3x - 18 = 0$
10. $x^2 - 3x - 10 = 0$

11. $6x^2 - 5x - 6 = 0$

12. $9x^2 - 12x - 5 = 0$

13. $x^2 - 2x - 10 = 0$

14. $x^2 + 6x - 10 = 0$

15. $x^2 - x = 14$

16. $x^2 - 5x = 10$

17. $6x^2 + 6x + 1 = 0$

18. $3x^2 - 5x + 1 = 0$

19. $9x^2 - 12x + 4 = 0$

20. $4x^2 + 12x + 9 = 0$

21. $4x^2 = 2x + 7$

22. $3x^2 = 6x - 1$

In Exercises 23–44, solve each equation by the method of your choice. Simplify irrational solutions, if possible.

23. $2x^2 - x = 1$

24. $3x^2 - 4x = 4$

25. $5x^2 + 2 = 11x$

26. $5x^2 = 6 - 13x$

27. $3x^2 = 60$

28. $2x^2 = 250$

29. $x^2 - 2x = 1$

30. $2x^2 + 3x = 1$

31. $(2x + 3)(x + 4) = 1$

32. $(2x - 5)(x + 1) = 2$

33. $(3x - 4)^2 = 16$

34. $(2x + 7)^2 = 25$

35. $3x^2 - 12x + 12 = 0$

36. $9 - 6x + x^2 = 0$

37. $4x^2 - 16 = 0$

38. $3x^2 - 27 = 0$

39. $x^2 + 9x = 0$

40. $x^2 - 6x = 0$

41. $\frac{3}{4}x^2 - \frac{5}{2}x - 2 = 0$

42. $\frac{1}{3}x^2 - \frac{1}{2}x - \frac{3}{2} = 0$

43. $(3x - 2)^2 = 10$

44. $(4x - 1)^2 = 15$

Practice PLUS

In Exercises 45–52, solve each equation by the method of your choice. Simplify irrational solutions, if possible.

45. $\frac{x^2}{x + 7} - \frac{3}{x + 7} = 0$

46. $\frac{x^2}{x + 9} - \frac{11}{x + 9} = 0$

47. $(x + 2)^2 + x(x + 1) = 4$

48. $(x - 1)(3x + 2) = -7(x - 1)$

49. $2x^2 - 9x - 3 = 9 - 9x$

50. $3x^2 - 6x - 3 = 12 - 6x$

51. $\frac{1}{x} + \frac{1}{x + 3} = \frac{1}{4}$

52. $\frac{1}{x} + \frac{2}{x + 3} = \frac{1}{4}$

Application Exercises

53. A football is kicked straight up from a height of 4 feet with an initial speed of 60 feet per second. The formula

$$h = -16t^2 + 60t + 4$$

describes the ball's height above the ground, h, in feet, t seconds after it is kicked. How long will it take for the football to hit the ground? Use a calculator and round to the nearest tenth of a second.

54. Standing on a platform 50 feet high, a person accidentally fires a gun straight into the air. The formula

$$h = -16t^2 + 100t + 50$$

describes the bullet's height above the ground, h, in feet, t seconds after the gun is fired. How long will it take for the bullet to hit the ground? Use a calculator and round to the nearest tenth of a second.

The height of the arch supporting the bridge shown in the figure is modeled by

$$h = -0.05x^2 + 27,$$

where x is the distance, in feet, from the center of the arch. Use this formula to solve Exercises 55–56.

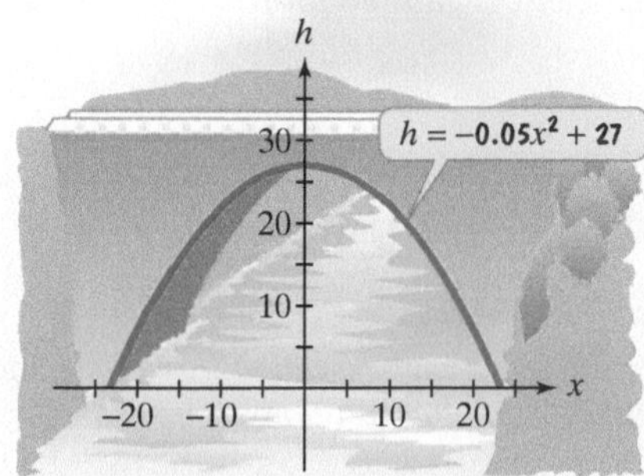

55. How far to the right of the center is the height 22 feet?

56. How far to the right of the center is the height 7 feet?

Because of radio, television, and the Internet, the number of people reading newspapers is continuing to decline. The bar graph shows the average daily newspaper circulation in the United States, in millions, for five selected years. The data can be modeled by the formula

$$N = -0.015x^2 + 1.15x + 41,$$

where N is the average daily U.S. newspaper circulation, in millions, x years after 1940. Use this information to solve Exercises 57–58.

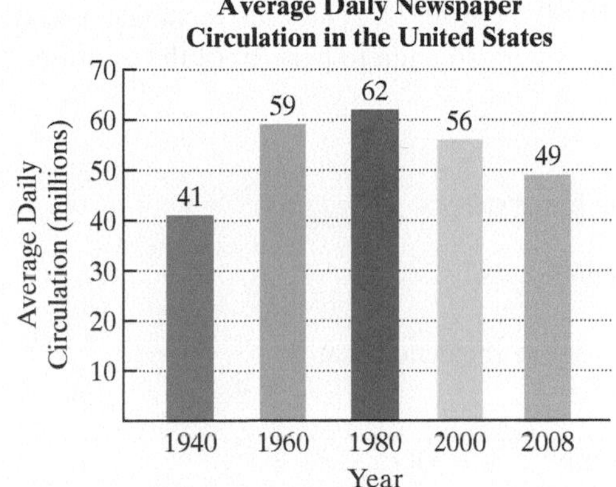

Source: Newspaper Association of America

57. a. According to the model, what was the average daily U.S. newspaper circulation in 2000? How well does the model describe the actual number displayed by the bar graph?

    b. If trends shown by the model continue, in which year will the average daily newspaper circulation be 37 million?

58. a. According to the model, what was the average daily U.S. newspaper circulation in 1980? Does the model underestimate or overestimate the actual number displayed by the bar graph? By how much?

    b. If trends shown by the model continue, in which year will the average daily newspaper circulation be 23 million?

59. The length of a rectangle is 3 meters longer than the width. If the area is 36 square meters, find the rectangle's dimensions. Round to the nearest tenth of a meter.

60. The length of a rectangle is 2 meters longer than the width. If the area is 10 square meters, find the rectangle's dimensions. Round to the nearest tenth of a meter.

61. The hypotenuse of a right triangle is 4 feet long. One leg is 1 foot longer than the other. Find the lengths of the legs. Round to the nearest tenth of a foot.

62. The hypotenuse of a right triangle is 6 feet long. One leg is 1 foot shorter than the other. Find the lengths of the legs. Round to the nearest tenth of a foot.

63. If you have not yet done so, read the Blitzer Bonus. In this exercise, you will use the golden rectangles shown to obtain an exact value for Φ, the ratio of the long side to the short side in a golden rectangle of any size.

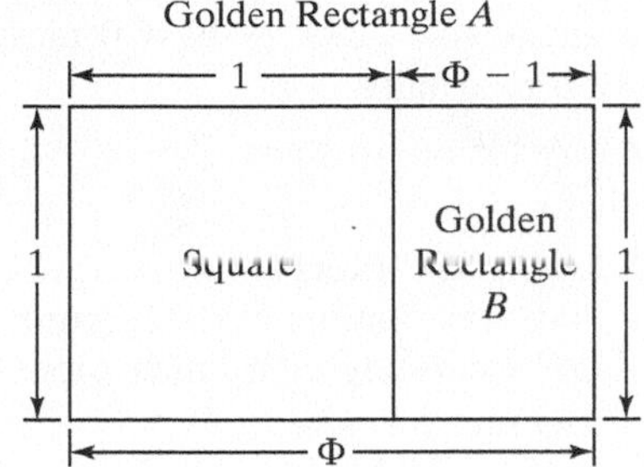

    a. The golden ratio in rectangle A, or the ratio of the long side to the short side, can be modeled by $\frac{\Phi}{1}$. Write a fractional expression that models the golden ratio in rectangle B.

    b. Set the expression for the golden ratio in rectangle A equal to the expression for the golden ratio in rectangle B. Solve the resulting proporation using the quadratic formula. Express Φ as an exact value in simplified radical form.

    c. Use your solution from part (b) to complete this statement: The ratio of the long side to the short side in a golden rectangle of any size is ____________ to 1.

64. Consider two formulas that approximate the dosage of a drug prescribed for children:

$$\text{Young's rule:} \quad C = \frac{DA}{A + 12}$$

$$\text{Cowling's rule:} \quad C = \frac{D(A + 1)}{24}.$$

In each formula, A = the child's age, in years, D = an adult dosage, and C = the proper child's dosage. The formulas apply for ages 2 through 13, inclusive. At which age, to the nearest tenth of a year, do the two formulas give the same dosage?

Writing in Mathematics

65. What is the quadratic formula and why is it useful?

66. Without going into specific details for each step, describe how the quadratic formula is derived.

67. Explain how to solve $x^2 + 6x + 8 = 0$ using the quadratic formula.

68. If you are given a quadratic equation, how do you determine which method to use to solve it?

Critical Thinking Exercises

Make Sense? *In Exercises 69–72, determine whether each statement "makes sense" or "does not make sense" and explain your reasoning.*

69. Because I want to solve $25x^2 - 49 = 0$ fairly quickly, I'll use the quadratic formula.
70. The fastest way for me to solve $x^2 - x - 2 = 0$ is to use the quadratic formula.
71. The data showing the percentage of the United States population that was foreign-born (**Figure 5**) could be described more accurately by a linear model than by the quadratic model that was given.
72. I simplified $\frac{3 + 2\sqrt{3}}{2}$ to $3 + \sqrt{3}$ because 2 is a factor of $2\sqrt{3}$.

In Exercises 73–76, determine whether each statement is true or false. If the statement is false, make the necessary change(s) to produce a true statement.

73. The quadratic formula can be expressed as
$$x = -b \pm \frac{\sqrt{b^2 - 4ac}}{2a}.$$
74. The solutions $\frac{4 \pm \sqrt{3}}{2}$ can be simplified to $2 \pm \sqrt{3}$.
75. For the quadratic equation $-2x^2 + 3x = 0$, we have $a = -2$, $b = 3$, and $c = 0$.
76. Any quadratic equation that can be solved by completing the square can be solved by the quadratic formula.
77. The radicand of the quadratic formula, $b^2 - 4ac$, can be used to determine whether $ax^2 + bx + c = 0$ has solutions that are rational, irrational, or not real numbers. Explain how this works. Is it possible to determine the kinds of answers that one will obtain to a quadratic equation without actually solving the equation? Explain.
78. Solve: $x^2 + 2\sqrt{3}x - 9 = 0$.
79. A rectangular vegetable garden is 5 feet wide and 9 feet long. The garden is to be surrounded by a tile border of uniform width. If there are 40 square feet of tile for the border, how wide, to the nearest tenth of a foot, should it be?

Technology Exercises

80. Graph the formula in Exercise 53,
$$y = -16x^2 + 60x + 4,$$
in a [0, 4, 1] by [0, 65, 5] viewing rectangle. Use the graph to verify your solution to the exercise.

81. Graph the formula in Exercise 57,
$$y = -0.015x^2 + 1.15x + 41,$$
in a [0, 90, 1] by [0, 70, 1] viewing rectangle. Use the graph to verify your solution to part (b) of the exercise.

Review Exercises

82. Evaluate: $125^{-\frac{2}{3}}$.

83. Rationalize the denominator: $\frac{12}{3 + \sqrt{5}}$.

84. Multiply: $(x - y)(x^2 + xy + y^2)$.

Preview Exercises

Exercises 85–87 will help you prepare for the material covered in the next section.

85. Can squaring a real number result in a negative number? Based on your answer, are $\sqrt{-1}$ and $\sqrt{-4}$ real numbers?

In Exercises 86–87, list the numbers from each set that are: **a.** *rational numbers;* **b.** *irrational numbers;* **c.** *real numbers;* **d.** *not real numbers. (Hint: Your answer to each question in Exercise 85 should be "no.")*

86. $\{-\sqrt{5}, -\sqrt{4}, \sqrt{-1}, \sqrt{-4}, \sqrt{1}, \sqrt{5}\}$

87. $\{-\sqrt{9}, -\sqrt{7}, \sqrt{-9}, \sqrt{-7}, \sqrt{0}, \sqrt{7}, \sqrt{9}\}$

MID-CHAPTER CHECK POINT Section 1–Section 3

What You Know: We saw that not all quadratic equations can be solved by factoring. We learned three new methods for solving these equations—the square root property, completing the square, and the quadratic formula. We also learned to determine the most efficient technique to use when solving a quadratic equation.

In Exercises 1–12, solve each equation by the method of your choice. Simplify irrational solutions, if possible.

1. $(3x - 2)^2 = 100$

2. $15x^2 = 5x$

3. $x^2 - 2x - 10 = 0$

4. $x^2 - 8x + 16 = 7$

5. $3x^2 - x - 2 = 0$

6. $6x^2 = 10x - 3$

7. $x^2 + (x + 1)^2 = 25$

8. $(x + 5)^2 = 40$

9. $2(x^2 - 8) = 11 - x^2$

10. $2x^2 + 5x + 1 = 0$

11. $(x - 8)(2x - 3) = 34$

12. $x + \frac{16}{x} = 8$

13. Solve by completing the square: $x^2 + 14x - 32 = 0.$

14. Find the missing length in the right triangle. Express the answer in simplified radical form.

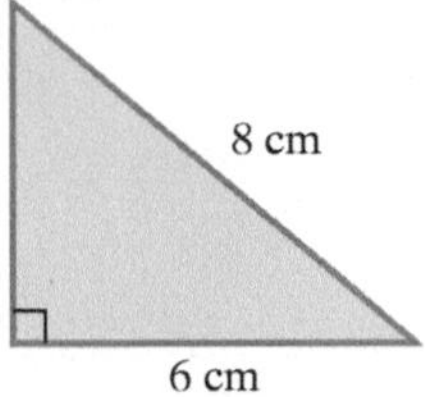

15. Find the distance between $(-3, 2)$ and $(9, -3)$.

16. The figure shows a right triangle whose hypotenuse measures 20 inches and whose leg measurements are in the ratio 3:4. Find the length of each leg.

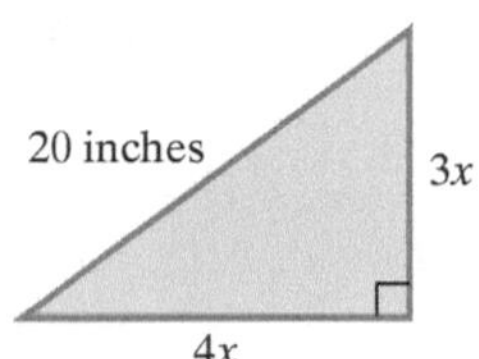

SECTION 4

Imaginary Numbers as Solutions of Quadratic Equations

Objectives

1. Express square roots of negative numbers in terms of i.
2. Solve quadratic equations with imaginary solutions.

Who is this kid warning us about our eyeballs turning black if we attempt to find the square root of -9? Don't believe what you hear on the street. Although square roots of negative numbers are not real numbers, they do play a significant role in algebra. In this section, we move beyond the real numbers and discuss square roots with negative radicands.

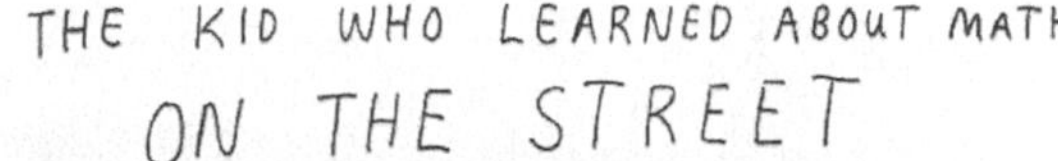

Copyright © 2011 by Roz Chast/The New Yorker Collection/The Cartoon bank.

1 Express square roots of negative numbers in terms of i.

The Imaginary Unit i

Throughout this chapter, we have avoided quadratic equations that have no real numbers as solutions. A fairly simple example is the equation

$$x^2 = -1.$$

Because the square of a real number is never negative, there is no real number x such that $x^2 = -1$. To provide a setting in which such equations have solutions, mathematicians invented an expanded system of numbers, the *complex numbers.* The *imaginary number i*, defined to be a solution to the equation $x^2 = -1$, is the basis of this new set.

The Imaginary Unit *i*

The **imaginary unit** i is defined as

$$i = \sqrt{-1}, \quad \text{where} \quad i^2 = -1.$$

Using the imaginary unit i, we can express the square root of any negative number as a real multiple of i. For example,

$$\sqrt{-25} = \sqrt{25(-1)} = \sqrt{25}\sqrt{-1} = 5i.$$

We can check this result by squaring $5i$ and obtaining -25.

$$(5i)^2 = 5^2i^2 = 25(-1) = -25$$

The Square Root of a Negative Number

If b is a positive real number, then

$$\sqrt{-b} = \sqrt{b(-1)} = \sqrt{b}\sqrt{-1} = \sqrt{b}\,i \quad \text{or} \quad i\sqrt{b}.$$

EXAMPLE 1 Expressing Square Roots of Negative Numbers as Multiples of *i*

Write as a multiple of i:

a. $\sqrt{-9}$ **b.** $\sqrt{-7}$ **c.** $\sqrt{-8}$.

Solution

a. $\sqrt{-9} = \sqrt{9(-1)} = \sqrt{9}\sqrt{-1} = 3i$

b. $\sqrt{-7} = \sqrt{7(-1)} = \sqrt{7}\sqrt{-1} = \sqrt{7}i$

c. $\sqrt{-8} = \sqrt{8(-1)} = \sqrt{8}\sqrt{-1} = \sqrt{4 \cdot 2}\sqrt{-1} = 2\sqrt{2}i$

Be sure not to write i under the radical.

In order to avoid writing i under a radical, let's agree to write i *before* any radical. Consequently, we express the multiple of i in part (b) as $i\sqrt{7}$ and the multiple of i in part (c) as $2i\sqrt{2}$. ■

Great Question!

Now that we've introduced square roots of negative numbers, can I still use the rule $\sqrt{ab} = \sqrt{a}\sqrt{b}$?

We allow the use of the product rule

$$\sqrt{ab} = \sqrt{a}\sqrt{b}$$

when a is positive and b is -1. However, you cannot use $\sqrt{ab} = \sqrt{a}\sqrt{b}$ when both a and b are negative.

✓ **CHECK POINT 1** Write as a multiple of i:

a. $\sqrt{-16}$ **b.** $\sqrt{-5}$ **c.** $\sqrt{-50}$.

A new system of numbers, called *complex numbers*, is based on adding multiples of i, such as $5i$, to the real numbers.

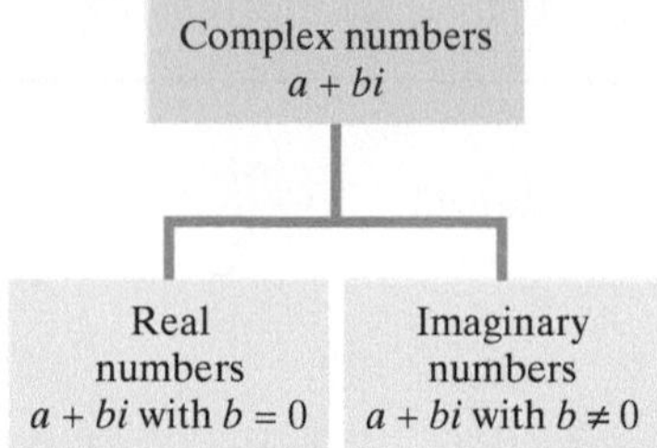

Figure 7
The complex number system

Complex Numbers and Imaginary Numbers

The set of all numbers in the form

$$a + bi$$

with real numbers a and b, and i, the imaginary unit, is called the set of **complex numbers**. The real number a is called the **real part** and the real number b is called the **imaginary part** of the complex number $a + bi$. If $b \neq 0$, then the complex number is called an **imaginary number** (see **Figure 7**).

Here are some examples of complex numbers. Each number can be written in the form $a + bi$.

$-4 + 6i$ — a, the real part, is -4. b, the imaginary part, is 6.

$2i = 0 + 2i$ — a, the real part, is 0. b, the imaginary part, is 2.

$3 = 3 + 0i$ — a, the real part, is 3. b, the imaginary part, is 0.

Can you see that b, the imaginary part, is not zero in the first two complex numbers? Because $b \neq 0$, these complex numbers are imaginary numbers. By contrast, the imaginary part of the complex number on the right, $3 + 0i$, is zero. This complex number is not an imaginary number. The number 3, or $3 + 0i$, is a real number.

2 Solve quadratic equations with imaginary solutions.

Solving Quadratic Equations with Imaginary Solutions

The equation $x^2 = -25$ has no real solutions, but it does have imaginary solutions.

$x^2 = -25$ — No real number squared results in a negative number.

$x = \pm\sqrt{-25}$ — Apply the square root property.

$x = \pm 5i$ — $\sqrt{-25} = \sqrt{25(-1)} = \sqrt{25}\sqrt{-1} = 5i$

The solutions are $5i$ and $-5i$. The next examples involve quadratic equations that have no real solutions, but do have imaginary solutions.

EXAMPLE 2 Solving a Quadratic Equation Using the Square Root Property

Solve: $(x + 4)^2 = -36$.

Solution

$(x + 4)^2 = -36$ — This is the given equation.

$x + 4 = \sqrt{-36}$ or $x + 4 = -\sqrt{-36}$ — Apply the square root property. Equivalently, $x + 4 = \pm\sqrt{-36}$.

$x + 4 = 6i$ $\quad$ $x + 4 = -6i$ — $\sqrt{-36} = \sqrt{36(-1)} = \sqrt{36}\sqrt{-1} = 6i$

$x = -4 + 6i$ $\quad$ $x = -4 - 6i$ — Solve the equations by subtracting 4 from both sides.

Check $-4 + 6i$:

$$(x + 4)^2 = -36$$
$$(-4 + 6i + 4)^2 \stackrel{?}{=} -36$$
$$(6i)^2 \stackrel{?}{=} -36$$
$$36i^2 \stackrel{?}{=} -36$$
$$36(-1) \stackrel{?}{=} -36$$
$$-36 = -36, \text{ true}$$

Check $-4 - 6i$:

$$(x + 4)^2 = -36$$
$$(-4 - 6i + 4)^2 \stackrel{?}{=} -36$$
$$(-6i)^2 \stackrel{?}{=} -36$$
$$36i^2 \stackrel{?}{=} -36$$
$$36(-1) \stackrel{?}{=} -36$$
$$-36 = -36, \text{ true}$$

The imaginary solutions are $-4 + 6i$ and $-4 - 6i$. The solution set is $\{-4 + 6i, -4 - 6i\}$ or $\{-4 \pm 6i\}$. ■

✓ **CHECK POINT 2** Solve: $(x + 2)^2 = -25$.

EXAMPLE 3 Solving a Quadratic Equation Using the Quadratic Formula

Solve: $x^2 - 2x + 2 = 0$.

Solution Because the trinomial on the left side is prime, we solve using the quadratic formula.

$$x^2 - 2x + 2 = 0$$

$a = 1$ $b = -2$ $c = 2$

$$x = \frac{-b \pm \sqrt{b^2 - 4ac}}{2a}$$ Use the quadratic formula.

$$x = \frac{-(-2) \pm \sqrt{(-2)^2 - 4(1)(2)}}{2(1)}$$ Substitute the values for a, b, and c: $a = 1$, $b = -2$, and $c = 2$.

$$= \frac{2 \pm \sqrt{-4}}{2}$$ $(-2)^2 - 4(1)(2) = 4 - 8 = -4$

$$= \frac{2 \pm \sqrt{4(-1)}}{2}$$

$$= \frac{2 \pm 2i}{2}$$ $\sqrt{4(-1)} = \sqrt{4}\sqrt{-1} = 2i$

$$= \frac{2(1 \pm i)}{2}$$ Factor out 2 from the numerator.

$$= 1 \pm i$$ Divide the numerator and denominator by 2.

The imaginary solutions are $1 + i$ and $1 - i$. The solution set is $\{1 \pm i\}$. ■

Using Technology

Graphic Connections

The graph of

$$y = x^2 - 2x + 2$$

has no x-intercepts, so

$$x^2 - 2x + 2 = 0$$

has no real solutions. However, the equation does have imaginary solutions.

$y = x^2 - 2x + 2$

[−10, 10, 1] by [−10, 10, 1]

✓ **CHECK POINT 3** Solve: $x^2 + 6x + 13 = 0$.

CONCEPT AND VOCABULARY CHECK

Fill in each blank so that the resulting statement is true.

1. The imaginary unit i is defined as $i =$ ____________, where $i^2 =$ ____________.
2. $\sqrt{-25} = \sqrt{25(-1)} = \sqrt{25}\sqrt{-1} =$ ____________.
3. The set of all numbers in the form $a + bi$ is called the set of ____________ numbers. If $b \neq 0$, then the number is also called a/an ____________ number. If $b = 0$, then the number is also called a/an ____________ number.
4. $x = \frac{4 \pm \sqrt{-4}}{2}$ simplifies to $x =$ ____________.

4 EXERCISE SET

MyMathLab®

Watch the videos in MyMathLab

Download the MyDashBoard App

Practice Exercises

In Exercises 1–16, express each number in terms of i.

1. $\sqrt{-36}$ **2.** $\sqrt{-49}$

3. $\sqrt{-13}$ **4.** $\sqrt{-19}$

5. $\sqrt{-50}$ **6.** $\sqrt{-12}$

7. $\sqrt{-20}$ **8.** $\sqrt{-300}$

9. $-\sqrt{-28}$ **10.** $-\sqrt{-150}$

11. $7 + \sqrt{-16}$ **12.** $9 + \sqrt{-4}$

13. $10 + \sqrt{-3}$ **14.** $5 + \sqrt{-5}$

15. $6 - \sqrt{-98}$ **16.** $6 - \sqrt{-18}$

In Exercises 17–24, solve each quadratic equation using the square root property. Express imaginary solutions in a + bi form.

17. $(x - 3)^2 = -9$

18. $(x - 5)^2 = -36$

19. $(x + 7)^2 = -64$

20. $(x + 12)^2 = -100$

21. $(x - 2)^2 = -7$

22. $(x - 1)^2 = -13$

23. $(y + 3)^2 = -18$

24. $(y + 4)^2 = -48$

In Exercises 25–36, solve each quadratic equation using the quadratic formula.

25. $x^2 + 4x + 5 = 0$

26. $x^2 + 2x + 2 = 0$

27. $x^2 - 6x + 13 = 0$

28. $x^2 - 6x + 10 = 0$

29. $x^2 - 12x + 40 = 0$

30. $x^2 - 4x + 29 = 0$

31. $x^2 = 10x - 27$

32. $x^2 = 4x - 7$

33. $5x^2 = 2x - 3$

34. $6x^2 = -2x - 1$

35. $2y^2 = 4y - 5$

36. $5y^2 = 6y - 7$

Practice PLUS

In Exercises 37–42, solve each equation by the method of your choice.

37. $12x^2 + 35 = 8x^2 + 15$ **38.** $8x^2 - 9 = 5x^2 - 30$

39. $\frac{x + 3}{5} = \frac{x - 2}{x}$ **40.** $\frac{x + 4}{4} = \frac{x - 5}{x - 2}$

41. $\frac{1}{x + 1} - \frac{1}{2} = \frac{1}{x}$ **42.** $\frac{4}{x} = \frac{8}{x^2} + 1$

Application Exercises

43. The personnel manager of a roller skate company knows that the company's weekly revenue, R, in thousands of dollars, can be modeled by the formula

$$R = -2x^2 + 36x,$$

where x is the price of a pair of skates, in dollars. A job applicant promises the personnel manager an advertising campaign guaranteed to generate $200,000 in weekly revenue. Substitute 200 for R in the given formula and solve the equation. Are the solutions real numbers? Explain why the applicant will or will not be hired in the advertising department.

44. A football is kicked straight up from a height of 4 feet with an initial speed of 60 feet per second. The formula

$$h = -16t^2 + 60t + 4$$

describes the ball's height above the ground, h, in feet, t seconds after it is kicked. Will the ball reach a height of 80 feet? Substitute 80 for h in the given formula and solve the equation. Are the solutions real numbers? Explain why the ball will or will not reach 80 feet.

Writing in Mathematics

45. What is the imaginary unit i?

46. Explain how to write $\sqrt{-64}$ as a multiple of i.

47. What is a complex number?

48. What is an imaginary number?

49. Why is every real number also a complex number?

50. Explain each of the three jokes in the cartoon on page 647.

Critical Thinking Exercises

Make Sense? *In Exercises 51–54, determine whether each statement "makes sense" or "does not make sense" and explain your reasoning.*

51. The word *imaginary* in imaginary numbers tells me that these numbers are undefined.

52. Writing i before any radical helps me to avoid placing i in the radicand.

53. By writing the imaginary number $6i$, I can immediately see that 6 is the constant and i is the variable.

54. When I use the quadratic formula to solve a quadratic equation and $b^2 - 4ac$ is negative, I can be certain that the equation has two imaginary solutions.

In Exercises 55–58, determine whether each statement is true or false. If the statement is false, make the necessary change(s) to produce a true statement.

55. $-\sqrt{-9} = -(-3) = 3$

56. The complex number $a + 0i$ is the real number a.

57. $2 + \sqrt{-4} = 2 - 2i$

58. $\frac{2 \pm 4i}{2} = 1 \pm 4i$

59. Show that $1 + i$ is a solution of $x^2 - 2x + 2 = 0$ by substituting $1 + i$ for x. You should obtain

$$(1 + i)^2 - 2(1 + i) + 2.$$

Square $1 + i$ as you would a binomial. Distribute -2 as indicated. Then simplify the resulting expression by combining like terms and replacing i^2 with -1. You should obtain 0. Use this procedure to show that $1 - i$ is the equation's other solution.

60. Prove that there is no real number such that when twice the number is subtracted from its square, the difference is -5.

Technology Exercises

61. Reread Exercise 43. Use your graphing utility to illustrate the problem's solution by graphing $y = -2x^2 + 36x$ and $y = 200$ in a [0, 20, 1] by [0, 210, 30] viewing rectangle. Explain how the two graphs show that weekly revenue will not reach \$200,000 and, therefore, the applicant will not be hired.

62. Reread Exercise 44. Use your graphing utility to illustrate the problem's solution by graphing $y = -16x^2 + 60x + 4$ and $y = 80$ in a [0, 4, 1] by [0, 100, 10] viewing rectangle. Explain how the graphs show that the ball will not reach a height of 80 feet.

Review Exercises

In Exercises 63–65, graph each equation in a rectangular coordinate system.

63. $y = \frac{1}{3}x - 2$

64. $2x - 3y = 6$

65. $x = -2$

Preview Exercises

Exercises 66–68 will help you prepare for the material covered in the next section.

66. Use point plotting to graph $y = x^2 + 4x + 3$. Select integers from -5 to 1, inclusive, for x.

67. Replace y with 0 and find the x-intercepts for the graph of $y = x^2 - 2x - 3$.

68. Replace x with 0 and find the y-intercept for the graph of $y = x^2 - 2x - 3$.

SECTION 5

Graphs of Quadratic Equations

Objectives

1. Understand the characteristics of graphs of quadratic equations.
2. Find a parabola's intercepts.
3. Find a parabola's vertex.
4. Graph quadratic equations.
5. Solve problems using a parabola's vertex.

Many sports involve objects that are thrown, kicked, or hit, and then proceed with no additional force of their own. Such objects are called **projectiles**. Paths of projectiles, as well as their heights over time, can be modeled by quadratic equations. In this section, you will learn to use graphs of quadratic equations to gain a visual understanding of the algebra that describes football, baseball, basketball, the shot put, and other projectile sports.

Marcin Janiec/Fotolia

1 Understand the characteristics of graphs of quadratic equations.

Graphs of Quadratic Equations

The graph of any quadratic equation

$$y = ax^2 + bx + c, \quad a \neq 0$$

is called a **parabola**. Parabolas are shaped like bowls or inverted bowls, as shown in **Figure 8**. If the coefficient of x^2 (the value of a in $ax^2 + bx + c$) is positive, the parabola opens upward. If the coefficient of x^2 is negative, the parabola opens downward. The **vertex** (or turning point) of the parabola is the lowest point, or minimum point, on the graph when it opens upward and the highest point, or maximum point, on the graph when it opens downward.

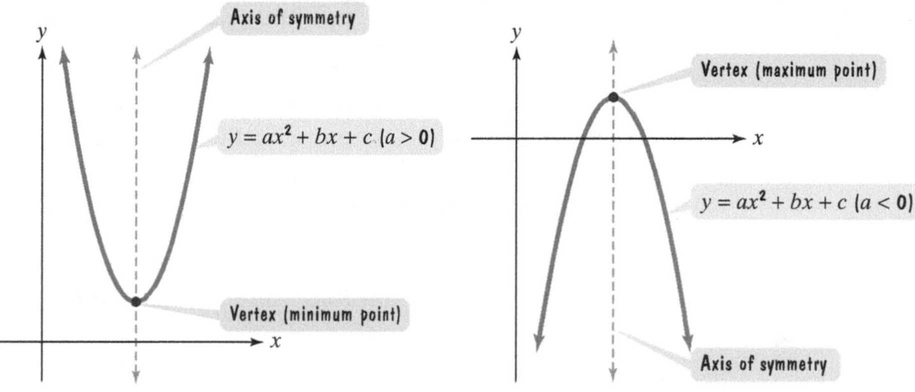

Figure 8 Characteristics of graphs of quadratic equations

Look at the unusual image of the word *mirror* shown on the right. The artist, Scott Kim, has created the image so that the two halves of the whole are mirror images of each other. A parabola shares this kind of symmetry. A "mirror line" through the vertex, called the **axis of symmetry**, divides the figure in half. If a parabola is folded along its axis of symmetry, the two halves match exactly.

EXAMPLE 1 Using Point Plotting to Graph a Parabola

Consider the equation $y = x^2 + 4x + 3$.

a. Is the graph a parabola that opens upward or downward?

b. Use point plotting to graph the parabola. Select integers from -5 to 1, inclusive, for x.

Solution

a. To determine whether a parabola opens upward or downward, we begin by identifying a, the coefficient of x^2. The following voice balloons show the values for a, b, and c in $y = x^2 + 4x + 3$. Notice that we wrote x^2 as $1x^2$.

$$y = 1x^2 + 4x + 3$$

a, the coefficient of x^2, is 1. | *b*, the coefficient of x, is 4. | *c*, the constant term, is 3.

When a is greater than 0, a parabola opens upward. When a is less than 0, a parabola opens downward. Because $a = 1$, which is greater than 0, the parabola opens upward.

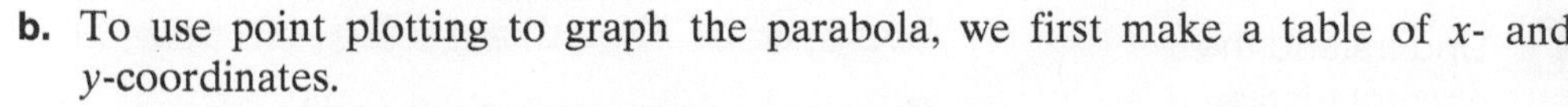

b. To use point plotting to graph the parabola, we first make a table of x- and y-coordinates.

x	$y = x^2 + 4x + 3$	(x, y)
−5	$y = (-5)^2 + 4(-5) + 3 = 8$	(−5, 8)
−4	$y = (-4)^2 + 4(-4) + 3 = 3$	(−4, 3)
−3	$y = (-3)^2 + 4(-3) + 3 = 0$	(−3, 0)
−2	$y = (-2)^2 + 4(-2) + 3 = -1$	(−2, −1)
−1	$y = (-1)^2 + 4(-1) + 3 = 0$	(−1, 0)
0	$y = 0^2 + 4(0) + 3 = 3$	(0, 3)
1	$y = 1^2 + 4(1) + 3 = 8$	(1, 8)

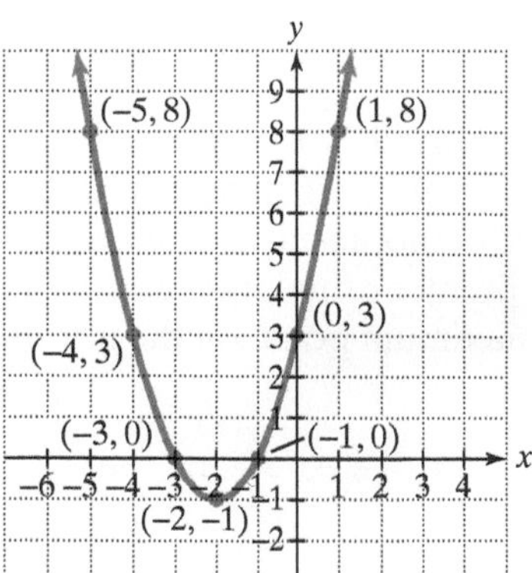

Figure 9
The graph of $y = x^2 + 4x + 3$

Then we plot the points and connect them with a smooth curve. The graph of $y = x^2 + 4x + 3$ is shown in **Figure 9**. ■

✓ **CHECK POINT 1** Consider the equation $y = x^2 - 6x + 8$.

a. Is the graph a parabola that opens upward or downward?

b. Use point plotting to graph the parabola. Select integers from 0 to 6, inclusive, for x.

Several points are important when graphing a quadratic equation. These points, labeled in **Figure 10**, are the x-intercepts (although not every parabola has two x-intercepts), the y-intercept, and the vertex. Let's see how we can locate these points.

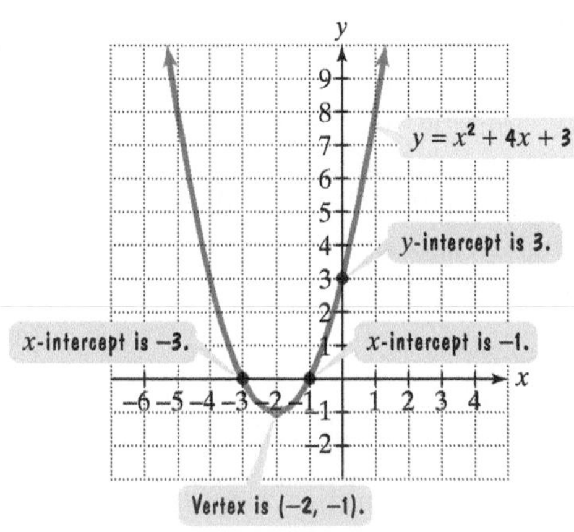

Figure 10 Useful points in graphing a parabola

2 Find a parabola's intercepts.

Finding a Parabola's x-Intercepts

At each point where a parabola crosses the x-axis, the value of y equals 0. Thus, the x-intercepts can be found by replacing y with 0 in $y = ax^2 + bx + c$. Use factoring or the quadratic formula to solve the resulting quadratic equation for x.

EXAMPLE 2 Finding a Parabola's x-Intercepts

Find the x-intercepts for the parabola whose equation is $y = x^2 + 4x + 3$.

Solution Replace y with 0 in $y = x^2 + 4x + 3$. We obtain $0 = x^2 + 4x + 3$, or $x^2 + 4x + 3 = 0$. We can solve this equation by factoring.

$$x^2 + 4x + 3 = 0$$
$$(x + 3)(x + 1) = 0$$
$$x + 3 = 0 \quad \text{or} \quad x + 1 = 0$$
$$x = -3 \qquad\qquad x = -1$$

Thus, the x-intercepts are -3 and -1. The parabola passes through $(-3, 0)$ and $(-1, 0)$, as shown in **Figure 10.** ■

✓ CHECK POINT 2 Find the x-intercepts for the parabola whose equation is $y = x^2 - 6x + 8$.

Finding a Parabola's *y*-Intercept

At the point where a parabola crosses the y-axis, the value of x equals 0. Thus, the y-intercept can be found by replacing x with 0 in $y = ax^2 + bx + c$. Simple arithmetic will produce a value for y, which is the y-intercept.

EXAMPLE 3 Finding a Parabola's *y*-Intercept

Find the y-intercept for the parabola whose equation is $y = x^2 + 4x + 3$.

Solution Replace x with 0 in $y = x^2 + 4x + 3$.

$$y = 0^2 + 4 \cdot 0 + 3 = 0 + 0 + 3 = 3$$

The y-intercept is 3. The parabola passes through $(0, 3)$, as shown in **Figure 10.** ■

✓ CHECK POINT 3 Find the y-intercept for the parabola whose equation is $y = x^2 - 6x + 8$.

3 Find a parabola's vertex.

Finding a Parabola's Vertex

Keep in mind that a parabola's vertex is its turning point. The x-coordinate of the vertex for the parabola in **Figure 10**, -2, is midway between the x-intercepts, -3 and -1. If a parabola has two x-intercepts, they are found by solving $ax^2 + bx + c = 0$. The solutions of this equation,

$$x = \frac{-b - \sqrt{b^2 - 4ac}}{2a} \quad \text{and} \quad x = \frac{-b + \sqrt{b^2 - 4ac}}{2a},$$

are the x-intercepts. The value of x midway between these intercepts is $x = \frac{-b}{2a}$. This equation can be used to find the x-coordinate of the vertex even when no x-intercepts exist.

The Vertex of a Parabola

For a parabola whose equation is $y = ax^2 + bx + c$,

1. The x-coordinate of the vertex is $\frac{-b}{2a}$.
2. The y-coordinate of the vertex is found by substituting the x-coordinate into the parabola's equation and evaluating.

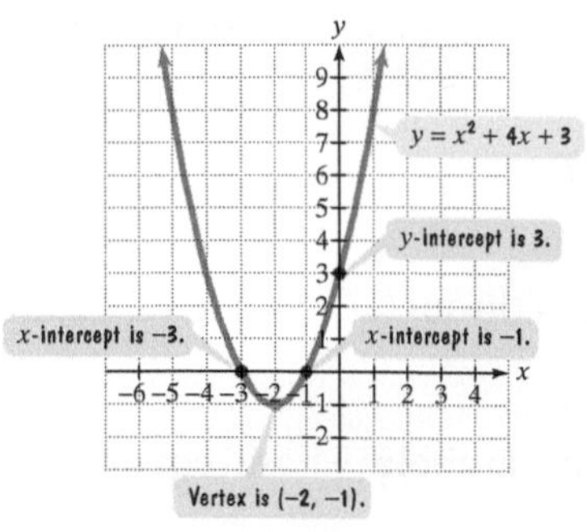
$y = x^2 + 4x + 3$
y-intercept is 3.
x-intercept is −3.
x-intercept is −1.
Vertex is (−2, −1).

Figure 10 (repeated)

EXAMPLE 4 Finding a Parabola's Vertex

Find the vertex for the parabola whose equation is $y = x^2 + 4x + 3$.

Solution In the equation $y = x^2 + 4x + 3$, $a = 1$ and $b = 4$.

$$x\text{-coordinate of vertex} = \frac{-b}{2a} = \frac{-4}{2 \cdot 1} = \frac{-4}{2} = -2$$

To find the y-coordinate of the vertex, we substitute -2 for x in $y = x^2 + 4x + 3$ and then evaluate.

$$y\text{-coordinate of vertex} = (-2)^2 + 4(-2) + 3 = 4 + (-8) + 3 = -1$$

The vertex is $(-2, -1)$, as shown in **Figure 10**. ■

✓ **CHECK POINT 4** Find the vertex for the parabola whose equation is $y = x^2 - 6x + 8$.

---

4 Graph quadratic equations.

A Strategy for Graphing Quadratic Equations

Here is a procedure to sketch the graph of the quadratic equation $y = ax^2 + bx + c$:

Graphing Quadratic Equations

The graph of $y = ax^2 + bx + c$, called a parabola, can be graphed using the following steps:

1. Determine whether the parabola opens upward or downward. If $a > 0$, it opens upward. If $a < 0$, it opens downward.
2. Determine the vertex of the parabola. The x-coordinate is $\frac{-b}{2a}$.
   The y-coordinate is found by substituting the x-coordinate into the parabola's equation and evaluating.
3. Find any x-intercepts by replacing y with 0. Solve the resulting quadratic equation for x. The real solutions are the x-intercepts.
4. Find the y-intercept by replacing x with 0. Because $y = a \cdot 0^2 + b \cdot 0 + c$ simplifies to $y = c$, the y-intercept is c, the constant term, and the parabola passes through $(0, c)$.
5. Plot the intercepts and the vertex.
6. Connect these points with a smooth curve.

EXAMPLE 5 Graphing a Parabola

Graph the quadratic equation: $y = x^2 - 2x - 3$.

Solution We can graph this equation by following the steps in the box.

Step 1. Determine how the parabola opens. Note that a, the coefficient of x^2, is 1. Thus, $a > 0$; this positive value tells us that the parabola opens upward.

Step 2. Find the vertex. We know that the x-coordinate of the vertex is $\frac{-b}{2a}$. Let's identify the numbers a, b, and c in the given equation, which is in the form $y = ax^2 + bx + c$.

$$y = x^2 - 2x - 3$$

$a = 1$ $b = -2$ $c = -3$

Now we substitute the values of a and b, $a = 1$ and $b = -2$, into the expression for the x-coordinate:

$$x\text{-coordinate of vertex} = \frac{-b}{2a} = \frac{-(-2)}{2(1)} = \frac{2}{2} = 1.$$

The x-coordinate of the vertex is 1. We can substitute 1 for x in the equation $y = x^2 - 2x - 3$ to find the y-coordinate:

$$y\text{-coordinate of vertex} = 1^2 - 2 \cdot 1 - 3 = 1 - 2 - 3 = -4.$$

The vertex is $(1, -4)$.

Step 3. Find the x-intercepts. Replace y with 0 in $y = x^2 - 2x - 3$. We obtain $0 = x^2 - 2x - 3$ or $x^2 - 2x - 3 = 0$. We can solve this equation by factoring.

$$x^2 - 2x - 3 = 0$$
$$(x - 3)(x + 1) = 0$$
$$x - 3 = 0 \quad \text{or} \quad x + 1 = 0$$
$$x = 3 \qquad\qquad x = -1$$

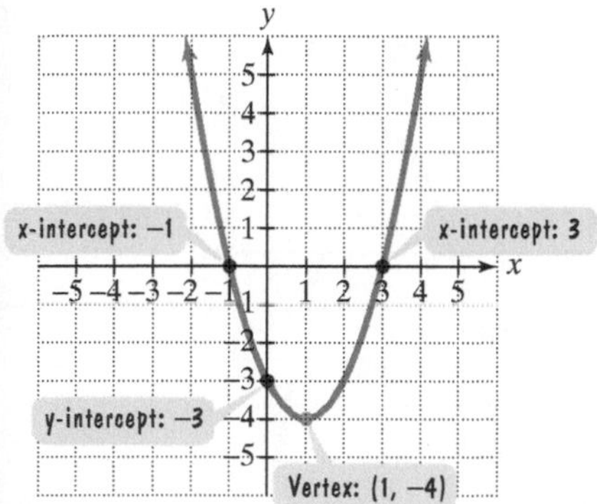

Figure 11
The graph of $y = x^2 - 2x - 3$

The x-intercepts are 3 and -1. The parabola passes through $(3, 0)$ and $(-1, 0)$.

Step 4. Find the y-intercept. Replace x with 0 in $y = x^2 - 2x - 3$:

$$y = 0^2 - 2 \cdot 0 - 3 = 0 - 0 - 3 = -3.$$

The y-intercept is -3. The parabola passes through $(0, -3)$.

Steps 5 and 6. Plot the intercepts and the vertex. Connect these points with a smooth curve. The intercepts and the vertex are shown as the four labeled points in **Figure 11**. Also shown is the graph of the quadratic equation, obtained by connecting the points with a smooth curve. ■

✓ **CHECK POINT 5** Graph the quadratic equation: $y = x^2 + 6x + 5$.

EXAMPLE 6 Graphing a Parabola

Graph the quadratic equation: $y = -x^2 + 4x - 1$.

Solution

Step 1. Determine how the parabola opens. Note that a, the coefficient of x^2, is -1. Thus, $a < 0$; this negative value tells us that the parabola opens downward.

Step 2. Find the vertex. The x-coordinate of the vertex is $\frac{-b}{2a}$.

$$y = -x^2 + 4x - 1$$

$a = -1$ $b = 4$ $c = -1$

$$x\text{-coordinate of vertex} = \frac{-b}{2a} = \frac{-4}{2(-1)} = \frac{-4}{-2} = 2$$

Substitute 2 for x in $y = -x^2 + 4x - 1$ to find the y-coordinate:

$$y\text{-coordinate of vertex} = -2^2 + 4 \cdot 2 - 1 = -4 + 8 - 1 = 3.$$

The vertex is $(2, 3)$.

Step 3. Find the x-intercepts. Replace y with 0 in $y = -x^2 + 4x - 1$. We obtain $0 = -x^2 + 4x - 1$ or $-x^2 + 4x - 1 = 0$. This equation cannot be solved by factoring. We will use the quadratic formula to solve it.

$$a = -1, \quad b = 4, \quad c = -1$$

$$x = \frac{-b \pm \sqrt{b^2 - 4ac}}{2a} = \frac{-4 \pm \sqrt{4^2 - 4(-1)(-1)}}{2(-1)} = \frac{-4 \pm \sqrt{16 - 4}}{-2}$$

$$x = \frac{-4 + \sqrt{12}}{-2} \approx 0.3 \quad \text{or} \quad x = \frac{-4 - \sqrt{12}}{-2} \approx 3.7$$

The x-intercepts are approximately 0.3 and 3.7. The parabola passes through (0.3, 0) and (3.7, 0).

Step 4. Find the y-intercept. Replace x with 0 in $y = -x^2 + 4x - 1$:

$$y = -0^2 + 4 \cdot 0 - 1 = -1.$$

The y-intercept is -1. The parabola passes through $(0, -1)$.

Steps 5 and 6. Plot the intercepts and the vertex. Connect these points with a smooth curve. The intercepts and the vertex are shown as the four labeled points in **Figure 12**. Also shown is the graph of the quadratic equation, obtained by connecting the points with a smooth curve.

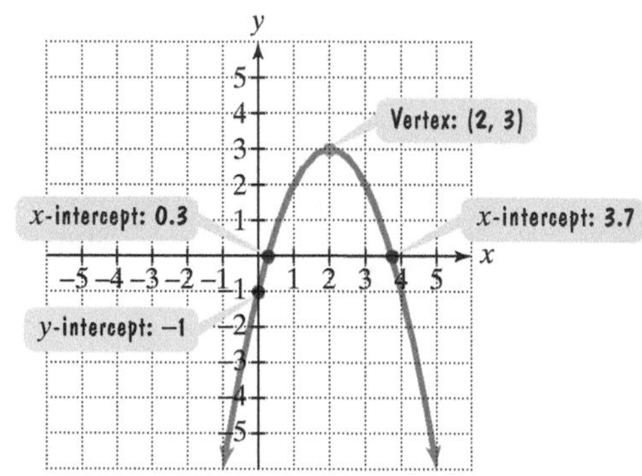

Figure 12
The graph of $y = -x^2 + 4x - 1$ ■

✓ **CHECK POINT 6** Graph the quadratic equation: $y = -x^2 - 2x + 5$.

---

5 Solve problems using a parabola's vertex.

Applications

Many applied problems involve finding the maximum or minimum value of equations in the form $y = ax^2 + bx + c$. The vertex of the graph is the point of interest. If $a < 0$, the parabola opens downward and the vertex is its highest point. If $a > 0$, the parabola opens upward and the vertex is its lowest point.

EXAMPLE 7 The Parabolic Path of a Punted Football

Figure 13 shows that when a football is kicked, the nearest defensive player is 6 feet from the point of impact with the kicker's foot. The height of the punted football, y, in feet, can be modeled by

$$y = -0.01x^2 + 1.18x + 2,$$

where x is the ball's horizontal distance, in feet, from the point of impact with the kicker's foot.

a. What is the maximum height of the punt and how far from the point of impact does this occur?

b. How far must the nearest defensive player, who is 6 feet from the kicker's point of impact, reach to block the punt?

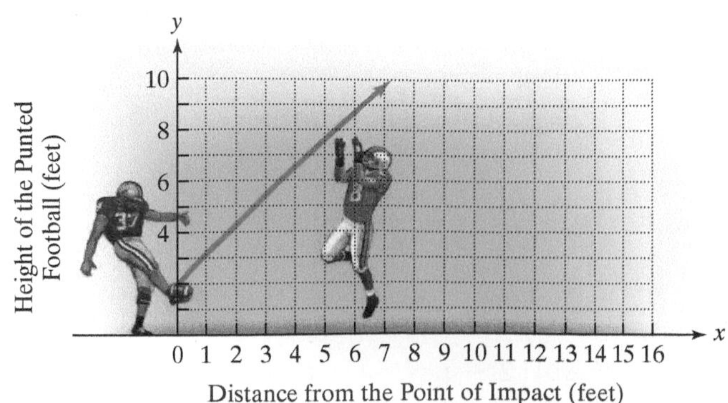

Figure 13

c. If the ball is not blocked by the defensive player, how far down the field will it go before hitting the ground?

d. Graph the equation that models the football's parabolic path.

Solution

a. We begin by identifying the numbers a, b, and c in the given model.

$$y = -0.01x^2 + 1.18x + 2$$

$a = -0.01$ $b = 1.18$ $c = 2$

Because the coefficient of x^2, -0.01, is negative, the parabola opens downward and the vertex is the highest point on the graph. The y-coordinate of the vertex gives the maximum height of the punt and the x-coordinate reveals how far from the point of impact this occurs.

$$x\text{-coordinate of vertex} = \frac{-b}{2a} = \frac{-1.18}{2(-0.01)} = \frac{-1.18}{-0.02} = 59$$

Substitute 59 for x in $y = -0.01x^2 + 1.18x + 2$ to find the y-coordinate.

$$y\text{-coordinate of vertex} = -0.01(59)^2 + 1.18(59) + 2$$
$$= -34.81 + 69.62 + 2 = 36.81$$

The vertex is (59, 36.81). The maximum height of the punt is 36.81 feet and this occurs 59 feet from the kicker's point of impact.

b. **Figure 13** shows that the defensive player is 6 feet from the kicker's point of impact. To block the punt, he must touch the football along its parabolic path. This means that we must find the height of the ball 6 feet from the kicker. Replace x with 6 in the given model, $y = -0.01x^2 + 1.18x + 2$.

$$y = -0.01(6)^2 + 1.18(6) + 2 = -0.36 + 7.08 + 2 = 8.72$$

The defensive player must reach 8.72 feet above the ground to block the punt.

c. Assuming that the ball is not blocked by the defensive player, we are interested in how far down the field it will go before hitting the ground. We are looking for the ball's horizontal distance, x, when its height above the ground, y, is 0 feet. To find this x-intercept, replace y with 0 in $y = -0.01x^2 + 1.18x + 2$. We obtain $0 = -0.01x^2 + 1.18x + 2$, or $-0.01x^2 + 1.18x + 2 = 0$. The equation cannot be solved by factoring. We will use the quadratic formula to solve it.

Use a calculator to evaluate the radicand.

$$x = \frac{-b \pm \sqrt{b^2 - 4ac}}{2a} = \frac{-1.18 \pm \sqrt{(1.18)^2 - 4(-0.01)(2)}}{2(-0.01)} = \frac{-1.18 \pm \sqrt{1.4724}}{-0.02}$$

$$x = \frac{-1.18 + \sqrt{1.4724}}{-0.02} \quad \text{or} \quad x = \frac{-1.18 - \sqrt{1.4724}}{-0.02}$$

$$x \approx -1.7 \qquad\qquad x \approx 119.7$$

Use a calculator and round to the nearest tenth.

Reject this value. We are interested in the football's height corresponding to horizontal distances from its point of impact onward, or $x \geq 0$.

If the football is not blocked by the defensive player, it will go approximately 119.7 feet down the field before hitting the ground.

d. In terms of graphing the model for the football's parabolic path, $y = -0.01x^2 + 1.18x + 2$, we have already determined the vertex and the appropriate x-intercept.

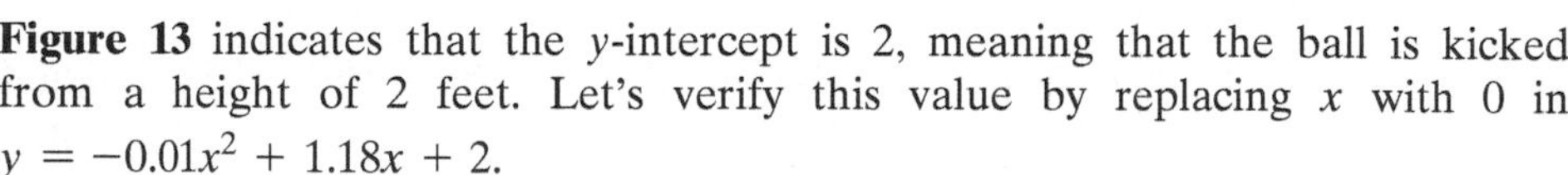
vertex: (59, 36.81)
The ball's maximum height, 36.81 feet, occurs at a horizontal distance of 59 feet.
x-intercept: 119.7
The ball's maximum horizontal distance is approximately 119.7 feet.

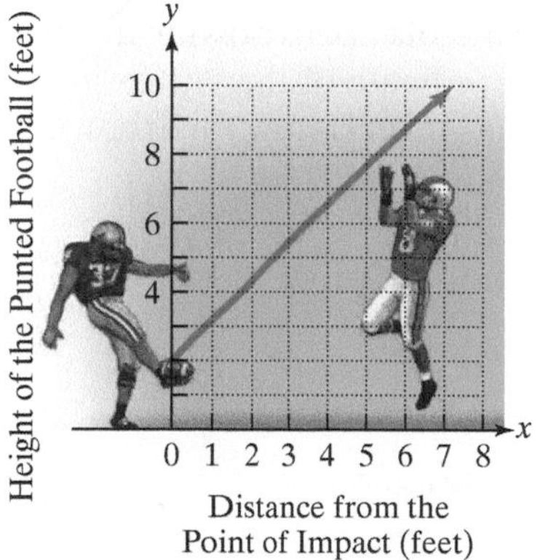
Height of the Punted Football (feet)
Distance from the Point of Impact (feet)

Figure 13 (repeated)

Figure 13 indicates that the y-intercept is 2, meaning that the ball is kicked from a height of 2 feet. Let's verify this value by replacing x with 0 in $y = -0.01x^2 + 1.18x + 2$.

$$y = -0.01 \cdot 0^2 + 1.18 \cdot 0 + 2 = 0 + 0 + 2 = 2$$

Using the vertex, (59, 36.81), the x-intercept, 119.7, and the y-intercept, 2, the graph of the equation that models the football's parabolic path is shown in **Figure 14**. The graph is shown only for $x \geq 0$, indicating horizontal distances that begin at the football's impact with the kicker's foot and end with the ball hitting the ground.

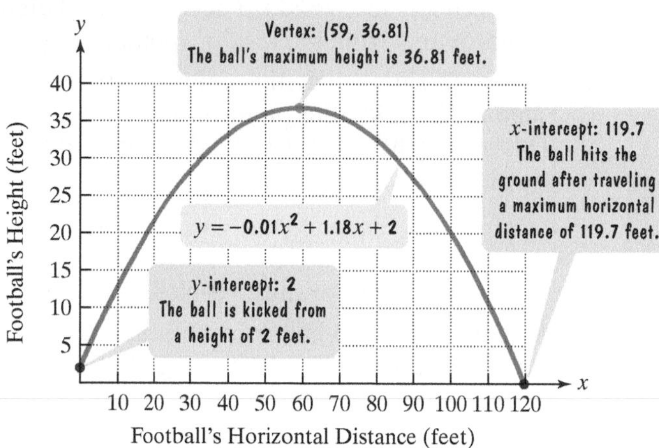
Vertex: (59, 36.81)
The ball's maximum height is 36.81 feet.
x-intercept: 119.7
The ball hits the ground after traveling a maximum horizontal distance of 119.7 feet.
y = −0.01x² + 1.18x + 2
y-intercept: 2
The ball is kicked from a height of 2 feet.
Football's Height (feet)
Football's Horizontal Distance (feet)

Figure 14 The parabolic path of a punted football ■

✓ **CHECK POINT 7** An archer's arrow follows a parabolic path. The height of the arrow, y, in feet, can be modeled by

$$y = -0.005x^2 + 2x + 5,$$

where x is the arrow's horizontal distance, in feet.

a. What is the maximum height of the arrow and how far from its release does this occur?

b. Find the horizontal distance the arrow travels before it hits the ground. Round to the nearest foot.

c. Graph the equation that models the arrow's parabolic path.

CONCEPT AND VOCABULARY CHECK

Fill in each blank so that the resulting statement is true.

1. The graph of any quadratic equation $y = ax^2 + bx + c, a \neq 0$, is called a/an ______________.
2. The graph of $y = ax^2 + bx + c$ opens upward if ______________ and opens downward if ______________.
3. The x-intercepts for the graph of $y = ax^2 + bx + c$ can be found by determining the real solutions of the equation ______________.
4. The y-intercept for the graph of $y = ax^2 + bx + c$ can be determined by replacing x with ______________.
5. The x-coordinate of the vertex of the graph of $y = ax^2 + bx + c$ is ______________. The y-coordinate of the vertex is found by substituting ________________ into the equation and evaluating.

5 EXERCISE SET

MyMathLab®

Watch the videos in MyMathLab

Download the MyDashBoard App

Practice Exercises

In Exercises 1–4 determine if the parabola whose equation is given opens upward or downward.

1. $y = x^2 - 4x + 3$
2. $y = x^2 - 6x + 5$
3. $y = -2x^2 + x + 6$
4. $y = -2x^2 - 4x + 6$

In Exercises 5–10, find the x-intercepts for the parabola whose equation is given. If the x-intercepts are irrational numbers, round your answers to the nearest tenth.

5. $y = x^2 - 4x + 3$
6. $y = x^2 - 6x + 5$
7. $y = -x^2 + 8x - 12$
8. $y = -x^2 - 2x + 3$
9. $y = x^2 + 2x - 4$
10. $y = x^2 + 8x + 14$

In Exercises 11–18, find the y-intercept for the parabola whose equation is given.

11. $y = x^2 - 4x + 3$
12. $y = x^2 - 6x + 5$
13. $y = -x^2 + 8x - 12$
14. $y = -x^2 - 2x + 3$
15. $y = x^2 + 2x - 4$
16. $y = x^2 + 8x + 14$
17. $y = x^2 + 6x$
18. $y = x^2 + 8x$

In Exercises 19–24, find the vertex for the parabola whose equation is given.

19. $y = x^2 - 4x + 3$
20. $y = x^2 - 6x + 5$
21. $y = 2x^2 + 4x - 6$
22. $y = -2x^2 - 4x - 2$
23. $y = x^2 + 6x$
24. $y = x^2 + 8x$

In Exercises 25–36, graph the parabola whose equation is given.

25. $y = x^2 + 8x + 7$
26. $y = x^2 + 10x + 9$
27. $y = x^2 - 2x - 8$
28. $y = x^2 + 4x - 5$
29. $y = -x^2 + 4x - 3$
30. $y = -x^2 + 2x + 3$
31. $y = x^2 - 1$
32. $y = x^2 - 4$
33. $y = x^2 + 2x + 1$
34. $y = x^2 - 2x + 1$
35. $y = -2x^2 + 4x + 5$
36. $y = -3x^2 + 6x - 2$

Practice PLUS

In Exercises 37–44, find the vertex for the parabola whose equation is given by first writing the equation in the form $y = ax^2 + bx + c$.

37. $y = (x - 3)^2 + 2$
38. $y = (x - 4)^2 + 3$
39. $y = (x + 5)^2 - 4$
40. $y = (x + 6)^2 - 5$
41. $y = 2(x - 1)^2 - 3$
42. $y = 2(x - 1)^2 - 4$
43. $y = -3(x + 2)^2 + 5$
44. $y = -3(x + 4)^2 + 6$
45. Generalize your work in Exercises 37–44 and complete the following statement: For a parabola whose equation is $y = a(x - h)^2 + k$, the vertex is the point ____.

Application Exercises

An athlete whose event is the shot put releases the shot with the same initial velocity, but at different angles. The figure shows the parabolic paths for shots released at angles of 35° and 65°. Exercises 46–47 are based on the equations that model the parabolic paths.

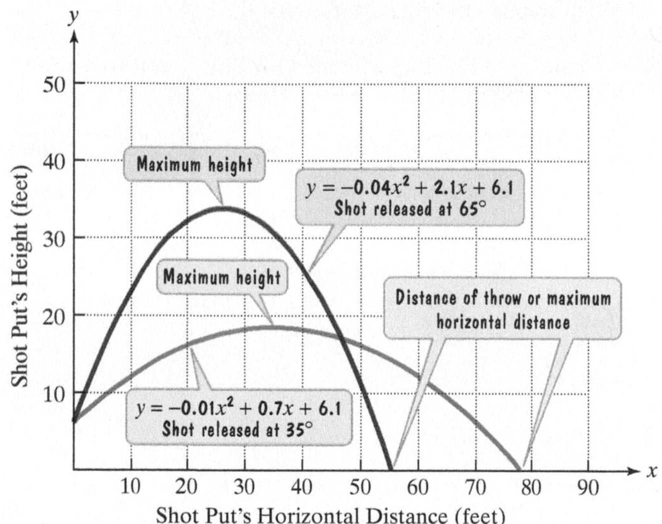

46. When the shot is released at an angle of 65°, its height, y, in feet, can be modeled by

$$y = -0.04x^2 + 2.1x + 6.1,$$

where x is the shot's horizontal distance, in feet, from its point of release. Use this model to solve parts (a) through (c) and verify your answers using the red graph.

a. What is the maximum height, to the nearest tenth of a foot, of the shot and how far from its point of release does this occur?

b. What is the shot's maximum horizontal distance, to the nearest tenth of a foot, or the distance of the throw?

c. From what height was the shot released?

47. When the shot is released at an angle of 35°, its height, y, in feet, can be modeled by

$$y = -0.01x^2 + 0.7x + 6.1,$$

where x is the shot's horizontal distance, in feet, from its point of release. Use this model to solve parts (a) through (c) and verify your answers using the blue graph.

a. What is the maximum height of the shot and how far from its point of release does this occur?

b. What is the shot's maximum horizontal distance, to the nearest tenth of a foot, or the distance of the throw?

c. From what height was the shot released?

48. A ball is thrown upward and outward from a height of 6 feet. The height of the ball, y, in feet, can be modeled by

$$y = -0.8x^2 + 2.4x + 6,$$

where x is the ball's horizontal distance, in feet, from where it was thrown.

a. What is the maximum height of the ball and how far from where it was thrown does this occur?

b. How far does the ball travel horizontally before hitting the ground? Round to the nearest tenth of a foot.

c. Graph the equation that models the ball's parabolic path.

49. A ball is thrown upward and outward from a height of 6 feet. The height of the ball, y, in feet, can be modeled by

$$y = -0.8x^2 + 3.2x + 6,$$

where x is the ball's horizontal distance, in feet, from where it was thrown.

a. What is the maximum height of the ball and how far from where it was thrown does this occur?

b. How far does the ball travel horizontally before hitting the ground? Round to the nearest tenth of a foot.

c. Graph the equation that models the ball's parabolic path.

50. You have 120 feet of fencing to enclose a rectangular plot that borders on a river. If you do not fence the side along the river, find the length and width of the plot that will maximize the area. What is the largest area that can be enclosed?

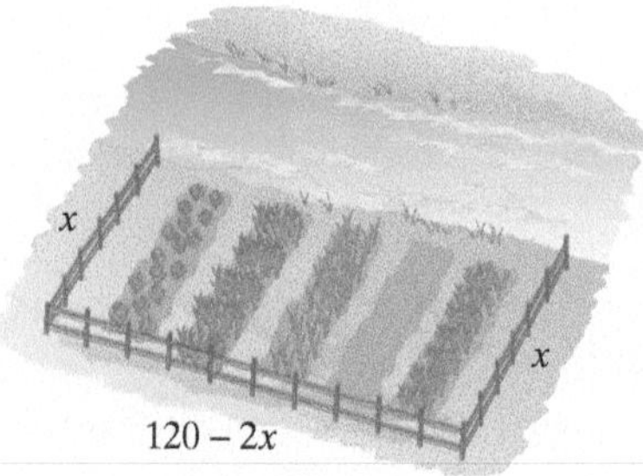

51. You have 100 yards of fencing to enclose a rectangular area, as shown in the figure. Find the dimensions of the rectangle that maximize the enclosed area. What is the maximum area?

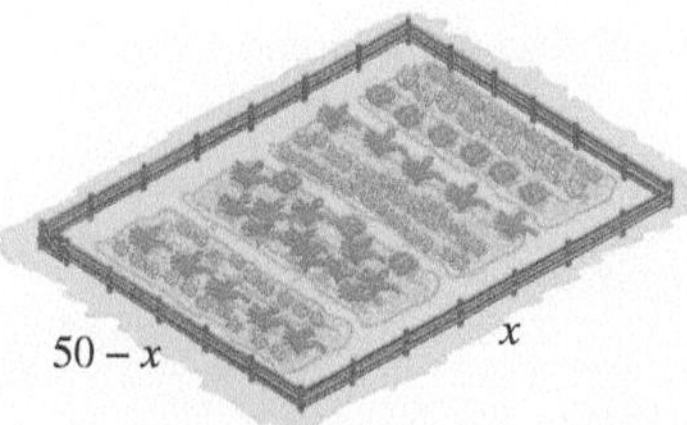

Writing in Mathematics

52. What is a parabola? Describe its shape.

53. Explain how to decide whether a parabola opens upward or downward.

54. If a parabola has two x-intercepts, explain how to find them.

55. Explain how to find a parabola's y-intercept.

56. Describe how to find a parabola's vertex.

57. A parabola that opens upward has its vertex at (1, 2). Describe as much as you can about the parabola based on this information. Include in your discussion the number of x-intercepts, if any, for the parabola.

Critical Thinking Exercises

Make Sense? *In Exercises 58–61, determine whether each statement "makes sense" or "does not make sense" and explain your reasoning.*

58. I must have made an error when graphing this parabola because it is symmetric with respect to the y-axis.

59. Parabolas that open up appear to form smiles ($a > 0$), while parabolas that open down frown ($a < 0$).

60. I threw a baseball vertically upward and its path was a parabola.

61. **Figure 13** shows that a linear model provides a better description of the football's path than a quadratic model.

In Exercises 62–65, determine whether each statement is true or false. If the statement is false, make the necessary change(s) to produce a true statement.

62. The x-coordinate of the vertex of the parabola whose equation is $y = ax^2 + bx + c$ is $\frac{b}{2a}$.

63. If a parabola has only one x-intercept, then the x-intercept is also the vertex.

64. There is no relationship between the graph of $y = ax^2 + bx + c$ and the number of real solutions of the equation $ax^2 + bx + c = 0$.

65. If $y = 4x^2 - 40x + 4$, then the vertex is the highest point on the graph.

66. Find two numbers whose sum is 200 and whose product is a maximum.

67. Graph $y = 2x^2 - 8$ and $y = -2x^2 + 8$ in the same rectangular coordinate system. What are the coordinates of the points of intersection?

68. A parabola has x-intercepts at 3 and 7, a y-intercept at -21, and (5, 4) for its vertex. Write the parabola's equation.

Technology Exercises

69. Use a graphing utility to verify any five of your hand-drawn graphs in Exercises 25–36.

70. **a.** Use a graphing utility to graph $y = 2x^2 - 82x + 720$ in a standard viewing rectangle. What do you observe?

b. Find the coordinates of the vertex for the given quadratic equation.

c. The answer to part (b) is $(20.5, -120.5)$. Because the leading coefficient, 2 of $y = 2x^2 - 82x + 720$ is positive, the vertex is a minimum point on the graph. Use this fact to help find a viewing rectangle that will give a relatively complete picture of the parabola. With an axis of symmetry at $x = 20.5$, the setting for x should extend past this, so try Xmin = 0 and Xmax = 30. The setting for y should include (and probably go below) the y-coordinate of the graph's minimum point, so try Ymin = -130. Experiment with Ymax until your utility shows the parabola's major features.

d. In general, explain how knowing the coordinates of a parabola's vertex can help determine a reasonable viewing rectangle on a graphing utility for obtaining a complete picture of the parabola.

In Exercises 71–74, find the vertex for each parabola. Then determine a reasonable viewing rectangle on your graphing utility and use it to graph the parabola.

71. $y = -0.25x^2 + 40x$

72. $y = -4x^2 + 20x + 160$

73. $y = 5x^2 + 40x + 600$

74. $y = 0.01x^2 + 0.6x + 100$

Review Exercises

In Exercises 75–77, solve each equation or system of equations.

75. $7(x - 2) = 10 - 2(x + 3)$

76. $\frac{7}{x + 2} + \frac{2}{x + 3} = \frac{1}{x^2 + 5x + 6}$

77. $\begin{cases} 5x - 3y = -13 \\ x = 2 - 4y \end{cases}$

Preview Exercises

Exercises 78–80 will help you prepare for the material covered in the next section.

78. Here are two sets of ordered pairs:

set 1: $\{(1, 5), (2, 5)\}$
set 2: $\{(5, 1), (5, 2)\}$.

In which set is each x-coordinate paired with one and only one y-coordinate?

79. Here are two graphs:

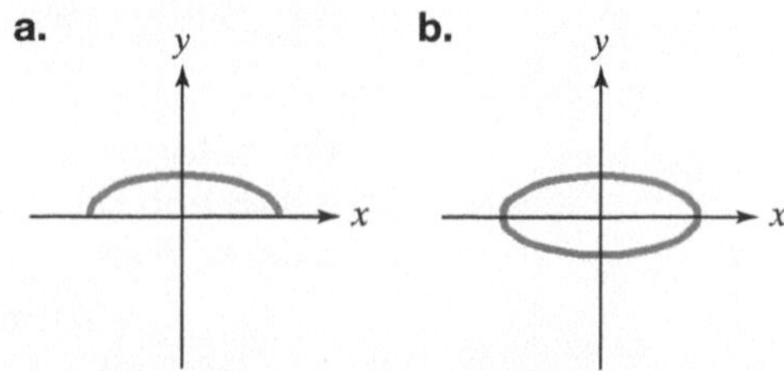

In which graph is each x-coordinate paired with one and only one y-coordinate?

80. Evaluate $x^2 + 3x + 5$ for $x = -3$.

SECTION 6

Introduction to Functions

Objectives

1. Find the domain and range of a relation.
2. Determine whether a relation is a function.
3. Evaluate a function.
4. Use the vertical line test to identify functions.
5. Find function values for functions that model data.

Andrey Yurlov/Shutterstock

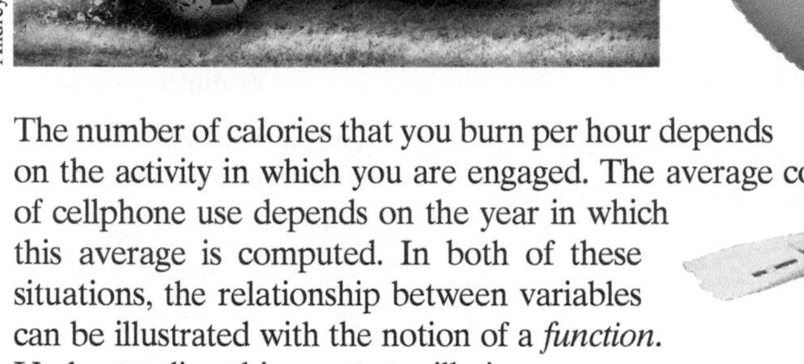

Michael A Keller/Photolibrary New York

The number of calories that you burn per hour depends on the activity in which you are engaged. The average cost of cellphone use depends on the year in which this average is computed. In both of these situations, the relationship between variables can be illustrated with the notion of a *function*. Understanding this concept will give you a new perspective on many ordinary situations. Much of your work in subsequent algebra courses will be devoted to the important topic of functions and how they model your world.

1 Find the domain and range of a relation.

Relations

Studies show that exercise can promote good long-term health no matter how much you weigh. A brisk half-hour walk each day is enough to get the benefits. Combined with a healthy diet, it also helps to stave off obesity. How many calories does your workout burn? The graph in **Figure 15** shows the calories burned per hour in six activities.

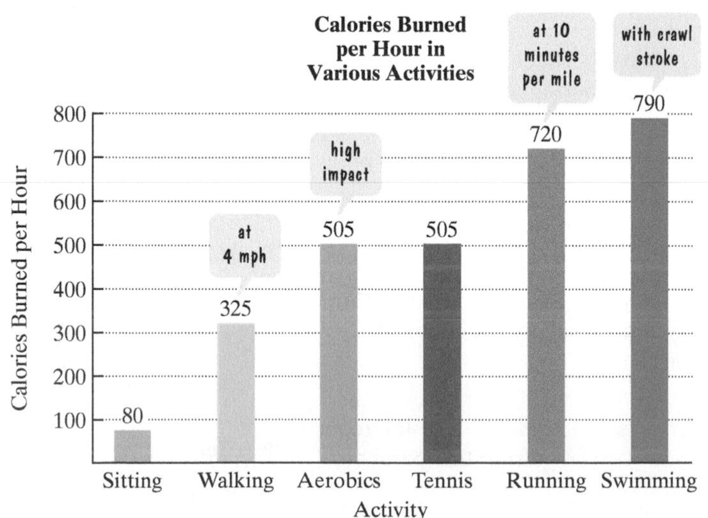

Figure 15
Counting calories

Source: FITRESOURCE.COM

The information shown in the bar graph indicates a correspondence between the activities and calories burned per hour. We can write this correspondence using a set of ordered pairs:

$$\{(\text{sitting}, 80), (\text{walking}, 325), (\text{aerobics}, 505), (\text{tennis}, 505), (\text{running}, 720), (\text{swimming}, 790)\}.$$

These braces indicate that we are representing a set.

The mathematical term for a set of ordered pairs is a **relation**.

Definition of a Relation

A **relation** is any set of ordered pairs. The set of all first components of the ordered pairs is called the **domain** of the relation and the set of all second components is called the **range** of the relation.

EXAMPLE 1 Finding the Domain and Range of a Relation

Find the domain and range of the relation:

$$\{(\text{sitting}, 80), (\text{walking}, 325), (\text{aerobics}, 505), (\text{tennis}, 505), (\text{running}, 720), (\text{swimming}, 790)\}.$$

Solution The domain is the set of all first components. Thus, the domain is

$$\{\text{sitting, walking, aerobics, tennis, running, swimming}\}.$$

Parentheses and square brackets are not used to represent sets.

The range is the set of all second components. Thus, the range is

$$\{80, 325, 505, 720, 790\}.$$

Although both aerobics and tennis burn 505 calories per hour, it is not necessary to list 505 twice. ■

✓ **CHECK POINT 1** The following set shows calories burned per hour in activities not included in **Figure 15**. Find the domain and range of the relation:

$$\{(\text{golf}, 250), (\text{lawn mowing}, 325), (\text{water skiing}, 430), (\text{hiking}, 430), (\text{bicycling}, 720)\}.$$

with cart

at 15 mph

---

2 Determine whether a relation is a function.

Functions

Shown in the margin are the calories burned per hour for the activities in the bar graph in **Figure 15**. We've used this information to define two relations. **Figure 16(a)** shows a correspondence between activities and calories burned. **Figure 16(b)** shows a correspondence between calories burned and activities.

Activity	Calories Burned per hour
Sitting	80
Walking	325
Aerobics	505
Tennis	505
Running	720

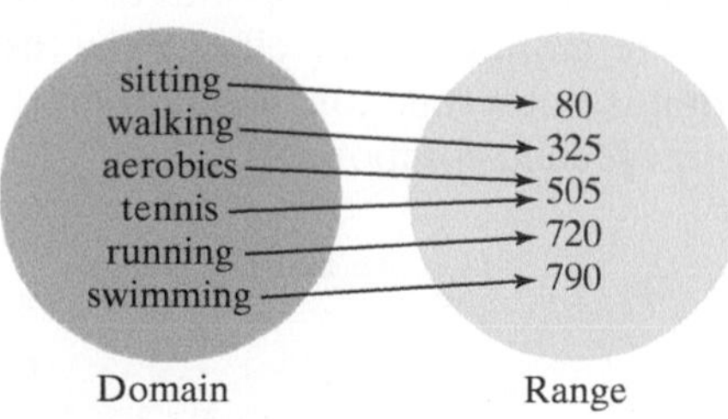

Figure 16(a) Activities correspond to calories burned.

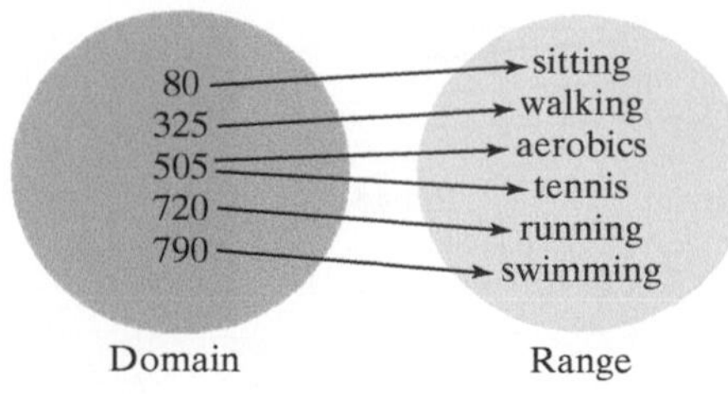

Figure 16(b) Calories burned correspond to activities.

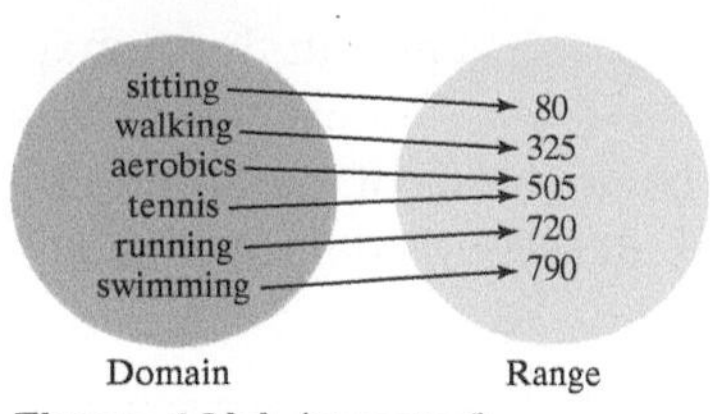

Figure 16(a) (repeated)

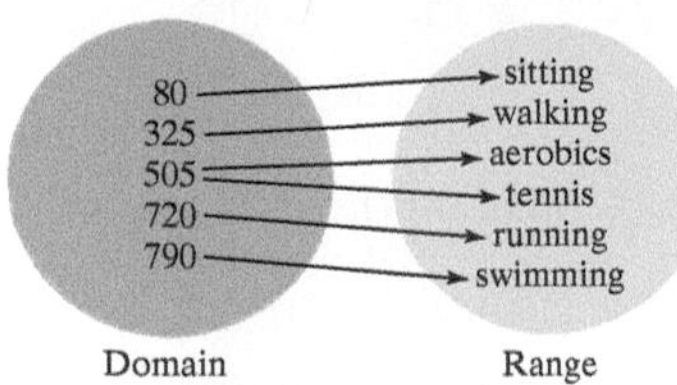

Figure 16(b) (repeated)

A relation in which each member of the domain corresponds to exactly one member of the range is a **function**. Can you see that the relation in **Figure 16(a)** is a function? Each activity in the domain corresponds to exactly one number representing calories burned per hour in the range. If we know the activity, we know the calories burned per hour. Notice that more than one element in the domain can correspond to the same element in the range: Aerobics and tennis both burn 505 calories per hour.

Is the relation in **Figure 16(b)** a function? Does each member of the domain correspond to precisely one member of the range? This relation is not a function because there is a member of the domain that corresponds to two members of the range:

(505, aerobics) (505, tennis).

The member of the domain, 505, corresponds to both aerobics and tennis. If we know the calories burned per hour, 505, we cannot be sure of the activity. Because **a function is a relation in which no two ordered pairs have the same first component and different second components**, the ordered pairs (505, aerobics) and (505, tennis) are not ordered pairs of a function.

Same first component

(505, aerobics) (505, tennis)

Different second components

Definition of a Function

A **function** is a relation in which each member of the domain corresponds to exactly one member of the range. No two ordered pairs of a function can have the same first component and different second components.

EXAMPLE 2 Determining Whether a Relation Is a Function

Determine whether each relation is a function:

a. $\{(1, 6), (2, 6), (3, 8), (4, 9)\}$ **b.** $\{(6, 1), (6, 2), (8, 3), (9, 4)\}$.

Solution We begin by making a figure for each relation that shows the domain and the range (**Figure 17**).

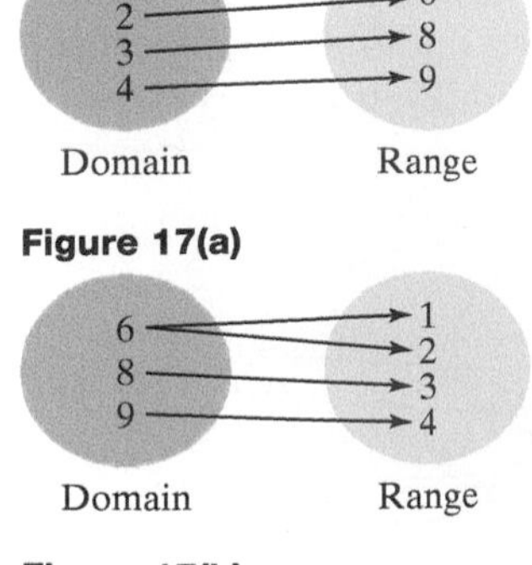

Figure 17(a)

Figure 17(b)

a. **Figure 17(a)** shows that every element in the domain corresponds to exactly one element in the range. The element 1 in the domain corresponds to the element 6 in the range. Furthermore, 2 corresponds to 6, 3 corresponds to 8, and 4 corresponds to 9. No two ordered pairs in the given relation have the same first component and different second components. Thus, the relation is a function.

b. **Figure 17(b)** shows that 6 corresponds to both 1 and 2. If any element in the domain corresponds to more than one element in the range, the relation is not a function. This relation is not a function: Two ordered pairs have the same first component and different second components.

Same first component

(6, 1) (6, 2)

Different second components

■

Look at **Figure 17(a)** on the previous page again. The fact that 1 and 2 in the domain correspond to the same number, 6, in the range does not violate the definition of a function. **A function can have two different first components with the same second component.** By contrast, a relation is not a function when two different ordered pairs have the same first component and different second components. Thus, the relation in **Figure 17(b)** is not a function.

✓ CHECK POINT 2 Determine whether each relation is a function:

a. $\{(1, 2), (3, 4), (5, 6), (5, 8)\}$

b. $\{(1, 2), (3, 4), (6, 5), (8, 5)\}$.

3 Evaluate a function.

Functions as Equations and Function Notation

Functions are usually given in terms of equations rather than as sets of ordered pairs. For example, here is an equation that shows a woman's cholesterol level as a function of her age:

$$y = 1.17x + 147.15.$$

The variable x represents a woman's age, in years. The variable y represents her cholesterol level. For each age, x, the equation gives one and only one cholesterol level, y. The variable y is a function of the variable x.

When an equation represents a function, the function is often named by a letter such as f, g, h, F, G, or H. Any letter can be used to name a function. Suppose that f names a function. Think of the domain as the set of the function's inputs and the range as the set of the function's outputs. As shown in **Figure 18**, the input is represented by x and the output by $f(x)$. The special notation $f(x)$, read "f of x" or "f at x," represents the **value of the function at the number x.**

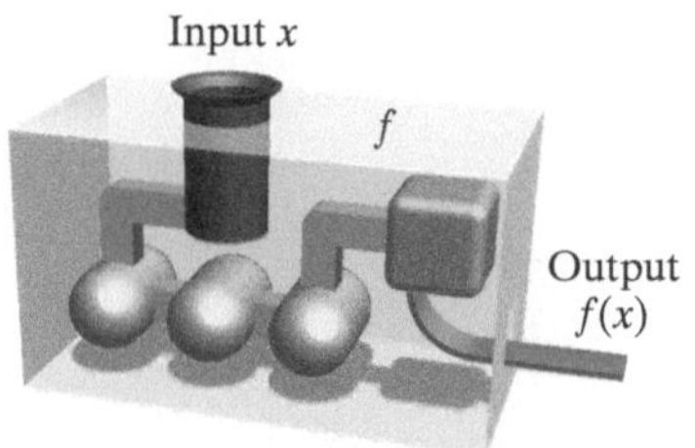

Figure 18 A function as a machine with inputs and outputs

Let's make this clearer by considering a specific example. We know the equation

$$y = 1.17x + 147.15$$

defines y as a function of x. We'll name the function f. Now, we can apply our new function notation.

Input	Output	Equation	
x	$f(x)$	$f(x) = 1.17x + 147.15$	We read this equation as "f of x equals $1.17x + 147.15$."

Suppose we are interested in finding $f(30)$, the function's output when the input is 30. To find the value of the function at 30, we substitute 30 for x. We are **evaluating the function** at 30.

$$f(x) = 1.17x + 147.15 \quad \text{This is the given function.}$$
$$f(30) = 1.17(30) + 147.15 \quad \text{The input is 30.}$$
$$= 35.1 + 147.15 \quad \text{Multiply.}$$
$$= 182.25 \quad \text{Add.}$$

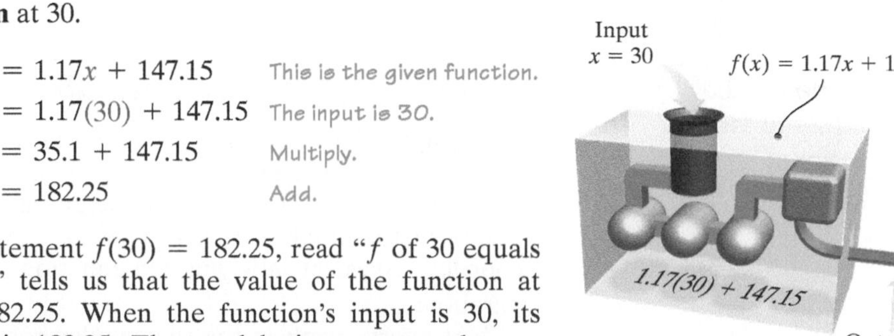

Figure 19 A function machine at work

The statement $f(30) = 182.25$, read "f of 30 equals 182.25," tells us that the value of the function at 30 is 182.25. When the function's input is 30, its output is 182.25. The model gives us exactly one cholesterol level for a 30-year-old woman, namely 182.25. **Figure 19** illustrates the input and output in terms of a function machine.

Great Question!

Doesn't $f(x)$ indicate that I need to multiply f and x?

The notation $f(x)$ does *not* mean "f times x." The notation describes the value of the function at x.

EXAMPLE 3 Evaluating a Function

If $f(x) = 3x + 1$, find each of the following:

a. $f(5)$ **b.** $f(-4)$ **c.** $f(0)$.

Solution We substitute 5, −4, and 0, respectively, for x in the function's equation, $f(x) = 3x + 1$.

a. $f(5) = 3 \cdot 5 + 1 = 15 + 1 = 16$ *f of 5 equals 16.*

b. $f(-4) = 3(-4) + 1 = -12 + 1 = -11$ *f of −4 equals −11.*

c. $f(0) = 3 \cdot 0 + 1 = 0 + 1 = 1$ *f of 0 equals 1.* ■

The function $f(x) = 3x + 1$ is an example of a *linear function*. **Linear functions** have equations of the form $f(x) = mx + b$.

✓ **CHECK POINT 3** If $f(x) = 4x + 3$, find each of the following:

a. $f(5)$ **b.** $f(-2)$ **c.** $f(0)$.

EXAMPLE 4 Evaluating a Function

If $g(x) = x^2 + 3x + 5$, find each of the following:

a. $g(2)$ **b.** $g(-3)$ **c.** $g(0)$.

Solution We substitute 2, −3, and 0, respectively, for x in the function's equation, $g(x) = x^2 + 3x + 5$.

a. $g(2) = 2^2 + 3 \cdot 2 + 5 = 4 + 6 + 5 = 15$ *g of 2 is 15.*

b. $g(-3) = (-3)^2 + 3(-3) + 5 = 9 + (-9) + 5 = 5$ *g of −3 is 5.*

c. $g(0) = 0^2 + 3 \cdot 0 + 5 = 0 + 0 + 5 = 5$ *g of 0 is 5.* ■

The function in Example 4 is a *quadratic function*. **Quadratic functions** have equations of the form $f(x) = ax^2 + bx + c, a \neq 0$.

✓ **CHECK POINT 4** If $g(x) = x^2 + 4x + 3$, find each of the following:

a. $g(5)$ **b.** $g(-4)$ **c.** $g(0)$.

4 Use the vertical line test to identify functions.

Graphs of Functions and the Vertical Line Test

The **graph of a function** is the graph of its ordered pairs. For example, the graph of $f(x) = 3x + 1$ is the set of points (x, y) in the rectangular coordinate system satisfying the equation $y = 3x + 1$. Thus, the graph of f is a line with slope 3 and y-intercept 1. Similarly, the graph of $f(x) = x^2 + 3x + 5$ is the set of points (x, y) in the rectangular coordinate system satisfying the equation $y = x^2 + 3x + 5$. Thus, the graph of g is a parabola.

Not every graph in the rectangular coordinate system is the graph of a function. The definition of a function specifies that no value of x can be paired with two or more

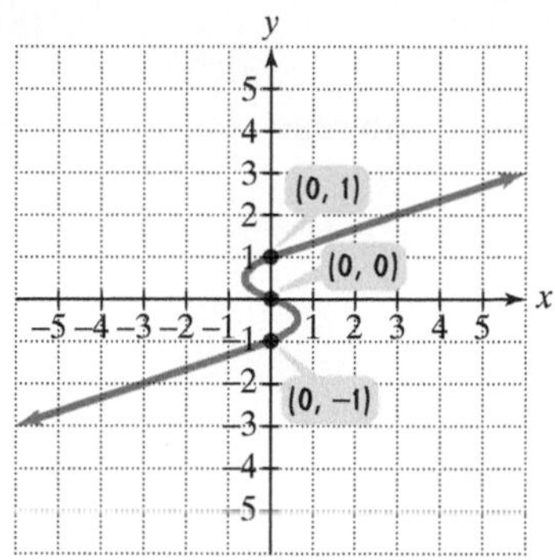

Figure 20 y is not a function of x because 0 is paired with three values of y, namely, 1, 0, and -1.

different values of y. Consequently, if a graph contains two or more different points with the same first coordinate, the graph cannot represent a function. This is illustrated in **Figure 20**. Observe that points sharing a common first coordinate are vertically above or below each other.

This observation is the basis of a useful test for determining whether a graph defines y as a function of x. The test is called the **vertical line test**.

The Vertical Line Test for Functions

If any vertical line intersects a graph in more than one point, the graph does not define y as a function of x.

EXAMPLE 5 Using the Vertical Line Test

Use the vertical line test to identify graphs in which y is a function of x.

a. 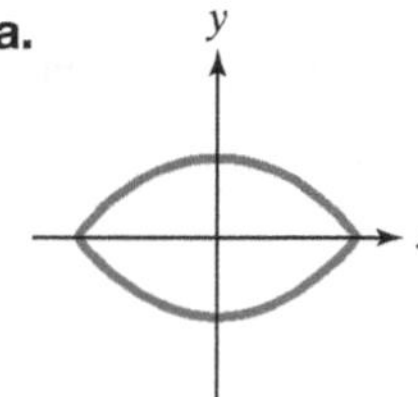

b. 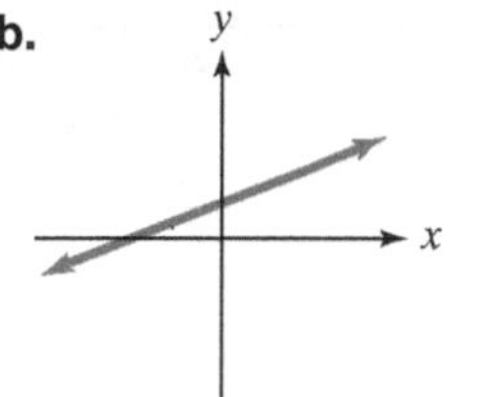

c.

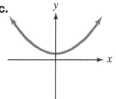

d. 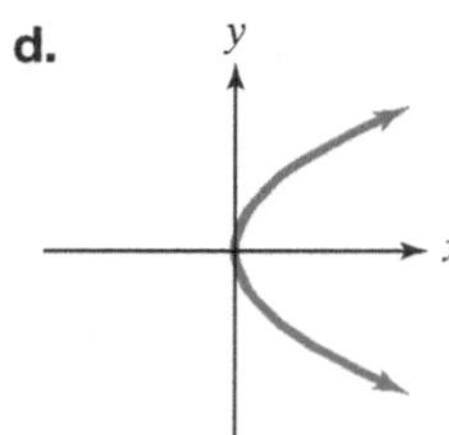

Solution y is a function of x for the graphs in (b) and (c).

a. 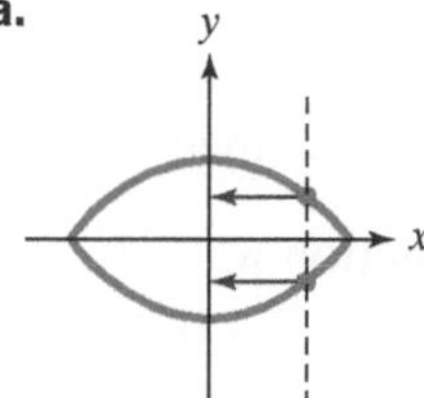

y **is not a function** of x. Two values of y correspond to one x-value.

b. 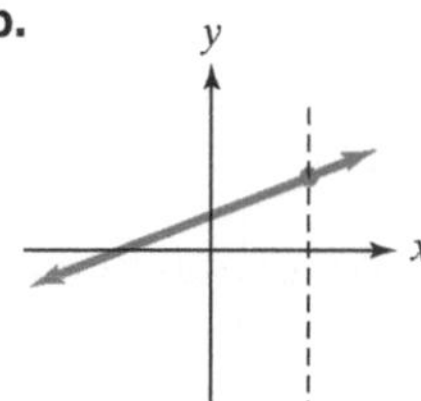

y **is a function** of x.

c. 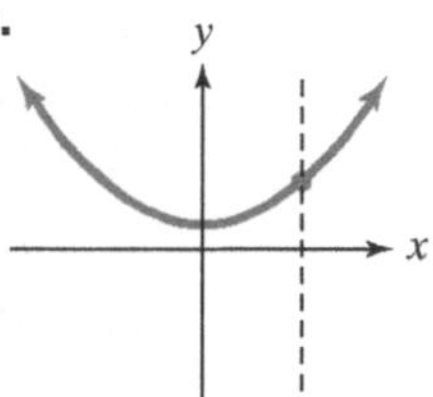

y **is a function** of x.

d. 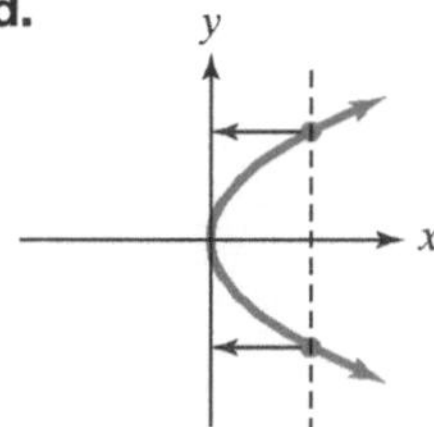

y **is not a function** of x. Two values of y correspond to one x-value.

■

✓ **CHECK POINT 5** Use the vertical line test to identify graphs in which y is a function of x.

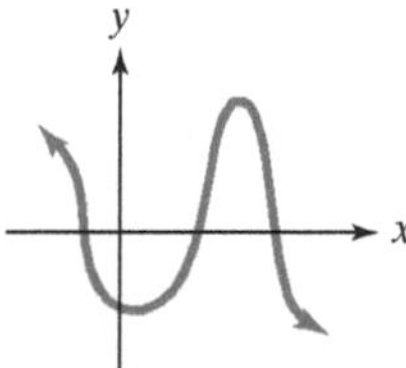

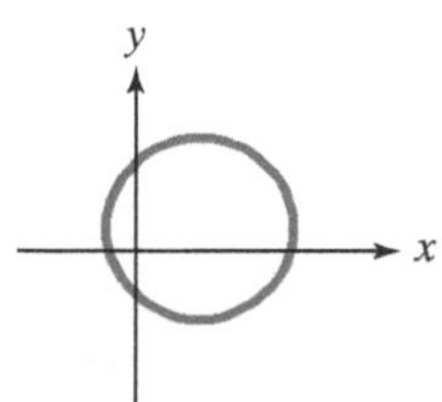

5 Find function values for functions that model data.

Applications

Like formulas, functions can be obtained from verbal conditions or from actual data. Throughout your next algebra course, you'll have lots of practice doing this. For now, let's make sure that we can find and interpret function values for functions that were obtained from modeling data.

EXAMPLE 6 Sixty and Beyond

Figure 21 shows your chances of surviving to various ages once you reach 60.

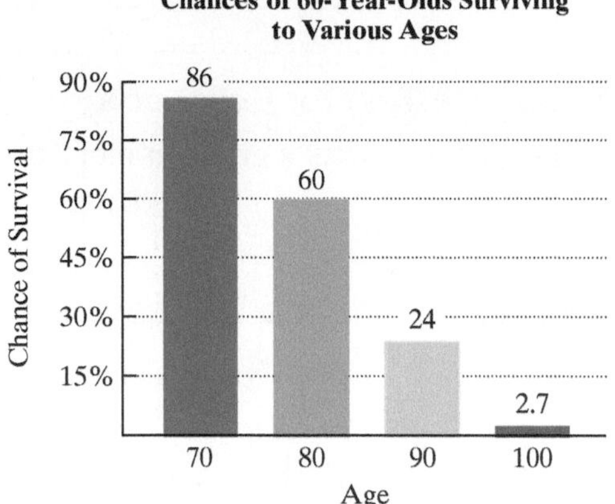

Figure 21

Source: National Center for Health Statistics, 2003 data

The functions

$$f(x) = -2.9x + 286$$
$$\text{and } g(x) = 0.01x^2 - 4.9x + 370$$

model the chance, as a percent, that a 60-year-old will survive to age x. Which model serves as a better description for the chance of surviving to age 70?

Solution We evaluate each function at 70 by substituting 70 for x in the function's equation. The graph in **Figure 21** indicates that 60-year-olds have an 86% chance of surviving to 70. The evaluation that comes closer to 86 will serve as the better description.

$f(x) = -2.9x + 286$ This is the given linear function.

$f(70) = -2.9(70) + 286$ Replace x with 70.

$= 83$ Use a calculator.

We see that $f(70) = 83$. The linear model indicates an 83% chance of surviving to 70.

$g(x) = 0.01x^2 - 4.9x + 370$ This is the given quadratic function.

$g(70) = 0.01(70)^2 - 4.9(70) + 370$ Replace each occurrence of x with 70.

$= 76$ Use a calculator.

We see that $g(70) = 76$. The quadratic model indicates a 76% chance of surviving to 70.

- $f(70) = 83$ (Linear function)
- $g(70) = 76$ (Quadratic function)
- Chance of surviving to 70 is 86 percent. (Actual data)

We see that the linear function f serves as a better description of the data. ■

Using Technology

Graphing utilities can be used to evaluate functions. The screens below show the evaluation of

$$f(x) = -2.9x + 286 \quad \text{and} \quad g(x) = 0.01x^2 - 4.9x + 370$$

at 70 on a TI-84 Plus graphing calculator. The function f is named Y_1 and the function g is named Y_2.

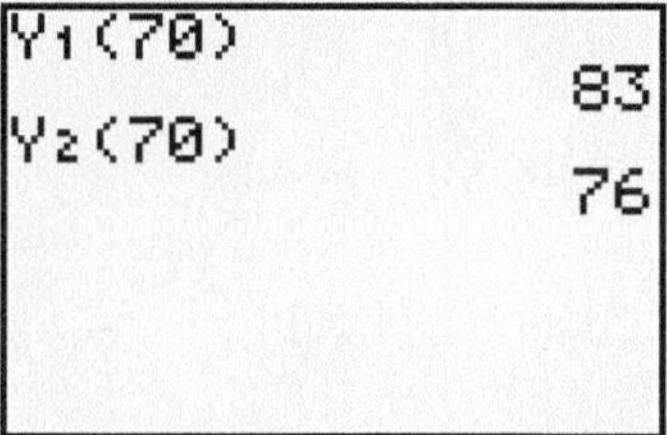

✓ **CHECK POINT 6** Use the functions in Example 6 to solve this exercise.

a. According to the linear function, what is the chance that a 60-year-old will survive to age 90?

b. According to the quadratic function, what is the chance that a 60-year-old will survive to age 90?

c. Which model serves as a better description for the chance of survival displayed by the bar graph in **Figure 21**?

Achieving Success

A recent government study cited in *Math: A Rich Heritage* (Globe Fearon Educational Publisher) found this simple fact: **The more college mathematics courses you take, the greater your earning potential will be.** Even jobs that do not require a college degree require mathematical thinking that involves attending to precision, making sense of complex problems, and persevering in solving them. No other discipline comes close to math in offering a more extensive set of tools for application and intellectual development. Take as much math as possible as you continue your journey into higher education.

CONCEPT AND VOCABULARY CHECK

Fill in each blank so that the resulting statement is true.

1. Any set of ordered pairs is called a/an ______________. The set of all first components of the ordered pairs is called the ______________. The set of all second components of the ordered pairs is called the ______________.
2. A set of ordered pairs in which each first component corresponds to exactly one second component is called a/an ______________.
3. The notation $f(x)$ describes the value of ______________ at ______________.
4. A function of the form $f(x) = mx + b$ is called a/an ______________ function.
5. A function of the form $f(x) = ax^2 + bx + c, a \neq 0$, is called a/an ______________ function.
6. If any vertical line intersects a graph ______________, the graph does not define y as a/an ______________ of x.

6 EXERCISE SET

MyMathLab®

Watch the videos in MyMathLab

Download the MyDashBoard App

Practice Exercises

In Exercises 1–8, determine whether each relation is a function. Give the domain and range for each relation.

1. $\{(1, 2), (3, 4), (5, 5)\}$

2. $\{(4, 5), (6, 7), (8, 8)\}$

3. $\{(3, 4), (3, 5), (4, 4), (4, 5)\}$

4. $\{(5, 6), (5, 7), (6, 6), (6, 7)\}$

5. $\{(-3, -3), (-2, -2), (-1, -1), (0, 0)\}$

6. $\{(-7, -7), (-5, -5), (-3, -3), (0, 0)\}$

7. $\{(1, 4), (1, 5), (1, 6)\}$

8. $\{(4, 1), (5, 1), (6, 1)\}$

In Exercises 9–24, evaluate each function at the given values.

9. $f(x) = x + 5$
 a. $f(7)$ **b.** $f(-6)$ **c.** $f(0)$

10. $f(x) = x + 6$
 a. $f(4)$ **b.** $f(-8)$ **c.** $f(0)$

11. $f(x) = 7x$
 a. $f(10)$ **b.** $f(-4)$ **c.** $f(0)$

12. $f(x) = 9x$
 a. $f(10)$ **b.** $f(-5)$ **c.** $f(0)$

13. $f(x) = 8x - 3$
 a. $f(12)$ **b.** $f(-\frac{1}{2})$ **c.** $f(0)$

14. $f(x) = 6x - 5$
 a. $f(12)$ **b.** $f(-\frac{1}{2})$ **c.** $f(0)$

15. $g(x) = x^2 + 3x$
 a. $g(2)$ **b.** $g(-2)$ **c.** $g(0)$

16. $g(x) = x^2 + 7x$
 a. $g(2)$ **b.** $g(-2)$ **c.** $g(0)$

17. $h(x) = x^2 - 2x + 3$
 a. $h(4)$ **b.** $h(-4)$ **c.** $h(0)$

18. $h(x) = x^2 - 4x + 5$
 a. $h(4)$ **b.** $h(-4)$ **c.** $h(0)$

19. $f(x) = 5$
 a. $f(9)$ **b.** $f(-9)$ **c.** $f(0)$

20. $f(x) = 7$
 a. $f(10)$ **b.** $f(-10)$ **c.** $f(0)$

21. $f(r) = \sqrt{r + 6} + 3$
 a. $f(-6)$ **b.** $f(10)$

22. $f(r) = \sqrt{25 - r} - 6$
 a. $f(16)$ **b.** $f(-24)$

23. $f(x) = \dfrac{x}{|x|}$
 a. $f(6)$ **b.** $f(-6)$

24. $f(x) = \dfrac{x}{|x|}$
 a. $f(5)$ **b.** $f(-5)$

In Exercises 25–32, use the vertical line test to identify graphs in which y is a function of x.

25.

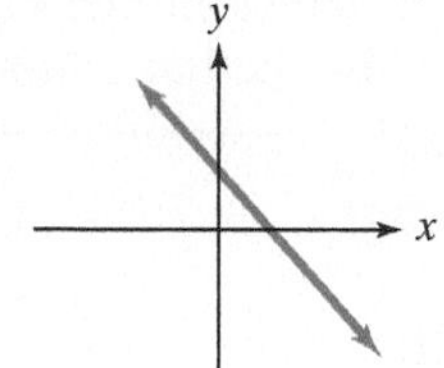

26.

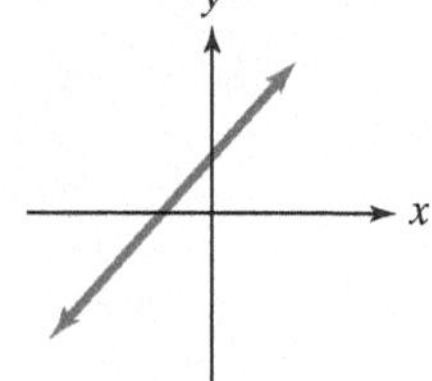

27.

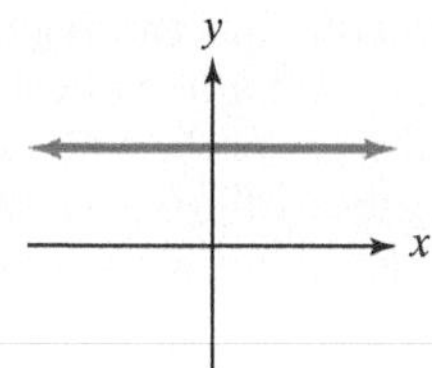

28.

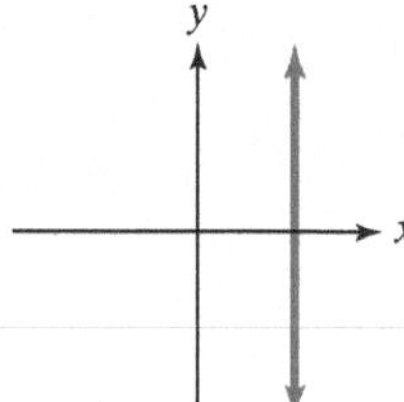

29.

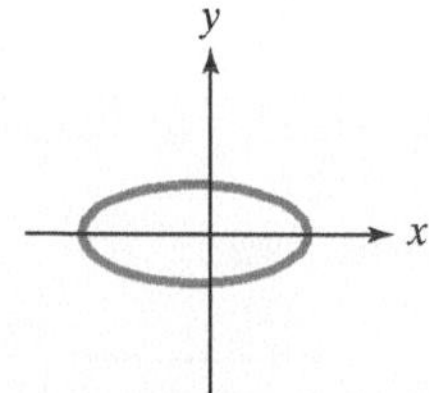

30.

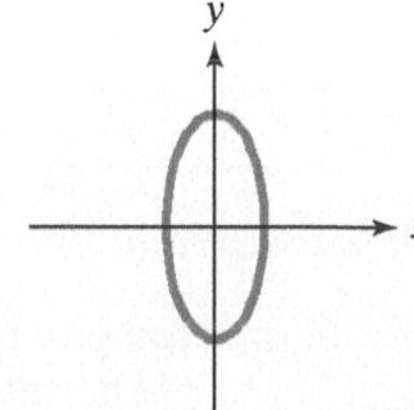

31.

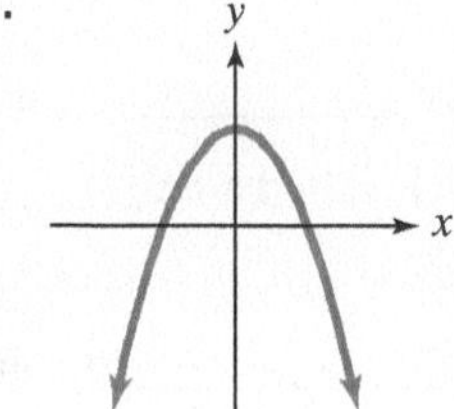

32.

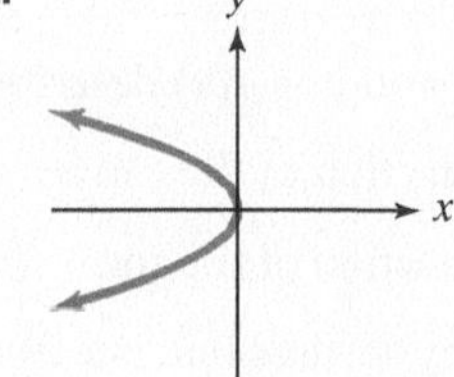

Practice PLUS

In Exercises 33–36, express each function as a set of ordered pairs.

33. $f(x) = 2x + 3$; domain: $\{-1, 0, 1\}$

34. $f(x) = 3x + 5$; domain: $\{-1, 0, 1\}$

35. $g(x) = x - x^2$; domain: the set of integers from -2 to 2, inclusive

36. $g(x) = x - |x|$; domain: the set of integers from -2 to 2, inclusive

In Exercises 37–40, find

$$\frac{f(x) - f(h)}{x - h}$$

and simplify.

37. $f(x) = 6x + 7$

38. $f(x) = 8x + 9$

39. $f(x) = x^2 - 1$

40. $f(x) = x^3 - 1$

Application Exercises

The bar graph shows minimum legal ages for sex and marriage in five selected countries. Use this information to solve Exercises 41–42. (We did not include data for the United States because the legal age of sexual consent varies according to state law. Furthermore, women are allowed to marry younger than men: 16 for women and 18 for men.)

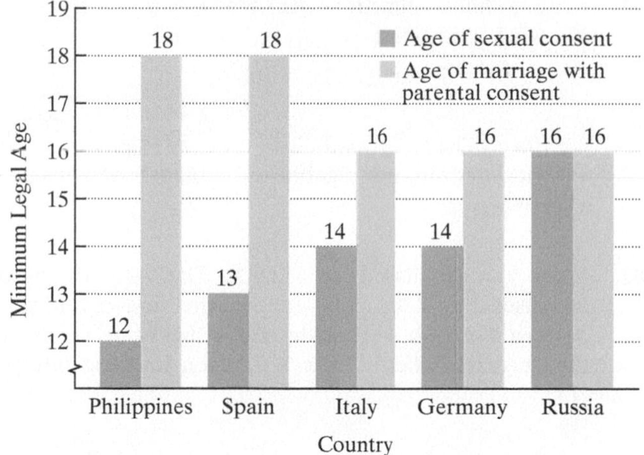

Source: Mitchell Beazley, *Snapshot: The Visual Almanac for Our World Today*, Octopus Publishing, 2009

41. **a.** Write a set of five ordered pairs in which countries correspond to the minimum legal age of sexual consent. Each ordered pair should be in the form

(country, minimum legal age of sexual consent).

b. Is the relation in part (a) a function? Explain your answer.

c. Write a set of five ordered pairs in which the minimum legal age of sexual consent corresponds to a country. Each ordered pair should be in the form

(minimum legal age of sexual consent, country).

d. Is the relation in part (c) a function?

42. **a.** Write a set of five ordered pairs in which countries correspond to the minimum legal age of marriage with parental consent. Each ordered pair should be in the form

(country, minimum legal age of marriage with parental consent).

b. Is the relation in part (a) a function? Explain your answer.

c. Write a set of five ordered pairs in which the minimum legal age of marriage with parental consent corresponds to a country. Each ordered pair should be in the form

(minimum legal age of marriage with parental consent, country).

d. Is the relation in part (c) a function?

The function $f(x) = 0.76x + 171.4$ models the cholesterol level of an American man as a function of his age, x, in years. Use the function to solve Exercises 43–44.

43. Find and interpret $f(20)$.

44. Find and interpret $f(50)$.

The bar graphs and the quadratic functions that model the data shown below and on the next page indicate that the cheaper cellphone calls got, the more Americans wanted to talk. Use the appropriate data to solve Exercises 45–46.

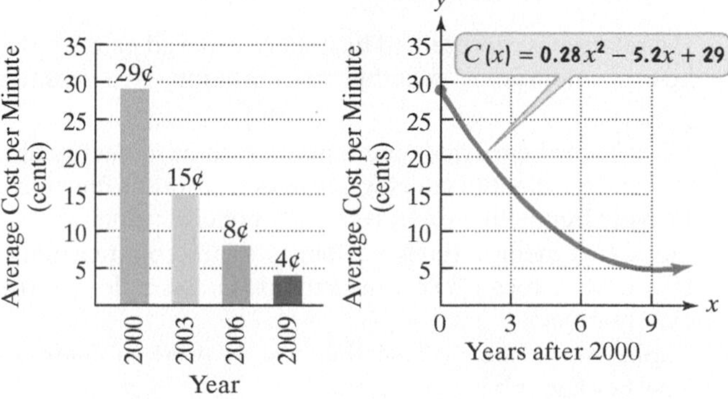

Source: Forbes

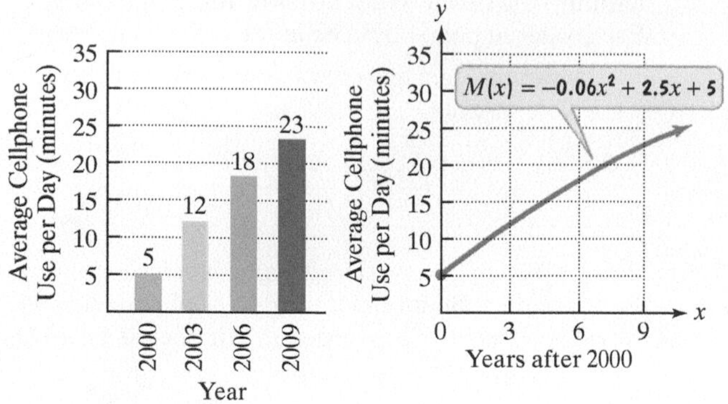

Source: Forbes

45. The function

$$C(x) = 0.28x^2 - 5.2x + 29$$

models the average cost of cellphone use per minute, $C(x)$, in cents, x years after 2000.

a. Find $C(9)$. Round to the nearest whole number and interpret the result.

b. Does the rounded value you obtained in part (a) underestimate or overestimate the value displayed by the bar graph at the bottom of the previous page? By how much?

c. Find and interpret $C(0)$. How is this shown on the graph of C on the previous page?

46. The function

$$M(x) = -0.06x^2 + 2.5x + 5$$

models the average cellphone use per day, $M(x)$, in minutes, x years after 2000.

a. Find $M(9)$. Round to the nearest whole number and interpret the result.

b. How does the rounded value you obtained in part (a) compare with the value displayed by the bar graph shown above?

c. Find and interpret $M(0)$. How is the shown on the graph of M?

Writing in Mathematics

47. If a relation is represented by a set of ordered pairs, explain how to determine whether the relation is a function.

48. Your friend heard that functions are studied in intermediate and college algebra courses. He asks you what a function is. Provide him with a clear, relatively concise response.

49. Does $f(x)$ mean f times x when referring to a function f? If not, what does $f(x)$ mean? Provide an example with your explanation.

50. Explain how the vertical line test is used to determine whether a graph is a function.

51. For people filing a single return, federal income tax is a function of adjusted gross income. For each value of adjusted gross income, there is a specific tax to be paid. By contrast, the price of a house is not a function of the lot size on which the house sits. Houses on same-sized lots can sell for many different prices.

a. Describe an everyday situation between variables that is a function.

b. Describe an everyday situation between variables that is not a function.

Critical Thinking Exercises

Make Sense? *In Exercises 52–55, determine whether each statement "makes sense" or "does not make sense" and explain your reasoning.*

52. My body temperature is a function of the time of day.

53. My height is a function of my age.

54. Using $f(x) = 3x + 2$, I found $f(50)$ by applying the distributive property to $(3x + 2)50$.

55. A function models how a woman's cholesterol level depends on her age, so the domain is the set of various cholesterol levels.

In Exercises 56–59, determine whether each statement is true or false. If the statement is false, make the necessary change(s) to produce a true statement.

56. All relations are functions.

57. No two ordered pairs of a function can have the same second component and different first components.

58. The graph of every line is a function.

59. A horizontal line can intersect the graph of a function at more than one point.

60. Write a linear function, $f(x) = mx + b$, satisfying the following conditions:

$$f(0) = 7 \text{ and } f(1) = 10.$$

61. If $f(x) = ax^2 + bx + c$ and $r = \dfrac{-b + \sqrt{b^2 - 4ac}}{2a}$, find $f(r)$ without doing any algebra and explain how you arrived at your result.

62. A car was purchased for \$22,500. The value of the car decreases by \$3200 per year for the first seven years. Write a function V that describes the value of the car after x years, where $0 \le x \le 7$. Then find and interpret $V(3)$.

Review Exercises

63. Write 0.00397 in scientific notation.

64. Divide: $\dfrac{x^3 + 7x^2 - 2x + 3}{x - 2}$.

65. Solve:

$$\begin{cases} 3x + 2y = 6 \\ 8x - 3y = 1 \end{cases}$$

GROUP PROJECT

The bar graph preceding Exercises 41 and 42 and each of these exercises in Exercise Set 6 illustrates that if a relation is a function, reversing the components in each of its ordered pairs may result in a relation that is no longer a function. Group members should find examples of bar graphs that illustrate this idea. Consult almanacs, newspapers, magazines, or the Internet. The group should select the graph with the most intriguing data. For the graph selected, write and solve a problem with four parts similar to Exercise 41 or 42.

Summary

Definitions and Concepts	Examples

Section 1 Solving Quadratic Equations by the Square Root Property

The Square Root Property

If u is an algebraic expression and d is a positive real number, then

If $u^2 = d$, then $u = \sqrt{d}$ or $u = -\sqrt{d}$.

Equivalently,

If $u^2 = d$, then $u = \pm\sqrt{d}$.

Solve:

$$(x-1)^2 = 7.$$
$$x - 1 = \pm\sqrt{7}$$
$$x = 1 \pm \sqrt{7}$$

The solution set is $\{1 \pm \sqrt{7}\}$.

The Pythagorean Theorem

The sum of the squares of the lengths of the legs of a right triangle equals the square of the length of the hypotenuse.

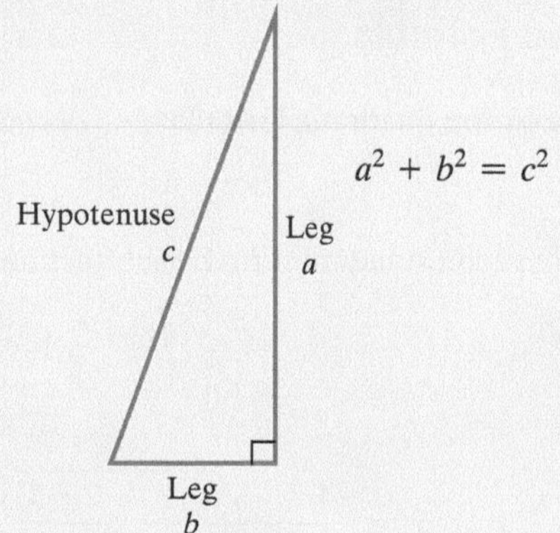

$$a^2 + b^2 = c^2$$

Find a.

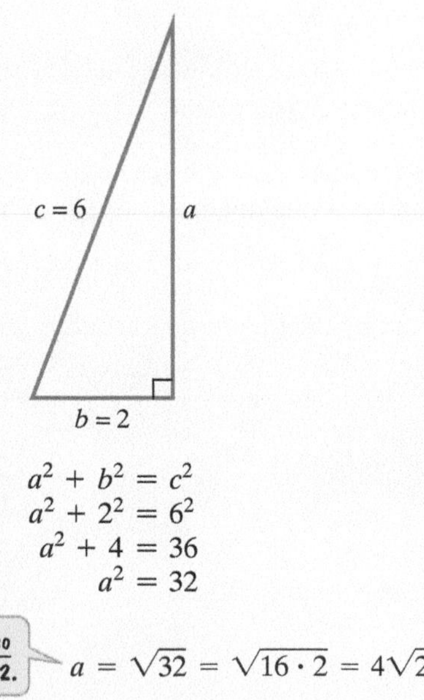

$$a^2 + b^2 = c^2$$
$$a^2 + 2^2 = 6^2$$
$$a^2 + 4 = 36$$
$$a^2 = 32$$

a must be positive, so do not use $a = -\sqrt{32}$.

$$a = \sqrt{32} = \sqrt{16 \cdot 2} = 4\sqrt{2}$$

The Distance Formula

The distance, d, between the points (x_1, y_1) and (x_2, y_2) is given by

$$d = \sqrt{(x_2 - x_1)^2 + (y_2 - y_1)^2}.$$

Find the distance between $(-3, -5)$ and $(6, -2)$.

$$d = \sqrt{[6-(-3)]^2 + [-2-(-5)]^2}$$
$$= \sqrt{9^2+3^2} = \sqrt{81+9} = \sqrt{90} = \sqrt{9 \cdot 10} = 3\sqrt{10} \approx 9.49$$

Definitions and Concepts	Examples

Section 2 Solving Quadratic Equations by Completing the Square

Completing the Square

If $x^2 + bx$ is a binomial, then by adding $\left(\frac{b}{2}\right)^2$, the square of half the coefficient of x, you will obtain a perfect square trinomial. That is,

$$x^2 + bx + \left(\frac{b}{2}\right)^2 = \left(x + \frac{b}{2}\right)^2.$$

Complete the square: $x^2 + 10x$.

Add $\left(\frac{10}{2}\right)^2 = 5^2$, or 25.

$$x^2 + 10x + 25 = (x + 5)^2$$

Solving Quadratic Equations by Completing the Square

1. If the coefficient of x^2 is not 1, divide both sides by this coefficient.
2. Isolate variable terms on one side.
3. Complete the square by adding the square of half the coefficient of x to both sides.
4. Factor the perfect square trinomial.
5. Solve by applying the square root property.

Solve by completing the square:

$$2x^2 + 12x - 4 = 0.$$

$$\frac{2x^2}{2} + \frac{12x}{2} - \frac{4}{2} = \frac{0}{2} \quad \text{Divide by 2.}$$

$$x^2 + 6x - 2 = 0 \quad \text{Simplify.}$$

$$x^2 + 6x = 2 \quad \text{Add 2.}$$

The coefficient of x is 6. Half of 6 is 3, and $3^2 = 9$. Add 9 to both sides.

$$x^2 + 6x + 9 = 2 + 9$$

$$(x + 3)^2 = 11$$

$$x + 3 = \pm\sqrt{11}$$

$$x = -3 \pm \sqrt{11}$$

The solution set is $\{-3 \pm \sqrt{11}\}$.

Section 3 The Quadratic Formula

The solutions of a quadratic equation in standard form

$$ax^2 + bx + c = 0, \quad a \neq 0,$$

are given by the quadratic formula

$$x = \frac{-b \pm \sqrt{b^2 - 4ac}}{2a}.$$

Solve by the quadratic formula:

$$2x^2 + 4x = 5.$$

First write in standard form by subtracting 5 from both sides.

$$2x^2 + 4x - 5 = 0$$

$a = 2$ $\quad b = 4$ $\quad c = -5$

$$x = \frac{-4 \pm \sqrt{4^2 - 4 \cdot 2(-5)}}{2 \cdot 2}$$

$$= \frac{-4 \pm \sqrt{16 - (-40)}}{4}$$

$$= \frac{-4 \pm \sqrt{56}}{4} = \frac{-4 \pm \sqrt{4 \cdot 14}}{4}$$

$$= \frac{-4 \pm 2\sqrt{14}}{4}$$

$$= \frac{2(-2 \pm \sqrt{14})}{2 \cdot 2} = \frac{-2 \pm \sqrt{14}}{2}$$

Definitions and Concepts	Examples

Section 4 Imaginary Numbers as Solutions of Quadratic Equations

The imaginary unit i is defined as

$$i = \sqrt{-1}, \quad \text{where} \quad i^2 = -1.$$

The set of numbers in the form $a + bi$ is called the set of complex numbers. If $b = 0$, the complex number is a real number. If $b \neq 0$, the complex number is called an imaginary number.

- $\sqrt{-36} = \sqrt{36(-1)} = \sqrt{36}\sqrt{-1} = 6i$
- $\sqrt{-50} = \sqrt{50(-1)} = \sqrt{25 \cdot 2}\sqrt{-1} = 5i\sqrt{2}$

Some quadratic equations have complex solutions that are imaginary numbers.

Solve: $x^2 - 2x + 2 = 0$.

$a = 1$ $b = -2$ $c = 2$

$$x = \frac{-b \pm \sqrt{b^2 - 4ac}}{2a} = \frac{-(-2) \pm \sqrt{(-2)^2 - 4 \cdot 1 \cdot 2}}{2 \cdot 1}$$

$$= \frac{2 \pm \sqrt{4 - 8}}{2} = \frac{2 \pm \sqrt{-4}}{2} = \frac{2 \pm \sqrt{4(-1)}}{2}$$

$$= \frac{2 \pm 2i}{2} = \frac{2(1 \pm i)}{2} = 1 \pm i$$

The solution set is $\{1 \pm i\}$.

Section 5 Graphs of Quadratic Equations

The graph of $y = ax^2 + bx + c$, called a parabola, can be graphed using the following steps:

1. If $a > 0$, the parabola opens upward. If $a < 0$, it opens downward.
2. Find the vertex, the lowest point if the parabola opens upward and the highest point if it opens downward. The x-coordinate of the vertex is $\frac{-b}{2a}$. Substitute this value into the parabola's equation to find the y-coordinate.
3. Find any x-intercepts by letting $y = 0$ and solving the resulting equation.
4. Find the y-intercept by letting $x = 0$.
5. Plot the intercepts and the vertex.
6. Connect these points with a smooth curve.

Graph: $y = x^2 - 2x - 8$.

$a = 1$ $b = -2$ $c = -8$

- $a > 0$, so the parabola opens upward.
- Vertex: x-coordinate $= \frac{-b}{2a} = \frac{-(-2)}{2 \cdot 1} = 1$

  y-coordinate $= 1^2 - 2 \cdot 1 - 8 = -9$

  Vertex is $(1, -9)$.
- x-intercepts: Let $y = 0$.

$$x^2 - 2x - 8 = 0$$
$$(x - 4)(x + 2) = 0$$
$$x - 4 = 0 \quad \text{or} \quad x + 2 = 0$$
$$x = 4 \qquad\qquad x = -2$$

  The parabola passes through $(4, 0)$ and $(-2, 0)$.
- y-intercept: Let $x = 0$.

$$y = 0^2 - 2 \cdot 0 - 8 = 0 - 0 - 8 = -8$$

  The parabola passes through $(0, -8)$.

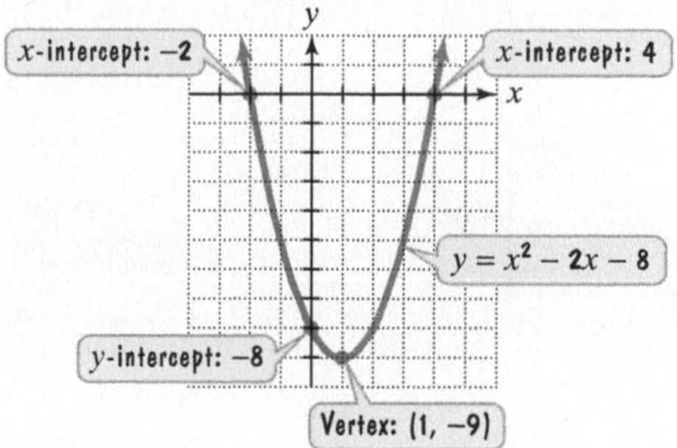

Definitions and Concepts	Examples

Section 6 Introduction to Functions

A relation is any set of ordered pairs. The set of first components is the domain and the set of second components is the range. A function is a relation in which each member of the domain corresponds to exactly one member of the range. No two ordered pairs of a function can have the same first component and different second components.

The domain of the relation $\{(1, 2), (3, 4), (3, 7)\}$ is $\{1, 3\}$. The range is $\{2, 4, 7\}$. The relation is not a function: 3, in the domain, corresponds to both 4 and 7 in the range.

If a function is defined as an equation, the notation $f(x)$, read "f of x" or "f at x," describes the value of the function at the number x.

If $f(x) = x^2 - 5x + 4$, find $f(3)$.

$$f(3) = 3^2 - 5 \cdot 3 + 4 = 9 - 15 + 4 = -2$$

Thus, f of 3 is -2.

The Vertical Line Test for Functions

If any vertical line intersects a graph in more than one point, the graph does not define y as a function of x.

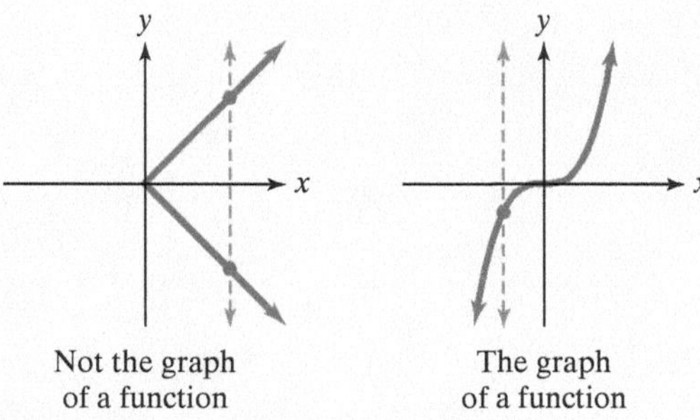

Not the graph of a function

The graph of a function

REVIEW EXERCISES

1 *In Exercises 1–8, solve each quadratic equation by the square root property. If possible, simplify radicals or rationalize denominators.*

1. $x^2 = 64$
2. $x^2 = 17$
3. $2x^2 = 150$
4. $(x - 3)^2 = 9$
5. $(y + 4)^2 = 5$
6. $3y^2 - 5 = 0$
7. $(2x - 7)^2 = 25$
8. $(x + 5)^2 = 12$

In Exercises 9–11, use the Pythagorean Theorem to find the missing length in each right triangle. Express the answer in radical form and simplify, if possible.

9.

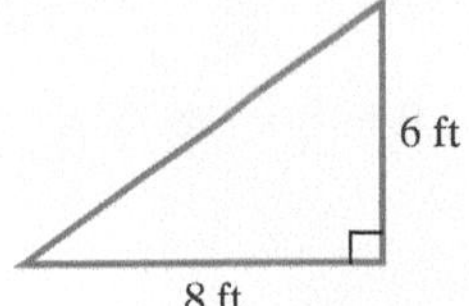

10.

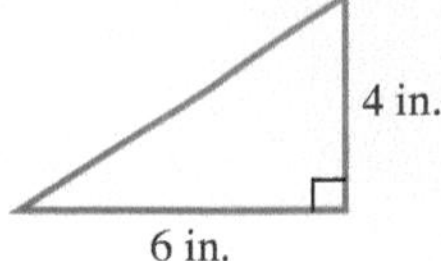

11.

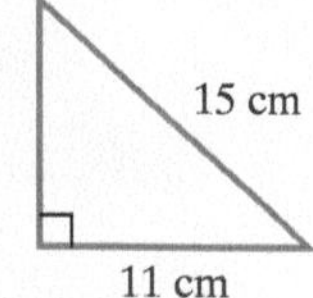

Use the Pythagorean Theorem to solve Exercises 12–13.

12. How far away from the building shown in the figure is the bottom of the ladder?

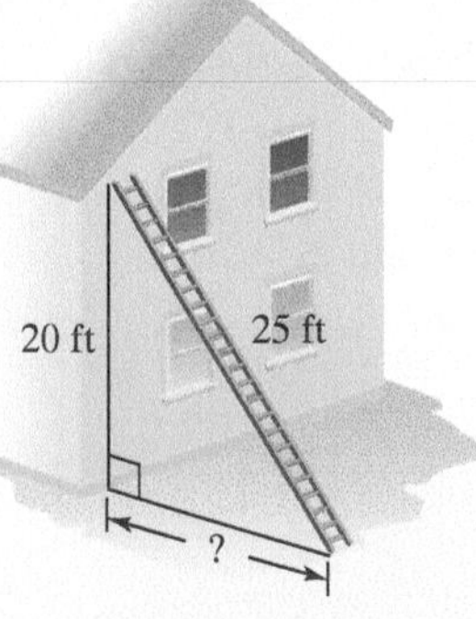

13. A vertical pole is to be supported by three wires. Each wire is 13 yards long and is anchored 5 yards from the base of the pole. How far up the pole will the wires be attached?

14. The weight of a human fetus is modeled by the formula $W = 3t^2$, where W is the weight, in grams, and t is the time, in weeks, $0 \le t \le 39$. After how many weeks does the fetus weigh 1200 grams?

15. The distance, d, in feet, that an object falls in t seconds is modeled by the formula $d = 16t^2$. If you dive from a height of 100 feet, how long will it take to hit the water?

In Exercises 16–17, find the distance between each pair of points. Express answers in simplified radical form and, if necessary, round to two decimal places.

16. $(-3, -2)$ and $(1, -5)$

17. $(3, 8)$ and $(5, 4)$

2 *In Exercises 18–21, complete the square for each binomial. Then factor the resulting perfect square trinomial.*

18. $x^2 + 16x$

19. $x^2 - 6x$

20. $x^2 + 3x$

21. $x^2 - 5x$

In Exercises 22–24, solve each quadratic equation by completing the square.

22. $x^2 - 12x + 27 = 0$

23. $x^2 - 6x + 4 = 0$

24. $3x^2 - 12x + 11 = 0$

3 *In Exercises 25–27, solve each equation using the quadratic formula. Simplify irrational solutions, if possible.*

25. $2x^2 + 5x - 3 = 0$

26. $x^2 = 2x + 4$

27. $3x^2 + 5 = 9x$

In Exercises 28–32, solve each equation by the method of your choice. Simplify irrational solutions, if possible.

28. $2x^2 - 11x + 5 = 0$

29. $(3x + 5)(x - 3) = 5$

30. $3x^2 - 7x + 1 - 0$

31. $x^2 - 9 = 0$

32. $(2x - 3)^2 = 5$

33. The amount spent by governments and businesses worldwide on goods and services to thwart terrorists is increasing. The formula

$$T = 0.6x^2 + 5.4x + 28$$

models the amount spent to fight terrorism, T, in billions of dollars, x years after 2003. (*Source*: Homeland Security Research)

a. How much was spent to fight terrorism in 2007?

b. By which year is the amount spent to fight terrorism expected to reach $160 billion?

4 *In Exercises 34–37, express each number in terms of i.*

34. $\sqrt{-81}$

35. $\sqrt{-23}$

36. $\sqrt{-48}$

37. $3 + \sqrt{-49}$

Exercises 38–42 involve quadratic equations with imaginary solutions. Solve each equation.

38. $x^2 = -100$

39. $5x^2 = -125$

40. $(2x + 1)^2 = -8$

41. $x^2 - 4x + 13 = 0$

42. $3x^2 - x + 2 = 0$

5 *In Exercises 43–46,*

a. *Determine if the parabola whose equation is given opens upward or downward.*

b. *Find the parabola's x-intercepts. If they are irrational, round to the nearest tenth.*

c. *Find the parabola's y-intercept.*

d. *Find the parabola's vertex.*

e. *Graph the parabola.*

43. $y = x^2 - 6x - 7$

44. $y = -x^2 - 2x + 3$

45. $y = -3x^2 + 6x + 1$

46. $y = x^2 - 4x$

47. Fireworks are launched into the air. The formula

$$y = -16x^2 + 200x + 4$$

models the fireworks' height, y, in feet, x seconds after they are launched. When should the fireworks explode so that they go off at the greatest height? What is that height?

48. A quarterback tosses a football to a receiver 40 yards downfield. The formula

$$y = -0.025x^2 + x + 6$$

models the football's height, y, in feet, when it is x yards from the quarterback.

a. How many yards from the quarterback does the football reach its greatest height? What is that height?

b. If a defender is 38 yards from the quarterback, how far must he reach to deflect or catch the ball?

c. If the football is neither deflected by the defender nor caught by the receiver, how many yards will it go, to the nearest tenth of a yard, before hitting the ground?

d. Graph the equation that models the football's parabolic path.

6 *In Exercises 49–51, determine whether each relation is a function. Give the domain and range for each relation.*

49. $\{(2, 7), (3, 7), (5, 7)\}$

50. $\{(1, 10), (2, 500), (3, \pi)\}$

51. $\{(12, 13), (14, 15), (12, 19)\}$

In Exercises 52–53, evaluate each function at the given values.

52. $f(x) = 3x - 4$

a. $f(-5)$ **b.** $f(6)$ **c.** $f(0)$

53. $g(x) = x^2 - 5x + 2$

a. $g(-4)$ **b.** $g(3)$ **c.** $g(0)$

In Exercises 54–57, use the vertical line test to identify graphs in which y is a function of x.

54.

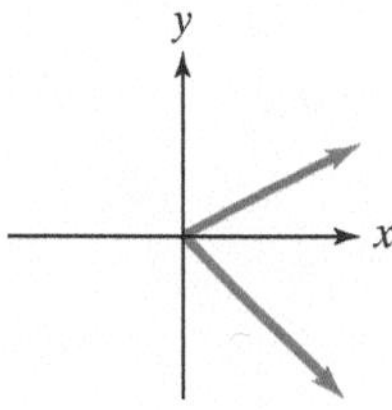

55.

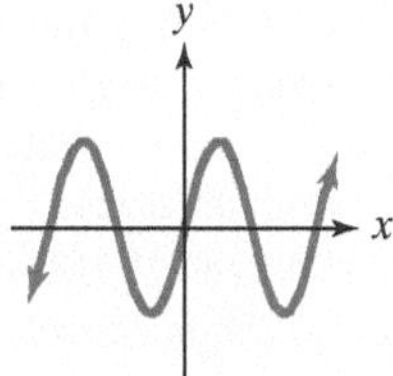

56.

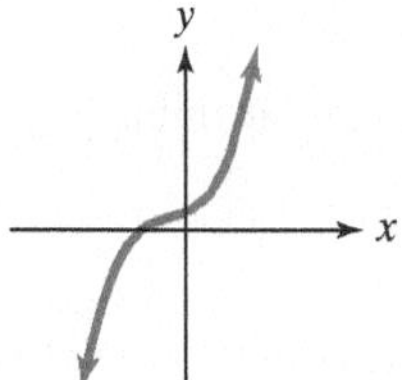

57.

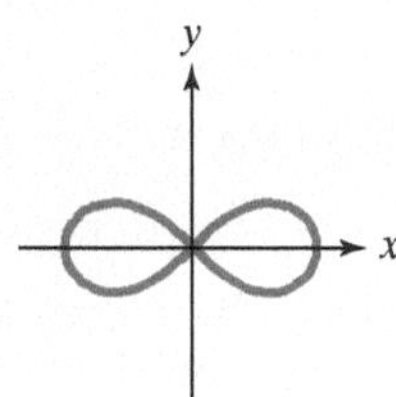

58. Whether on the slopes or at the shore, people are exposed to harmful amounts of the sun's skin-damaging ultraviolet (UV) rays. The quadratic function

$$D(x) = 0.8x^2 - 17x + 109$$

models the average time in which skin damage begins for burn-prone people, $D(x)$, in minutes, where x is the UV index, or measure of the sun's UV intensity. The graph of D is shown for a UV index from 1 (low) to 11 (high).

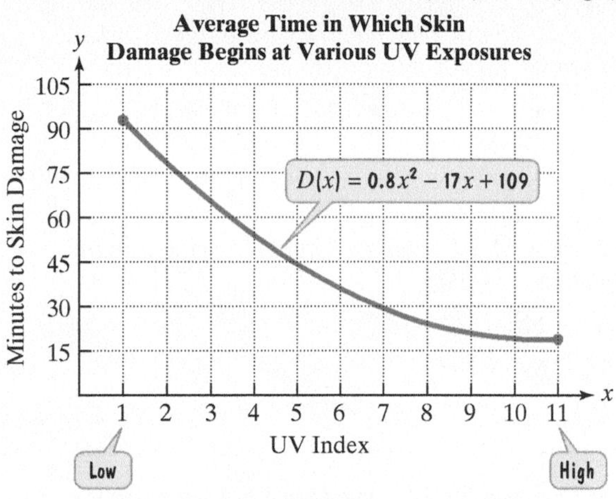

Source: National Oceanic and Atmospheric Administration

a. Find and interpret $D(1)$. How is this shown on the graph of D?

b. Find and interpret $D(10)$. How is this shown on the graph of D?

CHAPTER TEST

Step-by-step test solutions are found on the Chapter Test Prep Videos available in MyMathLab® or on YouTube (search "BlitzerIntroAlg" and click on "Channels").

In Exercises 1–2, solve by the square root property.

1. $3x^2 = 48$

2. $(x - 3)^2 = 5$

3. To find the distance across a lake, a surveyor inserts poles at P and Q, measuring the respective distances to point R, as shown in the figure. Use the surveyor's measurements given in the figure to find the distance PQ across the lake in simplified radical form.

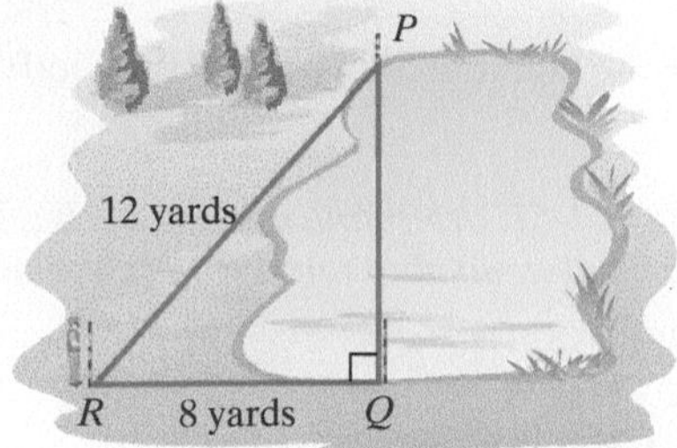

4. Find the distance between $(3, -2)$ and $(-4, 1)$. Express the answer in radical form and then round to two decimal places.

5. Solve by completing the square: $x^2 + 4x - 3 = 0$.

In Exercises 6–10, solve each equation by the method of your choice. Simplify irrational solutions, if possible.

6. $3x^2 + 5x + 1 = 0$

7. $(3x - 5)(x + 2) = -6$

8. $(2x + 1)^2 = 36$

9. $2x^2 = 6x - 1$

10. $2x^2 + 9x = 5$

In Exercises 11–12, express each number in terms of i.

11. $\sqrt{-121}$ **12.** $\sqrt{-75}$

In Exercises 13–15, solve each quadratic equation. Express imaginary solutions in a + bi form.

13. $x^2 + 36 = 0$ **14.** $(x - 5)^2 = -25$

15. $x^2 - 2x + 5 = 0$

In Exercises 16–17, graph each parabola whose equation is given. Label the x-intercepts, the y-intercept, and the vertex.

16. $y = x^2 + 2x - 8$

17. $y = -2x^2 + 16x - 24$

A batter hits a baseball into the air. The formula

$$y = -16x^2 + 64x + 5$$

models the baseball's height above the ground, y, in feet, x seconds after it is hit. Use the formula to solve Exercises 18–19.

18. When does the baseball reach its maximum height? What is that height?

19. After how many seconds does the baseball hit the ground? Round to the nearest tenth of a second.

In Exercises 20–21, determine whether each relation is a function. Give the domain and range for each relation.

20. $\{(1, 2), (3, 4), (5, 6), (6, 6)\}$

21. $\{(2, 1), (4, 3), (6, 5), (6, 6)\}$

22. If $f(x) = 7x - 3$, find $f(10)$.

23. If $g(x) = x^2 - 3x + 7$, find $g(-2)$.

In Exercises 24–25, identify the graph or graphs in which y is a function of x.

24.

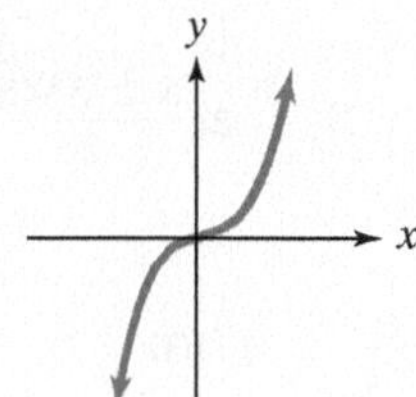

25.

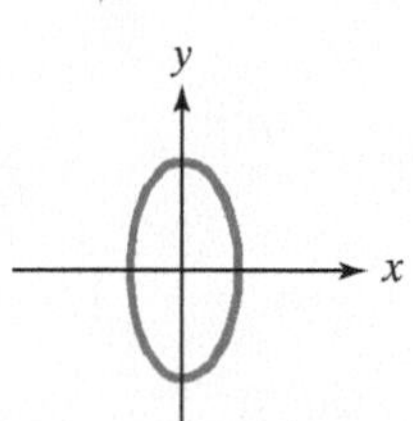

26. In a round-robin chess tournament, each player is paired with every other player once. The function

$$f(x) = \frac{x^2 - x}{2}$$

models the number of chess games, $f(x)$, that must be played in a round-robin tournament with x chess players. Find and interpret $f(9)$.

Answers to Selected Exercises

Section 1 Check Point Exercises

1. a. -6 and 6, or $\{\pm 6\}$ **b.** $-\sqrt{3}$ and $\sqrt{3}$, or $\{\pm\sqrt{3}\}$ **c.** $\pm\frac{\sqrt{14}}{2}$ or $\left\{\pm\frac{\sqrt{14}}{2}\right\}$ **2.** -2 and 8, or $\{-2, 8\}$ **3.** $2 \pm \sqrt{7}$ or $\{2 \pm \sqrt{7}\}$ **4.** $10\sqrt{21}$ in. ≈ 45.8 in. **5.** 13 units

Concept and Vocabulary Check

1. $\pm\sqrt{d}$ **2.** right; hypotenuse; legs **3.** right; legs; the square of the length of the hypotenuse **4.** $\sqrt{(x_2 - x_1)^2 + (y_2 - y_1)^2}$

Exercise Set 1

1. ± 4 or $\{\pm 4\}$ **3.** ± 9 or $\{\pm 9\}$ **5.** $\pm\sqrt{7}$ or $\{\pm\sqrt{7}\}$ **7.** $\pm 5\sqrt{2}$ or $\{\pm 5\sqrt{2}\}$ **9.** ± 2 or $\{\pm 2\}$ **11.** $\pm\frac{7}{2}$ or $\left\{\pm\frac{7}{2}\right\}$ **13.** ± 5 or $\{\pm 5\}$ **15.** $\pm\frac{\sqrt{6}}{3}$ or $\left\{\pm\frac{\sqrt{6}}{3}\right\}$ **17.** $\pm\frac{\sqrt{35}}{5}$ or $\left\{\pm\frac{\sqrt{35}}{5}\right\}$ **19.** -1 and 7, or $\{-1, 7\}$ **21.** -16 and 6, or $\{-16, 6\}$ **23.** $-\frac{5}{3}$ and $\frac{1}{3}$, or $\left\{-\frac{5}{3}, \frac{1}{3}\right\}$ **25.** $5 \pm \sqrt{3}$ or $\{5 \pm \sqrt{3}\}$ **27.** $-8 \pm \sqrt{11}$ or $\{-8 \pm \sqrt{11}\}$ **29.** $4 \pm 3\sqrt{2}$ or $\{4 \pm 3\sqrt{2}\}$ **31.** -6 and 2, or $\{-6, 2\}$ **33.** -3 and 9, or $\{-3, 9\}$ **35.** $5 \pm \sqrt{2}$ or $\{5 \pm \sqrt{2}\}$ **37.** $-1 \pm \sqrt{5}$ or $\{-1 \pm \sqrt{5}\}$ **39.** $7 \pm 2\sqrt{3}$ or $\{7 \pm 2\sqrt{3}\}$ **41.** 17 m **43.** 39 m **45.** 12 cm **47.** $5\sqrt{7}$ m **49.** $\sqrt{17}$ or 4.12 units **51.** 17 units **53.** $3\sqrt{5}$ or 6.71 units **55.** $\sqrt{41}$ or 6.40 units **57.** 16 units **59.** -2 and 8 **61.** -3 and $\frac{5}{3}$ **63.** $r = \frac{\sqrt{A\pi}}{\pi}$ **65.** $d = \frac{\sqrt{kI}}{I}$ **67.** $2\sqrt{41}$ ft **69.** $90\sqrt{2}$ ft **71.** 6 in. **73.** 6 weeks **75.** 5 sec **77.** 8 m **79.** 10 in. **85.** makes sense **87.** makes sense **89.** false **91.** true **93.** -7 and 1 **95.** -2 and 4, or $\{-2, 4\}$ **96.** $2(2x + 3)(3x - 1)$ **97.** $\frac{x - 3}{3(x - 2)}$ **98.** -6 or $\{-6\}$ **99.** $(x + 4)^2$ **100.** $(x - 7)^2$ **101.** $\left(x + \frac{5}{2}\right)^2$

Section 2 Check Point Exercises

1. a. $x^2 + 10x + 25 = (x+5)^2$ **b.** $x^2 - 6x + 9 = (x-3)^2$ **c.** $x^2 + 3x + \frac{9}{4} = \left(x + \frac{3}{2}\right)^2$

2. a. -7 and 1, or $\{-7, 1\}$ **b.** $5 \pm \sqrt{7}$ or $\{5 \pm \sqrt{7}\}$ **3.** $\frac{5 \pm 3\sqrt{3}}{2}$ or $\left\{\frac{5 \pm 3\sqrt{3}}{2}\right\}$

Concept and Vocabulary Check

1. 81 **2.** 9 **3.** $\frac{49}{4}$ **4.** $\frac{25}{16}$ **5.** $\left(\frac{b}{2}\right)^2$ or $\frac{b^2}{4}$ **6.** 100 **7.** 1 **8.** $\frac{1}{4}$

Exercise Set 2

1. $x^2 + 10x + 25 = (x+5)^2$ **3.** $x^2 - 2x + 1 = (x-1)^2$ **5.** $x^2 + 5x + \frac{25}{4} = \left(x + \frac{5}{2}\right)^2$ **7.** $x^2 - 7x + \frac{49}{4} = \left(x - \frac{7}{2}\right)^2$

9. $x^2 + \frac{1}{2}x + \frac{1}{16} = \left(x + \frac{1}{4}\right)^2$ **11.** $x^2 - \frac{4}{3}x + \frac{4}{9} = \left(x - \frac{2}{3}\right)^2$ **13.** -5 and 1, or $\{-5, 1\}$ **15.** 4 and 6, or $\{4, 6\}$

17. $1 \pm \sqrt{6}$ or $\{1 \pm \sqrt{6}\}$ **19.** $-2 \pm \sqrt{3}$ or $\{-2 \pm \sqrt{3}\}$ **21.** -4 and 7, or $\{-4, 7\}$ **23.** $\frac{-3 \pm \sqrt{13}}{2}$ or $\left\{\frac{-3 \pm \sqrt{13}}{2}\right\}$

25. $\frac{7 \pm \sqrt{37}}{2}$ or $\left\{\frac{7 \pm \sqrt{37}}{2}\right\}$ **27.** $\frac{1 \pm \sqrt{13}}{2}$ or $\left\{\frac{1 \pm \sqrt{13}}{2}\right\}$ **29.** $\frac{1}{2}$ and 1, or $\left\{\frac{1}{2}, 1\right\}$ **31.** $\frac{-5 \pm \sqrt{3}}{2}$ or $\left\{\frac{-5 \pm \sqrt{3}}{2}\right\}$

33. $\frac{1 \pm \sqrt{13}}{4}$ or $\left\{\frac{1 \pm \sqrt{13}}{4}\right\}$ **35.** $1 \pm \sqrt{7}$ or $\{1 \pm \sqrt{7}\}$ **37.** $\frac{1 \pm \sqrt{29}}{2}$ or $\left\{\frac{1 \pm \sqrt{29}}{2}\right\}$ **39.** $-5b$ and b, or $\{-5b, b\}$

43. makes sense **45.** makes sense **47.** false **49.** false **51.** $x^2 - 20x + 100$

53. $-\frac{b}{2} \pm \sqrt{\frac{b^2}{4} - c}, \frac{-b \pm \sqrt{b^2 - 4ac}}{2}, \left\{-\frac{b}{2} \pm \sqrt{\frac{b^2}{4} - c}\right\}$, or $\left\{\frac{-b \pm \sqrt{b^2 - 4ac}}{2}\right\}$ **55.** $\frac{11}{(x-3)(x-4)}$ **56.** $\frac{x}{3}$

57. 3 or $\{3\}$ **58.** $\frac{1}{2}; -5$ **59.** $\frac{2}{3}$ **60.** $1 + \sqrt{7}; 1 - \sqrt{7}$

Section 3 Check Point Exercises

1. $-\frac{1}{2}$ and $\frac{1}{4}$, or $\left\{-\frac{1}{2}, \frac{1}{4}\right\}$ **2.** $3 \pm \sqrt{5}$ or $\{3 \pm \sqrt{5}\}$ **3.** 2036

Concept and Vocabulary Check

1. $\frac{-b \pm \sqrt{b^2 - 4ac}}{2a}$ **2.** 3; 10; -8 **3.** 1; 8; -29 **4.** 6; -3; -4 **5.** $-\frac{1}{3}$; 2 **6.** $-4 \pm 3\sqrt{5}$

7. the square root property **8.** factoring and the zero-product principle **9.** the quadratic formula

Exercise Set 3

1. -3 and -2, or $\{-3, -2\}$ **3.** $\frac{-5 \pm \sqrt{13}}{2}$ or $\left\{\frac{-5 \pm \sqrt{13}}{2}\right\}$ **5.** $-2 \pm \sqrt{10}$ or $\{-2 \pm \sqrt{10}\}$ **7.** $-2 \pm \sqrt{11}$ or $\{-2 \pm \sqrt{11}\}$

9. -3 and 6, or $\{-3, 6\}$ **11.** $-\frac{2}{3}$ and $\frac{3}{2}$, or $\left\{-\frac{2}{3}, \frac{3}{2}\right\}$ **13.** $1 \pm \sqrt{11}$ or $\{1 \pm \sqrt{11}\}$ **15.** $\frac{1 \pm \sqrt{57}}{2}$ or $\left\{\frac{1 \pm \sqrt{57}}{2}\right\}$

17. $\frac{-3 \pm \sqrt{3}}{6}$ or $\left\{\frac{-3 \pm \sqrt{3}}{6}\right\}$ **19.** $\frac{2}{3}$ or $\left\{\frac{2}{3}\right\}$ **21.** $\frac{1 \pm \sqrt{29}}{4}$ or $\left\{\frac{1 \pm \sqrt{29}}{4}\right\}$ **23.** $-\frac{1}{2}$ and 1, or $\left\{-\frac{1}{2}, 1\right\}$ **25.** $\frac{1}{5}$ and 2, or $\left\{\frac{1}{5}, 2\right\}$

27. $\pm 2\sqrt{5}$ or $\{\pm 2\sqrt{5}\}$ **29.** $1 \pm \sqrt{2}$ or $\{1 \pm \sqrt{2}\}$ **31.** $\frac{-11 \pm \sqrt{33}}{4}$ or $\left\{\frac{-11 \pm \sqrt{33}}{4}\right\}$ **33.** 0 and $\frac{8}{3}$, or $\left\{0, \frac{8}{3}\right\}$ **35.** 2 or $\{2\}$

37. -2 and 2, or $\{-2, 2\}$ **39.** -9 and 0, or $\{-9, 0\}$ **41.** $-\frac{2}{3}$ and 4, or $\left\{-\frac{2}{3}, 4\right\}$ **43.** $\frac{2 \pm \sqrt{10}}{3}$ or $\left\{\frac{2 \pm \sqrt{10}}{3}\right\}$ **45.** $\pm\sqrt{3}$ or $\{\pm\sqrt{3}\}$

47. $-\frac{5}{2}$ and 0, or $\left\{-\frac{5}{2}, 0\right\}$ **49.** $\pm\sqrt{6}$ or $\{\pm\sqrt{6}\}$ **51.** $\frac{5 \pm \sqrt{73}}{2}$ or $\left\{\frac{5 \pm \sqrt{73}}{2}\right\}$ **53.** about 3.8 sec **55.** 10 ft

57. a. 56 million; perfectly well; It gives the actual number. **b.** 2020 **59.** width: 4.7 m; length: 7.7 m **61.** 2.3 and 3.3 ft

63. a. $\frac{1}{\Phi - 1}$ **b.** $\Phi = \frac{1 + \sqrt{5}}{2}$ **c.** $\frac{1 + \sqrt{5}}{2}$ **69.** does not make sense **71.** does not make sense **73.** false **75.** true **79.** about 1.2 feet

81.

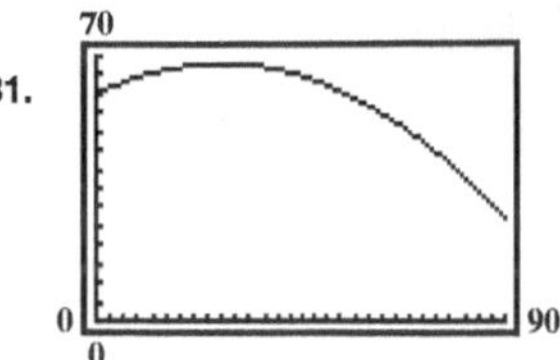

82. $\frac{1}{25}$ **83.** $9 - 3\sqrt{5}$ **84.** $x^3 - y^3$ **85.** no; no **86. a.** $-\sqrt{4}, \sqrt{1}$ **b.** $-\sqrt{5}, \sqrt{5}$ **c.** $-\sqrt{5}, -\sqrt{4}, \sqrt{1}, \sqrt{5}$ **d.** $\sqrt{-4}, \sqrt{-1}$
87. a. $-\sqrt{9}, \sqrt{0}, \sqrt{9}$ **b.** $-\sqrt{7}, \sqrt{7}$ **c.** $-\sqrt{9}, -\sqrt{7}, \sqrt{0}, \sqrt{9}, \sqrt{7}$ **d.** $\sqrt{-9}, \sqrt{-7}$

Mid-Chapter Check Point Exercises

1. $-\frac{8}{3}$ and 4, or $\left\{-\frac{8}{3}, 4\right\}$ **2.** 0 and $\frac{1}{3}$, or $\left\{0, \frac{1}{3}\right\}$ **3.** $1 \pm \sqrt{11}$ or $\{1 \pm \sqrt{11}\}$ **4.** $4 \pm \sqrt{7}$ or $\{4 \pm \sqrt{7}\}$ **5.** $-\frac{2}{3}$ and 1, or $\left\{-\frac{2}{3}, 1\right\}$
6. $\frac{5 \pm \sqrt{7}}{6}$ or $\left\{\frac{5 \pm \sqrt{7}}{6}\right\}$ **7.** -4 and 3, or $\{-4, 3\}$ **8.** $-5 \pm 2\sqrt{10}$ or $\{-5 \pm 2\sqrt{10}\}$ **9.** -3 and 3, or $\{-3, 3\}$
10. $\frac{-5 \pm \sqrt{17}}{4}$ or $\left\{\frac{-5 \pm \sqrt{17}}{4}\right\}$ **11.** $-\frac{1}{2}$ and 10, or $\left\{-\frac{1}{2}, 10\right\}$ **12.** 4 or $\{4\}$ **13.** -16 and 2, or $\{-16, 2\}$ **14.** $2\sqrt{7}$ cm
15. 13 units **16.** 12 in. and 16 in.

Section 4 Check Point Exercises

1. a. $4i$ **b.** $i\sqrt{5}$ **c.** $5i\sqrt{2}$ **2.** $-2 + 5i$ and $-2 - 5i$, or $\{-2 \pm 5i\}$ **3.** $-3 \pm 2i$ or $\{-3 \pm 2i\}$

Concept and Vocabulary Check

1. $\sqrt{-1}; -1$ **2.** $5i$ **3.** complex; imaginary; real **4.** $2 \pm i$

Exercise Set 4

1. $6i$ **3.** $i\sqrt{13}$ **5.** $5i\sqrt{2}$ **7.** $2i\sqrt{5}$ **9.** $-2i\sqrt{7}$ **11.** $7 + 4i$ **13.** $10 + i\sqrt{3}$ **15.** $6 - 7i\sqrt{2}$ **17.** $3 \pm 3i$ or $\{3 \pm 3i\}$
19. $-7 \pm 8i$ or $\{-7 \pm 8i\}$ **21.** $2 \pm i\sqrt{7}$ or $\{2 \pm i\sqrt{7}\}$ **23.** $-3 \pm 3i\sqrt{2}$ or $\{-3 \pm 3i\sqrt{2}\}$ **25.** $-2 \pm i$ or $\{-2 \pm i\}$ **27.** $3 \pm 2i$ or $\{3 \pm 2i\}$
29. $6 \pm 2i$ or $\{6 \pm 2i\}$ **31.** $5 \pm i\sqrt{2}$ or $\{5 \pm i\sqrt{2}\}$ **33.** $\frac{1 \pm i\sqrt{14}}{5}$ or $\left\{\frac{1 \pm i\sqrt{14}}{5}\right\}$ **35.** $\frac{2 \pm i\sqrt{6}}{2}$ or $\left\{\frac{2 \pm i\sqrt{6}}{2}\right\}$ **37.** $\pm i\sqrt{5}$ or $\{\pm i\sqrt{5}\}$
39. $1 \pm 3i$ or $\{1 \pm 3i\}$ **41.** $\frac{-1 \pm i\sqrt{7}}{2}$ or $\left\{\frac{-1 \pm i\sqrt{7}}{2}\right\}$ **43.** $9 \pm i\sqrt{19}$ are not real numbers. Applicant will not be hired. Answers will vary.
51. does not make sense **53.** does not make sense **55.** false **57.** false

63.

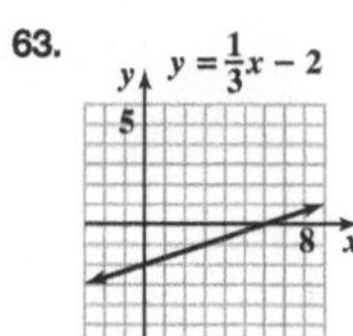

64.

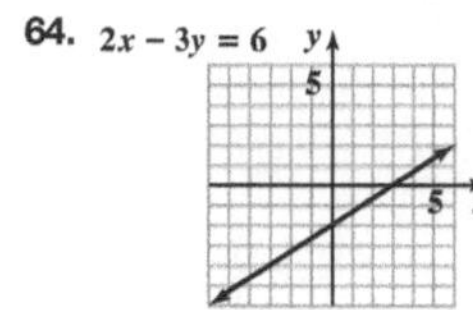

65.

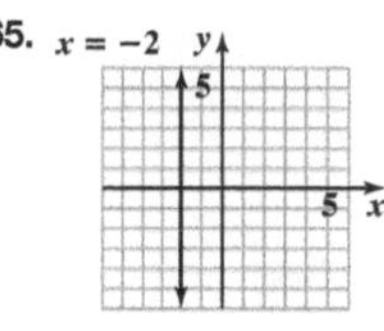

66.

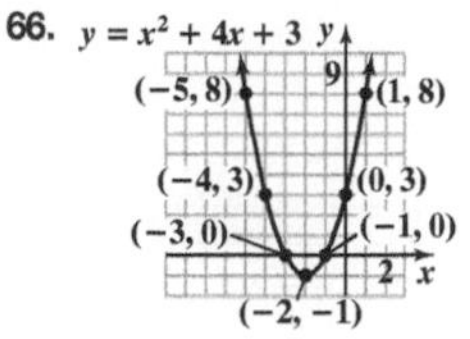

67. -1 and 3 **68.** -3

Section 5 Check Point Exercises

1. a. upward **b.**

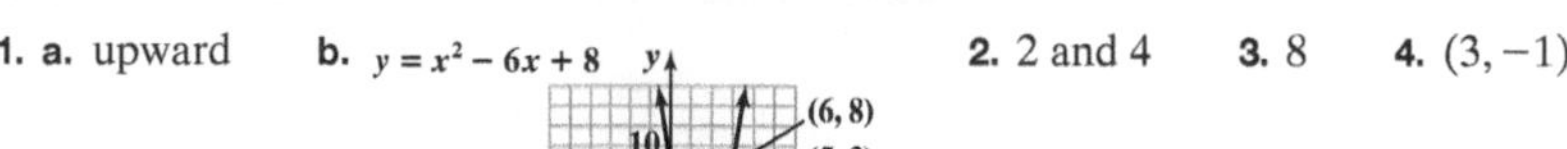

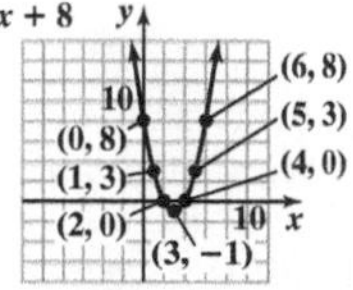

2. 2 and 4 **3.** 8 **4.** $(3, -1)$

5.

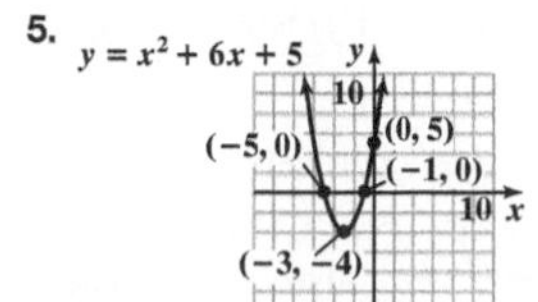

6.

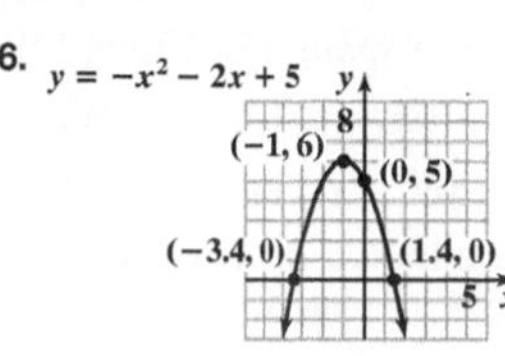

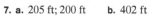

7. a. 205 ft; 200 ft **b.** 402 ft **c.**

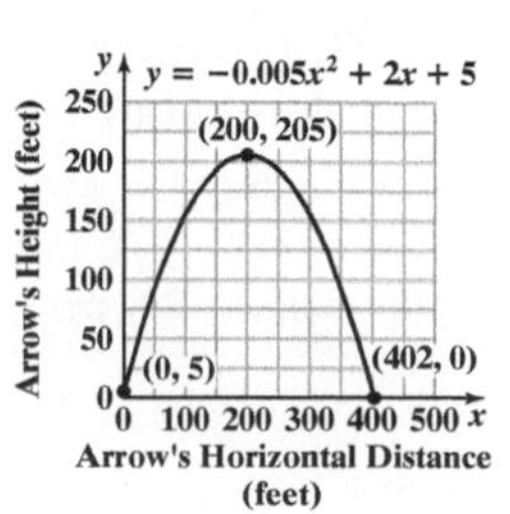

Concept and Vocabulary Check

1. parabola **2.** $a > 0; a < 0$ **3.** $ax^2 + bx + c = 0$ **4.** 0 **5.** $-\frac{b}{2a}; -\frac{b}{2a}$ or the x-coordinate

Exercise Set 5

1. upward **3.** downward **5.** 1 and 3 **7.** 2 and 6 **9.** 1.2 and -3.2 **11.** 3 **13.** -12 **15.** -4 **17.** 0 **19.** $(2, -1)$
21. $(-1, -8)$ **23.** $(-3, -9)$

25. $y = x^2 + 8x + 7$

27. $y = x^2 - 2x - 8$

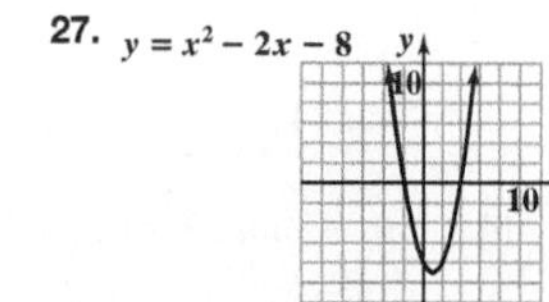

29. $y = -x^2 + 4x - 3$

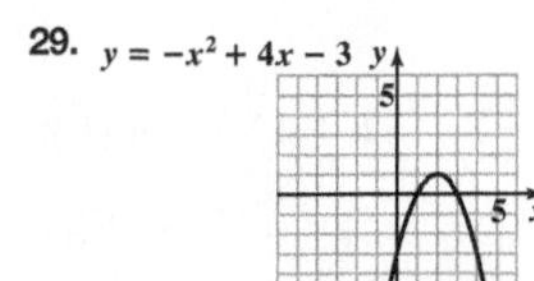

31. $y = x^2 - 1$

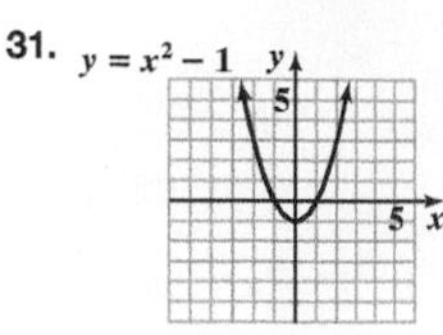

33. $y = x^2 + 2x + 1$

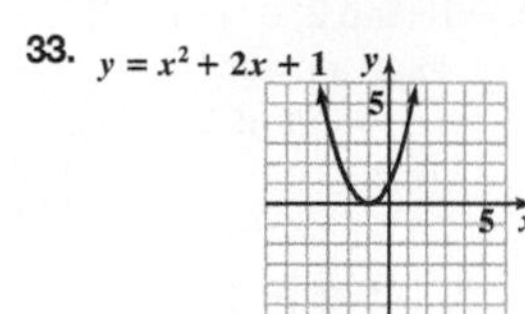

35. $y = -2x^2 + 4x + 5$

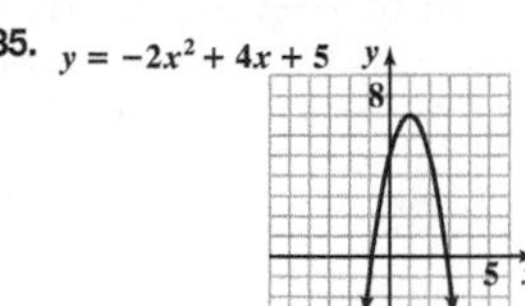

37. $(3, 2)$ **39.** $(-5, -4)$ **41.** $(1, -3)$ **43.** $(-2, 5)$ **45.** (h, k) **47.** **a.** 18.35 ft; 35 ft **b.** 77.8 ft **c.** 6.1 ft

49. **a.** 9.2 ft; 2 ft **b.** 5.4 ft **c.** $y = -0.8x^2 + 3.2x + 6$; (2, 9.2); (0, 6); (5.4, 0); Ball's Vertical Distance (feet); Ball's Horizontal Distance (feet) **51.** 25 yd by 25 yd; 625 sq yd

59. makes sense **61.** does not make sense **63.** true **65.** false **67.** $y = 2x^2 - 8$; $y = -2x^2 + 8$; $(-2, 0)$ and $(2, 0)$

71. (80, 1600); Answers will vary. **73.** $(-4, 520)$; Answers will vary. **75.** 2 or $\{2\}$ **76.** $-\frac{8}{3}$ or $\left\{-\frac{8}{3}\right\}$

77. $(-2, 1)$ or $\{(-2, 1)\}$ **78.** set 1 **79.** graph a **80.** 5

Section 6 Check Point Exercises

1. domain: {golf, lawn mowing, water skiing, hiking, bicycling}; range: {250, 325, 430, 720} **2.** **a.** not a function **b.** function
3. **a.** 23 **b.** -5 **c.** 3 **4.** **a.** 48 **b.** 3 **c.** 3 **5.** **a.** function **b.** function **c.** not a function
6. **a.** 25% **b.** 10% **c.** function f, the linear function

Concept and Vocabulary Check

1. relation; domain; range **2.** function **3.** f; x **4.** linear **5.** quadratic **6.** more than once; function

Exercise Set 6

1. function; domain: {1, 3, 5}; range: {2, 4, 5} **3.** not a function; domain: {3, 4}; range: {4, 5} **5.** function; domain: $\{-3, -2, -1, 0\}$; range: $\{-3, -2, -1, 0\}$ **7.** not a function; domain: {1}; range: {4, 5, 6} **9.** **a.** 12 **b.** -1 **c.** 5 **11.** **a.** 70 **b.** -28 **c.** 0
13. **a.** 93 **b.** -7 **c.** -3 **15.** **a.** 10 **b.** -2 **c.** 0 **17.** **a.** 11 **b.** 27 **c.** 3 **19.** **a.** 5 **b.** 5 **c.** 5 **21.** **a.** 3 **b.** 7
23. **a.** 1 **b.** -1 **25.** function **27.** function **29.** not a function **31.** function **33.** $\{(-1, 1), (0, 3), (1, 5)\}$
35. $\{(-2, -6), (-1, -2), (0, 0), (1, 0), (2, -2)\}$ **37.** 6 **39.** $x + h$ **41.** **a.** {(Philippines, 12), (Spain, 13), (Italy, 14), (Germany, 14), (Russia, 16)}
b. Yes; Each country corresponds to exactly one age. **c.** {(12, Philippines), (13, Spain), (14, Italy), (14, Germany), (16, Russia)}
d. No; 14 in the domain corresponds to two members of the range, Italy and Germany. **43.** 186.6; At age 20, an American man's cholesterol level is 186.6, or approx 187. **45.** **a.** $C(9) \approx 5$; In 2009, cellphone use cost approximately 5¢ per minute. **b.** overestimates by 1¢ **c.** $C(0) = 29$; In 2000, cellphone use cost approximately 29¢ per minute.; by the point (0, 29) **53.** makes sense **55.** does not make sense **57.** false **59.** true
61. $f(r) = 0$; r is a solution of the quadratic equation $ax^2 + bx + c = 0$. **63.** 3.97×10^{-3} **64.** $x^2 + 9x + 16 + \frac{35}{x - 2}$ **65.** $\left(\frac{4}{5}, \frac{9}{5}\right)$ or $\left\{\left(\frac{4}{5}, \frac{9}{5}\right)\right\}$

Review Exercises

1. -8 and 8, or $\{-8, 8\}$ **2.** $\pm\sqrt{17}$ or $\{\pm\sqrt{17}\}$ **3.** $\pm 5\sqrt{3}$ or $\{\pm 5\sqrt{3}\}$ **4.** 0 and 6, or $\{0, 6\}$ **5.** $-4 \pm \sqrt{5}$ or $\{-4 \pm \sqrt{5}\}$
6. $\pm\frac{\sqrt{15}}{3}$ or $\left\{\pm\frac{\sqrt{15}}{3}\right\}$ **7.** 1 and 6, or $\{1, 6\}$ **8.** $-5 \pm 2\sqrt{3}$ or $\{-5 \pm 2\sqrt{3}\}$ **9.** 10 ft **10.** $2\sqrt{13}$ in. **11.** $2\sqrt{26}$ cm
12. 15 ft **13.** 12 yd **14.** 20 weeks **15.** 2.5 sec **16.** 5 units **17.** $2\sqrt{5}$ or 4.47 units **18.** $x^2 + 16x + 64 = (x + 8)^2$

19. $x^2 - 6x + 9 = (x - 3)^2$ **20.** $x^2 + 3x + \frac{9}{4} = \left(x + \frac{3}{2}\right)^2$ **21.** $x^2 - 5x + \frac{25}{4} = \left(x - \frac{5}{2}\right)^2$ **22.** 3 and 9, or {3, 9}
23. $3 \pm \sqrt{5}$ or $\{3 \pm \sqrt{5}\}$ **24.** $\frac{6 \pm \sqrt{3}}{3}$ or $\left\{\frac{6 \pm \sqrt{3}}{3}\right\}$ **25.** -3 and $\frac{1}{2}$, or $\left\{-3, \frac{1}{2}\right\}$ **26.** $1 \pm \sqrt{5}$ or $\{1 \pm \sqrt{5}\}$
27. $\frac{9 \pm \sqrt{21}}{6}$ or $\left\{\frac{9 \pm \sqrt{21}}{6}\right\}$ **28.** $\frac{1}{2}$ and 5, or $\left\{\frac{1}{2}, 5\right\}$ **29.** -2 and $\frac{10}{3}$, or $\left\{-2, \frac{10}{3}\right\}$ **30.** $\frac{7 \pm \sqrt{37}}{6}$ or $\left\{\frac{7 \pm \sqrt{37}}{6}\right\}$ **31.** -3 and 3, or $\{-3, 3\}$
32. $\frac{3 \pm \sqrt{5}}{2}$ or $\left\{\frac{3 \pm \sqrt{5}}{2}\right\}$ **33. a.** \$59.2 billion **b.** 2014 **34.** $9i$ **35.** $i\sqrt{23}$ **36.** $4i\sqrt{3}$ **37.** $3 + 7i$ **38.** $\pm 10i$ or $\{\pm 10i\}$
39. $\pm 5i$ or $\{\pm 5i\}$ **40.** $\frac{-1 \pm 2i\sqrt{2}}{2}$ or $\left\{\frac{-1 \pm 2i\sqrt{2}}{2}\right\}$ **41.** $2 \pm 3i$ or $\{2 \pm 3i\}$ **42.** $\frac{1 \pm i\sqrt{23}}{6}$ or $\left\{\frac{1 \pm i\sqrt{23}}{6}\right\}$

43. a. upward **b.** -1 and 7 **c.** -7 **d.** $(3, -16)$ **e.**

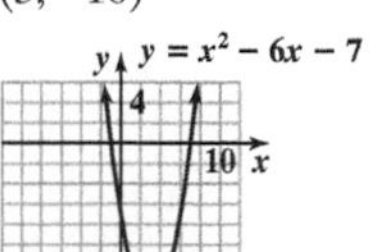

44. a. downward **b.** -3 and 1 **c.** 3 **d.** $(-1, 4)$ **e.**

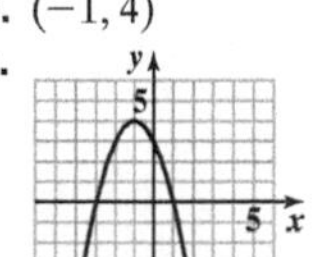

45. a. downward **b.** -0.2 and 2.2 **c.** 1 **d.** $(1, 4)$ **e.**

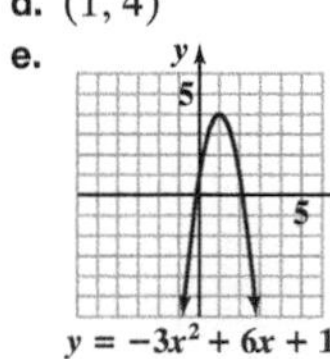

46. a. upward **b.** 0 and 4 **c.** 0 **d.** $(2, -4)$ **e.**

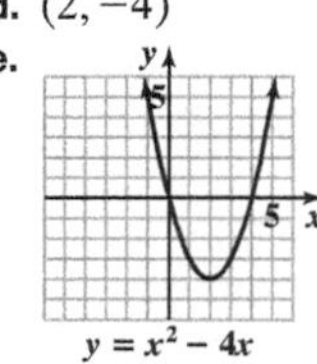

47. 6.25 sec; 629 ft **48. a.** 20 yd; 16 ft **b.** 7.9 ft **c.** 45.3 yd **d.**

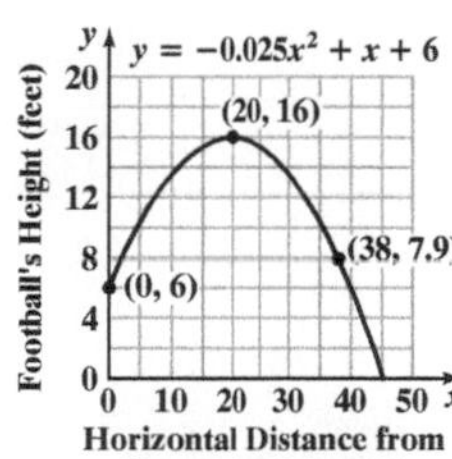

49. function; domain: {2, 3, 5}; range: {7} **50.** function; domain: {1, 2, 3}; range: {10, 500, π} **51.** not a function; domain: {12, 14}; range: {13, 15, 19} **52. a.** -19 **b.** 14 **c.** -4 **53. a.** 38 **b.** -4 **c.** 2 **54.** not a function **55.** function **56.** function **57.** not a function **58. a.** $D(1) = 92.8$; Skin damage begins for burn-prone people after 92.8 minutes when the sun's UV index is 1.; by the point (1, 92.8) **b.** $D(10) = 19$; Skin damage for burn-prone people after 19 minutes when the sun's UV index is 10.; by the point (10, 19)

Chapter Test

1. -4 and 4, or $\{-4, 4\}$ **2.** $3 \pm \sqrt{5}$ or $\{3 \pm \sqrt{5}\}$ **3.** $4\sqrt{5}$ yd **4.** $\sqrt{58}$ or 7.62 units **5.** $-2 \pm \sqrt{7}$ or $\{-2 \pm \sqrt{7}\}$
6. $\frac{-5 \pm \sqrt{13}}{6}$ or $\left\{\frac{-5 \pm \sqrt{13}}{6}\right\}$ **7.** $-\frac{4}{3}$ and 1, or $\left\{-\frac{4}{3}, 1\right\}$ **8.** $-\frac{7}{2}$ and $\frac{5}{2}$, or $\left\{-\frac{7}{2}, \frac{5}{2}\right\}$ **9.** $\frac{3 \pm \sqrt{7}}{2}$ or $\left\{\frac{3 \pm \sqrt{7}}{2}\right\}$
10. -5 and $\frac{1}{2}$, or $\left\{-5, \frac{1}{2}\right\}$ **11.** $11i$ **12.** $5i\sqrt{3}$ **13.** $\pm 6i$ or $\{\pm 6i\}$ **14.** $5 \pm 5i$ or $\{5 \pm 5i\}$ **15.** $1 \pm 2i$ or $\{1 \pm 2i\}$

16.

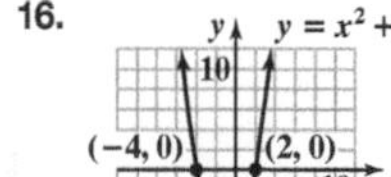

17.

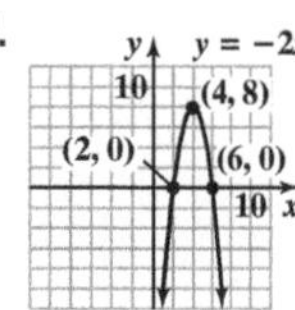

16. 2 sec; 69 ft **19.** 4.1 sec **20.** function; domain: {1, 3, 5, 6}; range: {2, 4, 6} **21.** not a function; domain: {2, 4, 6}; range: {1, 3, 5, 6}
22. 67 **23.** 17 **24.** function **25.** not a function **26.** 36; In a tournament with 9 chess players, 36 games must be played.

Problem Solving and Critical Thinking

How would your lifestyle change if a gallon of gas cost \$9.15? Or if the price of a staple such as milk was \$15? That's how much those products would cost if their prices had increased at the same rate college tuition has increased since 1980.

TUITION AND FEES AT FOUR-YEAR COLLEGES

	School Year Ending 2000	School Year Ending 2008
Public	\$3362	\$6185
Private	\$15,518	\$23,712

Source: The College Board

If these trends continue, what can we expect by the 2010s and beyond? We can answer this question by using estimation techniques that allow us to represent the data mathematically. With such representations, called *mathematical models*, we can gain insights and predict what might occur in the future on a variety of issues, ranging from college costs to global warming.

Mathematical models involving college costs are developed in Example 8 and Check Point 8 of Section 2. In Exercise 16 of the chapter test, you will approach our climate crisis mathematically by developing a model for data related to global warming.

Graduation cap: Stephen Coburn/shutterstock images; Child holding calculator: iofoto/shutterstock images

From Chapter 1 of *Thinking Mathematically*, Fifth Edition, Robert F. Blitzer.

OBJECTIVES

1 | Understand and use inductive reasoning.
2 | Understand and use deductive reasoning.

1 Inductive and Deductive Reasoning

One of the new frontiers of mathematics suggests that there is an underlying order in things that appear to be random, such as the hiss and crackle of background noises as you tune a radio. Irregularities in the heartbeat, some of them severe enough to cause a heart attack, or irregularities in our sleeping patterns, such as insomnia, are examples of chaotic behavior. Chaos in the mathematical sense does not mean a complete lack of form or arrangement. In mathematics, chaos is used to describe something that appears to be random but is not actually random. The patterns of chaos appear in images like the one shown on the left, called the Mandelbrot set. Magnified portions of this image yield repetitions of the original structure, as well as new and unexpected patterns. The Mandelbrot set transforms the hidden structure of chaotic events into a source of wonder and inspiration.

R.F. Voss "29-Fold M-set Seahorse" computer-generated image.

A magnification of the Mandelbrot set

Many people associate mathematics with tedious computation, meaningless algebraic procedures, and intimidating sets of equations. The truth is that mathematics is the most powerful means we have of exploring our world and describing how it works. The word *mathematics* comes from the Greek word *mathematikos*, which means "inclined to learn." To be mathematical literally means to be inquisitive, open-minded, and interested in a lifetime of pursuing knowledge!

Mathematics and Your Life

A major goal of this book is to show you how mathematics can be applied to your life in interesting, enjoyable, and meaningful ways. The ability to think mathematically and reason with quantitative issues will help you so that you can:

- order and arrange your world by using sets to sort and classify information
- use logic to evaluate the arguments of others and become a more effective advocate for your own beliefs
- understand the relationship between cutting-edge technology and ancient systems of number representation
- put the numbers you encounter in the news, ranging from the national debt to costs for President Obama's 2009 economic stimulus package, into perspective
- use mathematical models to gain insights into a variety of issues, including the positive benefits that humor and laughter can have on your life
- use basic ideas about savings, loans, and investments to achieve your financial goals
- use geometry to study the shape of your world, enhancing your appreciation of nature's patterns and beauty

- develop an understanding of the fundamentals of statistics and how these numbers are used to make decisions
- understand the mathematical paradoxes of voting in a democracy, increasing your ability to function as a more fully aware citizen
- use graph theory to examine how mathematics is used to solve problems in the business world

"It is better to take what may seem to be too much math rather than too little. Career plans change, and one of the biggest roadblocks in undertaking new educational or training goals is poor preparation in mathematics. Furthermore, not only do people qualify for more jobs with more math, they are also better able to perform their jobs."

Occupational Outlook Quarterly

Mathematics and Your Career

Generally speaking, the income of an occupation is related to the amount of education required. This, in turn, is usually related to the skill level required in language and mathematics. With our increasing reliance on technology, the more mathematics you know, the more career choices you will have.

Mathematics and Your World

Mathematics is a science that helps us recognize, classify, and explore the hidden patterns of our universe. Focusing on areas as different as planetary motion, animal markings, shapes of viruses, aerodynamics of figure skaters, and the very origin of the universe, mathematics is the most powerful tool available for revealing the underlying structure of our world. Within the last 30 years, mathematicians have even found order in chaotic events such as the uncontrolled storm of noise in the nerve cells of the brain during an epileptic seizure.

1 Understand and use inductive reasoning.

Inductive Reasoning

Mathematics involves the study of patterns. In everyday life, we frequently rely on patterns and routines to draw conclusions. Here is an example:

> The last six times I went to the beach, the traffic was light on Wednesdays and heavy on Sundays. My conclusion is that weekdays have lighter traffic than weekends.

This type of reasoning process is referred to as *inductive reasoning*, or *induction*.

INDUCTIVE REASONING

Inductive reasoning is the process of arriving at a general conclusion based on observations of specific examples.

Although inductive reasoning is a powerful method of drawing conclusions, we can never be absolutely certain that these conclusions are true. For this reason, the conclusions are called **conjectures**, **hypotheses**, or educated guesses. A strong inductive argument does not guarantee the truth of the conclusion, but rather provides strong support for the conclusion. If there is just one case for which the conjecture does not hold, then the conjecture is false. Such a case is called a **counterexample**.

EXAMPLE 1 Finding a Counterexample

The ten symbols that we use to write numbers, namely 0, 1, 2, 3, 4, 5, 6, 7, 8, and 9, are called **digits**. In each example shown below, the sum of two two-digit numbers is a three-digit number.

$$\begin{array}{r} 47 \\ +73 \\ \hline 120 \end{array} \qquad \begin{array}{r} 56 \\ +46 \\ \hline 102 \end{array}$$

Two-digit numbers

Three-digit sums

Is the sum of two two-digit numbers always a three-digit number? Find a counter-example to show that the statement

The sum of two two-digit numbers is a three-digit number

is false.

Solution There are many counterexamples, but we need to find only one. Here is an example that makes the statement false:

Two-digit numbers

$$\begin{array}{r} 56 \\ +43 \\ \hline 99 \end{array}$$

This is a two-digit sum, not a three-digit sum.

This example is a counterexample that shows the statement

The sum of two two-digit numbers is a three-digit number

is false.

STUDY TIP

After working each Check Point, check your answer in the answer section before continuing your reading.

Find a counterexample to show that the statement

The product of two two-digit numbers is a three-digit number

is false.

Here are two examples of inductive reasoning:

- **Strong Inductive Argument** In a random sample of 380,000 freshmen at 722 four-year colleges, 25% said they frequently came to class without completing readings or assignments. (*Source*: National Survey of Student Engagement) We can conclude that there is a 95% probability that between 24.84% and 25.15% of all college freshmen frequently come to class unprepared.

You will learn how observations from a randomly selected group, one in which each member of the population has an equal chance of being selected can provide probabilities of what is true about an entire population.

- **Weak Inductive Argument** Men have difficulty expressing their feelings. Neither my dad nor my boyfriend has ever cried in front of me.

When generalizing from observations about your own circumstances and experiences, avoid jumping to hasty conclusions based on a few observations. Psychologists theorize that we do this - that is, place everyone in a neat category - to feel more secure about ourselves and our relationships to others.

Inductive reasoning is extremely important to mathematicians. Discovery in mathematics often begins with an examination of individual cases to reveal patterns about numbers.

EXAMPLE 2 Using Inductive Reasoning

Identify a pattern in each list of numbers. Then use this pattern to find the next number.

a. 3, 12, 21, 30, 39, _____ **b.** 3, 12, 48, 192, 768, _____

c. 3, 4, 6, 9, 13, 18, _____ **d.** 3, 6, 18, 36, 108, 216, _____

Solution

a. Because 3, 12, 21, 30, 39, _____ is increasing relatively slowly, let's use addition as the basis for our individual observations.

"For thousands of years, people have loved numbers and found patterns and structures among them. The allure of numbers is not limited to or driven by a desire to change the world in a practical way. When we observe how numbers are connected to one another, we are seeing the inner workings of a fundamental concept."

Edward B. Burger and Michael Starbird, *Coincidences, Chaos, and All That Math Jazz*, W. W. Norton and Company, 2005

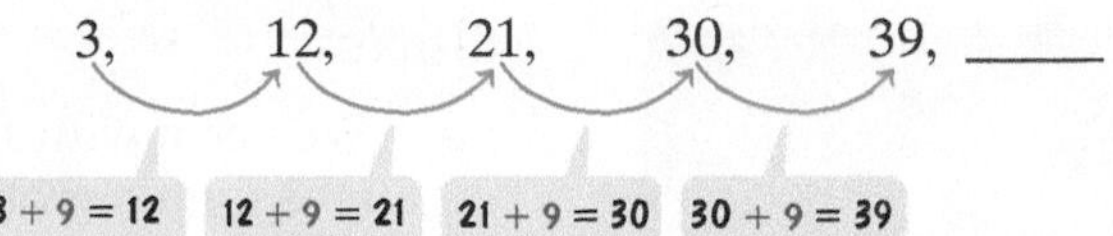

Generalizing from these observations, we conclude that each number after the first is obtained by adding 9 to the previous number. Using this pattern, the next number is 39 + 9, or 48.

b. Because 3, 12, 48, 192, 768, ____ is increasing relatively rapidly, let's use multiplication as the basis for our individual observations.

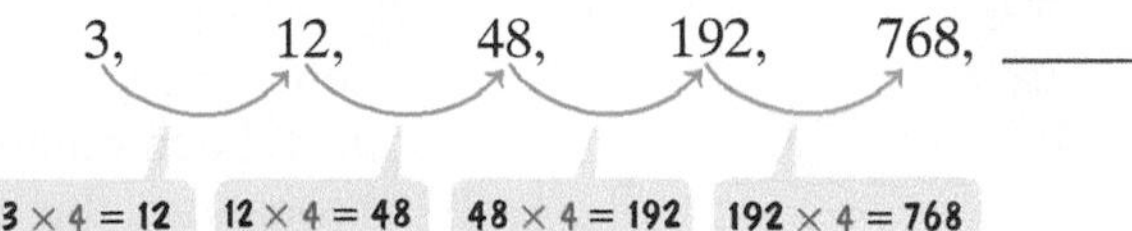

Generalizing from these observations, we conclude that each number after the first is obtained by multiplying the previous number by 4. Using this pattern, the next number is 768 × 4, or 3072.

c. Because 3, 4, 6, 9, 13, 18, ____ is increasing relatively slowly, let's use addition as the basis for our individual observations.

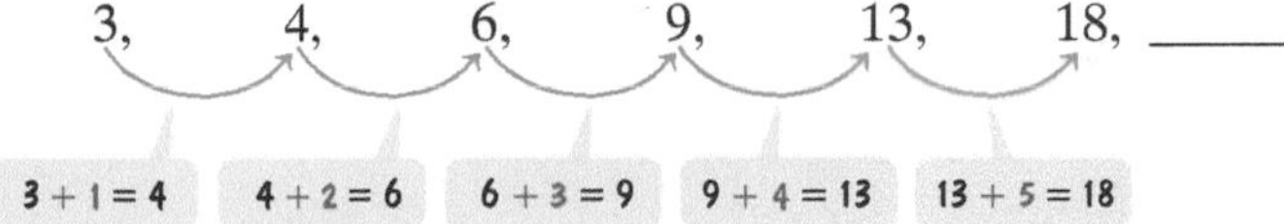

Generalizing from these observations, we conclude that each number after the first is obtained by adding a counting number to the previous number. The additions begin with 1 and continue through each successive counting number. Using this pattern, the next number is 18 + 6, or 24.

d. Because 3, 6, 18, 36, 108, 216, ____ is increasing relatively rapidly, let's use multiplication as the basis for our individual observations.

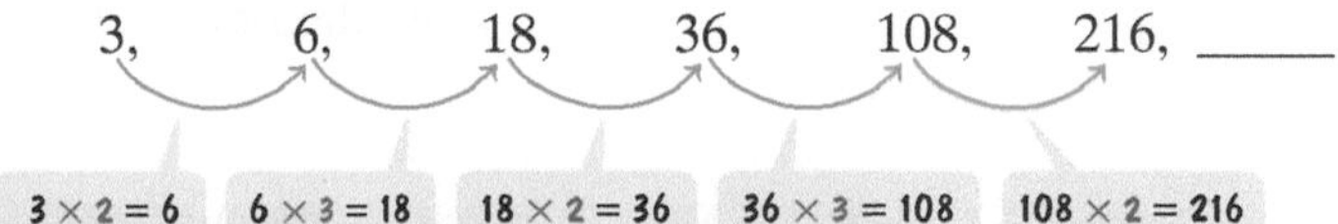

Generalizing from these observations, we conclude that each number after the first is obtained by multiplying the previous number by 2 or by 3. The multiplications begin with 2 and then alternate, multiplying by 2, then 3, then 2, then 3, and so on. Using this pattern, the next number is 216 × 3, or 648.

CHECK POINT 2 Identify a pattern in each list of numbers. Then use this pattern to find the next number.

a. 3, 9, 15, 21, 27, ____ **b.** 2, 10, 50, 250, ____

c. 3, 6, 18, 72, 144, 432, 1728, ____

d. 1, 9, 17, 3, 11, 19, 5, 13, 21, ____

In our next example, the patterns are a bit more complex than the additions and multiplications we encountered in Example 2.

EXAMPLE 3 Using Inductive Reasoning

Identify a pattern in each list of numbers. Then use this pattern to find the next number.

a. 1, 1, 2, 3, 5, 8, 13, 21, ____ **b.** 23, 54, 95, 146, 117, 98, ____

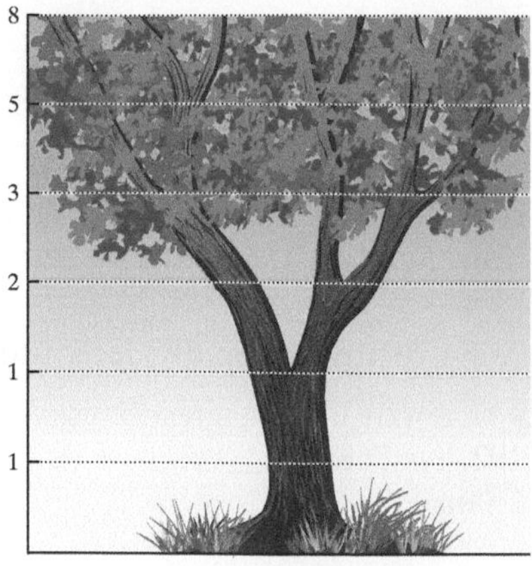

As this tree branches, the number of branches forms the Fibonacci sequence.

Solution

a. We begin with 1, 1, 2, 3, 5, 8, 13, 21. Starting with the third number in the list, let's form our observations by comparing each number with the two numbers that immediately precede it.

1, 1, 2, 3, 5, 8, 13, 21, _____

2	3	5	8	13	21
preceded by 1 and 1: $1 + 1 = 2$	preceded by 1 and 2: $1 + 2 = 3$	preceded by 2 and 3: $2 + 3 = 5$	preceded by 3 and 5: $3 + 5 = 8$	preceded by 5 and 8: $5 + 8 = 13$	preceded by 8 and 13: $8 + 13 = 21$

Generalizing from these observations, we conclude that the first two numbers are 1. Each number thereafter is the sum of the two preceding numbers. Using this pattern, the next number is $13 + 21$, or 34. (The numbers 1, 1, 2, 3, 5, 8, 13, 21, and 34 are the first nine terms of the *Fibonacci sequence.*)

b. Now, we consider 23, 54, 95, 146, 117, 98. Let's use the digits that form each number as the basis for our individual observations. Focus on the sum of the digits, as well as the final digit increased by 1.

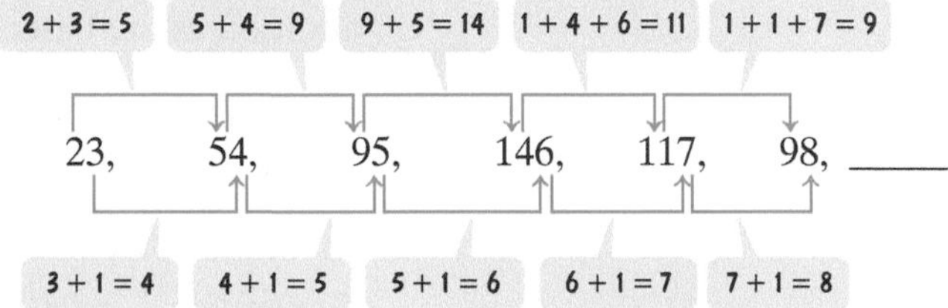

Generalizing from these observations, we conclude that for each number after the first, we obtain the first digit or the first two digits by adding the digits of the previous number. We obtain the last digit by adding 1 to the final digit of the preceding number. Applying this pattern to find the number that follows 98, the first two digits are $9 + 8$, or 17. The last digit is $8 + 1$, or 9. Thus, the next number in the list is 179.

STUDY TIP

The illusion in **Figure 1** is an ambiguous figure containing two patterns, where it is not clear which pattern should predominate. Do you see a wine goblet or two faces looking at each other? Like this ambiguous figure, some lists of numbers can display more than one pattern, particularly if only a few numbers are given. Inductive reasoning can result in more than one probable next number in a list.

FIGURE 1

Example: 1, 2, 4, _____

Pattern: Each number after the first is obtained by multiplying the previous number by 2. The missing number is 4×2, or 8.

Pattern: Each number after the first is obtained by adding successive counting numbers, starting with 1, to the previous number. The second number is $1 + 1$, or 2. The third number is $2 + 2$, or 4. The missing number is $4 + 3$, or 7.

Inductive reasoning can also result in different patterns that produce the same probable next number in a list.

Example: 1, 4, 9, 16, 25, _____

Pattern: Start by adding 3 to the first number. Then add successive odd numbers, 5, 7, 9, and so on. The missing number is $25 + 11$, or 36.

Pattern: Each number is obtained by squaring its position in the list: The first number is $1^2 = 1 \times 1 = 1$, the second number is $2^2 = 2 \times 2 = 4$, the third number is $3^2 = 3 \times 3 = 9$, and so on. The missing sixth number is $6^2 = 6 \times 6$, or 36.

The numbers that we found in Examples 2 and 3 are probable numbers. Perhaps you found patterns other than the ones we pointed out that might have resulted in different answers.

Identify a pattern in each list of numbers. Then use this pattern to find the next number.

a. 1, 3, 4, 7, 11, 18, 29, 47, ____

b. 2, 3, 5, 9, 17, 33, 65, 129, ____

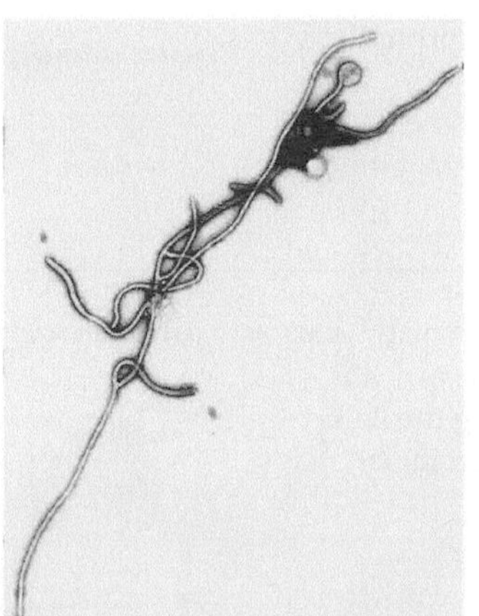

This electron microscope photograph shows the knotty shape of the Ebola virus. LSHTM\Getty Images Inc. - Stone Allstock

Mathematics is more than recognizing number patterns. It is about the patterns that arise in the world around us. For example, by describing patterns formed by various kinds of knots, mathematicians are helping scientists investigate the knotty shapes and patterns of viruses. One of the weapons used against viruses is based on recognizing visual patterns in the possible ways that knots can be tied.

Our next example deals with recognizing visual patterns.

EXAMPLE 4 Finding the Next Figure in a Visual Sequence

Describe two patterns in this sequence of figures. Use the patterns to draw the next figure in the sequence.

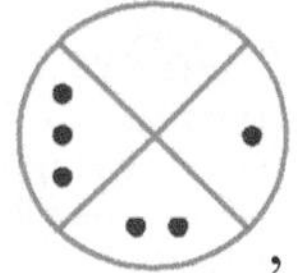, 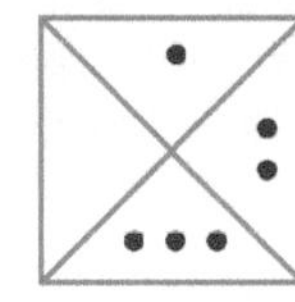, 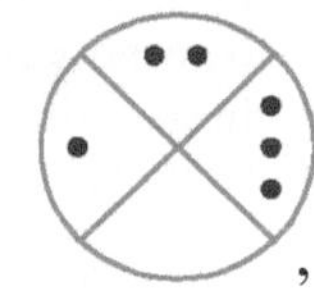, 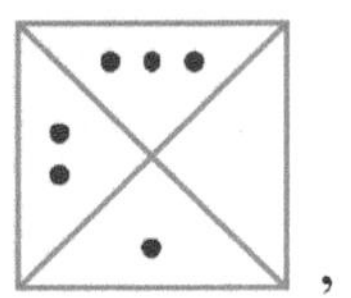, ________

Solution The more obvious pattern is that the figures alternate between circles and squares. We conclude that the next figure will be a circle. We can identify the second pattern in the four regions containing no dots, one dot, two dots, and three dots. The dots are placed in order (no dots, one dot, two dots, three dots) in a clockwise direction. However, the entire pattern of the dots rotates counterclockwise as we follow the figures from left to right.

This means that the next figure should be a circle with a single dot in the right-hand region, two dots in the bottom region, three dots in the left-hand region, and no dots in the top region. This figure is drawn in **Figure 2**.

FIGURE 2

Describe two patterns in this sequence of figures. Use the patterns to draw the next figure in the sequence.

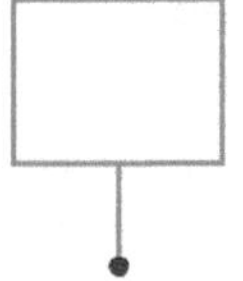, 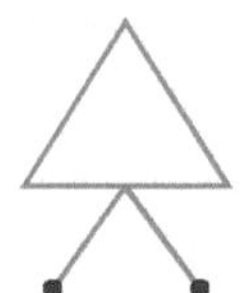, , 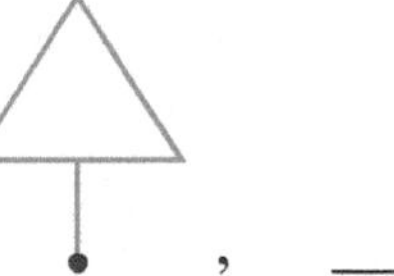, ________

2 Understand and use deductive reasoning.

Deductive Reasoning

We use inductive reasoning in everyday life. Many of the conjectures that come from this kind of thinking seem highly likely, although we can never be absolutely certain that they are true. Another method of reasoning, called *deductive reasoning*, or *deduction*, can be used to prove that some conjectures are true.

DEDUCTIVE REASONING

Deductive reasoning is the process of proving a specific conclusion from one or more general statements. A conclusion that is proved to be true by deductive reasoning is called a **theorem**.

Deductive reasoning allows us to draw a specific conclusion from one or more general statements. Here are two examples of deductive reasoning. Notice that in both everyday situations, the general statement from which the conclusion is drawn is implied rather than directly stated.

Everyday Situation	Deductive Reasoning
One player to another in a Scrabble game: "You have to remove those five letters. You can't use TEXAS as a word."	• All proper names are prohibited in Scrabble. (general statement) TEXAS is a proper name. Therefore, TEXAS is prohibited in Scrabble. (conclusion)
Advice to college freshmen on choosing classes: "Never sign up for a 7 A.M. class. Yes, you did it in high school, but Mom was always there to keep waking you up, and if by some miracle you do make it to an early class, you will sleep through the lecture when you get there." (*Source: How to Survive Your Freshman Year*, Hundreds of Heads Books, 2004)	• All people need to sleep at 7 A.M. (general statement) You sign up for a class at 7 A.M. Therefore, you'll sleep through the lecture or not even make it to class. (conclusion) It is possible to prove this conclusion from the general statement in the first line. But is the general statement really true? Can we make assumptions about the sleeping patterns of all people, or are we using deductive reasoning to reinforce an untrue reality assumption?

Our next example illustrates the difference between inductive and deductive reasoning. The first part of the example involves reasoning that moves from specific examples to a general statement, illustrating inductive reasoning. The second part of the example begins with the general case rather than specific examples and illustrates deductive reasoning. To begin the general case, we use a letter to represent any one of various numbers. A letter used to represent any number in a collection of numbers is called a **variable**.

STUDY TIP

In case you have forgotten some basic terms of arithmetic, the following list should be helpful.

Sum:	the result of addition
Difference:	the result of subtraction
Product:	the result of multiplication
Quotient:	the result of division

EXAMPLE 5 Using Inductive and Deductive Reasoning

Consider the following procedure:

Select a number. Multiply the number by 6. Add 8 to the product. Divide this sum by 2. Subtract 4 from the quotient.

a. Repeat this procedure for at least four different numbers. Write a conjecture that relates the result of this process to the original number selected.

b. Use the variable n to represent the original number and use deductive reasoning to prove the conjecture in part (a).

Solution

a. First, let us pick our starting numbers. We will use 4, 7, 11, and 100, but we could pick any four numbers. Next we will apply the procedure given in this example to 4, 7, 11, and 100, four individual cases, in **Table 1**.

TABLE 1 Applying a Procedure to Four Individual Cases

Select a number.	4	7	11	100
Multiply the number by 6.	$4 \times 6 = 24$	$7 \times 6 = 42$	$11 \times 6 = 66$	$100 \times 6 = 600$
Add 8 to the product.	$24 + 8 = 32$	$42 + 8 = 50$	$66 + 8 = 74$	$600 + 8 = 608$
Divide this sum by 2.	$\frac{32}{2} = 16$	$\frac{50}{2} = 25$	$\frac{74}{2} = 37$	$\frac{608}{2} = 304$
Subtract 4 from the quotient.	$16 - 4 = 12$	$25 - 4 = 21$	$37 - 4 = 33$	$304 - 4 = 300$

Because we are asked to write a conjecture that relates the result of this process to the original number selected, let us focus on the result of each case.

Original number selected	4	7	11	100
Result of the process	12	21	33	300

Do you see a pattern? Our conjecture is that the result of the process is three times the original number selected. We have used inductive reasoning.

b. Now we begin with the general case rather than specific examples. We use the variable n to represent any number.

Select a number. — n

Multiply the number by 6. — $6n$ (This means 6 times n.)

Add 8 to the product. — $6n + 8$

Divide this sum by 2. — $\frac{6n + 8}{2} = \frac{6n}{2} + \frac{8}{2} = 3n + 4$

Subtract 4 from the quotient. — $3n + 4 - 4 = 3n$

Using the variable n to represent any number, the result is $3n$, or three times the number n. This proves that the result of the procedure is three times the original number selected for any number. We have used deductive reasoning.

CHECK POINT 5 Consider the following procedure:

Select a number. Multiply the number by 4. Add 6 to the product. Divide this sum by 2. Subtract 3 from the quotient.

a. Repeat this procedure for at least four different numbers. Write a conjecture that relates the result of this process to the original number selected.

b. Use the variable n to represent the original number and use deductive reasoning to prove the conjecture in part (a).

Exercise Set 1

STUDY TIP

Researchers say the mind can be strengthened, just like your muscles, with regular training and rigorous practice. Think of the book's exercise sets as brain calisthenics. If you're feeling a bit sluggish before any of your mental workouts, try this warmup:

In the list below, say the color the word is printed in, not the word itself. Once you can do this in 15 seconds without an error, the warmup is over and it's time to move on to the assigned exercises.

Blue Yellow Red Green Yellow Green Blue Red Yellow Red

Practice Exercises

In Exercises 1–8, find a counterexample to show that each of the statements is false.

1. No U.S. president has been younger than 65 at the time of his inauguration.
2. No singers appear in movies.
3. If a number is multiplied by itself, the result is even.
4. The sum of two three-digit numbers is a four-digit number.
5. Adding the same number to both the numerator and the denominator (top and bottom) of a fraction does not change the fraction's value.
6. If the difference between two numbers is odd, then the two numbers are both odd.
7. If a number is added to itself, the sum is greater than the original number.
8. If 1 is divided by a number, the quotient is less than that number.

In Exercises 9–38, identify a pattern in each list of numbers. Then use this pattern to find the next number. (More than one pattern might exist, so it is possible that there is more than one correct answer.)

9. 8, 12, 16, 20, 24, _____

10. 19, 24, 29, 34, 39, _____

11. 37, 32, 27, 22, 17, _____

12. 33, 29, 25, 21, 17, _____

13. 3, 9, 27, 81, 243, _____

14. 2, 8, 32, 128, 512, _____

15. 1, 2, 4, 8, 16, _____

16. 1, 5, 25, 125, _____

17. 1, 4, 1, 8, 1, 16, 1, _____

18. 1, 4, 1, 7, 1, 10, 1, _____

19. 4, 2, 0, −2, −4, _____

20. 6, 3, 0, −3, −6, _____

21. $\frac{1}{2}, \frac{1}{6}, \frac{1}{10}, \frac{1}{14}, \frac{1}{18},$ _____

22. $1, \frac{1}{2}, \frac{1}{3}, \frac{1}{4}, \frac{1}{5},$ _____

23. $1, \frac{1}{3}, \frac{1}{9}, \frac{1}{27},$ _____

24. $1, \frac{1}{2}, \frac{1}{4}, \frac{1}{8},$ _____

25. 3, 7, 12, 18, 25, 33, _____

26. 2, 5, 9, 14, 20, 27, _____

27. 3, 6, 11, 18, 27, 38, _____

28. 2, 5, 10, 17, 26, 37, _____

29. 3, 7, 10, 17, 27, 44, _____

30. 2, 5, 7, 12, 19, 31, _____

31. 2, 7, 12, 5, 10, 15, 8, 13, _____

32. 3, 9, 15, 5, 11, 17, 7, 13, _____

33. 3, 6, 5, 10, 9, 18, 17, 34, _____

34. 2, 6, 5, 15, 14, 42, 41, 123, _____

35. 64, −16, 4, −1, _____

36. 125, −25, 5, −1, _____

37. $(6, 2), (0, -4), \left(7\frac{1}{2}, 3\frac{1}{2}\right), (2, -2), (3, \_\_\_\_)$

38. $\left(\frac{2}{3}, \frac{4}{9}\right), \left(\frac{1}{5}, \frac{1}{25}\right), (7, 49), \left(-\frac{5}{6}, \frac{25}{36}\right), \left(-\frac{4}{7}, \_\_\_\_\_\right)$

In Exercises 39–42, identify a pattern in each sequence of figures. Then use the pattern to find the next figure in the sequence.

39.

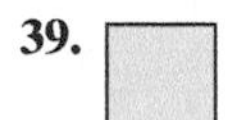 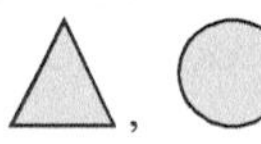 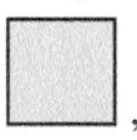 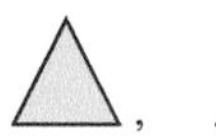 _____

40.

 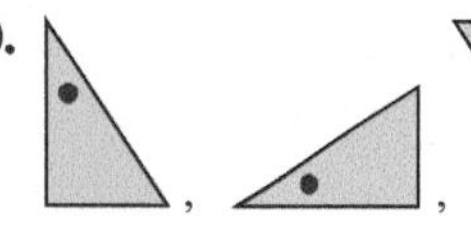 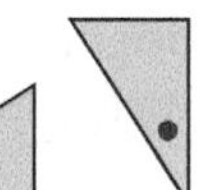 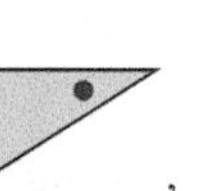 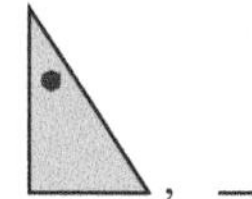 _____

41.

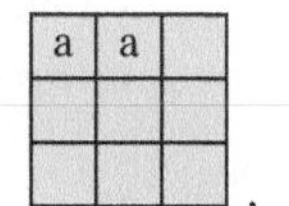

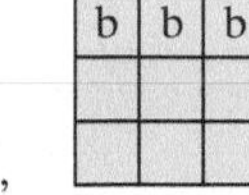

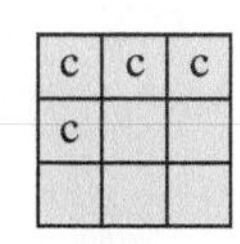

_____

42.

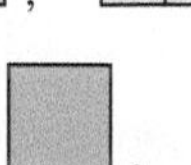 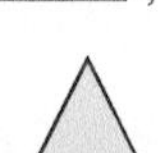 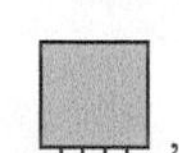 _____

Exercises 43–46 describe procedures that are to be applied to numbers. In each exercise,

a. *Repeat the procedure for four numbers of your choice. Write a conjecture that relates the result of the process to the original number selected.*

b. *Use the variable n to represent the original number and use deductive reasoning to prove the conjecture in part (a).*

43. Select a number. Multiply the number by 4. Add 8 to the product. Divide this sum by 2. Subtract 4 from the quotient.

44. Select a number. Multiply the number by 3. Add 6 to the product. Divide this sum by 3. Subtract the original selected number from the quotient.

45. Select a number. Add 5. Double the result. Subtract 4. Divide by 2. Subtract the original selected number.

46. Select a number. Add 3. Double the result. Add 4. Divide by 2. Subtract the original selected number.

In Exercises 47–52, use inductive reasoning to predict the next line in each sequence of computations. Then use a calculator or perform the arithmetic by hand to determine whether your conjecture is correct.

47.
$$1 + 2 = \frac{2 \times 3}{2}$$
$$1 + 2 + 3 = \frac{3 \times 4}{2}$$
$$1 + 2 + 3 + 4 = \frac{4 \times 5}{2}$$
$$1 + 2 + 3 + 4 + 5 = \frac{5 \times 6}{2}$$

48.
$$3 + 6 = \frac{6 \times 3}{2}$$
$$3 + 6 + 9 = \frac{9 \times 4}{2}$$
$$3 + 6 + 9 + 12 = \frac{12 \times 5}{2}$$
$$3 + 6 + 9 + 12 + 15 = \frac{15 \times 6}{2}$$

49.
$$1 + 3 = 2 \times 2$$
$$1 + 3 + 5 = 3 \times 3$$
$$1 + 3 + 5 + 7 = 4 \times 4$$
$$1 + 3 + 5 + 7 + 9 = 5 \times 5$$

50.
$$\frac{1}{1 \times 2} + \frac{1}{2 \times 3} = \frac{2}{3}$$
$$\frac{1}{1 \times 2} + \frac{1}{2 \times 3} + \frac{1}{3 \times 4} = \frac{3}{4}$$
$$\frac{1}{1 \times 2} + \frac{1}{2 \times 3} + \frac{1}{3 \times 4} + \frac{1}{4 \times 5} = \frac{4}{5}$$

51.
$$9 \times 9 + 7 = 88$$
$$98 \times 9 + 6 = 888$$
$$987 \times 9 + 5 = 8888$$
$$9876 \times 9 + 4 = 88{,}888$$

52.
$$1 \times 9 - 1 = 8$$
$$21 \times 9 - 1 = 188$$
$$321 \times 9 - 1 = 2888$$
$$4321 \times 9 - 1 = 38{,}888$$

Practice Plus

In Exercises 53–54, use inductive reasoning to predict the next line in each sequence of computations. Then use a calculator or perform the arithmetic by hand to determine whether your conjecture is correct.

53.
$$33 \times 3367 = 111{,}111$$
$$66 \times 3367 = 222{,}222$$
$$99 \times 3367 = 333{,}333$$
$$132 \times 3367 = 444{,}444$$

54.
$$1 \times 8 + 1 = 9$$
$$12 \times 8 + 2 = 98$$
$$123 \times 8 + 3 = 987$$
$$1234 \times 8 + 4 = 9876$$
$$12{,}345 \times 8 + 5 = 98{,}765$$

55. Study the pattern in these examples:

$$a^2 \# a^4 = a^{10} \quad a^3 \# a^2 = a^7 \quad a^5 \# a^3 = a^{11}.$$

Select the equation that describes the pattern.

a. $a^x \# a^y = a^{2x+y}$

b. $a^x \# a^y = a^{x+2y}$

c. $a^x \# a^y = a^{x+y+4}$

d. $a^x \# a^y = a^{xy+2}$

56. Study the pattern in these examples:

$$a^5 * a^3 * a^2 = a^5 \quad a^3 * a^7 * a^2 = a^6 \quad a^2 * a^4 * a^8 = a^7.$$

Select the equation that describes the pattern.

a. $a^x * a^y * a^z = a^{x+y+z}$

b. $a^x * a^y * a^z = a^{\frac{xyz}{2}}$

c. $a^x * a^y * a^z = a^{\frac{x+y+z}{2}}$

d. $a^x * a^y * a^z = a^{\frac{xy}{2}+z}$

Application Exercises

In Exercises 57–60, identify the reasoning process, induction or deduction, in each example. Explain your answer.

57. It can be shown that

$$1 + 2 + 3 + \cdots + n = \frac{n(n+1)}{2}.$$

I can use this formula to conclude that the sum of the first one hundred counting numbers, $1 + 2 + 3 + \cdots + 100$, is

$$\frac{100(100+1)}{2} = \frac{100(101)}{2} = 50(101), \text{ or } 5050.$$

58. An HMO does a follow-up study on 200 randomly selected patients given a flu shot. None of these people became seriously ill with the flu. The study concludes that all HMO patients be urged to get a flu shot in order to prevent a serious case of the flu.

59. The data in the graph are from a random sample of 1200 full-time four-year undergraduate college students on 100 U.S. campuses.

The Greatest Problems on Campus

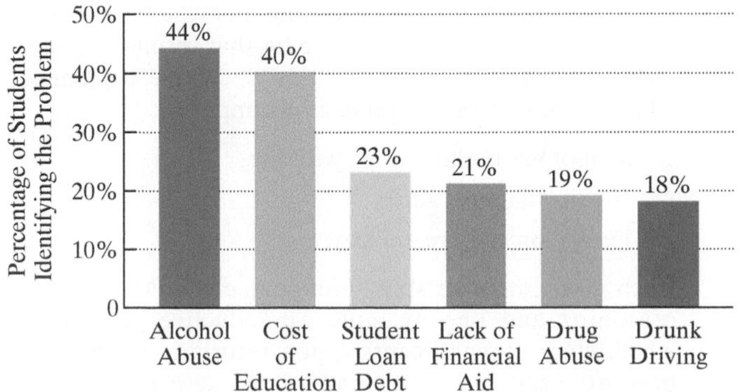

Source: Student Monitor LLC

We can conclude that there is a high probability that approximately 44% of all full-time four-year college students in the United States believe that alcohol abuse is the greatest problem on campus.

60. The course policy states that work turned in late will be marked down a grade. I turned in my report a day late, so it was marked down from B to C.

61. The ancient Greeks studied **figurate numbers**, so named because of their representations as geometric arrangements of points.

Triangular Numbers

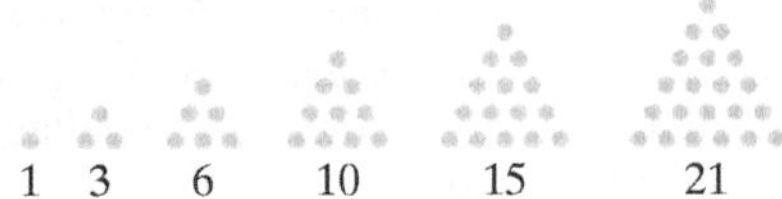

Square Numbers

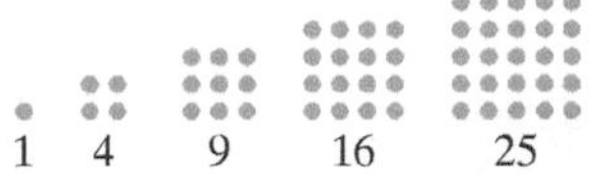

Pentagonal Numbers

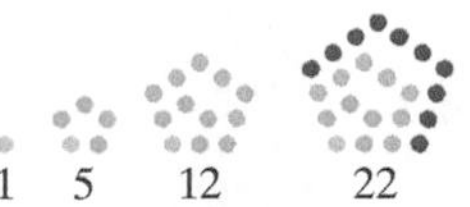

a. Use inductive reasoning to write the five triangular numbers that follow 21.

b. Use inductive reasoning to write the five square numbers that follow 25.

c. Use inductive reasoning to write the five pentagonal numbers that follow 22.

d. Use inductive reasoning to complete this statement: If a triangular number is multiplied by 8 and then 1 is added to the product, a _____ number is obtained.

62. The triangular arrangement of numbers shown below is known as **Pascal's triangle**, credited to French mathematician Blaise Pascal (1623–1662). Use inductive reasoning to find the six numbers designated by question marks.

```
          1
        1   1
      1   2   1
    1   3   3   1
  1   4   6   4   1
?   ?   ?   ?   ?   ?
```

Writing in Mathematics

Writing about mathematics will help you to learn mathematics. Use complete sentences to respond to the questions. Some writing exercises can be answered in a sentence; others require a paragraph or two. You can decide how much you need to write as long as your writing clearly and directly answers the question in the exercise. Standard references such as a dictionary and a thesaurus may be helpful.

63. The word *induce* comes from a Latin term meaning to lead. Explain what leading has to do with inductive reasoning.

64. Describe what is meant by deductive reasoning. Give an example.

65. Give an example of a decision that you made recently in which the method of reasoning you used to reach the decision was induction. Describe your reasoning process.

Critical Thinking Exercises

Make Sense? *In Exercises 66–69, determine whether each statement makes sense or does not make sense, and explain your reasoning.*

66. I use deductive reasoning to draw conclusions that are not certain, but likely.

67. Additional information may strengthen or weaken the probability of my inductive arguments.

68. I used the data shown in the bar graph, which summarizes a random sample of 752 college seniors, to conclude with certainty that 51% of all graduating college females expect to earn $30,000 or less after graduation.

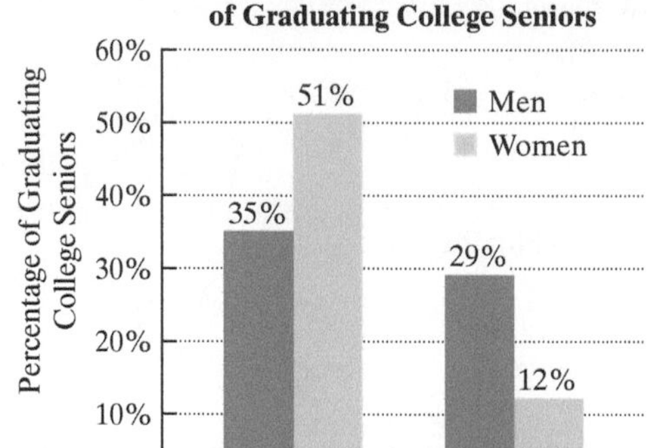

Source: Duquesne University Senior Economic Expectation research survey

69. I used the data shown in the bar graph for Exercise 68, which summarizes a random sample of 752 college seniors, to conclude inductively that a greater percentage of male graduates expect higher first-year income than female graduates.

70. If $(6 - 2)^2 = 36 - 24 + 4$ and $(8 - 5)^2 = 64 - 80 + 25$, use inductive reasoning to write a compatible expression for $(11 - 7)^2$.

71. The rectangle shows an array of nine numbers represented by combinations of the variables a, b, and c.

$a + b$	$a - b - c$	$a + c$
$a - b + c$	a	$a + b - c$
$a - c$	$a + b + c$	$a - b$

a. Determine the nine numbers in the array for $a = 10, b = 6$, and $c = 1$. What do you observe about the sum of the numbers in all rows, all columns, and the two diagonals?

b. Repeat part (a) for $a = 12, b = 5$, and $c = 2$.

c. Repeat part (a) for values of a, b, and c of your choice.

d. Use the results of parts (a) through (c) to make an inductive conjecture about the rectangular array of nine numbers represented by a, b, and c.

e. Use deductive reasoning to prove your conjecture in part (d).

72. Write a list of numbers that has two patterns so that the next number in the list can be 15 or 20.

73. a. Repeat the following procedure with at least five people. Write a conjecture that relates the result of the procedure to each person's birthday.

Take the number of the month of your birthday (January = 1, February = 2, . . . , December = 12), multiply by 5, add 6, multiply this sum by 4, add 9, multiply this new sum by 5, and add the number of the day on which you were born. Finally, subtract 165.

b. Let M represent the month number and let D represent the day number of any person's birthday. Use deductive reasoning to prove your conjecture in part (a).

Technology Exercises

74. a. Use a calculator to find 6×6, 66×66, 666×666, and 6666×6666.

b. Describe a pattern in the numbers being multiplied and the resulting products.

c. Use the pattern to write the next two multiplications and their products. Then use your calculator to verify these results.

d. Is this process an example of inductive or deductive reasoning? Explain your answer.

75. a. Use a calculator to find 3367×3, 3367×6, 3367×9, and 3367×12.

b. Describe a pattern in the numbers being multiplied and the resulting products.

c. Use the pattern to write the next two multiplications and their products. Then use your calculator to verify these results.

d. Is this process an example of inductive or deductive reasoning? Explain your answer.

Group Exercise

76. Stereotyping refers to classifying people, places, or things according to common traits. Prejudices and stereotypes can function as assumptions in our thinking, appearing in inductive and deductive reasoning. For example, it is not difficult to find inductive reasoning that results in generalizations such as these, as well as deductive reasoning in which these stereotypes serve as assumptions:

School has nothing to do with life.

Intellectuals are nerds.

People on welfare are lazy.

Each group member should find one example of inductive reasoning and one example of deductive reasoning in which stereotyping occurs. Upon returning to the group, present each example and then describe how the stereotyping results in faulty conjectures or prejudging situations and people.

OBJECTIVES

1 | Use estimation techniques to arrive at an approximate answer to a problem.
2 | Apply estimation techniques to information given by graphs.
3 | Develop mathematical models that estimate relationships between variables.

2 Estimation, Graphs, and Mathematical Models

If present trends continue, is it possible that our descendants could live to be 200 years of age? To answer this question, we need to examine data for life expectancy and develop estimation techniques for representing the data mathematically. In this section, you will learn estimation methods that will enable you to obtain mathematical representations of data displayed by graphs, using these representations to predict what might occur in the future.

Mark Gamba\CORBIS-NY

Estimation

1 | Use estimation techniques to arrive at an approximate answer to a problem.

Estimation is the process of arriving at an approximate answer to a question. For example, companies estimate the amount of their products consumers are likely to use, and economists estimate financial trends. If you are about to cross a street, you may estimate the speed of oncoming cars so that you know whether or not to wait before crossing. Rounding numbers is also an estimation method. You might round a number without even being aware that you are doing so. You may say that you are 20 years old, rather than 20 years 5 months, or that you will be home in about a half-hour, rather than 25 minutes.

You will find estimation to be equally valuable in your work for this class. Making mistakes with a calculator or a computer is easy. Estimation can tell us whether the answer displayed for a computation makes sense.

In this section, we demonstrate several estimation methods. In the second part of the section, we apply these techniques to information given by graphs.

Performing computations using rounded numbers is one way to check whether an answer displayed by a calculator or a computer is reasonable. Rounding whole numbers depends on knowing the place values of the digits. (The digits that we use in base ten are 0, 1, 2, 3, 4, 5, 6, 7, 8, and 9. Know that there are other ways of representing numbers, including bases other than ten.) The place that a digit occupies in a number tells us its value in that number. Here is an example using world population at 8:35 A.M. Eastern Time on January 4, 2009.

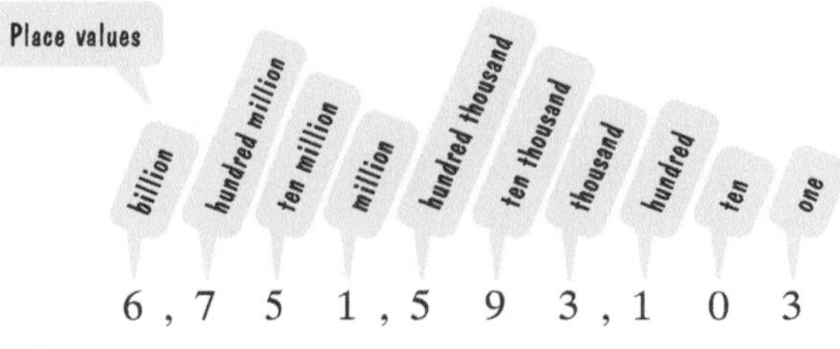

ROUNDING WHOLE NUMBERS

1. Look at the digit to the right of the digit where rounding is to occur.
2. **a.** If the digit to the right is 5 or greater, add 1 to the digit to be rounded. Replace all digits to the right with zeros.

   b. If the digit to the right is less than 5, do not change the digit to be rounded. Replace all digits to the right with zeros.

The symbol $\approx$ means *is approximately equal to*. We will use this symbol when rounding numbers.

EXAMPLE 1 Rounding a Whole Number

Round world population (6,751,593,103) as follows:

a. to the nearest million

b. to the nearest thousand.

Solution

a. $6{,}751{,}593{,}103 \approx 6{,}752{,}000{,}000$

Millions digit, where rounding is to occur | Digit to the right is 5. | Add 1 to the digit to be rounded. | Replace all digits to the right with zeros.

World population to the nearest million is six billion, seven hundred fifty-two million.

b. $6{,}751{,}593{,}103 \approx 6{,}751{,}593{,}000$

Thousands digit, where rounding is to occur | Digit to the right is less than 5. | Do not change the digit to be rounded. | Replace all digits to the right with zeros.

World population to the nearest thousand is six billion, seven hundred fifty-one million, five hundred ninety-three thousand.

Round world population (6,751,593,103) as follows:

a. to the nearest billion

b. to the nearest hundred million

c. to the nearest ten thousand.

Rounding can also be applied to decimal notation, used to denote a part of a whole. Once again, the place that a digit occupies tells us its value. Here's an example using the first seven digits of the number π (pi).

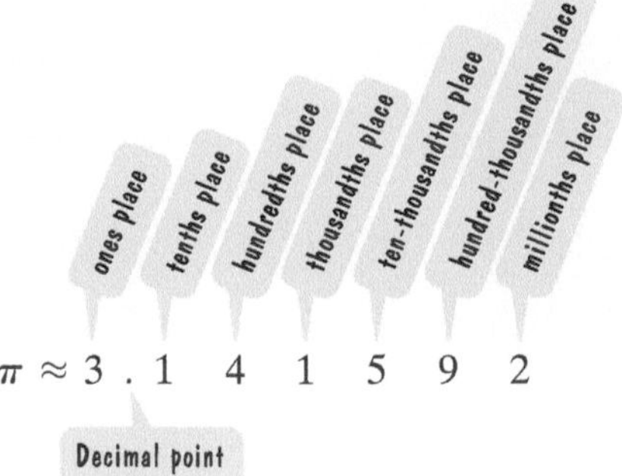

We round the decimal part of a decimal number in nearly the same way that we round whole numbers. The only difference is that we drop the digits to the right of the rounding place, rather than replacing these digits with zeros.

EXAMPLE 2 Rounding the Decimal Part of a Number

Round 3.141592, the first seven digits of π, as follows:

a. to the nearest hundredth

b. to the nearest thousandth.

Solution

a. $3.141592 \approx 3.14$

Hundredths digit, where rounding is to occur | Digit to the right is less than 5. | Do not change the digit to be rounded. | Drop all digits to the right.

The number π to the nearest hundredth is three and fourteen hundredths.

b. $3.141592 \approx 3.142$

Thousandths digit, where rounding is to occur | Digit to the right is 5. | Add 1 to the digit to be rounded. | Drop all digits to the right.

The number π to the nearest thousandth is three and one hundred forty-two thousandths.

CHECK POINT 2 Round 3.141592, the first seven digits of π, as follows:

a. to the nearest tenth

b. to the nearest ten-thousandth.

BLITZER BONUS

ESTIMATING SUPPORT FOR A CAUSE

Police often need to estimate the size of a crowd at a political demonstration. One way to do this is to select a reasonably sized rectangle within the crowd and estimate (or count) the number of people within the rectangle. Police then estimate the number of such rectangles it would take to completely fill the area occupied by the crowd. The police estimate is obtained by multiplying the number of such rectangles by the number of demonstrators in the representative rectangle. The organizers of the demonstration might give a larger estimate than the police to emphasize the strength of their support.

Ken Fisher\Getty Images Inc.-Stone Allstock

EXAMPLE 3 Estimation by Rounding

You purchased bread for \$2.59, detergent for \$2.17, a sandwich for \$3.65, an apple for \$0.47, and coffee for \$5.79. The total bill was given as \$18.67. Is this amount reasonable?

Solution If you are in the habit of carrying a calculator to the store, you can answer the question by finding the exact cost of the purchase. However, estimation can be used to determine if the bill is reasonable even if you do not have a calculator. We will round the cost of each item to the nearest dollar.

Round to the nearest dollar. | Use digits in the tenths place to do the rounding.

Bread	\$2.59	≈	\$3.00
Detergent	\$2.17	≈	\$2.00
Sandwich	\$3.65	≈	\$4.00
Apple	\$0.47	≈	\$0.00
Coffee	\$5.79	≈	\$6.00
			\$15.00

The total bill that you were given, \$18.67, seems a bit high compared to the \$15.00 estimate. You should check the bill before paying it. Adding the prices of all seven items gives the true total bill of \$14.67.

You and a friend ate lunch at Ye Olde Cafe. The check for the meal showed soup for \$2.40, tomato juice for \$1.25, a roast beef sandwich for \$4.60, a chicken salad sandwich for \$4.40, two coffees totaling \$1.40, apple pie for \$1.85, and chocolate cake for \$2.95.

a. Round the cost of each item to the nearest dollar and obtain an estimate for the food bill.

b. The total bill before tax was given as \$21.85. Is this amount reasonable?

EXAMPLE 4 Estimation by Rounding

A carpenter who works full time earns \$28 per hour.

a. Estimate the carpenter's weekly salary.

b. Estimate the carpenter's annual salary.

Solution

a. In order to simplify the calculation, we can round the hourly rate of \$28 to \$30. Be sure to write out the units for each number in the calculation. The work week is 40 hours per week and the rounded salary is \$30 per hour. We express this as

$$\frac{40 \text{ hours}}{\text{week}} \text{ and } \frac{\$30}{\text{hour}}.$$

The word *per* is represented by the division bar. We multiply these two numbers to estimate the carpenter's weekly salary. We cancel out units that are identical if they are above and below the division bar.

$$\frac{40 \cancel{\text{hours}}}{\text{week}} \times \frac{\$30}{\cancel{\text{hour}}} = \frac{\$1200}{\text{week}}$$

Thus, the carpenter earns approximately \$1200 per week, written $\approx$ \$1200.

b. For the estimate of annual salary, we may round 52 weeks to 50 weeks. The annual salary is approximately the product of \$1200 per week and 50 weeks per year:

$$\frac{\$1200}{\cancel{\text{week}}} \times \frac{50 \cancel{\text{weeks}}}{\text{year}} = \frac{\$60{,}000}{\text{year}}.$$

Thus, the carpenter earns approximately \$60,000 per year, or \$60,000 annually, written $\approx$\$60,000.

STUDY TIP

It does not matter whether a unit is singular, such as *week*, or plural, such as *weeks*. *Week* and *weeks* are identical units and can be canceled out, as shown on the right.

A landscape architect who works full time earns \$52 per hour.

a. Estimate the landscape architect's weekly salary.

b. Estimate the landscape architect's annual salary.

2 Apply estimation techniques to information given by graphs.

Estimation with Graphs

Magazines, newspapers, and websites often display information using circle, bar, and line graphs. The following examples illustrate how rounding and other estimation techniques can be applied to data displayed in each of these types of graphs.

Circle graphs, also called **pie charts**, show how a whole quantity is divided into parts. Circle graphs are divided into pieces, called **sectors. Figure 3** shows a circle graph that indicates how Americans disagree as to when "old age" begins.

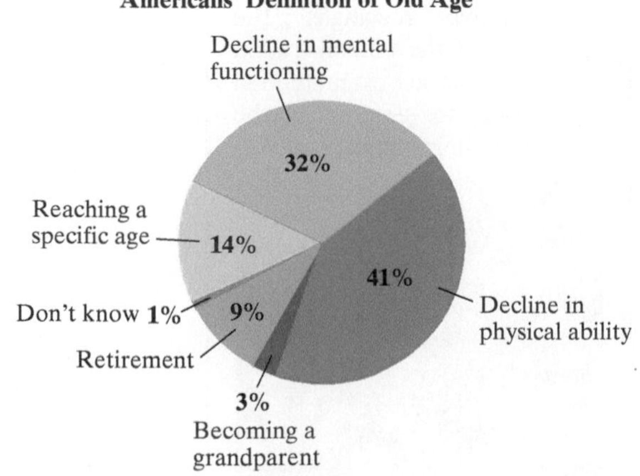

FIGURE 3
Source: American Demographics

In our next example, we will use the information in the circle graph at the bottom of the previous page to estimate a quantity. Although different rounding results in different estimates, the whole idea behind the rounding process is to make calculations simple.

EXAMPLE 5 Applying Estimation Techniques to a Circle Graph

According to the U.S. Census Bureau, in 2008, there were 220,948,915 Americans 20 years and older. Assuming the circle graph in **Figure 3** is representative of this age group,

a. Use the appropriate information displayed by the graph to determine a calculation that shows the number of Americans 20 years and older who define old age by a decline in physical ability.

b. Use rounding to find a reasonable estimate for this calculation.

Solution

a. The circle graph in **Figure 3** indicates that 41% of Americans define old age by a decline in physical ability. Among the 220,948,915 Americans 20 years and older, the number who define old age in this manner is determined by finding 41% of 220,948,915.

The number of Americans 20 and older who define old age by a decline in physical ability | is | 41% | of | the number of Americans 20 and older.

$$= 0.41 \times 220{,}948{,}915$$

b. We can use rounding to obtain a reasonable estimate of $0.41 \times 220{,}948{,}915$.

Round to the nearest ten million.

$$0.41 \times 220{,}948{,}915 \approx 0.4 \times 220{,}000{,}000 = 88{,}000{,}000$$

Round to the nearest tenth.

$$\begin{array}{r} 220{,}000{,}000 \\ \times \quad 0.4 \\ \hline 88{,}000{,}000.0 \end{array}$$

Our answer indicates that approximately 88,000,000 (88 million) Americans 20 years and older define old age by a decline in physical ability.

STUDY TIP

To convert a number from percent form to decimal form, move the decimal point two places to the left and drop the percent sign. Example:

$$41\% = 41.\% = 0.41\%$$

CHECK POINT 5 According to the U.S. Census Bureau, in 2008, there were 21,728,978 Americans between the ages of 15 to 19, inclusive. Assuming the circle graph in **Figure 3** on the previous page is representative of this age group,

a. Use the appropriate information displayed by the graph to determine a calculation that shows the number of Americans in this age group who define old age by a decline in mental functioning.

b. Use rounding to find a reasonable estimate for this calculation.

Bar graphs are convenient for showing comparisons among items. The bars may be either horizontal or vertical, and their heights or lengths are used to show the amounts of different items. **Figure 4** is an example of a typical bar graph. The graph shows life expectancy for American men and American women born in various years from 1960 through 2005.

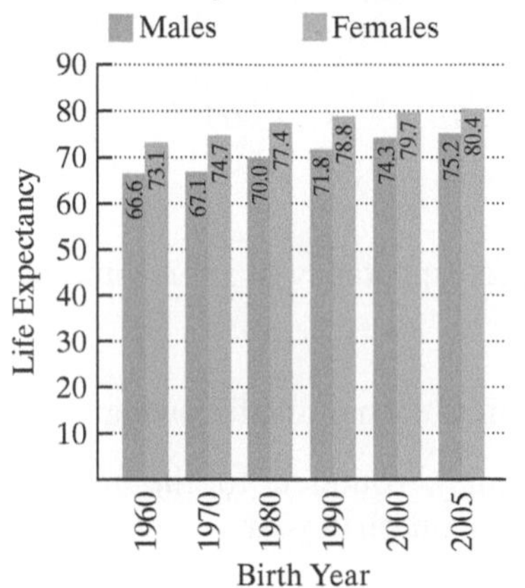

FIGURE 4
Source: National Center for Health Statistics

EXAMPLE 6 Applying Estimation and Inductive Reasoning to Data in a Bar Graph

Use the data for men in **Figure 4** to estimate each of the following:

a. a man's increased life expectancy, rounded to the nearest hundredth of a year, for each subsequent birth year

b. the life expectancy of a man born in 2020.

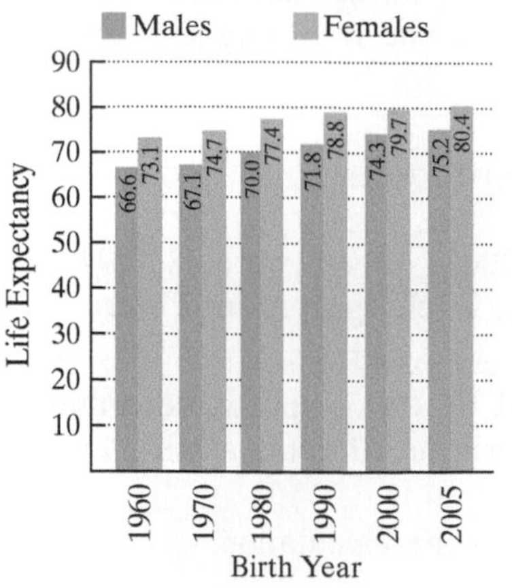

FIGURE 4 (repeated)

Solution

a. One way to estimate increased life expectancy for each subsequent birth year is to generalize from the information given for 1960 (male life expectancy: 66.6 years) and for 2005 (male life expectancy: 75.2 years). The average yearly increase in life expectancy is the change in life expectancy from 1960 to 2005 divided by the change in time from 1960 to 2005.

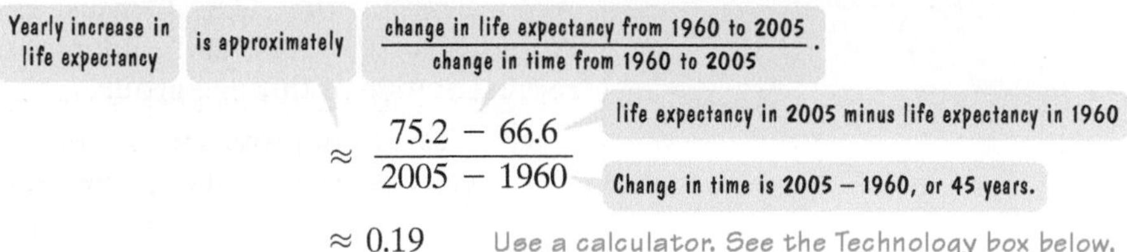

$$\approx \frac{75.2 - 66.6}{2005 - 1960}$$

life expectancy in 2005 minus life expectancy in 1960

Change in time is 2005 – 1960, or 45 years.

$$\approx 0.19$$

Use a calculator. See the Technology box below.

For each subsequent birth year, a man's life expectancy is increasing by approximately 0.19 year.

TECHNOLOGY

Here is the calculator keystroke sequence needed to perform the computation in Example 6(a).

(75.2 − 66.6) ÷ (2005 − 1960).

Press = on a scientific calculator or ENTER on a graphing calculator to display the answer. As specified, we round to the nearest hundredth.

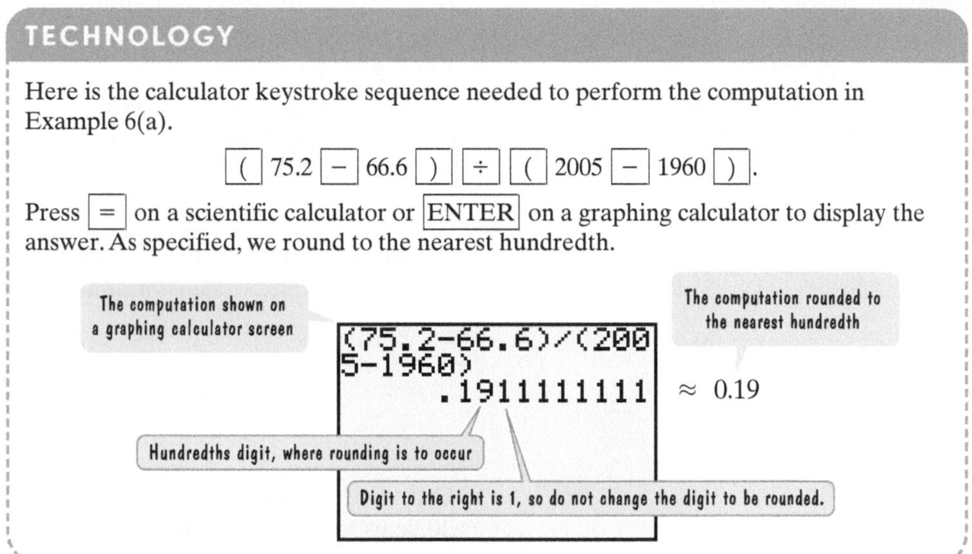

b. We can use our computation in part (a) to estimate the life expectancy of an American man born in 2020. The bar graph indicates that men born in 1960 had a life expectancy of 66.6 years. The year 2020 is 60 years after 1960 and life expectancy is increasing by approximately 0.19 year for each subsequent birth year.

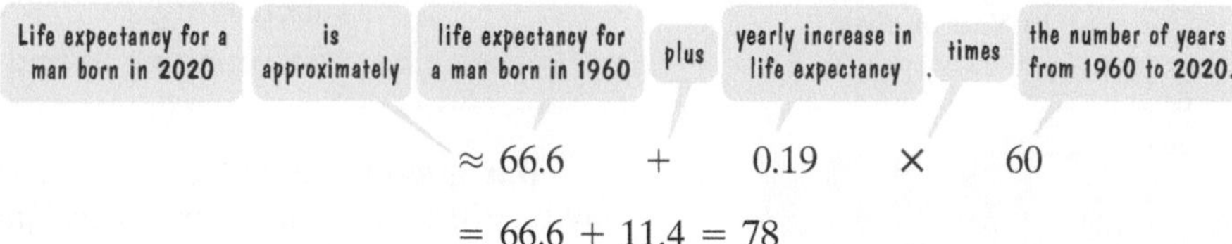

$$\approx 66.6 \quad + \quad 0.19 \quad \times \quad 60$$

$$= 66.6 + 11.4 = 78$$

An American man born in 2020 will have a life expectancy of approximately 78 years.

CHECK POINT 6

Use the data for women in **Figure 4** to estimate each of the following:

a. a woman's increased life expectancy, rounded to the nearest hundredth of a year, for each subsequent birth year

b. the life expectancy, to the nearest tenth of a year, of a woman born in 2050.

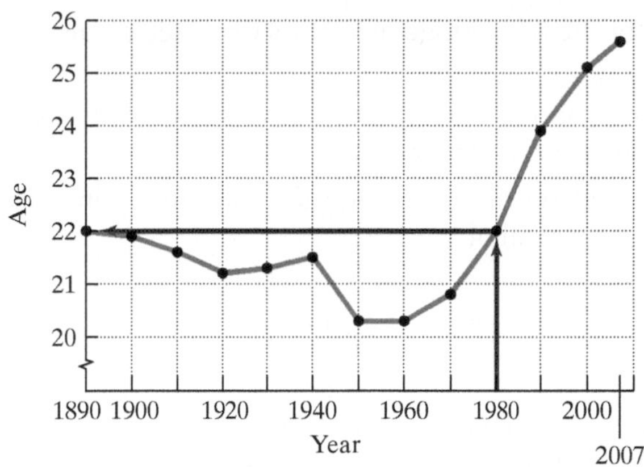

FIGURE 5
Source: U.S. Census Bureau

Line graphs are often used to illustrate trends over time. Some measure of time, such as months or years, frequently appears on the horizontal axis. Amounts are generally listed on the vertical axis. Points are drawn to represent the given information. The graph is formed by connecting the points with line segments.

Figure 5 is an example of a typical line graph. The graph shows the average age at which women in the United States married for the first time from 1890 through 2007. The years are listed on the horizontal axis and the ages are listed on the vertical axis. The symbol ⍭ on the vertical axis shows that there is a break in values between 0 and 20. Thus, the first tick mark on the vertical axis represents an average age of 20.

Figure 5 shows how to find the average age at which women married for the first time in 1980.

Step 1 Locate 1980 on the horizontal axis.
Step 2 Locate the point on the line graph above 1980.
Step 3 Read across to the corresponding age on the vertical axis.

The age is 22. Thus, in 1980, women in the United States married for the first time at an average age of 22.

EXAMPLE 7 Using a Line Graph

Alcohol and Marijuana Use by United States High School Seniors

FIGURE 6
Source: U.S. Department of Health and Human Services

The line graphs in **Figure 6** show the percentage of high school seniors who used alcohol or marijuana during the 30 days prior to being surveyed for the University of Michigan's *Monitoring the Future* study.

a. Find an estimate for the percentage of seniors who used marijuana in 1990.

b. In which five-year period did the percentage of seniors who used marijuana decrease at the greatest rate?

c. In which year labeled on the horizontal axis did 50% of the seniors use alcohol?

Solution

a. Estimating the Percentage Using Marijuana in 1990

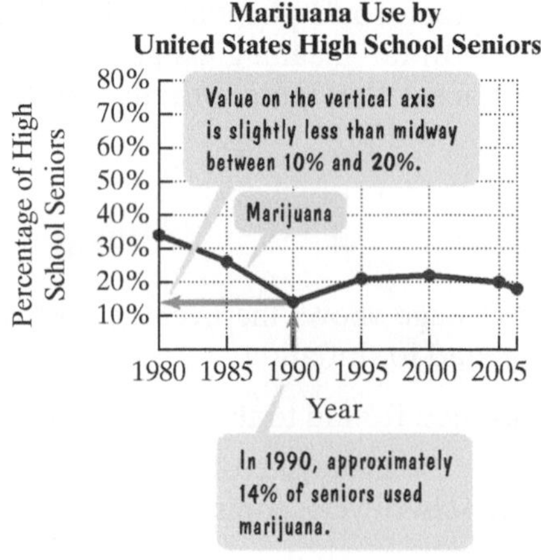

b. Identifying the Period of the Greatest Rate of Decreasing Marijuana Use

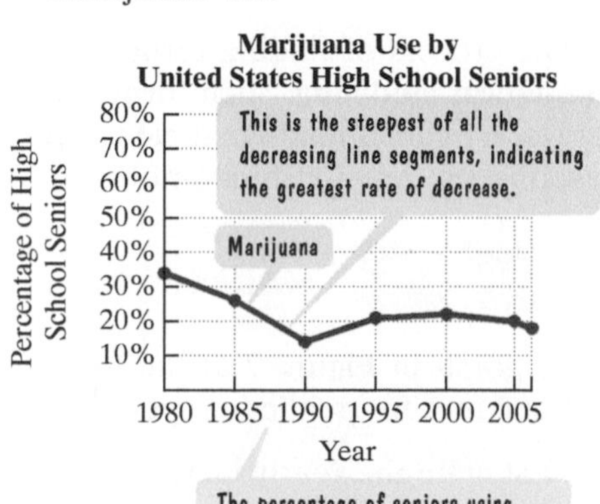

c. Identifying the Year when 50% of Seniors Used Alcohol

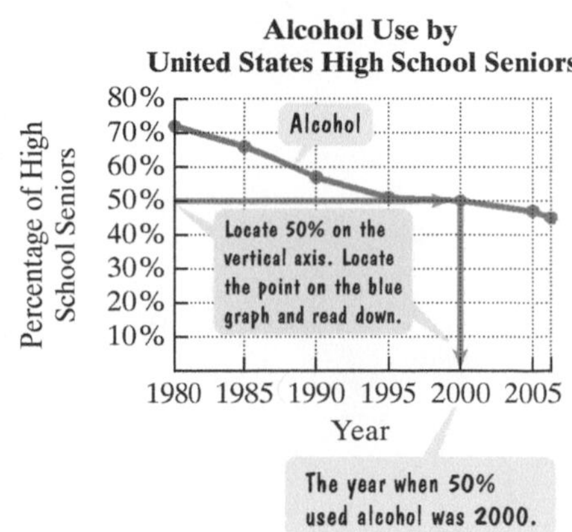

Use the line graphs in **Figure 6** on the previous page to solve this exercise.

a. Find an estimate for the percentage of seniors who used alcohol in 1985.

b. In which five-year period did the percentage of seniors who used marijuana decrease at the slowest rate?

c. In which year labeled on the horizontal axis did approximately 57% of the seniors use alcohol?

3 Develop mathematical models that estimate relationships between variables.

Mathematical Models

We have seen that American men born in 1960 have a life expectancy of 66.6 years, increasing by approximately 0.19 year for each subsequent birth year. We can use variables to express the life expectancy, E, for American men born x years after 1960.

Life expectancy for American men | is | life expectancy for a man born in 1960 | plus | yearly increase in life expectancy | times the number of birth years after 1960.

$$E = 66.6 + 0.19x$$

A **formula** is a statement of equality that uses letters to express a relationship between two or more variables. Thus, $E = 66.6 + 0.19x$ is a formula describing life expectancy, E, for American men born x years after 1960. Be aware that this formula provides *estimates* of life expectancy, as shown in **Table 2**.

TABLE 2 Comparing Given Data with Estimates Determined by a Formula

Birth Year	Life Expectancy: Given Data	Life Expectancy: Formula Estimate $E = 66.6 + 0.19x$
1960	66.6	$E = 66.6 + 0.19(0) = 66.6 + 0 = 66.6$
1970	67.1	$E = 66.6 + 0.19(10) = 66.6 + 1.9 = 68.5$
1980	70.0	$E = 66.6 + 0.19(20) = 66.6 + 3.8 = 70.4$
1990	71.8	$E = 66.6 + 0.19(30) = 66.6 + 5.7 = 72.3$
2000	74.3	$E = 66.6 + 0.19(40) = 66.6 + 7.6 = 74.2$
2005	75.2	$E = 66.6 + 0.19(45) = 66.6 + 8.55 = 75.15$

In each row, we substitute the number of years after 1960 for x. The better estimates occur in 1960, 1980, 2000, and 2005.

The process of finding formulas to describe real-world phenomena is called **mathematical modeling**. Such formulas, together with the meaning assigned to the variables, are called **mathematical models**. We often say that these formulas model, or describe, the relationships among the variables.

EXAMPLE 8 Modeling the Cost of Attending a Public College

The bar graph in **Figure 7** at the top of the next page shows the average cost of tuition and fees for public four-year colleges, adjusted for inflation.

a. Estimate the yearly increase in tuition and fees. Round to the nearest dollar.

b. Write a mathematical model that estimates the average cost of tuition and fees, T, at public four-year colleges for the school year ending x years after 2000.

c. Use the mathematical model from part (b) to project the average cost of tuition and fees at public four-year colleges for the school year ending in 2014.

Brian Snyder\Getty Images

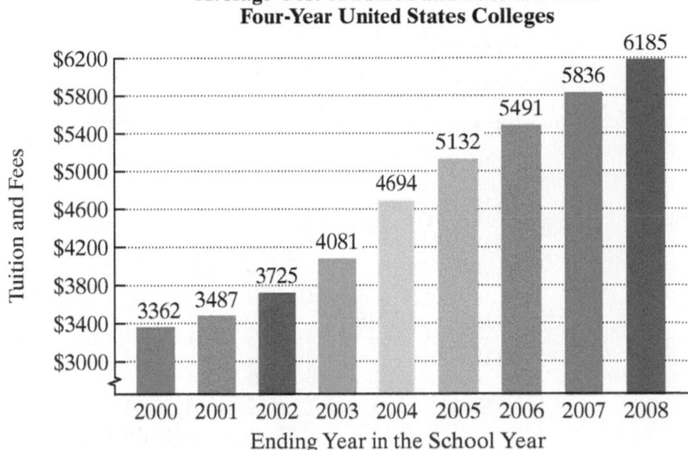

FIGURE 7
Source: The College Board

Solution

a. We can use the data from 2000 and 2008 to estimate the yearly increase in tuition and fees.

Yearly increase in tuition and fees | is approximately | $\dfrac{\text{change in tuition and fees from 2000 to 2008}}{\text{change in time from 2000 to 2008}}$.

$$\approx \frac{6185 - 3362}{2008 - 2000}$$

$$= \frac{2823}{8} = 352.875 \approx 353$$

Each year the average cost of tuition and fees for public four-year colleges is increasing by approximately $353.

b. Now we can use variables to obtain a mathematical model that estimates the average cost of tuition and fees, T, for the school year ending x years after 2000.

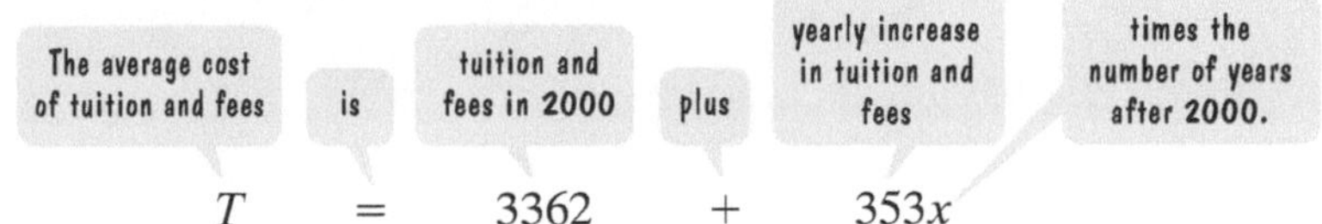

$$T \quad = \quad 3362 \quad + \quad 353x$$

The mathematical model $T = 3362 + 353x$ estimates the average cost of tuition and fees, T, at public four-year colleges for the school year ending x years after 2000.

c. Now let's use the mathematical model to project the average cost of tuition and fees for the school year ending in 2014. Because 2014 is 14 years after 2000, we substitute 14 for x.

$T = 3362 + 353x$ — This is the mathematical model from part (b).

$T = 3362 + 353(14)$ — Substitute 14 for x.

$= 3362 + 4942$ — Multiply: $353(14) = 4942$.

$= 8304$ — Add. On a calculator, enter 3362 [+] 353 [×] 14 and press [=] or [ENTER].

Our model projects that the average cost of tuition and fees at public four-year colleges for the school year ending in 2014 will be $8304.

CHECK POINT 8 The bar graph in **Figure 8** shows the average cost of tuition and fees for private four-year colleges, adjusted for inflation.

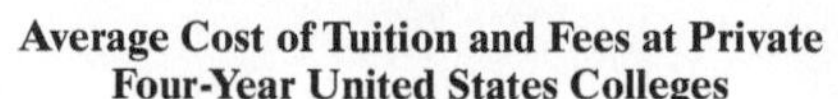

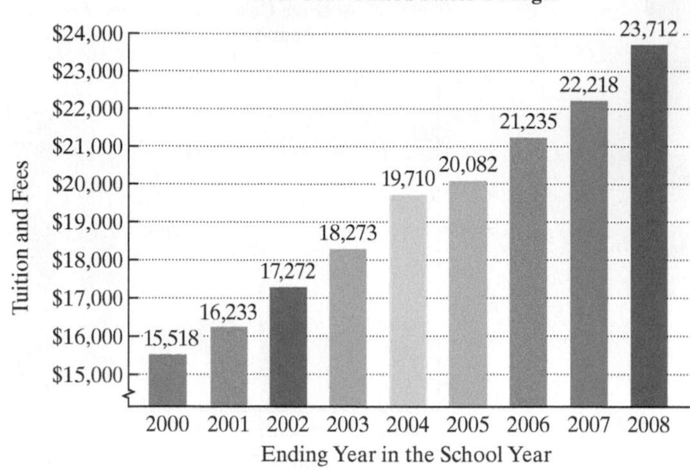

FIGURE 8
Source: The College Board

a. Estimate the yearly increase in tuition and fees. Round to the nearest dollar.

b. Write a mathematical model that estimates the average cost of tuition and fees, T, at private four-year colleges for the school year ending x years after 2000.

c. Use the mathematical model from part (b) to project the average cost of tuition and fees at private four-year colleges for the school year ending in 2012.

Sometimes a mathematical model gives an estimate that is not a good approximation or is extended to include values of the variable that do not make sense. In these cases, we say that **model breakdown** has occurred. Models that accurately describe data for the past ten years might not serve as reliable predictions for what can reasonably be expected to occur in the future. Model breakdown can occur when formulas are extended too far into the future.

Exercise Set 2

Practice Exercises

1. According to the U.S. Census Bureau, 55,444,562 Americans speak a language other than English at home. Round this number to the nearest **a.** hundred, **b.** thousand, **c.** ten thousand, **d.** hundred thousand, **e.** million, **f.** ten million.

2. According to the U.S. Bureau of Justice, there were 1,528,041 prisoners in the United States in 2007. Round this number to the nearest **a.** hundred, **b.** thousand, **c.** ten thousand, **d.** hundred thousand, **e.** million.

Pi goes on and on and on . . .
And e is just as cursed.
I wonder: Which is larger
When their digits are reversed?

Martin Gardner

Although most people are familiar with π, the number e is more significant in mathematics, showing up in problems involving population growth and compound interest, and at the heart of the statistical bell curve. One way to think of e is the dollar amount you would have in a savings account at the end of the year if you invested \$1 at the beginning of the year and the bank paid an annual interest rate of 100% compounded continuously (compounding interest every trillionth of a second, every quadrillionth of a second, etc.). Although continuous compounding sounds terrific, at the end of the year your \$1 would have grown to a mere \$e, or \$2.72, rounded to the nearest cent. Here is a better approximation for e.

$$e \approx 2.718281828459045$$

In Exercises 3–8, use this approximation to round e as specified.

3. to the nearest thousandth
4. to the nearest ten-thousandth
5. to the nearest hundred-thousandth
6. to the nearest millionth
7. to nine decimal places
8. to ten decimal places

In Exercises 9–34, because different rounding results in different estimates, there is not one single, correct answer to each exercise.

In Exercises 9–22, obtain an estimate for each computation by rounding the numbers so that the resulting arithmetic can easily be performed by hand or in your head. Then use a calculator to perform the computation. How reasonable is your estimate when compared to the actual answer?

9. $359 + 596$

10. $248 + 797$

11. $8.93 + 1.04 + 19.26$

12. $7.92 + 3.06 + 24.36$

13. $32.15 - 11.239$

14. $46.13 - 15.237$

15. 39.67×5.5

16. 78.92×6.5

17. 0.79×414

18. 0.67×211

19. $47.83 \div 2.9$

20. $54.63 \div 4.7$

21. 32% of 187,253

22. 42% of 291,506

In Exercises 23–34, determine each estimate without using a calculator. Then use a calculator to perform the computation necessary to obtain an exact answer. How reasonable is your estimate when compared to the actual answer?

23. Estimate the total cost of six grocery items if their prices are \$3.47, \$5.89, \$19.98, \$2.03, \$11.85, and \$0.23.

24. Estimate the total cost of six grocery items if their prices are \$4.23, \$7.79, \$28.97, \$4.06, \$13.43, and \$0.74.

25. A full-time employee who works 40 hours per week earns \$19.50 per hour. Estimate that person's annual income.

26. A full-time employee who works 40 hours per week earns \$29.85 per hour. Estimate that person's annual income.

27. You lease a car at \$605 per month for 3 years. Estimate the total cost of the lease.

28. You lease a car at \$415 per month for 4 years. Estimate the total cost of the lease.

29. A raise of \$310,000 is evenly distributed among 294 professors. Estimate the amount each professor receives.

30. A raise of \$310,000 is evenly distributed among 196 professors. Estimate the amount each professor receives.

31. If a person who works 40 hours per week earns \$61,500 per year, estimate that person's hourly wage.

32. If a person who works 40 hours per week earns \$38,950 per year, estimate that person's hourly wage.

33. The average life expectancy in Canada is 80.1 years. Estimate the country's life expectancy in hours.

34. The average life expectancy in Mozambique is 40.3 years. Estimate the country's life expectancy in hours.

Practice Plus

In Exercises 35–36, obtain an estimate for each computation without using a calculator. Then use a calculator to perform the computation. How reasonable is your estimate when compared to the actual answer?

35. $\dfrac{0.19996 \times 107}{0.509}$

36. $\dfrac{0.47996 \times 88}{0.249}$

37. Ten people ordered calculators. The least expensive was \$19.95 and the most expensive was \$39.95. Half ordered a \$29.95 calculator. Select the best estimate of the amount spent on calculators.

a. \$240 **b.** \$310 **c.** \$345 **d.** \$355

38. Ten people ordered calculators. The least expensive was \$4.95 and the most expensive was \$12.95. Half ordered a \$6.95 calculator. Select the best estimate of the amount spent on calculators.

a. \$160 **b.** \$105 **c.** \$75 **d.** \$55

39. Traveling at an average rate of between 60 and 70 miles per hour for 3 to 4 hours, select the best estimate for the distance traveled.

a. 90 miles **b.** 190 miles **c.** 225 miles **d.** 275 miles

40. Traveling at an average rate of between 40 and 50 miles per hour for 3 to 4 hours, select the best estimate for the distance traveled.

a. 120 miles **b.** 160 miles **c.** 195 miles **d.** 210 miles

41. Imagine that you counted 60 numbers per minute and continued to count nonstop until you reached 10,000. Determine a reasonable estimate of the number of hours it would take you to complete the counting.

42. Imagine that you counted 60 numbers per minute and continued to count nonstop until you reached one million. Determine a reasonable estimate of the number of days it would take you to complete the counting.

Application Exercises

The circle graph shows the percentage of the 221,730,462 American adults who drink caffeinated beverages on a daily basis and the number of cups consumed per day. Use this information to solve Exercises 43–44.

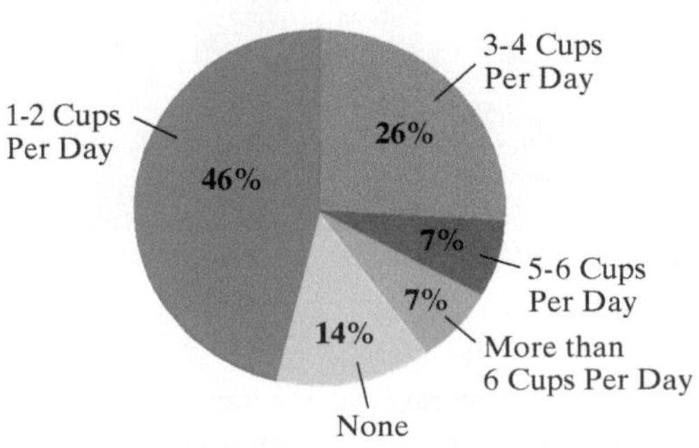

Source: Harris Interactive

43. Without using a calculator, estimate the number of American adults who drink from one to two cups of caffeinated beverages per day.

44. Without using a calculator, estimate the number of American adults who drink from three to four cups of caffeinated beverages per day.

An online test of English spelling looked at how well people spelled difficult words. The bar graph shows how many people per 100 spelled each word correctly. Use this information to solve Exercises 45–46.

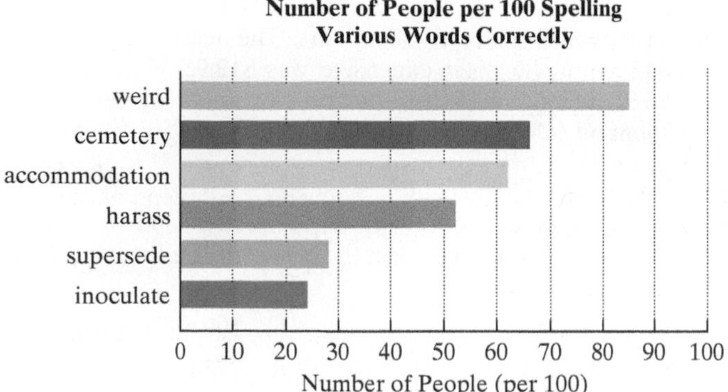

Source: Vivian Cook, *Accomodating Brocolli in the Cemetary or Why Can't Anybody Spell?*, Simon and Schuster, 2004

45. a. Estimate the number of people per 100 who spelled *weird* correctly.

b. In a group consisting of 8729 randomly selected people, estimate how many more people can correctly spell *weird* than *inoculate*.

46. a. Estimate the number of people per 100 who spelled *cemetery* correctly.

b. In a group consisting of 7219 randomly selected people, estimate how many more people can correctly spell *cemetery* than *supersede*.

Americans are getting married later in life, or not getting married at all. In 2006, nearly half of Americans ages 25 through 29 were unmarried. The bar graph shows the percentage of never-married men and women in this age group. Use this information to solve Exercises 47–48.

Percentage of United States Population Never Married, Ages 25–29

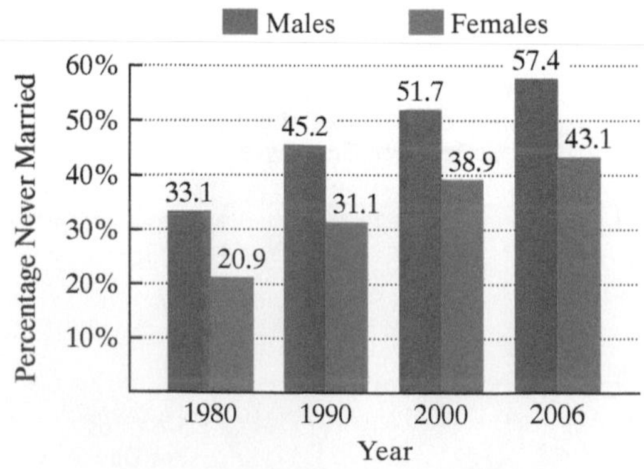

Source: U.S. Census Bureau

47. a. Estimate the average yearly increase in the percentage of never-married American males ages 25–29. Round the percent to the nearest tenth.

b. Estimate the percentage of never-married American males ages 25–29 in 2010.

48. a. Estimate the average yearly increase in the percentage of never-married American females ages 25–29. Round the percent to the nearest tenth.

b. Estimate the percentage of never-married American females ages 25–29 in 2010.

Even after a campaign to curb grade inflation, 51% of the grades given at Harvard in the 2005 school year were B+ or better. The graph shows the percentage of Harvard students with B+ averages or better for the period from 1960 through 2005. Use this information to solve Exercises 49–50.

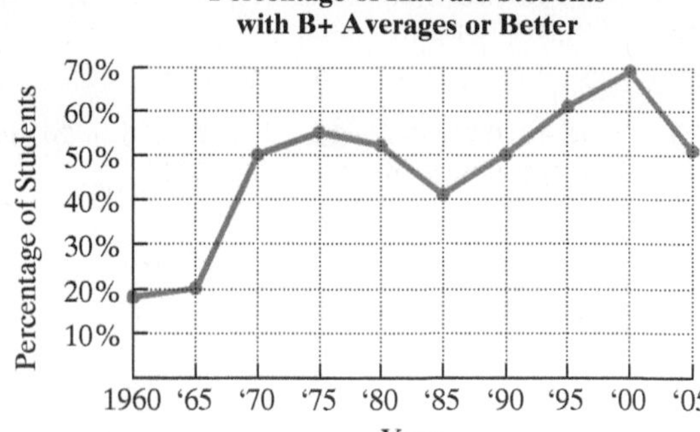

Source: Mother Jones, January/February 2008

49. a. For which year was the percentage of students with B+ averages or better at a maximum? Find a reasonable estimate of the percentage of students for that year.

b. In which five-year period did the percentage of students with B+ averages or better increase at the greatest rate?

c. In which year did 20% of the students have B+ averages or better?

50. a. For which year was the percentage of students with B+ averages or better at a minimum? Find a reasonable estimate of the percentage of students for that year.

b. In which five-year period did the percentage of students with B+ averages or better decrease at the greatest rate?

c. In which year did approximately 61% of the students have B+ averages or better?

The bar graph shows the population of the United States, in millions, for five selected years. Use this information to solve Exercises 51–52.

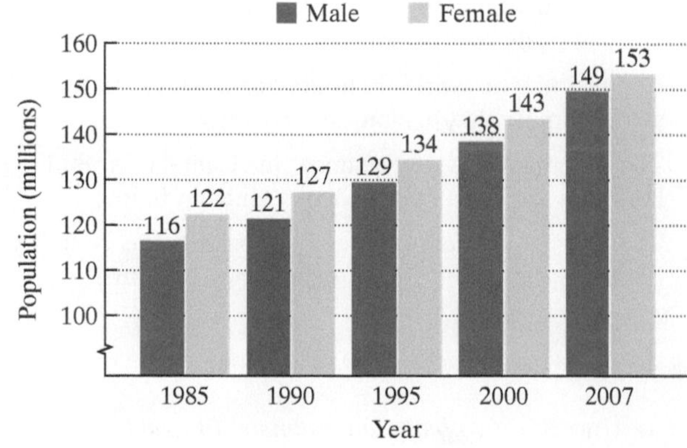

Source: U.S. Census Bureau

51. a. Estimate the yearly increase in the female population. Express the answer in millions, rounded to one decimal place.

b. Write a mathematical model that estimates the female U.S. population, F, in millions, x years after 1985.

c. Use the mathematical model from part (b) to project the female U.S. population, in millions, in 2020.

52. a. Estimate the yearly increase in the male population. Express the answer in millions and do not round.

b. Write a mathematical model that estimates the male U.S. population, M, in millions, x years after 1985.

c. Use the mathematical model from part (b) to project the male U.S. population, in millions, in 2020.

Writing in Mathematics

53. What is estimation? When is it helpful to use estimation?
54. Explain how to round 218,543 to the nearest thousand and to the nearest hundred thousand.
55. Explain how to round 14.26841 to the nearest hundredth and to the nearest thousandth.
56. What does the $\approx$ symbol mean?
57. In this era of calculators and computers, why is there a need to develop estimation skills?
58. Describe a circle graph.
59. Describe a bar graph.
60. Describe a line graph.
61. What does it mean when we say that a formula models real-world phenomena?
62. In 2000, there were 39.8 million Americans without health insurance. This number has increased by approximately 1.7 million people per year. Describe how to use this information to write a mathematical model that describes the number of Americans without health insurance, N, in millions, x years after 2000.
63. Explain how to use the mathematical model from Exercise 62 to predict how many Americans will not have health insurance in 2020. Describe one event that could occur in the future that would make this prediction highly inaccurate.
64. Describe one way in which you use estimation in a nonacademic area of your life.
65. A forecaster at the National Hurricane Center needs to estimate the time until a hurricane with high probability of striking South Florida will hit Miami. Is it better to overestimate or underestimate? Explain your answer.

Critical Thinking Exercises

Make Sense? *In Exercises 66–69, determine whether each statement makes sense or does not make sense, and explain your reasoning.*

66. When buying several items at the market, I use estimation before going to the cashier to be sure I have enough money to pay for the purchase.
67. It's not necessary to use estimation skills when using my calculator.
68. Being able to compute an exact answer requires a different ability than estimating the reasonableness of the answer.
69. My mathematical model estimates the data for the past ten years extremely well, so it will serve as an accurate prediction for what will occur in 2050.
70. Take a moment to read the verse preceding Exercises 3–8 that mentions the numbers π and e, whose decimal representations continue infinitely with no repeating patterns. The verse was written by the American mathematician (and accomplished amateur magician!) Martin Gardner (1914–), author of more than 60 books, and best known for his "Mathematical Games" column, which ran in *Scientific American* for 25 years. Explain the humor in Gardner's question.

In Exercises 71–74, match the story with the correct graph. The graphs are labeled (a), (b), (c), and (d).

71. As the blizzard got worse, the snow fell harder and harder.
72. The snow fell more and more softly.
73. It snowed hard, but then it stopped. After a short time, the snow started falling softly.
74. It snowed softly, and then it stopped. After a short time, the snow started falling hard.

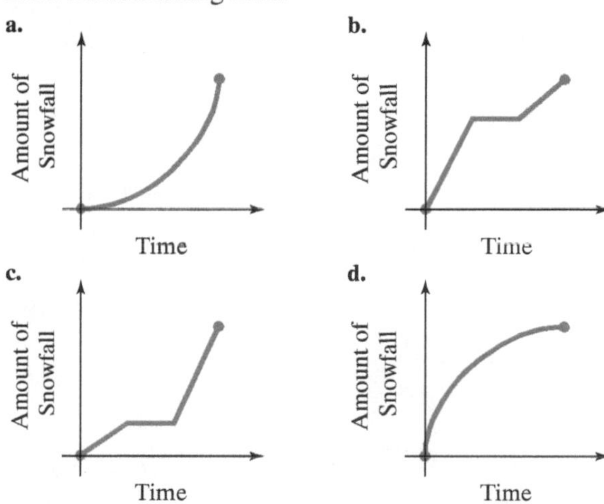

75. American children ages 2 to 17 spend 19 hours 40 minutes per week watching television. (*Source*: TV-Turnoff Network) From ages 2 through 17, inclusive, estimate the number of days an American child spends watching television. How many years, to the nearest tenth of a year, is that?
76. If you spend $1000 each day, estimate how long it will take to spend a billion dollars.

Group Exercises

77. Group members should devise an estimation process that can be used to answer each of the following questions. Use input from all group members to describe the best estimation process possible.

    a. Is it possible to walk from San Francisco to New York in a year?

    b. How much money is spent on ice cream in the United States each year?

78. Group members should begin by consulting an almanac, newspaper, magazine, or the Internet to find two graphs that show "intriguing" data changing from year to year. In one graph, the data values should be increasing relatively steadily. In the second graph, the data values should be decreasing relatively steadily. For each graph selected, write a mathematical model that estimates the changing variable x years after the graph's starting date. Then use each mathematical model to make predictions about what might occur in the future. Are there circumstances that might affect the accuracy of the prediction? List some of these circumstances.

OBJECTIVE

1 | Solve problems using the organization of the four-step problem-solving process.

3 Problem Solving

Critical thinking and problem solving are essential skills in both school and work. A model for problem solving was established by the charismatic teacher and mathematician George Polya (1887–1985) in *How to Solve It* (Princeton University Press, Princeton, NJ, 1957). This book, first published in 1945, has sold more than one million copies and is available in 17 languages. Using a four-step procedure for problem solving, Polya's book demonstrates how to think clearly in any field.

David Young-Wolff\PhotoEdit Inc.

1 | Solve problems using the organization of the four-step problem-solving process.

"If you don't know where you're going, you'll probably end up some place else."

Yogi Berra

POLYA'S FOUR STEPS IN PROBLEM SOLVING

Step 1 **Understand the problem.** Read the problem several times. The first reading can serve as an overview. In the second reading, write down what information is given and determine exactly what it is that the problem requires you to find.

Step 2 **Devise a plan.** The plan for solving the problem might involve one or more of these suggested problem-solving strategies:

- Use inductive reasoning to look for a pattern.
- Make a systematic list or a table.
- Use estimation to make an educated guess at the solution. Check the guess against the problem's conditions and work backward to eventually determine the solution.
- Try expressing the problem more simply and solve a similar simpler problem.
- Use trial and error.
- List the given information in a chart or table.
- Try making a sketch or a diagram to illustrate the problem.
- Relate the problem to a similar problem that you have seen before. Try applying the procedures used to solve the similar problem to the new one.
- Look for a "catch" if the answer seems too obvious. Perhaps the problem involves some sort of trick question deliberately intended to lead the problem solver in the wrong direction.
- Use the given information to eliminate possibilities.
- Use common sense.

Step 3 **Carry out the plan and solve the problem.**

Step 4 **Look back and check the answer.** The answer should satisfy the conditions of the problem. The answer should make sense and be reasonable. If this is not the case, recheck the method and any calculations. Perhaps there is an alternate way to arrive at a correct solution.

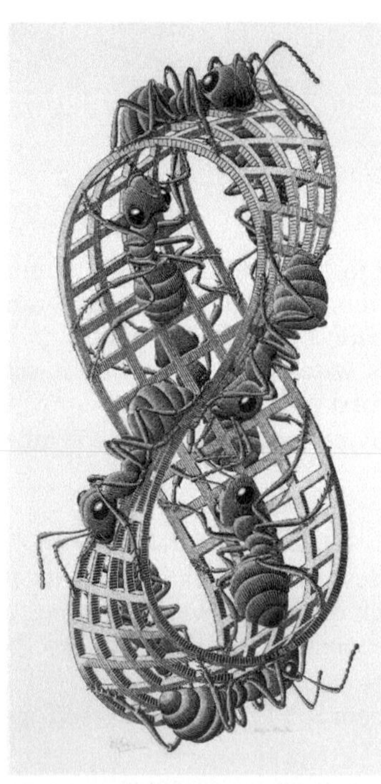

M.C. Escher's "Mobius Strip II" © 2009 The M.C. Scher Company-Holland. All rights reserved. M.C. Escher's "Mobius Strip II" ©2009 The M.C. Scher Company-Holland. All right reserved. www.mcsescher.com

STUDY TIP

Think of Polya's four steps as guidelines that will help you organize the process of problem solving, rather than a list of rigid rules that need to be memorized. You may be able to solve certain problems without thinking about or using every step in the four-step process.

The very first step in problem solving involves evaluating the given information in a deliberate manner. Is there enough given to solve the problem? Is the information relevant to the problem's solution or are some facts not necessary to arrive at a solution?

EXAMPLE 1 Finding What Is Missing

Which necessary piece of information is missing and prevents you from solving the following problem?

> A man purchased five shirts, each at the same discount price. How much did he pay for them?

Solution

Step 1 Understand the problem. Here's what is given:

> Number of shirts purchased: 5.

We must find how much the man paid for the five shirts.

Step 2 Devise a plan. The amount that the man paid for the five shirts is the number of shirts, 5, times the cost of each shirt. The discount price of each shirt is not given. This missing piece of information makes it impossible to solve the problem.

Which necessary piece of information is missing and prevents you from solving the following problem?

> The bill for your meal totaled $20.36, including the tax. How much change should you receive from the cashier?

EXAMPLE 2 Finding What Is Unnecessary

In the following problem, one more piece of information is given than is necessary for solving the problem. Identify this unnecessary piece of information. Then solve the problem.

> A roll of E-Z Wipe paper towels contains 100 sheets and costs $1.38. A comparable brand, Kwik-Clean, contains five dozen sheets per roll and costs $1.23. If you need three rolls of paper towels, which brand is the better value?

Solution

Step 1 Understand the problem. Here's what is given:

> E-Z Wipe: 100 sheets per roll; $1.38
>
> Kwik-Clean: 5 dozen sheets per roll; $1.23
>
> Needed: 3 rolls.

We must determine which brand offers the better value.

Step 2 Devise a plan. The brand with the better value is the one that has the lower price per sheet. Thus, we can compare the two brands by finding the cost for one sheet of E-Z Wipe and one sheet of Kwik-Clean. The price per sheet, or the *unit price*, is the price of a roll divided by the number of sheets in the roll. The fact that three rolls are required is not relevant to the problem. This unnecessary piece of information is not needed to find which brand is the better value.

BLITZER BONUS

UNIT PRICES AND SNEAKY PRICEJACKS

In *200% of Nothing* (John Wiley & Sons, 1993), author A. K. Dewdney writes, "It must be something of a corporate dream come true when a company charges more for a product and no one notices." He gives two examples of "sneaky pricejacks," both easily detected using unit prices. The manufacturers of Mennen Speed Stick deodorant increased the size of the package that held the stick, left the price the same, and reduced the amount of actual deodorant in the stick from 2.5 ounces to 2.25. Fabergé's Brut left the price and size of its cologne jar the same, but reduced its contents from 5 ounces to 4. Surprisingly, the new jar read, "Now, more Brut!" *Consumer Reports* contacted Fabergé to see how this could be possible. Their response: The new jar contained "more fragrance." *Consumer Reports* moaned, "Et tu Brut?"

Step 3 Carry out the plan and solve the problem.

E-Z Wipe:

$$\text{price per sheet} = \frac{\text{price of a roll}}{\text{number of sheets per roll}}$$

$$= \frac{\$1.38}{100 \text{ sheets}} = \$0.0138 \approx \$0.01$$

Kwik-Clean:

$$\text{price per sheet} = \frac{\text{price of a roll}}{\text{number of sheets per roll}}$$

$$= \frac{\$1.23}{60 \text{ sheets}} = \$0.0205 \approx \$0.02$$

5 dozen = 5 × 12, or 60 sheets

By comparing unit prices, we see that E-Z Wipe, at approximately $0.01 per sheet, is the better value.

Step 4 Look back and check the answer. We can double-check the arithmetic in each of our unit-price computations. We can also see if these unit prices satisfy the problem's conditions. The product of each brand's price per sheet and the number of sheets per roll should result in the given price for a roll.

E-Z Wipe: Check $0.0138 Kwik-Clean: Check $0.0205

$$\$0.0138 \times 100 = \$1.38 \qquad \$0.0205 \times 60 = \$1.23$$

These are the given prices for a roll of each respective brand.

The unit prices satisfy the problem's conditions.

A generalization of our work in Example 2 allows you to compare different brands and make a choice between various products of different sizes. When shopping at the supermarket, a useful number to keep in mind is a product's *unit price*. The **unit price** is the total price divided by the total units. Among comparable brands, the best value is the product with the lowest unit price, assuming that the units are kept uniform.

The word *per* is used to state unit prices. For example, if a 12-ounce box of cereal sells for $3.00, its unit price is determined as follows:

$$\text{Unit price} = \frac{\text{total price}}{\text{total units}} = \frac{\$3.00}{12 \text{ ounces}} = \$0.25 \text{ per ounce.}$$

CHECK POINT 2 Solve the following problem. If the problem contains information that is not relevant to its solution, identify this unnecessary piece of information.

A manufacturer packages its apple juice in bottles and boxes. A 128-ounce bottle costs $5.39 and a 9-pack of 6.75-ounce boxes costs $3.15. Which packaging option is the better value?

EXAMPLE 3 Applying the Four-Step Procedure

By paying $100 cash up front and the balance at $20 a week, how long will it take to pay for a bicycle costing $680?

Solution

Step 1 Understand the problem. Here's what is given:

Cost of the bicycle: $680
Amount paid in cash: $100
Weekly payments: $20.

STUDY TIP

An effective way to see if you understand a problem is to restate the problem in your own words.

If necessary, consult a dictionary to look up any unfamiliar words. The word *balance* means the amount still to be paid. We must find the balance to determine the number of weeks required to pay off the bicycle.

Step 2 Devise a plan. Subtract the amount paid in cash from the cost of the bicycle. This results in the amount still to be paid. Because weekly payments are \$20, divide the amount still to be paid by 20. This will give the number of weeks required to pay for the bicycle.

Step 3 Carry out the plan and solve the problem. Begin by finding the balance, the amount still to be paid for the bicycle.

\$680	cost of the bicycle
−\$100	amount paid in cash
\$580	amount still to be paid

Now divide the \$580 balance by \$20, the payment per week. The result of the division is the number of weeks needed to pay off the bicycle.

$$\frac{\$580}{\frac{\$20}{\text{week}}} = \$580 \times \frac{\text{week}}{\$20} = \frac{580 \text{ weeks}}{20} = 29 \text{ weeks}$$

It will take 29 weeks to pay for the bicycle.

Step 4 Look back and check the answer. We can certainly double-check the arithmetic either by hand or with a calculator. We can also see if the answer, 29 weeks to pay for the bicycle, satisfies the condition that the bicycle costs \$680.

This is the answer we are checking.

\$20	weekly payment	\$580	total of weekly payments
29	number of weeks	+\$100	amount paid in cash
\$580	total of weekly payments	\$680	cost of bicycle

The answer of 29 weeks satisfies the condition that the cost of the bicycle is \$680.

CHECK POINT 3 By paying \$350 cash up front and the balance at \$45 per month, how long will it take to pay for a computer costing \$980?

Making lists is a useful strategy in problem solving.

EXAMPLE 4 Solving a Problem by Making a List

Suppose you are an engineer programming the automatic gate for a 50-cent toll. The gate should accept exact change only. It should not accept pennies. How many coin combinations must you program the gate to accept?

Solution

Step 1 Understand the problem. The total change must always be 50 cents. One possible coin combination is two quarters. Another is five dimes. We need to count all such combinations.

Step 2 Devise a plan. Make a list of all possible coin combinations. Begin with the coins of larger value and work toward the coins of smaller value.

Step 3 Carry out the plan and solve the problem. First we must find all of the coins that are not pennies but can combine to form 50 cents. This includes half-dollars, quarters, dimes, and nickels. Now we can set up a table. We will use these coins as table headings.

Half-Dollars	Quarters	Dimes	Nickels

Half-Dollars	Quarters	Dimes	Nickels

Each row in the table (repeated above) will represent one possible combination for exact change. We start with the largest coin, the half-dollar. Only one half-dollar is needed to make exact change. No other coins are needed. Thus, we put a 1 in the half-dollars column and 0s in the other columns to represent the first possible combination.

Half-Dollars	Quarters	Dimes	Nickels
1	0	0	0

Likewise, two quarters are also exact change for 50 cents. We put a 0 in the half-dollars column, a 2 in the quarters column, and 0s in the columns for dimes and nickels.

Half-Dollars	Quarters	Dimes	Nickels
1	0	0	0
0	2	0	0

In this manner, we can find all possible combinations for exact change for the 50-cent toll. These combinations are shown in **Table 3**.

TABLE 3 Exact Change for 50 Cents: No Pennies

Half-Dollars	Quarters	Dimes	Nickels
1	0	0	0
0	2	0	0
0	1	2	1
0	1	1	3
0	1	0	5
0	0	5	0
0	0	4	2
0	0	3	4
0	0	2	6
0	0	1	8
0	0	0	10

Count the coin combinations shown in **Table 3**. How many coin combinations must the gate accept? You must program the gate to accept 11 coin combinations.

Step 4 Look back and check the answer. Double-check **Table 3** to make sure that no possible combinations have been omitted and that the total in each row is 50 cents. Double-check your count of the number of combinations.

Suppose you are an engineer programming the automatic gate for a 30-cent toll. The gate should accept exact change only. It should not accept pennies. How many coin combinations must you program the gate to accept?

BLITZER BONUS

TRICK QUESTIONS

Think about the following questions carefully before answering because each contains some sort of trick or catch.

> Sample: Do they have a fourth of July in England?
> Answer: Of course, they do. However, there is no national holiday on that date!

See if you can answer the questions that follow without developing mental whiplash. The answers appear in the answer section.

1. A farmer had 17 sheep. All but 12 died. How many sheep does the farmer have left?
2. Some months have 30 days. Some have 31. How many months have 28 days?
3. A doctor had a brother, but this brother had no brothers. What was the relationship between doctor and brother?
4. If you had only one match and entered a log cabin in which there was a candle, a fireplace, and a woodburning stove, which should you light first?

Sketches and diagrams are sometimes useful in problem solving.

EXAMPLE 5 Solving a Problem by Using a Diagram

Four runners are in a one-mile race: Maria, Aretha, Thelma, and Debbie. Points are awarded only to the women finishing first or second. The first-place winner gets more points than the second-place winner. How many different arrangements of first- and second-place winners are possible?

Jim Cummins\Jim Cummins Studio, Inc.

Solution

Step 1 Understand the problem. Three possibilities for first and second position are

Maria-Aretha
Maria-Thelma
Aretha-Maria.

Notice that Maria finishing first and Aretha finishing second is a different outcome than Aretha finishing first and Maria finishing second. Order makes a difference because the first-place winner gets more points than the second-place winner. We must count all possibilities for first and second position.

Step 2 Devise a plan. If Maria finishes first, then each of the other three runners could finish second:

First place	Second place	Possibilities for first and second place
Maria	Aretha	Maria-Aretha
	Thelma	Maria-Thelma
	Debbie	Maria-Debbie

Similarly, we can list each woman as the possible first-place runner. Then we will list the other three women as possible second-place runners. Next we will determine the possibilities for first and second place. This diagram will show how the runners can finish first or second.

Step 3 Carry out the plan and solve the problem. Now we complete the diagram started in step 2. The diagram is shown in **Figure 9**.

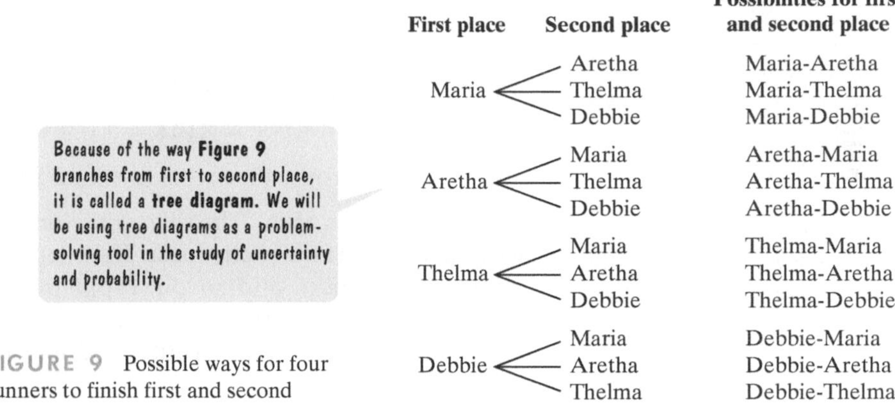

FIGURE 9 Possible ways for four runners to finish first and second

Count the number of possibilities shown under the third column, "Possibilities for first and second place." Can you see that there are 12 possibilities? Therefore, 12 different arrangements of first- and second-place winners are possible.

Step 4 Look back and check the answer. Check the diagram in **Figure 9** to make sure that no possible first- and second-place outcomes have been left out. Double-check your count for the winning pairs of runners.

CHECK POINT 5 Your "lecture wardrobe" is rather limited—just two pairs of jeans to choose from (one blue, one black) and three T-shirts to choose from (one beige, one yellow, and one blue). How many different outfits can you form?

Diagrams called *graphs* provide structures for describing relationships. In Example 6, we use such a diagram to illustrate the relationship between cities and one-way airfares between them.

EXAMPLE 6 Using a Reasonable Option to Solve a Problem with More Than One Solution

A sales director who lives in city A is required to fly to regional offices in cities B, C, D, and E. Other than starting and ending the trip in city A, there are no restrictions as to the order in which the other four cities are visited.

The one-way fares between each of the cities are given in **Table 4**. A diagram that illustrates this information is shown in **Figure 10**.

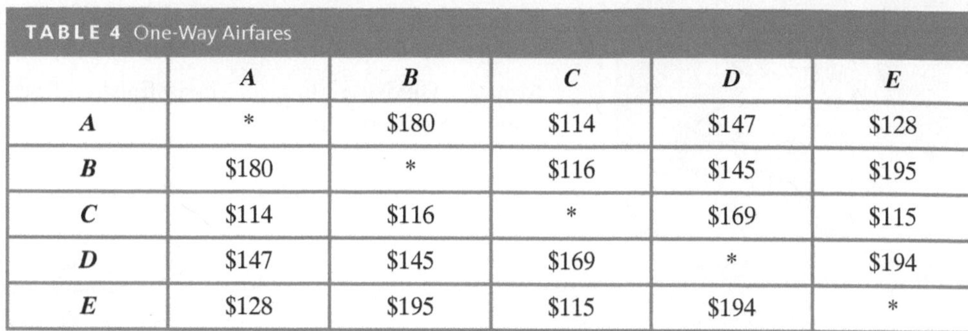

TABLE 4 One-Way Airfares

	A	B	C	D	E
A	*	$180	$114	$147	$128
B	$180	*	$116	$145	$195
C	$114	$116	*	$169	$115
D	$147	$145	$169	*	$194
E	$128	$195	$115	$194	*

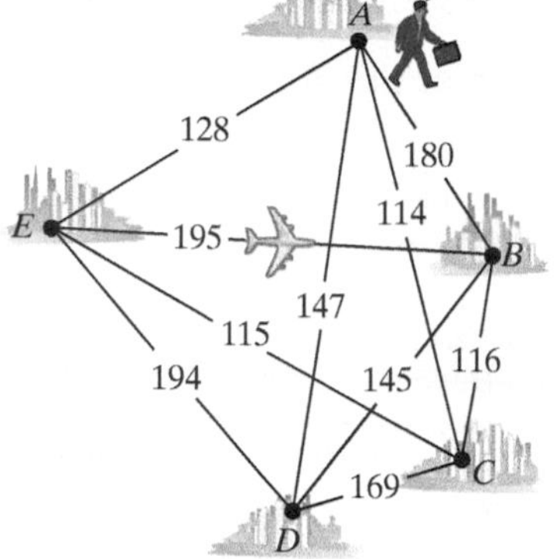

FIGURE 10

Give the sales director an order for visiting cities B, C, D, and E once, returning home to city A, for less than $750.

Solution

Step 1 Understand the problem. There are many ways to visit cities B, C, D, and E once, and return home to A. One route is

$$A, E, D, C, B, A.$$

Fly from A to E to D to C to B and then back to A.

The cost of this trip involves the sum of five costs, shown in both **Figure 10**:

$$\$128 + \$194 + \$169 + \$116 + \$180 = \$787.$$

We must find a route that costs less than $750.

Step 2 Devise a plan. The sales director starts at city A. From there, fly to the city to which the airfare is cheapest. Then from there fly to the next city to which the airfare is cheapest, and so on. From the last of the cities, fly home to city A. Compute the cost of this trip to see if it is less than $750. If it is not, use trial and error to find other possible routes and select an order (if there is one) whose cost is less than $750.

Step 3 Carry out the plan and solve the problem. See **Figure 11**. The route is indicated using red lines with arrows.

- Start at A.
- Choose the line segment with the smallest number: 114. Fly from A to C. (cost: $114)
- From C, choose the line segment with the smallest number that does not lead to A: 115. Fly from C to E. (cost: $115)
- From E, choose the line segment with the smallest number that does not lead to a city already visited: 194. Fly from E to D. (cost: $194)
- From D, there is little choice but to fly to B, the only city not yet visited. (cost: $145)
- From B, return home to A. (cost: $180)

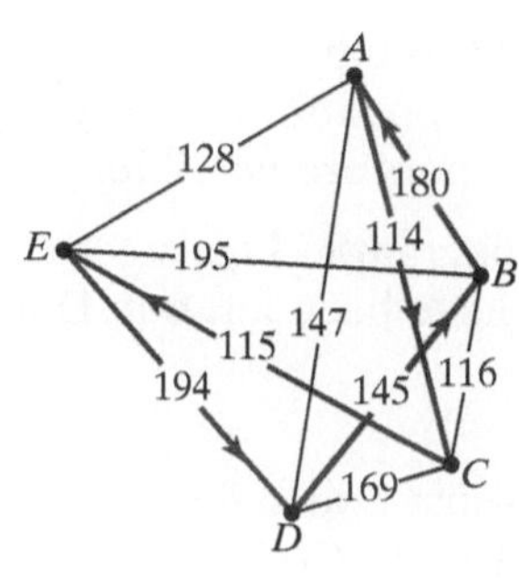

FIGURE 11

The route that we are considering is

$$A, C, E, D, B, A.$$

Let's see if the cost is less than $750. The cost is

$$\$114 + \$115 + \$194 + \$145 + \$180 = \$748.$$

Because the cost is less than $750, the sales director can follow the order A, C, E, D, B, A.

Step 4 Look back and check the answer. Use **Table 4** on the previous page or **Figure 11** to verify that the five numbers used in the sum shown above are correct. Use estimation to verify that $748 is a reasonable cost for the trip.

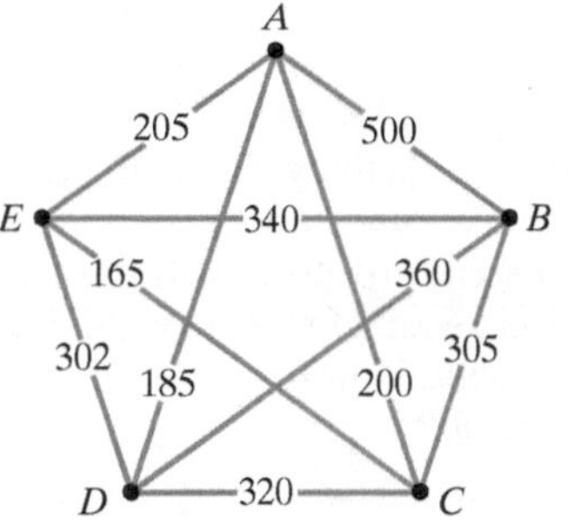

FIGURE 12

CHECK POINT 6 As in Example 6, a sales director who lives in city A is required to fly to regional offices in cities B, C, D, and E. The diagram in **Figure 12** shows the one-way airfares between any two cities. Give the sales director an order for visiting cities B, C, D, and E once, returning home to city A, for less than $1460.

Exercise Set 3

Everyone can become a better, more confident problem solver. As in learning any other skill, learning problem solving requires hard work and patience. Work as many problems as possible in this exercise set. You may feel confused once in a while, but do not be discouraged. Thinking about a particular problem and trying different methods can eventually lead to new insights. Be sure to check over each answer carefully!

Practice and Application Exercises

In Exercises 1–4, what necessary piece of information is missing that prevents solving the problem?

1. If a student saves $35 per week, how long will it take to save enough money to buy a computer?

2. If a steak sells for $8.15, what is the cost per pound?

3. If it takes you four minutes to read a page in a book, how many words can you read in one minute?

4. By paying $1500 cash and the balance in equal monthly payments, how many months would it take to pay for a car costing $12,495?

In Exercises 5–8, one more piece of information is given than is necessary for solving the problem. Identify this unnecessary piece of information. Then solve the problem.

5. A salesperson receives a weekly salary of $350. In addition, $15 is paid for every item sold in excess of 200 items. How much extra is received from the sale of 212 items?

6. You have $250 to spend and you need to purchase four new tires. If each tire weighs 21 pounds and costs $42 plus $2.50 tax, how much money will you have left after buying the tires?

7. A parking garage charges $2.50 for the first hour and $0.50 for each additional hour. If a customer gave the parking attendant $20.00 for parking from 10 A.M. to 3 P.M., how much did the garage charge?

8. An architect is designing a house. The scale on the plan is 1 inch = 6 feet. If the house is to have a length of 90 feet and a width of 30 feet, how long will the line representing the house's length be on the blueprint?

Use Polya's four-step method in problem solving to solve Exercises 9–40.

9. a. Which is the better value: a 15.3-ounce box of cereal for $3.37 or a 24-ounce box of cereal for $4.59?

b. The supermarket displays the unit price for the 15.3 ounce box in terms of cost per ounce, but displays the unit price for the 24-ounce box in terms of cost per pound. What are the unit prices, to the nearest cent, given by the supermarket?

c. Based on your work in parts (a) and (b), does the better value always have the lower displayed unit price? Explain your answer.

10. a. Which is the better value: a 12-ounce jar of honey for $2.25 or an 18-ounce jar of honey for $3.24?

b. The supermarket displays the unit price for the 12-ounce jar in terms of cost per ounce, but displays the unit price for the 18-ounce jar in terms of cost per quart. Assuming 32 ounces in a quart, what are the unit prices, to the nearest cent, given by the supermarket?

c. Based on your work in parts (a) and (b), does the better value always have the lower displayed unit price? Explain your answer.

11. One person earns $48,000 per year. Another earns $3750 per month. How much more does the first person earn in a year than the second?

12. At the beginning of a year, the odometer on a car read 25,124 miles. At the end of the year, it read 37,364 miles. If the car averaged 24 miles per gallon, how many gallons of gasoline did it use during the year?

13. A television sells for $750. Instead of paying the total amount at the time of the purchase, the same television can be bought by paying $100 down and $50 a month for 14 months. How much is saved by paying the total amount at the time of the purchase?

14. In a basketball game, the Bulldogs scored 34 field goals, each counting 2 points, and 13 foul goals, each counting 1 point. The Panthers scored 38 field goals and 8 foul goals. Which team won? By how many points did it win?

15. Calculators were purchased at $65 per dozen and sold at $20 for three calculators. Find the profit on six dozen calculators.

16. Pens are bought at 95¢ per dozen and sold in groups of four for $2.25. Find the profit on 15 dozen pens.

17. Each day a small business owner sells 200 pizza slices at $1.50 per slice and 85 sandwiches at $2.50 each. If business expenses come to $60 per day, what is the owner's profit for a ten-day period?

18. A college tutoring center pays math tutors $5.15 per hour. Tutors earn an additional $1.20 per hour for each hour over 40 hours per week. A math tutor worked 42 hours one week and 45 hours the second week. How much did the tutor earn in this two-week period?

19. A car rents for $220 per week plus $0.25 per mile. Find the rental cost for a two-week trip of 500 miles for a group of three people.

20. A college graduate receives a salary of $2750 a month for her first job. During the year she plans to spend $4800 for rent, $8200 for food, $3750 for clothing, $4250 for household expenses, and $3000 for other expenses. With the money that is left, she expects to buy as many shares of stock at $375 per share as possible. How many shares will she be able to buy?

21. Charlene decided to ride her bike from her home to visit her friend Danny. Three miles away from home, her bike got a flat tire and she had to walk the remaining two miles to Danny's home. She could not repair the tire and had to walk all the way back home. How many more miles did Charlene walk than she rode?

22. A store received 200 containers of juice to be sold by April 1. Each container cost the store $0.75 and sold for $1.25. The store signed a contract with the manufacturer in which the manufacturer agreed to a $0.50 refund for every container not sold by April 1. If 150 containers were sold by April 1, how much profit did the store make?

23. A storeowner ordered 25 calculators that cost $30 each. The storeowner can sell each calculator for $35. The storeowner sold 22 calculators to customers. He had to return 3 calculators and pay a $2 charge for each returned calculator. Find the storeowner's profit.

24. New York City and Washington, D.C. are about 240 miles apart. A car leaves New York City at noon traveling directly south toward Washington, D.C. at 55 miles per hour. At the same time and along the same route, a second car leaves Washington, D.C. bound for New York City traveling directly north at 45 miles per hour. How far has each car traveled when the drivers meet for lunch at 2:24 P.M.?

25. An automobile purchased for $23,000 is worth $2700 after 7 years. Assuming that the car's value depreciated steadily from year to year, what was it worth at the end of the third year?

26. An automobile purchased for $34,800 is worth $8550 after 7 years. Assuming that the car's value depreciated steadily from year to year, what was it worth at the end of the third year?

27. A vending machine accepts nickels, dimes, and quarters. Exact change is needed to make a purchase. How many ways can a person with five nickels, three dimes, and two quarters make a 45-cent purchase from the machine?

28. How many ways can you make change for a quarter using only pennies, nickels, and dimes?

29. The members of the Student Activity Council on your campus are meeting to select two speakers for a month-long event celebrating artists and entertainers. The choices are Johnny Depp, Jamie Foxx, Jon Stewart, and Hilary Swank. How many different ways can the two speakers be selected?

30. The members of the Student Activity Council on your campus are meeting to select two speakers for a month-long event exploring why some people are most likely to succeed. The choices are Bill Clinton, Sean Combs, Donald Trump, Oprah Winfrey, and Tiger Woods. How many different ways can the two speakers be selected?

31. If you spend $4.79, in how many ways can you receive change from a five-dollar bill?

32. If you spend $9.74, in how many ways can you receive change from a ten-dollar bill?

33. You throw three darts at the board shown. Each dart hits the board and scores a 1, 5, or 10. How many different total scores can you make?

34. Suppose that you throw four darts at the board shown. With these four darts, there are 16 ways to hit four different numbers whose sum is 100. Describe one way you can hit four different numbers on the board that total 100.

35. Five housemates (A, B, C, D, and E) agreed to share the expenses of a party equally. If A spent $42, B spent $10, C spent $26, D spent $32, and E spent $30, who owes money after the party and how much do they owe? To whom is money owed and how much should they receive? In order to resolve these discrepancies, who should pay how much to whom?

36. Six houses are spaced equally around a circular road. If it takes 10 minutes to walk from the first house to the third house, how long would it take to walk all the way around the road?

37. If a test has four true/false questions, in how many ways can there be three answers that are false and one answer that is true?

38. There are five people in a room. Each person shakes the hand of every other person exactly once. How many handshakes are exchanged?

39. Five runners, Andy, Beth, Caleb, Darnell, and Ella, are in a one-mile race. Andy finished the race seven seconds before Caleb. Caleb finished the race two seconds before Beth. Beth finished the race six seconds after Darnell. Ella finished the race eight seconds after Darnell. In which order did the runners finish the race?

40. Eight teams are competing in a volleyball tournament. Any team that loses a game is eliminated from the tournament. How many games must be played to determine the tournament winner?

In Exercises 41–42, you have three errands to run around town, although in no particular order. You plan to start and end at home. You must go to the bank, the post office, and the dry cleaners. Distances, in miles, between any two of these locations are given in the diagram.

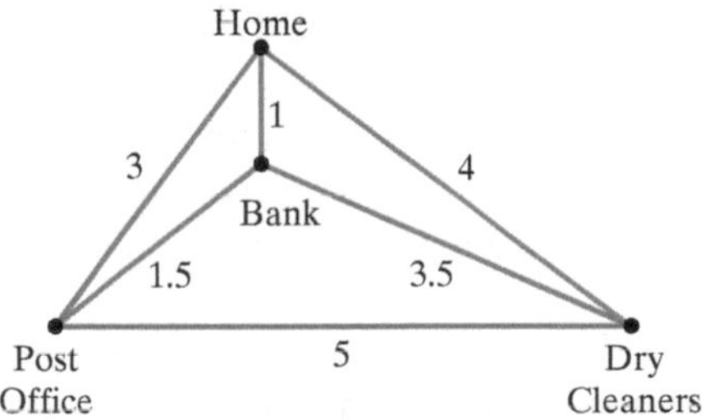

41. Determine a route whose distance is less than 12 miles for running the errands and returning home.

42. Determine a route whose distance exceeds 12 miles for running the errands and returning home.

43. The map shows five western states. Trace a route on the map that crosses each common state border exactly once.

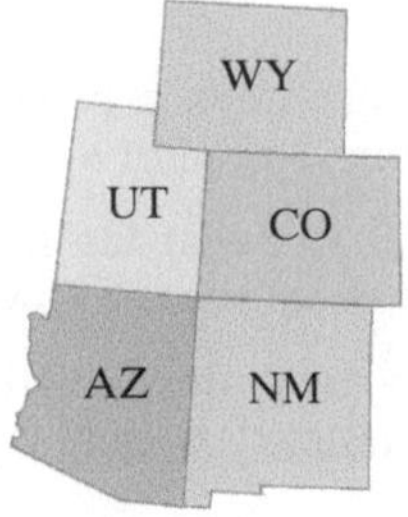

44. The layout of a city with land masses and bridges is shown. Trace a route that shows people how to walk through the city so as to cross each bridge exactly once.

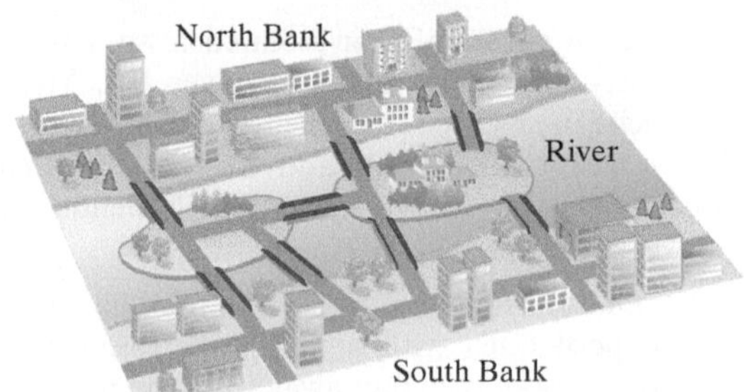

45. Jose, Bob, and Tony are college students living in adjacent dorm rooms. Bob lives in the middle dorm room. Their majors are business, psychology, and biology, although not necessarily in that order. The business major frequently uses the new computer in Bob's dorm room when Bob is in class. The psychology major and Jose both have 8 A.M. classes, and the psychology major knocks on Jose's wall to make sure he is awake. Determine Bob's major.

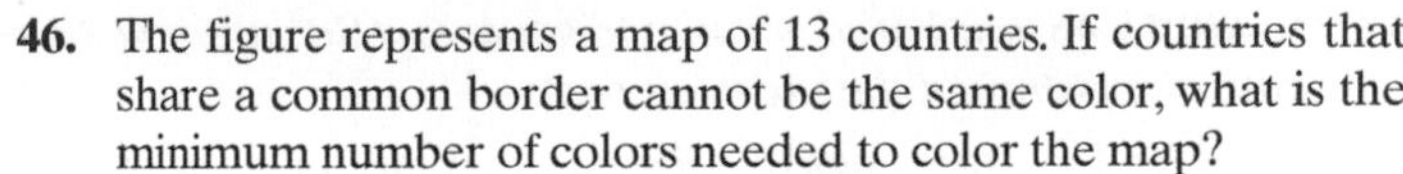

46. The figure represents a map of 13 countries. If countries that share a common border cannot be the same color, what is the minimum number of colors needed to color the map?

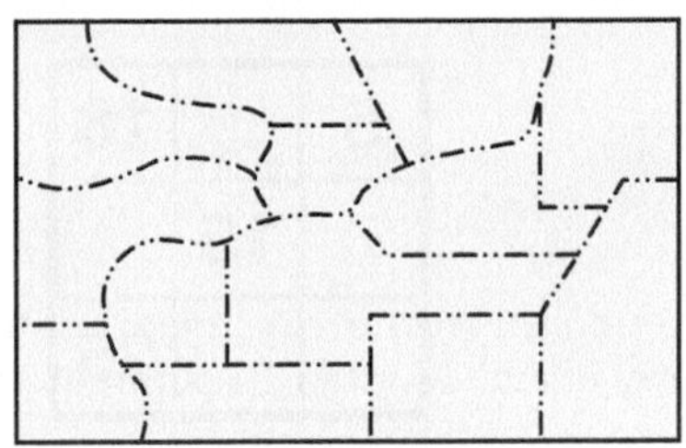

The sudoku (pronounced: sue-DOE-koo) craze, a number puzzle popular in Japan, hit the United States in 2005. A sudoku ("single number") puzzle consists of a 9-by-9 grid of 81 boxes subdivided into nine 3-by-3 squares. Some of the square boxes contain numbers. Here is an example:

2						6	7	
4	5							1
	9		7					
			3					
		4				2	8	
	1			2	4			
	8	3	9		7			
6	2			5		4	1	
							9	

The objective is to fill in the remaining squares so that every row, every column, and every 3-by-3 square contains each of the digits from 1 through 9 exactly once. (You can work this puzzle in Exercise 66, perhaps consulting one of the dozens of sudoku books in which the numerals 1 through 9 have created a cottage industry for publishers. There's even a Sudoku for Dummies.*)*

Trying to slot numbers into small checkerboard grids is not unique to sudoku. In Exercises 47–50, we explore some of the intricate patterns in other arrays of numbers, including magic squares. A ***magic square*** *is a square array of numbers arranged so that the numbers in all rows, all columns, and the two diagonals have the same sum. Here is an example of a magic square in which the sum of the numbers in each row, each column, and each diagonal is 15:*

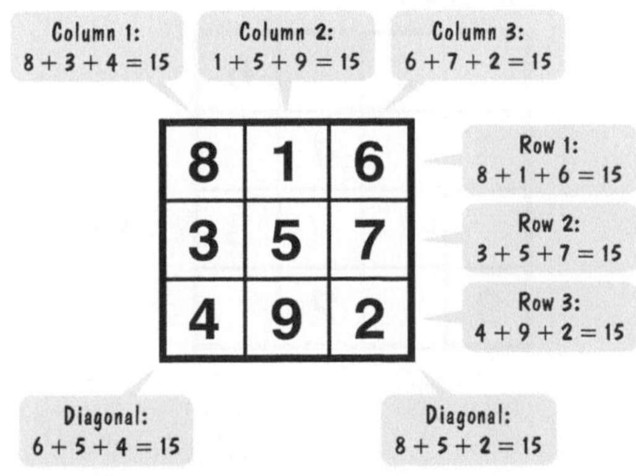

Exercises 47–48 are based on magic squares. (Be sure you have read the discussion on the previous page.)

47. a. Use the properties of a magic square to fill in the missing numbers.

5		18
	15	
		25

b. Show that the number of letters in the word for each number in the square in part (a) generates another magic square.

48. a. Use the properties of a magic square to fill in the missing numbers.

96		37	45
	43		
		25	57
23		82	78

b. Show that if you reverse the digits for each number in the square in part (a), another magic square is generated.

(*Source* for the *alphamagic square* in Exercise 47 and the *mirrormagic square* in Exercise 48: Clifford A. Pickover, *A Passion for Mathematics*, John Wiley & Sons, Inc., 2005)

49. As in sudoku, fill in the missing numbers in the 3-by-3 square so that it contains each of the digits from 1 through 9 exactly once. Furthermore, in this *antimagic square*, the rows, the columns, and the two diagonals must have *different sums*.

9		7
	1	
3		5

50. The missing numbers in the 4-by-4 array are one-digit numbers. The sums for each row, each column, and one diagonal are listed in the voice balloons outside the array. Find the missing numbers.

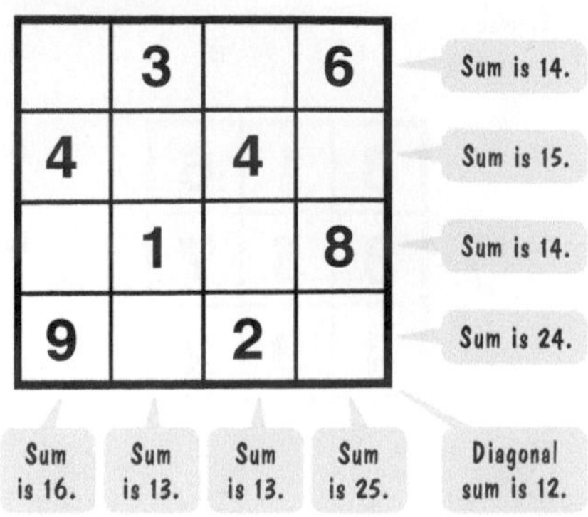

51. Some numbers in the printing of a division problem have become illegible. They are designated below by *. Fill in the blanks.

```
      1**
  **)4***
     28
     *56
     ***
      ***
      ***
        0
```

Writing in Mathematics

In Exercises 52–54, explain the plan needed to solve the problem.

52. If you know how much was paid for several pounds of steak, find the cost of one pound.

53. If you know a person's age, find the year in which that person was born.

54. If you know how much you earn each hour, find your yearly income.

55. Write your own problem that can be solved using the four-step procedure. Then use the four steps to solve the problem.

Critical Thinking Exercises

Make Sense? *In Exercises 56–59, determine whether each statement makes sense or does not make sense, and explain your reasoning.*

56. Polya's four steps in problem solving make it possible for me to solve any mathematical problem easily and quickly.

57. I used Polya's four steps in problem solving to deal with a personal problem in need of a creative solution.

58. I find it helpful to begin the problem-solving process by restating the problem in my own words.

59. When I get bogged down with a problem, there's no limit to the amount of time I should spend trying to solve it.

60. Gym lockers are to be numbered from 1 through 99 using metal numbers to be nailed onto each locker. How many 7s are needed?

61. You are on vacation in an isolated town. Everyone in the town was born there and has never left. You develop a toothache and check out the two dentists in town. One dentist has gorgeous teeth and one has teeth that show the effects of poor dental work. Which dentist should you choose and why?

62. India Jones is standing on a large rock in the middle of a square pool filled with hungry, man-eating piranhas. The edge of the pool is 20 feet away from the rock. India's mom wants to rescue her son, but she is standing on the edge of the pool with only two planks, each $19\frac{1}{2}$ feet long. How can India be rescued using the two planks?

63. One person tells the truth on Monday, Tuesday, Wednesday, and Thursday, but lies on all other days. A second person lies on Tuesday, Wednesday, and Thursday, but tells the truth on all other days. If both people state "I lied yesterday," then what day of the week is it today?

64. (This logic problem dates back to the eighth century.) A farmer needs to take his goat, wolf, and cabbage across a stream. His boat can hold him and one other passenger (the goat, wolf, or cabbage). If he takes the wolf with him, the goat will eat the cabbage. If he takes the cabbage, the wolf will eat the goat. Only when the farmer is present are the cabbage and goat safe from their respective predators. How does the farmer get everything across the stream?

65. As in sudoku, fill in the missing numbers along the sides of the triangle so that it contains each of the digits from 1 through 9 exactly once. Furthermore, each side of the triangle should contain four digits whose sum is 17.

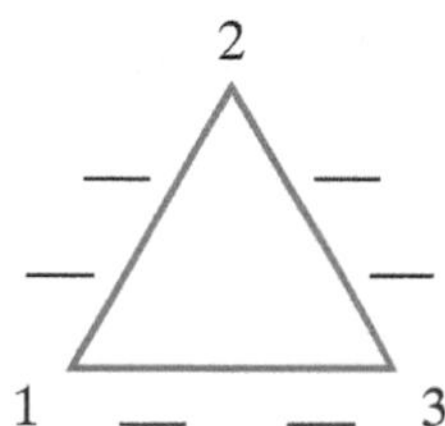

66. Solve the sudoku puzzle in the middle of the right column on page 35.

67. A version of this problem, called the *missing dollar problem*, first appeared in 1933. Three people eat at a restaurant and receive a total bill for $30. They divide the amount equally and pay $10 each. The waiter gives the bill and the $30 to the manager, who realizes there is an error: The correct charge should be only $25. The manager gives the waiter five $1 bills to return to the customers, with the restaurant's apologies. However, the waiter is dishonest, keeping $2 and giving back only $3 to the customers. In conclusion, each of the three customers has paid $9 and the waiter has stolen $2, giving a total of $29. However, the original bill was $30. Where has the missing dollar gone?

68. A firefighter spraying water on a fire stood on the middle rung of a ladder. When the smoke became less thick, the firefighter moved up 4 rungs. However it got too hot, so the firefighter backed down 6 rungs. Later, the firefighter went up 7 rungs and stayed until the fire was out. Then, the firefighter climbed the remaining 4 rungs and entered the building. How many rungs does the ladder have?

69. The Republic of Margaritaville is composed of four states: A, B, C, and D. According to the country's constitution, the congress will have 30 seats, divided among the four states according to their respective populations. The table shows each state's population.

POPULATION OF MARGARITAVILLE BY STATE

State	A	B	C	D	Total
Population (in thousands)	275	383	465	767	1890

Allocate the 30 congressional seats among the four states in a fair manner.

Group Exercises

Exercises 70–74 describe problems that have many plans for finding an answer. Group members should describe how the four steps in problem solving can be applied to find a solution. It is not necessary to actually solve each problem. Your professor will let the group know if the four steps should be described verbally by a group spokesperson or in essay form.

70. How much will it cost to install bicycle racks on campus to encourage students to use bikes, rather than cars, to get to campus?

71. How many new counselors are needed on campus to prevent students from waiting in long lines for academic advising?

72. By how much would taxes in your state have to be increased to cut tuition at community colleges and state universities in half?

73. Is your local electric company overcharging its customers?

74. Should solar heating be required for all new construction in your community?

75. Group members should describe a problem in need of a solution. Then, as in Exercises 70–74, describe how the four steps in problem solving can be applied to find a solution.

Chapter Summary, Review, and Test

Summary – Definitions and Concepts

	Examples
1 Inductive and Deductive Reasoning	
a. Inductive reasoning is the process of arriving at a general conclusion based on observations of specific examples. The conclusion is called a conjecture or a hypothesis. A case for which a conjecture is false is called a counterexample.	Ex. 1 Ex. 2 Ex. 3 Ex. 4
b. Deductive reasoning is the process of proving a specific conclusion from one or more general statements. The statement that is proved is called a theorem.	Ex. 5

2 Estimation, Graphs, and Mathematical Models

a. The procedure for rounding whole numbers is given in the box on page 14. The symbol ≈ means *is approximately equal to.*	Ex. 1
b. Decimal parts of numbers are rounded in nearly the same way as whole numbers. However, digits to the right of the rounding place are dropped.	Ex. 2
c. Estimation is the process of arriving at an approximate answer to a question. Computations can be estimated by using rounding that results in simplified arithmetic.	Ex. 3 Ex. 4
d. Estimation is useful when interpreting information given by circle, bar, or line graphs.	Ex. 5 Ex. 6 Ex. 7
e. The process of finding formulas to describe real-world phenomena is called mathematical modeling. Such formulas, together with the meaning assigned to the variables, are called mathematical models.	Ex. 8

3 Problem Solving

1. Understand the problem.	Ex. 1
2. Devise a plan.	Ex. 2
3. Carry out the plan and solve the problem.	Ex. 3
4. Look back and check the answer.	Ex. 4
	Ex. 5
	Ex. 6

Review Exercises

1

1. Which reasoning process is shown in the following example? Explain your answer.

All books by Stephen King have made the best-seller list. *Carrie* is a novel by Stephen King. Therefore, *Carrie* was on the best-seller list.

2. Which reasoning process is shown in the following example? Explain your answer.

All books by Stephen King have made the best-seller list. Therefore, it is highly probable that the novel King is currently working on will make the best-seller list.

In Exercises 3–10, identify a pattern in each list of numbers. Then use this pattern to find the next number.

3. 4, 9, 14, 19,

4. 7, 14, 28, 56,

5. 1, 3, 6, 10, 15,

6. $\frac{3}{4}, \frac{3}{5}, \frac{1}{2}, \frac{3}{7},$

7. 40, −20, 10, −5,

8. 40, −20, −80, −140,

9. 2, 2, 4, 6, 10, 16, 26,

10. 2, 6, 12, 36, 72, 216,

11. Identify a pattern in the following sequence of figures. Then use the pattern to find the next figure in the sequence.

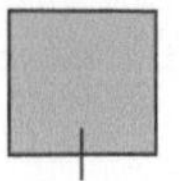, 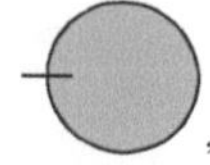, 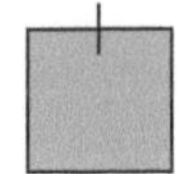, 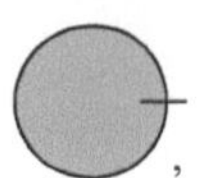, ______

In Exercises 12–13, use inductive reasoning to predict the next line in each sequence of computations. Then perform the arithmetic to determine whether your conjecture is correct.

12.
$$2 = 4 - 2$$
$$2 + 4 = 8 - 2$$
$$2 + 4 + 8 = 16 - 2$$
$$2 + 4 + 8 + 16 = 32 - 2$$

13.
$$111 \div 3 = 37$$
$$222 \div 6 = 37$$
$$333 \div 9 = 37$$

14. Consider the following procedure:

Select a number. Double the number. Add 4 to the product. Divide the sum by 2. Subtract 2 from the quotient.

- **a.** Repeat the procedure for four numbers of your choice. Write a conjecture that relates the result of the process to the original number selected.
- **b.** Represent the original number by the variable n and use deductive reasoning to prove the conjecture in part (a).

2

15. In 2006, there were 4,265,996 live births in the United States. (*Source*: National Center for Health Statistics)

Round the number of live births to the nearest

- **a.** hundred.
- **b.** thousand.
- **c.** hundred thousand.
- **d.** million.

16. A magnified view of the boundary of this black "buglike" shape, called the Mandelbrot set, was illustrated in the Section 1 opener on page 2.

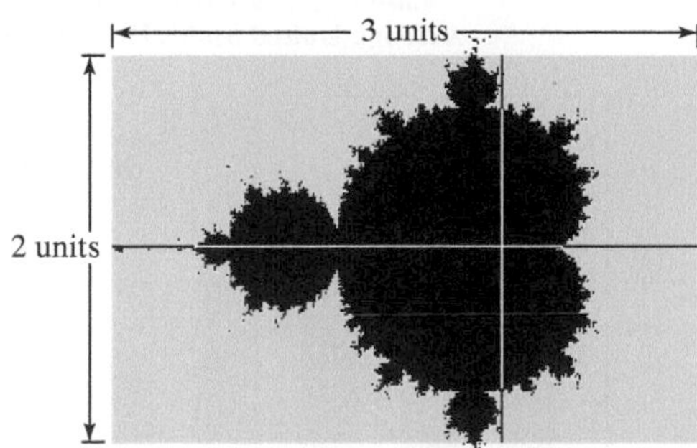

The area of the yellow rectangular region is the product of its length, 3 units, and its width, 2 units, or 6 square units. It is conjectured that the area of the black buglike region representing the Mandelbrot set is

$$\sqrt{6\pi - 1} - e \approx 1.5065916514855 \text{ square units.}$$

(*Source*: Robert P. Munafo, *Mandelbrot Set Glossary and Encyclopedia*)

Round the area of the Mandelbrot set to

a. the nearest tenth.

b. the nearest hundredth.

c. the nearest thousandth.

d. seven decimal places.

In Exercises 17–20, obtain an estimate for each computation by rounding the numbers so that the resulting arithmetic can easily be performed by hand or in your head. Then use a calculator to perform the computation. How reasonable is your estimate when compared to the actual answer?

17. $1.57 + 4.36 + 9.78$

18. 8.83×49

19. $19.894 \div 4.179$

20. 62.3% of 3847.6

In Exercises 21–24, determine each estimate without using a calculator. Then use a calculator to perform the computation necessary to obtain an exact answer. How reasonable is your estimate when compared to the actual answer?

21. Estimate the total cost of six grocery items if their prices are \$8.47, \$0.89, \$2.79, \$0.14, \$1.19, and \$4.76.

22. Estimate the salary of a worker who works for 78 hours at \$6.85 per hour.

23. At a yard sale, a person bought 21 books at \$0.85 each, two chairs for \$11.95 each, and a ceramic plate for \$14.65. Estimate the total amount spent.

24. The circle graph shows the most important issues for college students in 2008.

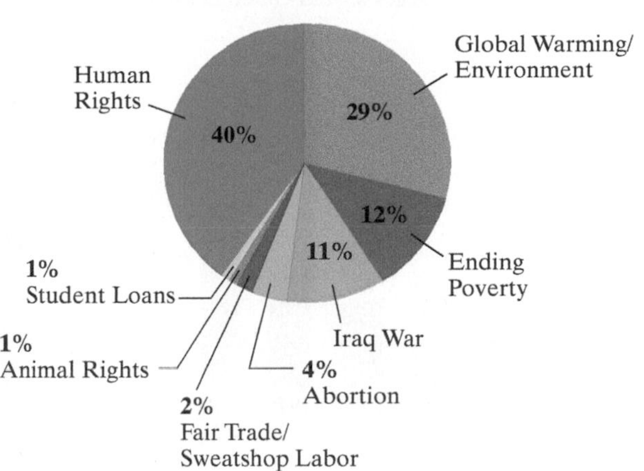

Source: Mother Jones, September/October 2008

Assume the circle graph is representative of college students who received bachelor's degrees in 2008. Among the 1,585,326 college students who received bachelor's degrees in 2008, estimate the number for whom the most important issue was global warming.

25. A small private school employs ten teachers with salaries ranging from \$817 to \$992 per week. Which of the following is the best estimate of the monthly payroll for the teachers?

a. \$30,000 **b.** \$36,000

c. \$42,000 **d.** \$50,000

26. Select the best estimate for the number of seconds in a day.

a. 1500 **b.** 15,000

c. 86,000 **d.** 100,000

27. Imagine the entire global population as a village of precisely 200 people. The bar graph shows some numeric observations based on this scenario.

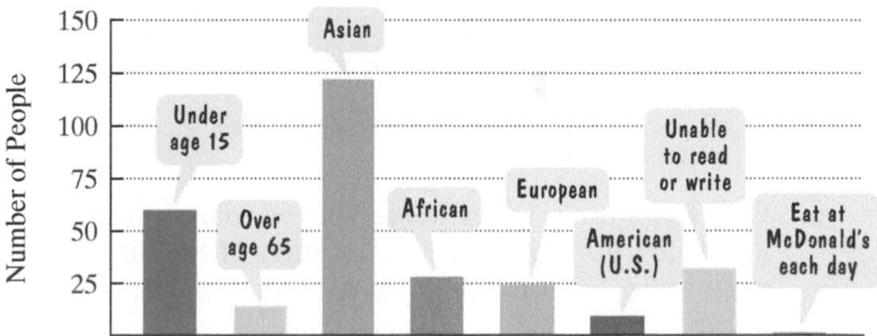

Source: Gary Rimmer, *Number Freaking*, The Disinformation Company Ltd.

a. Which group in the village has a population that exceeds 100? Estimate this group's population.

b. World population is approximately 33 million times the population of the village of 200 people. Use this observation to estimate the number of people in the world, in millions, unable to read or write.

28. The bar graph shows the percentage of people 25 years of age and older who were college graduates in the United States for seven selected years.

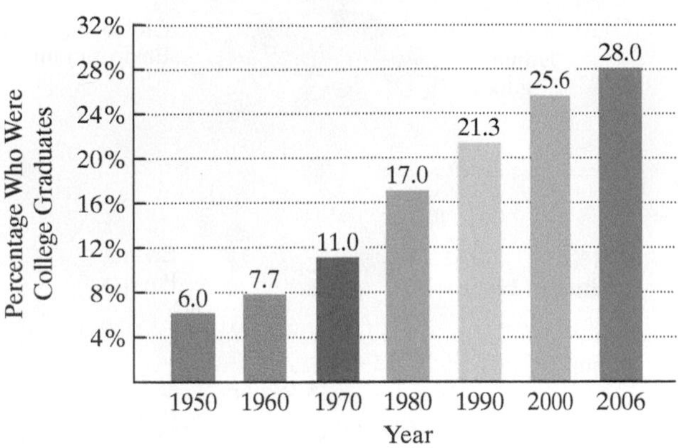

Source: U.S. Census Bureau

a. Estimate the average yearly increase in the percentage of college graduates. Round to the nearest tenth of a percent.

b. If the trend shown by the graph continues, estimate the percentage of people 25 years of age and older who will be college graduates in 2020.

29. During a diagnostic evaluation, a 33-year-old woman experienced a panic attack a few minutes after she had been asked to relax her whole body. The graph shows the rapid increase in heart rate during the panic attack.

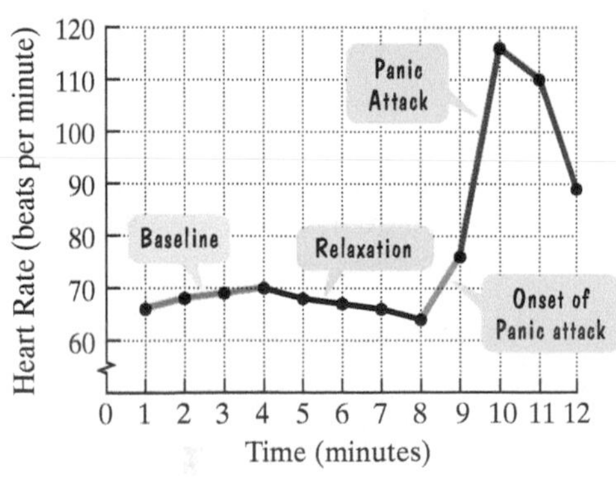

Source: Davis and Palladino, *Psychology*, Fifth Edition, Prentice Hall, 2007.

a. Use the graph to estimate the woman's maximum heart rate during the first 12 minutes of the diagnostic evaluation. After how many minutes did this occur?

b. Use the graph to estimate the woman's minimum heart rate during the first 12 minutes of the diagnostic evaluation. After how many minutes did this occur?

c. During which time period did the woman's heart rate increase at the greatest rate?

d. After how many minutes was the woman's heart rate approximately 75 beats per minute?

30. The number of TV channels is increasing. The bar graph shows the total channels available in the average U.S. household from 2000 through 2006.

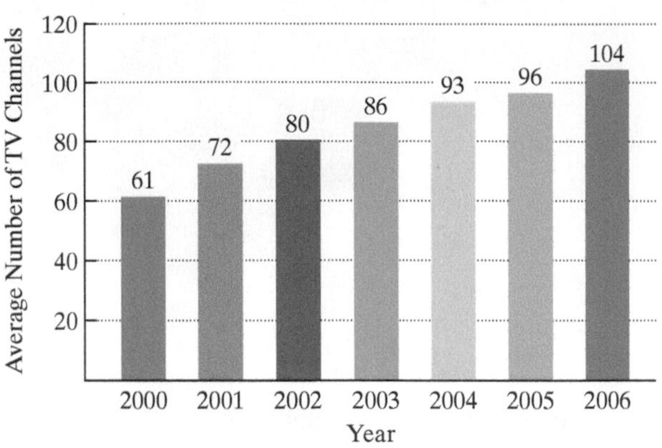

Source: Nielsen Media Research

a. Estimate the yearly increase in the number of TV channels. Round to the nearest whole number.

b. Write a mathematical model that estimates the number of TV channels in the average U.S. household, T, x years after 2000.

c. Use your mathematical model from part (b) to project the number of TV channels in the average U.S. household in 2014.

3

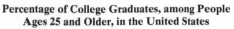

31. What necessary piece of information is missing that prevents solving the following problem?

If 3 milligrams of a medicine is given for every 20 pounds of body weight, how many milligrams should be given to a six-year-old child?

32. In the following problem, there is one more piece of information given than is necessary for solving the problem. Identify this unnecessary piece of information. Then solve the problem.

A taxicab charges $3.00 for the first mile and 50 cents for each additional half-mile. After a six-mile trip, a customer handed the taxi driver a $20 bill. Find the cost of the trip.

Use the four-step method in problem solving to solve Exercises 33–38.

33. If there are seven frankfurters in one pound, how many pounds would you buy for a picnic to supply 28 people with two frankfurters each?

34. A car rents for $175 per week plus $0.30 per mile. Find the rental cost for a three-week trip of 1200 miles.

35. You are choosing between two plans at a discount warehouse. Plan A offers an annual membership fee of $100 and you pay 80% of the manufacturer's recommended list price. Plan B offers an annual membership fee of $40 and you pay 90% of the manufacturer's recommended list price.

If you anticipate purchasing $1500 of merchandise in a year, which plan offers the better deal? By how much?

36. Miami is on Eastern Standard Time and San Francisco is on Pacific Standard Time, three hours earlier than Eastern Standard Time. A flight leaves Miami at 10 A.M. Eastern Standard Time, stops for 45 minutes in Houston, Texas, and arrives in San Francisco at 1:30 P.M. Pacific time. What is the actual flying time from Miami to San Francisco?

37. An automobile purchased for $37,000 is worth $2600 after eight years. Assuming that the value decreased steadily each year, what was the car worth at the end of the fifth year?

38. Suppose you are an engineer programming the automatic gate for a 35-cent toll. The gate is programmed for exact change only and will not accept pennies. How many coin combinations must you program the gate to accept?

Chapter Test

CHAPTER Test Prep VIDEOS

Step-by-step test solutions are found on the Chapter Test Prep Videos available on YouTube (search "Blitzer, Thinking Mathematically" and click on "Channels").

1. Which reasoning process is shown in the following example?

The course policy states that if you turn in at least 80% of the homework, your lowest exam grade will be dropped. I turned in 90% of the homework, so my lowest grade will be dropped.

2. Which reasoning process is shown in the following example?

We examine the fingerprints of 1000 people. No two individuals in this group of people have identical fingerprints. We conclude that for all people, no two people have identical fingerprints.

In Exercises 3–6, find the next number, computation, or figure, as appropriate.

3. 0, 5, 10, 15,

4. $\frac{1}{6}, \frac{1}{12}, \frac{1}{24}, \frac{1}{48},$

5.
$3367 \times 3 = 10{,}101$
$3367 \times 6 = 20{,}202$
$3367 \times 9 = 30{,}303$
$3367 \times 12 = 40{,}404$

6. 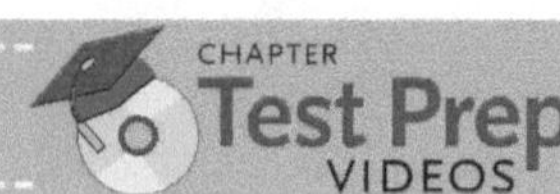 ______

7. Consider the following procedure:

Select a number. Multiply the number by 4. Add 8 to the product. Divide the sum by 2. Subtract 4 from the quotient.

a. Repeat this procedure for three numbers of your choice. Write a conjecture that relates the result of the process to the original number selected.

b. Represent the original number by the variable n and use deductive reasoning to prove the conjecture in part (a).

8. Round 3,279,425 to the nearest hundred thousand.

9. Round 706.3849 to the nearest hundredth.

In Exercises 10–13, determine each estimate without using a calculator. Different rounding results in different estimates, so there is not one single correct answer to each exercise. Use rounding to make the resulting calculations simple.

10. For a spring break vacation, a student needs to spend $47.00 for gas, $311.00 for food, and $405.00 for a hotel room. If the student takes $681.79 from savings, estimate how much more money is needed for the vacation.

11. The cost for opening a restaurant is $485,000. If 19 people decide to share equally in the business, estimate the amount each must contribute.

12. Find an estimate of 0.48992×121.976.

13. The graph shows the composition of a typical American community's trash.

Types of Trash in an American Community by Percentage of Total Weight

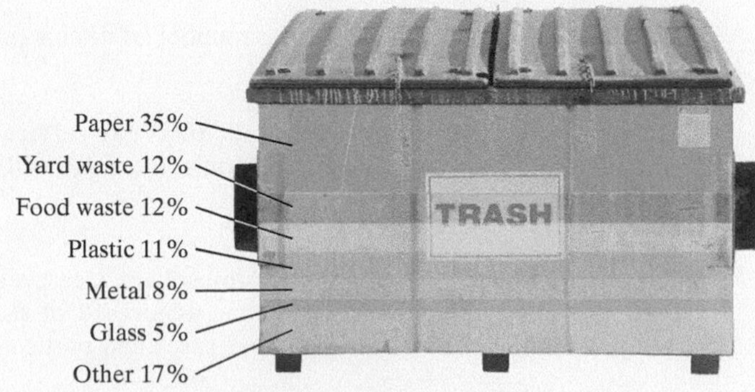

Source: U.S. Environmental Protection Agency

Across the United States, people generate approximately 512 billion pounds of trash per year. Estimate the number of pounds of trash in the form of plastic.

14. If the odometer of a car reads 71,911.5 miles and it averaged 28.9 miles per gallon, select the best estimate for the number of gallons of gasoline used.

a. 2400 **b.** 3200 **c.** 4000
d. 4800 **e.** 5600

15. The stated intent of the 1994 "don't ask, don't tell" policy was to reduce the number of discharges of gay men and lesbians from the military. The line graph shows the number of active-duty gay servicemembers discharged from the military for homosexuality under the policy.

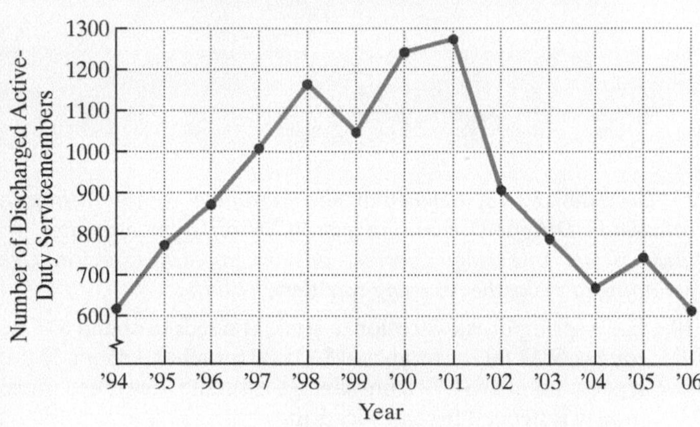

Source: General Accountability Office

a. For the period shown, in which year did the number of discharges reach a maximum? Find a reasonable estimate of the number of discharges for that year.

b. For the period shown, in which year did the number of discharges reach a minimum? Find a reasonable estimate of the number of discharges for that year.

c. In which one-year period did the number of discharges decrease at the greatest rate?

d. In which year were approximately 1000 gay servicemembers discharged under the "don't ask, don't tell" policy?

16. The amount of carbon dioxide in the atmosphere, measured in parts per million, has been increasing as a result of the burning of oil and coal. The buildup of gases and particles traps heat and raises the planet's temperature. The bar graph shows the average atmospheric concentration of carbon dioxide for seven selected years.

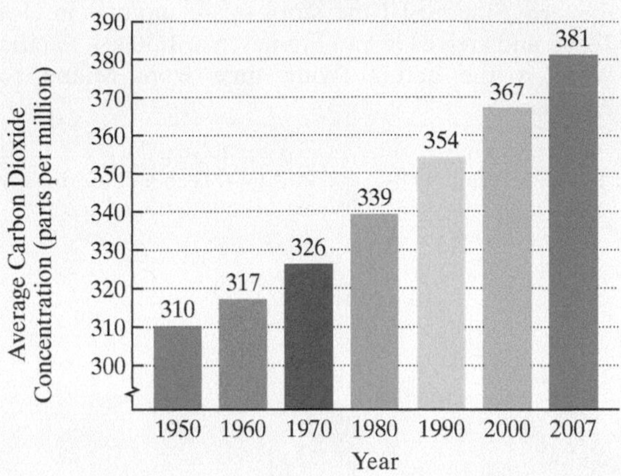

Source: National Oceanic and Atmospheric Administration

a. Estimate the yearly increase in the average atmospheric concentration of carbon dioxide. Express the answer in parts per million, rounded to the nearest hundredth.

b. Write a mathematical model that estimates the average atmospheric concentration of carbon dioxide, C, in parts per million, x years after 1950.

c. If the trend shown by the data continues, use your mathematical model from part (b) to project the average atmospheric concentration of carbon dioxide in 2050.

17. The cost of renting a boat from Estes Rental is \$9 per 15 minutes. The cost from Ship and Shore Rental is \$20 per half-hour. If you plan to rent the boat for three hours, which business offers the better deal and by how much?

18. A bus operates between Miami International Airport and Miami Beach, 10 miles away. It makes 20 round trips per day carrying 32 passengers per trip. If the fare each way is \$11.00, how much money is taken in from one day's operation?

19. By paying \$50 cash up front and the balance at \$35 a week, how long will it take to pay for a computer costing \$960?

20. In 2000, the population of Greece was 10,600,000, with projections of a population decrease of 28,000 people per year. In the same year, the population of Belgium was 10,200,000, with projections of a population decrease of 12,000 people per year.

(*Source:* United Nations)

According to these projections, which country will have the greater population in 2035 and by how many more people?

Answers to Selected Exercises

Section 1

Check Point Exercises

1. Answers will vary; an example is $40 \times 40 = 1600$. **2. a.** Each number in the list is obtained by adding 6 to the previous number.; 33 **b.** Each number in the list is obtained by multiplying the previous number by 5.; 1250 **c.** To get the second number, multiply the previous number by 2. Then multiply by 3 and then by 4. Then multiply by 2, then by 3, and then by 4, repeatedly.; 3456 **d.** To get the second number, add 8 to the previous number. Then add 8 and then subtract 14. Then add 8, then add 8, and then subtract 14, repeatedly.; 7 **3. a.** Starting with the third number, each number is the sum of the previous two numbers.; 76 **b.** Starting with the second number, each number is one less than twice the previous number.; 257

4. The figures alternate between rectangles and triangles, and the number of appendages follows the pattern: one, two, three, one, two, three, etc.;

5. a. The result of the process is two times the original number selected.
b. Using n to represent the original number, we have

Select a number:	n
Multiply the number by 4:	$4n$
Add 6 to the product:	$4n + 6$
Divide this sum by 2:	$\frac{4n+6}{2} = 2n + 3$
Subtract 3 from the quotient:	$2n + 3 - 3 = 2n$.

Exercise Set 1

1. Answers will vary; an example is: Barack Obama was younger than 65 at the time of his inauguration. **3.** Answers will vary; an example is: 3 multiplied by itself is 9, which is not even.

5. Answers will vary; an example is: Adding 1 to the numerator and denominator of $\frac{1}{2}$ results in $\frac{2}{3}$, which is not equal to $\frac{1}{2}$.

7. Answers will vary; an example is: When -1 is added to itself, the result is -2, which is less than -1. **9.** Each number in the list is obtained by adding 4 to the previous number.; 28 **11.** Each number in the list is obtained by subtracting 5 from the previous number.; 12 **13.** Each number in the list is obtained by multiplying the previous number by 3.; 729 **15.** Each number in the list is obtained by multiplying the previous number by 2.; 32 **17.** The numbers in the list alternate between 1 and numbers obtained by multiplying the number prior to the previous number by 2.; 32 **19.** Each number in the list is obtained by subtracting 2 from the previous number.; -6

21. Each number in the list is obtained by adding 4 to the denominator of the previous fraction.; $\frac{1}{22}$

23. Each number in the list is obtained by multiplying the previous number by $\frac{1}{3}$.; $\frac{1}{81}$

25. The second number is obtained by adding 4 to the first number. The third number is obtained by adding 5 to the second number. The number being added to the previous number increases by 1 each time.; 42 **27.** The second number is obtained by adding 3 to the first number. The third number is obtained by adding 5 to the second number. The number being added to the previous number increases by 2 each time.; 51 **29.** Starting with the third number, each number is the sum of the previous two numbers.; 71 **31.** To get the second number, add 5 to the previous number. Then add 5 and then subtract 7. Then add 5, then add 5, and then subtract 7, repeatedly.; 18 **33.** The second number is obtained by multiplying the first number by 2. The third number is obtained by subtracting 1 from the second number. Then multiply by 2 and then subtract 1, repeatedly.; 33

35. Each number in the list is obtained by multiplying the previous number by $-\frac{1}{4}$.; $\frac{1}{4}$

37. For each pair in the list, the second number is obtained by subtracting 4 from the first number.; -1

39. The pattern is: square, triangle, circle, square, triangle, circle, etc.;

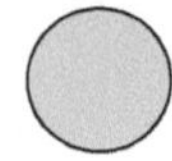

41. Each figure contains the letter of the alphabet following the letter in the previous figure with one more occurrence than in the previous figure.;

d	d	d
d	d	

43. a. The result of the process is two times the original number selected.
b. Using n to represent the original number, we have

Select a number:	n
Multiply the number by 4:	$4n$
Add 8 to the product:	$4n + 8$
Divide this sum by 2:	$\frac{4n+8}{2} = 2n + 4$
Subtract 4 from the quotient:	$2n + 4 - 4 = 2n$.

45. a. The result of the process is 3.
b. Using n to represent the original number as we have

Select a number:	n
Add 5:	$n + 5$
Double the result:	$2(n + 5) = 2n + 10$
Subtract 4:	$2n + 10 - 4 = 2n + 6$
Divide by 2:	$\frac{2n+6}{2} = n + 3$
Subtract n:	$n + 3 - n = 3$.

47. $1 + 2 + 3 + 4 + 5 + 6 = \frac{6 \times 7}{2}$; $21 = 21$ **49.** $1 + 3 + 5 + 7 + 9 + 11 = 6 \times 6$; $36 = 36$ **51.** $98{,}765 \times 9 + 3 = 888{,}888$; correct **53.** $165 \times 3367 = 555{,}555$; correct **55.** b **57.** deductive reasoning; Answers will vary. **59.** inductive reasoning; Answers will vary. **61. a.** 28, 36, 45, 55, 66 **b.** 36, 49, 64, 81, 100 **c.** 35, 51, 70, 92, 117 **d.** square **67.** makes sense **69.** makes sense

71. a.

16	3	11
5	10	15
9	17	4

The sums are all 30. **b.**

17	5	14
9	12	15
10	19	7

The sums are all 36. **c.** For any values of a, b, and c, the sums of all rows, all columns, and both diagonals are the same. **d.** The sums of the expressions in each row, each column, and each diagonal is $3a$. **e.** Add the variable expressions in a, b, and c, in each row, each column, and each diagonal. The sum is always $3a$.
73. a. The result is a three-or four-digit number in which the thousands and hundreds places represent the month of the birthday and the tens and ones places represent the day of the birthday. **b.** $5[4(5M + 6) + 9] + D - 165 = 100M + D$ **75. a.** 10,101; 20,202; 30,303; 40,404 **b.** In the multiplications, the first factor is always 3367, and the second factors are consecutive multiples of 3, beginning with $3 \times 1 = 3$.; The second and fourth digits of the products are always 0; the first, third, and last digits are the same within each product; this digit is 1 in the first product and increases by 1 in each subsequent product. **c.** $3367 \times 15 = 50{,}505$; $3367 \times 18 = 60{,}606$ **d.** inductive reasoning; Answers will vary.

Section 2

Check Point Exercises

1. a. 7,000,000,000 **b.** 6,800,000,000 **c.** 6,751,590,000 **2. a.** 3.1 **b.** 3.1416 **3. a.** \$2, \$1, \$5, \$4, \$1, \$2, and \$3; ≈ \$18 **b.** no **4. a.** ≈ \$2000 per wk **b.** ≈ \$100,000 per yr **5. a.** $0.32 \times 21{,}728{,}978$ **b.** $0.3 \times 22{,}000{,}000 = 6{,}600{,}000$; Approximately 6,600,000 Americans between the ages of 15 and 19, inclusive, define old age by a decline in mental functioning. **6. a.** ≈ 0.16 yr for each subsequent birth year **b.** ≈ 87.5 yr **7. a.** 66% **b.** 2000 through 2005 **c.** 1990 **8. a.** \$1024 **b.** $T = 15{,}518 + 1024x$ **c.** \$27,806

Exercise Set 2

1. a. 55,444,600 **b.** 55,445,000 **c.** 55,440,000 **d.** 55,400,000 **e.** 55,000,000 **f.** 60,000,000 **3.** 2.718 **5.** 2.71828 **7.** 2.718281828 **9.** $350 + 600 = 950$; 955; reasonably well **11.** $9 + 1 + 19 = 29$; 29.23; quite well **13.** $32 - 11 = 21$; 20.911; quite well **15.** $40 \times 6 = 240$; 218.185; not so well **17.** $0.8 \times 400 = 320$; 327.06; reasonably well **19.** $48 \div 3 = 16$; ≈ 16.49; quite well **21.** 30% of 200,000 is 60,000.; 59,920.96; quite well **23.** ≈ \$43 **25.** ≈ \$40,000 per yr **27.** ≈ \$24,000 **29.** ≈ \$1000 **31.** ≈ \$30 per hr **33.** ≈ 700,800 hr **35.** ≈ 40; ≈ 42.03; quite reasonable **37.** b **39.** c **41.** ≈ 3 hr **43.** ≈ 100,000,000 American adults **45. a.** ≈ 85 people per 100 **b.** ≈ 5400 people **47. a.** ≈ 0.9% per yr **b.** 60.1% **49. a.** 2000; 69% or 70% **b.** 1965 through 1970 **c.** 1965 **51. a.** 1.4 million **b.** $F = 122 + 1.4x$ **c.** 171 million **67.** does not make sense **69.** does not make sense **71.** a **73.** b **75.** ≈ 667 days; ≈ 1.8 yr

Section 3

Check Point Exercises

1. the amount of money given to the cashier **2.** The 128-ounce bottle at approximately 4¢ an ounce is the better value. **3.** 14 months **4.** 5 combinations **5.** 6 outfits **6.** A route that will cost less than \$1460 is A, D, E, C, B, A.

Trick Questions

1. 12 **2.** 12 **3.** sister and brother **4.** match

Exercise Set 3

1. the price of the computer **3.** the number of words on the page **5.** unnecessary information: weekly salary of \$350; extra pay: \$180 **7.** unnecessary information: \$20 given to the parking attendant; charge: \$4.50 **9. a.** 24-ounce box for \$4.59 **b.** 22¢ per ounce for the 15.3-ounce box and \$3.06 per pound for the 24-ounce box **c.** no; Answers will vary. **11.** \$3000 **13.** \$50 **15.** \$90 **17.** \$4525 **19.** \$565 **21.** 4 mi **23.** \$104 **25.** \$14,300 **27.** 5 ways **29.** 6 ways **31.** 9 ways **33.** 10 different total scores **35.** B owes \$18 and C owes \$2.; A is owed \$14, D is owed \$4, and E is owed \$2.; B should give A \$14 and D \$4, while C should give E \$2. **37.** 4 ways **39.** Andy, Darnell, Caleb, Beth, Ella **41.** Home, Bank, Post Office, Dry Cleaners, Home

43. Sample answer:
CO, WY, UT, AZ, NM, CO, UT

45. Bob's major is psychology.

47. a.

5	22	18
28	15	2
12	8	25

b.

4	9	8
11	7	3
6	5	10

49.

9	6	7
8	1	4
3	2	5

51.

```
     156
28)4368
   28
   156
   140
    168
    168
      0
```

57. makes sense **59.** does not make sense **61.** the dentist with poor dental work **63.** Friday

65. Sample answer:

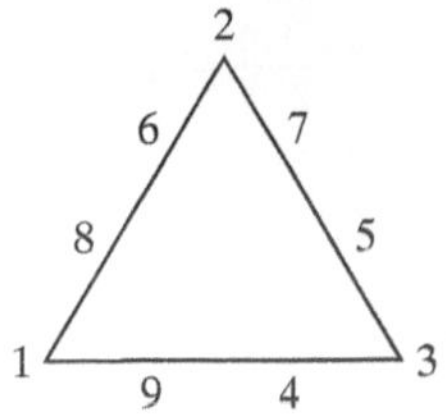

67. There is no missing dollar; in the end, the customers paid a total of \$27 of which \$25 went to the restaurant and \$2 was stolen by the waiter.
69. Answers will vary; an example is

State	A	B	C	D
Congressional Seats	4	6	8	12

Chapter Review Exercises

1. deductive reasoning: Answers will vary. **2.** inductive reasoning; Answers will vary. **3.** Each number in the list is obtained by adding 5 to the previous number.; 24 **4.** Each number in the list is obtained by multiplying the previous number by 2.; 112 **5.** The successive differences are consecutive counting numbers beginning with 2.; 21 **6.** Each number in the list is obtained by writing a fraction with a denominator that is one more than the denominator of the previous fraction before it is reduced to lowest terms.; $\frac{3}{8}$ **7.** Each number in the list is obtained by multiplying the previous number by $-\frac{1}{2}$.; $\frac{5}{2}$ **8.** Each number in the list is obtained by subtracting 60 from the previous number; −200.
9. Each number beginning with the third number is the sum of the two previous numbers.; 42 **10.** To get the second number, multiply the first number by 3. Then multiply the second number by 2 to get the third number. Then multiply by 3 and then by 2, repeatedly.; 432 **11.** The figures alternate between squares and circles, and in each figure the tick mark has been rotated 90° clockwise from its position in the previous figure.;
12. $2 + 4 + 8 + 16 + 32 = 64 - 2$; correct **13.** $444 \div 12 = 37$; correct
14. a. The result is the original number.
b. Using n to represent the original number, we have

Select a number:	n
Double the number:	$2n$
Add 4 to the product:	$2n + 4$
Divide the sum by 2:	$\frac{2n + 4}{2} = n + 2$
Subtract 2 from the quotient:	$n + 2 - 2 = n$.

15. a. 4,266,000 **b.** 4,266,000 **c.** 4,300,000 **d.** 4,000,000 **16. a.** 1.5 **b.** 1.51 **c.** 1.507 **d.** 1.5065917 **17.** ≈ 16; 15.71; quite reasonable **18.** ≈ 450; 432.67; somewhat reasonable **19.** ≈ 5; ≈ 4.76; quite reasonable **20.** ≈ 2400; 2397.0548; quite reasonable **21.** ≈ $18.00 **22.** ≈ $560 **23.** ≈ $60 **24.** ≈ 480,000 students **25.** b **26.** c **27. a.** Asian; ≈ 122 **b.** ≈ 990 million **28. a.** ≈ 0.4% per yr **b.** 34% **29. a.** 115 beats per min; 10 min **b.** 64 beats per min; 8 min **c.** between 9 and 10 minutes **d.** 9 min **30. a.** 7 channels per yr **b.** $T = 61 + 7x$ **c.** 159 channels **31.** the weight of the child **32.** unnecessary information: $20 given to driver; cost of trip: $8.00 **33.** 8 lb **34.** $885 **35.** Plan A; $90 **36.** 5.75 hr or 5 hr 45 min **37.** $15,500 **38.** 6 combinations

Chapter Test

1. deductive **2.** inductive **3.** Each number in the list is obtained by adding 5 to the previous number.; 20
4. Each number in the list is obtained by multiplying the previous number by $\frac{1}{2}$.; $\frac{1}{96}$ **5.** $3367 \times 15 = 50{,}505$
6. The outer figure is always a square; the inner figure follows the pattern: triangle, circle, square, triangle, circle, square, etc.; the number of appendages on the outer square alternates between 1 and 2.;
7. a. The original number is doubled.
b. Using n to represent the original number, we have

Select a number:	n
Multiply the number by 4:	$4n$
Add 8 to the product:	$4n + 8$
Divide the sum by 2:	$\frac{4n + 8}{2} = 2n + 4$
Subtract 4 from the quotient:	$2n + 4 - 4 = 2n$.

8. 3,300,000 **9.** 706.38 **10.** ≈ $90 **11.** ≈ $25,000 per person **12.** ≈ 60 **13.** ≈ 50 billion pounds **14.** a **15. a.** 2001; ≈ 1275 discharges **b.** 2006; 610 discharges **c.** between 2001 and 2002 **d.** 1997 **16. a.** 1.25 ppm per yr **b.** $C = 310 + 1.25x$ **c.** 435 ppm **17.** Estes Rental; $12 **18.** $14,080 **19.** 26 weeks **20.** Belgium; 160,000 people

Set Theory

Our bodies are fragile and complex, vulnerable to disease and easily damaged. The sequencing of the human genome in 2003—all 140,000 genes—should lead to rapid advances in treating heart disease, cancer, depression, Alzheimer's, and AIDS. Neural stem cell research could make it possible to repair brain damage and even re-create whole parts of the brain. There appears to be no limit to the parts of our bodies that can be replaced. By contrast, at the start of the twentieth century, we lacked even a basic understanding of the different types of human blood. The discovery of blood types, organized into collections called *sets* and illustrated by a special set diagram, rescued surgery patients from random, often lethal, transfusions. In this sense, the set diagram for blood types that you will encounter in this chapter reinforces our optimism that life does improve and that we are better off today than we were one hundred years ago.

Organizing and visually representing sets of human blood types is presented in the Blitzer Bonus at the end of Section 4. The vital role that this representation plays in blood transfusions is developed in Exercises 113–117 of Exercise Set 4.
Michael Dwyer\AP Wide World Photos

From Chapter 2 of *Thinking Mathematically*, Fifth Edition, Robert F. Blitzer.

OBJECTIVES

1 | Use three methods to represent sets.
2 | Define and recognize the empty set.
3 | Use the symbols $\in$ and $\notin$.
4 | Apply set notation to sets of natural numbers.
5 | Determine a set's cardinal number.
6 | Recognize equivalent sets.
7 | Distinguish between finite and infinite sets.
8 | Recognize equal sets.

1 Basic Set Concepts

PhotoAlto\Alamy Images

We tend to place things in categories, which allows us to order and structure the world. For example, to which populations do you belong? Do you categorize yourself as a college student? What about your gender? What about your academic major or your ethnic background? Our minds cannot find order and meaning without creating collections. Mathematicians call such collections *sets*. A **set** is a collection of objects whose contents can be clearly determined. The objects in a set are called the **elements**, or **members**, of the set.

A set must be **well defined**, meaning that its contents can be clearly determined. Using this criterion, the collection of actors who have won Academy Awards is a set. We can always determine whether or not a particular actor is an element of this collection. By contrast, consider the collection of great actors. Whether or not a person belongs to this collection is a matter of how we interpret the word *great*. In this text, we will only consider collections that form well-defined sets.

1 | Use three methods to represent sets.

Methods for Representing Sets

An example of a set is the set of the days of the week, whose elements are Monday, Tuesday, Wednesday, Thursday, Friday, Saturday, and Sunday.

Capital letters are generally used to name sets. Let's use W to represent the set of the days of the week.

Three methods are commonly used to designate a set. One method is a **word description**. We can describe set W as the set of the days of the week. A second method is the **roster method**. This involves listing the elements of a set inside a pair of braces, { }. The braces at the beginning and end indicate that we are representing a set. The roster form uses commas to separate the elements of the set. Thus, we can designate the set W by listing its elements:

W = {Monday, Tuesday, Wednesday, Thursday, Friday, Saturday, Sunday}.

Grouping symbols such as parentheses, ( ), and square brackets, [ ], are not used to represent sets. Only commas are used to separate the elements of a set. Separators such as colons or semicolons are not used. Finally, the order in which the elements are listed in a set is not important. Thus, another way of expressing the set of the days of the week is

W = {Saturday, Sunday, Monday, Tuesday, Wednesday, Thursday, Friday}.

EXAMPLE 1 Representing a Set Using a Description

Write a word description of the set

P = {Washington, Adams, Jefferson, Madison, Monroe}.

Solution Set P is the set of the first five presidents of the United States.

Write a word description of the set

$$L = \{a, b, c, d, e, f\}.$$

EXAMPLE 2 Representing a Set Using the Roster Method

Set C is the set of U.S. coins with a value of less than a dollar. Express this set using the roster method.

Solution

$$C = \{\text{penny, nickel, dime, quarter, half-dollar}\}$$

Set M is the set of months beginning with the letter A. Express this set using the roster method.

The third method for representing a set is with **set-builder notation**. Using this method, the set of the days of the week can be expressed as

$$W = \{x \mid x \text{ is a day of the week}\}.$$

Set W | is | the set of | all elements x | such that

We read this notation as "Set W is the set of all elements x such that x is a day of the week." Before the vertical line is the variable x, which represents an element in general. After the vertical line is the condition x must meet in order to be an element of the set.

Table 1 contains two examples of sets, each represented with a word description, the roster method, and set-builder notation.

STUDY TIP

Any letter can be used to represent the variable in set-builder notation. Thus, $\{x|x$ is a day of the week$\}$, $\{y|y$ is a day of the week$\}$, and $\{z|z$ is a day of the week$\}$ all represent the same set.

The Beatles climbed to the top of the British music charts in 1963, conquering the United States a year later. Globe Photos, Inc.

TABLE 1 Sets Using Three Designations

Word Description	Roster Method	Set-Builder Notation
B is the set of members of the Beatles in 1963.	B = {George Harrison, John Lennon, Paul McCartney, Ringo Starr}	$B = \{x\|x$ was a member of the Beatles in 1963$\}$
S is the set of states whose names begin with the letter A.	S = {Alabama, Alaska, Arizona, Arkansas}	$S = \{x\|x$ is a U.S. state whose name begins with the letter A$\}$

EXAMPLE 3 Converting from Set-Builder to Roster Notation

Express set

$$A = \{x|x \text{ is a month that begins with the letter M}\}$$

using the roster method.

Solution Set A is the set of all elements x such that x is a month beginning with the letter M. There are two such months, namely March and May. Thus,

$$A = \{\text{March, May}\}.$$

Express the set

$$O = \{x|x \text{ is a positive odd number less than } 10\}$$

using the roster method.

The representation of some sets by the roster method can be rather long, or even impossible, if we attempt to list every element. For example, consider the set of all lowercase letters of the English alphabet. If L is chosen as a name for this set, we can use set-builder notation to represent L as follows:

$$L = \{x \mid x \text{ is a lowercase letter of the English alphabet}\}.$$

A complete listing using the roster method is rather tedious:

$$L = \{\text{a, b, c, d, e, f, g, h, i, j, k, l, m, n, o, p, q, r, s, t, u, v, w, x, y, z}\}.$$

We can shorten the listing in set L by writing

$$L = \{\text{a, b, c, d}, \dots, \text{z}\}.$$

The three dots after the element d, called an *ellipsis*, indicate that the elements in the set continue in the same manner up to and including the last element z.

BLITZER BONUS

THE LOSS OF SETS

John Tenniel, colored by Fritz Kredel Illustration by John Tenniel, colored by Fritz Kredel. Discoveries(R). Gallimard Jeunesse Publishers.

Have you ever considered what would happen if we suddenly lost our ability to recall categories and the names that identify them? This is precisely what happened to Alice, the heroine of Lewis Carroll's *Through the Looking Glass*, as she walked with a fawn in "the woods with no names."

> So they walked on together through the woods, Alice with her arms clasped lovingly round the soft neck of the Fawn, till they came out into another open field, and here the Fawn gave a sudden bound into the air, and shook itself free from Alice's arm. "I'm a Fawn!" it cried out in a voice of delight. "And, dear me! you're a human child!" A sudden look of alarm came into its beautiful brown eyes, and in another moment it had darted away at full speed.

By realizing that Alice is a member of the set of human beings, which in turn is part of the set of dangerous things, the fawn is overcome by fear. Thus, the fawn's experience is determined by the way it structures the world into sets with various characteristics.

2 Define and recognize the empty set.

The Empty Set

Consider the following sets:

$$\{x \mid x \text{ is a fawn that speaks}\}$$

$$\{x \mid x \text{ is a number greater than 10 and less than 4}\}.$$

Can you see what these sets have in common? They both contain no elements. There are no fawns that speak. There are no numbers that are both greater than 10 and also less than 4. Sets such as these that contain no elements are called the *empty set*, or the *null set*.

THE EMPTY SET

The **empty set**, also called the **null set**, is the set that contains no elements. The empty set is represented by $\{\ \}$ or $\varnothing$.

Notice that $\{\ \}$ **and** $\varnothing$ **have the same meaning**. However, **the empty set is not represented by** $\{\varnothing\}$. This notation represents a set containing the element $\varnothing$.

BLITZER BONUS

THE MUSICAL SOUNDS OF THE EMPTY SET

John Cage (1912–1992), the American avant-garde composer, translated the empty set into the quietest piece of music ever written. His piano composition *4′33″* requires the musician to sit frozen in silence at a piano stool for 4 minutes, 33 seconds, or 273 seconds. (The significance of 273 is that at approximately −273°C, all molecular motion stops.) The set

$\{x \mid x$ is a musical sound from *4′33″*$\}$

is the empty set. There are no musical sounds in the composition. Mathematician Martin Gardner wrote, "I have not heard *4′33″* performed, but friends who have tell me it is Cage's finest composition."

EXAMPLE 4 Recognizing the Empty Set

Which one of the following is the empty set?

a. $\{0\}$ **b.** 0

c. $\{x \mid x$ is a number less than 4 or greater than $10\}$

d. $\{x \mid x$ is a square with exactly three sides$\}$

Solution

a. $\{0\}$ is a set containing one element, 0. Because this set contains an element, it is not the empty set.

b. 0 is a number, not a set, so it cannot possibly be the empty set. It does, however, represent the number of members of the empty set.

c. $\{x \mid x$ is a number less than 4 or greater than $10\}$ contains all numbers that are either less than 4, such as 3, or greater than 10, such as 11. Because some elements belong to this set, it cannot be the empty set.

d. $\{x \mid x$ is a square with exactly three sides$\}$ contains no elements. There are no squares with exactly three sides. This set is the empty set.

CHECK POINT 4 Which one of the following is the empty set?

a. $\{x \mid x$ is a number less than 3 or greater than $5\}$

b. $\{x \mid x$ is a number less than 3 and greater than $5\}$

c. nothing **d.** $\{\varnothing\}$

3 Use the symbols $\in$ and $\notin$.

Notations for Set Membership

We now consider two special notations that indicate whether or not a given object belongs to a set.

THE NOTATIONS $\in$ AND $\notin$

The symbol $\in$ is used to indicate that an object is an element of a set. The symbol $\in$ is used to replace the words "is an element of."

The symbol $\notin$ is used to indicate that an object is *not* an element of a set. The symbol $\notin$ is used to replace the words "is not an element of."

EXAMPLE 5 Using the Symbols $\in$ and $\notin$

Determine whether each statement is true or false:

a. $\text{r} \in \{\text{a, b, c}, \ldots, \text{z}\}$ **b.** $7 \notin \{1, 2, 3, 4, 5\}$ **c.** $\{\text{a}\} \in \{\text{a, b}\}$.

Solution

a. Because r is an element of the set $\{\text{a, b, c}, \ldots, \text{z}\}$, the statement

$$\text{r} \in \{\text{a, b, c}, \ldots, \text{z}\}$$

is true.

Observe that an element can belong to a set in roster notation when three dots appear even though the element is not listed.

b. Because 7 is not an element of the set $\{1, 2, 3, 4, 5\}$, the statement

$$7 \notin \{1, 2, 3, 4, 5\}$$

is true.

c. Because $\{\text{a}\}$ is a set and the set $\{\text{a}\}$ is not an element of the set $\{\text{a, b}\}$, the statement

$$\{\text{a}\} \in \{\text{a, b}\}$$

is false.

STUDY TIP

A set can be an element of another set. For example, $\{\{a, b\}, c\}$ is a set with two elements. One element is the set $\{a, b\}$ and the other element is the letter c. Thus, $\{a, b\} \in \{\{a, b\}, c\}$ and $c \in \{\{a, b\}, c\}$.

CHECK POINT 5 Determine whether each statement is true or false:

a. $8 \in \{1, 2, 3, \ldots, 10\}$

b. $r \notin \{a, b, c, z\}$

c. $\{\text{Monday}\} \in \{x \mid x \text{ is a day of the week}\}$.

4 Apply set notation to sets of natural numbers.

Sets of Natural Numbers

For much of the remainder of this section, we will focus on the set of numbers used for counting:

$$\{1, 2, 3, 4, 5, 6, 7, 8, 9, 10, 11, \ldots\}.$$

The set of counting numbers is also called the set of **natural numbers**. We represent this set by the bold face letter **N**.

THE SET OF NATURAL NUMBERS

$$\mathbf{N} = \{1, 2, 3, 4, 5, \ldots\}$$

The three dots, or ellipsis, after the 5 indicate that there is no final element and that the listing goes on forever.

EXAMPLE 6 Representing Sets of Natural Numbers

Express each of the following sets using the roster method:

a. Set A is the set of natural numbers less than 5.

b. Set B is the set of natural numbers greater than or equal to 25.

c. $E = \{x \mid x \in \mathbf{N} \text{ and } x \text{ is even}\}$.

Solution

a. The natural numbers less than 5 are 1, 2, 3, and 4. Thus, set A can be expressed using the roster method as

$$A = \{1, 2, 3, 4\}.$$

b. The natural numbers greater than or equal to 25 are 25, 26, 27, 28, and so on. Set B in roster form is

$$B = \{25, 26, 27, 28, \ldots\}.$$

The three dots show that the listing goes on forever.

c. The set-builder notation

$$E = \{x \mid x \in \mathbf{N} \text{ and } x \text{ is even}\}$$

indicates that we want to list the set of all x such that x is an element of the set of natural numbers and x is even. The set of numbers that meets both conditions is the set of even natural numbers. The set in roster form is

$$E = \{2, 4, 6, 8, \ldots\}.$$

Express each of the following sets using the roster method:

a. Set A is the set of natural numbers less than or equal to 3.

b. Set B is the set of natural numbers greater than 14.

c. $O = \{x \mid x \in \mathbf{N} \text{ and } x \text{ is odd}\}$.

Inequality symbols are frequently used to describe sets of natural numbers. **Table 2** reviews basic inequality notation.

TABLE 2 Inequality Notation and Sets

Inequality Symbol and Meaning		Example: Set-Builder Notation	Example: Roster Method
$x < a$	x is less than a.	$\{x \mid x \in \mathbf{N} \text{ and } x < 4\}$ — x is a natural number less than 4.	$\{1, 2, 3\}$
$x \le a$	x is less than or equal to a.	$\{x \mid x \in \mathbf{N} \text{ and } x \le 4\}$ — x is a natural number less than or equal to 4.	$\{1, 2, 3, 4\}$
$x > a$	x is greater than a.	$\{x \mid x \in \mathbf{N} \text{ and } x > 4\}$ — x is a natural number greater than 4.	$\{5, 6, 7, 8, \ldots\}$
$x \ge a$	x is greater than or equal to a.	$\{x \mid x \in \mathbf{N} \text{ and } x \ge 4\}$ — x is a natural number greater than or equal to 4.	$\{4, 5, 6, 7, \ldots\}$
$a < x < b$	x is greater than a and less than b.	$\{x \mid x \in \mathbf{N} \text{ and } 4 < x < 8\}$ — x is a natural number greater than 4 and less than 8.	$\{5, 6, 7\}$
$a \le x \le b$	x is greater than or equal to a and less than or equal to b.	$\{x \mid x \in \mathbf{N} \text{ and } 4 \le x \le 8\}$ — x is a natural number greater than or equal to 4 and less than or equal to 8.	$\{4, 5, 6, 7, 8\}$
$a \le x < b$	x is greater than or equal to a and less than b.	$\{x \mid x \in \mathbf{N} \text{ and } 4 \le x < 8\}$ — x is a natural number greater than or equal to 4 and less than 8.	$\{4, 5, 6, 7\}$
$a < x \le b$	x is greater than a and less than or equal to b.	$\{x \mid x \in \mathbf{N} \text{ and } 4 < x \le 8\}$ — x is a natural number greater than 4 and less than or equal to 8.	$\{5, 6, 7, 8\}$

STUDY TIP

A page of sheet music, filled with symbols and notations, *represents* a piece of music. Similarly, the symbols and notations throughout this book are representations of mathematical ideas. Mathematical notation no more *is* mathematics than musical notation *is* music. As you become familiar with various mathematical notations, the ideas represented by the symbols can then live and breathe in your mind.

EXAMPLE 7 Representing Sets of Natural Numbers

Express each of the following sets using the roster method:

a. $\{x \mid x \in \mathbf{N} \text{ and } x \le 100\}$ **b.** $\{x \mid x \in \mathbf{N} \text{ and } 70 \le x < 100\}$.

Solution

a. $\{x \mid x \in \mathbf{N} \text{ and } x \le 100\}$ represents the set of natural numbers less than or equal to 100. This set can be expressed using the roster method as

$$\{1, 2, 3, 4, \ldots, 100\}.$$

b. $\{x \mid x \in \mathbf{N} \text{ and } 70 \le x < 100\}$ represents the set of natural numbers greater than or equal to 70 and less than 100. This set in roster form is $\{70, 71, 72, 73, \ldots, 99\}$.

 Express each of the following sets using the roster method:

a. $\{x | x \in \mathbf{N} \text{ and } x < 200\}$

b. $\{x | x \in \mathbf{N} \text{ and } 50 < x \leq 200\}$.

5 Determine a set's cardinal number.

Cardinality and Equivalent Sets

The number of elements in a set is called the **cardinal number**, or **cardinality**, of the set. For example, the set $\{a, e, i, o, u\}$ contains five elements and therefore has the cardinal number 5. We can also say that the set has a cardinality of 5.

DEFINITION OF A SET'S CARDINAL NUMBER

The **cardinal number** of set A, represented by $n(A)$, is the number of distinct elements in set A. The symbol $n(A)$ is read "n of A."

Notice that the cardinal number of a set refers to the number of *distinct*, or different, elements in the set. **Repeating elements in a set neither adds new elements to the set nor changes its cardinality.** For example, $A = \{3, 5, 7\}$ and $B = \{3, 5, 5, 7, 7, 7\}$ represent the same set with three distinct elements, 3, 5, and 7. Thus, $n(A) = 3$ and $n(B) = 3$.

EXAMPLE 8 Determining a Set's Cardinal Number

Find the cardinal number of each of the following sets:

a. $A = \{7, 9, 11, 13\}$

b. $B = \{0\}$

c. $C = \{13, 14, 15, \ldots, 22, 23\}$

d. $\varnothing$.

Solution The cardinal number for each set is found by determining the number of elements in the set.

a. $A = \{7, 9, 11, 13\}$ contains four distinct elements. Thus, the cardinal number of set A is 4. We also say that set A has a cardinality of 4, or $n(A) = 4$.

b. $B = \{0\}$ contains one element, namely 0. The cardinal number of set B is 1. Therefore, $n(B) = 1$.

c. Set $C = \{13, 14, 15, \ldots, 22, 23\}$ lists only five elements. However, the three dots indicate that the natural numbers from 16 through 21 are also in the set. Counting the elements in the set, we find that there are 11 natural numbers in set C. The cardinality of set C is 11, and $n(C) = 11$.

d. The empty set, $\varnothing$, contains no elements. Thus, $n(\varnothing) = 0$.

CHECK POINT 8 Find the cardinal number of each of the following sets:

a. $A = \{6, 10, 14, 15, 16\}$

b. $B = \{872\}$

c. $C = \{9, 10, 11, \ldots, 15, 16\}$

d. $D = \{\ \}$.

6 Recognize equivalent sets.

Sets that contain the same number of elements are said to be *equivalent*.

DEFINITION OF EQUIVALENT SETS

Set A is **equivalent** to set B means that set A and set B contain the same number of elements. For equivalent sets, $n(A) = n(B)$.

Here is an example of two equivalent sets:

$n(A) = n(B) = 5$

$$A = \{x \mid x \text{ is a vowel}\} \quad = \quad \{a, e, i, o, u\}$$

$$\updownarrow\ \updownarrow\ \updownarrow\ \updownarrow\ \updownarrow$$

$$B = \{x \mid x \in \mathbf{N} \text{ and } 3 \leq x \leq 7\} = \{3, 4, 5, 6, 7\}.$$

It is not necessary to count elements and arrive at 5 to determine that these sets are equivalent. The lines with arrowheads, $\updownarrow$, indicate that each element of set A can be paired with exactly one element of set B and each element of set B can be paired with exactly one element of set A. We say that the sets can be placed in a **one-to-one correspondence**.

ONE-TO-ONE CORRESPONDENCES AND EQUIVALENT SETS

1. If set A and set B can be placed in a one-to-one correspondence, then A is equivalent to B: $n(A) = n(B)$.
2. If set A and set B cannot be placed in a one-to-one correspondence, then A is not equivalent to B: $n(A) \neq n(B)$.

EXAMPLE 9 Determining If Sets Are Equivalent

In most societies, women say they prefer to marry men who are older than themselves, whereas men say they prefer women who are younger. **Figure 1** shows the preferred age difference in a mate in five selected countries.

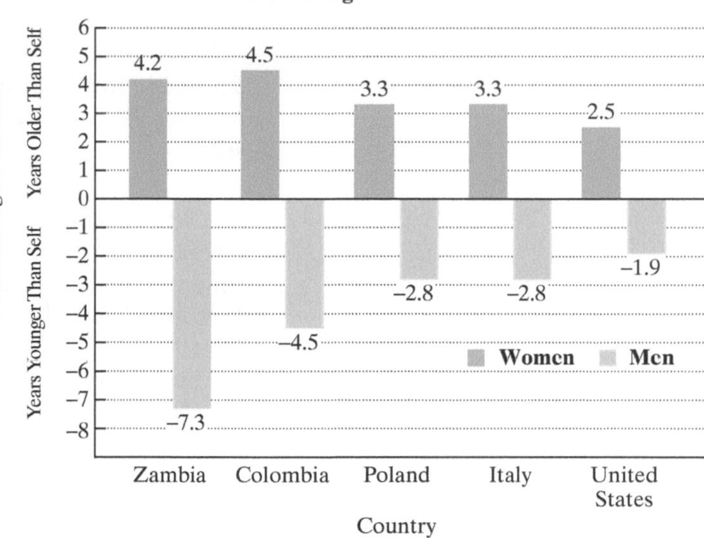

FIGURE 1

Source: Carole Wade and Carol Tavris, *Psychology*, Sixth Edition, Prentice Hall, 2000.

Let

A = the set of the five countries shown in **Figure 1**

B = the set of the average number of years women in each of these countries prefer men who are older than themselves.

Are these sets equivalent? Explain.

Solution Let's begin by expressing each set in roster form.

$$A = \{\text{Zambia, Colombia, Poland, Italy, U.S.}\}$$

$$\updownarrow \qquad \updownarrow \qquad \searrow\ \swarrow \qquad \updownarrow$$

$$B = \{\ 4.2, \qquad 4.5, \qquad 3.3, \qquad 2.5\ \}$$

Do not write 3.3 twice. We are interested in each set's distinct elements.

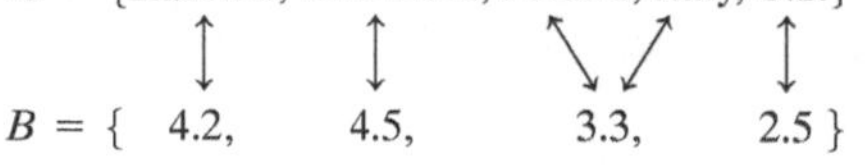

A = {Zambia, Colombia, Poland, Italy, U.S.}
B = { 4.2, 4.5, 3.3, 2.5 }

The sets in roster form (repeated)

There are two ways to determine that these sets are not equivalent.

Method 1. Trying to Set Up a One-to-One Correspondence

The lines with arrowheads between the sets in roster form indicate that the correspondence between the sets is not one-to-one. The elements Poland and Italy from set A are both paired with the element 3.3 from set B. These sets are not equivalent.

Method 2. Counting Elements

Set A contains five distinct elements: $n(A) = 5$. Set B contains four distinct elements: $n(B) = 4$. Because the sets do not contain the same number of elements, they are not equivalent.

CHECK POINT 9 Let

A = the set of the five countries shown in **Figure 1** on the previous page

B = the set of the average number of years men in each of these countries prefer women who are younger than themselves.

Are these sets equivalent? Explain.

7 Distinguish between finite and infinite sets.

Finite and Infinite Sets

Example 9 illustrated that to compare the cardinalities of two sets, pair off their elements. If there is not a one-to-one correspondence, the sets have different cardinalities and are not equivalent. Although this idea is obvious in the case of *finite sets*, some unusual conclusions emerge when dealing with *infinite sets*.

FINITE SETS AND INFINITE SETS

Set A is a **finite set** if $n(A) = 0$ (that is, A is the empty set) or $n(A)$ is a natural number. A set whose cardinality is not 0 or a natural number is called an **infinite set**.

An example of an infinite set is the set of natural numbers, **N** = $\{1, 2, 3, 4, 5, 6, \ldots\}$, where the ellipsis indicates that there is no last, or final, element. Does this set have a cardinality? The answer is yes, albeit one of the strangest numbers you've ever seen. The set of natural numbers is assigned the infinite cardinal number $\aleph_0$ (read: "aleph-null," aleph being the first letter of the Hebrew alphabet). What follows is a succession of mind-boggling results, including a hierarchy of different infinite numbers in which $\aleph_0$ is the smallest infinity:

$$\aleph_0 < \aleph_1 < \aleph_2 < \aleph_3 < \aleph_4 < \aleph_5 \ldots .$$

These ideas, which are impossible for our imaginations to grasp, are developed in Section 2 and the Blitzer Bonus at the end of that section.

8 Recognize equal sets.

Equal Sets

We conclude this section with another important concept of set theory, equality of sets.

DEFINITION OF EQUALITY OF SETS

Set A is **equal** to set B means that set A and set B contain exactly the same elements, regardless of order or possible repetition of elements. We symbolize the equality of sets A and B using the statement $A = B$.

For example, if $A = \{w, x, y, z\}$ and $B = \{z, y, w, x\}$, then $A = B$ because the two sets contain exactly the same elements.

Because equal sets contain the same elements, they also have the same cardinal number. For example, the equal sets $A = \{w, x, y, z\}$ and $B = \{z, y, w, x\}$

> **STUDY TIP**
>
> In English, the words *equal* and *equivalent* often mean the same thing. This is not the case in set theory. **Equal sets** contain the **same elements. Equivalent sets** contain the **same number of elements**. If two sets are equal, then they must be equivalent. However, if two sets are equivalent, they are not necessarily equal.

have four elements each. Thus, both sets have the same cardinal number: 4. Notice that a possible one-to-one correspondence between the equal sets A and B can be obtained by pairing each element with itself:

$$A = \{\text{w, x, y, z}\}$$
$$B = \{\text{z, y, w, x}\}$$

This illustrates an important point: **If two sets are equal, then they must be equivalent.**

EXAMPLE 10 Determining Whether Sets Are Equal

Determine whether each statement is true or false:

a. $\{4, 8, 9\} = \{8, 9, 4\}$ **b.** $\{1, 3, 5\} = \{0, 1, 3, 5\}$.

Solution

a. The sets $\{4, 8, 9\}$ and $\{8, 9, 4\}$ contain exactly the same elements. Therefore, the statement

$$\{4, 8, 9\} = \{8, 9, 4\}$$

is true.

b. As we look at the given sets, $\{1, 3, 5\}$ and $\{0, 1, 3, 5\}$, we see that 0 is an element of the second set, but not the first. The sets do not contain exactly the same elements. Therefore, the sets are not equal. This means that the statement

$$\{1, 3, 5\} = \{0, 1, 3, 5\}$$

is false.

Determine whether each statement is true or false:

a. $\{\text{O, L, D}\} = \{\text{D, O, L}\}$ **b.** $\{4, 5\} = \{5, 4, \varnothing\}$.

Exercise Set 1

Practice Exercises

In Exercises 1–6, determine which collections are not well defined and therefore not sets.

1. The collection of U.S. presidents
2. The collection of part-time and full-time students currently enrolled at your college
3. The collection of the five worst U.S. presidents
4. The collection of elderly full-time students currently enrolled at your college
5. The collection of natural numbers greater than one million
6. The collection of even natural numbers greater than 100

In Exercises 7–14, write a word description of each set. (More than one correct description may be possible.)

7. {Mercury, Venus, Earth, Mars, Jupiter, Saturn, Uranus, Neptune}
8. {Saturday, Sunday}
9. {January, June, July}
10. {April, August}
11. $\{6, 7, 8, 9, \dots\}$
12. $\{9, 10, 11, 12, \dots\}$
13. $\{6, 7, 8, 9, \dots, 20\}$
14. $\{9, 10, 11, 12, \dots, 25\}$

In Exercises 15–32, express each set using the roster method.

15. The set of the four seasons in a year
16. The set of months of the year that have exactly 30 days
17. $\{x \mid x$ is a month that ends with the letters b-e-r$\}$
18. $\{x \mid x$ is a lowercase letter of the alphabet that follows d and comes before j$\}$
19. The set of natural numbers less than 4
20. The set of natural numbers less than or equal to 6
21. The set of odd natural numbers less than 13
22. The set of even natural numbers less than 10
23. $\{x \mid x \in \mathbf{N} \text{ and } x \le 5\}$
24. $\{x \mid x \in \mathbf{N} \text{ and } x \le 4\}$
25. $\{x \mid x \in \mathbf{N} \text{ and } x > 5\}$

26. $\{x \mid x \in \mathbf{N} \text{ and } x > 4\}$

27. $\{x \mid x \in \mathbf{N} \text{ and } 6 < x \leq 10\}$

28. $\{x \mid x \in \mathbf{N} \text{ and } 7 < x \leq 11\}$

29. $\{x \mid x \in \mathbf{N} \text{ and } 10 \leq x < 80\}$

30. $\{x \mid x \in \mathbf{N} \text{ and } 15 \leq x < 60\}$

31. $\{x \mid x + 5 = 7\}$

32. $\{x \mid x + 3 = 9\}$

In Exercises 33–46, determine which sets are the empty set.

33. $\{\varnothing, 0\}$

34. $\{0, \varnothing\}$

35. $\{x \mid x$ is a woman who served as U.S. president before 2000$\}$

36. $\{x \mid x$ is a living U.S. president born before 1200$\}$

37. $\{x \mid x$ is the number of women who served as U.S. president before 2000$\}$

38. $\{x \mid x$ is the number of living U.S. presidents born before 1200$\}$

39. $\{x \mid x$ is a U.S. state whose name begins with the letter X$\}$

40. $\{x \mid x$ is a month of the year whose name begins with the letter X$\}$

41. $\{x \mid x < 2 \text{ and } x > 5\}$

42. $\{x \mid x < 3 \text{ and } x > 7\}$

43. $\{x \mid x \in \mathbf{N} \text{ and } 2 < x < 5\}$

44. $\{x \mid x \in \mathbf{N} \text{ and } 3 < x < 7\}$

45. $\{x \mid x$ is a number less than 2 or greater than 5$\}$

46. $\{x \mid x$ is a number less than 3 or greater than 7$\}$

In Exercises 47–66, determine whether each statement is true or false.

47. $3 \in \{1, 3, 5, 7\}$

48. $6 \in \{2, 4, 6, 8, 10\}$

49. $12 \in \{1, 2, 3, \ldots, 14\}$

50. $10 \in \{1, 2, 3, \ldots, 16\}$

51. $5 \in \{2, 4, 6, \ldots, 20\}$

52. $8 \in \{1, 3, 5, \ldots 19\}$

53. $11 \notin \{1, 2, 3, \ldots, 9\}$

54. $17 \notin \{1, 2, 3, \ldots, 16\}$

55. $37 \notin \{1, 2, 3, \ldots, 40\}$

56. $26 \notin \{1, 2, 3, \ldots, 50\}$

57. $4 \notin \{x \mid x \in \mathbf{N}$ and x is even$\}$

58. $2 \in \{x \mid x \in \mathbf{N}$ and x is odd$\}$

59. $13 \notin \{x \mid x \in \mathbf{N} \text{ and } x < 13\}$

60. $20 \notin \{x \mid x \in \mathbf{N} \text{ and } x < 20\}$

61. $16 \notin \{x \mid x \in \mathbf{N} \text{ and } 15 \leq x < 20\}$

62. $19 \notin \{x \mid x \in \mathbf{N} \text{ and } 16 \leq x < 21\}$

63. $\{3\} \in \{3, 4\}$

64. $\{7\} \in \{7, 8\}$

65. $-1 \notin \mathbf{N}$

66. $-2 \notin \mathbf{N}$

In Exercises 67–80, find the cardinal number for each set.

67. $A = \{17, 19, 21, 23, 25\}$

68. $A = \{16, 18, 20, 22, 24, 26\}$

69. $B = \{2, 4, 6, \ldots, 30\}$

70. $B = \{1, 3, 5, \ldots, 21\}$

71. $C = \{x \mid x$ is a day of the week that begins with the letter A$\}$

72. $C = \{x \mid x$ is a month of the year that begins with the letter W$\}$

73. $D = \{\text{five}\}$

74. $D = \{\text{six}\}$

75. $A = \{x \mid x$ is a letter in the word *five*$\}$

76. $A = \{x \mid x$ is a letter in the word *six*$\}$

77. $B = \{x \mid x \in \mathbf{N} \text{ and } 2 \leq x < 7\}$

78. $B = \{x \mid x \in \mathbf{N} \text{ and } 3 \leq x < 10\}$

79. $C = \{x \mid x < 4 \text{ and } x \geq 12\}$

80. $C = \{x \mid x < 5 \text{ and } x \geq 15\}$

In Exercises 81–90,

a. *Are the sets equivalent? Explain.*

b. *Are the sets equal? Explain.*

81. A is the set of students at your college. B is the set of students majoring in business at your college.

82. A is the set of states in the United States. B is the set of people who are now governors of the states in the United States.

83. $A = \{1, 2, 3, 4, 5\}$
$B = \{0, 1, 2, 3, 4\}$

84. $A = \{1, 3, 5, 7, 9\}$
$B = \{2, 4, 6, 8, 10\}$

85. $A = \{1, 1, 1, 2, 2, 3, 4\}$
$B = \{4, 3, 2, 1\}$

86. $A = \{0, 1, 1, 2, 2, 2, 3, 3, 3, 3\}$
$B = \{3, 2, 1, 0\}$

87. $A = \{x \mid x \in \mathbf{N} \text{ and } 6 \leq x < 10\}$
$B = \{x \mid x \in \mathbf{N} \text{ and } 9 < x \leq 13\}$

88. $A = \{x \mid x \in \mathbf{N} \text{ and } 12 < x \leq 17\}$
$B = \{x \mid x \in \mathbf{N} \text{ and } 20 \leq x < 25\}$

89. $A = \{x \mid x \in \mathbf{N} \text{ and } 100 \leq x \leq 105\}$
$B = \{x \mid x \in \mathbf{N} \text{ and } 99 < x < 106\}$

90. $A = \{x \mid x \in \mathbf{N} \text{ and } 200 \leq x \leq 206\}$
$B = \{x \mid x \in \mathbf{N} \text{ and } 199 < x < 207\}$

In Exercises 91–96, determine whether each set is finite or infinite.

91. $\{x \mid x \in \mathbf{N} \text{ and } x \geq 100\}$

92. $\{x \mid x \in \mathbf{N} \text{ and } x \geq 50\}$

93. $\{x \mid x \in \mathbf{N} \text{ and } x \leq 1{,}000{,}000\}$

94. $\{x \mid x \in \mathbf{N} \text{ and } x \leq 2{,}000{,}000\}$

95. The set of natural numbers less than 1

96. The set of natural numbers less than 0

Practice Plus

In Exercises 97–100, express each set using set-builder notation. Use inequality notation to express the condition x must meet in order to be a member of the set. (More than one correct inequality may be possible.)

97. $\{61, 62, 63, 64, \ldots\}$

98. $\{36, 37, 38, 39, \ldots\}$

99. $\{61, 62, 63, 64, \ldots, 89\}$

100. $\{36, 37, 38, 39, \ldots, 59\}$

In Exercises 101–104, give examples of two sets that meet the given conditions. If the conditions are impossible to satisfy, explain why.

101. The two sets are equivalent but not equal.

102. The two sets are equivalent and equal.

103. The two sets are equal but not equivalent.

104. The two sets are neither equivalent nor equal.

Application Exercises

The bar graph shows the countries with the greatest percentage of their population having used marijuana. In Exercises 105–112, use the information given by the graph to represent each set by the roster method, or use the appropriate notation to indicate that the set is the empty set.

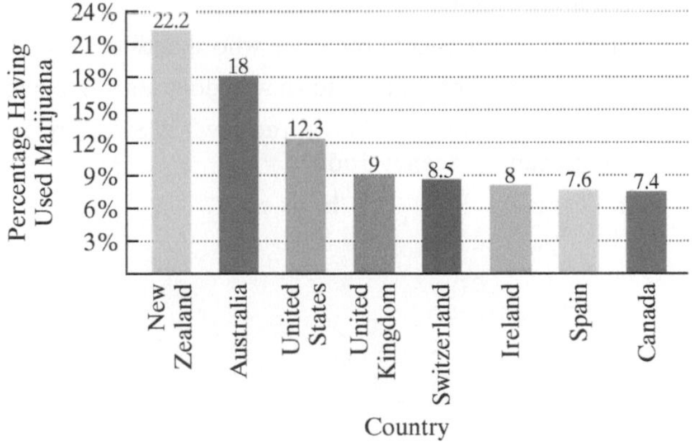

Source: Organization for Economic Cooperation and Development

105. The set of countries in which the percentage having used marijuana exceeds 12%

106. The set of countries in which the percentage having used marijuana exceeds 9%

107. The set of countries in which the percentage having used marijuana is at least 8% and at most 18%

108. The set of countries in which the percentage having used marijuana is at least 8.5% and at most 20%

109. $\{x | x$ is a country in which $8\% \leq$ percentage having used marijuana $< 12.3\%\}$

110. $\{x | x$ is a country in which $7.6\% \leq$ percentage having used marijuana $< 9\%\}$

111. $\{x | x$ is a country in which the percentage having used marijuana $> 22.2\%\}$

112. $\{x | x$ is a country in which the percentage having used marijuana $\geq 22.2\%\}$

A study of 900 working women in Texas showed that their feelings changed throughout the day. The line graph in the next column shows 15 different times in a day and the average level of happiness for the women at each time. Based on the information given by the graph, represent each of the sets in Exercises 113–116 using the roster method.

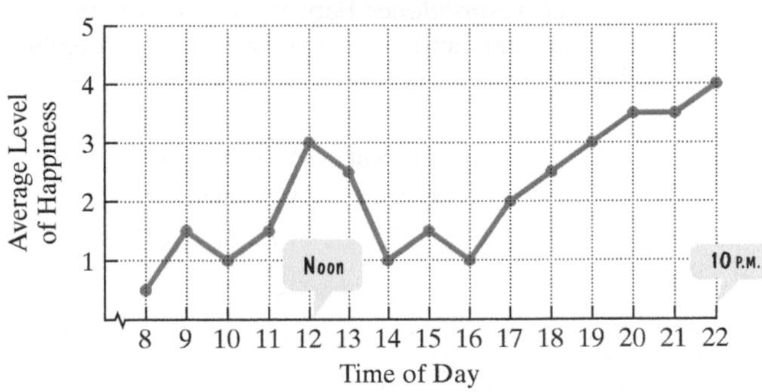

Source: D. Kahneman et al. "A Survey Method for Characterizing Daily Life Experience," *Science*.

113. $\{x | x$ is a time of the day when the average level of happiness was $3\}$

114. $\{x | x$ is a time of the day when the average level of happiness was $1\}$

115. $\{x | x$ is a time of the day when

$$3 < \text{average level of happiness} < 4\}$$

116. $\{x | x$ is a time of the day when

$$3 < \text{average level of happiness} \leq 4\}$$

117. Do the results of Exercise 113 or 114 indicate a one-to-one correspondence between the set representing the time of day and the set representing average level of happiness? Are these sets equivalent?

Writing in Mathematics

118. What is a set?

119. Describe the three methods used to represent a set. Give an example of a set represented by each method.

120. What is the empty set?

121. Explain what is meant by *equivalent sets*.

122. Explain what is meant by *equal sets*.

123. Use cardinality to describe the difference between a finite set and an infinite set.

Critical Thinking Exercises

Make Sense? *In Exercises 124–127, determine whether each statement makes sense or does not make sense, and explain your reasoning.*

124. I used the roster method to express the set of countries that I have visited.

125. I used the roster method and natural numbers to express the set of average daily Fahrenheit temperatures throughout the month of July in Vostok Station, Antarctica, the coldest month in one of the coldest locations in the world.

126. Using this bar graph that shows the average number of hours that Americans sleep per day, I can see that there is a one-to-one correspondence between the set of six ages on the horizontal axis and the set of the average number of hours that men sleep per day.

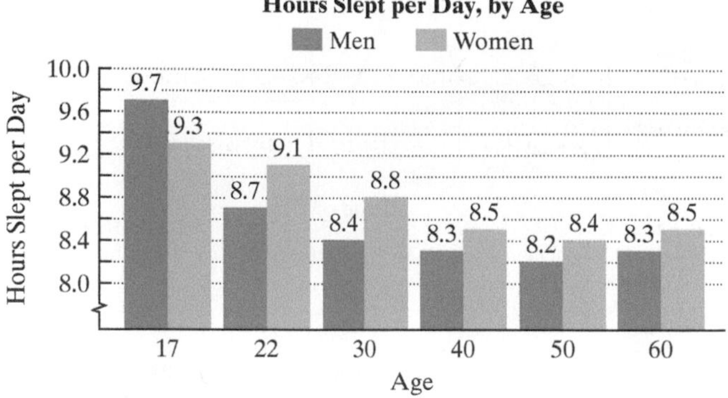

Source: ATUS, Bureau of Labor Statistics

127. Using the bar graph in Exercise 126, I can see that there is a one-to-one correspondence between the set of the average number of hours that men sleep per day and the set of the average number of hours that women sleep per day.

In Exercises 128–135, determine whether each statement is true or false. If the statement is false, make the necessary change(s) to produce a true statement.

128. Two sets can be equal but not equivalent.

129. Any set in roster notation that contains three dots must be an infinite set.

130. $n(\varnothing) = 1$

131. Some sets that can be written in set-builder notation cannot be written in roster form.

132. The set of fractions between 0 and 1 is an infinite set.

133. The set of multiples of 4 between 0 and 4,000,000,000 is an infinite set.

134. If the elements in a set cannot be counted in a trillion years, the set is an infinite set.

135. Because 0 is not a natural number, it can be deleted from any set without changing the set's cardinality.

136. In a certain town, a barber shaves all those men and only those men who do not shave themselves. Consider each of the following sets:

$A = \{x | x \text{ is a man of the town who shaves himself}\}$

$B = \{x | x \text{ is a man of the town who does not shave himself}\}.$

The one and only barber in the town is Sweeney Todd. If s represents Sweeney Todd,

a. is $s \in A$? **b.** is $s \in B$?

OBJECTIVES

1 Recognize subsets and use the notation $\subseteq$.

2 Recognize proper subsets and use the notation $\subset$.

3 Determine the number of subsets of a set.

4 Apply concepts of subsets and equivalent sets to infinite sets.

2 Subsets

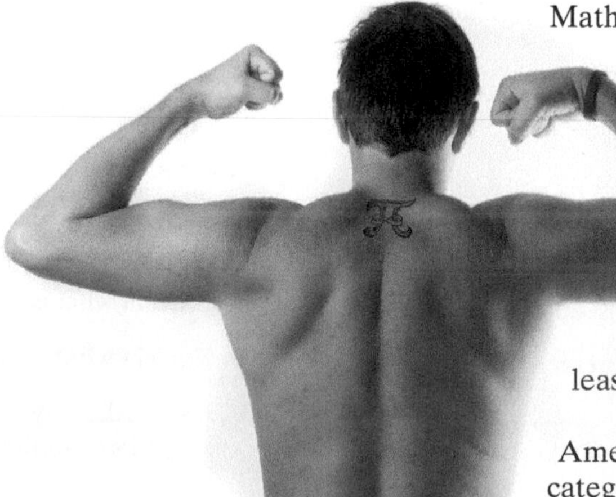

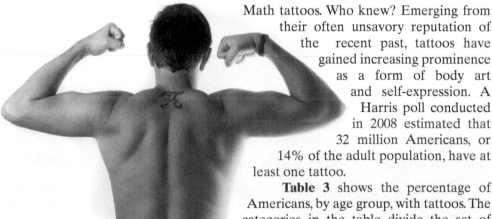

Martin Allinger\Shutterstock

Math tattoos. Who knew? Emerging from their often unsavory reputation of the recent past, tattoos have gained increasing prominence as a form of body art and self-expression. A Harris poll conducted in 2008 estimated that 32 million Americans, or 14% of the adult population, have at least one tattoo.

Table 3 shows the percentage of Americans, by age group, with tattoos. The categories in the table divide the set of tattooed Americans into smaller sets, called *subsets*, based on age. The age subsets can be broken into still-smaller subsets. For example, tattooed Americans ages 25–29 can be categorized by gender, political party affiliation, race/ethnicity, or any other area of interest. This suggests numerous possible subsets of the set of Americans with tattoos. Every American in each of these subsets is also a member of the set of tattooed Americans.

TABLE 3 Percentage of Tattooed Americans, by Age Group

Age Group	Percent Tattooed
18–24	9%
25–29	32%
30–39	25%
40–49	12%
50–64	8%
65+	9%

Source: Harris Interactive

Subsets

Situations in which all the elements of one set are also elements of another set are described by the following definition:

1 Recognize subsets and use the notation $\subseteq$.

DEFINITION OF A SUBSET OF A SET

Set A is a **subset** of set B, expressed as

$$A \subseteq B,$$

if every element in set A is also an element in set B.

Let's apply this definition to the set of people ages 25–29 in **Table 3**.

The set of tattooed Americans in the 25-29 age group | is a subset of | the set of all tattooed Americans.

$$\{x \mid x \text{ is a tattooed American and } 25 \leq x\text{'s age} \leq 29\} \subseteq \{x \mid x \text{ is a tattooed American}\}$$

Every person in this set, to the left of the subset symbol, | is also a member of this set, to the right of the subset symbol.

Observe that a subset is itself a set.

The notation $A \not\subseteq B$ means that A **is not a subset** of B. Set A is not a subset of set B if there is at least one element of set A that is not an element of set B. For example, consider the following sets:

$$A = \{1, 2, 3\} \quad \text{and} \quad B = \{1, 2\}.$$

Can you see that 3 is an element of set A that is not in set B? Thus, set A is not a subset of set B: $A \not\subseteq B$.

We can show that $A \subseteq B$ by showing that every element of set A also occurs as an element of set B. We can show that $A \not\subseteq B$ by finding one element of set A that is not in set B.

The eight planets in Earth's solar system

No, we did not forget Pluto. In 2006, based on the requirement that a planet must dominate its own orbit (Pluto is slave to Neptune's orbit), the International Astronomical Union removed Pluto from the list of planets and decreed that it belongs to a new category of heavenly body, a "dwarf planet."

EXAMPLE 1 Using the Symbols $\subseteq$ and $\not\subseteq$

Write $\subseteq$ or $\not\subseteq$ in each blank to form a true statement:

a. $A = \{1, 3, 5, 7\}$
$B = \{1, 3, 5, 7, 9, 11\}$
A____B

b. $A = \{x \mid x \text{ is a letter in the word } \textit{proof}\}$
$B = \{y \mid y \text{ is a letter in the word } \textit{roof}\}$
A____B

c. $A = \{x \mid x \text{ is a planet of Earth's solar system}\}$
$B = \{\text{Mercury, Venus, Earth, Mars, Jupiter, Saturn, Uranus, Neptune}\}$
A____B.

Solution

a. All the elements of $A = \{1, 3, 5, 7\}$ are also contained in $B = \{1, 3, 5, 7, 9, 11\}$. Therefore, set A is a subset of set B:

$$A \subseteq B.$$

b. Let's write the set of letters in the word *proof* and the set of letters in the word *roof* in roster form. In each case, we consider only the distinct elements, so there is no need to repeat the o.

$$A = \{\text{p, r, o, f}\} \qquad B = \{\text{r, o, f}\}$$

The element p is in set A but not in set B.

Because there is an element in set A that is not in set B, set A is not a subset of set B:

$$A \not\subseteq B.$$

c. All the elements of

$$A = \{x|x \text{ is a planet of Earth's solar system}\}$$

are contained in

$$B = \{\text{Mercury, Venus, Earth, Mars, Jupiter, Saturn, Uranus, Neptune}\}.$$

Because all elements in set A are also in set B, set A is a subset of set B:

$$A \subseteq B.$$

Furthermore, the sets are equal $(A = B)$.

Write $\subseteq$ or $\nsubseteq$ in each blank to form a true statement:

a. $A = \{1, 3, 5, 6, 9, 11\}$
$B = \{1, 3, 5, 7\}$
A_____B

b. $A = \{x|x$ is a letter in the word *roof*$\}$
$B = \{y|y$ is a letter in the word *proof*$\}$
A_____B

c. $A = \{x|x$ is a day of the week$\}$
$B = \{$Monday, Tuesday, Wednesday, Thursday, Friday, Saturday, Sunday$\}$
A_____B

2 Recognize proper subsets and use the notation $\subset$.

Proper Subsets

In Example 1(c) and Check Point 1(c), the given sets are equal and illustrate that **every set is a subset of itself.** If A is any set, then $A \subseteq A$ because it is obvious that each element of A is a member of A.

If we know that set A is a subset of set B and we exclude the possibility of the sets being equal, then set A is called a *proper subset* of set B, written $A \subset B$.

DEFINITION OF A PROPER SUBSET OF A SET

Set A is a **proper subset** of set B, expressed as $A \subset B$, if set A is a subset of set B and sets A and B are not equal $(A \neq B)$.

Try not to confuse the symbols for subset, $\subseteq$, and proper subset, $\subset$. In some subset examples, both symbols can be placed between sets:

Set A — Set B — Set A — Set B

$$\{1, 3\} \subseteq \{1, 3, 5\} \quad \textit{and} \quad \{1, 3\} \subset \{1, 3, 5\}.$$

A is a subset of B. Every element in A is also an element in B.

A is a proper subset of B because A and B are not equal sets.

By contrast, there are subset examples where only the symbol $\subseteq$ can be placed between sets:

Set A — Set B

$$\{1, 3, 5\} \subseteq \{1, 3, 5\}.$$

A is a subset of B. Every element in A is also an element in B. A is not a proper subset of B because $A = B$. The symbol $\subset$ should not be placed between the sets.

Because the lower part of the subset symbol in $A \subseteq B$ suggests an equal sign, it is *possible* that sets A and B are equal, although they do not have to be. By contrast, the missing lower line for the proper subset symbol in $A \subset B$ indicates that sets A and B *cannot* be equal.

STUDY TIP

- The notation for "is a subset of," $\subseteq$, is similar to the notation for "is less than or equal to," $\leq$. Because the notations share similar ideas, $A \subseteq B$ applies to finite sets only if the cardinal number of set A is less than or equal to the cardinal number of set B.
- The notation for "is a proper subset of," $\subset$, is similar to the notation for "is less than," $<$. Because the notations share similar ideas, $A \subset B$ applies to finite sets only if the cardinal number of set A is less than the cardinal number of set B.

EXAMPLE 2 Using the Symbols $\subseteq$ and $\subset$

Write $\subseteq$, $\subset$, or both in each blank to form a true statement:

a. $A = \{x \mid x \text{ is a person and } x \text{ lives in San Francisco}\}$

$B = \{x \mid x \text{ is a person and } x \text{ lives in California}\}$

A_____B

b. $A = \{2, 4, 6, 8\}$

$B = \{2, 8, 4, 6\}$

A_____B.

Solution

a. We begin with $A = \{x \mid x \text{ is a person and } x \text{ lives in San Francisco}\}$ and $B = \{x \mid x \text{ a person and } x \text{ lives in California}\}$. Every person living in San Francisco is also a person living in California. Because each person in set A is contained in set B, set A is a subset of set B:

$$A \subseteq B.$$

Can you see that the two sets do not contain exactly the same elements and, consequently, are not equal? A person living in California outside San Francisco is in set B, but not in set A. Because the sets are not equal, set A is a proper subset of set B:

$$A \subset B.$$

The symbols $\subseteq$ and $\subset$ can both be placed in the blank to form a true statement.

b. Every number in $A = \{2, 4, 6, 8\}$ is contained in $B = \{2, 8, 4, 6\}$, so set A is a subset of set B:

$$A \subseteq B.$$

Because the sets contain exactly the same elements and are equal, set A is *not* a proper subset of set B. The symbol $\subset$ cannot be placed in the blank if we want to form a true statement. (Because set A is not a proper subset of set B, it is correct to write $A \not\subset B$.)

Write $\subseteq$, $\subset$, or both in each blank to form a true statement:

a. $A = \{2, 4, 6, 8\}$

$B = \{2, 8, 4, 6, 10\}$

A_____B

b. $A = \{x \mid x \text{ is a person and } x \text{ lives in Atlanta}\}$

$B = \{x \mid x \text{ is a person and } x \text{ lives in Georgia}\}$

A_____B.

STUDY TIP

Do not confuse the symbols $\in$ and $\subseteq$. The symbol $\in$ means "is an element of" and the symbol $\subseteq$ means "is a subset of." Notice the differences among the following true statements:

$4 \in \{4, 8\}$ — 4 is an element of the set {4, 8}.

$\{4\} \subseteq \{4, 8\}$ — The set containing 4 is a subset of the set {4, 8}.

$\{4\} \notin \{4, 8\}$. — The set containing 4 is not an element of {4, 8}, although $\{4\} \in \{\{4\}, \{8\}\}$.

Subsets and the Empty Set

The meaning of $A \subseteq B$ leads to some interesting properties of the empty set.

EXAMPLE 3 The Empty Set as a Subset

Let $A = \{\ \}$ and $B = \{1, 2, 3, 4, 5\}$. Is $A \subseteq B$?

Solution A is not a subset of B ($A \not\subseteq B$) if there is at least one element of set A that is not an element of set B. Because A represents the empty set, there are no elements in set A, period, much less elements in A that do not belong to B. Because we cannot find an element in $A = \{\ \}$ that is not contained in $B = \{1, 2, 3, 4, 5\}$, this means that $A \subseteq B$. Equivalently, $\varnothing \subseteq B$.

CHECK POINT 3 Let $A = \{\ \}$ and $B = \{6, 7, 8\}$. Is $A \subseteq B$?

Example 3 illustrates the principle that **the empty set is a subset of every set.** Furthermore, the empty set is a proper subset of every set except itself.

THE EMPTY SET AS A SUBSET

1. For any set B, $\varnothing \subseteq B$.
2. For any set B other than the empty set, $\varnothing \subset B$.

3 Determine the number of subsets of a set.

The Number of Subsets of a Given Set

If a set contains n elements, how many subsets can be formed? Let's observe some special cases, namely sets with 0, 1, 2, and 3 elements. We can use inductive reasoning to arrive at a general conclusion. We begin by listing subsets and counting the number of subsets in our list. This is shown in **Table 4**.

TABLE 4 The Number of Subsets: Some Special Cases

Set	Number of Elements	List of All Subsets	Number of Subsets
$\{\ \}$	0	$\{\ \}$	1
$\{a\}$	1	$\{a\}, \{\ \}$	2
$\{a, b\}$	2	$\{a, b\}, \{a\}, \{b\}, \{\ \}$	4
$\{a, b, c\}$	3	$\{a, b, c\}$, $\{a, b\}, \{a, c\}, \{b, c\}$, $\{a\}, \{b\}, \{c\}, \{\ \}$	8

Table 4 suggests that when we increase the number of elements in the set by one, the number of subsets doubles. The number of subsets appears to be a power of 2.

Number of elements	0	1	2	3
Number of subsets	$1 = 2^0$	$2 = 2^1$	$4 = 2 \times 2 = 2^2$	$8 = 2 \times 2 \times 2 = 2^3$

STUDY TIP

If powers of 2 have you in an exponentially increasing state of confusion, here's a list of values that should be helpful. Observe how rapidly these values are increasing.

Powers of 2

$2^0 = 1$
$2^1 = 2$
$2^2 = 2 \times 2 = 4$
$2^3 = 2 \times 2 \times 2 = 8$
$2^4 = 2 \times 2 \times 2 \times 2 = 16$
$2^5 = 2 \times 2 \times 2 \times 2 \times 2 = 32$
$2^6 = 64$
$2^7 = 128$
$2^8 = 256$
$2^9 = 512$
$2^{10} = 1024$
$2^{11} = 2048$
$2^{12} = 4096$
$2^{15} = 32{,}768$
$2^{20} = 1{,}048{,}576$
$2^{25} = 33{,}554{,}432$
$2^{30} = 1{,}073{,}741{,}824$

The power of 2 is the same as the number of elements in the set. Using inductive reasoning, if the set contains n elements, then the number of subsets that can be formed is 2^n.

NUMBER OF SUBSETS

The number of subsets of a set with n elements is 2^n.

For a given set, we know that every subset except the set itself is a proper subset. In **Table 4**, we included the set itself when counting the number of subsets. If we want to find the number of proper subsets, we must exclude counting the given set, thereby decreasing the number by 1.

NUMBER OF PROPER SUBSETS

The number of proper subsets of a set with n elements is $2^n - 1$.

EXAMPLE 4 Finding the Number of Subsets and Proper Subsets

Find the number of subsets and the number of proper subsets for each set:

a. $\{a, b, c, d, e\}$

b. $\{x | x \in \mathbf{N} \text{ and } 9 \leq x \leq 15\}$.

Solution

a. A set with n elements has 2^n subsets. Because the set $\{a, b, c, d, e\}$ contains 5 elements, there are $2^5 = 2 \times 2 \times 2 \times 2 \times 2 = 32$ subsets. Of these, we must exclude counting the given set as a proper subset, so there are $2^5 - 1 = 32 - 1 = 31$ proper subsets.

b. We can write $\{x | x \in \mathbf{N} \text{ and } 9 \leq x \leq 15\}$ in roster form as $\{9, 10, 11, 12, 13, 14, 15\}$. Because this set contains 7 elements, there are $2^7 = 2 \times 2 \times 2 \times 2 \times 2 \times 2 \times 2 = 128$ subsets. Of these, there are $2^7 - 1 = 128 - 1 = 127$ proper subsets.

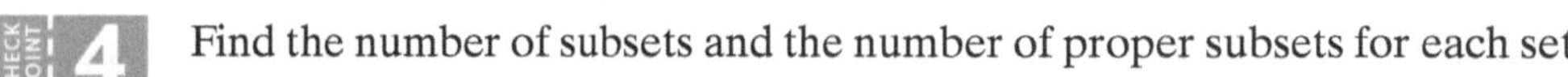

CHECK POINT 4 Find the number of subsets and the number of proper subsets for each set:

a. $\{a, b, c, d\}$

b. $\{x | x \in \mathbf{N} \text{ and } 3 \leq x \leq 8\}$.

4 Apply concepts of subsets and equivalent sets to infinite sets.

The Number of Subsets of Infinite Sets

In Section 1, we mentioned that the infinite set of natural numbers, $\{1, 2, 3, 4, 5, 6, \ldots\}$, is assigned the cardinal number $\aleph_0$ (read "aleph-null"), called a *transfinite* cardinal number. Equivalently, there are $\aleph_0$ natural numbers.

Once we accept the cardinality of sets with infinitely many elements, a surreal world emerges in which there is no end to an ascending hierarchy of infinities. Because the set of natural numbers contains $\aleph_0$ elements, it has $2^{\aleph_0}$ subsets, where $2^{\aleph_0} > \aleph_0$. Denoting $2^{\aleph_0}$ by $\aleph_1$, we have $\aleph_1 > \aleph_0$. Because the set of subsets of the natural numbers contains $\aleph_1$ elements, it has $2^{\aleph_1}$ subsets, where $2^{\aleph_1} > \aleph_1$. Denoting $2^{\aleph_1}$ by $\aleph_2$, we now have $\aleph_2 > \aleph_1 > \aleph_0$. Continuing in this manner, $\aleph_0$ is the "smallest" transfinite cardinal number in an infinite hierarchy of different infinities!

"Infinity is where things happen that don't."

W. W. Sawyer, *Prelude to Mathematics*, Penguin Books, 1960

BLITZER BONUS

CARDINAL NUMBERS OF INFINITE SETS

PJ Crook "Time and Time Again" 1981. Courtesy Loch Gallery, Toronto.

The mirrors in the painting *Time and Time Again* have the effect of repeating the image infinitely many times, creating an endless tunnel of mirror images. There is something quite fascinating about the idea of endless infinity. Did you know that for thousands of years religious leaders warned that human beings should not examine the nature of the infinite? Religious teaching often equated infinity with the concept of a Supreme Being. One of the last victims of the Inquisition, Giordano Bruno, was burned at the stake for his explorations into the characteristics of infinity. It was not until the 1870s that the German mathematician Georg Cantor (1845–1918) began a careful analysis of the mathematics of infinity.

It was Cantor who assigned the transfinite cardinal number $\aleph_0$ to the set of natural numbers. He used one-to-one correspondences to establish some surprising equivalences between the set of natural numbers and its proper subsets. Here are two examples:

$$\begin{array}{rl} \text{Natural Numbers:} & \{1, 2, 3, 4, 5, 6, \ldots, n, \ldots\} \\ & \ \ \updownarrow\ \updownarrow\ \updownarrow\ \updownarrow\ \updownarrow\ \updownarrow \qquad \updownarrow \\ \text{Even Natural Numbers:} & \{2, 4, 6, 8, 10, 12, \ldots, 2n, \ldots\} \end{array}$$

Each natural number, n, is paired with its double, $2n$, in the set of even natural numbers.

$$\begin{array}{rl} \text{Natural Numbers:} & \{1, 2, 3, 4, 5, 6, \ldots, n, \ldots\} \\ & \ \ \updownarrow\ \updownarrow\ \updownarrow\ \updownarrow\ \updownarrow\ \updownarrow \qquad \searrow \\ \text{Odd Natural Numbers:} & \{1, 3, 5, 7, 9, 11, \ldots, 2n - 1, \ldots\} \end{array}$$

Each natural number, n, is paired with 1 less than its double, $2n - 1$, in the set of odd natural numbers.

These one-to-one correspondences indicate that the set of even natural numbers and the set of odd natural numbers are equivalent to the set of all natural numbers. In fact, an infinite set, such as the natural numbers, can be *defined* as any set that can be placed in a one-to-one correspondence with a proper subset of itself. This definition boggles the mind because it implies that part of a set has the same number of objects as the entire set. There are $\aleph_0$ even natural numbers, $\aleph_0$ odd natural numbers, and $\aleph_0$ natural numbers. Because the even and odd natural numbers combined make up the entire set of natural numbers, we are confronted with an unusual statement of transfinite arithmetic:

$$\aleph_0 + \aleph_0 = \aleph_0.$$

As Cantor continued studying infinite sets, his observations grew stranger and stranger. It was Cantor who showed that some infinite sets contain more elements than others. This was too much for his colleagues, who considered this work ridiculous. Cantor's mentor, Leopold Kronecker, told him, "Look at the crazy ideas that are now surfacing with your work with infinite sets. How can one infinity be greater than another? Best to ignore such inconsistencies. By considering these monsters and infinite numbers mathematics, I will make sure that you never gain a faculty position at the University of Berlin." Although Cantor was not burned at the stake, universal condemnation of his work resulted in numerous nervous breakdowns. His final days, sadly, were spent in a psychiatric hospital. However, Cantor's work later regained the respect of mathematicians. Today, he is seen as a great mathematician who demystified infinity.

Exercise Set 2

Practice Exercises

In Exercises 1–18, write $\subseteq$ *or* $\not\subseteq$ *in each blank so that the resulting statement is true.*

1. $\{1, 2, 5\}$ ____ $\{1, 2, 3, 4, 5, 6, 7\}$

2. $\{2, 3, 7\}$ ____ $\{1, 2, 3, 4, 5, 6, 7\}$

3. $\{-3, 0, 3\}$ ____ $\{-3, -1, 1, 3\}$

4. $\{-4, 0, 4\}$ ____ $\{-4, -3, -1, 1, 3, 4\}$

5. {Monday, Friday} ____ {Saturday, Sunday, Monday, Tuesday, Wednesday}

6. {Mercury, Venus, Earth} ____ {Venus, Earth, Mars, Jupiter}

7. $\{x|x$ is a cat$\}$ ____ $\{x|x$ is a black cat$\}$

8. $\{x|x$ is a dog$\}$ ____ $\{x|x$ is a pure-bred dog$\}$

9. {c, o, n, v, e, r, s, a, t, i, o, n} ____ {v, o, i, c, e, s, r, a, n, t, o, n}

10. {r, e, v, o, l, u, t, i, o, n} _____ {t, o, l, o, v, e, r, u, i, n}

11. $\{\frac{4}{7}, \frac{9}{13}\}$ _____ $\{\frac{7}{4}, \frac{13}{9}\}$

12. $\{\frac{1}{2}, \frac{1}{3}\}$ _____ {2, 3, 5}

13. ∅ _____ {2, 4, 6}

14. ∅ _____ {1, 3, 5}

15. {2, 4, 6} _____ ∅

16. {1, 3, 5} _____ ∅

17. { } _____ ∅

18. ∅ _____ { }

In Exercises 19–40, determine whether $\subseteq$, $\subset$, *both, or neither can be placed in each blank to form a true statement.*

19. {V, C, R} _____ {V, C, R, S}

20. {F, I, N} _____ {F, I, N, K}

21. {0, 2, 4, 6, 8} _____ {8, 0, 6, 2, 4}

22. {9, 1, 7, 3, 4} _____ {1, 3, 4, 7, 9}

23. $\{x \mid x$ is a man$\}$ _____ $\{x \mid x$ is a woman$\}$

24. $\{x \mid x$ is a woman$\}$ _____ $\{x \mid x$ is a man$\}$

25. $\{x \mid x$ is a man$\}$ _____ $\{x \mid x$ is a person$\}$

26. $\{x \mid x$ is a woman$\}$ _____ $\{x \mid x$ is a person$\}$

27. $\{x \mid x$ is a man or a woman$\}$ _____ $\{x \mid x$ is a person$\}$

28. $\{x \mid x$ is a woman or a man$\}$ _____ $\{x \mid x$ is a person$\}$

29. $A = \{x \mid x \in \mathbf{N}$ and $5 < x < 12\}$
$B =$ the set of natural numbers between 5 and 12
A ___ B

30. $A = \{x \mid x \in \mathbf{N}$ and $3 < x < 10\}$
$B =$ the set of natural numbers between 3 and 10
A ___ B

31. $A = \{x \mid x \in \mathbf{N}$ and $5 < x < 12\}$
$B =$ the set of natural numbers between 3 and 17
A ___ B

32. $A = \{x \mid x \in \mathbf{N}$ and $3 < x < 10\}$
$B =$ the set of natural numbers between 2 and 16
A ___ B

33. $A = \{x \mid x \in \mathbf{N}$ and $5 < x < 12\}$
$B = \{x \mid x \in \mathbf{N}$ and $2 \le x \le 11\}$
A ___ B

34. $A = \{x \mid x \in \mathbf{N}$ and $3 < x < 10\}$
$B = \{x \mid x \in \mathbf{N}$ and $2 \le x \le 8\}$
A ___ B

35. ∅ ___ {7, 8, 9, . . . , 100}

36. ∅ ___ {101, 102, 103, . . . , 200}

37. {7, 8, 9, . . .} _____ ∅

38. {101, 102, 103, . . .} _____ ∅

39. ∅ _____ { }

40. { } _____ ∅

In Exercises 41–54, determine whether each statement is true or false. If the statement is false, explain why.

41. Ralph ∈ {Ralph, Alice, Trixie, Norton}

42. Canada ∈ {Mexico, United States, Canada}

43. Ralph ⊆ {Ralph, Alice, Trixie, Norton}

44. Canada ⊆ {Mexico, United States, Canada}

45. {Ralph} ⊆ {Ralph, Alice, Trixie, Norton}

46. {Canada} ⊆ {Mexico, United States, Canada}

47. ∅ ∈ {Archie, Edith, Mike, Gloria}

48. ∅ ⊆ {Charlie Chaplin, Groucho Marx, Woody Allen}

49. {5} ∈ {{5}, {9}}

50. {1} ∈ {{1}, {3}}

51. {1, 4} ⊈ {4, 1}

52. {1, 4} ⊄ {4, 1}

53. 0 ∉ ∅

54. {0} ⊈ ∅

In Exercises 55–60, list all the subsets of the given set.

55. {border collie, poodle}

56. {Romeo, Juliet}

57. {t, a, b}

58. {I, II, III}

59. {0}

60. ∅

In Exercises 61–68, calculate the number of subsets and the number of proper subsets for each set.

61. {2, 4, 6, 8}

62. $\{\frac{1}{2}, \frac{1}{3}, \frac{1}{4}, \frac{1}{5}\}$

63. {2, 4, 6, 8, 10, 12}

64. {a, b, c, d, e, f}

65. $\{x \mid x$ is a day of the week$\}$

66. $\{x \mid x$ is a U.S. coin worth less than a dollar$\}$

67. $\{x \mid x \in \mathbf{N}$ and $2 < x < 6\}$

68. $\{x \mid x \in \mathbf{N}$ and $2 \le x \le 6\}$

Practice Plus

In Exercises 69–82, determine whether each statement is true or false. If the statement is false, make the necessary change(s) to produce a true statement.

69. The set {1, 2, 3, . . . , 1000} has 2^{1000} proper subsets.

70. The set {1, 2, 3, . . . , 10,000} has $2^{10,000}$ proper subsets.

71. $\{x \mid x \in \mathbf{N}$ and $30 < x < 50\} \subseteq \{x \mid x \in \mathbf{N}$ and $30 \le x \le 50\}$

72. $\{x \mid x \in \mathbf{N}$ and $20 \le x \le 60\} \not\subseteq \{x \mid x \in \mathbf{N}$ and $20 < x < 60\}$

73. ∅ ⊈ {∅, {∅}}

74. {∅} ⊈ {∅, {∅}}

75. ∅ ∈ {∅, {∅}}

76. {∅} ∈ {∅, {∅}}

77. If $A \subseteq B$ and $d \in A$, then $d \in B$.

78. If $A \subseteq B$ and $B \subseteq C$, then $A \subseteq C$.

79. If set A is equivalent to the set of natural numbers, then $n(A) = \aleph_0$.

80. If set A is equivalent to the set of even natural numbers, then $n(A) = \aleph_0$.

81. The set of subsets of {a, e, i, o, u} contains 64 elements.

82. The set of subsets of {a, b, c, d, e, f} contains 128 elements.

Application Exercises

Sets and subsets allow us to order and structure data. In the data shown below, the set of tattooed Americans is divided into subsets categorized by party affiliation. These subsets are further broken down into subsets categorized by gender. All numbers in the branching tree diagram are based on the number of people per 10,000 American adults.

Breakdown of Tattooed Americans by Party Affiliation and Gender

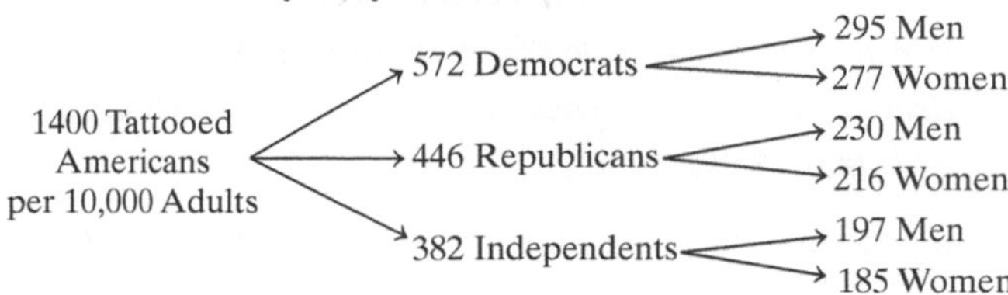

Source: Harris Interactive

Based on the tree diagram on the bottom of the previous page, let

T = the set of tattooed Americans

R = the set of tattooed Republicans

D = the set of tattooed Democrats

M = the set of tattooed Democratic men

W = the set of tattooed Democratic women.

In Exercises 83–92, determine whether each statement is true or false. If the statement is false, make the necessary change(s) to produce a true statement.

83. $D \in T$

84. $R \in T$

85. $M \subset T$

86. $W \subset T$

87. If $x \in D$, then $x \in W$.

88. If $x \in D$, then $x \in M$.

89. If $x \in R$, then $x \notin D$.

90. If $x \in D$, then $x \notin R$.

91. The set of elements in M and W combined is equal to set D.

92. The set of elements in M and W combined is equivalent to set D.

93. Houses in Euclid Estates are all identical. However, a person can purchase a new house with some, all, or none of a set of options. This set includes {pool, screened-in balcony, lake view, alarm system, upgraded landscaping}. How many options are there for purchasing a house in this community?

94. A cheese pizza can be ordered with some, all, or none of the following set of toppings: {beef, ham, mushrooms, sausage, peppers, pepperoni, olives, prosciutto, onion}. How many different variations are available for ordering a pizza?

95. Based on more than 1500 ballots sent to film notables, the American Film Institute rated the top U.S. movies. The Institute selected *Citizen Kane* (1941), *Casablanca* (1942), *The Godfather* (1972), *Gone With the Wind* (1939), *Lawrence of Arabia* (1962), and *The Wizard of Oz* (1939) as the top six films. Suppose that you have all six films on DVD and decide to view some, all, or none of these films. How many viewing options do you have?

96. A small town has four police cars. If a radio dispatcher receives a call, depending on the nature of the situation, no cars, one car, two cars, three cars, or all four cars can be sent. How many options does the dispatcher have for sending the police cars to the scene of the caller?

97. According to the U.S. Census Bureau, the most ethnically diverse U.S. cities are New York City, Los Angeles, Miami, Chicago, Washington, D.C., Houston, San Diego, and Seattle. If you decide to visit some, all, or none of these cities, how many travel options do you have?

98. Some of the movies with all-time high box office grosses include

Titanic ($601 million), *Star Wars: Episode IV—A New Hope* ($461 million), *Shrek* 2 ($441 million),
E. T. the Extra-Terrestrial ($435 million),
Star Wars: Episode I—The Phantom Menace ($431 million),
Pirates of the Carribean: Dead Man's Chest ($421 million), and
Spider-Man ($404 million).

Suppose that you have all seven films on DVD and decide, over the course of a week, to view some, all, or none of these films. How many viewing options do you have?

Writing in Mathematics

99. Explain what is meant by a subset.

100. What is the difference between a subset and a proper subset?

101. Explain why the empty set is a subset of every set.

102. Describe the difference between the symbols $\in$ and $\subseteq$. Explain how each symbol is used.

103. Describe the formula for finding the number of subsets for a given set. Give an example.

104. Describe how to find the number of proper subsets for a given set. Give an example.

Critical Thinking Exercises

Make Sense? *In Exercises 105–108, determine whether each statement makes sense or does not make sense, and explain your reasoning.*

105. The set of my six rent payments from January through June is a subset of the set of my 12 cable television payments from January through December.

106. Every time I increase the number of elements in a set by one, I double the number of subsets.

107. Because Exercises 93–98 involve different situations, I cannot solve them by the same method.

108. I recently purchased a set of books and am deciding which books, if any, to take on vacation. The number of subsets of my set of books gives me the number of different combinations of the books that I can take.

In Exercises 109–112, determine whether each statement is true or false. If the statement is false, make the necessary change(s) to produce a true statement

109. The set {3} has 2^3, or eight, subsets.

110. All sets have subsets.

111. Every set has a proper subset.

112. The set {3, {1, 4}} has eight subsets.

113. Suppose that a nickel, a dime, and a quarter are on a table. You may select some, all, or none of the coins. Specify all of the different amounts of money that can be selected.

114. If a set has 127 proper subsets, how many elements are there in the set?

Group Exercises

115. This activity is a group research project and should result in a presentation made by group members to the entire class. Georg Cantor was certainly not the only genius in history who faced criticism during his lifetime, only to have his work acclaimed as a masterpiece after his death. Describe the life and work of three other people, including at least one mathematician, who faced similar circumstances.

116. Research useful Web sites and present a report on infinite sets and their cardinalities. Explain why the sets of whole numbers, integers, and rational numbers each have cardinal number $\aleph_0$. Be sure to define these sets and show the one-to-one correspondences between each set and the set of natural numbers. Then explain why the set of real numbers does not have cardinal number $\aleph_0$ by describing how a real number can always be left out in a pairing with the natural numbers. Spice up the more technical aspects of your report with ideas you discovered about infinity that you find particularly intriguing.

OBJECTIVES

1. Understand the meaning of a universal set.
2. Understand the basic ideas of a Venn diagram.
3. Use Venn diagrams to visualize relationships between two sets.
4. Find the complement of a set.
5. Find the intersection of two sets.
6. Find the union of two sets.
7. Perform operations with sets.
8. Determine sets involving set operations from a Venn diagram.
9. Understand the meaning of *and* and *or*.
10. Use the formula for $n(A \cup B)$.

3 Venn Diagrams and Set Operations

SíTV, a 24-hour cable channel targeted to young U.S. Latinos, was launched in 2004 and is now in more than 18 million households. Its motto: "Speak English. Live Latin." As Latino spending power steadily rises, corporate America has discovered that Hispanic Americans, particularly young spenders between the ages of 14 and 34, want to be spoken to in English, even as they stay true to their Latino identity.

What is the primary language spoken at home by U.S. Hispanics? In this section, we use sets to analyze the answer to this question. By doing so, you will see how sets and their visual representations provide precise ways of organizing, classifying, and describing a wide variety of data.

Si TV, Inc.

1 | Understand the meaning of a universal set.

Universal Sets and Venn Diagrams

The circle graph in **Figure 2** categorizes America's 46 million Hispanics by the primary language spoken at home. The graph's sectors define four sets:

- the set of U.S. Hispanics who speak Spanish at home
- the set of U.S. Hispanics who speak English at home
- the set of U.S. Hispanics who speak both Spanish and English at home
- the set of U.S. Hispanics who speak neither Spanish nor English at home.

Languages Spoken at Home by U.S. Hispanics

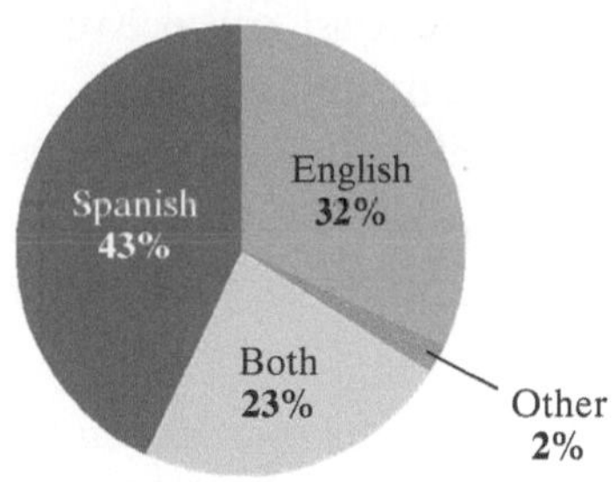

FIGURE 2
Source: Time

In discussing sets, it is convenient to refer to a general set that contains all elements under discussion. This general set is called the *universal set*. A **universal set**, symbolized by U, is a set that contains all the elements being considered in a given discussion or problem. Thus, a convenient universal set for the sets described above is

$$U = \text{the set of U.S. Hispanics.}$$

Notice how this universal set restricts our attention so that we can divide it into the four subsets shown by the circle graph in **Figure 2**.

2 | Understand the basic ideas of a Venn diagram.

We can obtain a more thorough understanding of sets and their relationship to a universal set by considering diagrams that allow visual analysis. **Venn diagrams**, named for the British logician John Venn (1834–1923), are used to show the visual relationship among sets.

Figure 3 is a Venn diagram. The universal set is represented by a region inside a rectangle. Subsets within the universal set are depicted by circles, or sometimes by ovals or other shapes. In this Venn diagram, set A is represented by the light blue region inside the circle.

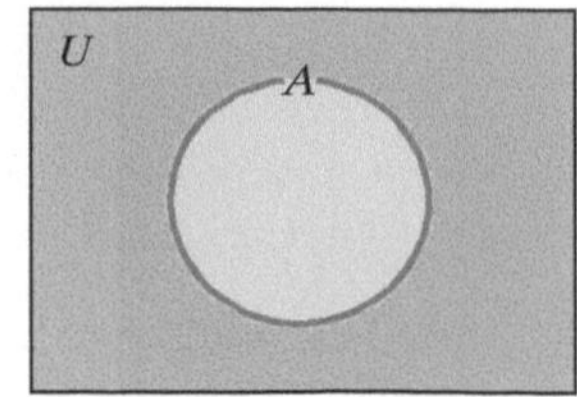

FIGURE 3

The dark blue region in **Figure 3** represents the set of elements in the universal set U that are not in set A. By combining the regions shown by the light blue shading and the dark blue shading, we obtain the universal set, U.

STUDY TIP

The size of the circle representing set A in a Venn diagram has nothing to do with the number of elements in set A.

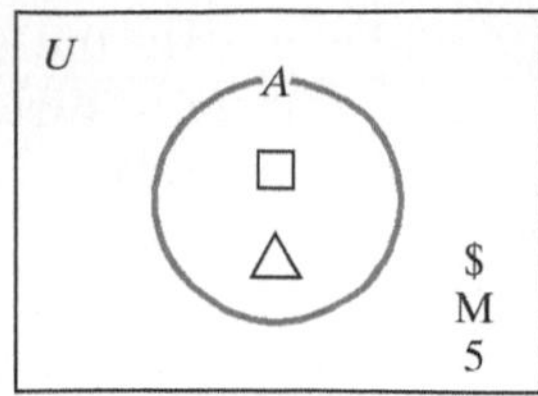

FIGURE 4

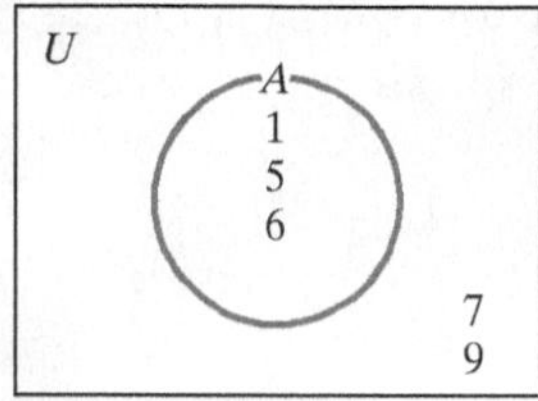

FIGURE 5

EXAMPLE 1 Determining Sets from a Venn Diagram

Use the Venn diagram in **Figure 4** to determine each of the following sets:

a. U **b.** A **c.** the set of elements in U that are not in A.

Solution

a. Set U, the universal set, consists of all the elements within the rectangle. Thus, $U = \{\square, \triangle, \$, \text{M}, 5\}$.

b. Set A consists of all the elements within the circle. Thus, $A = \{\square, \triangle\}$.

c. The set of elements in U that are not in A, shown by the set of all the elements outside the circle, is $\{\$, \text{M}, 5\}$.

Use the Venn diagram in **Figure 5** to determine each of the following sets:

a. U

b. A

c. the set of elements in U that are not in A.

3 Use Venn diagrams to visualize relationships between two sets.

Representing Two Sets in a Venn Diagram

There are a number of different ways to represent two subsets of a universal set in a Venn diagram. To help understand these representations, consider the following scenario:

You need to determine whether there is sufficient support on campus to have a blood drive. You take a survey to obtain information, asking students

Would you be willing to donate blood?

Would you be willing to help serve a free breakfast to blood donors?

Set A represents the set of students willing to donate blood. Set B represents the set of students willing to help serve breakfast to donors. Possible survey results include the following:

- No students willing to donate blood are willing to serve breakfast, and vice versa.
- All students willing to donate blood are willing to serve breakfast.
- The same students who are willing to donate blood are willing to serve breakfast.
- Some of the students willing to donate blood are willing to serve breakfast.

We begin by using Venn diagrams to visualize these results. To do so, we consider four basic relationships and their visualizations.

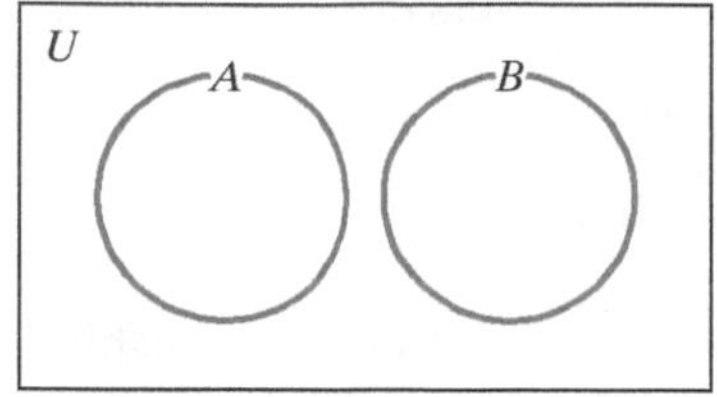

FIGURE 6

Relationship 1: Disjoint Sets Two sets that have no elements in common are called **disjoint sets.** Two disjoint sets, A and B, are shown in the Venn diagram in **Figure 6**. Disjoint sets are represented as circles that do not overlap. No elements of set A are elements of set B, and vice versa.

Since set A represents the set of students willing to donate blood and set B represents the set of students willing to serve breakfast to donors, the set diagram illustrates

No students willing to donate blood are willing to serve breakfast, and vice versa.

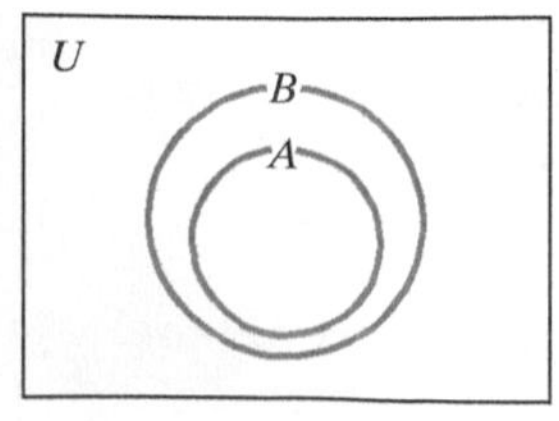

FIGURE 7

Relationship 2: Proper Subsets If set A is a proper subset of set B ($A \subset B$), the relationship is shown in the Venn diagram in **Figure 7**. All elements of set A are elements of set B. If an x representing an element is placed inside circle A, it automatically falls inside circle B.

Since set A represents the set of students willing to donate blood and set B represents the set of students willing to serve breakfast to donors, the set diagram illustrates

All students willing to donate blood are willing to serve breakfast.

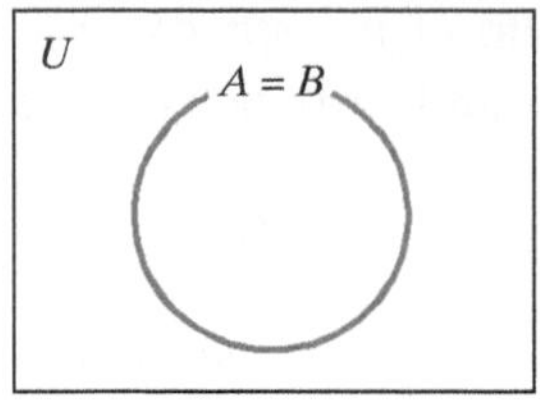

FIGURE 8

Relationship 3: Equal Sets If $A = B$, then set A contains exactly the same elements as set B. This relationship is shown in the Venn diagram in **Figure 8**. Because all elements in set A are in set B, and vice versa, this diagram illustrates that when $A = B$, then $A \subseteq B$ and $B \subseteq A$.

Since set A represents the set of students willing to donate blood and set B represents the set of students willing to serve breakfast to donors, the set diagram illustrates

The same students who are willing to donate blood are willing to serve breakfast.

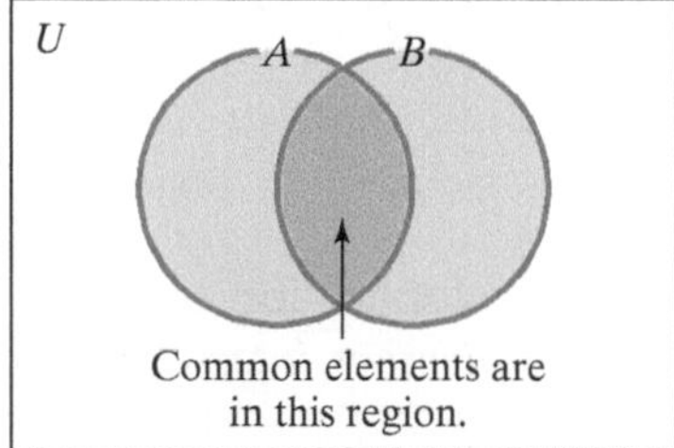

FIGURE 9

Relationship 4: Sets with Some Common Elements In mathematics, the word *some* means *there exists at least one*. If set A and set B have at least one element in common, then the circles representing the sets must overlap. This is illustrated in the Venn diagram in **Figure 9**.

Since set A represents the set of students willing to donate blood and set B represents the set of students willing to serve breakfast to donors, the presence of at least one student in the dark blue region in **Figure 9** illustrates

Some students willing to donate blood are willing to serve breakfast.

In **Figure 10**, we've numbered each of the regions in the Venn diagram in **Figure 9**. Let's make sure we understand what these regions represent in terms of the campus blood drive scenario. Remember that A is the set of blood donors and B is the set of breakfast servers.

In **Figure 10**, we'll start with the innermost region, region II, and work outward to region IV.

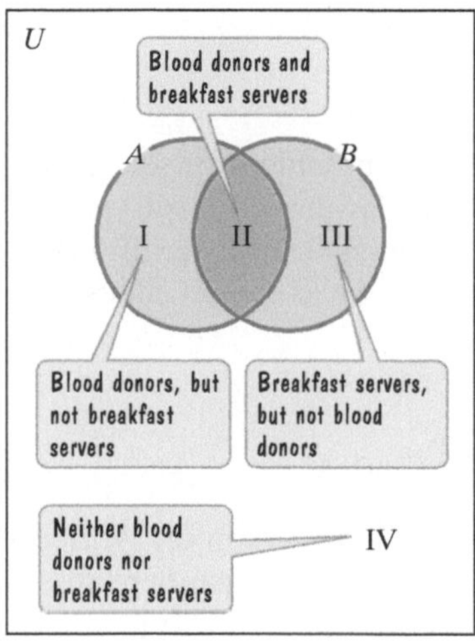

A: Set of blood donors
B: Set of breakfast servers

FIGURE 10

Region II	This region represents the set of students willing to donate blood and serve breakfast. The elements that belong to both set A and set B are in this region.
Region I	This region represents the set of students willing to donate blood but not serve breakfast. The elements that belong to set A but not to set B are in this region.
Region III	This region represents the set of students willing to serve breakfast but not donate blood. The elements that belong to set B but not to set A are in this region.
Region IV	This region represents the set of students surveyed who are not willing to donate blood and are not willing to serve breakfast. The elements that belong to the universal set U that are not in sets A or B are in this region.

EXAMPLE 2 Determining Sets from a Venn Diagram

Use the Venn diagram in **Figure 11** to determine each of the following sets:

a. U **b.** B

c. the set of elements in A but not B

d. the set of elements in U that are not in B

e. the set of elements in both A and B.

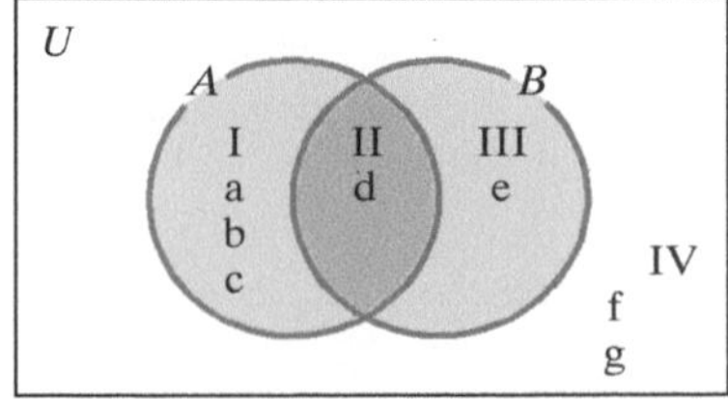

FIGURE 11

Solution

a. Set U, the universal set, consists of all elements within the rectangle. Taking the elements in regions I, II, III, and IV, we obtain $U = \{a, b, c, d, e, f, g\}$.

b. Set B consists of the elements in regions II and III. Thus, $B = \{d, e\}$.

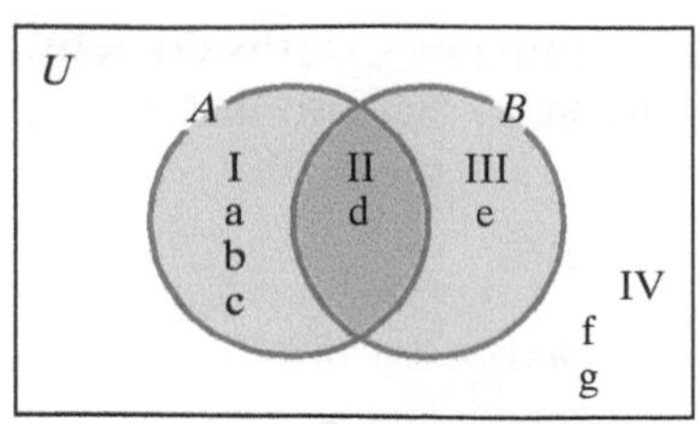
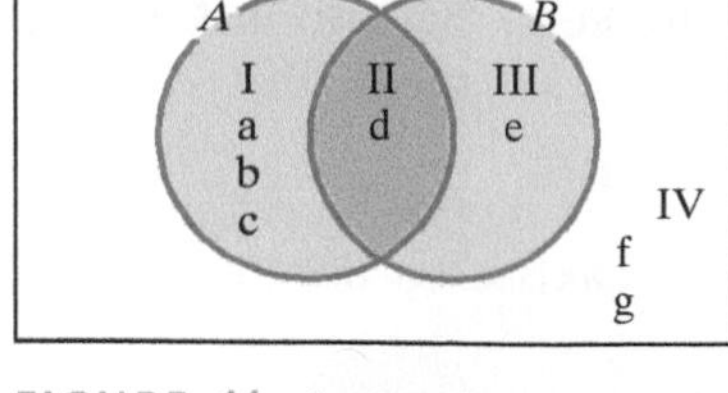

FIGURE 11 (repeated)

c. The set of elements in A but not B, found in region I, is $\{a, b, c\}$.

d. The set of elements in U that are not in B, found in regions I and IV, is $\{a, b, c, f, g\}$.

e. The set of elements in both A and B, found in region II, is $\{d\}$.

Use the Venn diagram in **Figure 11** to determine each of the following sets:

a. A

b. the set of elements in B but not A

c. the set of elements in U that are not in A

d. the set of elements in U that are not in A or B.

4 Find the complement of a set.

The Complement of a Set

In arithmetic, we use operations such as addition and multiplication to combine numbers. We now turn to three set operations, called *complement, intersection*, and *union*. We begin by defining a set's complement.

DEFINITION OF THE COMPLEMENT OF A SET

The **complement** of set A, symbolized by A', is the set of all elements in the universal set that are *not* in A. This idea can be expressed in set-builder notation as follows:

$$A' = \{x \mid x \in U \text{ and } x \notin A\}.$$

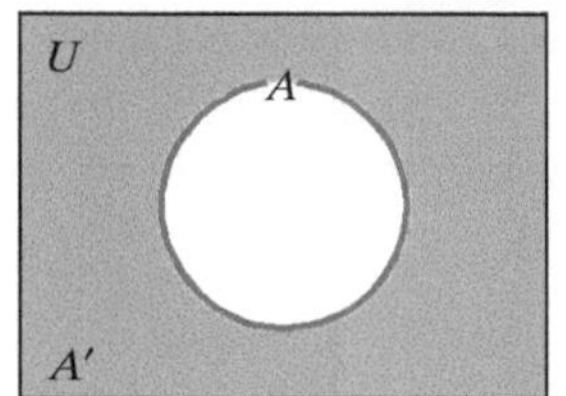

FIGURE 12

The shaded region in **Figure 12** represents the complement of set A, or A'. This region lies outside circle A, but within the rectangular universal set.

In order to find A', a universal set U must be given. A fast way to find A' is to cross out the elements in U that are given to be in set A. A' is the set that remains.

EXAMPLE 3 Finding a Set's Complement

Let $U = \{1, 2, 3, 4, 5, 6, 7, 8, 9\}$ and $A = \{1, 3, 4, 7\}$. Find A'.

Solution Set A' contains all the elements of set U that are not in set A. Because set A contains the elements 1, 3, 4, and 7, these elements cannot be members of set A':

$$\{\not{1}, 2, \not{3}, \not{4}, 5, 6, \not{7}, 8, 9\}.$$

Thus, set A' contains 2, 5, 6, 8, and 9:

$$A' = \{2, 5, 6, 8, 9\}.$$

A Venn diagram illustrating A and A' is shown in **Figure 13**.

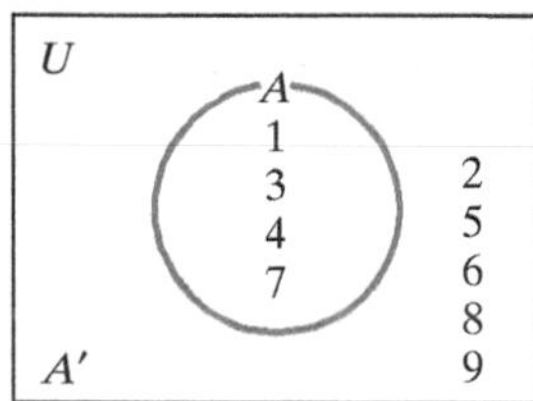

FIGURE 13

CHECK POINT 3 Let $U = \{a, b, c, d, e\}$ and $A = \{a, d\}$. Find A'.

5 Find the intersection of two sets.

The Intersection of Sets

If A and B are sets, we can form a new set consisting of all elements that are in both A and B. This set is called the *intersection* of the two sets.

DEFINITION OF THE INTERSECTION OF SETS

The **intersection** of sets A and B, written $A \cap B$, is the set of elements common to both set A and set B. This definition can be expressed in set-builder notation as follows:

$$A \cap B = \{x \mid x \in A \quad \text{and} \quad x \in B\}.$$

In Example 4, we are asked to find the intersection of two sets. This is done by listing the common elements of both sets. Because the intersection of two sets is also a set, we enclose these elements with braces.

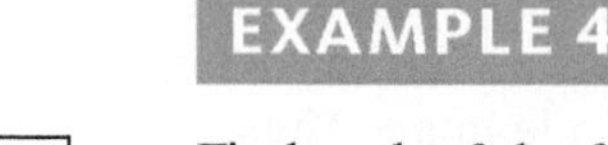

EXAMPLE 4 Finding the Intersection of Two Sets

Find each of the following intersections:

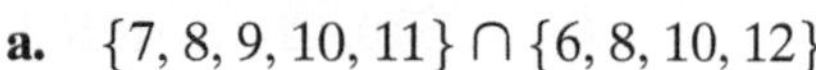

a. $\{7, 8, 9, 10, 11\} \cap \{6, 8, 10, 12\}$

b. $\{1, 3, 5, 7, 9\} \cap \{2, 4, 6, 8\}$

c. $\{1, 3, 5, 7, 9\} \cap \emptyset$.

Solution

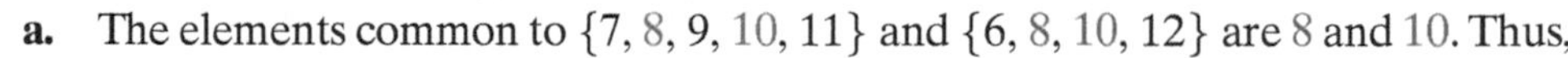

a. The elements common to $\{7, 8, 9, 10, 11\}$ and $\{6, 8, 10, 12\}$ are 8 and 10. Thus,

$$\{7, 8, 9, 10, 11\} \cap \{6, 8, 10, 12\} = \{8, 10\}.$$

The Venn diagram in **Figure 14** illustrates this situation.

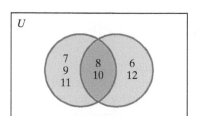

FIGURE 14 The numbers 8 and 10 belong to both sets.

b. The sets $\{1, 3, 5, 7, 9\}$ and $\{2, 4, 6, 8\}$ have no elements in common. Thus,

$$\{1, 3, 5, 7, 9\} \cap \{2, 4, 6, 8\} = \emptyset.$$

The Venn diagram in **Figure 15** illustrates this situation. The sets are disjoint.

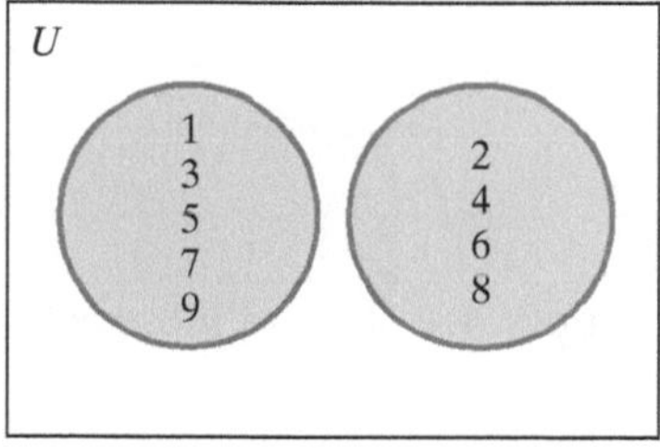

FIGURE 15 These disjoint sets have no common elements.

c. There are no elements in $\emptyset$, the empty set. This means that there can be no elements belonging to both $\{1, 3, 5, 7, 9\}$ and $\emptyset$. Therefore,

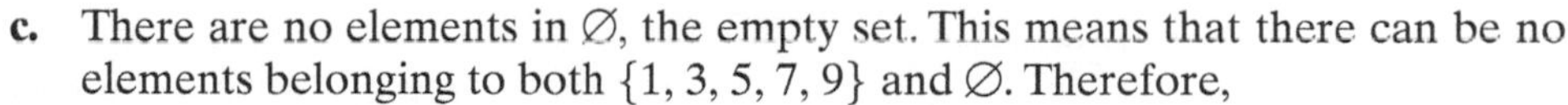

$$\{1, 3, 5, 7, 9\} \cap \emptyset = \emptyset.$$

CHECK POINT 4 Find each of the following intersections:

a. $\{1, 3, 5, 7, 10\} \cap \{6, 7, 10, 11\}$

b. $\{1, 2, 3\} \cap \{4, 5, 6, 7\}$

c. $\{1, 2, 3\} \cap \emptyset$.

6 Find the union of two sets.

The Union of Sets

Another set that we can form from sets A and B consists of elements that are in A or B or in both sets. This set is called the *union* of the two sets.

DEFINITION OF THE UNION OF SETS

The **union** of sets A and B, written $A \cup B$, is the set of elements that are members of set A or of set B or of both sets. This definition can be expressed in set-builder notation as follows:

$$A \cup B = \{x \mid x \in A \quad \text{or} \quad x \in B\}.$$

We can find the union of set A and set B by listing the elements of set A. Then, we include any elements of set B that have not already been listed. Enclose all elements that are listed with braces. This shows that the union of two sets is also a set.

EXAMPLE 5 Finding the Union of Two Sets

Find each of the following unions:

a. $\{7, 8, 9, 10, 11\} \cup \{6, 8, 10, 12\}$

b. $\{1, 3, 5, 7, 9\} \cup \{2, 4, 6, 8\}$

c. $\{1, 3, 5, 7, 9\} \cup \emptyset$.

Solution This example uses the same sets as in Example 4. However, this time we are finding the unions of the sets, rather than their intersections.

a. To find $\{7, 8, 9, 10, 11\} \cup \{6, 8, 10, 12\}$, start by listing all the elements from the first set, namely 7, 8, 9, 10, and 11. Now list all the elements from the second set that are not in the first set, namely 6 and 12. The union is the set consisting of all these elements. Thus,

$$\{7, 8, 9, 10, 11\} \cup \{6, 8, 10, 12\} = \{6, 7, 8, 9, 10, 11, 12\}.$$

b. To find $\{1, 3, 5, 7, 9\} \cup \{2, 4, 6, 8\}$, list the elements from the first set, namely 1, 3, 5, 7, and 9. Now add to the list the elements in the second set that are not in the first set. This includes every element in the second set, namely 2, 4, 6, and 8. The union is the set consisting of all these elements, so

$$\{1, 3, 5, 7, 9\} \cup \{2, 4, 6, 8\} = \{1, 2, 3, 4, 5, 6, 7, 8, 9\}.$$

c. To find $\{1, 3, 5, 7, 9\} \cup \varnothing$, list the elements from the first set, namely 1, 3, 5, 7, and 9. Because there are no elements in $\varnothing$, the empty set, there are no additional elements to add to the list. Thus,

$$\{1, 3, 5, 7, 9\} \cup \varnothing = \{1, 3, 5, 7, 9\}.$$

STUDY TIP

When finding the union of two sets, some elements may appear in both sets. List these common elements only once, *not twice*, in the union of the sets.

Examples 4 and 5 illustrate the role that the empty set plays in intersection and union.

THE EMPTY SET IN INTERSECTION AND UNION

For any set A,

1. $A \cap \varnothing = \varnothing$
2. $A \cup \varnothing = A$.

Find each of the following unions:

a. $\{1, 3, 5, 7, 10\} \cup \{6, 7, 10, 11\}$

b. $\{1, 2, 3\} \cup \{4, 5, 6, 7\}$

c. $\{1, 2, 3\} \cup \varnothing$.

7 Perform operations with sets.

Performing Set Operations

Some problems involve more than one set operation. The set notation specifies the order in which we perform these operations. **Always begin by performing any operations inside parentheses.** Here are two examples involving sets we will find in Example 6.

- Finding $(A \cup B)'$

  Step 1. Parentheses indicate to first find the union of A and B.

  Step 2. Find the complement of $A \cup B$.

- Finding $A' \cap B'$

  Step 1. Find the complement of A.

  Step 2. Find the complement of B.

  Step 3. Find the intersection of A' and B'.

STUDY TIP

The words *union* and *intersection* are helpful in distinguishing these two operations. Union, as in a marriage union, suggests joining things, or uniting them. Intersection, as in the intersection of two crossing streets, brings to mind the area common to both, suggesting things that overlap.

EXAMPLE 6 Performing Set Operations

Given

$$U = \{1, 2, 3, 4, 5, 6, 7, 8, 9, 10\}$$
$$A = \{1, 3, 7, 9\}$$
$$B = \{3, 7, 8, 10\},$$

find each of the following sets:

a. $(A \cup B)'$ **b.** $A' \cap B'$.

Solution

a. To find $(A \cup B)'$ we will first work inside the parentheses and determine $A \cup B$. Then we'll find the complement of $A \cup B$, namely $(A \cup B)'$.

$$A \cup B = \{1, 3, 7, 9\} \cup \{3, 7, 8, 10\}$$ These are the given sets.

$$= \{1, 3, 7, 8, 9, 10\}$$ Join (unite) the elements, listing the common elements (3 and 7) only once.

Now find $(A \cup B)'$, the complement of $A \cup B$.

$$(A \cup B)' = \{1, 3, 7, 8, 9, 10\}'$$

$$= \{2, 4, 5, 6\}$$ List the elements in the universal set that are not listed in {1, 3, 7, 8, 9, 10}: {~~1~~, 2, ~~3~~, 4, 5, 6, ~~7~~, ~~8~~, ~~9~~, ~~10~~}.

b. To find $A' \cap B'$, we must first identify the elements in A' and B'. Set A' is the set of elements of U that are not in set A:

$$A' = \{2, 4, 5, 6, 8, 10\}.$$ List the elements in the universal set that are not listed in A = {1, 3, 7, 9}: {~~1~~, 2, ~~3~~, 4, 5, 6, ~~7~~, 8, ~~9~~, 10}.

Set B' is the set of elements of U that are not in set B:

$$B' = \{1, 2, 4, 5, 6, 9\}.$$ List the elements in the universal set that are not listed in B = {3, 7, 8, 10}: {1, 2, ~~3~~, 4, 5, 6, ~~7~~, ~~8~~, 9, ~~10~~}.

Now we can find $A' \cap B'$, the set of elements belonging to both A' and to B':

$$A' \cap B' = \{2, 4, 5, 6, 8, 10\} \cap \{1, 2, 4, 5, 6, 9\}$$
$$= \{2, 4, 5, 6\}.$$ The numbers 2, 4, 5, and 6 are common to both sets.

CHECK POINT 6 Given $U = \{a, b, c, d, e\}$, $A = \{b, c\}$, and $B = \{b, c, e\}$, find each of the following sets:

a. $(A \cup B)'$ **b.** $A' \cap B'$.

EXAMPLE 7 Determining Sets from a Venn Diagram

8 Determine sets involving set operations from a Venn diagram.

The Venn diagram in **Figure 16** percolates with interesting numbers. Use the diagram to determine each of the following sets:

a. $A \cup B$ **b.** $(A \cup B)'$ **c.** $A \cap B$

d. $(A \cap B)'$ **e.** $A' \cap B$ **f.** $A \cup B'$.

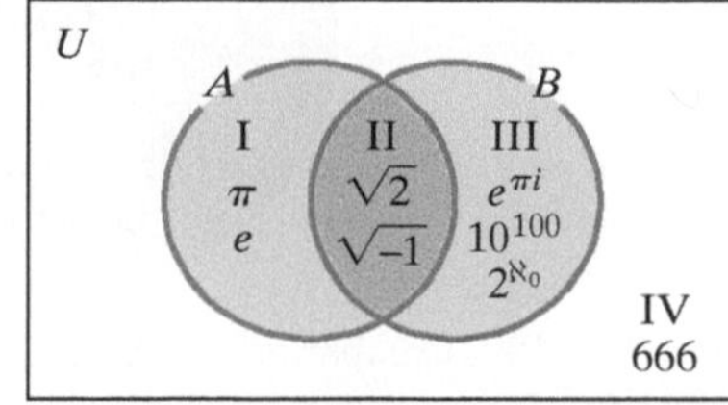

FIGURE 16

Solution Refer to **Figure 16**, repeated below.

Set to Determine	Description of Set	Regions in Venn Diagram in Figure 16	Set in Roster Form
a. $A \cup B$	set of elements in A or B or both	I, II, III	$\{\pi, e, \sqrt{2}, \sqrt{-1}, e^{\pi i}, 10^{100}, 2^{\aleph_0}\}$
b. $(A \cup B)'$	set of elements in U that are not in $A \cup B$	IV	$\{666\}$
c. $A \cap B$	set of elements in both A and B	II	$\{\sqrt{2}, \sqrt{-1}\}$
d. $(A \cap B)'$	set of elements in U that are not in $A \cap B$	I, III, IV	$\{\pi, e, e^{\pi i}, 10^{100}, 2^{\aleph_0}, 666\}$
e. $A' \cap B$	set of elements that are not in A and are in B	III	$\{e^{\pi i}, 10^{100}, 2^{\aleph_0}\}$
f. $A \cup B'$	set of elements that are in A or not in B or both	I, II, IV	$\{\pi, e, \sqrt{2}, \sqrt{-1}, 666\}$

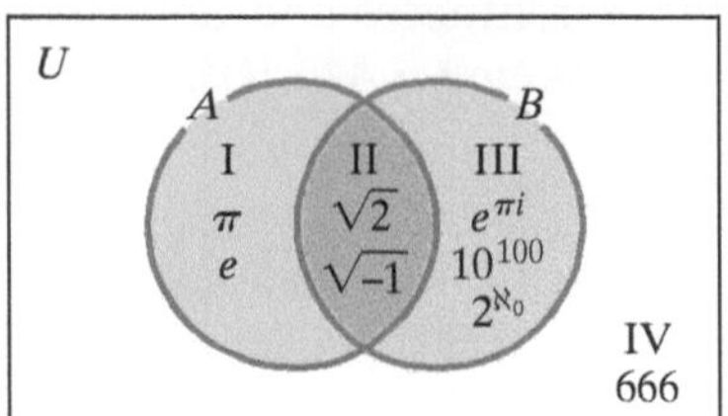

FIGURE 16 (repeated)

Use the Venn diagram in **Figure 17** to determine each of the following sets:

a. $A \cap B$
b. $(A \cap B)'$
c. $A \cup B$
d. $(A \cup B)'$
e. $A' \cup B$
f. $A \cap B'$.

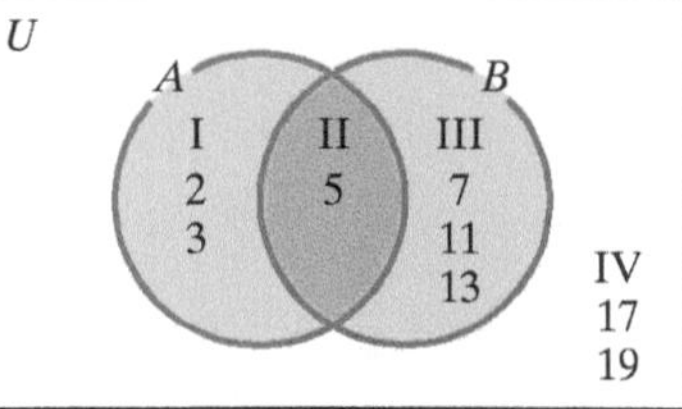

FIGURE 17

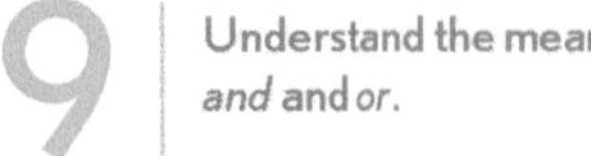

Understand the meaning of *and* and *or*.

Sets and Precise Use of Everyday English

Set operations and Venn diagrams provide precise ways of organizing, classifying, and describing the vast array of sets and subsets we encounter every day. Let's see how this applies to the sets from the beginning of this section:

U = the set of U.S. Hispanics
S = the set of U.S. Hispanics who speak Spanish at home
E = the set of U.S. Hispanics who speak English at home.

When describing collections in everyday English, the word **or** refers to the **union** of sets. Thus, U.S. Hispanics who speak Spanish or English at home means those who speak Spanish or English or both. The word **and** refers to the **intersection** of sets. Thus, U.S. Hispanics who speak Spanish and English at home means those who speak both languages.

In **Figure 18**, we revisit the circle graph showing languages spoken at home by U.S. Hispanics. To the right of the circle graph, we've organized the data using a Venn diagram. The voice balloons indicate how the Venn diagram provides a more accurate understanding of the subsets and their data.

Languages Spoken at Home by U.S. Hispanics

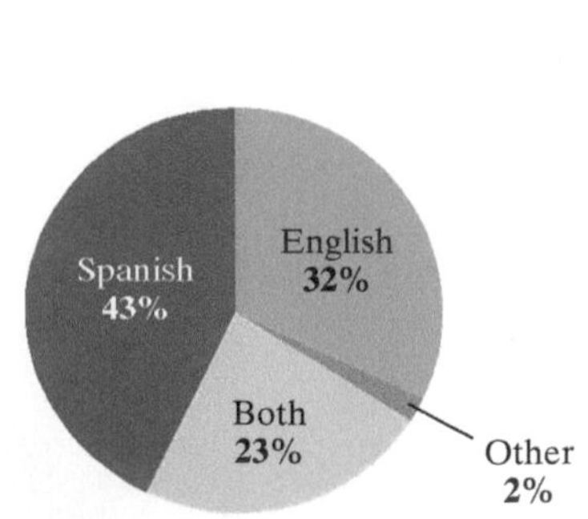

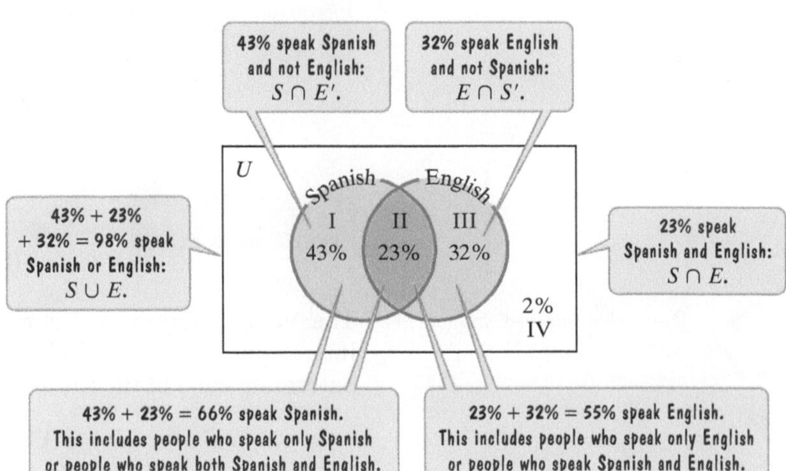

FIGURE 18 Comparing a circle graph and a Venn diagram
Source: Time

10 Use the formula for $n(A \cup B)$.

The Cardinal Number of the Union of Two Finite Sets

Can the number of elements in A or B, $n(A \cup B)$, be determined by adding the number of elements in A and the number of elements in B, $n(A) + n(B)$? The answer is no. **Figure 19** illustrates that by doing this, we are counting elements in both sets, $A \cap B$, or region II, twice.

To find the number of elements in the union of finite sets A and B, add the number of elements in A and the number of elements in B. Then subtract the number of elements common to both sets. We perform this subtraction so that we do not count the number of elements in the intersection twice, once for $n(A)$, and again for $n(B)$.

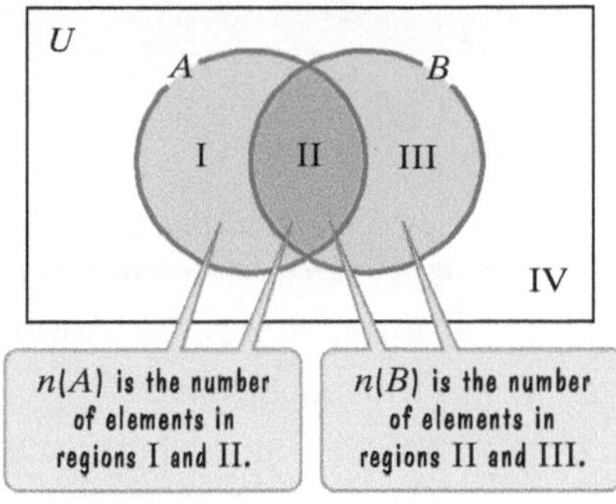
U
A
B
I
II
III
IV
n(A) is the number of elements in regions I and II.
n(B) is the number of elements in regions II and III.

FIGURE 19

FORMULA FOR THE CARDINAL NUMBER OF THE UNION OF TWO FINITE SETS

$$n(A \cup B) = n(A) + n(B) - n(A \cap B)$$

The number of elements in A or B | is | the number of elements in A plus the number of elements in B | minus the number of elements in A and B.

EXAMPLE 8 Using the Formula for $n(A \cup B)$

Some of the results of the campus blood drive survey indicated that 490 students were willing to donate blood, 340 students were willing to help serve a free breakfast to blood donors, and 120 students were willing to donate blood and serve breakfast. How many students were willing to donate blood or serve breakfast?

Solution Let A = the set of students willing to donate blood and B = the set of students willing to serve breakfast. We are interested in how many students were willing to donate blood or serve breakfast. Thus, we need to determine $n(A \cup B)$.

number of blood donors or breakfast servers | number of blood donors | number of breakfast servers | number of blood donors and breakfast servers

$$\begin{aligned} n(A \cup B) &= n(A) + n(B) - n(A \cap B) \\ &= 490 + 340 - 120 \\ &= 830 - 120 \\ &= 710 \end{aligned}$$

We see that 710 students were willing to donate blood or serve a free breakfast.

CHECK POINT 8 The admissions department at a college looked at the registration of 500 of its students and found the following results: 244 students were registered in a mathematics class, 230 students were registered in an English class, and 89 students were registered in a math class and an English class. How many students were registered in a math class or an English class?

Exercise Set 3

Practice Exercises

In Exercises 1–4, describe a universal set U that includes all elements in the given sets. Answers may vary.

1. $A = \{$Bach, Mozart, Beethoven$\}$
$B = \{$Brahms, Schubert$\}$

2. $A = \{$William Shakespeare, Charles Dickens$\}$
$B = \{$Mark Twain, Robert Louis Stevenson$\}$

3. $A = \{$Pepsi, Sprite$\}$
$B = \{$Coca Cola, Seven-Up$\}$

4. $A = \{$Acura RSX, Toyota Camry, Mitsubishi Lancer$\}$
$B = \{$Dodge Ram, Chevrolet Impala$\}$

In Exercises 5–8, let $U = \{a, b, c, d, e, f, g\}$, $A = \{a, b, f, g\}$, $B = \{c, d, e\}$, $C = \{a, g\}$, *and* $D = \{a, b, c, d, e, f\}$.
Use the roster method to write each of the following sets.

5. A' **6.** B' **7.** C' **8.** D'

In Exercises 9–12, let $U = \{1, 2, 3, 4, \ldots, 20\}$, $A = \{1, 2, 3, 4, 5\}$, $B = \{6, 7, 8, 9\}$, $C = \{1, 3, 5, 7, \ldots, 19\}$, *and* $D = \{2, 4, 6, 8, \ldots, 20\}$.
Use the roster method to write each of the following sets.

9. A' **10.** B' **11.** C' **12.** D'

In Exercises 13–16, let $U = \{1, 2, 3, 4, \ldots\}$, $A = \{1, 2, 3, 4, \ldots, 20\}$, $B = \{1, 2, 3, 4, \ldots, 50\}$, $C = \{2, 4, 6, 8, \ldots\}$, *and* $D = \{1, 3, 5, 7, \ldots\}$.
Use the roster method to write each of the following sets.

13. A' **14.** B' **15.** C' **16.** D'

In Exercises 17–40, let

$$U = \{1, 2, 3, 4, 5, 6, 7\}$$
$$A = \{1, 3, 5, 7\}$$
$$B = \{1, 2, 3\}$$
$$C = \{2, 3, 4, 5, 6\}.$$

Find each of the following sets.

17. $A \cap B$ **18.** $B \cap C$ **19.** $A \cup B$
20. $B \cup C$ **21.** A' **22.** B'
23. $A' \cap B'$ **24.** $B' \cap C$ **25.** $A \cup C'$
26. $B \cup C'$ **27.** $(A \cap C)'$ **28.** $(A \cap B)'$
29. $A' \cup C'$ **30.** $A' \cup B'$ **31.** $(A \cup B)'$
32. $(A \cup C)'$ **33.** $A \cup \varnothing$ **34.** $C \cup \varnothing$
35. $A \cap \varnothing$ **36.** $C \cap \varnothing$ **37.** $A \cup U$
38. $B \cup U$ **39.** $A \cap U$ **40.** $B \cap U$

In Exercises 41–66, let

$$U = \{a, b, c, d, e, f, g, h\}$$
$$A = \{a, g, h\}$$
$$B = \{b, g, h\}$$
$$C = \{b, c, d, e, f\}.$$

Find each of the following sets.

41. $A \cap B$ **42.** $B \cap C$ **43.** $A \cup B$
44. $B \cup C$ **45.** A' **46.** B'
47. $A' \cap B'$ **48.** $B' \cap C$ **49.** $A \cup C'$
50. $B \cup C'$ **51.** $(A \cap C)'$ **52.** $(A \cap B)'$
53. $A' \cup C'$ **54.** $A' \cup B'$ **55.** $(A \cup B)'$
56. $(A \cup C)'$ **57.** $A \cup \varnothing$ **58.** $C \cup \varnothing$
59. $A \cap \varnothing$ **60.** $C \cap \varnothing$ **61.** $A \cup U$
62. $B \cup U$ **63.** $A \cap U$ **64.** $B \cap U$
65. $(A \cap B) \cup B'$ **66.** $(A \cup B) \cap B'$

In Exercises 67–78, use the Venn diagram to represent each set in roster form.

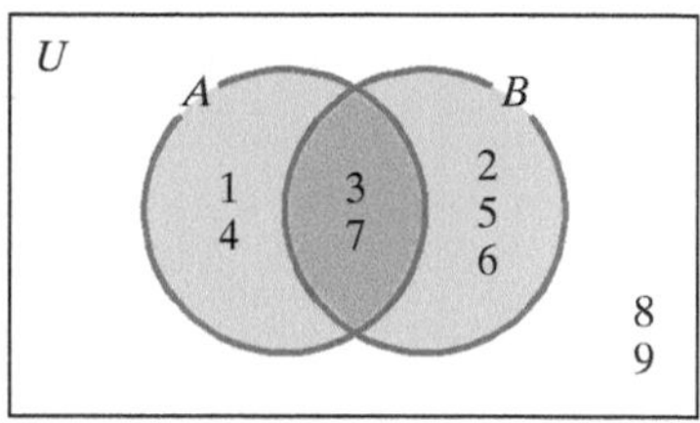

67. A **68.** B **69.** U
70. $A \cup B$ **71.** $A \cap B$ **72.** A'
73. B' **74.** $(A \cap B)'$ **75.** $(A \cup B)'$
76. $A' \cap B$ **77.** $A \cap B'$ **78.** $A \cup B'$

In Exercises 79–92, use the Venn diagram to determine each set or cardinality.

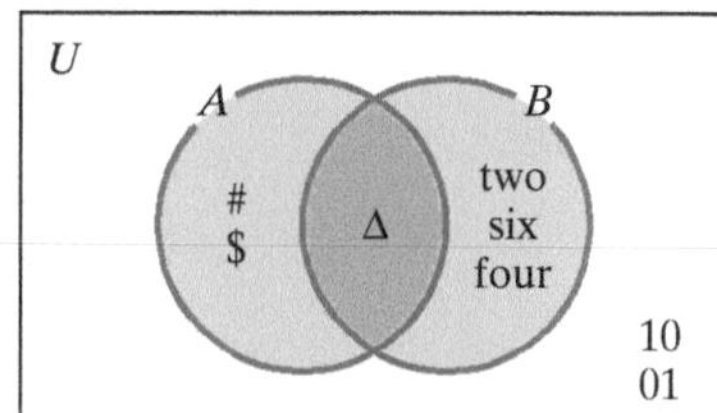

79. B **80.** A **81.** $A \cup B$
82. $A \cap B$ **83.** $n(A \cup B)$ **84.** $n(A \cap B)$
85. $n(A')$ **86.** $n(B')$ **87.** $(A \cap B)'$
88. $(A \cup B)'$ **89.** $A' \cap B$ **90.** $A \cap B'$
91. $n(U) - n(B)$ **92.** $n(U) - n(A)$

Use the formula for the cardinal number of the union of two sets to solve Exercises 93–96.

93. Set A contains 17 elements, set B contains 20 elements, and 6 elements are common to sets A and B. How many elements are in $A \cup B$?

94. Set A contains 30 elements, set B contains 18 elements, and 5 elements are common to sets A and B. How many elements are in $A \cup B$?

95. Set A contains 8 letters and 9 numbers. Set B contains 7 letters and 10 numbers. Four letters and 3 numbers are common to both sets A and B. Find the number of elements in set A or set B.

96. Set A contains 12 numbers and 18 letters. Set B contains 14 numbers and 10 letters. One number and 6 letters are common to both sets A and B. Find the number of elements in set A or set B.

Practice Plus

In Exercises 97–104, let

$$U = \{x \mid x \in \mathbf{N} \text{ and } x < 9\}$$
$$A = \{x \mid x \text{ is an odd natural number and } x < 9\}$$
$$B = \{x \mid x \text{ is an even natural number and } x < 9\}$$
$$C = \{x \mid x \in \mathbf{N} \text{ and } 1 < x < 6\}.$$

Find each of the following sets.

97. $A \cup B$ **98.** $B \cup C$

99. $A \cap U$ **100.** $A \cup U$

101. $A \cap C'$ **102.** $A \cap B'$

103. $(B \cap C)'$ **104.** $(A \cap C)'$

In Exercises 105–108, use the Venn diagram to determine each set or cardinality.

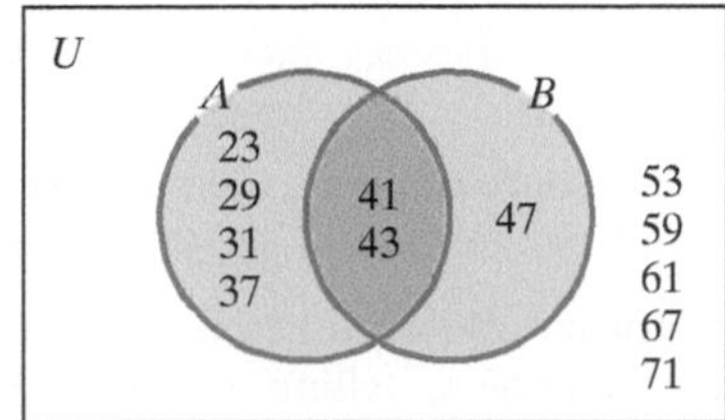

105. $A \cup (A \cup B)'$

106. $(A' \cap B) \cup (A \cap B)$

107. $n(U)[n(A \cup B) - n(A \cap B)]$

108. $n(A \cap B)[n(A \cup B) - n(A')]$

Application Exercises

A math tutor working with a small group of students asked each student when he or she had studied for class the previous weekend. Their responses are shown in the Venn diagram.

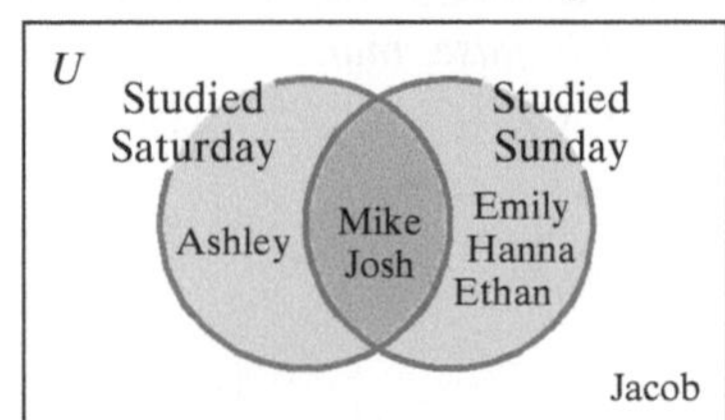

In Exercises 109–116, use the Venn diagram to list the elements of each set in roster form.

109. The set of students who studied Saturday

110. The set of students who studied Sunday

111. The set of students who studied Saturday or Sunday

112. The set of students who studied Saturday and Sunday

113. The set of students who studied Saturday and not Sunday

114. The set of students who studied Sunday and not Saturday

115. The set of students who studied neither Saturday nor Sunday

116. The set of students surveyed by the math tutor

The bar graph shows the percentage of Americans with gender preferences for various jobs.

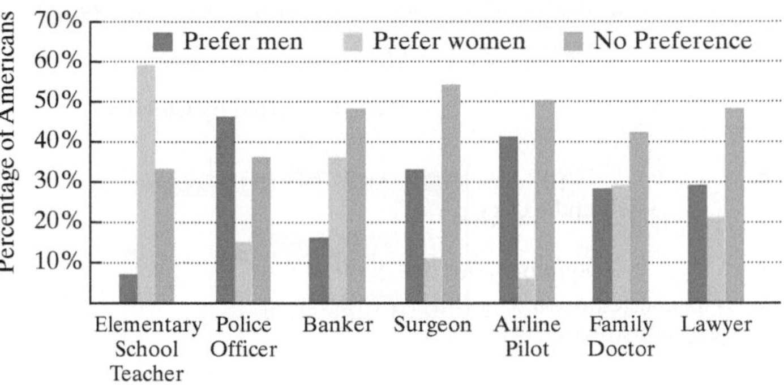

Source: Pew Research Center

In Exercises 117–122, use the information in the graph to place the indicated job in the correct region of the following Venn diagram.

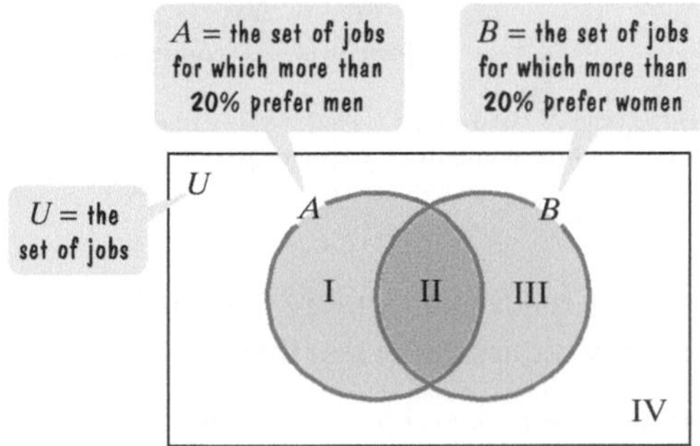

117. elementary school teacher **118.** police officer

119. surgeon **120.** banker

121. family doctor **122.** lawyer

A **palindromic number** *is a natural number whose value does not change if its digits are reversed. Examples of palindromic numbers are 11, 454, and 261,162. In Exercises 123–132, use this definition to place the indicated natural number in the correct region of the following Venn diagram.*

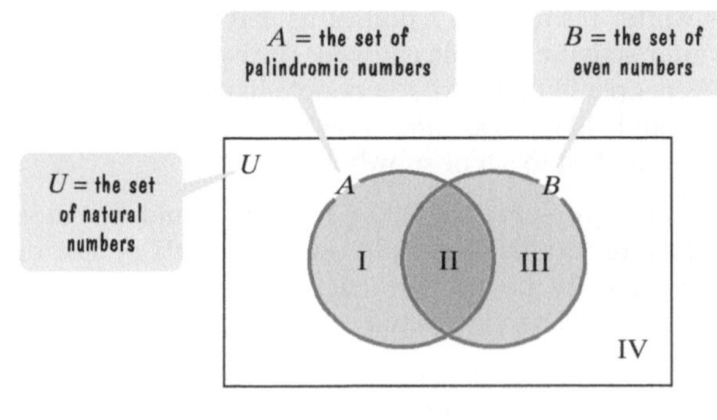

123. 11 **124.** 22

125. 15 **126.** 17

127. 454 **128.** 101

129. 9558 **130.** 9778

131. 9559 **132.** 9779

As a result of cultural expectations about what is appropriate behavior for each gender, boys and girls differ substantially in their toy preferences. The graph shows the percentage of boys and girls asking for various types of toys in letters to Santa Claus. Use the information in the graph to write each set in Exercises 133–138 in roster form or express the set as ∅.

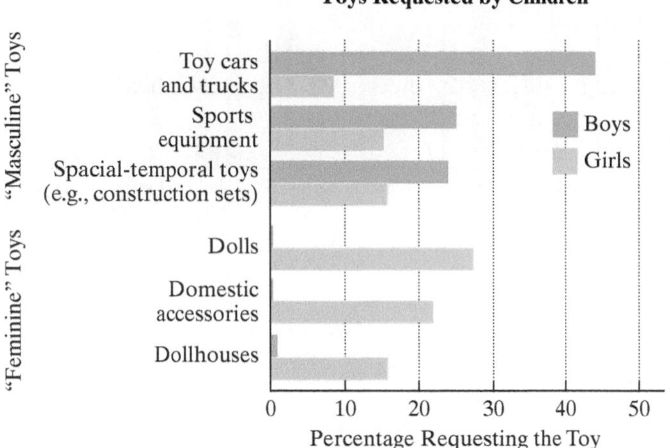

Source: Richard, J. G., & Simpson, C. H. (1982). Children, gender and social structure: An analysis of the contents of letters to Santa Claus. *Child Development*, 53, 429–436.

133. $\{x|x$ is a toy requested by more than 10% of the boys$\} \cap \{x|x$ is a toy requested by less than 20% of the girls$\}$

134. $\{x|x$ is a toy requested by fewer than 5% of the boys$\} \cap \{x|x$ is a toy requested by fewer than 20% of the girls$\}$

135. $\{x|x$ is a toy requested by more than 10% of the boys$\} \cup \{x|x$ is a toy requested by less than 20% of the girls$\}$

136. $\{x|x$ is a toy requested by fewer than 5% of the boys$\} \cup \{x|x$ is a toy requested by fewer than 20% of the girls$\}$

137. The set of toys requested by more than 40% of the boys and more than 10% of the girls

138. The set of toys requested by more than 40% of the boys or more than 10% of the girls

139. A winter resort took a poll of its 350 visitors to see which winter activities people enjoyed. The results were as follows: 178 people liked to ski, 154 people liked to snowboard, and 49 people liked to ski and snowboard. How many people in the poll liked to ski or snowboard?

140. A pet store surveyed 200 pet owners and obtained the following results: 96 people owned cats, 97 people owned dogs, and 29 people owned cats and dogs. How many people in the survey owned cats or dogs?

Writing in Mathematics

141. Describe what is meant by a universal set. Provide an example.

142. What is a Venn diagram and how is it used?

143. Describe the Venn diagram for two disjoint sets. How does this diagram illustrate that the sets have no common elements?

144. Describe the Venn diagram for proper subsets. How does this diagram illustrate that the elements of one set are also in the second set?

145. Describe the Venn diagram for two equal sets. How does this diagram illustrate that the sets are equal?

146. Describe the Venn diagram for two sets with common elements. How does the diagram illustrate this relationship?

147. Describe what is meant by the complement of a set.

148. Is it possible to find a set's complement if a universal set is not given? Explain your answer.

149. Describe what is meant by the intersection of two sets. Give an example.

150. Describe what is meant by the union of two sets. Give an example.

151. Describe how to find the cardinal number of the union of two finite sets.

Critical Thinking Exercises

Make Sense? *In Exercises 152–155, determine whether each statement makes sense or does not make sense, and explain your reasoning.*

152. Set A and set B share only one element, so I don't need to use overlapping circles to visualize their relationship.

153. Even if I'm not sure how mathematicians define irrational and complex numbers, telling me how these sets are related, I can construct a Venn diagram illustrating their relationship.

154. If I am given sets A and B, the set $(A \cup B)'$ indicates I should take the union of the complement of A and the complement of B.

155. I suspect that at least 90% of college students have no preference whether their professor is a man or a woman, so I should place college professors in region IV of the Venn diagram that precedes Exercises 117–122.

In Exercises 156–163, determine whether each statement is true or false. If the statement is false, make the necessary change(s) to produce a true statement.

156. $n(A \cup B) = n(A) + n(B)$

157. $A \cap A' = \varnothing$

158. $(A \cup B) \subseteq A$

159. If $A \subseteq B$, then $A \cap B = B$.

160. $A \cap U = U$

161. $A \cup \varnothing = \varnothing$

162. If $A \subseteq B$, then $A \cap B = \varnothing$.

163. If $B \subseteq A$, then $A \cap B = B$.

In Exercises 164–167, assume $A \neq B$. Draw a Venn diagram that correctly illustrates the relationship between the sets.

164. $A \cap B = A$

165. $A \cap B = B$

166. $A \cup B = A$

167. $A \cup B = B$

OBJECTIVES

1 | Perform set operations with three sets.
2 | Use Venn diagrams with three sets.
3 | Use Venn diagrams to prove equality of sets.

4 Set Operations and Venn Diagrams with Three Sets

Should your blood type determine what you eat? The blood-type diet, developed by naturopathic physician Peter D'Adamo, is based on the theory that people with different blood types require different diets for optimal health. D'Adamo gives very detailed recommendations for what people with each type should and shouldn't eat. For example, he says shitake mushrooms are great for type B's, but bad for type O's. Type B? Type O? In this section, we present a Venn diagram with three sets that will give you a unique perspective on the different types of human blood. Despite this perspective, we'll have nothing to say about shitakes, avoiding the question as to whether or not the blood-type diet really works.

funkyfood London/Paul Williams\Alamy Images

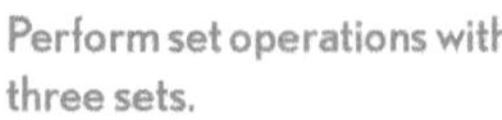

1 | Perform set operations with three sets.

Set Operations with Three Sets

We now know how to find the union and intersection of two sets. We also know how to find a set's complement. In Example 1, we apply set operations to situations containing three sets.

EXAMPLE 1 Set Operations with Three Sets

Given

$$U = \{1, 2, 3, 4, 5, 6, 7, 8, 9\}$$
$$A = \{1, 2, 3, 4, 5\}$$
$$B = \{1, 2, 3, 6, 8\}$$
$$C = \{2, 3, 4, 6, 7\},$$

find each of the following sets:

a. $A \cup (B \cap C)$ **b.** $(A \cup B) \cap (A \cup C)$ **c.** $A \cap (B \cup C')$.

Solution Before determining each set, let's be sure we perform the operations in the correct order. Remember that we begin by performing any set operations inside parentheses.

- Finding $A \cup (B \cap C)$

  Step 1. Find the intersection of B and C.

  Step 2. Find the union of A and $(B \cap C)$.

- Finding $(A \cup B) \cap (A \cup C)$

  Step 1. Find the union of A and B.

  Step 2. Find the union of A and C.

  Step 3. Find the intersection of $(A \cup B)$ and $(A \cup C)$.

- Finding $A \cap (B \cup C')$

  Step 1. Find the complement of C.

  Step 2. Find the union of B and C'.

  Step 3. Find the intersection of A and $(B \cup C')$.

a. To find $A \cup (B \cap C)$, first find the set within the parentheses, $B \cap C$:

$$B \cap C = \{1, 2, 3, 6, 8\} \cap \{2, 3, 4, 6, 7\} = \{2, 3, 6\}.$$

Common elements are 2, 3, and 6.

Now finish the problem by finding $A \cup (B \cap C)$:

$$A \cup (B \cap C) = \{1, 2, 3, 4, 5\} \cup \{2, 3, 6\} = \{1, 2, 3, 4, 5, 6\}.$$

List all elements in A and then add the only unlisted element in $B \cap C$, namely 6.

b. To find $(A \cup B) \cap (A \cup C)$, first find the sets within parentheses. Start with $A \cup B$:

$$A \cup B = \{1, 2, 3, 4, 5\} \cup \{1, 2, 3, 6, 8\} = \{1, 2, 3, 4, 5, 6, 8\}.$$

List all elements in A and then add the unlisted elements in B, namely 6 and 8.

Now find $A \cup C$:

$$A \cup C = \{1, 2, 3, 4, 5\} \cup \{2, 3, 4, 6, 7\} = \{1, 2, 3, 4, 5, 6, 7\}.$$

List all elements in A and then add the unlisted elements in C, namely 6 and 7.

Now finish the problem by finding $(A \cup B) \cap (A \cup C)$:

$$(A \cup B) \cap (A \cup C) = \{1, 2, 3, 4, 5, 6, 8\} \cap \{1, 2, 3, 4, 5, 6, 7\} = \{1, 2, 3, 4, 5, 6\}.$$

Common elements are 1, 2, 3, 4, 5, and 6.

c. As in parts (a) and (b), to find $A \cap (B \cup C')$, begin with the set in parentheses. First we must find C', the set of elements in U that are not in C:

$$C' = \{1, 5, 8, 9\}.$$

List the elements in U that are not in $C = \{2, 3, 4, 6, 7\}$: $\{1, \not{2}, \not{3}, \not{4}, 5, \not{6}, \not{7}, 8, 9\}$.

Now we can identify elements of $B \cup C'$:

$$B \cup C' = \{1, 2, 3, 6, 8\} \cup \{1, 5, 8, 9\} = \{1, 2, 3, 5, 6, 8, 9\}.$$

List all elements in B and then add the unlisted elements in C', namely 5 and 9.

Now finish the problem by finding $A \cap (B \cup C')$:

$$A \cap (B \cup C') = \{1, 2, 3, 4, 5\} \cap \{1, 2, 3, 5, 6, 8, 9\} = \{1, 2, 3, 5\}.$$

Common elements are 1, 2, 3, and 5.

CHECK POINT 1 Given $U = \{a, b, c, d, e, f\}$, $A = \{a, b, c, d\}$, $B = \{a, b, d, f\}$, and $C = \{b, c, f\}$, find each of the following sets:

a. $A \cup (B \cap C)$

b. $(A \cup B) \cap (A \cup C)$

c. $A \cap (B \cup C')$.

2 Use Venn diagrams with three sets.

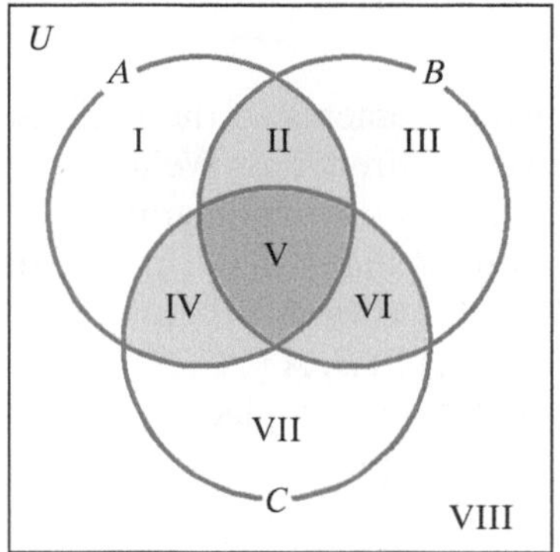

FIGURE 20 Three intersecting sets separate the universal set into eight regions.

Venn Diagrams with Three Sets

Venn diagrams can contain three or more sets, such as the diagram in **Figure 20**. The three sets in the figure separate the universal set, U, into eight regions. The numbering of these regions is arbitrary—that is, we can number any region as I, any region as II, and so on. Here is a description of each region, starting with the innermost region, region V, and working outward to region VIII.

The Region Shown in Dark Blue

Region V — This region represents elements that are common to sets A, B, and C: $A \cap B \cap C$.

The Regions Shown in Light Blue

Region II — This region represents elements in both sets A and B that are not in set C: $(A \cap B) \cap C'$.

Region IV — This region represents elements in both sets A and C that are not in set B: $(A \cap C) \cap B'$.

Region VI — This region represents elements in both sets B and C that are not in set A: $(B \cap C) \cap A'$.

The Regions Shown in White

Region I — This region represents elements in set A that are in neither sets B nor C: $A \cap (B' \cap C')$.

Region III — This region represents elements in set B that are in neither sets A nor C: $B \cap (A' \cap C')$.

Region VII — This region represents elements in set C that are in neither sets A nor B: $C \cap (A' \cap B')$.

Region VIII — This region represents elements in the universal set U that are not in sets A, B, or C: $A' \cap B' \cap C'$.

EXAMPLE 2 Determining Sets from a Venn Diagram with Three Intersecting Sets

Use the Venn diagram in **Figure 21** to determine each of the following sets:

a. A **b.** $A \cup B$ **c.** $B \cap C$

d. C' **e.** $A \cap B \cap C$.

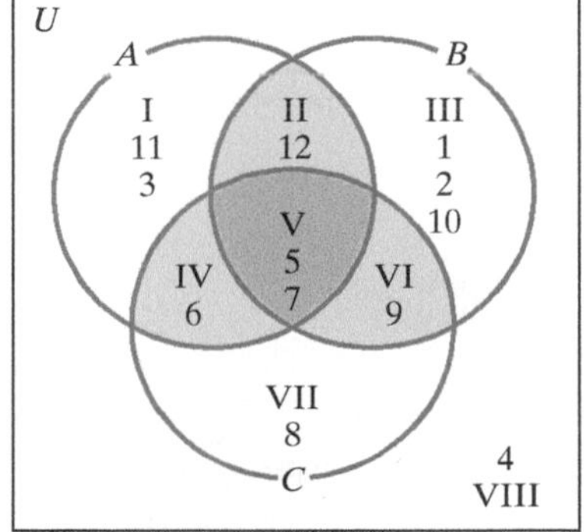

FIGURE 21

Solution

Set to Determine	Description of Set	Regions in Venn Diagram	Set in Roster Form
a. A	set of elements in A	I, II, IV, V	{11, 3, 12, 6, 5, 7}
b. $A \cup B$	set of elements in A or B or both	I, II, III, IV, V, VI	{11, 3, 12, 1, 2, 10, 6, 5, 7, 9}
c. $B \cap C$	set of elements in both B and C	V, VI	{5, 7, 9}
d. C'	set of elements in U that are not in C	I, II, III, VIII	{11, 3, 12, 1, 2, 10, 4}
e. $A \cap B \cap C$	set of elements in A and B and C	V	{5, 7}

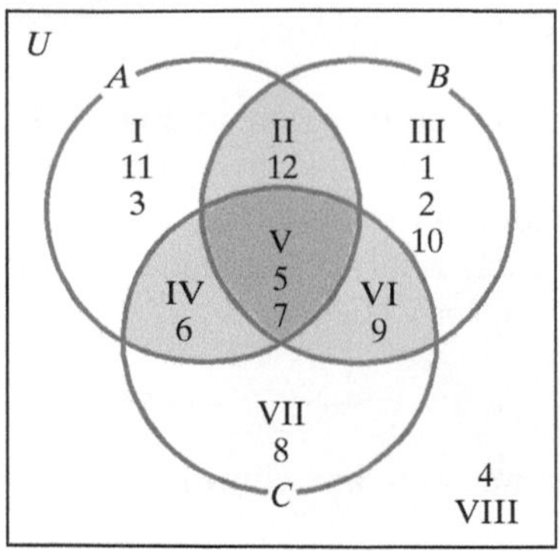

FIGURE 21 (repeated)

CHECK POINT 2 Use the Venn diagram in **Figure 21** to determine each of the following sets:

a. C **b.** $B \cup C$

c. $A \cap C$ **d.** B'

e. $A \cup B \cup C$.

In Example 2, we used a Venn diagram showing elements in the regions to determine various sets. Now we are going to reverse directions. We'll use sets A, B, C, and U to determine the elements in each region of a Venn diagram.

To construct a Venn diagram illustrating the elements in A, B, C, and U, **start by placing elements into the innermost region and work outward**. Because the four inner regions represent various intersections, find $A \cap B$, $A \cap C$, $B \cap C$, and $A \cap B \cap C$. Then use these intersections and the given sets to place the various elements into regions. This procedure is illustrated in Example 3.

EXAMPLE 3 Determining a Venn Diagram from Sets

Construct a Venn diagram illustrating the following sets:

$$A = \{a, d, e, g, h, i, j\}$$
$$B = \{b, e, g, h, l\}$$
$$C = \{a, c, e, h\}$$
$$U = \{a, b, c, d, e, f, g, h, i, j, k, l\}.$$

Solution We begin by finding four intersections. In each case, common elements are shown in red.

- $A \cap B = \{a, d, e, g, h, i, j\} \cap \{b, e, g, h, l\} = \{e, g, h\}$
- $A \cap C = \{a, d, e, g, h, i, j\} \cap \{a, c, e, h\} = \{a, e, h\}$
- $B \cap C = \{b, e, g, h, l\} \cap \{a, c, e, h\} = \{e, h\}$
- $A \cap B \cap C = \{e, g, h\} \cap \{a, c, e, h\} = \{e, h\}$

This is $A \cap B$ from above.

Now we can place elements into regions, starting with the innermost region, region V, and working outward.

STEP 1

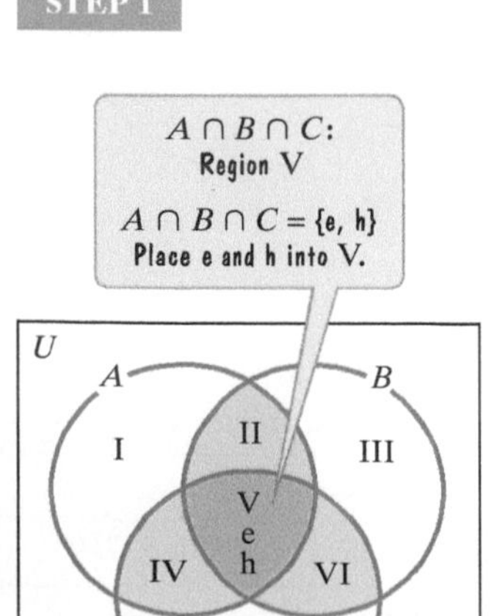

STEP 2

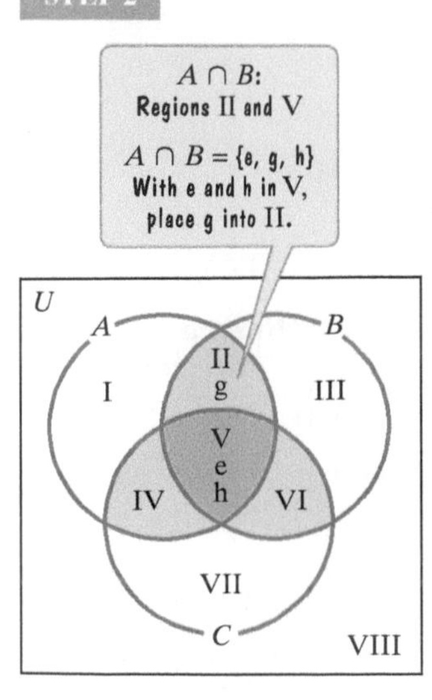

STEP 3

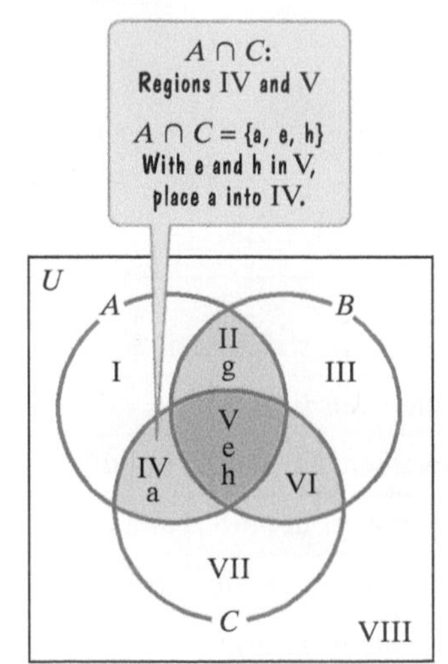

STEP 4

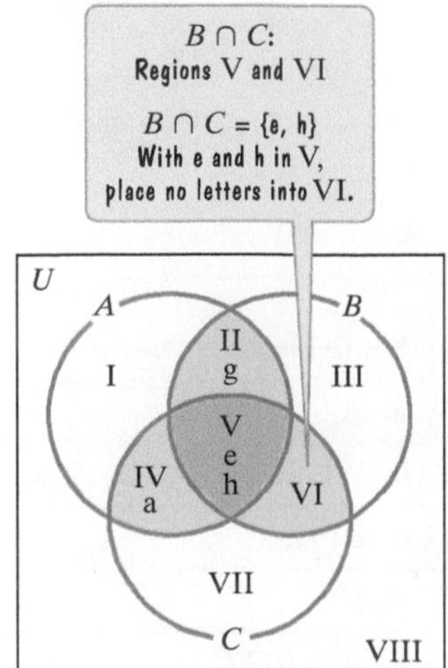

STEP 5

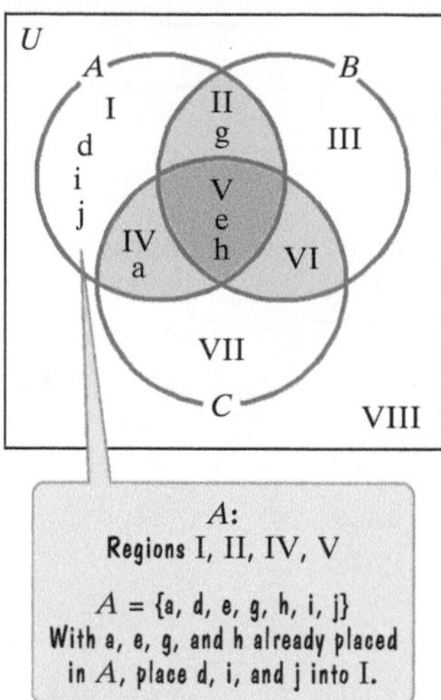

STEP 6

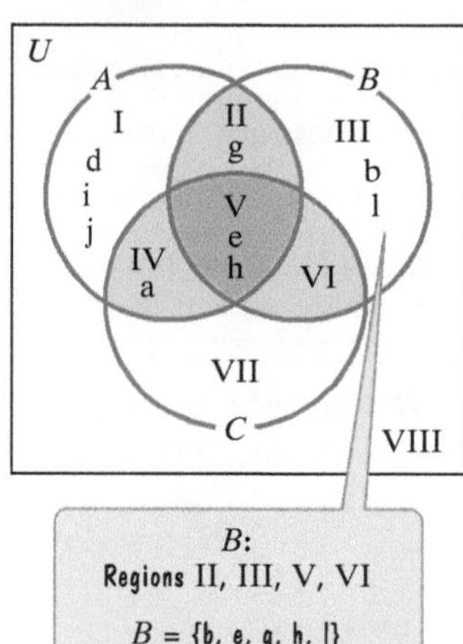

STEP 7

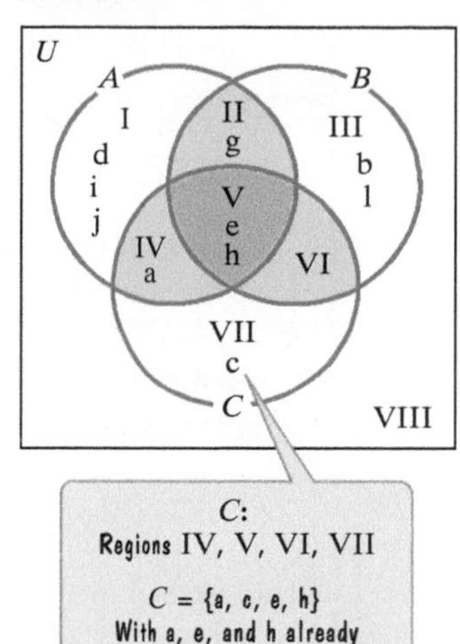

STEP 8

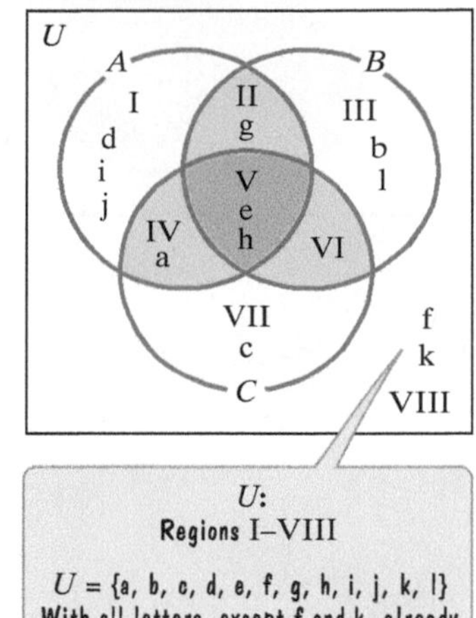

The completed Venn diagram in step 8 illustrates the given sets.

CHECK POINT 3 Construct a Venn diagram illustrating the following sets:

$$A = \{1, 3, 6, 10\}$$
$$B = \{4, 7, 9, 10\}$$
$$C = \{3, 4, 5, 8, 9, 10\}$$
$$U = \{1, 2, 3, 4, 5, 6, 7, 8, 9, 10\}.$$

3 Use Venn diagrams to prove equality of sets.

Proving the Equality of Sets

Throughout Section 3, you were given two sets A and B and their universl set U and asked to find $(A \cap B)'$ and $A' \cup B'$. In each example, $(A \cap B)'$ and $A' \cup B'$ resulted in the same set. This occurs regardless of which sets we choose for A and B in a universal set U. Examining these individual cases and applying inductive reasoning, a conjecture (or educated guess) is that $(A \cap B)' = A' \cup B'$.

We can apply deductive reasoning to *prove* the statement $(A \cap B)' = A' \cup B'$ for *all* sets A and B in any universal set U. To prove that $(A \cap B)'$ and $A' \cup B'$ are equal, we use a Venn diagram. If both sets are represented by the same regions in this general diagram, then this proves that they are equal. Example 4 shows how this is done.

STUDY TIP

In summary, here are two forms of reasoning.

- **Inductive Reasoning:** Starts with individual observations and works to a general conjecture (or educated guess)
- **Deductive Reasoning:** Starts with general cases and works to the proof of a specific statement (or theorem)

EXAMPLE 4 Proving the Equality of Sets

Use the Venn diagram in **Figure 22** to prove that

$$(A \cap B)' = A' \cup B'.$$

Solution Begin by identifying the regions representing $(A \cap B)'$.

Set	Regions in the Venn Diagram
A	I, II
B	II, III
$A \cap B$	II (This is the region common to A and B.)
$(A \cap B)'$	I, III, IV (These are the regions in U that are not in $A \cap B$.)

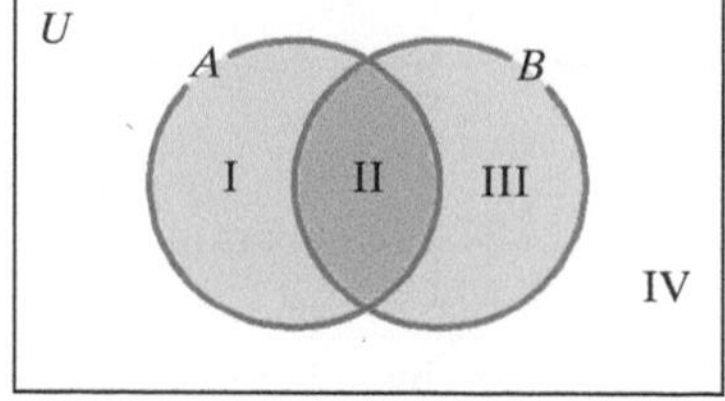

FIGURE 22

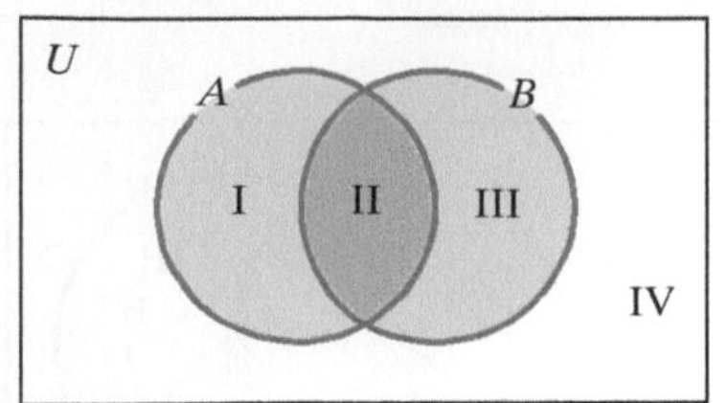

FIGURE 22 (repeated)

Next, find the regions in **Figure 22** representing $A' \cup B'$.

Set	Regions in the Venn Diagram
A'	III, IV (These are the regions not in A.)
B'	I, IV (These are the regions not in B.)
$A' \cup B'$	I, III, IV (These are the regions obtained by uniting the regions representing A' and B'.)

Both $(A \cap B)'$ and $A' \cup B'$ are represented by the same regions, I, III, and IV, of the Venn diagram. This result proves that

$$(A \cap B)' = A' \cup B'$$

for all sets A and B in any universal set U.

Can you see how we applied deductive reasoning in Example 4? We started with the two general sets in the Venn diagram in **Figure 22** and worked to the specific conclusion that $(A \cap B)'$ and $A' \cup B'$ represent the same regions in the diagram. Thus, the statement $(A \cap B)' = A' \cup B'$ is a theorem.

Use the Venn diagram in **Figure 22** to solve this exercise.

a. Which region represents $(A \cup B)'$?

b. Which region represents $A' \cap B'$?

c. Based on parts (a) and (b), what can you conclude?

The statements proved in Example 4 and Check Point 4 are known as *De Morgan's laws*, named for the British logician Augustus De Morgan (1806–1871).

STUDY TIP

Learn the pattern of De Morgan's laws. They are extremely important in logic.

DE MORGAN'S LAWS

$(A \cap B)' = A' \cup B'$: The complement of the intersection of two sets is the union of the complements of those sets.

$(A \cup B)' = A' \cap B'$: The complement of the union of two sets is the intersection of the complements of those sets.

EXAMPLE 5 Proving the Equality of Sets

Use a Venn diagram to prove that

$$A \cup (B \cap C) = (A \cup B) \cap (A \cup C).$$

Solution Use a Venn diagram with three sets A, B, and C, as shown in **Figure 23**. Begin by identifying the regions representing $A \cup (B \cap C)$.

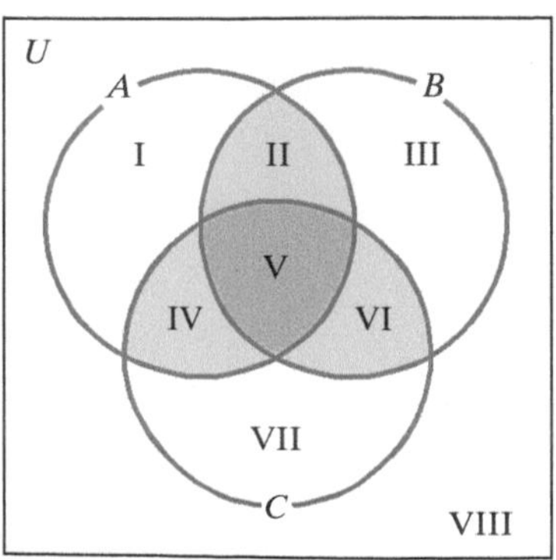

FIGURE 23

Set	Regions in the Venn Diagram
A	I, II, IV, V
$B \cap C$	V, VI (These are the regions common to B and C.)
$A \cup (B \cap C)$	I, II, IV, V, VI (These are the regions obtained by uniting the regions representing A and $B \cap C$.)

Next, find the regions representing $(A \cup B) \cap (A \cup C)$.

Set	Regions in the Venn Diagram
A	I, II, IV, V
B	II, III, V, VI
C	IV, V, VI, VII
$A \cup B$	I, II, III, IV, V, VI (Unite the regions representing A and B.)
$A \cup C$	I, II, IV, V, VI, VII (Unite the regions representing A and C.)
$(A \cup B) \cap (A \cup C)$	I, II, IV, V, VI (These are the regions common to $A \cup B$ and $A \cup C$.)

Both $A \cup (B \cap C)$ and $(A \cup B) \cap (A \cup C)$ are represented by the same regions, I, II, IV, V, and VI, of the Venn diagram. This result proves that

$$A \cup (B \cap C) = (A \cup B) \cap (A \cup C)$$

for all sets A, B, and C in any universal set U. Thus, the statement is a theorem.

CHECK POINT 5 Use the Venn diagram in **Figure 23** to solve this exercise.

a. Which regions represent $A \cap (B \cup C)$?

b. Which regions represent $(A \cap B) \cup (A \cap C)$?

c. Based on parts (a) and (b), what can you conclude?

BLITZER BONUS

BLOOD TYPES AND VENN DIAGRAMS

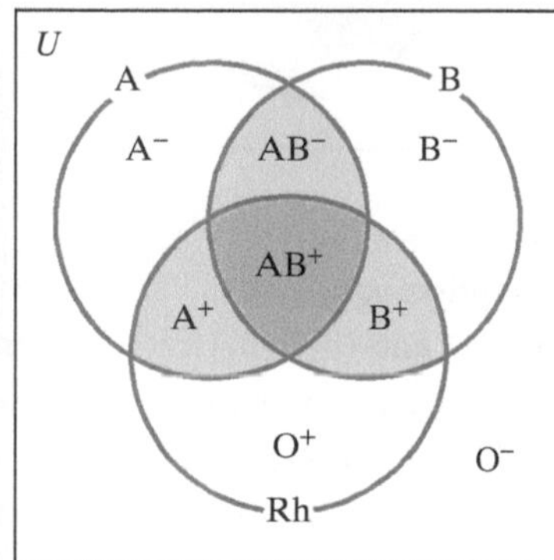

FIGURE 24 Human blood types

In the early 1900s, the Austrian immunologist Karl Landsteiner discovered that all blood is not the same. Blood serum drawn from one person often clumped when mixed with the blood cells of another. The clumping was caused by different antigens, proteins, and carbohydrates that trigger antibodies and fight infection. Landsteiner classified blood types based on the presence or absence of the antigens A, B, and Rh in red blood cells. The Venn diagram in **Figure 24** contains eight regions representing the eight common blood groups.

In the Venn diagram, blood with the Rh antigen is labeled positive and blood lacking the Rh antigen is labeled negative. The region where the three circles intersect represents type AB^+, indicating that a person with this blood type has the antigens A, B, and Rh. Observe that type O blood (both positive and negative) lacks A and B antigens. Type O^- lacks all three antigens, A, B, and Rh.

In blood transfusions, the recipient must have all or more of the antigens present in the donor's blood. This discovery rescued surgery patients from random, often lethal, transfusions. This knowledge made the massive blood drives during World War I possible. Eventually, it made the modern blood bank possible as well.

Exercise Set 4

Practice Exercises

In Exercises 1–12, let

$$U = \{1, 2, 3, 4, 5, 6, 7\}$$
$$A = \{1, 3, 5, 7\}$$
$$B = \{1, 2, 3\}$$
$$C = \{2, 3, 4, 5, 6\}.$$

Find each of the following sets.

1. $A \cup (B \cap C)$

2. $A \cap (B \cup C)$

3. $(A \cup B) \cap (A \cup C)$

4. $(A \cap B) \cup (A \cap C)$

5. $A' \cap (B \cup C')$

6. $C' \cap (A \cup B')$

7. $(A' \cap B) \cup (A' \cap C')$

8. $(C' \cap A) \cup (C' \cap B')$

9. $(A \cup B \cup C)'$

10. $(A \cap B \cap C)'$

11. $(A \cup B)' \cap C$

12. $(B \cup C)' \cap A$

In Exercises 13–24, let

$$U = \{a, b, c, d, e, f, g, h\}$$
$$A = \{a, g, h\}$$
$$B = \{b, g, h\}$$
$$C = \{b, c, d, e, f\}.$$

Find each of the following sets.

13. $A \cup (B \cap C)$ **14.** $A \cap (B \cup C)$

15. $(A \cup B) \cap (A \cup C)$ **16.** $(A \cap B) \cup (A \cap C)$

17. $A' \cap (B \cup C')$ **18.** $C' \cap (A \cup B')$

19. $(A' \cap B) \cup (A' \cap C')$ **20.** $(C' \cap A) \cup (C' \cap B')$

21. $(A \cup B \cup C)'$ **22.** $(A \cap B \cap C)'$

23. $(A \cup B)' \cap C$ **24.** $(B \cup C)' \cap A$

In Exercises 25–32, use the Venn diagram shown to answer each question.

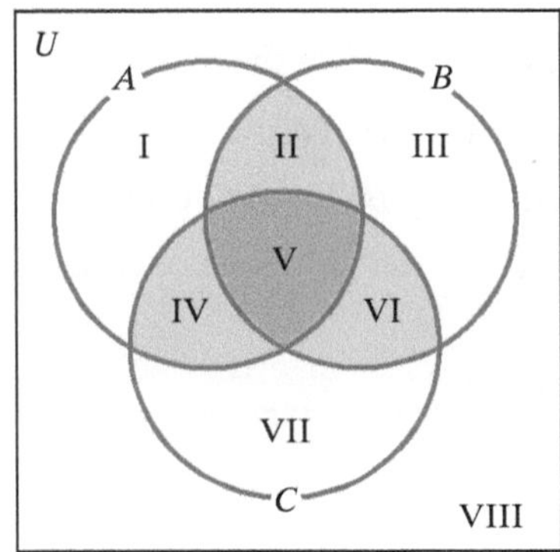

25. Which regions represent set B?

26. Which regions represent set C?

27. Which regions represent $A \cup C$?

28. Which regions represent $B \cup C$?

29. Which regions represent $A \cap B$?

30. Which regions represent $A \cap C$?

31. Which regions represent B'?

32. Which regions represent C'?

In Exercises 33–44, use the Venn diagram to represent each set in roster form.

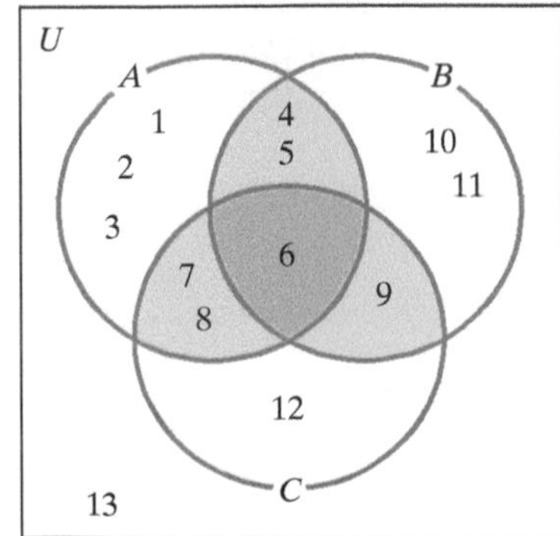

33. A **34.** B

35. $A \cup B$ **36.** $B \cup C$

37. $(A \cup B)'$ **38.** $(B \cup C)'$

39. $A \cap B$ **40.** $A \cap C$

41. $A \cap B \cap C$ **42.** $A \cup B \cup C$

43. $(A \cap B \cap C)'$ **44.** $(A \cup B \cup C)'$

In Exercises 45–48, construct a Venn diagram illustrating the given sets.

45. $A = \{4, 5, 6, 8\}, B = \{1, 2, 4, 5, 6, 7\},$
$C = \{3, 4, 7\}, U = \{1, 2, 3, 4, 5, 6, 7, 8, 9\}$

46. $A = \{a, e, h, i\}, B = \{b, c, e, f, h, i\},$
$C = \{e, f, g\}, U = \{a, b, c, d, e, f, g, h, i\}$

47. $A = \{+, -, \times, \div, \rightarrow, \leftrightarrow\}$
$B = \{\times, \div, \rightarrow\}$
$C = \{\wedge, \vee, \rightarrow, \leftrightarrow\}$
$U = \{+, -, \times, \div, \wedge, \vee, \rightarrow, \leftrightarrow, \sim\}$

48. $A = \{x_3, x_9\}$
$B = \{x_1, x_2, x_3, x_5, x_6\}$
$C = \{x_3, x_4, x_5, x_6, x_9\}$
$U = \{x_1, x_2, x_3, x_4, x_5, x_6, x_7, x_8, x_9\}$

Use the Venn diagram shown to solve Exercises 49–52.

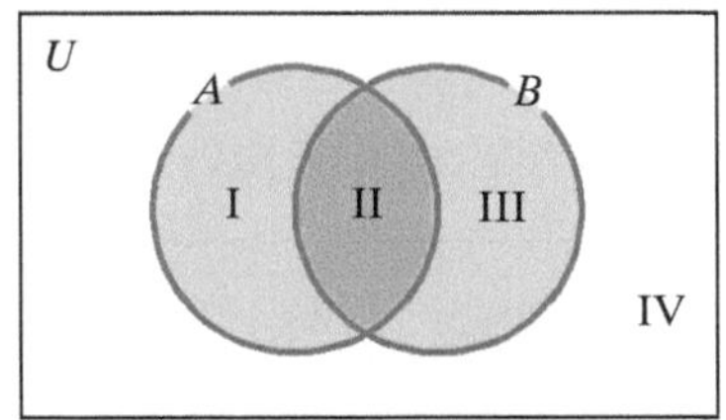

49. **a.** Which region represents $A \cap B$?
b. Which region represents $B \cap A$?
c. Based on parts (a) and (b), what can you conclude?

50. **a.** Which regions represents $A \cup B$?
b. Which regions represents $B \cup A$?
c. Based on parts (a) and (b), what can you conclude?

51. **a.** Which region(s) represents $(A \cap B)'$?
b. Which region(s) represents $A' \cap B'$?
c. Based on parts (a) and (b), are $(A \cap B)'$ and $A' \cap B'$ equal for all sets A and B? Explain your answer.

52. **a.** Which region(s) represents $(A \cup B)'$?
b. Which region(s) represents $A' \cup B'$?
c. Based on parts (a) and (b), are $(A \cup B)'$ and $A' \cup B'$ equal for all sets A and B? Explain your answer.

In Exercises 53–58, use the Venn diagram for Exercises 49–52 to determine whether the given sets are equal for all sets A and B.

53. $A' \cup B, \quad A \cap B'$ **54.** $A' \cap B, \quad A \cup B'$

55. $(A \cup B)', \quad (A \cap B)'$ **56.** $(A \cup B)', \quad A' \cap B$

57. $(A' \cap B)', \quad A \cup B'$ **58.** $(A \cup B')', \quad A' \cap B$

Use the Venn diagram shown to solve Exercises 59–62.

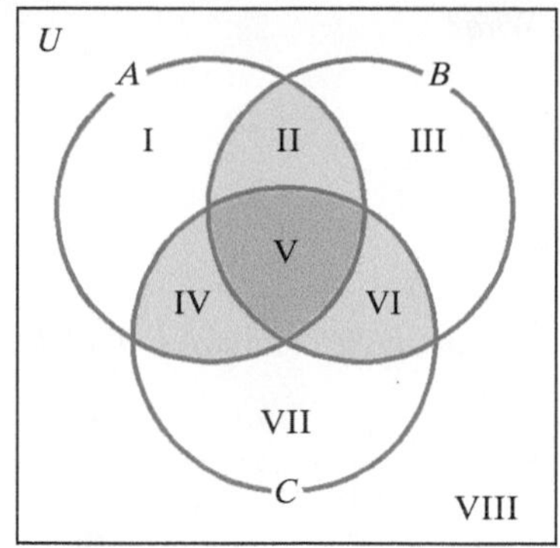

59. **a.** Which regions represent $(A \cap B) \cup C$?

b. Which regions represent $(A \cup C) \cap (B \cup C)$?

c. Based on parts (a) and (b), what can you conclude?

60. **a.** Which regions represent $(A \cup B) \cap C$?

b. Which regions represent $(A \cap C) \cup (B \cap C)$?

c. Based on parts (a) and (b), what can you conclude?

61. **a.** Which regions represent $A \cap (B \cup C)$?

b. Which regions represent $A \cup (B \cap C)$?

c. Based on parts (a) and (b), are $A \cap (B \cup C)$ and $A \cup (B \cap C)$ equal for all sets A, B, and C? Explain your answer.

62. **a.** Which regions represent $C \cup (B \cap A)$?

b. Which regions represent $C \cap (B \cup A)$?

c. Based on parts (a) and (b), are $C \cup (B \cap A)$ and $C \cap (B \cup A)$ equal for all sets A, B, and C? Explain your answer.

In Exercises 63–68, use the Venn diagram shown above to determine which statements are true for all sets A, B, and C, and, consequently, are theorems.

63. $A \cap (B \cup C) = (A \cap B) \cup C$

64. $A \cup (B \cap C) = (A \cup B) \cap C$

65. $B \cup (A \cap C) = (A \cup B) \cap (B \cup C)$

66. $B \cap (A \cup C) = (A \cap B) \cup (B \cap C)$

67. $A \cap (B \cup C)' = A \cap (B' \cap C')$

68. $A \cup (B \cap C)' = A \cup (B' \cup C')$

Practice Plus

69. **a.** Let $A = \{c\}$, $B = \{a, b\}$, $C = \{b, d\}$, and $U = \{a, b, c, d, e, f\}$. Find $A \cup (B' \cap C')$ and $(A \cup B') \cap (A \cup C')$.

b. Let $A = \{1, 3, 7, 8\}$, $B = \{2, 3, 6, 7\}$, $C = \{4, 6, 7, 8\}$, and $U = \{1, 2, 3, \ldots, 8\}$. Find $A \cup (B' \cap C')$ and $(A \cup B') \cap (A \cup C')$.

c. Based on your results in parts (a) and (b), use inductive reasoning to write a conjecture that relates $A \cup (B' \cap C')$ and $(A \cup B') \cap (A \cup C')$.

d. Use deductive reasoning to determine whether your conjecture in part (c) is a theorem.

70. **a.** Let $A = \{3\}$, $B = \{1, 2\}$, $C = \{2, 4\}$, and $U = \{1, 2, 3, 4, 5, 6\}$. Find $(A \cup B)' \cap C$ and $A' \cap (B' \cap C)$.

b. Let $A = \{d, f, g, h\}$, $B = \{a, c, f, h\}$, $C = \{c, e, g, h\}$, and $U = \{a, b, c, \ldots, h\}$. Find $(A \cup B)' \cap C$ and $A' \cap (B' \cap C)$.

c. Based on your results in parts (a) and (b), use inductive reasoning to write a conjecture that relates and $A' \cap (B' \cap C)$.

d. Use deductive reasoning to determine whether your conjecture in part (c) is a theorem.

In Exercises 71–78, use the symbols A, B, C, ∩, ∪, and ′, as necessary, to describe each shaded region. More than one correct symbolic description may be possible.

71.

72.

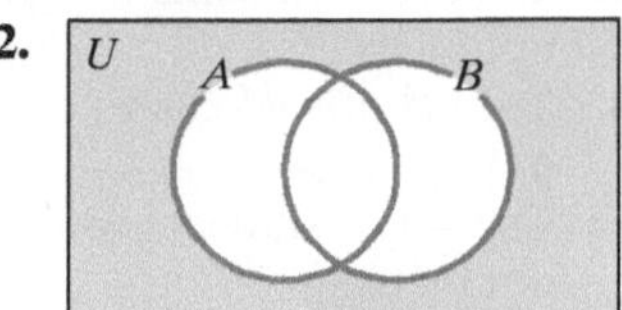

73.

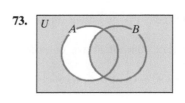

74.

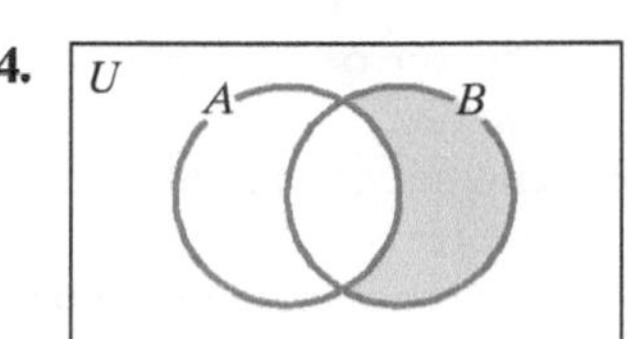

75.

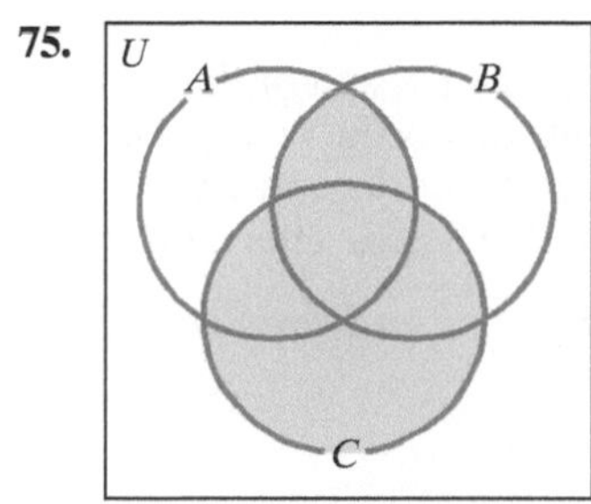

76.

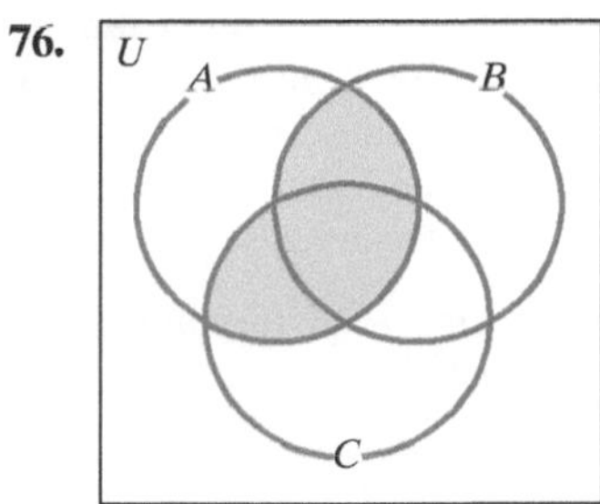

77.

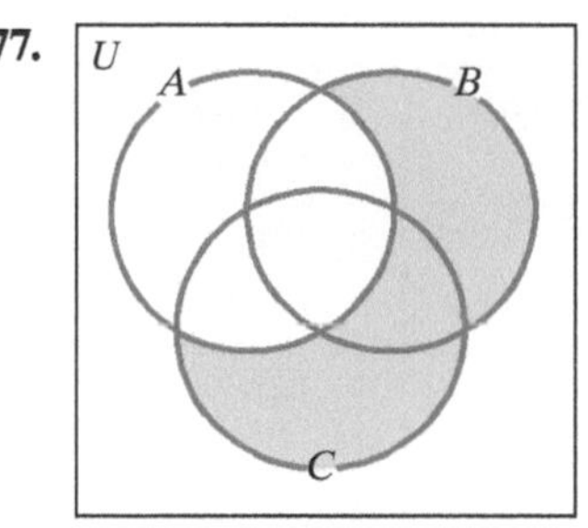

78.

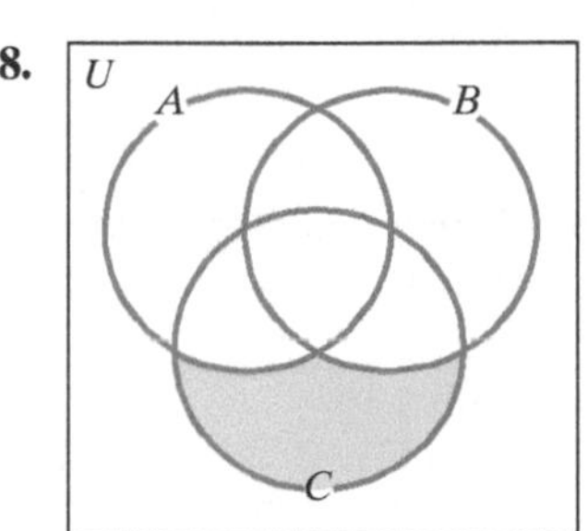

Application Exercises

A math tutor working with a small study group has classified students in the group by whether or not they scored 90% or above on each of three tests. The results are shown in the Venn diagram.

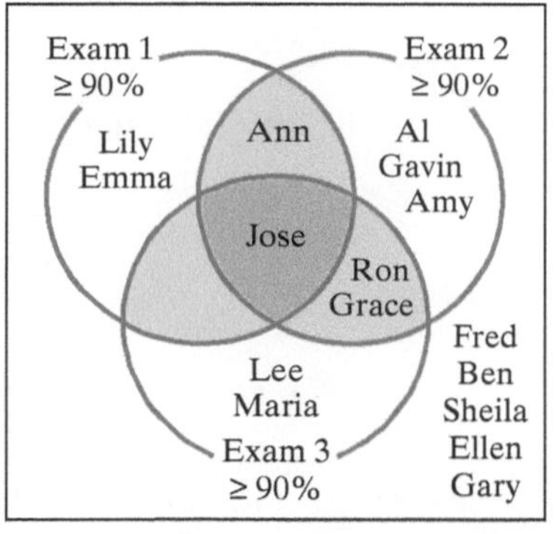

In Exercises 79–90, use the Venn diagram at the bottom of the previous page to represent each set in roster form.

79. The set of students who scored 90% or above on exam 2

80. The set of students who scored 90% or above on exam 3

81. The set of students who scored 90% or above on exam 1 and exam 3

82. The set of students who scored 90% or above on exam 1 and exam 2

83. The set of students who scored 90% or above on exam 1 and not on exam 2

84. The set of students who scored 90% or above on exam 3 and not on exam 1

85. The set of students who scored 90% or above on exam 1 or not on exam 2

86. The set of students who scored 90% or above on exam 3 or not on exam 1

87. The set of students who scored 90% or above on *exactly one* test

88. The set of students who scored 90% or above on *at least two* tests

89. The set of students who scored 90% or above on exam 2 and not on exam 1 and exam 3

90. The set of students who scored 90% or above on exam 1 and not on exam 2 and exam 3

91. Use the Venn diagram shown at the bottom of the previous page to describe a set of students that is the empty set.

92. Use the Venn diagram shown at the bottom of the previous page to describe the set {Fred, Ben,Sheila, Ellen, Gary}.

The chart shows the most popular shows on television in 2006, 2007, and 2008.

MOST POPULAR TELEVISION SHOWS

2006	2007	2008
1. *American Idol*	1. *American Idol*	1. *American Idol*
2. *CSI*	2. *Dancing with the Stars*	2. *Dancing with the Stars*
3. *Desperate Housewives*	3. *CSI*	3. *NBC Sunday Night Football*
4. *Grey's Anatomy*	4. *Grey's Anatomy*	4. *CSI*
5. *Without a Trace*	5. *House*	5. *Grey's Anatomy*
6. *Dancing with the Stars*	6. *Desperate Housewives*	6. *Samantha Who?*

Source: Nielsen Media Research

In Exercises 93–98, use the Venn diagram to indicate in which region, I through VIII, each television show should be placed.

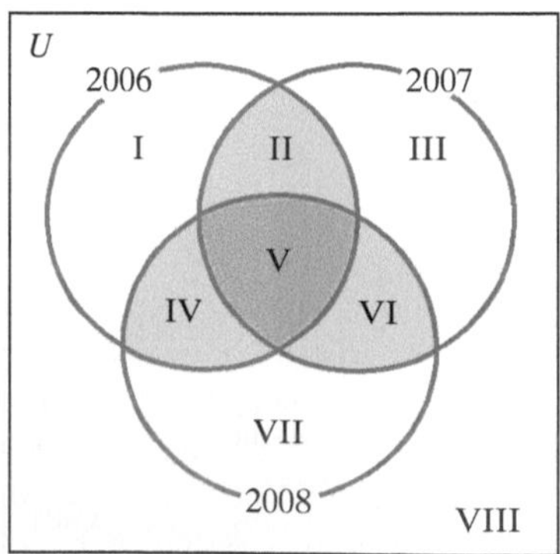

93. *Desperate Housewives*

94. *Samantha Who?*

95. *CSI*

96. *Grey's Anatomy*

97. *House*

98. *60 Minutes*

The chart shows the top single recordings of all time.

TOP SINGLE RECORDINGS

Title	Artist or Group	Sales	Year Released
"Candle in the Wind"	Elton John	37 million	1997
"White Christmas"	Bing Crosby	30 million	1942
"Rock Around the Clock"	Bill Haley and His Comets	17 million	1954
"I Want to Hold Your Hand"	The Beatles	12 million	1963
"It's Now or Never"	Elvis Presley	10 million	1960
"Hey Jude"	The Beatles	10 million	1968
"I Will Always Love You"	Whitney Houston	10 million	1992
"Hound Dog"	Elvis Presley	9 million	1956
"Diana"	Paul Anka	9 million	1957
"I'm a Believer"	The Monkees	8 million	1966

Source: RIAA

In Exercises 99–104, use the Venn diagram to indicate in which region, I through VIII, each recording should be placed.

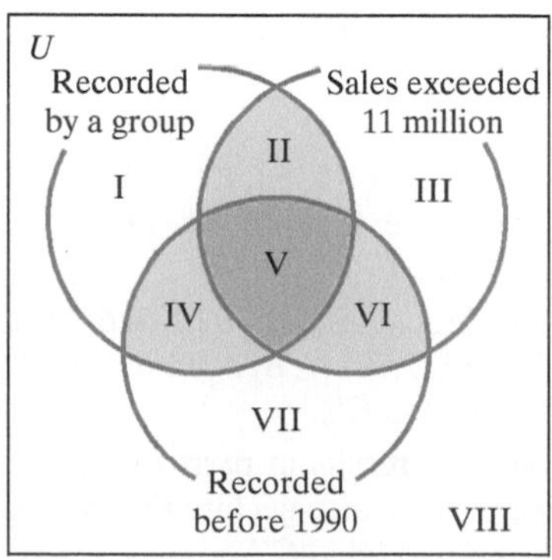

99. "Candle in the Wind"

100. "White Christmas"

101. "I Want to Hold Your Hand"

102. "Hey Jude"

103. "Diana"

104. "I'm a Believer"

105. The chart shows three health indicators for seven countries or regions.

WORLDWIDE HEALTH INDICATORS

Country/ Region	Male Life Expectancy	Female Life Expectancy	Persons per Doctor
United States	74.8	80.1	360
Italy	77.6	83.2	180
Russia	59.9	73.3	240
East Africa	46.9	48.2	13,620
Japan	78.6	85.6	530
England	75.9	81.0	720
Iran	68.6	71.4	1200

Source: Time Almanac 2009

Let U = the set of countries/regions shown in the chart, A = the set of countries/regions with male life expectancy that exceeds 75 years, B = the set of countries/regions with female life expectancy that exceeds 80 years, and C = the set of countries/regions with fewer than 400 persons per doctor. Use the information in the chart to construct a Venn diagram that illustrates these sets.

106. The chart shows the ten films nominated for the most Oscars.

FILMS WITH THE MOST OSCAR NOMINATIONS

Film	Nominations	Awards	Year
All About Eve	14	6	1950
Titanic	14	11	1997
Gone with the Wind	13	8	1939
From Here to Eternity	13	8	1953
Shakespeare in Love	13	7	1998
Mary Poppins	13	5	1964
Who's Afraid of Virginia Woolf?	13	5	1966
Forrest Gump	13	6	1994
The Lord of the Rings: The Fellowship of the Ring	13	4	2001
Chicago	13	6	2004

Source: Academy of Motion Picture Arts and Sciences

Using abbreviated film titles, let $U = \{Eve, Titanic, Wind, Eternity, Love, Poppins, Woolf, Gump, Ring, Chicago\}$, A = the set of films nominated for 14 Oscars, B = the set of films that won at least 7 Oscars, and C = the set of films that won Oscars after 1965. Use the information in the chart to construct a Venn diagram that illustrates these sets.

Writing in Mathematics

107. If you are given four sets, A, B, C, and U, describe what is involved in determining $(A \cup B)' \cap C$. Be as specific as possible in your description.

108. Describe how a Venn diagram can be used to prove that $(A \cup B)'$ and $A' \cap B'$ are equal sets.

Critical Thinking Exercises

Make Sense? *In Exercises 109–112, determine whether each statement makes sense or does not make sense, and explain your reasoning.*

109. I constructed a Venn diagram for three sets by placing elements into the outermost region and working inward.

110. This Venn diagram showing color combinations from red, green, and blue illustrates that white is a combination of all three colors and black uses none of the colors.

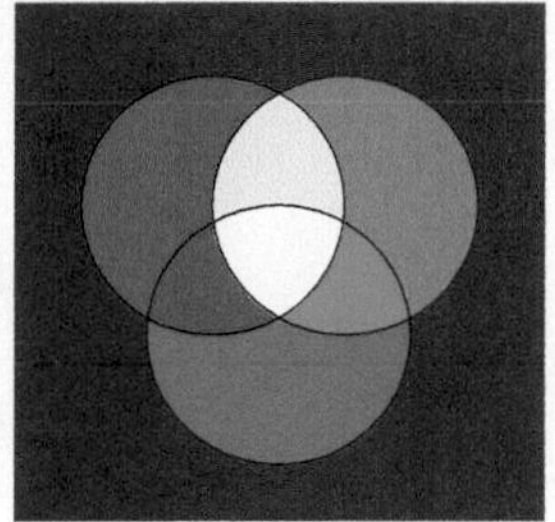

111. I used a Venn diagram to prove that $(A \cup B)'$ and $A' \cup B'$ are not equal.

112. I found 50 examples of two sets, A and B, for which $(A \cup B)'$ and $A' \cap B'$ resulted in the same set, so this proves that $(A \cup B)' = A' \cap B'$.

The eight blood types discussed in the last Blitzer Bonus are shown once again in the Venn diagram. In blood transfusions, the set of antigens in a donor's blood must be a subset of the set of antigens in a recipient's blood. Thus, the recipient must have all or more of the antigens present in the donor's blood. Use this information to solve Exercises 113–116.

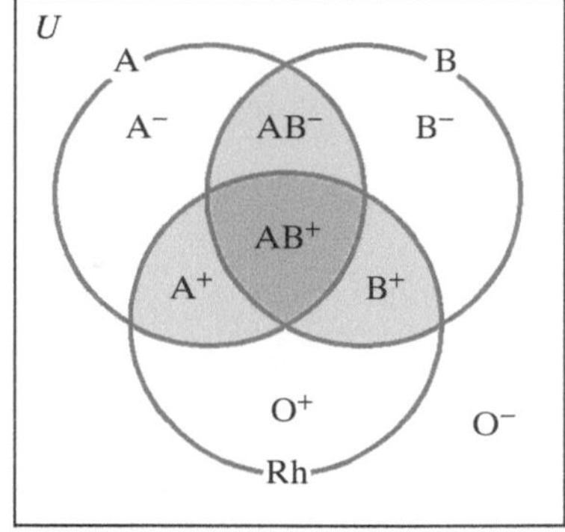

Human blood types

113. What is the blood type of a universal recipient?

114. What is the blood type of a universal donor?

115. Can an A^+ person donate blood to an A^- person?

116. Can an A^- person donate blood to an A^+ person?

Group Exercises

117. Each group member should find out his or her blood type. (If you cannot obtain this information, select a blood type that you find appealing!) Read the introduction to Exercises 113–116. Referring to the Venn diagram for these exercises, each group member should determine all other group members to whom blood can be donated and from whom it can be received.

118. The group should define three sets, each of which categorizes U, the set of students in the group, in different ways. Examples include the set of students with blonde hair, the set of students no more than 23 years old, and the set of students whose major is undecided. Once you have defined the sets, construct a Venn diagram with three intersecting sets and eight regions. Each student should determine which region he or she belongs to. Illustrate the sets by writing each first name in the appropriate region.

OBJECTIVES

1 | Use Venn diagrams to visualize a survey's results.

2 | Use survey results to complete Venn diagrams and answer questions about the survey.

5 Survey Problems

Terrazas Glavan Monica-Unep\Alamy Images.

Mexico's 2006 election, its closest-ever race for president, exposed an emerging trend in Latin America: a sharpening divide between the rich and the poor. Although Mexico's economy expanded by 4.4% in 2004 and 3% in 2005, at the end of 2005, almost half of the country's 107 million people still lived in poverty. (*Source*: *Newsweek*, July 17, 2006) **Figure 25** shows that Mexicans tend to see societal injustice, rather than personal laziness, as the primary cause of poverty.

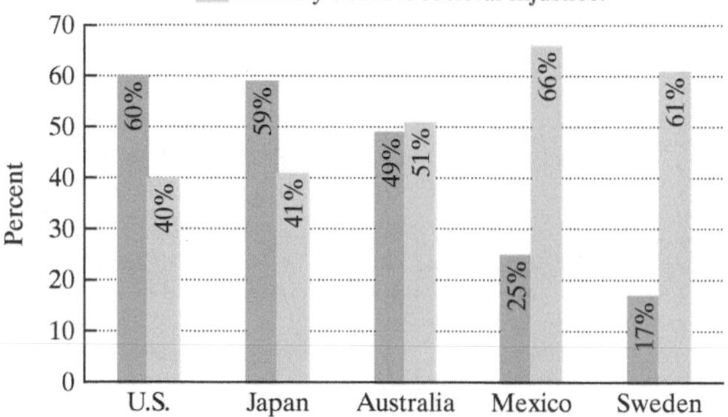

FIGURE 25 Percentages for each country may not total 100% because less frequently identified primary causes of poverty were omitted from the graph. *Source:* Ronald Inglehart et al., *World Values Surveys and European Values Surveys*

Suppose a survey is taken that asks randomly selected adults in the United States and Mexico the following question:

Do you agree or disagree that the primary cause of poverty is societal injustice?

In this section, you will see how sets and Venn diagrams are used to tabulate information collected in such a survey. In survey problems, it is helpful to remember that **and** means **intersection**, **or** means **union**, and **not** means **complement**. Furthermore, *but* means the same thing as *and*. Thus, **but** means **intersection**.

1 | Use Venn diagrams to visualize a survey's results.

Visualizing the Results of a Survey

In Section 1, we defined the cardinal number of set A, denoted by $n(A)$, as the number of elements in set A. Venn diagrams are helpful in determining a set's cardinality.

EXAMPLE 1 Using a Venn Diagram to Visualize the Results of a Survey

We return to the campus survey in which students were asked two questions:

Would you be willing to donate blood?

Would you be willing to help serve a free breakfast to blood donors?

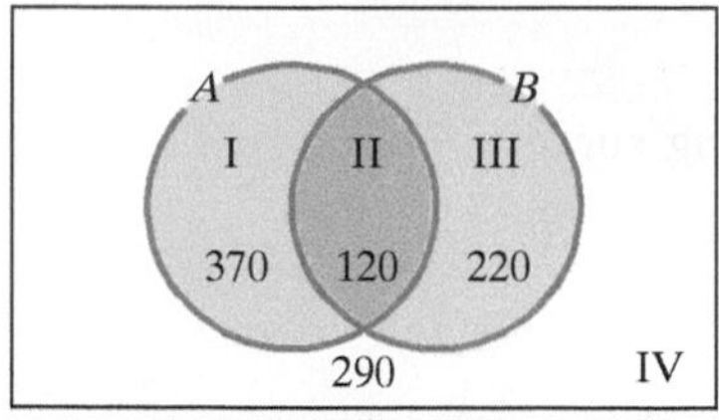

A: Set of students willing to donate blood
B: Set of students willing to serve breakfast to donors

FIGURE 26 Results of a survey

Set A represents the set of students willing to donate blood. Set B represents the set of students willing to help serve breakfast to donors. The survey results are summarized in **Figure 26**. Use the diagram to answer the following questions:

a. How many students are willing to donate blood?
b. How many students are willing to help serve a free breakfast to blood donors?
c. How many students are willing to donate blood and serve breakfast?
d. How many students are willing to donate blood or serve breakfast?
e. How many students are willing to donate blood but not serve breakfast?
f. How many students are willing to serve breakfast but not donate blood?
g. How many students are neither willing to donate blood nor serve breakfast?
h. How many students were surveyed?

Solution

a. The number of students willing to donate blood can be determined by adding the numbers in regions I and II. Thus, $n(A) = 370 + 120 = 490$. There are 490 students willing to donate blood.

b. The number of students willing to help serve a free breakfast to blood donors can be determined by adding the numbers in regions II and III. Thus, $n(B) = 120 + 220 = 340$. There are 340 students willing to help serve breakfast.

c. The number of students willing to donate blood and serve breakfast appears in region II, the region representing the intersection of the two sets. Thus, $n(A \cap B) = 120$. There are 120 students willing to donate blood and serve breakfast.

d. The number of students willing to donate blood or serve breakfast is found by adding the numbers in regions I, II, and III, representing the union of the two sets. We see that $n(A \cup B) = 370 + 120 + 220 = 710$. Therefore, 710 students in the survey are willing to donate blood or serve breakfast.

e. The region representing students who are willing to donate blood but not serve breakfast, $A \cap B'$, is region I. We see that 370 of the students surveyed are willing to donate blood but not serve breakfast.

f. Region III represents students willing to serve breakfast but not donate blood: $B \cap A'$. We see that 220 students surveyed are willing to help serve breakfast but not donate blood.

g. Students who are neither willing to donate blood nor serve breakfast, $A' \cap B'$, fall within the universal set, but outside circles A and B. Thcsc students fall in region IV, where the Venn diagram indicates that there are 290 elements. There are 290 students in the survey who are neither willing to donate blood nor serve breakfast.

h. We can find the number of students surveyed by adding the numbers in regions I, II, III, and IV. Thus, $n(U) = 370 + 120 + 220 + 290 = 1000$. There were 1000 students surveyed.

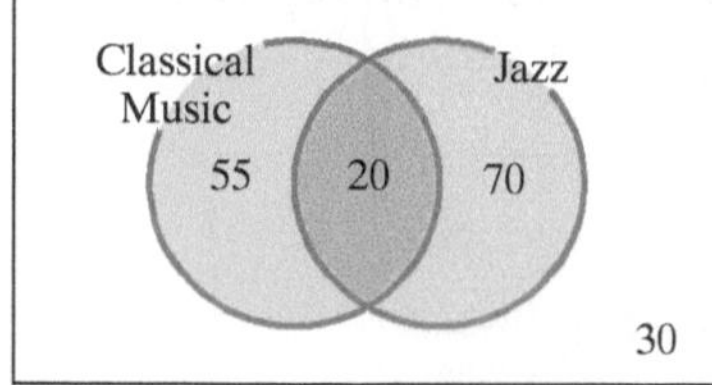

FIGURE 27

CHECK POINT 1 In a survey on musical tastes, respondents were asked: Do you listen to classical music? Do you listen to jazz? The survey results are summarized in **Figure 27**. Use the diagram to answer the following questions.

a. How many respondents listened to classical music?
b. How many respondents listened to jazz?
c. How many respondents listened to both classical music and jazz?
d. How many respondents listened to classical music or jazz?
e. How many respondents listened to classical music but not jazz?
f. How many respondents listened to jazz but not classical music?
g. How many respondents listened to neither classical music nor jazz?
h. How many people were surveyed?

2 Use survey results to complete Venn diagrams and answer questions about the survey.

Solving Survey Problems

Venn diagrams are used to solve problems involving surveys. Here are the steps needed to solve survey problems:

SOLVING SURVEY PROBLEMS

1. Use the survey's description to define sets and draw a Venn diagram.
2. Use the survey's results to determine the cardinality for each region in the Venn diagram. **Start with the intersection of the sets, the innermost region, and work outward.**
3. Use the completed Venn diagram to answer the problem's questions.

EXAMPLE 2 Surveying People's Attitudes

A survey is taken that asks 2000 randomly selected U.S. and Mexican adults the following question:

Do you agree or disagree that the primary cause of poverty is societal injustice?

The results of the survey showed that

1060 people agreed with the statement.

400 Americans agreed with the statement.

Source: World Values Surveys

If half the adults surveyed were Americans,

a. How many Mexicans agreed with the statement?

b. How many Mexicans disagreed with the statement?

Solution

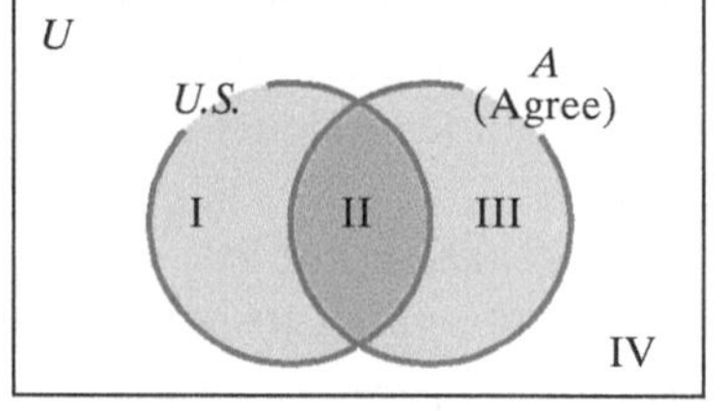
U
U.S.
A
(Agree)
I
II
III
IV

FIGURE 28

Step 1 Define sets and draw a Venn diagram. The Venn diagram in **Figure 28** shows two sets. Set *U.S.* is the set of Americans surveyed. Set *A* (labeled "Agree") is the set of people surveyed who agreed with the statement. By representing the Americans surveyed with circle *U.S.*, we do not need a separate circle for the Mexicans. The group of people outside circle *U.S.* must be the set of Mexicans. Similarly, by visualizing the set of people who agreed with the statement as circle *A*, we do not need a separate circle for those who disagreed. The group of people outside circle *A* (Agree) must be the set of people disagreeing with the statement.

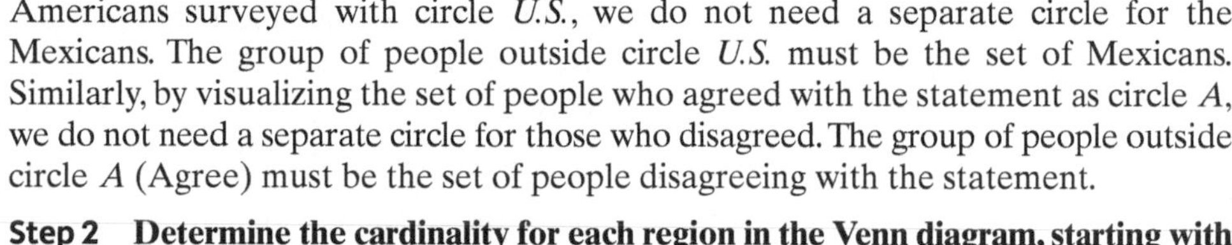

Step 2 Determine the cardinality for each region in the Venn diagram, starting with the innermost region and working outward. We are given the following cardinalities:

There were 2000 people surveyed: $n(U) = 2000$.

Half the people surveyed were Americans: $n(U.S.) = 1000$.

The number of people who agreed with the statement was 1060: $n(A) = 1060$.

There were 400 Americans who agreed with the statement: $n(U.S. \cap A) = 400$.

Now let's use these numbers to determine the cardinality of each region, starting with region II, moving outward to regions I and III, and ending with region IV.

Start with region II.

U, U.S., A, I, II 400, III, IV

II represents the set of Americans who agreed with the statement. We are given that $n(U.S. \cap A) = 400$.

Move out to region I.

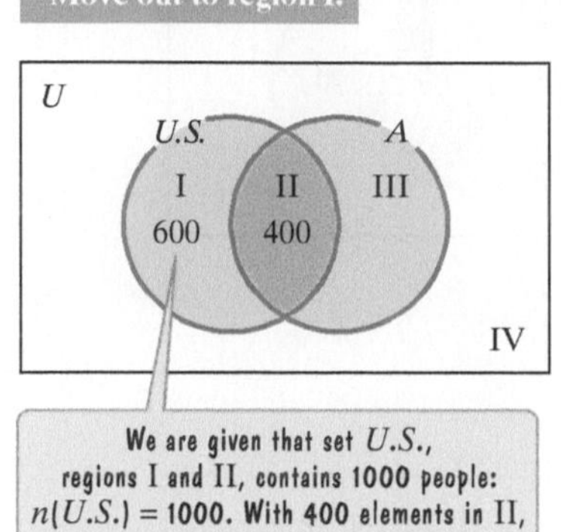
U
U.S.
A
I
600
II
400
III
IV
We are given that set U.S., regions I and II, contains 1000 people: n(U.S.) = 1000. With 400 elements in II, this leaves 1000 − 400 = 600 people in I.

Move out to region III.

U; U.S.; A; I 600; II 400; III 660; IV

We are given that set A, regions II and III, contains 1060 people: $n(A) = 1060$. With 400 elements in II, this leaves $1060 - 400 = 660$ people in III.

End with IV, the outer region.

U; U.S.; A; I 600; II 400; III 660; IV 340

We are given that set U, regions I, II, III, and IV, contains 2000 people: $n(U) = 2000$. With $600 + 400 + 660 = 1660$ elements in I, II, and III, this leaves $2000 - 1660 = 340$ people in IV.

Is the Primary Cause of Poverty Societal Injustice?

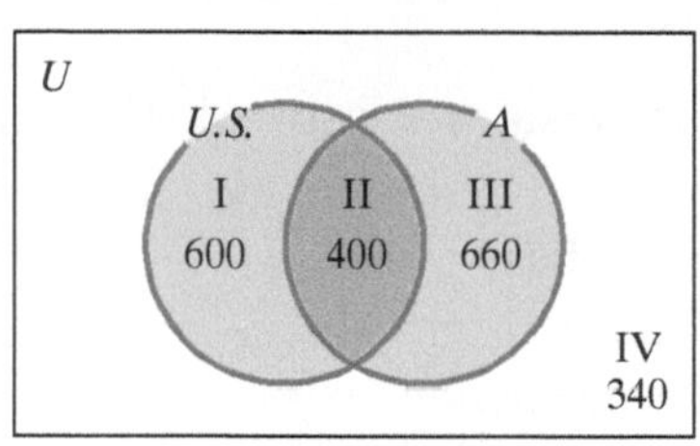

FIGURE 29

Step 3 Use the completed Venn diagram to answer the problem's questions. The completed Venn diagram that illustrates the survey's results is shown in **Figure 29**.

a. The Mexicans who agreed with the statement are those members of the set of people who agreed who are not Americans, shown in region III. This means that 660 Mexicans agreed that societal injustice is the primary cause of poverty.

b. The Mexicans who disagreed with the statement can be found outside the circles of people who agreed and people who are Americans. This corresponds to region IV, whose cardinality is 340. Thus, 340 Mexicans disagreed that societal injustice is the primary cause of poverty.

In a Gallup poll, 2000 U.S. adults were selected at random and asked to agree or disagree with the following statement:

Job opportunities for women are not equal to those for men.

The results of the survey showed that

1190 people agreed with the statement.

700 women agreed with the statement.

Source: The People's Almanac

If half the people surveyed were women,

a. How many men agreed with the statement?

b. How many men disagreed with the statement?

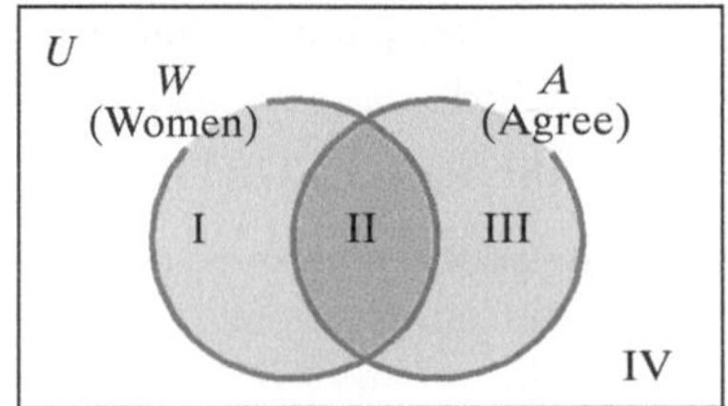

When tabulating survey results, more than two circles within a Venn diagram are often needed. For example, consider a *Time*/CNN poll that sought to determine how Americans felt about reserving a certain number of college scholarships exclusively for minorities and women. Respondents were asked the following question:

Do you agree or disagree with the following statement: Colleges should reserve a certain number of scholarships exclusively for minorities and women?

Source: Time Almanac

Suppose that we want the respondents to the poll to be identified by gender (man or woman), ethnicity (African American or other), and whether or not they agreed with the statement. A Venn diagram into which the results of the survey can be tabulated is shown in **Figure 30**.

Based on our work in Example 2, we only used one circle in the Venn diagram to indicate the gender of the respondent. We used M for men, so the set of women respondents, M', consists of the regions outside circle M. Similarly, we used B for the set of African-American respondents, so the regions outside circle B account for all other ethnicities. Finally, we used A for the set of respondents who agreed with the statement. Those who disagreed lie outside circle A.

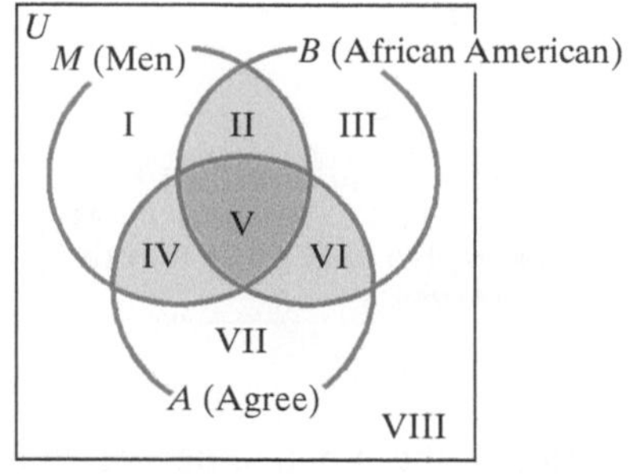

FIGURE 30

In the next example, we create a Venn diagram with three intersecting sets to illustrate a survey's results. In our final example, we use this Venn diagram to answer questions about the survey.

EXAMPLE 3 Constructing a Venn Diagram for a Survey

Sixty people were contacted and responded to a movie survey. The following information was obtained:

a. 6 people liked comedies, dramas, and science fiction.
b. 13 people liked comedies and dramas.
c. 10 people liked comedies and science fiction.
d. 11 people liked dramas and science fiction.
e. 26 people liked comedies.
f. 21 people liked dramas.
g. 25 people liked science fiction.

Use a Venn diagram to illustrate the survey's results.

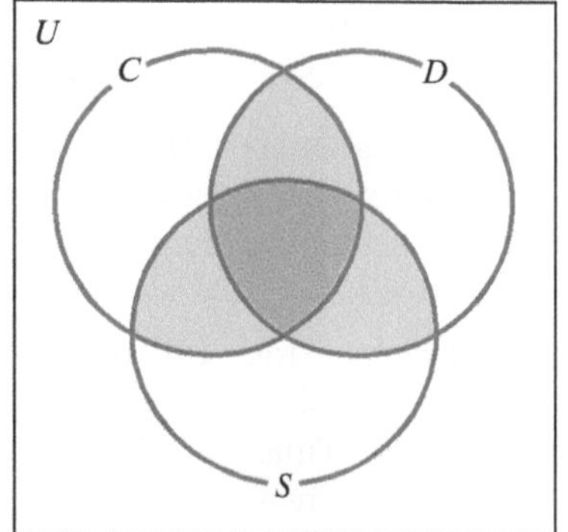
U
C
D
S

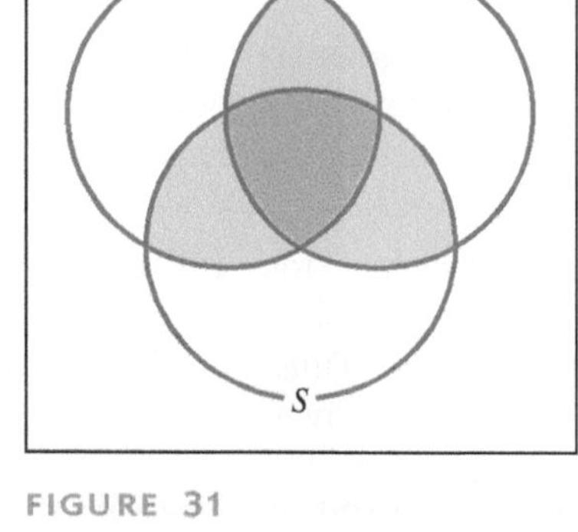

FIGURE 31

Solution The set of people surveyed is a universal set with 60 elements containing three subsets:

C = the set of those who like comedies
D = the set of those who like dramas
S = the set of those who like science fiction.

We draw these sets in **Figure 31**. Now let's use the numbers in (a) through (g), as well as the fact that 60 people were surveyed, which we call condition (h), to determine the cardinality of each region in the Venn diagram.

STUDY TIP

After entering the cardinality of the innermost region, work outward and use subtraction to obtain subsequent cardinalities. The phrase

SURVEY SUBTRACT

is a helpful reminder of these repeated subtractions.

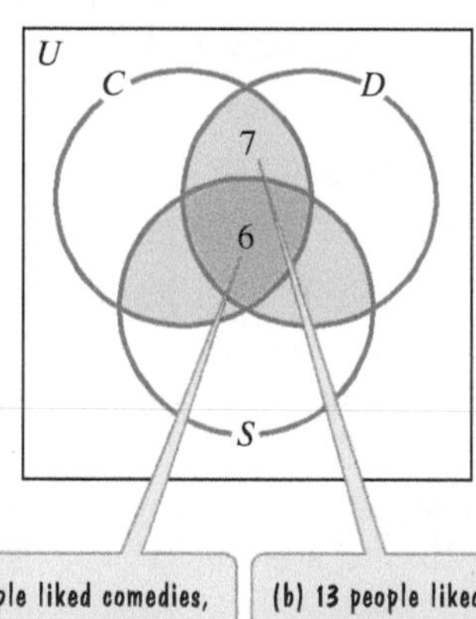
U
C
D
7
6
S
(a) 6 people liked comedies, drama, and science fiction: $n(C \cap D \cap S) = 6$.
(b) 13 people liked comedies and drama: $n(C \cap D) = 13$. With 6 counted, there are $13 - 6 = 7$ people in this region.

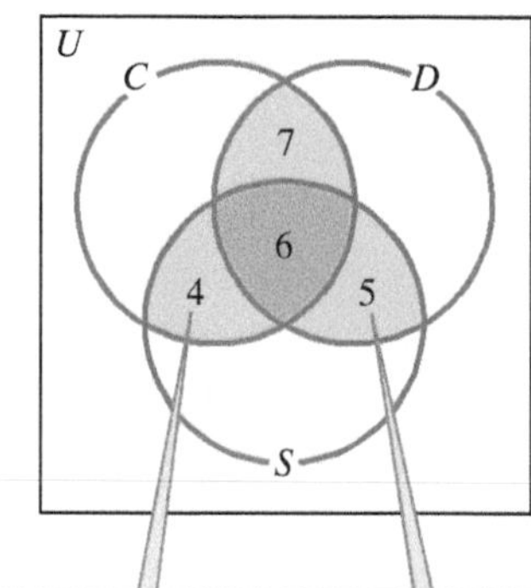
U
C
D
7
6
4
5
S
(c) 10 people liked comedies and science fiction: $n(C \cap S) = 10$. With 6 counted, there are $10 - 6 = 4$ people in this region.
(d) 11 people liked drama and science fiction: $n(D \cap S) = 11$. With 6 counted, there are $11 - 6 = 5$ people in this region.

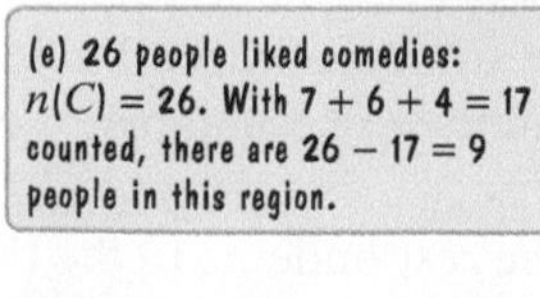
(e) 26 people liked comedies: $n(C) = 26$. With $7 + 6 + 4 = 17$ counted, there are $26 - 17 = 9$ people in this region.
(f) 21 people liked dramas: $n(D) = 21$. With $7 + 6 + 5 = 18$ counted, there are $21 - 18 = 3$ people in this region.
U
C
D
9
7
3
6
4
5
10
S
16
(g) 25 people liked science fiction: $n(S) = 25$. With $4 + 6 + 5 = 15$ counted, there are $25 - 15 = 10$ people in this region.
(h) 60 people were surveyed: $n(U) = 60$. With $9 + 7 + 3 + 4 + 6 + 5 + 10 = 44$ counted, there are $60 - 44 = 16$ people in this region.

With a cardinality in each region, we have completed the Venn diagram that illustrates the survey's results.

A survey of 250 memorabilia collectors showed the following results: 108 collected baseball cards. 92 collected comic books. 62 collected stamps. 29 collected baseball cards and comic books. 5 collected baseball cards and stamps. 2 collected comic books and stamps. 2 collected all three types of memorabilia. Use a Venn diagram to illustrate the survey's results.

EXAMPLE 4 Using a Survey's Venn Diagram

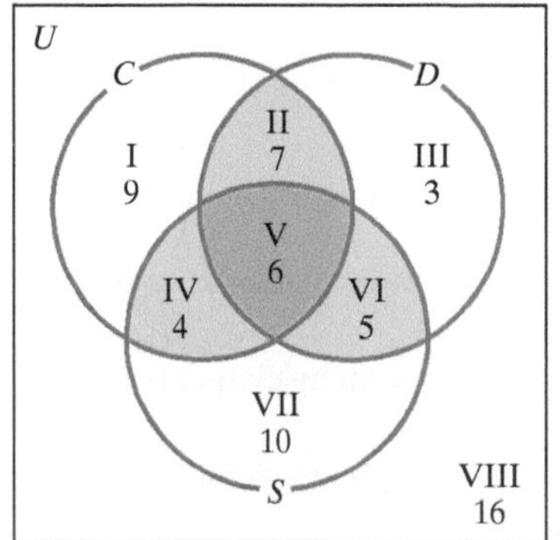

FIGURE 32

The Venn diagram in **Figure 32** shows the results of the movie survey in Example 3. How many of those surveyed liked

a. comedies, but neither dramas nor science fiction?
b. dramas and science fiction, but not comedies?
c. dramas or science fiction, but not comedies?
d. exactly one movie style?
e. at least two movie styles?
f. none of the movie styles?

Solution

$C \cap (D' \cap S')$

a. Those surveyed who liked comedies, but neither dramas nor science fiction, are represented in region I. There are 9 people in this category.

$(D \cap S) \cap C'$

b. Those surveyed who liked dramas and science fiction, but not comedies, are represented in region VI. There are 5 people in this category.

c. We are interested in those surveyed who liked dramas or science fiction, but not comedies:

Dramas or science fiction, | but | not comedies

$$(D \cup S) \cap C'.$$

Regions II, III, IV, V, VI, VII | Regions III, VI, VII, VIII

The intersection of the regions in the voice balloons consists of the common regions shown in red, III, VI, and VII. There are $3 + 5 + 10 = 18$ elements in these regions. There are 18 people who liked dramas or science fiction, but not comedies.

d. Those surveyed who liked exactly one movie style are represented in regions I, III, and VII. There are $9 + 3 + 10 = 22$ elements in these regions. Thus, 22 people liked exactly one movie style.

e. Those surveyed who liked at least two movie styles are people who liked two or more types of movies. People who liked two movie styles are represented in regions II, IV, and VI. Those who liked three movie styles are represented in region V. Thus, we add the number of elements in regions II, IV, V, and VI: $7 + 4 + 6 + 5 = 22$. Thus, 22 people liked at least two movie styles.

f. Those surveyed who liked none of the movie styles are represented in region VIII. There are 16 people in this category.

Use the Venn diagram you constructed in Check Point 3 to determine how many of those surveyed collected

a. comic books, but neither baseball cards nor stamps.
b. baseball cards and stamps, but not comic books.
c. baseball cards or stamps, but not comic books.
d. exactly two types of memorabilia.
e. at least one type of memorabilia.
f. none of the types of memorabilia.

Exercise Set 5

Practice Exercises

Use the accompanying Venn diagram, which shows the number of elements in regions I through IV, to answer the questions in Exercises 1–8.

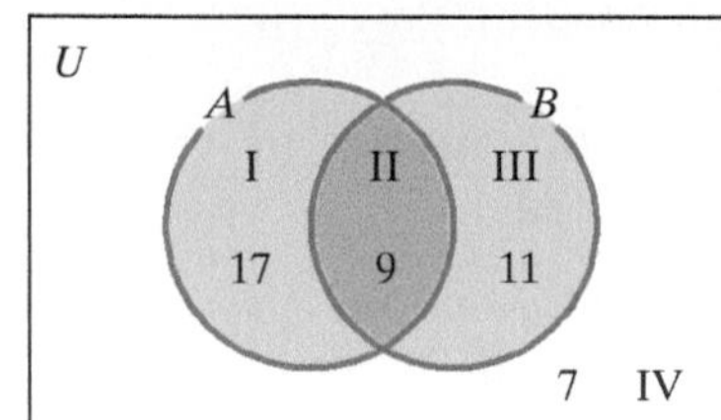

1. How many elements belong to set A?
2. How many elements belong to set B?
3. How many elements belong to set A but not set B?
4. How many elements belong to set B but not set A?
5. How many elements belong to set A or set B?
6. How many elements belong to set A and set B?
7. How many elements belong to neither set A nor set B?
8. How many elements are there in the universal set?

Use the accompanying Venn diagram, which shows the number of elements in region II, to answer Exercises 9–10.

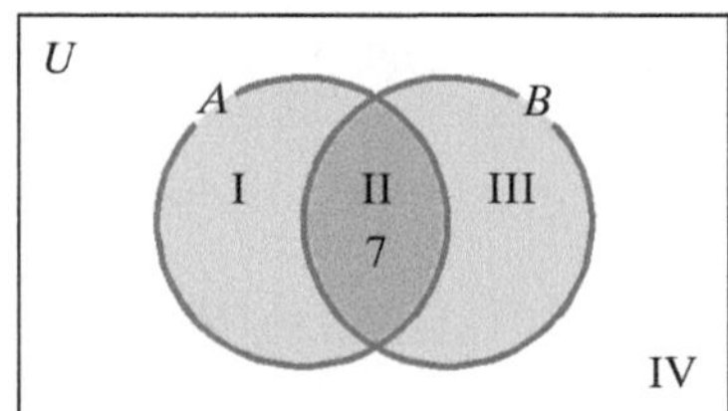

9. If $n(A) = 21$, $n(B) = 29$, and $n(U) = 48$, find the number of elements in each of regions I, III, and IV.
10. If $n(A) = 23$, $n(B) = 27$, and $n(U) = 53$, find the number of elements in each of regions I, III, and IV.

Use the accompanying Venn diagram, which shows the cardinality of each region, to answer Exercises 11–26.

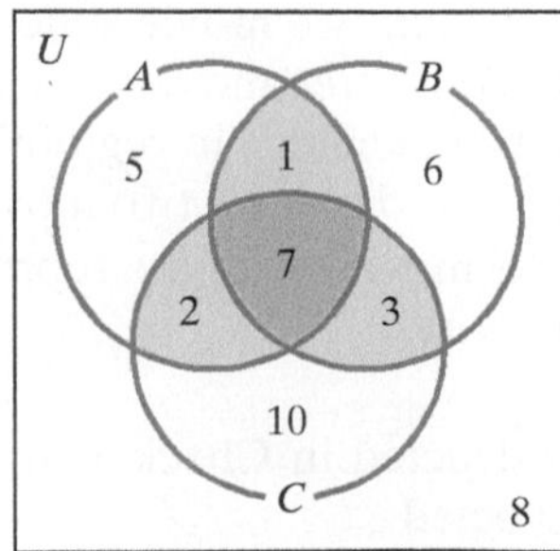

11. How many elements belong to set B?
12. How many elements belong to set A?
13. How many elements belong to set A but not set C?
14. How many elements belong to set B but not set A?
15. How many elements belong to set A or set C?
16. How many elements belong to set A or set B?
17. How many elements belong to set A and set C?
18. How many elements belong to set A and set B?
19. How many elements belong to set B and set C, but not to set A?
20. How many elements belong to set A and set C, but not to set B?
21. How many elements belong to set B or set C, but not to set A?
22. How many elements belong to set A or set C, but not to set B?
23. Considering sets A, B, and C, how many elements belong to exactly one of these sets?
24. Considering sets A, B, and C, how many elements belong to exactly two of these sets?
25. Considering sets A, B, and C, how many elements belong to at least one of these sets?
26. Considering sets A, B, and C, how many elements belong to at least two of these sets?

The accompanying Venn diagram shows the number of elements in region V. In Exercises 27–28, use the given cardinalities to determine the number of elements in each of the other seven regions.

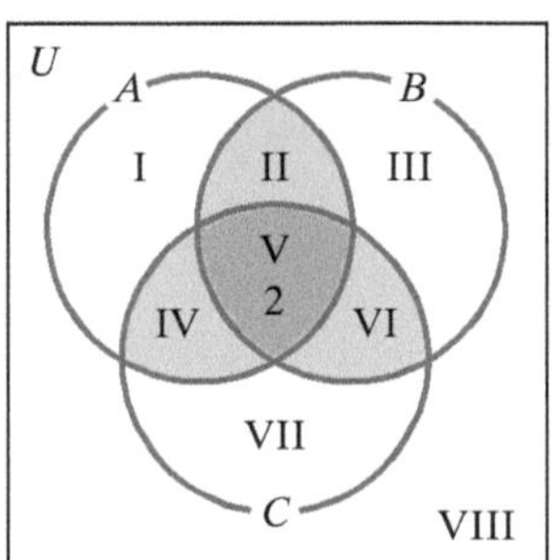

27. $n(U) = 30, n(A) = 11, n(B) = 8, n(C) = 14,$
$n(A \cap B) = 3, n(A \cap C) = 5, n(B \cap C) = 3$
28. $n(U) = 32, n(A) = 21, n(B) = 15, n(C) = 14,$
$n(A \cap B) = 6, n(A \cap C) = 7, n(B \cap C) = 8$

Practice Plus

In Exercises 29–32, use the Venn diagram and the given conditions to determine the number of elements in each region, or explain why the conditions are impossible to meet.

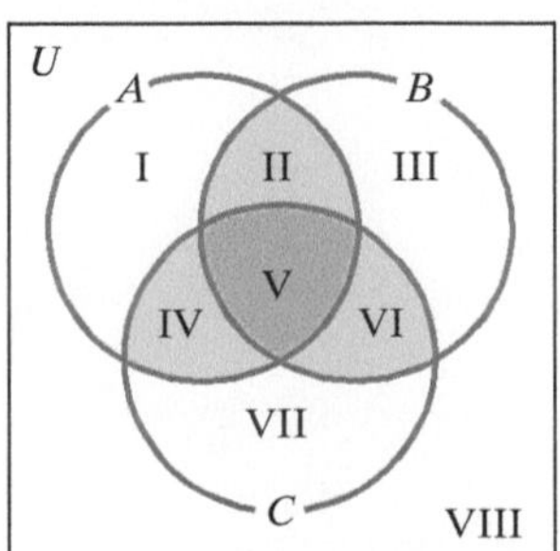

29. $n(U) = 38, n(A) = 26, n(B) = 21, n(C) = 18,$
$n(A \cap B) = 17, n(A \cap C) = 11, n(B \cap C) = 8,$
$n(A \cap B \cap C) = 7$

(In Exercises 30–32, continue to refer to the Venn diagram at the bottom of the previous page.)

30. $n(U) = 42, n(A) = 26, n(B) = 22, n(C) = 25,$
$n(A \cap B) = 17, n(A \cap C) = 11, n(B \cap C) = 9,$
$n(A \cap B \cap C) = 5$

31. $n(U) = 40, n(A) = 10, n(B) = 11, n(C) = 12,$
$n(A \cap B) = 6, n(A \cap C) = 9, n(B \cap C) = 7,$
$n(A \cap B \cap C) = 2$

32. $n(U) = 25, n(A) = 8, n(B) = 9, n(C) = 10,$
$n(A \cap B) = 6, n(A \cap C) = 9, n(B \cap C) = 8,$
$n(A \cap B \cap C) = 5$

Application Exercises

As discussed in the text, a poll asked respondents if they agreed with the statement

Colleges should reserve a certain number of scholarships exclusively for minorities and women.

Hypothetical results of the poll are tabulated in the Venn diagram. Use these cardinalities to solve Exercises 33–38.

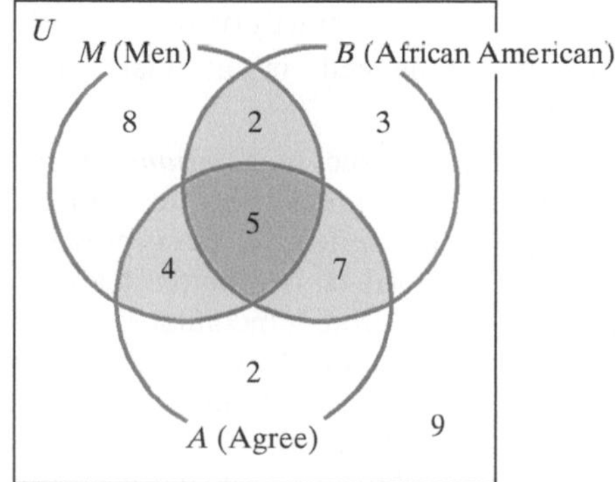

33. How many respondents agreed with the statement?

34. How many respondents disagreed with the statement?

35. How many women agreed with the statement?

36. How many people who are not African American agreed with the statement?

37. How many women who are not African American disagreed with the statement?

38. How many men who are not African American disagreed with the statement?

39. A pollster conducting a telephone poll of a city's residents asked two questions:

1. Do you currently smoke cigarettes?
2. Regardless of your answer to question 1, would you support a ban on smoking in all city parks?

a. Construct a Venn diagram that allows the respondents to the poll to be identified by whether or not they smoke cigarettes and whether or not they support the ban.

b. Write the letter b in every region of the diagram that represents smokers polled who support the ban.

c. Write the letter c in every region of the diagram that represents nonsmokers polled who support the ban.

d. Write the letter d in every region of the diagram that represents nonsmokers polled who do not support the ban.

40. A pollster conducting a telephone poll at a college campus asked students two questions:

1. Do you binge drink three or more times per month?
2. Regardless of your answer to question 1, are you frequently behind in your school work?

a. Construct a Venn diagram that allows the respondents to the poll to be identified by whether or not they binge drink and whether or not they frequently fall behind in school work.

b. Write the letter b in every region of the diagram that represents binge drinkers who are frequently behind in school work.

c. Write the letter c in every region of the diagram that represents students polled who do not binge drink but who are frequently behind in school work.

d. Write the letter d in every region of the diagram that represents students polled who do not binge drink and who do not frequently fall behind in their school work.

41. A pollster conducting a telephone poll asked three questions:

1. Are you religious?
2. Have you spent time with a person during his or her last days of a terminal illness?
3. Should assisted suicide be an option for terminally ill people?

a. Construct a Venn diagram with three circles that can assist the pollster in tabulating the responses to the three questions.

b. Write the letter b in every region of the diagram that represents all religious persons polled who are not in favor of assisted suicide for the terminally ill.

c. Write the letter c in every region of the diagram that represents the people polled who do not consider themselves religious, who have not spent time with a terminally ill person during his or her last days, and who are in favor of assisted suicide for the terminally ill.

d. Write the letter d in every region of the diagram that represents the people polled who consider themselves religious, who have not spent time with a terminally ill person during his or her last days, and who are not in favor of assisted suicide for the terminally ill.

e. Write the letter e in a region of the Venn diagram other than those in parts (b)–(d) and then describe who in the poll is represented by this region.

42. A poll asks respondents the following question:

Do you agree or disagree with this statement: In order to address the trend in diminishing male enrollment, colleges should begin special efforts to recruit men?

a. Construct a Venn diagram with three circles that allows the respondents to be identified by gender (man or woman), education level (college or no college), and whether or not they agreed with the statement.

b. Write the letter b in every region of the diagram that represents men with a college education who agreed with the statement.

c. Write the letter c in every region of the diagram that represents women who disagreed with the statement.

d. Write the letter d in every region of the diagram that represents women without a college education who agreed with the statement.

e. Write the letter e in a region of the Venn diagram other than those in parts (b)–(d) and then describe who in the poll is represented by this region.

In Exercises 43–48, construct a Venn diagram and determine the cardinality for each region. Use the completed Venn diagram to answer the questions.

43. A survey of 75 college students was taken to determine where they got the news about what's going on in the world. Of those surveyed, 29 students got the news from newspapers, 43 from television, and 7 from both newspapers and television.

Of those surveyed,

a. How many got the news from only newspapers?

b. How many got the news from only television?

c. How many got the news from newspapers or television?

d. How many did not get the news from either newspapers or television?

44. A survey of 120 college students was taken at registration. Of those surveyed, 75 students registered for a math course, 65 for an English course, and 40 for both math and English.

Of those surveyed,

a. How many registered only for a math course?

b. How many registered only for an English course?

c. How many registered for a math course or an English course?

d. How many did not register for either a math course or an English course?

45. A survey of 80 college students was taken to determine the musical styles they listened to. Forty-two students listened to rock, 34 to classical, and 27 to jazz. Twelve students listened to rock and jazz, 14 to rock and classical, and 10 to classical and jazz. Seven students listened to all three musical styles.

Of those surveyed,

a. How many listened to only rock music?

b. How many listened to classical and jazz, but not rock?

c. How many listened to classical or jazz, but not rock?

d. How many listened to music in exactly one of the musical styles?

e. How many listened to music in at least two of the musical styles?

f. How many did not listen to any of the musical styles?

46. A survey of 180 college men was taken to determine participation in various campus activities. Forty-three students were in fraternities, 52 participated in campus sports, and 35 participated in various campus tutorial programs. Thirteen students participated in fraternities and sports, 14 in sports and tutorial programs, and 12 in fraternities and tutorial programs. Five students participated in all three activities.

Of those surveyed,

a. How many participated in only campus sports?

b. How many participated in fraternities and sports, but not tutorial programs?

c. How many participated in fraternities or sports, but not tutorial programs?

d. How many participated in exactly one of these activities?

e. How many participated in at least two of these activities?

f. How many did not participate in any of the three activities?

47. An anonymous survey of college students was taken to determine behaviors regarding alcohol, cigarettes, and illegal drugs. The results were as follows: 894 drank alcohol regularly, 665 smoked cigarettes, 192 used illegal drugs, 424 drank alcohol regularly and smoked cigarettes, 114 drank alcohol regularly and used illegal drugs, 119 smoked cigarettes and used illegal drugs, 97 engaged in all three behaviors, and 309 engaged in none of these behaviors.

Source: Jamie Langille, University of Nevada Las Vegas

a. How many students were surveyed?

Of those surveyed,

b. How many drank alcohol regularly or smoked cigarettes?

c. How many used illegal drugs only?

d. How many drank alcohol regularly and smoked cigarettes, but did not use illegal drugs?

e. How many drank alcohol regularly or used illegal drugs, but did not smoke cigarettes?

f. How many engaged in exactly two of these behaviors?

g. How many engaged in at least one of these behaviors?

48. In the August 2005 issue of *Consumer Reports*, readers suffering from depression reported that alternative treatments were less effective than prescription drugs. Suppose that 550 readers felt better taking prescription drugs, 220 felt better through meditation, and 45 felt better taking St. John's wort. Furthermore, 95 felt better using prescription drugs and meditation, 17 felt better using prescription drugs and St. John's wort, 35 felt better using meditation and St. John's wort, 15 improved using all three treatments, and 150 improved using none of these treatments. (Hypothetical results are partly based on percentages given in *Consumer Reports*.)

a. How many readers suffering from depression were included in the report?

Of those included in the report,

b. How many felt better using prescription drugs or meditation?

c. How many felt better using St. John's wort only?

d. How many improved using prescription drugs and meditation, but not St. John's wort?

e. How many improved using prescription drugs or St. John's wort, but not meditation?

f. How many improved using exactly two of these treatments?

g. How many improved using at least one of these treatments?

Writing in Mathematics

49. Suppose that you are drawing a Venn diagram to sort and tabulate the results of a survey. If results are being tabulated along gender lines, explain why only a circle representing women is needed, rather than two separate circles representing the women surveyed and the men surveyed.

50. Suppose that you decide to use two sets, M and W, to sort and tabulate the responses for men and women in a survey. Describe the set of people represented by regions II and IV in the Venn diagram shown. What conclusion can you draw?

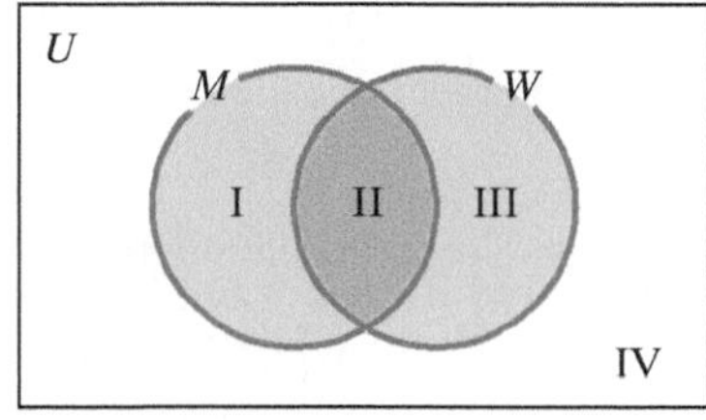

Critical Thinking Exercises

Make Sense? *In Exercises 51–54, determine whether each statement makes sense or does not make sense, and explain your reasoning.*

51. A survey problem must present the information in exactly the same order in which I determine cardinalities from innermost to outermost region.

Exercises 52–54 are based on the graph that shows the percentage of smokers and nonsmokers suffering from various ailments. Use the graph to determine whether each statement makes sense.

Percentage of United States Adults Suffering from Various Ailments

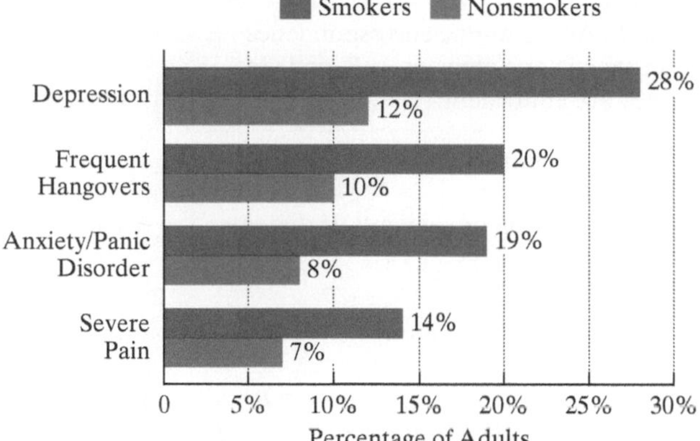

Source: MARS OTC/DTC

52. I represented the data for depression using the following Venn diagram:

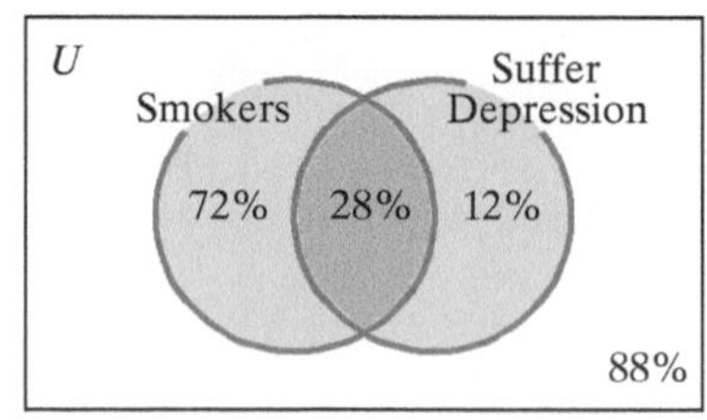

53. I improved the Venn diagram in Exercise 52 by adding a third circle for nonsmokers.

54. I used a single Venn diagram to represent all the data displayed by the bar graph.

In Exercises 55–58, determine whether each statement is true or false. If the statement is false, make the necessary change(s) to produce a true statement.

55. In a survey, 110 students were taking mathematics, 90 were taking psychology, and 20 were taking neither. Thus, 220 students were surveyed.

56. If $A \cap B = \varnothing$, then $n(A \cup B) = n(A) + n(B)$.

57. When filling in cardinalities for regions in a two-set Venn diagram, the innermost region, the intersection of the two sets, should be the last region to be filled in.

58. $n(A')$ can be obtained by subtracting $n(A)$ from $n(U)$.

59. In a survey of 150 students, 90 were taking mathematics and 30 were taking psychology.

a. What is the least number of students who could have been taking both courses?

b. What is the greatest number of students who could have been taking both courses?

c. What is the greatest number of students who could have been taking neither course?

60. A person applying for the position of college registrar submitted the following report to the college president on 90 students: 31 take math; 28 take chemistry; 42 take psychology; 9 take math and chemistry; 10 take chemistry and psychology; 6 take math and psychology; 4 take all three subjects; and 20 take none of these courses. The applicant was not hired. Explain why.

Group Exercise

61. This group activity is intended to provide practice in the use of Venn diagrams to sort responses to a survey. The group will determine the topic of the survey. Although you will not actually conduct the survey, it might be helpful to imagine carrying out the survey using the students on your campus.

a. In your group, decide on a topic for the survey.

b. Devise three questions that the pollster will ask to the people who are interviewed.

c. Construct a Venn diagram that will assist the pollster in sorting the answers to the three questions. The Venn diagram should contain three intersecting circles within a universal set and eight regions.

d. Describe what each of the regions in the Venn diagram represents in terms of the questions in your poll.

Chapter Summary, Review, and Test

Summary –Definitions and Concepts

Examples

1 Basic Set Concepts

a. A set is a collection of objects whose contents can be clearly determined. The objects in a set are called the elements, or members, of the set.

b. Sets can be designated by word descriptions, the roster method (a listing within braces, separating elements with commas), or set-builder notation: Ex. 1 Ex. 2 Ex. 3

$$\{ \quad x \quad | \quad \text{condition (s)} \}.$$

The set of — all elements x — such that — x meets these conditions

c. The empty set, or the null set, represented by { } or ∅, is a set that contains no elements. Ex. 4

d. The symbol ∈ means that an object is an element of a set. The symbol ∉ means that an object is not an element of a set. Ex. 5

e. The set of natural numbers is $\mathbf{N} = \{1, 2, 3, 4, 5, \dots\}$. Inequality symbols, summarized in Table 2, are frequently used to describe sets of natural numbers. Ex. 6 Ex. 7

f. The cardinal number of a set A, $n(A)$, is the number of distinct elements in set A. Repeating elements in a set neither adds new elements to the set nor changes its cardinality. Ex. 8

g. Equivalent sets have the same number of elements, or the same cardinality. A one-to-one correspondence between sets A and B means that each element in A can be paired with exactly one element in B, and vice versa. If two sets can be placed in a one-to-one correspondence, then they are equivalent. Ex. 9

h. Set A is a finite set if $n(A) = 0$ or if $n(A)$ is a natural number. A set that is not finite is an infinite set.

i. Equal sets have exactly the same elements, regardless of order or possible repetition of elements. If two sets are equal, then they must be equivalent. Ex. 10

2 Subsets

a. Set A is a subset of set B, expressed as $A \subseteq B$, if every element in set A is also in set B. The notation $A \nsubseteq B$ means that set A is not a subset of set B, so there is at least one element of set A that is not an element of set B. Ex. 1

b. Set A is a proper subset of set B, expressed as $A \subset B$, if A is a subset of B and $A \neq B$. Ex. 2

c. The empty set is a subset of every set. Ex. 3

d. A set with n elements has 2^n subsets and $2^n - 1$ proper subsets. Ex. 4

3 Venn Diagrams and Set Operations

a. A universal set, symbolized by U, is a set that contains all the elements being considered in a given discussion or problem. Ex. 1

b. Venn Diagrams: Representing Two Subsets of a Universal Set Ex. 2

U A B

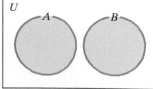

No A are B.
A and B are disjoint.

U B A

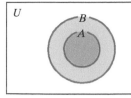

All A are B.
$A \subset B$

U A = B

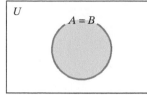

A and B are equal sets.

U A B

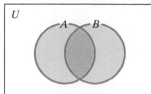

Some (at least one) A are B.

c. A' (the complement of set A), which can be read A prime or **not** A, is the set of all elements in the universal set that are not in A. Ex. 3

d. $A \cap B$ (A intersection B), which can be read set A **and** set B, is the set of elements common to both set A and set B. Ex. 4

e. $A \cup B$ (A union B), which can be read set A **or** set B, is the set of elements that are members of set A or of set B or of both sets. Ex. 5

f. Some problems involve more than one set operation. Begin by performing any operations inside parentheses. Ex. 6

g. Elements of sets involving a variety of set operations can be determined from Venn diagrams. Ex. 7

h. Cardinal Number of the Union of Two Finite Sets Ex. 8

$$n(A \cup B) = n(A) + n(B) - n(A \cap B)$$

4 Set Operations and Venn Diagrams with Three Sets

a. When using set operations involving three sets, begin by performing operations within parentheses.  Ex. 17

b. The figure below shows a Venn diagram with three intersecting sets that separate the universal set, U, into eight regions. Elements of sets involving a variety of set operations can be determined from this Venn diagram.  Ex. 2

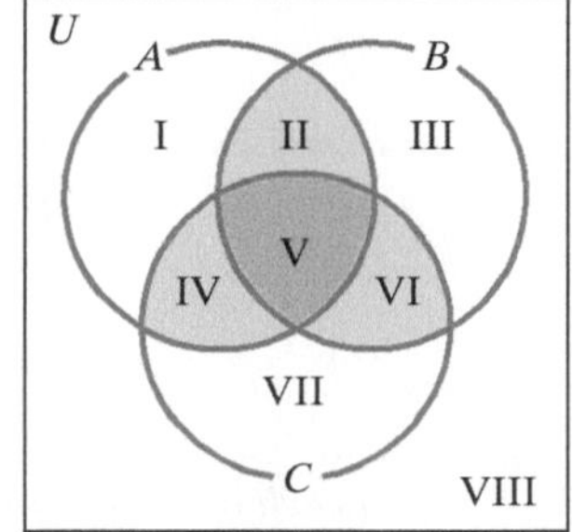

c. To construct a Venn diagram illustrating the elements in A, B, C, and U, first find $A \cap B$, $A \cap C$, $B \cap C$, and $A \cap B \cap C$. Then place elements into the eight regions shown above, starting with the innermost region, region V, and working outward to region VIII. Ex. 3

d. If two specific sets represent the same regions of a general Venn diagram, then this deductively proves that the two sets are equal. Ex. 4, Ex. 5

5 Survey Problems

a. Venn diagrams can be used to organize information collected in surveys. When interpreting cardinalities in such diagrams, *and* and *but* mean intersection, *or* means union, and *not* means complement. Ex. 1

b. To solve a survey problem, Ex. 2
1. Define sets and draw a Venn diagram. Ex. 3
2. Fill in the cardinality of each region, starting with the innermost region and working outward. Ex. 4
3. Use the completed diagram to answer the problem's questions.

Review Exercises

1

In Exercises 1–2, write a word description of each set. (More than one correct description may be possible.)

1. {Tuesday, Thursday}

2. $\{1, 2, 3, \ldots, 10\}$

In Exercises 3–5, express each set using the roster method.

3. $\{x \mid x \text{ is a letter in the word } miss\}$

4. $\{x \mid x \in \mathbf{N} \text{ and } 8 \le x < 13\}$

5. $\{x \mid x \in \mathbf{N} \text{ and } x \le 30\}$

In Exercises 6–7, determine which sets are the empty set.

6. $\{\varnothing\}$

7. $\{x \mid x < 4 \text{ and } x \ge 6\}$

In Exercises 8–9, fill in the blank with either $\in$ *or* $\notin$ *to make each statement true.*

8. 93 ____ $\{1, 2, 3, 4, \ldots, 99, 100\}$

9. {d} ____ {a, b, c, d, e}

In Exercises 10–11, find the cardinal number for each set.

10. $A = \{x \mid x \text{ is a month of the year}\}$

11. $B = \{18, 19, 20, \ldots, 31, 32\}$

In Exercises 12–13, fill in the blank with either $=$ *or* $\neq$ *to make each statement true.*

12. $\{0, 2, 4, 6, 8\}$______$\{8, 2, 6, 4\}$

13. $\{x \mid x \in \mathbf{N}$ and $x > 7\}$______$\{8, 9, 10, \ldots, 100\}$

In Exercises 14–15, determine if the pairs of sets are equivalent, equal, both, or neither.

14. $A = \{x \mid x$ is a lowercase letter that comes before f in the English alphabet$\}$
$B = \{2, 4, 6, 8, 10\}$

15. $A = \{x \mid x \in \mathbf{N}$ and $3 < x < 7\}$
$B = \{4, 5, 6\}$

In Exercises 16–17, determine whether each set is finite or infinite.

16. $\{x \mid x \in \mathbf{N}$ and $x < 50{,}000\}$

17. $\{x \mid x \in \mathbf{N}$ and x is even$\}$

2

In Exercises 18–20, write $\subseteq$ *or* $\nsubseteq$ *in each blank so that the resulting statement is true.*

18. {penny, nickel, dime}
______{half-dollar, quarter, dime, nickel, penny}

19. $\{-1, 0, 1\}$______$\{-3, -2, -1, 1, 2, 3\}$

20. $\varnothing$______$\{x \mid x$ is an odd natural number$\}$

In Exercises 21–22, determine whether $\subseteq$, $\subset$, *both, or neither can be placed in each blank to form a true statement.*

21. $\{1, 2\}$______$\{1, 1, 2, 2\}$

22. $\{x \mid x$ is a person living in the United States$\}$
______$\{y \mid y$ is a person living on planet Earth$\}$

In Exercises 23–29, determine whether each statement is true or false. If the statement is false, explain why.

23. Texas $\in$ {Oklahoma, Louisiana, Georgia, South Carolina}

24. $4 \subseteq \{2, 4, 6, 8, 10, 12\}$

25. $\{e, f, g\} \subset \{d, e, f, g, h, i\}$

26. $\{\ominus, \varnothing\} \subset \{\varnothing, \ominus\}$

27. $\{3, 7, 9\} \subseteq \{9, 7, 3, 1\}$

28. {six} has 2^6 subsets.

29. $\varnothing \subseteq \{\ \}$

30. List all subsets for the set $\{1, 5\}$. Which one of these subsets is not a proper subset?

In Exercises 31–32, find the number of subsets and the number of proper subsets for each set.

31. $\{2, 4, 6, 8, 10\}$

32. $\{x \mid x$ is a month that begins with the letter J$\}$

3

In Exercises 33–37, let $U = \{1, 2, 3, 4, 5, 6, 7, 8\}$, $A = \{1, 2, 3, 4\}$, *and* $B = \{1, 2, 4, 5\}$. *Find each of the following sets.*

33. $A \cap B$

34. $A \cup B'$

35. $A' \cap B$

36. $(A \cup B)'$

37. $A' \cap B'$

In Exercises 38–45, use the Venn diagram to represent each set in roster form.

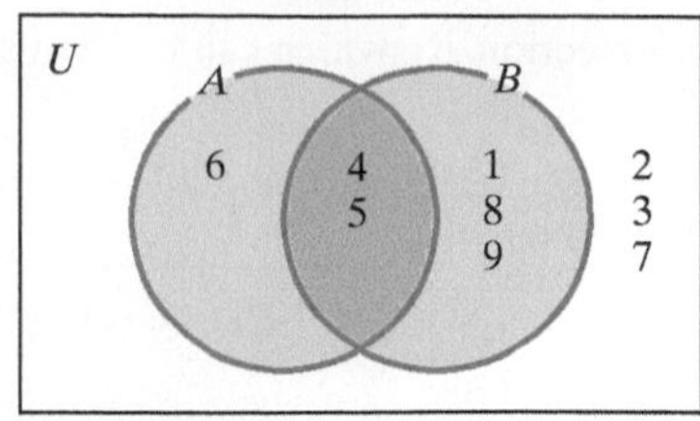

38. A

39. B'

40. $A \cup B$

41. $A \cap B$

42. $(A \cap B)'$

43. $(A \cup B)'$

44. $A \cap B'$

45. U

46. Set A contains 25 elements, set B contains 17 elements, and 9 elements are common to sets A and B. How many elements are in $A \cup B$?

4

In Exercises 47–48, let

$$U = \{1, 2, 3, 4, 5, 6, 7, 8\}$$
$$A = \{1, 2, 3, 4\}$$
$$B = \{1, 2, 4, 5\}$$
$$C = \{1, 5\}.$$

Find each of the following sets.

47. $A \cup (B \cap C)$

48. $(A \cap C)' \cup B$

In Exercises 49–54, use the Venn diagram to represent each set in roster form.

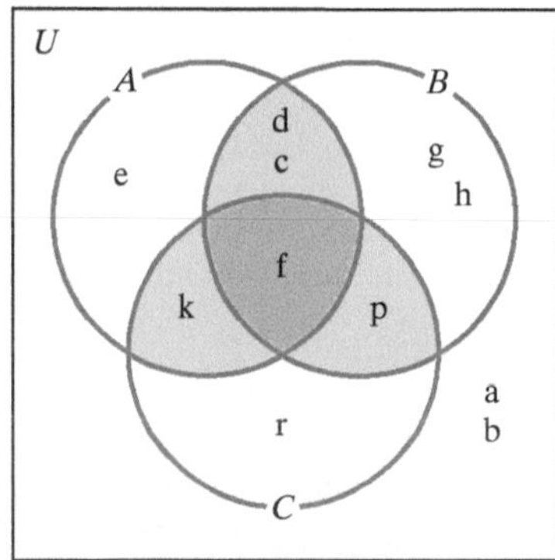

49. $A \cup C$

50. $B \cap C$

51. $(A \cap B) \cup C$

52. $A \cap C'$

53. $(A \cap C)'$

54. $A \cap B \cap C$

55. Construct a Venn diagram illustrating the following sets: $A = \{q, r, s, t, u\}$, $B = \{p, q, r\}$, $C = \{r, u, w, y\}$, and $U = \{p, q, r, s, t, u, v, w, x, y\}$.

56. Use a Venn diagram with two intersecting circles to prove that

$$(A \cup B)' = A' \cap B'.$$

57. Use a Venn diagram with three intersecting circles to determine whether the following statement is a theorem:

$$A \cap (B \cup C) = A \cup (B \cap C).$$

58. *The Penguin Atlas of Women in the World* uses maps and graphics to present data on how women live across continents and cultures. The table is based on data from the atlas.

WOMEN IN THE WORLD: SCHOOL, WORK, AND LITERACY

	Percentage of College Students Who Are Women	Percentage of Women Working for Pay	Percentage of Women Who Are Illiterate
United States	57%	59%	1%
Italy	57%	37%	2%
Turkey	43%	28%	20%
Norway	60%	63%	1%
Pakistan	46%	33%	65%
Iceland	65%	71%	1%
Mexico	51%	40%	10%

Source: The Penguin Atlas of Women in the World, 2009

The data can be organized in the following Venn diagram:

Women in the World

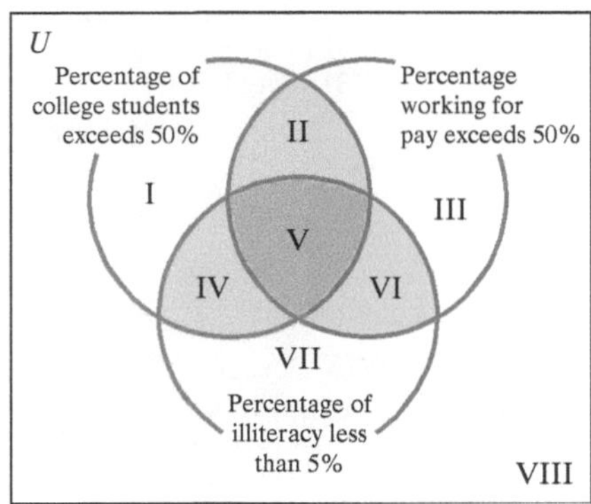

Use the data to determine the region in the Venn diagram into which each of the seven countries should be placed.

5

59. A pollster conducting a telephone survey of college students asked two questions:

1. Are you a registered Republican?
2. Are you in favor of the death penalty?

a. Construct a Venn diagram with two circles that can assist the pollster in tabulating the responses to the two questions.

b. Write the letter b in every region of the diagram that represents students polled who are registered Republicans who are not in favor of the death penalty.

c. Write the letter c in every region of the diagram that represents students polled who are not registered Republicans and who are in favor of the death penalty.

In Exercises 60–61, construct a Venn diagram and determine the cardinality for each region. Use the completed Venn diagram to answer the questions.

60. A survey of 1000 American adults was taken to analyze their investments. Of those surveyed, 650 had invested in stocks, 550 in bonds, and 400 in both stocks and bonds. Of those surveyed,

a. How many invested in only stocks?

b. How many invested in stocks or bonds?

c. How many did not invest in either stocks or bonds?

61. A survey of 200 students at a nonresidential college was taken to determine how they got to campus during the fall term. Of those surveyed, 118 used cars, 102 used public transportation, and 70 used bikes. Forty-eight students used cars and public transportation, 38 used cars and bikes, and 26 used public transportation and bikes. Twenty-two students used all three modes of transportation.
Of those surveyed,

a. How many used only public transportation?

b. How many used cars and public transportation, but not bikes?

c. How many used cars or public transportation, but not bikes?

d. How many used exactly two of these modes of transportation?

e. How many did not use any of the three modes of transportation to get to campus?

Chapter Test

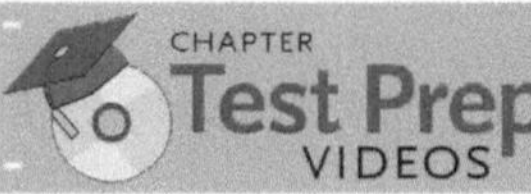

Step-by-step test solutions are found on the Chapter Test Prep Videos available on YouTube (search "Blitzer, Thinking Mathematically" and click on "Channels").

1. Express the following set using the roster method:
$\{x \mid x \in \mathbf{N} \text{ and } 17 < x \le 24\}$.

In Exercises 2–9, determine whether each statement is true or false. If the statement is false, explain why.

2. $\{6\} \in \{1, 2, 3, 4, 5, 6, 7\}$

3. If $A = \{x \mid x \text{ is a day of the week}\}$ and $B = \{2, 4, 6, \ldots, 14\}$, then sets A and B are equivalent.

4. $\{2, 4, 6, 8\} = \{8, 8, 6, 6, 4, 4, 2\}$

5. $\{d, e, f, g\} \subseteq \{a, b, c, d, e, f\}$

6. $\{3, 4, 5\} \subset \{x \mid x \in \mathbf{N} \text{ and } x < 6\}$

7. $14 \notin \{1, 2, 3, 4, \ldots, 39, 40\}$

8. $\{a, b, c, d, e\}$ has 25 subsets.

9. The empty set is a proper subset of any set, including itself.

10. List all subsets for the set $\{6, 9\}$. Which of these subsets is not a proper subset?

In Exercises 11–15, let

$$U = \{a, b, c, d, e, f, g\}$$
$$A = \{a, b, c, d\}$$
$$B = \{c, d, e, f\}$$
$$C = \{a, e, g\}.$$

Find each of the following sets or cardinalities.

11. $A \cup B$

12. $(B \cap C)'$

13. $A \cap C'$

14. $(A \cup B) \cap C$

15. $n(A \cup B')$

In Exercises 16–18, use the Venn diagram to represent each set in roster form.

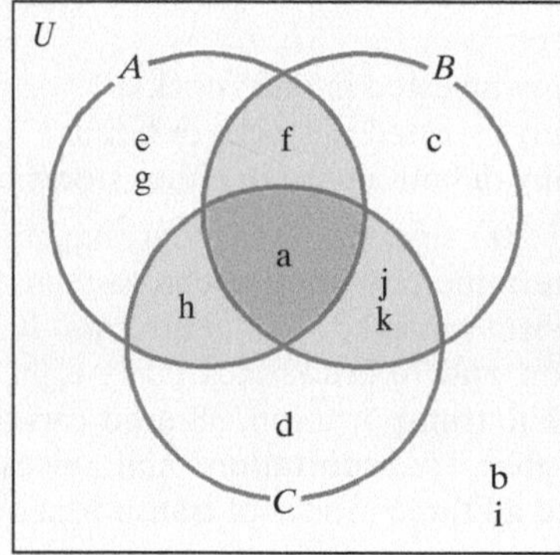

16. A'

17. $A \cap B \cap C$

18. $(A \cap B) \cup (A \cap C)$

19. Construct a Venn diagram illustrating the following sets: $A = \{1, 4, 5\}$, $B = \{1, 5, 6, 7\}$, and $U = \{1, 2, 3, 4, 5, 6, 7\}$.

20. Use the Venn diagram shown to determine whether the following statement is a theorem:

$$A' \cap (B \cup C) = (A' \cap B) \cup (A' \cap C).$$

Show work clearly as you develop the regions representing each side of the statement.

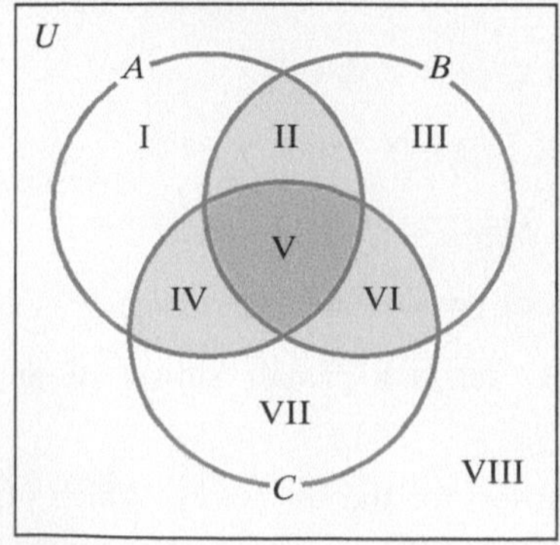

21. Here is a list of some famous people on whom the FBI kept files:

Famous Person	Length of FBI File
Bud Abbott (entertainer)	14 pages
Charlie Chaplin (entertainer)	2063 pages
Albert Einstein (scientist)	1800 pages
Martin Luther King, Jr. (civil rights leader)	17,000 pages
Elvis Presley (entertainer)	663 pages
Jackie Robinson (athlete)	131 pages
Eleanor Roosevelt (first lady; U.N. representative)	3000 pages
Frank Sinatra (entertainer)	1275 pages

Source: Paul Grobman, *Vital Statistics*, Plume, 2005.

The data can be organized in the following Venn diagram:

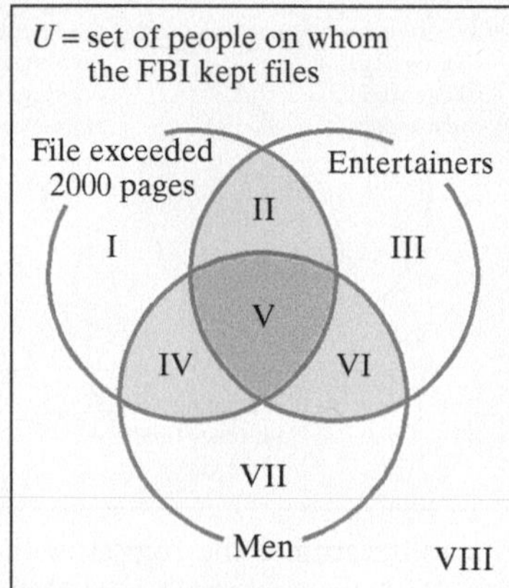

Use the data to determine the region in the Venn diagram into which each of the following people should be placed.

a. Chaplin **b.** Einstein **c.** King
d. Roosevelt **e.** Sinatra

22. A winter resort took a poll of its 350 visitors to see which winter activities people enjoyed. The results were as follows: 178 liked to ski, 154 liked to snowboard, 57 liked to ice skate, 49 liked to ski and snowboard, 15 liked to ski and ice skate, 2 liked to snowboard and ice skate, and 2 liked all three activities.

a. Use a Venn diagram to illustrate the survey's results.

Use the Venn diagram to determine how many of those surveyed enjoyed

b. exactly one of these activities.

c. none of these activities.

d. at least two of these activities.

e. snowboarding and ice skating, but not skiing.

f. snowboarding or ice skating, but not skiing.

g. only skiing.

Answers to Selected Exercises

Section 1

Check Point Exercises

1. L is the set of the first six letters of the alphabet. **2.** $M = \{\text{April, August}\}$ **3.** $O = \{1, 3, 5, 7, 9\}$ **4. a.** not the empty set **b.** empty set **c.** not the empty set **d.** not the empty set **5. a.** true **b.** true **c.** false **6. a.** $A = \{1, 2, 3\}$ **b.** $B = \{15, 16, 17, 18, \ldots\}$ **c.** $O = \{1, 3, 5, 7, \ldots\}$ **7. a.** $\{1, 2, 3, 4, \ldots, 199\}$ **b.** $\{51, 52, 53, 54, \ldots, 200\}$ **8. a.** $n(A) = 5$ **b.** $n(B) = 1$ **c.** $n(C) = 8$ **d.** $n(D) = 0$ **9.** No; the sets do not contain the same number of distinct elements. **10. a.** true **b.** false

Exercise Set 1

1. well defined; set **3.** not well defined; not a set **5.** well defined; set **7.** the set of planets in our solar system **9.** the set of months that begin with J **11.** the set of natural numbers greater than 5 **13.** the set of natural numbers between 6 and 20, inclusive **15.** {winter, spring, summer, fall} **17.** {September, October, November, December} **19.** $\{1, 2, 3\}$ **21.** $\{1, 3, 5, 7, 9, 11\}$ **23.** $\{1, 2, 3, 4, 5\}$ **25.** $\{6, 7, 8, 9, \ldots\}$ **27.** $\{7, 8, 9, 10\}$ **29.** $\{10, 11, 12, 13, \ldots, 79\}$ **31.** $\{2\}$ **33.** not the empty set **35.** empty set **37.** not the empty set **39.** empty set **41.** empty set **43.** not the empty set **45.** not the empty set **47.** true **49.** true **51.** false **53.** true **55.** false **57.** false **59.** true **61.** false **63.** false **65.** true **67.** 5 **69.** 15 **71.** 0 **73.** 1 **75.** 4 **77.** 5 **79.** 0 **81. a.** not equivalent; Answers will vary. **b.** not equal; Answers will vary. **83. a.** equivalent; Answers will vary. **b.** not equal; Answers will vary. **85. a.** equivalent; Answers will vary. **b.** equal; Answers will vary. **87. a.** equivalent; Answers will vary. **b.** not equal; Answers will vary. **89. a.** equivalent; Answers will vary. **b.** equal; Answers will vary. **91.** infinite **93.** finite **95.** finite **97.** $\{x \mid x \in \mathbf{N} \text{ and } x \geq 61\}$ **99.** $\{x \mid x \in \mathbf{N} \text{ and } 61 \leq x \leq 89\}$ **101.** Answers will vary; an example is: $\{0, 1, 2, 3\}$ and $\{1, 2, 3, 4\}$. **103.** impossible; Answers will vary. **105.** {New Zealand, Australia, United States} **107.** {Australia, United States, United Kingdom, Switzerland, Ireland} **109.** {United Kingdom, Switzerland, Ireland} **111.** $\varnothing$ or { } **113.** $\{12, 19\}$ **115.** $\{20, 21\}$ **117.** no one-to-one correspondence; not equivalent **125.** does not make sense **127.** makes sense **129.** false **131.** true **133.** false **135.** false

Section 2

Check Point Exercises

1. a. $\not\subseteq$ **b.** $\subseteq$ **c.** $\subseteq$ **2. a.** $\subseteq, \subset$ **b.** $\subseteq, \subset$ **3.** yes **4. a.** 16; 15 **b.** 64; 63

Exercise Set 2

1. $\subseteq$ **3.** $\not\subseteq$ **5.** $\not\subseteq$ **7.** $\not\subseteq$ **9.** $\subseteq$ **11.** $\not\subseteq$ **13.** $\subseteq$ **15.** $\not\subseteq$ **17.** $\subseteq$ **19.** both **21.** $\subseteq$ **23.** neither **25.** both **27.** $\subseteq$ **29.** $\subseteq$ **31.** both **33.** both **35.** both **37.** neither **39.** $\subseteq$ **41.** true **43.** false; Answers will vary. **45.** true **47.** false; Answers will vary. **49.** true **51.** false; Answers will vary. **53.** true **55.** $\varnothing$, {border collie}, {poodle}, {border collie, poodle} **57.** $\varnothing$, {t}, {a}, {b}, {t, a}, {t, b}, {a, b}, {t, a, b} **59.** $\varnothing$ and $\{0\}$ **61.** 16; 15 **63.** 64; 63 **65.** 128; 127 **67.** 8; 7 **69.** false; The set $\{1, 2, 3, \ldots, 1000\}$ has $2^{1000} - 1$ proper subsets. **71.** true **73.** false; $\varnothing \subseteq \{\varnothing, \{\varnothing\}\}$ **75.** true **77.** true **79.** true **81.** false; The set of subsets of {a, e, i, o, u} contains 32 elements. **83.** false; $D \subseteq T$ **85.** true **87.** false; If $x \in W$, then $x \in D$. **89.** true **91.** true **93.** 32 **95.** 64 **97.** 256 **105.** does not make sense **107.** does not make sense **109.** false **111.** false **113.** \$0.00, \$0.05, \$0.10, \$0.15, \$0.25, \$0.30, \$0.35, and \$0.40

Section 3

Check Point Exercises

1. a. $\{1, 5, 6, 7, 9\}$ **b.** $\{1, 5, 6\}$ **c.** $\{7, 9\}$ **2. a.** {a, b, c, d} **b.** {e} **c.** {e, f, g} **d.** {f, g} **3.** {b, c, e} **4. a.** $\{7, 10\}$ **b.** $\varnothing$ **c.** $\varnothing$ **5. a.** $\{1, 3, 5, 6, 7, 10, 11\}$ **b.** $\{1, 2, 3, 4, 5, 6, 7\}$ **c.** $\{1, 2, 3\}$ **6. a.** {a, d} **b.** {a, d} **7. a.** $\{5\}$ **b.** $\{2, 3, 7, 11, 13, 17, 19\}$ **c.** $\{2, 3, 5, 7, 11, 13\}$ **d.** $\{17, 19\}$ **e.** $\{5, 7, 11, 13, 17, 19\}$ **f.** $\{2, 3\}$ **8.** 385 students

Exercise Set 3

1. the set of all composers **3.** the set of all brands of soft drinks **5.** {c, d, e} **7.** {b, c, d, e, f} **9.** $\{6, 7, 8, 9, \ldots, 20\}$ **11.** $\{2, 4, 6, 8, \ldots, 20\}$ **13.** $\{21, 22, 23, 24, \ldots\}$ **15.** $\{1, 3, 5, 7, \ldots\}$ **17.** $\{1, 3\}$ **19.** $\{1, 2, 3, 5, 7\}$ **21.** $\{2, 4, 6\}$ **23.** $\{4, 6\}$ **25.** $\{1, 3, 5, 7\}$ or A **27.** $\{1, 2, 4, 6, 7\}$ **29.** $\{1, 2, 4, 6, 7\}$ **31.** $\{4, 6\}$ **33.** $\{1, 3, 5, 7\}$ or A **35.** $\varnothing$ **37.** $\{1, 2, 3, 4, 5, 6, 7\}$ or U **39.** $\{1, 3, 5, 7\}$ or A **41.** {g, h} **43.** {a, b, g, h} **45.** {b, c, d, e, f} or C **47.** {c, d, e, f} **49.** {a, g, h} or A **51.** {a, b, c, d, e, f, g, h} or U **53.** {a, b, c, d, e, f, g, h} or U **55.** {c, d, e, f} **57.** {a, g, h} or A **59.** $\varnothing$ **61.** {a, b, c, d, e, f, g, h} or U **63.** {a, g, h} or A **65.** {a, c, d, e, f, g, h} **67.** $\{1, 3, 4, 7\}$ **69.** $\{1, 2, 3, 4, 5, 6, 7, 8, 9\}$ **71.** $\{3, 7\}$ **73.** $\{1, 4, 8, 9\}$ **75.** $\{8, 9\}$ **77.** $\{1, 4\}$ **79.** {$\triangle$, two, four, six} **81.** {$\triangle$, #, \$, two, four, six} **83.** 6 **85.** 5 **87.** {#, \$, two, four, six, 10, 01} **89.** {two, four, six} **91.** 4 **93.** 31 **95.** 27 **97.** $\{1, 2, 3, 4, 5, 6, 7, 8\}$ or U **99.** $\{1, 3, 5, 7\}$ or A **101.** $\{1, 7\}$ **103.** $\{1, 3, 5, 6, 7, 8\}$ **105.** $\{23, 29, 31, 37, 41, 43, 53, 59, 61, 67, 71\}$ **107.** 60 **109.** {Ashley, Mike, Josh} **111.** {Ashley, Mike, Josh, Emily, Hanna, Ethan} **113.** {Ashley} **115.** {Jacob} **117.** III **119.** I **121.** II **123.** I **125.** IV **127.** II **129.** III **131.** I **133.** {spacial-temporal toys, sports equipment, toy cars and trucks} **135.** {dollhouses, spacial-temporal toys, sports equipment, toy cars and trucks} **137.** $\varnothing$ **139.** 283 people **153.** makes sense **155.** makes sense **157.** true **159.** false **161.** false **163.** true

165.

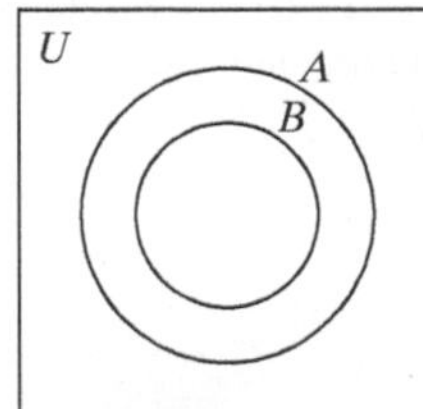

167.

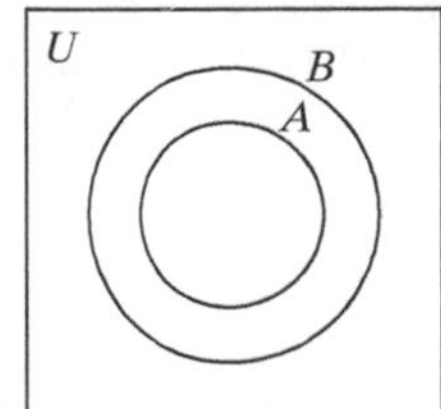

Section 4

Check Point Exercises

1. a. {a, b, c, d, f} **b.** {a, b, c, d, f} **c.** {a, b, d}
2. a. {5, 6, 7, 8, 9} **b.** {1, 2, 5, 6, 7, 8, 9, 10, 12} **c.** {5, 6, 7} **d.** {3, 4, 6, 8, 11} **e.** {1, 2, 3, 5, 6, 7, 8, 9, 10, 11, 12}
3.

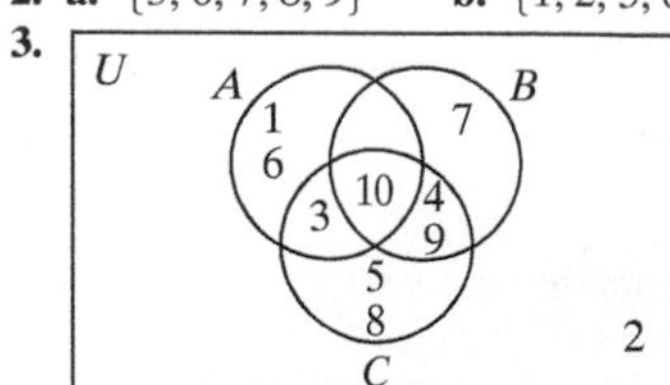

4. a. IV **b.** IV **c.** $(A \cup B)' = A' \cap B'$ **5. a.** II, IV, and V **b.** II, IV, and V **c.** $A \cap (B \cup C) = (A \cap B) \cup (A \cap C)$

Exercise Set 4

1. {1, 2, 3, 5, 7} **3.** {1, 2, 3, 5, 7} **5.** {2} **7.** {2} **9.** ∅ **11.** {4, 6} **13.** {a, b, g, h} **15.** {a, b, g, h} **17.** {b} **19.** {b} **21.** ∅ **23.** {c, d, e, f} **25.** II, III, V, and VI **27.** I, II, IV, V, VI, and VII **29.** II and V **31.** I, IV, VII, and VIII **33.** {1, 2, 3, 4, 5, 6, 7, 8} **35.** {1, 2, 3, 4, 5, 6, 7, 8, 9, 10, 11} **37.** {12, 13} **39.** {4, 5, 6} **41.** {6} **43.** {1, 2, 3, 4, 5, 7, 8, 9, 10, 11, 12, 13}
45.

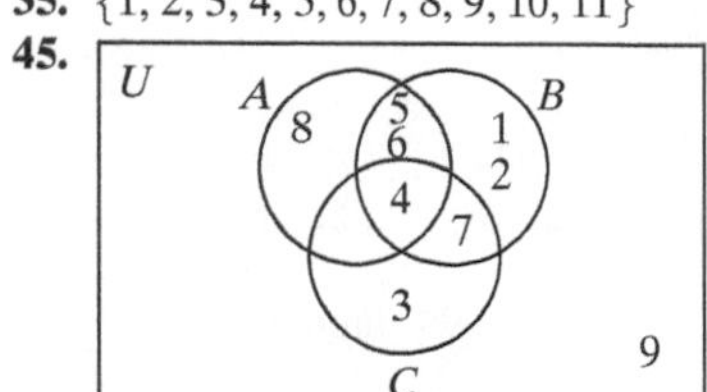

47.

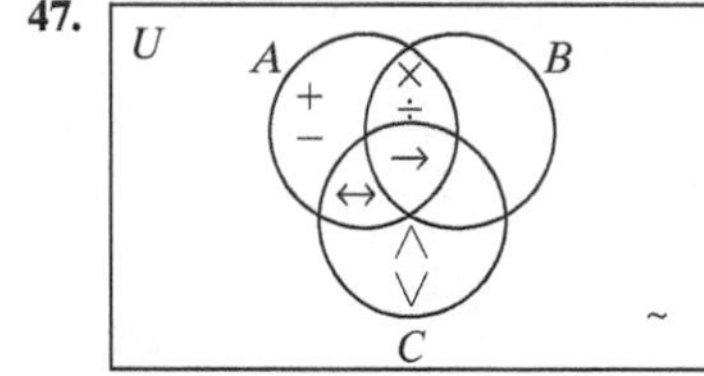

49. a. II **b.** II **c.** $A \cap B = B \cap A$ **51. a.** I, III, and IV **b.** IV **c.** no; Answers will vary. **53.** not equal **55.** not equal **57.** equal **59. a.** II, IV, V, VI, and VII **b.** II, IV, V, VI, and VII **c.** $(A \cap B) \cup C = (A \cup C) \cap (B \cup C)$ **61. a.** II, IV, and V **b.** I, II, IV, V, and VI **c.** no; Answers will vary. **63.** not true **65.** true; theorem **67.** true; theorem **69. a.** {c, e, f}; {c, e, f} **b.** {1, 3, 5, 7, 8}; {1, 3, 5, 7, 8} **c.** $A \cup (B' \cap C') = (A \cup B') \cap (A \cup C')$ **d.** theorem **71.** $(A \cap B)' \cap (A \cup B)$ **73.** $A' \cup B$ **75.** $(A \cap B) \cup C$ **77.** $A' \cap (B \cup C)$ **79.** {Ann, Jose, Al, Gavin, Amy, Ron, Grace} **81.** {Jose} **83.** {Lily, Emma} **85.** {Lily, Emma, Ann, Jose, Lee, Maria, Fred, Ben, Sheila, Ellen, Gary} **87.** {Lily, Emma, Al, Gavin, Amy, Lee, Maria} **89.** {Al, Gavin, Amy} **91.** The set of students who scored 90% or above on exam 1 and exam 3 but not on exam 2 **93.** II **95.** V **97.** III **99.** III **101.** V **103.** VII **105.**

U
A
B
Japan
England
Italy
U.S.
Russia
C
Iran
East Africa

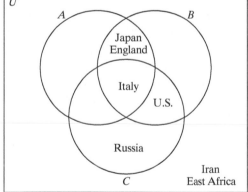

109. does not make sense **111.** makes sense **113.** AB+ **115.** no

Section 5

Check Point Exercises

1. a. 75 **b.** 90 **c.** 20 **d.** 145 **e.** 55 **f.** 70 **g.** 30 **h.** 175 **2. a.** 490 men **b.** 510 men
3.

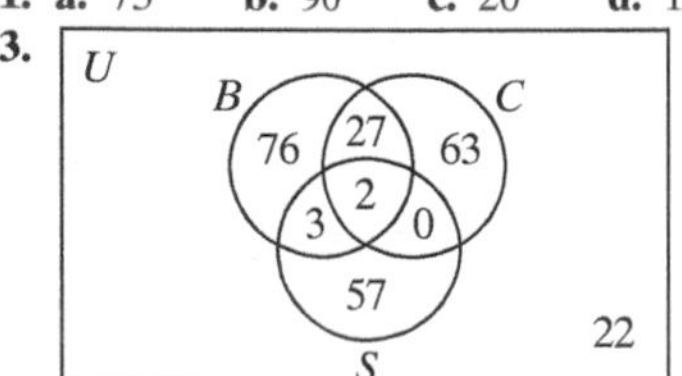

4. a. 63 **b.** 3 **c.** 136 **d.** 30 **e.** 228 **f.** 22

Exercise Set 5

1. 26 **3.** 17 **5.** 37 **7.** 7 **9.** I: 14; III: 22; IV: 5 **11.** 17 **13.** 6 **15.** 28 **17.** 9 **19.** 3 **21.** 19 **23.** 21 **25.** 34 **27.** I: 5; II: 1; III: 4; IV: 3; VI: 1; VII: 8; VIII: 6 **29.** I: 5; II: 10; III: 3; IV: 4; V: 7; VI: 1; VII: 6; VIII: 2 **31.** impossible; There are only 10 elements in set A but there are 13 elements in set A that are also in sets B or C. A similar problem exists for set C. **33.** 18 **35.** 9 **37.** 9

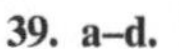

39. a–d.

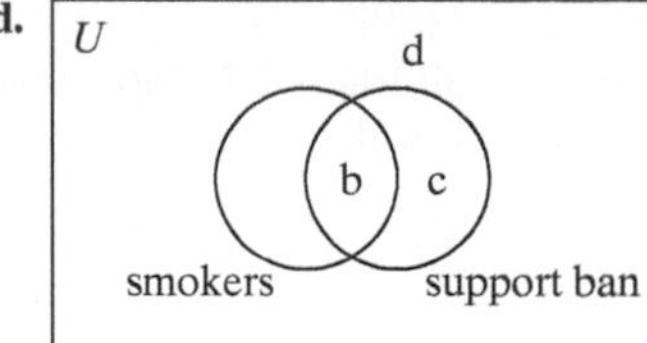

41. a–d.

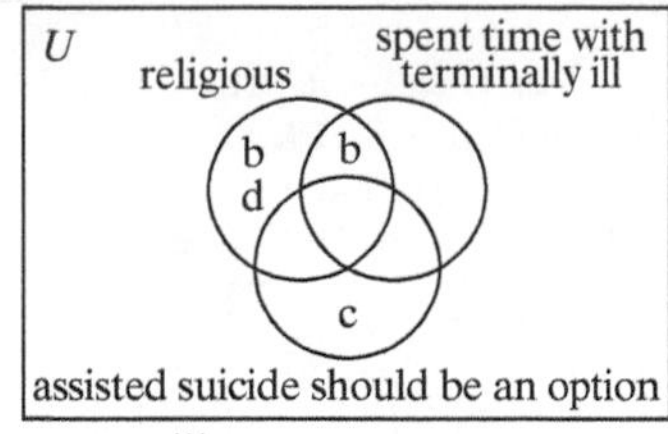

e. Answers will vary.

43.

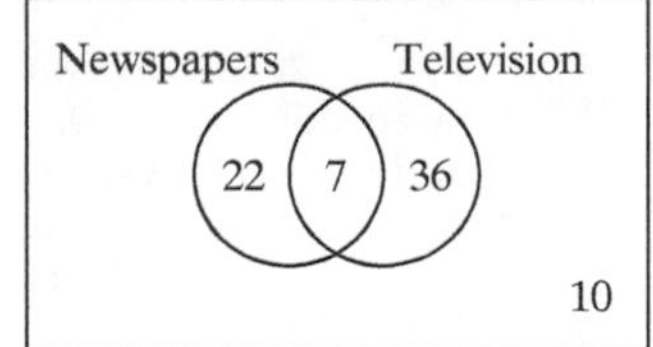

a. 22 **b.** 36 **c.** 65 **d.** 10

45.

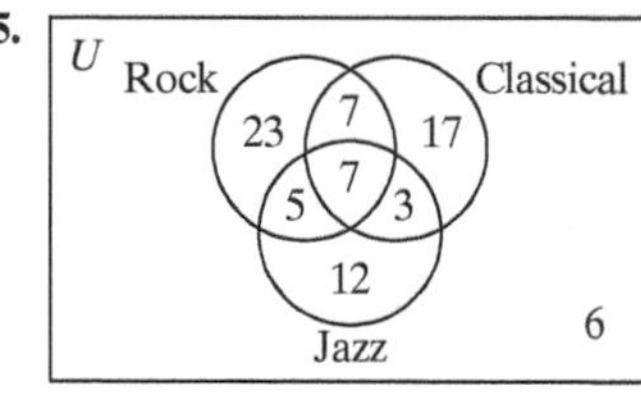

a. 23 **b.** 3 **c.** 32 **d.** 52 **e.** 22 **f.** 6

47. a. 1500 **b.** 1135 **c.** 56 **d.** 327 **e.** 526 **f.** 366 **g.** 1191 **51.** does not make sense **53.** does not make sense
55. false **57.** false **59. a.** 0 **b.** 30 **c.** 60

Chapter Review Exercises

1. the set of days of the week beginning with the letter T **2.** the set of natural numbers between 1 and 10, inclusive **3.** {m, i, s}
4. {8, 9, 10, 11, 12} **5.** {1, 2, 3, ..., 30} **6.** not empty **7.** empty set **8.** $\in$ **9.** $\notin$ **10.** 12 **11.** 15 **12.** $\neq$ **13.** $\neq$
14. equivalent **15.** both **16.** finite **17.** infinite **18.** $\subseteq$ **19.** $\not\subseteq$ **20.** $\subseteq$ **21.** $\subseteq$ **22.** both **23.** false; Answers will vary.
24. false; Answers will vary. **25.** true **26.** false; Answers will vary. **27.** true **28.** false; It has $2^1 = 2$ subsets. **29.** true
30. $\varnothing$, {1}, {5}, {1, 5}; {1, 5} **31.** 32; 31 **32.** 8; 7 **33.** {1, 2, 4} **34.** {1, 2, 3, 4, 6, 7, 8} **35.** {5} **36.** {6, 7, 8} **37.** {6, 7, 8}
38. {4, 5, 6} **39.** {2, 3, 6, 7} **40.** {1, 4, 5, 6, 8, 9} **41.** {4, 5} **42.** {1, 2, 3, 6, 7, 8, 9} **43.** {2, 3, 7} **44.** {6}
45. {1, 2, 3, 4, 5, 6, 7, 8, 9} **46.** 33 **47.** {1, 2, 3, 4, 5} **48.** {1, 2, 3, 4, 5, 6, 7, 8} or U **49.** {c, d, e, f, k, p, r} **50.** {f, p}
51. {c, d, f, k, p, r} **52.** {c, d, e} **53.** {a, b, c, d, e, g, h, p, r} **54.** {f}

55.

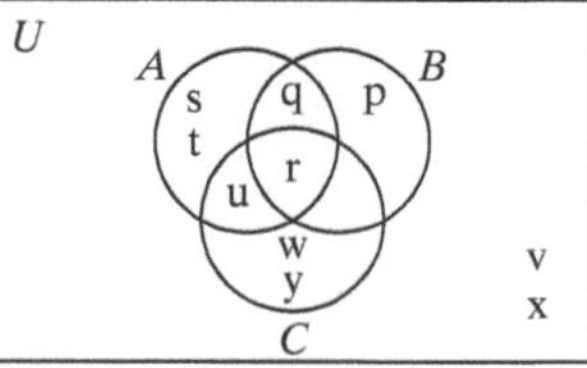

56. Use Figure 22.

Set	Regions in the Venn Diagram
A	I, II
B	II, III
$A \cup B$	I, II, III
$(A \cup B)'$	IV

Set	Regions in the Venn Diagram
A'	III, IV
B'	I, IV
$A' \cap B'$	IV

Since $(A \cup B)'$ and $A' \cap B'$ are represented by the same region, $(A \cup B)' = A' \cap B'$.

57. Use Figure 23.

Set	Regions in the Venn Diagram
A	I, II, IV, V
B	II, III, V, VI
C	IV, V, VI, VII
$B \cup C$	II, III, IV, V, VI, VII
$A \cap (B \cup C)$	II, IV, V

Set	Regions in the Venn Diagram
A	I, II, IV, V
B	II, III, V, VI
C	IV, V, VI, VII
$B \cap C$	V, VI
$A \cup (B \cap C)$	I, II, IV, V, VI

Since $A \cap (B \cup C)$ and $A \cup (B \cap C)$ are not represented by the same regions, $A \cap (B \cup C) = A \cup (B \cap C)$ is false.

58. United States: V; Italy: IV; Turkey: VIII; Norway: V; Pakistan: VIII; Iceland: V; Mexico: I

59. a–c.

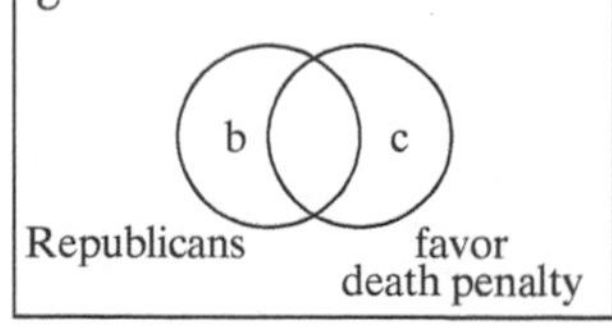

60. a. 250 **b.** 800 **c.** 200 **61. a.** 50 **b.** 26 **c.** 130 **d.** 46 **e.** 0

Chapter Test

1. {18, 19, 20, 21, 22, 23, 24} **2.** false; Answers will vary. **3.** true **4.** true **5.** false; Answers will vary. **6.** true **7.** false; Answers will vary. **8.** false; Answers will vary. **9.** false; Answers will vary. **10.** ∅, {6}, {9}, {6, 9}; {6, 9} **11.** {a, b, c, d, e, f} **12.** {a, b, c, d, f, g} **13.** {b, c, d} **14.** {a, e} **15.** 5 **16.** {b, c, d, i, j, k} **17.** {a} **18.** {a, f, h}

19.

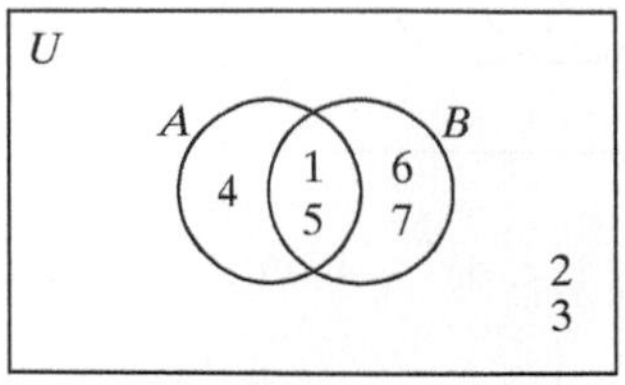

20. theorem **21. a.** V **b.** VII **c.** IV **d.** I **e.** VI

22. a.

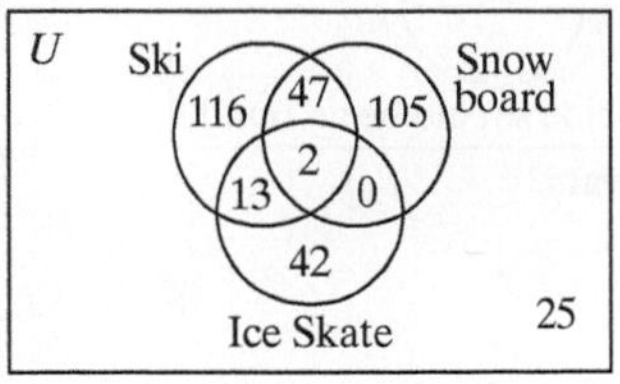

b. 263 **c.** 25 **d.** 62 **e.** 0 **f.** 147 **g.** 116

Logic

We are inundated with arguments that attempt to convince us of a variety of claims. P. T. Barnum (1810–1891), cofounder of the circus called "the Greatest Show on Earth," shamelessly engaged in the art of ballyhoo and humbug, feeding the public "bonafide baloney, with no truth in it." His philosophy: There is a sucker born every minute.

Logic is a kind of self-defense to avoid being suckered in by the Barnums of the world. It will enable you to apply deductive reasoning to arrive at valid conclusions in complicated situations and to avoid being fooled into believing things for which insufficient reasons are available. The rules of logic will help you to evaluate the vast array of claims facing you as a consumer, a citizen, a student, and a human being. Understanding logic will also allow you to construct better and more convincing arguments of your own, thereby becoming a more effective advocate for your beliefs.

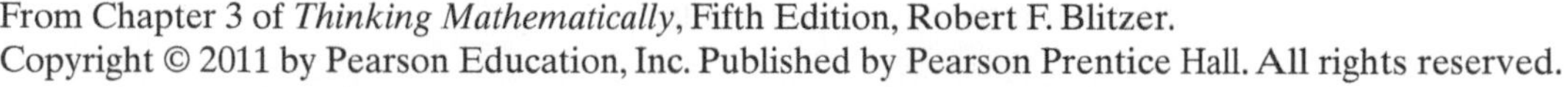
From Chapter 3 of *Thinking Mathematically*, Fifth Edition, Robert F. Blitzer.

OBJECTIVES

1 | Identify English sentences that are statements.
2 | Express statements using symbols.
3 | Form the negation of a statement.
4 | Express negations using symbols.
5 | Translate a negation represented by symbols into English.
6 | Express quantified statements in two ways.
7 | Write negations of quantified statements.

1 Statements, Negations, and Quantified Statements

History is filled with bad predictions. Here are examples of statements that turned out to be notoriously false:

> *"The actual building of roads devoted to motor cars will not occur in the future."*
>
> *Harper's Weekly*, August 2, 1902

> *"Everything that can be invented has been invented."*
>
> CHARLES H. DUELL, Commissioner, U.S. Office of Patents, 1899

> *"The abdomen, the chest, and the brain will forever be shut from the intrusion of the wise and humane surgeon."*
>
> JOHN ERICKSEN, Queen Victoria's surgeon, 1873

> *"Television won't be able to hold onto any market. People will soon get tired of staring at a plywood box every night."*
>
> DARRYL F. ZANUCK, 1949

> *"Whatever happens in Vietnam, I can conceive of nothing except military victory."*
>
> LYNDON B. JOHNSON, in a speech at West Point, 1967

> *"When the President does it, that means that it is not illegal."*
>
> RICHARD M. NIXON, TV interview with David Frost, May 20, 1977

Understanding that these statements are false enables us to negate each statement mentally and, with the assistance of historical perspective, obtain a true statement. We begin our study of logic by looking at statements and their negations.

1 | Identify English sentences that are statements.

Statements and Using Symbols to Represent Statements

In everyday English, we use many different kinds of sentences. Some of these sentences are clearly true or false. Others are opinions, questions, and exclamations such as *Help*! or *Fire*! However, in logic we are concerned solely with statements, and not all English sentences are statements.

DEFINITION OF A STATEMENT

A **statement** is a sentence that is either true or false, but not both simultaneously.

Here are two examples of statements:

1. London is the capital of England.
2. William Shakespeare wrote the last episode of *The Sopranos*.

Statement 1 is true and statement 2 is false. Shakespeare had nothing to do with *The Sopranos* (perhaps writer's block after *Macbeth*).

As long as a sentence is either true or false, *even if we do not know which it is*, then that sentence is a statement. For example, the sentence

The United States has the world's highest divorce rate

is a statement. It's clearly either true or false, and it's not necessary to know which it is.

Some sentences, such as commands, questions, and opinions, are not statements because they are not either true or false. The following sentences are not statements:

1. Read pages 23–57. (This is an order or command.)
2. If I start losing my memory, how will I know? (This is a question.)
3. *Titanic* is the greatest movie of all time. (This is an opinion.)

2 Express statements using symbols.

In symbolic logic, we use lowercase letters such as p, q, r, and s to represent statements. Here are two examples:

p: London is the capital of England.

q: William Shakespeare wrote the last episode of *The Sopranos*.

The letter p represents the first statement.
The letter q represents the second statement.

3 Form the negation of a statement.

Negating Statements

The sentence "London is the capital of England" is a true statement. The *negation* of this statement, "London is not the capital of England," is a false statement. The **negation** of a true statement is a false statement and the negation of a false statement is a true statement.

EXAMPLE 1 Forming Negations

Form the negation of each statement:

a. Shakespeare wrote the last episode of *The Sopranos*.

b. Today is not Monday.

Solution

a. The most common way to negate this statement is to introduce *not* into the sentence. The negation is

Shakespeare did not write the last episode of *The Sopranos*.

The English language provides many ways of expressing a statement's meaning. Here is another way to express the negation:

It is not true that Shakespeare wrote the last episode of *The Sopranos*.

b. The negation of "Today is not Monday" is

It is not true that today is not Monday.

The negation is more naturally expressed in English as

Today is Monday.

CHECK POINT 1 Form the negation of each statement:

a. Paris is the capital of Spain.

b. July is not a month.

4 Express negations using symbols.

The negation of statement p is expressed by writing $\sim p$. We read this as "not p" or "It is not true that p."

EXAMPLE 2 Expressing Negations Symbolically

Let p and q represent the following statements:

p: Shakespeare wrote the last episode of *The Sopranos*.

q: Today is not Monday.

Express each of the following statements symbolically:

a. Shakespeare did not write the last episode of *The Sopranos*.

b. Today is Monday.

STUDY TIP

Letters such as p, q, or r can represent any statement, including English statements containing the word *not*. When choosing letters to represent statements, you may prefer to use the symbol $\sim$ with negated English statements. However, it is not wrong to let p, q, or r represent such statements.

Solution

a. Shakespeare did not write the last episode of *The Sopranos* is the negation of statement p. Therefore, it is expressed symbolically as $\sim p$.

b. Today is Monday is the negation of statement q. Therefore, it is expressed symbolically as $\sim q$.

CHECK POINT 2 Let p and q represent the following statements:

p: Paris is the capital of Spain.

q: July is not a month.

Express each of the following statements symbolically:

a. Paris is not the capital of Spain.

b. July is a month.

5 Translate a negation represented by symbols into English.

In Example 2, we translated English statements into symbolic statements. In Example 3, we reverse the direction of our translation.

EXAMPLE 3 Translating a Symbolic Statement into Words

Let p represent the following statement:

p: The United States has the world's highest divorce rate.

Express the symbolic statement $\sim p$ in words.

Solution The symbol $\sim$ is translated as "not." Therefore, $\sim p$ represents

The United States does not have the world's highest divorce rate.

This can also be expressed as

It is not true that the United States has the world's highest divorce rate.

CHECK POINT 3 Let q represent the following statement:

q: Chicago O'Hare is the world's busiest airport.

Express the symbolic statement $\sim q$ in words.

6 Express quantified statements in two ways.

Quantified Statements

In English, we frequently encounter statements containing the words **all**, **some**, and **no** (or **none**). These words are called **quantifiers**. A statement that contains one of these words is a **quantified statement**. Here are some examples:

All poets are writers.
Some people are bigots.
No common colds are fatal.
Some students do not work hard.

Using our knowledge of the English language, we can express each of these quantified statements in two equivalent ways, that is, in two ways that have exactly the same meaning. These equivalent statements are shown in **Table 1**.

TABLE 1 Equivalent Ways of Expressing Quantified Statements

Statement	An Equivalent Way to Express the Statement	Example (Two Equivalent Quantified Statements)
All A are B.	There are no A that are not B.	All poets are writers. There are no poets that are not writers.
Some A are B.	There exists at least one A that is a B.	Some people are bigots. At least one person is a bigot.
No A are B.	All A are not B.	No common colds are fatal. All common colds are not fatal.
Some A are not B.	Not all A are B.	Some students do not work hard. Not all students work hard.

7 Write negations of quantified statements.

Forming the negation of a quantified statement can be a bit tricky. Suppose we want to negate the statement "All writers are poets." Because this statement is false, its negation must be true. The negation is "Not all writers are poets." This means the same thing as "Some writers are not poets." Notice that the negation is a true statement.

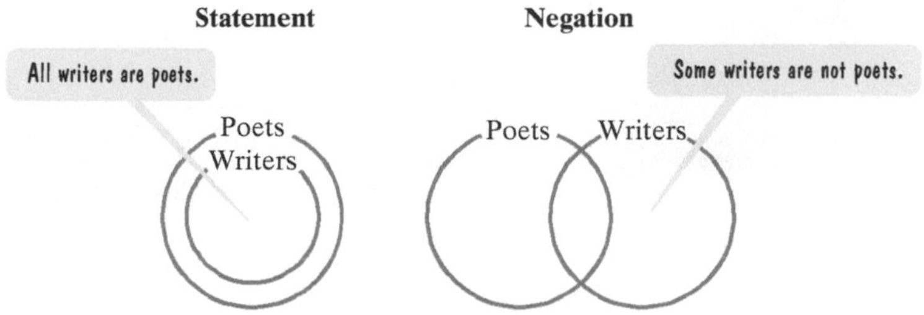

STUDY TIP

The negation of "All writers are poets" cannot be "No writers are poets" because both statements are false. The negation of a false statement must be a true statement. In general, the negation of "All A are B" is *not* "No A are B."

In general, the negation of "All A are B" is "Some A are not B." Likewise, the negation of "Some A are not B" is "All A are B."

Now let's investigate how to negate a statement with the word *some*. Consider the statement "Some canaries weigh 50 pounds." Because *some* means "there exists at least one," the negation is "It is not true that there is at least one canary that weighs 50 pounds." Because it is not true that there is even one such critter, we can express the negation as "No canary weighs 50 pounds."

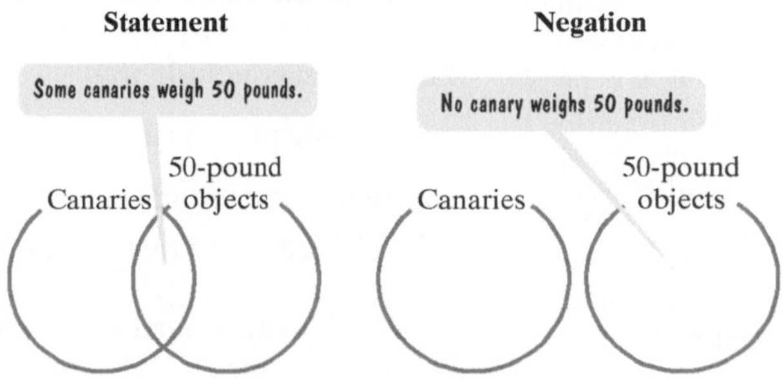

In general, the negation of "Some A are B" is "No A are B." Likewise, the negation of "No A are B" is "Some A are B."

Negations of quantified statements are summarized in **Table 2**.

TABLE 2 Negations of Quantified Statements

Statement	Negation	Example (A Quantified Statement and Its Negation)
All A are B.	Some A are not B.	All people take exams honestly. Negation: Some people do not take exams honestly.
Some A are B.	No A are B.	Some roads are open. Negation: No roads are open.

(The negations of the statements in the second column are the statements in the first column.)

STUDY TIP

This diagram should help you remember the negations for quantified statements. The statements diagonally opposite each other are negations.

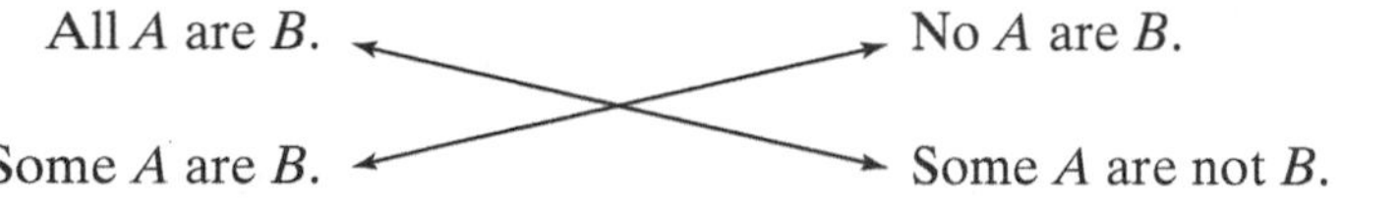
All A are B.
No A are B.
Some A are B.
Some A are not B.

BLITZER BONUS

Four Enterprise officers (clockwise from lower left): Kirk, McCoy, Uhura, Spock
Paramount Pictures\Picture Desk, Inc./Kobal Collection

LOGIC AND *STAR TREK*

In the television series *Star Trek*, the crew of the *Enterprise* is held captive by an evil computer. The crew escapes after one of them tells the computer, "I am lying to you." If he says that he is lying and he *is* lying, then he isn't lying. But consider this: If he says that he is lying and he *isn't* lying, then he is lying. The sentence "I am lying to you" is not a statement because it is true and false simultaneously. Thinking about this sentence destroys the computer.

Table 3 contains examples of negations for each of the four kinds of quantified statements.

TABLE 3 Examples of Negations of Quantified Statements

Statement	Negation
All humans are mortal.	Some humans are not mortal.
Some students do not come to class prepared.	All students come to class prepared.
Some psychotherapists are in therapy.	No psychotherapists are in therapy.
No well-behaved dogs shred couches.	Some well-behaved dogs shred couches.

EXAMPLE 4 Negating a Quantified Statement

The mechanic told me, "All piston rings were replaced." I later learned that the mechanic never tells the truth. What can I conclude?

Solution Let's begin with the mechanic's statement:

All piston rings were replaced.

Because the mechanic never tells the truth, I can conclude that the truth is the negation of what I was told. The negation of "All A are B" is "Some A are not B." Thus, I can conclude that

Some piston rings were not replaced.

Because *some* means *at least one*, I can also correctly conclude that

At least one piston ring was not replaced.

CHECK POINT 4

The board of supervisors told us, "All new tax dollars will be used to improve education." I later learned that the board of supervisors never tells the truth. What can I conclude? Express the conclusion in two equivalent ways.

Exercise Set 1

Practice Exercises

In Exercises 1–14, determine whether or not each sentence is a statement.

1. René Descartes came up with the theory of analytic geometry by watching a fly walk across a ceiling.

2. As a young and struggling artist, Pablo Picasso kept warm by burning his own paintings.

3. On January 20, 2009, John McCain became America's 44th president.

4. On January 20, 2009, Barack Obama became America's first Hispanic president.

5. Take the most interesting classes you can find.

6. Don't try to study on a Friday night in the dorms.

7. The average human brain contains 100 billion neurons.

8. There are 2,500,000 rivets in the Eiffel Tower.

9. Is the unexamined life worth living?

10. Is this the best of all possible worlds?

11. All U.S. presidents with beards have been Republicans.

12. No U.S. president was an only child.

13. The shortest sentence in the English language is "Go!"

14. Go!

In Exercises 15–20, form the negation of each statement.

15. It is raining.

16. It is snowing.

17. The Dallas Cowboys are not the team with the most Super Bowl wins.

18. The New York Yankees are not the team with the most World Series wins.

19. It is not true that chocolate in moderation is good for the heart.

20. It is not true that Albert Einstein was offered the presidency of Israel.

In Exercises 21–24, let $p, q, r,$ and s represent the following statements:

p: One works hard.

q: One succeeds.

r: The temperature outside is not freezing.

s: It is not true that the heater is working.

Express each of the following statements symbolically.

21. One does not work hard.

22. One does not succeed.

23. The temperature outside is freezing.

24. The heater is working.

According to Condensed Knowledge: A Deliciously Irreverent Guide to Feeling Smart Again *(Harper Collins, 2004), each statement listed below is false.*

p: Listening to classical music makes infants smarter.

q: Subliminal advertising makes you buy things.

r: Sigmund Freud's father was not 20 years older than his mother.

s: Humans and bananas do not share approximately 60% of the same DNA structure.

In Exercises 25–28, use the representations shown at the bottom of the previous column to express each symbolic statement in words. What can you conclude about the resulting verbal statement?

25. $\sim p$ **26.** $\sim q$ **27.** $\sim r$ **28.** $\sim s$

In Exercises 29–42,

a. *Express the quantified statement in an equivalent way, that is, in a way that has exactly the same meaning.*

b. *Write the negation of the quantified statement. (The negation should begin with "all," "some," or "no.")*

29. All whales are mammals.

30. All journalists are writers.

31. Some students are business majors.

32. Some movies are comedies.

33. Some thieves are not criminals.

34. Some pianists are not keyboard players.

35. No Democratic presidents have been impeached.

36. No women have served as Supreme Court justices.

37. There are no seniors who did not graduate.

38. There are no applicants who were not hired.

39. Not all parrots are pets.

40. Not all dogs are playful.

41. All atheists are not churchgoers.

42. All burnt muffins are not edible.

Here's another list of false statements from Condensed Knowledge.

p: No Africans have Jewish ancestry.

q: No religious traditions recognize sexuality as central to their understanding of the sacred.

r: All rap is hip-hop.

s: Some hip-hop is not rap.

In Exercises 43–46, use the representations shown to express each symbolic statement in words. Verbal statements should begin with "all," "some," or "no." What can you conclude about each resulting verbal statement?

43. $\sim p$ **44.** $\sim q$ **45.** $\sim r$ **46.** $\sim s$

Practice Plus

Exercises 47–50 contain diagrams that show relationships between two sets. (These diagrams are just like Venn diagrams. However, the circles are not enclosed in a rectangle representing a universal set.)

a. *Use each diagram to write a statement beginning with the word "all," "some," or "no" that illustrates the relationship between the sets.*

b. *Determine if the statement in part (a) is true or false. If it is false, write its negation.*

47.

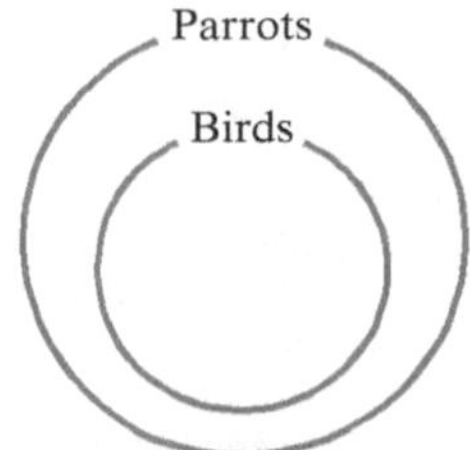

48.

Humans

Mammals

49. **50.**

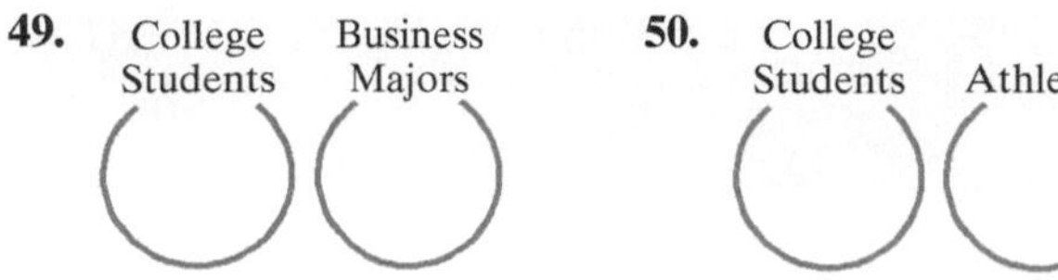

In Exercises 51–56,

a. *Express each statement in an equivalent way that begins with "all," "some," or "no."*

b. *Write the negation of the statement in part (a).*

51. Nobody doesn't like Sara Lee.
52. A problem well stated is a problem half solved.
53. Nothing is both safe and exciting.
54. Many a person has lived to regret a misspent youth.
55. Not every great actor is a Tom Hanks.
56. Not every generous philanthropist is a Bill Gates.

Application Exercises

In Exercises 57 and 58, choose the correct statement.

57. The City Council of a large northern metropolis promised its citizens that in the event of snow, all major roads connecting the city to its airport would remain open. The City Council did not keep its promise during the first blizzard of the season. Therefore, during the first blizzard:
a. No major roads connecting the city to the airport were open.
b. At least one major road connecting the city to the airport was not open.
c. At least one major road connecting the city to the airport was open.
d. The airport was forced to close.

58. During the Watergate scandal in 1974, President Richard Nixon assured the American people that "In all my years of public service, I have never obstructed justice." Later, events indicated that the president was not telling the truth. Therefore, in his years of public service:
a. Nixon always obstructed justice.
b. Nixon sometimes did not obstruct justice.
c. Nixon sometimes obstructed justice.
d. Nixon never obstructed justice.

Our culture celebrates romantic love—affection and sexual passion for another person—as the basis for marriage. However, the bar graph illustrates that in some countries, romantic love plays a less important role in marriage.

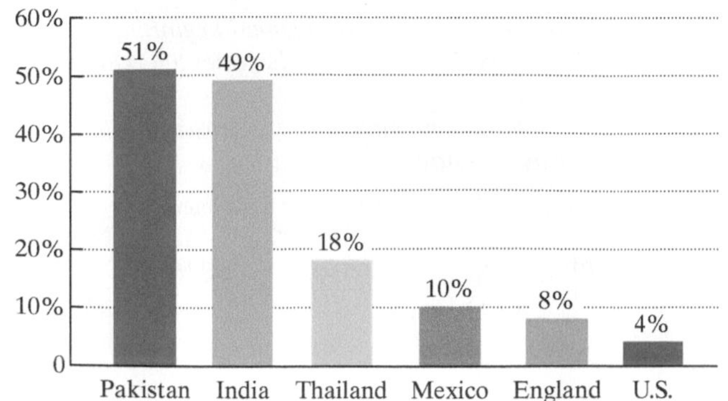

Source: Robert Levine, "Is Love a Luxury?" *American Demographics*

In Exercises 59–66, use the graph at the bottom of the previous column to determine whether each statement is true or false. If the statement is false, write its negation.

59. A majority of college students in Pakistan are willing to marry without romantic love.
60. Nearly half of India's college students are willing to marry without romantic love.
61. No college students in the United States are willing to marry without romantic love.
62. All college students in Pakistan are willing to marry without romantic love.
63. Not all college students in Mexico are willing to marry without romantic love.
64. Not all college students in England are willing to marry without romantic love.
65. The sentence "5% of college students in Australia are willing to marry without romantic love" is not a statement.
66. The sentence "12% of college students in the Philippines are willing to marry without romantic love" is not a statement.

Writing in Mathematics

67. What is a statement? Explain why commands, questions, and opinions are not statements.
68. Explain how to form the negation of a given English statement. Give an example.
69. Describe how the negation of statement p is expressed using symbols.
70. List the words identified as quantifiers. Give an example of a statement that uses each of these quantifiers.
71. Explain how to write the negation of a quantified statement in the form "All A are B." Give an example.
72. Explain how to write the negation of a quantified statement in the form "Some A are B." Give an example.
73. If the ancient Greek god Zeus could do anything, could he create a rock so huge that he could not move it? Explain your answer.

Critical Thinking Exercises

Make Sense? *In Exercises 74–77, determine whether each statement makes sense or does not make sense, and explain your reasoning.*

74. I have no idea if a particular sentence is true or false, so I cannot determine whether or not that sentence is a statement.
75. "All beagles are dogs" is true and "no beagles are dogs" is false, so the second statement must be the negation of the first statement.
76. Little Richard's "A-wop-bop-a-lula-a-wop-bam-boom!" is an exclamation and not a statement.
77. Researchers at Cambridge University made the following comments on how we read:

It deson't mtater waht oerdr the ltteres in a wrod are, so lnog as the frist and lsat ltteer are in the crorcet pclae. Tihs is bcuseae we dno't raed ervey lteter but the wrod as a wlohe.

Because of the incorrect spellings in these sentences, neither sentence is a statement.

78. Give an example of a sentence that is not a statement because it is true and false simultaneously.
79. Give an example in which the statement "Some A are not B" is true, but the statement "Some B are not A" is false.
80. The statement

She isn't dating him because he is muscular

is confusing because it can mean two different things. Describe the two different meanings that make this statement ambiguous.

OBJECTIVES

1 Express compound statements in symbolic form.
2 Express symbolic statements with parentheses in English.
3 Use the dominance of connectives.

2 Compound Statements and Connectives

What conditions enable us to flourish and our hearts to sing? Researchers in the new science of happiness have learned some surprising things about what it doesn't take to ring our inner chimes. Neither wealth nor a good education are sufficient for happiness. Put in another way, we should not rely on the following statement:

If you're wealthy or well educated, then you'll be happy.

We can break this statement down into three basic sentences:

You're wealthy. You're well educated. You'll be happy.

Jonathan Kitchen\Getty Images/Digital Vision

These sentences are called **simple statements** because each one conveys one idea with no connecting words. Statements formed by combining two or more simple statements are called **compound statements**. Words called **connectives** are used to join simple statements to form a compound statement. Connectives include words such as **and, or, if . . . then**, and **if and only if**.

Compound statements appear throughout written and spoken language. We need to be able to understand the logic of such statements to analyze information objectively. In this section, we analyze four kinds of compound statements.

1 Express compound statements in symbolic form.

And Statements

If p and q represent two simple statements, then **the compound statement "p and q" is symbolized by $p \wedge q$.** The compound statement formed by connecting statements with the word **and** is called a **conjunction**. The symbol for *and* is $\wedge$.

EXAMPLE 1 Translating from English to Symbolic Form

Let p and q represent the following simple statements:

p: It is after 5 P.M.
q: They are working.

Write each compound statement below in symbolic form:

a. It is after 5 P.M. and they are working.
b. It is after 5 P.M. and they are not working.

Solution

a. It is after 5 P.M. | and | they are working.

p $\wedge$ q

The symbolic form is $p \wedge q$.

b. It is after 5 P.M. | and | they are not working.

p $\wedge$ $\sim q$

The symbolic form is $p \wedge \sim q$.

STUDY TIP

You can remember $\wedge$, the symbol for *and*, by thinking of it as an A (for And) with the horizontal bar missing.

Use the representations in Example 1 on the previous page to write each compound statement below in symbolic form:

a. They are working and it is after 5 P.M.

b. It is not after 5 P.M. and they are working.

The English language has a variety of ways to express the connectives that appear in compound statements. **Table 4** shows a number of ways to translate $p \wedge q$ into English.

TABLE 4 Common English Expressions for $p \wedge q$

Symbolic Statement	English Statement	Example p: It is after 5 P.M. q: They are working.
$p \wedge q$	p and q.	It is after 5 P.M. and they are working.
$p \wedge q$	p but q.	It is after 5 P.M., but they are working.
$p \wedge q$	p yet q.	It is after 5 P.M., yet they are working.
$p \wedge q$	p nevertheless q.	It is after 5 P.M.; nevertheless, they are working.

STUDY TIP

Not every English statement with the word *and* is a conjunction.

- Not a conjunction:

  "Nonviolence and truth are inseparable."

  —GANDHI

  This statement cannot be broken down into two simple statements. It is itself a simple statement.

- Conjunction:

  Pizza and beer are not recommended for people with ulcers.

  Can be broken down as follows: Pizza is not recommended for people with ulcers and beer is not recommended for people with ulcers.

Or Statements

The connective *or* can mean two different things. For example, consider this statement:

I visited London or Paris.

The statement can mean

I visited London or Paris, but not both.

This is an example of the **exclusive or**, which means "one or the other, but not both." By contrast, the statement can mean

I visited London or Paris or both.

This is an example of the **inclusive or**, which means "either or both."

In this chapter and in mathematics in general, when the connective *or* appears, it means the *inclusive or*. If p and q represent two simple statements, then the compound statement "p or q" means p or q or both. The compound statement formed by connecting statements with the word *or* is called a **disjunction**. **The symbol for *or* is $\vee$. Thus, we can symbolize the compound statement "p or q or both" by $p \vee q$.**

EXAMPLE 2 Translating from English to Symbolic Form

Let p and q represent the following simple statements:

p: The bill receives majority approval.

q: The bill becomes a law.

Write each compound statement below in symbolic form:

a. The bill receives majority approval or the bill becomes a law.

b. The bill receives majority approval or the bill does not become a law.

Solution

a.

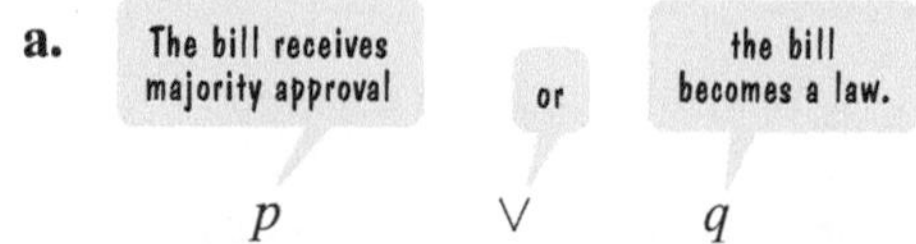
The bill receives majority approval
or
the bill becomes a law.
p
∨
q

The symbolic form is $p \vee q$.

b. The bill receives majority approval | or | the bill does not become a law.

$p \quad \vee \quad {\sim}q$

The symbolic form is $p \vee {\sim}q$.

CHECK POINT 2

Let p and q represent the following simple statements:

p: You graduate.

q: You satisfy the math requirement.

Write each compound statement below in symbolic form:

a. You graduate or you satisfy the math requirement.

b. You satisfy the math requirement or you do not graduate.

If-Then Statements

Writers
Poets
All poets are writers. If a person is a poet, then that person is a writer.

FIGURE 1

The diagram in **Figure 1** shows that

All poets are writers. (The set of poets is a subset of the set of writers.)

In Section 1, we saw that this can be expressed as

There are no poets that are not writers.

Another way of expressing this statement is

If a person is a poet, then that person is a writer.

The form of this statement is "If p, then q." **The compound statement "If p, then q" is symbolized by $p \rightarrow q$.** The compound statement formed by connecting statements with "if–then" is called a **conditional statement**. The symbol for "if–then" is $\rightarrow$.

In a conditional statement, the statement before the $\rightarrow$ connective is called the **antecedent**. The statement after the $\rightarrow$ connective is called the **consequent**:

antecedent $\rightarrow$ consequent.

EXAMPLE 3 Translating from English to Symbolic Form

Let p and q represent the following simple statements:

p: A person is a father.

q: A person is a male.

Write each compound statement below in symbolic form:

a. If a person is a father, then that person is a male.

b. If a person is a male, then that person is a father.

c. If a person is not a male, then that person is not a father.

Solution

We use p: A person is a father and q: A person is a male.

a. 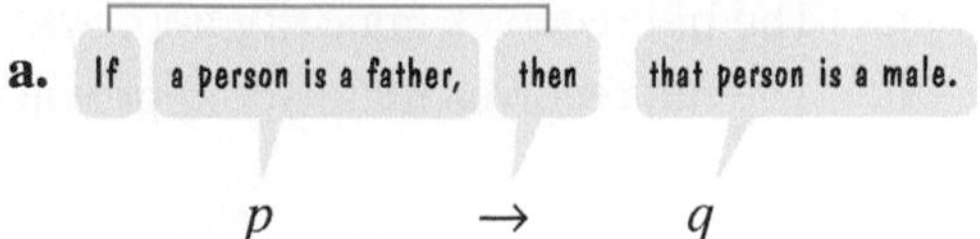

The symbolic form is $p \rightarrow q$.

b. 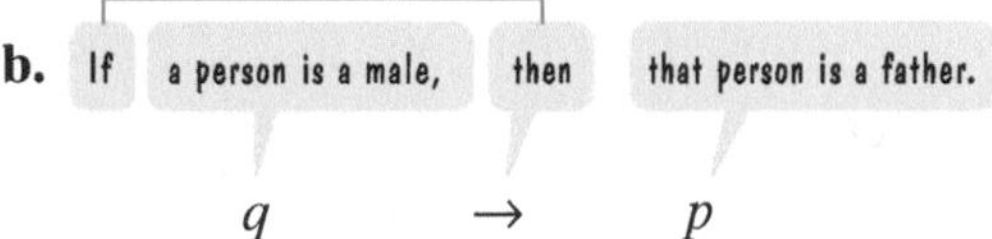

The symbolic form is $q \rightarrow p$.

c. 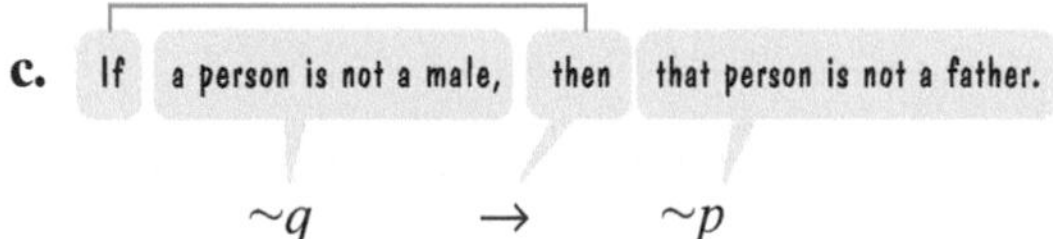

The symbolic form is $\sim q \rightarrow \sim p$.

CHECK POINT 3 Use the representations in Example 3 on the previous page to write each compound statement below in symbolic form:

a. If a person is not a father, then that person is not a male.

b. If a person is a male, then that person is not a father.

Conditional statements in English often omit the word *then* and simply use a comma. When *then* is included, the comma can be included or omitted. Here are some examples:

If a person is a father, then that person is a male.
If a person is a father then that person is a male.
If a person is a father, that person is a male.

Table 5 shows some of the common ways to translate $p \rightarrow q$ into English.

TABLE 5 Common English Expressions for $p \rightarrow q$

Symbolic Statement	English Statement	Example **p: A person is a father.** **q: A person is a male.**
$p \rightarrow q$	If p then q.	If a person is a father, then that person is a male.
$p \rightarrow q$	q if p.	A person is a male if that person is a father.
$p \rightarrow q$	p is sufficient for q.	Being a father is sufficient for being a male.
$p \rightarrow q$	q is necessary for p.	Being a male is necessary for being a father.
$p \rightarrow q$	p only if q.	A person is a father only if that person is a male.
$p \rightarrow q$	Only if q, p.	Only if a person is a male is that person a father.

STUDY TIP

The sufficient condition of a conditional statement is the part that precedes $\rightarrow$, or the antecedent. The necessary condition of a conditional statement is the part that follows $\rightarrow$, or the consequent.

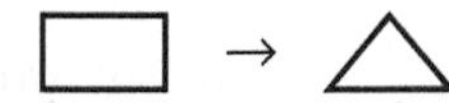

The *if* part or the *sufficient* part — The *only if* part or the *necessary* part

EXAMPLE 4 Translating from English to Symbolic Form

Let p and q represent the following simple statements:

p: We suffer huge budget deficits.

q: We control military spending.

Write the following compound statement in symbolic form:

Controlling military spending is necessary for not suffering huge budget deficits.

Solution The necessary part of a conditional statement follows the *if–then* connective. Because "controlling military spending" is the necessary part, we can rewrite the compound statement as follows:

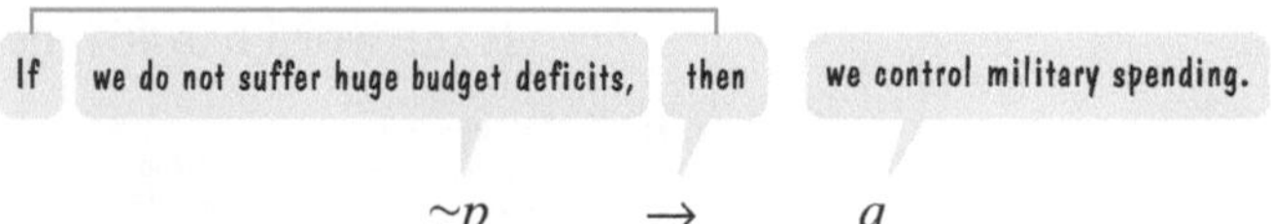
If
we do not suffer huge budget deficits,
then
we control military spending.

$\sim p \quad \rightarrow \quad q$

The symbolic form is $\sim p \rightarrow q$.

Use the representations in Example 4 to write the following compound statement in symbolic form.

Suffering huge budget deficits is necessary for not controlling military spending.

If and Only If Statements

If a conditional statement is true, reversing the antecedent and consequent may result in a statement that is not necessarily true:

- If a person is a father, then that person is a male. (true)
- If a person is a male, then that person is a father. (not necessarily true)

However, some true conditional statements are still true when the antecedent and consequent are reversed:

- If a person is an unmarried male, then that person is a bachelor. (true)
- If a person is a bachelor, then that person is an unmarried male. (also true)

Rather than deal with two separate conditionals, we can combine them into one *biconditional statement:*

A person is an unmarried male if and only if that person is a bachelor.

If p and q represent two simple statements, then **the compound statement "p if and only if q" is symbolized by $p \leftrightarrow q$.** The compound statement formed by connecting statements with *if and only if* is called a **biconditional**. The symbol for *if and only if* is $\leftrightarrow$. The phrase *if and only if* can be abbreviated as *iff.*

EXAMPLE 5 Translating from English to Symbolic Form

TABLE 6 Words with the Most Meanings in the *Oxford English Dictionary*

Word	Meanings
Set	464
Run	396
Go	368
Take	343
Stand	334

Table 6 shows that the word *set* has 464 meanings, making it the word with the most meanings in the English language. Let p and q represent the following simple statements:

p: The word is *set*.

q: The word has 464 meanings.

Write each of the compound statements below in its symbolic form:

a. The word is *set* if and only if the word has 464 meanings.

b. The word does not have 464 meanings if and only if the word is not *set*.

Solution

a. 

$p \quad \leftrightarrow \quad q$

The symbolic form is $p \leftrightarrow q$. Observe that each of the following statements is true:

If the word is *set*, then it has 464 meanings.

If the word has 464 meanings, then it is *set*.

b. 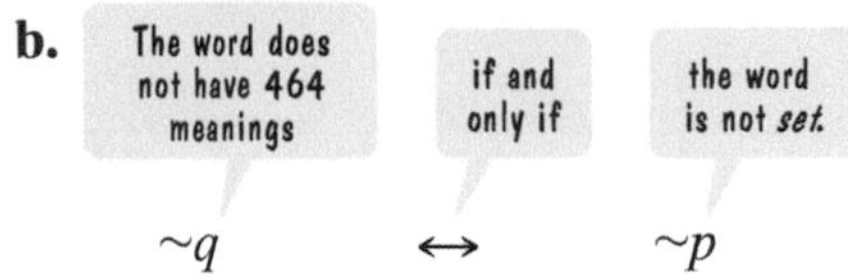

$\sim q \quad \leftrightarrow \quad \sim p$

The symbolic form is $\sim q \leftrightarrow \sim p$.

CHECK POINT 5 Let p and q represent the following simple statements:

p: The word is *run*.

q: The word has 396 meanings.

Write each of the compound statements below in its symbolic form:

a. The word has 396 meanings if and only if the word is *run*.

b. The word is not *run* if and only if the word does not have 396 meanings.

Table 7 shows some of the common ways to translate $p \leftrightarrow q$ into English.

TABLE 7 Common English Expressions for $p \leftrightarrow q$

Symbolic Statement	English Statement	Example **p: A person is an unmarried male.** **q: A person is a bachelor.**
$p \leftrightarrow q$	p if and only if q.	A person is an unmarried male if and only if that person is a bachelor.
$p \leftrightarrow q$	q if and only if p.	A person is a bachelor if and only if that person is an unmarried male.
$p \leftrightarrow q$	If p then q, and if q then p.	If a person is an unmarried male then that person is a bachelor, and if a person is a bachelor then that person is an unmarried male.
$p \leftrightarrow q$	p is necessary and sufficient for q.	Being an unmarried male is necessary and sufficient for being a bachelor.
$p \leftrightarrow q$	q is necessary and sufficient for p.	Being a bachelor is necessary and sufficient for being an unmarried male.

STUDY TIP

- $p \wedge q$ means the same thing as $q \wedge p$.
- $p \vee q$ means the same thing as $q \vee p$.
- $p \leftrightarrow q$ means the same thing as $q \leftrightarrow p$.

However,

- $p \rightarrow q$ does not necessarily mean the same thing as $q \rightarrow p$.

We'll have more to say about these observations throughout the chapter.

Table 8 summarizes the statements discussed in the first two sections of this chapter.

TABLE 8 Statements of Symbolic Logic

Name	Symbolic Form	Common English Translations
Negation	$\sim p$	Not p. It is not true that p.
Conjunction	$p \wedge q$	p and q. p but q.
Disjunction	$p \vee q$	p or q.
Conditional	$p \rightarrow q$	If p, then q. p is sufficient for q. q is necessary for p.
Biconditional	$p \leftrightarrow q$	p if and only if q. p is necessary and sufficient for q.

2 Express symbolic statements with parentheses in English.

Symbolic Statements with Parentheses

Parentheses in symbolic statements indicate which statements are to be grouped together. For example, $\sim(p \wedge q)$ means the negation of the entire statement $p \wedge q$. By contrast, $\sim p \wedge q$ means that only statement p is negated. We read $\sim(p \wedge q)$ as "it is not true that p and q." We read $\sim p \wedge q$ as "not p and q." Unless parentheses appear in a symbolic statement, the symbol $\sim$ negates only the statement that immediately follows it.

EXAMPLE 6 Expressing Symbolic Statements with and without Parentheses in English

Let p and q represent the following simple statements:

p: She is wealthy.

q: She is happy.

Write each of the following symbolic statements in words:

a. $\sim(p \wedge q)$ **b.** $\sim p \wedge q$ **c.** $\sim(p \vee q)$.

Solution The voice balloons illustrate the differences among the three statements.

- $\sim(p \wedge q)$
- $\sim p \wedge q$
- $\sim(p \vee q)$

It is not true that
she is wealthy and she is happy.
She is not wealthy
and
she is happy.
It is not true that
she is wealthy or she is happy.

a. The symbolic statement $\sim(p \wedge q)$ means the negation of the entire statement $p \wedge q$. A translation of $\sim(p \wedge q)$ is

It is not true that she is wealthy and happy.

We can also express this statement as

It is not true that she is both wealthy and happy.

b. A translation of $\sim p \wedge q$ is

She is not wealthy and she is happy.

c. The symbolic statement $\sim(p \vee q)$ means the negation of the entire statement $p \vee q$. A translation of $\sim(p \vee q)$ is

It is not true that she is wealthy or happy.

We can express this statement as

She is neither wealthy nor happy.

STUDY TIP

It is not always necessary to use p and q to represent two simple statements. You can select letters that help you remember what the statements represent. For example, in Example 6, you may prefer using w and h rather than p and q:

w: She is wealthy.

h: She is happy.

CHECK POINT 6 Let p and q represent the following simple statements:

p: He earns $105,000 yearly.

q: He is often happy.

Write each of the following symbolic statements in words:

a. $\sim(p \wedge q)$ **b.** $\sim q \wedge p$ **c.** $\sim(q \rightarrow p)$.

Many compound statements contain more than one connective. When expressed symbolically, parentheses are used to indicate which simple statements are grouped together. When expressed in English, commas are used to indicate the groupings. Here is a table that illustrates groupings using parentheses in symbolic statements and commas in English statements:

Symbolic Statement	Statements to Group Together	English Translation
$(q \wedge \sim p) \rightarrow \sim r$	$q \wedge \sim p$	If q and not p, then not r.
$q \wedge (\sim p \rightarrow \sim r)$	$\sim p \rightarrow \sim r$	q, and if not p then not r.

The statement in the first row is an *if–then* conditional statement. Notice that the symbol $\rightarrow$ is outside the parentheses. By contrast, the statement in the second row is an *and* conjunction. In this case, the symbol $\wedge$ is outside the parentheses. Notice that when we translate the symbolic statement into English, **the simple statements in parentheses appear on the same side of the comma**.

EXAMPLE 7 Expressing Symbolic Statements with Parentheses in English

Let p, q, and r represent the following simple statements:

p: A student misses lecture.

q: A student studies.

r: A student fails.

Write each of the symbolic statements below in words:

a. $(q \wedge \sim p) \rightarrow \sim r$ **b.** $q \wedge (\sim p \rightarrow \sim r)$.

Solution

a.

$$(q \wedge \sim p) \rightarrow \sim r$$

If [A student studies] and [A student does not miss lecture], then [A student does not fail.]

One possible English translation for the symbolic statement is

If a student studies and does not miss lecture, then the student does not fail.

Observe how the symbolic statements in parentheses appear on the same side of the comma in the English translation.

b.

$$q \wedge (\sim p \rightarrow \sim r)$$

[A student studies], and if [A student does not miss lecture] then [A student does not fail.]

One possible English translation for the symbolic statement is

A student studies, and if a student does not miss lecture then the student does not fail.

Once again, the symbolic statements in parentheses appear on the same side of the comma in the English statement.

CHECK POINT 7 Let p, q, and r represent the following simple statements:

p: The plant is fertilized.

q: The plant is not watered.

r: The plant wilts.

Write each of the symbolic statements in words:

a. $(p \wedge {\sim}q) \rightarrow {\sim}r$ **b.** $p \wedge ({\sim}q \rightarrow {\sim}r)$.

3 Use the dominance of connectives.

Dominance of Connectives

In Example 7, the statements $(q \wedge {\sim}p) \rightarrow {\sim}r$ and $q \wedge ({\sim}p \rightarrow {\sim}r)$ had different meanings. If we are given $q \wedge {\sim}p \rightarrow {\sim}r$ without parentheses, how do we know which statements to group together?

If a symbolic statement appears without parentheses, statements before and after the most *dominant connective* should be grouped. Symbolic connectives are categorized from the least dominant, negation, to the most dominant, the biconditional.

DOMINANCE OF CONNECTIVES

The **dominance of connectives** used in symbolic logic is defined in the following order:

1. Negation, $\sim$ 2. Conjunction, $\wedge$ Disjunction, $\vee$ 3. Conditional, $\rightarrow$ 4. Biconditional, $\leftrightarrow$

Least dominant — Same level of dominance — Most dominant

Table 9 shows a number of symbolic statements without parentheses. The meaning of each statement is then clarified by placing grouping symbols (parentheses), as needed, before and after the most dominant connective used.

TABLE 9 Using the Dominance of Connectives

Statement	Most Dominant Connective Highlighted in Red	Statement's Meaning Clarified with Grouping Symbols	Type of Statement
$p \rightarrow q \wedge {\sim}r$	$p \rightarrow q \wedge {\sim}r$	$p \rightarrow (q \wedge {\sim}r)$	Conditional
$p \wedge q \rightarrow {\sim}r$	$p \wedge q \rightarrow {\sim}r$	$(p \wedge q) \rightarrow {\sim}r$	Conditional
$p \leftrightarrow q \rightarrow r$	$p \leftrightarrow q \rightarrow r$	$p \leftrightarrow (q \rightarrow r)$	Biconditional
$p \rightarrow q \leftrightarrow r$	$p \rightarrow q \leftrightarrow r$	$(p \rightarrow q) \leftrightarrow r$	Biconditional
$p \wedge {\sim}q \rightarrow r \vee s$	$p \wedge {\sim}q \rightarrow r \vee s$	$(p \wedge {\sim}q) \rightarrow (r \vee s)$	Conditional
$p \wedge q \vee r$	$\wedge$ and $\vee$ have the same level of dominance.	The meaning is ambiguous.	?

Grouping symbols must be given with this statement to determine whether it means $(p \wedge q) \vee r$, a disjunction, or $p \wedge (q \vee r)$, a conjunction.

EXAMPLE 8 Using the Dominance of Connectives

Write each compound statement below in symbolic form:

a. I do not fail the course if and only if I study hard and I pass the final.

b. I do not fail the course if and only if I study hard, and I pass the final.

Solution We begin by assigning letters to the simple statements. Let each letter represent an English statement that is not negated. We can then represent any negated simple statement with the negation symbol, $\sim$. Use the following representations:

p: I fail the course.
q: I study hard.
r: I pass the final.

a.

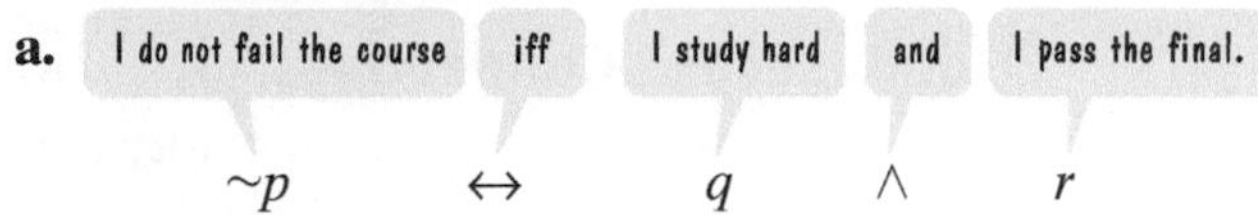

Because the most dominant connective that appears is $\leftrightarrow$, the symbolic form with parentheses is $\sim p \leftrightarrow (q \wedge r)$.

STUDY TIP

Only apply the dominance of connectives if grouping symbols (parentheses) are not given in compound symbolic statements or commas do not appear in compound English statements.

b.

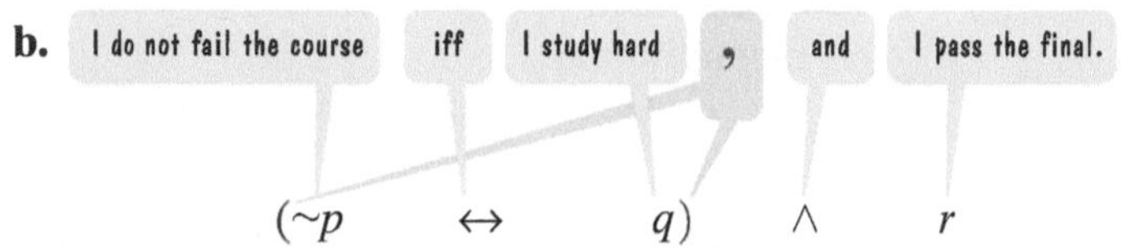

In this statement, the comma indicates the grouping, so it is not necessary to apply the dominance of connectives. The symbolic form of the statement is $(\sim p \leftrightarrow q) \wedge r$.

Write each compound statement below in symbolic form:

a. If there is too much homework or a teacher is boring then I do not take that class.

b. There is too much homework, or if a teacher is boring then I do not take that class.

Exercise Set 2

Practice Exercises

In Exercises 1–6, let p and q represent the following simple statements:

p: I'm leaving
q: You're staying.

Write each compound statement in symbolic form.

1. I'm leaving and you're staying.
2. You're staying and I'm leaving.
3. You're staying and I'm not leaving.
4. I'm leaving and you're not staying.
5. You're not staying, but I'm leaving.
6. I'm not leaving, but you're staying.

In Exercises 7–10, let p and q represent the following simple statements:

p: I study.
q: I pass the course.

Write each compound statement in symbolic form.

7. I study or I pass the course.
8. I pass the course or I study.
9. I study or I do not pass the course.
10. I do not study or I do not pass the course.

In Exercises 11–18, let p and q represent the following simple statements:

p: This is an alligator.
q: This is a reptile.

Write each compound statement in symbolic form.

11. If this is an alligator, then this is a reptile.
12. If this is a reptile, then this is an alligator.
13. If this is not an alligator, then this is not a reptile.
14. If this is not a reptile, then this is not an alligator.
15. This is not an alligator if it's not a reptile.
16. This is a reptile if it's an alligator.
17. Being a reptile is necessary for being an alligator.
18. Being an alligator is sufficient for being a reptile.

In Exercises 19–26, let p and q represent the following simple statements:

p: You are human.

q: You have feathers.

Write each compound statement in symbolic form.

19. You do not have feathers if you are human.

20. You are not human if you have feathers.

21. Not being human is necessary for having feathers.

22. Not having feathers is necessary for being human.

23. Being human is sufficient for not having feathers.

24. Having feathers is sufficient for not being human.

25. You have feathers only if you're not human.

26. You're human only if you do not have feathers.

In Exercises 27–32, let p and q represent the following simple statements:

p: The campus is closed.

q: It is Sunday.

Write each compound statement in symbolic form.

27. The campus is closed if and only if it is Sunday.

28. It is Sunday if and only if the campus is closed.

29. It is not Sunday if and only if the campus is not closed.

30. The campus is not closed if and only if it is not Sunday.

31. Being Sunday is necessary and sufficient for the campus being closed.

32. The campus being closed is necessary and sufficient for being Sunday.

In Exercises 33–40, let p and q represent the following simple statements:

p: The heater is working.

q: The house is cold.

Write each symbolic statement in words.

33. $\sim p \wedge q$ **34.** $p \wedge \sim q$ **35.** $p \vee \sim q$

36. $\sim p \vee q$ **37.** $p \rightarrow \sim q$ **38.** $q \rightarrow \sim p$

39. $p \leftrightarrow \sim q$ **40.** $\sim p \leftrightarrow q$

In Exercises 41–48, let q and r represent the following simple statements:

q: It is July 4th.

r: We are having a barbecue.

Write each symbolic statement in words.

41. $q \wedge \sim r$ **42.** $\sim q \wedge r$ **43.** $\sim q \vee r$

44. $q \vee \sim r$ **45.** $r \rightarrow \sim q$ **46.** $q \rightarrow \sim r$

47. $\sim q \leftrightarrow r$ **48.** $q \leftrightarrow \sim r$

In Exercises 49–58, let p and q represent the following simple statements:

p: Romeo loves Juliet.

q: Juliet loves Romeo.

Write each symbolic statement in words.

49. $\sim(p \wedge q)$ **50.** $\sim(q \wedge p)$ **51.** $\sim p \wedge q$

52. $\sim q \wedge p$ **53.** $\sim(q \vee p)$ **54.** $\sim(p \vee q)$

55. $\sim q \vee p$ **56.** $\sim p \vee q$ **57.** $\sim p \wedge \sim q$

58. $\sim q \wedge \sim p$

In Exercises 59–66, let p, q, and r represent the following simple statements:

p: The temperature outside is freezing.

q: The heater is working.

r: The house is cold.

Write each compound statement in symbolic form.

59. The temperature outside is freezing and the heater is working, or the house is cold.

60. If the temperature outside is freezing, then the heater is working or the house is not cold.

61. If the temperature outside is freezing or the heater is not working, then the house is cold.

62. It is not the case that if the house is cold then the heater is not working.

63. The house is cold, if and only if the temperature outside is freezing and the heater isn't working.

64. If the heater is working, then the temperature outside is freezing if and only if the house is cold.

65. Sufficient conditions for the house being cold are freezing outside temperatures and a heater not working.

66. A freezing outside temperature is both necessary and sufficient for a cold house if the heater is not working.

In Exercises 67–80, let p, q, and r represent the following simple statements:

p: The temperature is above 85°.

q: We finished studying.

r: We go to the beach.

Write each symbolic statement in words. If a symbolic statement is given without parentheses, place them, as needed, before and after the most dominant connective and then translate into English.

67. $(p \wedge q) \rightarrow r$ **68.** $(q \wedge r) \rightarrow p$

69. $p \wedge (q \rightarrow r)$ **70.** $p \wedge (r \rightarrow q)$

71. $\sim r \rightarrow \sim p \vee \sim q$ **72.** $\sim p \rightarrow q \vee r$

73. $(\sim r \rightarrow \sim q) \vee p$ **74.** $(\sim p \rightarrow \sim r) \vee q$

75. $r \leftrightarrow p \wedge q$ **76.** $r \leftrightarrow q \wedge p$

77. $(p \leftrightarrow q) \wedge r$ **78.** $q \rightarrow (r \leftrightarrow p)$

79. $\sim r \rightarrow \sim(p \wedge q)$ **80.** $\sim(p \wedge q) \rightarrow \sim r$

In Exercises 81–90, write each compound statement in symbolic form. Let letters assigned to the simple statements represent English sentences that are not negated. If commas do not appear in compound English statements, use the dominance of connectives to show grouping symbols (parentheses) in symbolic statements.

81. If I like the teacher or the course is interesting then I do not miss class.

82. If the lines go down or the transformer blows then we do not have power.

83. I like the teacher, or if the course is interesting then I do not miss class.

84. The lines go down, or if the transformer blows then we do not have power.

85. I miss class if and only if it's not true that both I like the teacher and the course is interesting.

86. We have power if and only if it's not true that both the lines go down and the transformer blows.

87. If I like the teacher I do not miss class if and only if the course is interesting.

88. If the lines go down we do not have power if and only if the transformer blows.
89. If I do not like the teacher and I miss class then the course is not interesting or I spend extra time reading the textbook.
90. If the lines do not go down and we have power then the transformer does not blow or there is an increase in the cost of electricity.

Practice Plus

In Exercises 91–96, write each compound statement in symbolic form. Assign letters to simple statements that are not negated and show grouping symbols in symbolic statements.

91. If it's not true that being French is necessary for being a Parisian then it's not true that being German is necessary for being a Berliner.
92. If it's not true that being English is necessary for being a Londoner then it's not true that being American is necessary for being a New Yorker.
93. Filing an income tax report and a complete statement of earnings is necessary for each taxpayer or an authorized tax preparer.
94. Falling in love with someone in your class or picking someone to hate are sufficient conditions for showing up to vent your emotions and not skipping.
(*Source:* Paraphrased from a student at the University of Georgia)
95. It is not true that being wealthy is a sufficient condition for being happy and living contentedly.
96. It is not true that being happy and living contentedly are necessary conditions for being wealthy.

In Exercises 97–100, use grouping symbols to clarify the meaning of each symbolic statement.

97. $p \rightarrow q \vee r \leftrightarrow p \wedge r$
98. $p \wedge q \rightarrow r \leftrightarrow p \vee r$
99. $p \rightarrow p \leftrightarrow p \wedge p \rightarrow \sim p$
100. $p \rightarrow p \leftrightarrow p \vee p \rightarrow \sim p$

Application Exercises

Exercises 101–106 contain statements made by well-known people. Use letters to represent each non-negated simple statement and rewrite the given compound statement in symbolic form.

101. "If you cannot get rid of the family skeleton, you may as well make it dance." (George Bernard Shaw)
102. "I wouldn't turn out the way I did if I didn't have all the old-fashioned values to rebel against." (Madonna)
103. "If you know what you believe then it makes it a lot easier to answer questions, and I can't answer your question." (George W. Bush)
104. "If you don't like what you're doing, you can always pick up your needle and move to another groove." (Timothy Leary)
105. "If I were an intellectual, I would be pessimistic about America, but since I'm not an intellectual, I am optimistic about America." (General Lewis B. Hershey, Director of the Selective Service during the Vietnam war) (For simplicity, regard "optimistic" as "not pessimistic.")
106. "You cannot be both a good socializer and a good writer." (Erskine Caldwell)

Writing in Mathematics

107. Describe what is meant by a compound statement.
108. What is a conjunction? Describe the symbol that forms a conjunction.
109. What is a disjunction? Describe the symbol that forms a disjunction.
110. What is a conditional statement? Describe the symbol that forms a conditional statement.
111. What is a biconditional statement? Describe the symbol that forms a biconditional statement.
112. Discuss the difference between the symbolic statements $\sim(p \wedge q)$ and $\sim p \wedge q$.
113. If a symbolic statement does not contain parentheses, how are the grouping symbols determined?
114. Suppose that a friend tells you, "This summer I plan to visit Paris or London." Under what condition can you conclude that if your friend visits Paris, London will not be visited? Under what condition can you conclude that if your friend visits Paris, London might be visited? Assuming your friend has told you the truth, what can you conclude if you know that Paris will not be visited? Explain each of your answers.

Critical Thinking Exercises

Make Sense? *In Exercises 115–118, determine whether each statement makes sense or does not make sense, and explain your reasoning.*

115. When the waiter asked if I would like soup or salad, he used the exclusive *or*. However when he asked if I would like coffee or dessert, he used the inclusive *or*.
116. When you wrote me that you planned to enroll in English and math or chemistry, I knew that if you didn't enroll in math, you'd be taking chemistry.
117. In China, the bride wears red, so wearing red is sufficient for being a Chinese bride.
118. Earth is the only planet not named after a god, so not being named after a god is both necessary and sufficient for a planet being Earth.
119. Use letters to represent each simple statement in the compound statement that follows. Then express the compound statement in symbolic form.

    Shooting unarmed civilians is morally justifiable if and only if bombing them is morally justifiable, and as the former is not morally justifiable, neither is the latter.
120. Using a topic on which you have strong opinions, write a compound statement that contains at least two different connectives. Then express the statement in symbolic form.

Group Exercise

121. Each group member should find a legal document that contains at least six connectives in one paragraph. The connectives should include at least three different kinds of connectives, such as *and*, *or*, *if–then*, and *if and only if*. Share your example with other members of the group and see if the group can explain what some of the more complicated statements actually mean.

OBJECTIVES

1 Use the definitions of negation, conjunction, and disjunction.
2 Construct truth tables.
3 Determine the truth value of a compound statement for a specific case.

3 Truth Tables for Negation, Conjunction, and Disjunction

In 2006, *USA Today* analyzed patterns in the deaths of four-year college students since January 2000. Their most dominant finding was that freshmen emerged as the class most likely to make a fatal mistake. Freshmen accounted for more than one-third of all undergraduate deaths, even though they made up only 24% of the population enrolled in four-year institutions.

In this section, you will work with two circle graphs based on data from the *USA Today* study. By determining when statements involving negation, ~ (not), conjunction, ∧ (and), and disjunction, ∨ (or), are true and when they are false, you will be able to draw conclusions from the data. Classifying a statement as true or false is called **assigning a truth value to the statement.**

Clara Shutterstock

1 Use the definitions of negation, conjunction, and disjunction.

Negation, ~

The negation of a true statement is a false statement. We can express this in a table in which T represents true and F represents false.

p	$\sim p$
T	F

The negation of a false statement is a true statement. This, too, can be shown in table form.

p	$\sim p$
F	T

Combining the two tables results in **Table 10**, called the **truth table for negation**. This truth table expresses the idea that $\sim p$ has the opposite truth value from p.

TABLE 10 Negation

p	$\sim p$
T	F
F	T

$\sim p$ has the opposite truth value from p.

I visited London and I visited Paris. (Top) Gala\SuperStock, Inc. (Bottom) Carole Elies\Getty Images Inc. - Stone Allstock

Conjunction, $\wedge$

A friend tells you, "I visited London and I visited Paris." In order to understand the truth values for this statement, let's break it down into its two simple statements:

p: I visited London.

q: I visited Paris.

There are four possible cases to consider.

Case 1. Your friend actually visited both cities, so p is true and q is true. The conjunction "I visited London and I visited Paris" is true because your friend did both things. If both p and q are true, the conjunction $p \wedge q$ is true. We can show this in truth table form:

p	q	$p \wedge q$
T	T	T

Case 2. Your friend actually visited London, but did not tell the truth about visiting Paris. In this case, p is true and q is false. Your friend didn't do what was stated, namely visit both cities, so $p \wedge q$ is false. If p is true and q is false, the conjunction $p \wedge q$ is false.

p	q	$p \wedge q$
T	F	F

Case 3. This time, London was not visited, but Paris was. This makes p false and q true. As in case 2, your friend didn't do what was stated, namely visit both cities, so $p \wedge q$ is false. If p is false and q is true, the conjunction $p \wedge q$ is false.

p	q	$p \wedge q$
F	T	F

Case 4. This time your friend visited neither city, so p is false and q is false. The statement that both were visited, $p \wedge q$, is false.

p	q	$p \wedge q$
F	F	F

Let's use a truth table to summarize all four cases. Only in the case that your friend visited London and visited Paris is the conjunction true. Each of the four cases appears in **Table 11**, the truth table for conjunction, $\wedge$. The definition of conjunction is given in words to the right of the table.

THE DEFINITION OF CONJUNCTION

TABLE 11 Conjunction

p	q	$p \wedge q$
T	T	T
T	F	F
F	T	F
F	F	F

A conjunction is true only when both simple statements are true.

Table 12 contains an example of each of the four cases in the conjunction truth table.

TABLE 12 Statements of Conjunction and Their Truth Values

Statement	Truth Value	Reason
$3 + 2 = 5$ and London is in England.	T	Both simple statements are true.
$3 + 2 = 5$ and London is in France.	F	The second simple statement is false.
$3 + 2 = 6$ and London is in England.	F	The first simple statement is false.
$3 + 2 = 6$ and London is in France.	F	Both simple statements are false.

STUDY TIP

As soon as you find one simple statement in a conjunction that is false, you know that the conjunction is false.

The statements that come before and after the main connective in a compound statement do not have to be simple statements. Consider, for example, the compound statement

$$(\sim p \vee q) \wedge \sim q.$$

The statements that make up this conjunction are $\sim p \vee q$ and $\sim q$. The conjunction is true only when both $\sim p \vee q$ and $\sim q$ are true. Notice that $\sim p \vee q$ is not a simple statement. We call $\sim p \vee q$ and $\sim q$ the *component statements* of the conjunction. The statements making up a compound statement are called **component statements**.

Disjunction, $\vee$

Now your friend states, "I will visit London or I will visit Paris." Because we assume that this is the inclusive "or," if your friend visits either or both of these cities, the truth has been told. The disjunction is false only in the event that neither city is visited. An *or* statement is true in every case, except when both component statements are false.

The truth table for disjunction, $\vee$, is shown in **Table 13**. The definition of disjunction is given in words to the right of the table.

THE DEFINITION OF DISJUNCTION

TABLE 13 Disjunction

p	q	$p \vee q$
T	T	T
T	F	T
F	T	T
F	F	F

A disjunction is false only when both component statements are false.

Table 14 contains an example of each of the four cases in the disjunction truth table.

TABLE 14 Statements of Disjunction and Their Truth Values

Statement	Truth Value	Reason
$3 + 2 = 5$ or London is in England.	T	Both component statements are true.
$3 + 2 = 5$ or London is in France.	T	The first component statement is true.
$3 + 2 = 6$ or London is in England.	T	The second component statement is true.
$3 + 2 = 6$ or London is in France.	F	Both component statements are false.

STUDY TIP

As soon as you find one component statement in a disjunction that is true, you know that the disjunction is true.

EXAMPLE 1 Using the Definitions of Negation, Conjunction, and Disjunction

Let p and q represent the following statements:

p: $10 > 4$

q: $3 < 5$.

Determine the truth value for each statement:

a. $p \wedge q$ **b.** $\sim p \wedge q$ **c.** $p \vee \sim q$ **d.** $\sim p \vee \sim q$.

Solution

a. $p \wedge q$ translates as

$10 > 4$ and $3 < 5$.

10 is greater than 4 is true. 3 is less than 5 is true.

By definition, a conjunction, $\wedge$, is true only when both component statements are true. Thus, $p \wedge q$ is a true statement.

b. $\sim p \wedge q$ translates as

$10 \ngtr 4$ and $3 < 5$.

10 is not greater than 4 is false. 3 is less than 5 is true.

By definition, a conjunction, $\wedge$, is true only when both component statements are true. In this conjunction, only one of the two component statements is true. Thus, $\sim p \wedge q$ is a false statement.

c. $p \vee \sim q$ translates as

$10 > 4$ or $3 \nless 5$.

10 is greater than 4 is true. 3 is not less than 5 is false.

By definition, a disjunction, $\vee$, is false only when both component statements are false. In this disjunction, only one of the two component statements is false. Thus, $p \vee \sim q$ is a true statement.

d. $\sim p \vee \sim q$ translates as

$10 \ngtr 4$ or $3 \nless 5$.

10 is not greater than 4 is false. 3 is not less than 5 is false.

By definition, a disjunction, $\vee$, is false only when both component statements are false. Thus, $\sim p \vee \sim q$ is a false statement.

CHECK POINT 1 Let p and q represent the following statements:

p: $3 + 5 = 8$

q: $2 \times 7 = 20$.

Determine the truth value for each statement:

a. $p \wedge q$ **b.** $p \wedge \sim q$

c. $\sim p \vee q$ **d.** $\sim p \vee \sim q$.

2 Construct truth tables.

Constructing Truth Tables

Truth tables can be used to gain a better understanding of English statements. The truth tables in this section are based on the definitions of negation, $\sim$, conjunction, $\wedge$, and disjunction, $\vee$. It is helpful to remember these definitions in words.

DEFINITIONS OF NEGATION, CONJUNCTION, AND DISJUNCTION

1. Negation $\sim$: not
   The negation of a statement has the opposite truth value from the statement.
2. Conjunction $\wedge$: and
   The only case in which a conjunction is true is when both component statements are true.
3. Disjunction $\vee$: or
   The only case in which a disjunction is false is when both component statements are false.

Breaking compound statements into component statements and applying these definitions will enable you to construct truth tables.

CONSTRUCTING TRUTH TABLES FOR COMPOUND STATEMENTS CONTAINING ONLY THE SIMPLE STATEMENTS p AND q

- List the four possible combinations of truth values for p and q.

p	q	
T	T	
T	F	
F	T	
F	F	

We will always list the combinations in this order. Although any order can be used, this standard order makes for a consistent presentation.

- Determine each column heading by reconstructing the given compound statement one component statement at a time. The final column heading should be the given compound statement.
- Use each column heading to fill in the four truth values.
  - → If a column heading involves negation, $\sim$ (not), fill in the column by looking back at the column that contains the statement that must be negated. Take the opposite of the truth values in this column.
  - → If a column heading involves the symbol for conjunction, $\wedge$ (and), fill in the truth values in the column by looking back at two columns—the column for the statement before the $\wedge$ connective and the column for the statement after the $\wedge$ connective. Fill in the column by applying the definition of conjunction, writing T only when both component statements are true.
  - → If a column heading involves the symbol for disjunction, $\vee$ (or), fill in the truth values in the column by looking back at two columns—the column for the statement before the $\vee$ connective and the column for the statement after the $\vee$ connective. Fill in the column by applying the definition of disjunction, writing F only when both component statements are false.

EXAMPLE 2 Constructing a Truth Table

Construct a truth table for

$$\sim(p \wedge q)$$

to determine when the statement is true and when the statement is false.

Solution The parentheses indicate that we must first determine the truth values for the conjunction $p \wedge q$. After this, we determine the truth values for the negation $\sim(p \wedge q)$ by taking the opposite of the truth values for $p \wedge q$.

BLITZER BONUS

LEWIS CARROLL IN LOGICAL WONDERLAND

One of the world's most popular logicians was Lewis Carroll (1832–1898), author of *Alice's Adventures in Wonderland* and *Through the Looking Glass*. Carroll's passion for word games and logic is evident throughout the Alice stories.

> "Speak when you're spoken to!" the Queen sharply interrupted her.
> "But if everybody obeyed that rule," said Alice, who was always ready for a little argument, "and if you only spoke when you were spoken to, and the other person always waited for *you* to begin, you see nobody would ever say anything, so that—"
>
> "Take some more tea," the March Hare said to Alice, very earnestly.
> "I've had nothing yet," Alice replied in an offended tone, "so I can't take more."
> "You mean you can't take *less*," said the Hatter. "It's very easy to take *more* than nothing."

Step 1 As with all truth tables, first list the simple statements on top. Then show all the possible truth values for these statements. In this case there are two simple statements and four possible combinations, or cases.

p	q	
T	T	
T	F	
F	T	
F	F	

Step 2 Make a column for $p \wedge q$, the statement within the parentheses in $\sim(p \wedge q)$. Use $p \wedge q$ as the heading for the column, and then fill in the truth values for the conjunction by looking back at the p and q columns. A conjunction is true only when both component statements are true.

p	q	$p \wedge q$
T	T	T
T	F	F
F	T	F
F	F	F

p and q are true, so $p \wedge q$ is true.

Step 3 Construct one more column for $\sim(p \wedge q)$. Fill in this column by negating the values in the $p \wedge q$ column. Using the negation definition, take the opposite of the truth values in the third column.

p	q	$p \wedge q$	$\sim(p \wedge q)$
T	T	T	F
T	F	F	T
F	T	F	T
F	F	F	T

Opposite truth values because we are negating column 3

This completes the truth table for $\sim(p \wedge q)$.

The final column in the truth table for $\sim(p \wedge q)$ tells us that the statement is false only when both p and q are true. For example, using

p: Harvard is a college (true)

q: Yale is a college (true),

the statement $\sim(p \wedge q)$ translates as

It is not true that Harvard and Yale are colleges.

This compound statement is false. It *is* true that Harvard and Yale are colleges.

CHECK POINT 2 Construct a truth table for $\sim(p \vee q)$ to determine when the statement is true and when the statement is false.

EXAMPLE 3 Constructing a Truth Table

Construct a truth table for

$$\sim p \vee \sim q$$

to determine when the statement is true and when the statement is false.

Solution Without parentheses, the negation symbol, $\sim$, negates only the statement that immediately follows it. Therefore, we first determine the truth values for $\sim p$ and for $\sim q$. Then we determine the truth values for the *or* disjunction, $\sim p \vee \sim q$.

Step 1 List the simple statements on top and show the four possible cases for the truth values.

p	q	
T	T	
T	F	
F	T	
F	F	

Step 2 Make columns for $\sim p$ and for $\sim q$. Fill in the $\sim p$ column by looking back at the p column, the first column, and taking the opposite of the truth values in that column. Fill in the $\sim q$ column by taking the opposite of the truth values in the second column, the q column.

Opposite truth values

p	q	$\sim p$	$\sim q$
T	T	F	F
T	F	F	T
F	T	T	F
F	F	T	T

Opposite truth values

Step 3 Construct one more column for $\sim p \vee \sim q$. To determine the truth values of $\sim p \vee \sim q$, look back at the $\sim p$ column, column 3, and the $\sim q$ column, column 4. Now use the disjunction definition on the entries in columns 3 and 4. Disjunction definition: An *or* statement is false only when both component statements are false. This occurs only in the first row.

p	q	$\sim p$	$\sim q$	$\sim p \vee \sim q$
T	T	F	F	F
T	F	F	T	T
F	T	T	F	T
F	F	T	T	T

$\sim p$ is false and $\sim q$ is false, so $\sim p \vee \sim q$ is false.

column 3 $\vee$ column 4

CHECK POINT 3 Construct a truth table for $\sim p \wedge \sim q$ to determine when the statement is true and when the statement is false.

EXAMPLE 4 Constructing a Truth Table

Construct a truth table for

$$(\sim p \vee q) \wedge \sim q$$

to determine when the statement is true and when the statement is false.

Solution The statement $(\sim p \vee q) \wedge \sim q$ is an *and* conjunction because the conjunction symbol, $\wedge$, is outside the parentheses. We cannot determine the truth values for the statement until we first determine the truth values for $\sim p \vee q$ and for $\sim q$, the component statements before and after the $\wedge$ connective:

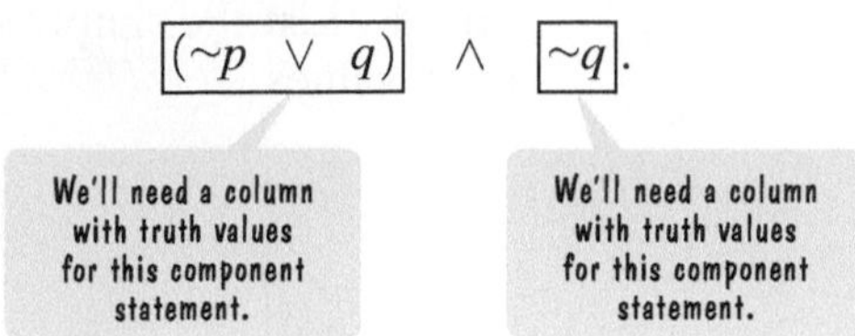
(~p ∨ q) ∧ ~q.
We'll need a column with truth values for this component statement.
We'll need a column with truth values for this component statement.

Step 1 The compound statement involves two simple statements and four possible cases.

p	q	
T	T	
T	F	
F	T	
F	F	

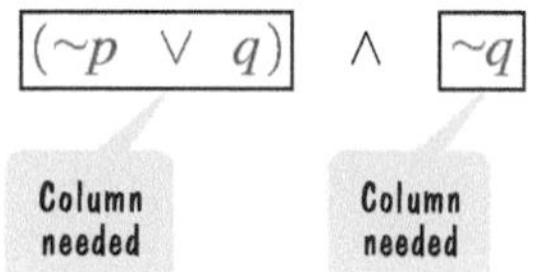
(~p ∨ q) ∧ ~q
Column needed
Column needed

Step 2 Because we need a column with truth values for $\sim p \vee q$, begin with $\sim p$. Use $\sim p$ as the heading. Fill in the column by looking back at the p column, column 1, and take the opposite of the truth values in that column.

p	q	$\sim p$
T	T	F
T	F	F
F	T	T
F	F	T

Opposite truth values

Step 3 Now add a $\sim p \vee q$ column. To determine the truth values of $\sim p \vee q$, look back at the $\sim p$ column, column 3, and the q column, column 2. Now use the disjunction definition on the entries in columns 3 and 2. Disjunction definition: An *or* statement is false only when both component statements are false. This occurs only in the second row.

p	q	$\sim p$	$\sim p \vee q$
T	T	F	T
T	F	F	F
F	T	T	T
F	F	T	T

$\sim p$ is false and q is false, so $\sim p \vee q$ is false.

column 3 $\vee$ column 2

Step 4 The statement following the $\wedge$ connective in $(\sim p \vee q) \wedge \sim q$ is $\sim q$, so add a $\sim q$ column. Fill in the column by looking back at the q column, column 2, and take the opposite of the truth values in that column.

p	q	$\sim p$	$\sim p \vee q$	$\sim q$
T	T	F	T	F
T	F	F	F	T
F	T	T	T	F
F	F	T	T	T

Opposite truth values

Step 5 The final column heading is

$$(\sim p \vee q) \wedge \sim q,$$

which is our given statement. To determine its truth values, look back at the $\sim p \vee q$ column, column 4, and the $\sim q$ column, column 5. Now use the conjunction definition on the entries in columns 4 and 5. Conjunction definition: An *and* statement is true only when both component statements are true. This occurs only in the last row.

p	q	$\sim p$	$\sim p \vee q$	$\sim q$	$(\sim p \vee q) \wedge \sim q$
T	T	F	T	F	F
T	F	F	F	T	F
F	T	T	T	F	F
F	F	T	T	T	T

$\sim p \vee q$ is true and $\sim q$ is true, so $(\sim p \vee q) \wedge \sim q$ is true.

column 4 $\wedge$ column 5

The truth table is now complete. By looking at the truth values in the last column, we can see that the compound statement

$$(\sim p \vee q) \wedge \sim q$$

is true only in the fourth row, that is, when p is false and q is false.

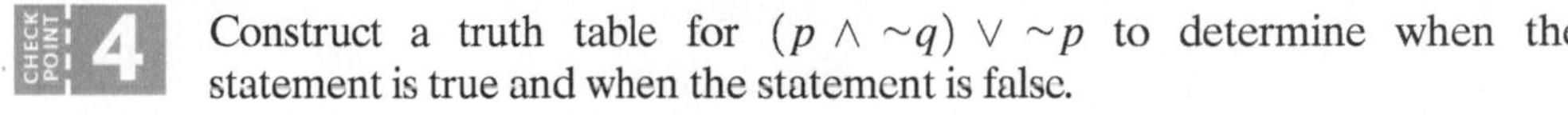

CHECK POINT 4 Construct a truth table for $(p \wedge \sim q) \vee \sim p$ to determine when the statement is true and when the statement is false.

Some compound statements, such as $p \vee \sim p$, consist of only one simple statement. In cases like this, there are only two true–false possibilities: p can be true or p can be false.

EXAMPLE 5 Constructing a Truth Table

Construct a truth table for

$$p \vee \sim p$$

to determine when the statement is true and when the statement is false.

Solution We first determine the truth values for $\sim p$. Then we determine the truth values for the *or* disjunction, $p \vee \sim p$.

Step 1 The compound statement involves one simple statement and two possible cases.

p	
T	
F	

Step 2 Add a column for $\sim p$.

p	$\sim p$
T	F
F	T

Take the opposite of the truth values in the first column.

Step 3 Construct one more column for $p \vee \sim p$.

p	$\sim p$	$p \vee \sim p$
T	F	T
F	T	T

Look back at columns 1 and 2 and apply the disjunction definition: An *or* statement is false only when both component statements are false. This does not occur in either row.

The truth table is now complete. By looking at the truth values in the last column, we can see that the compound statement $p \vee \sim p$ is true in all cases.

A compound statement that is always true is called a **tautology**. Example 5 proves that $p \vee \sim p$ is a tautology.

CHECK POINT 5 Construct a truth table for

$$p \wedge \sim p$$

to determine when the statement is true and when the statement is false.

BLITZER BONUS

TAUTOLOGIES AND COMMERCIALS

Think about the logic in the following statement from a commercial for a high-fiber cereal:

> Some studies suggest a high-fiber, low-fat diet may reduce the risk of some kinds of cancer.

From a strictly logical point of view, "may reduce" means "It may reduce the risk of cancer or it may not." The symbolic translation of this sentence, $p \vee \sim p$, is a tautology. The claim made in the cereal commercial can be made about any substance that is not known to actually cause cancer and, like $p \vee \sim p$, will always be true.

Some compound statements involve three simple statements, usually represented by p, q, and r. In this situation, there are eight different true–false combinations, shown in **Table 15**. The first column has four Ts followed by four Fs. The second column has two Ts, two Fs, two Ts, and two Fs. Under the third statement, r, T alternates with F. It is not necessary to list the eight cases in this order, but this systematic method ensures that no case is repeated and that all cases are included.

TABLE 15

	p	q	r
Case 1	T	T	T
Case 2	T	T	F
Case 3	T	F	T
Case 4	T	F	F
Case 5	F	T	T
Case 6	F	T	F
Case 7	F	F	T
Case 8	F	F	F

There are eight different true–false combinations for compound statements consisting of three simple statements.

EXAMPLE 6 Constructing a Truth Table with Eight Cases

a. Construct a truth table for the following statement:

I study hard and ace the final, or I fail the course.

b. Suppose that you study hard, you do not ace the final, and you fail the course. Under these conditions, is the compound statement in part (a) true or false?

Solution

a. We begin by assigning letters to the simple statements. Use the following representations:

p: I study hard.
q: I ace the final.
r: I fail the course.

Now we can write the given statement in symbolic form.

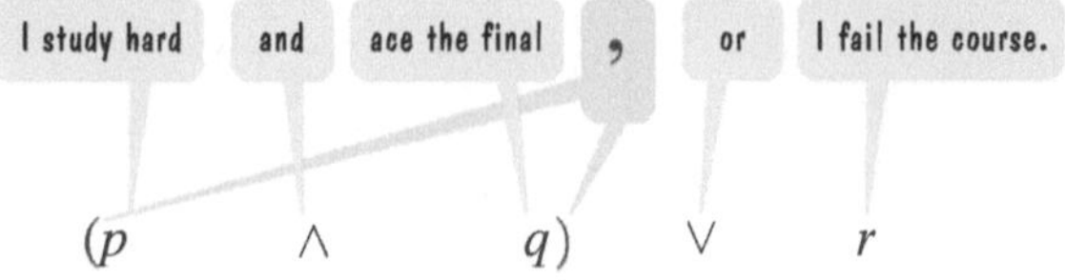

$$(p \wedge q) \vee r$$

The statement $(p \wedge q) \vee r$ is a disjunction because the *or* symbol, $\vee$, is outside the parentheses. We cannot determine the truth values for this disjunction until we have determined the truth values for $p \wedge q$ and for r, the statements before and after the $\vee$ connective. The completed truth table appears as follows:

The conjunction is true only when p, the first column, is true and q, the second column, is true.

The disjunction is false only when $p \wedge q$, column 4, is false and r, column 3, is false.

Show eight possible cases.

These are the conditions in part (b).

p	q	r	$p \wedge q$	$(p \wedge q) \vee r$
T	T	T	T	T
T	T	F	T	T
T	F	T	F	T
T	F	F	F	F
F	T	T	F	T
F	T	F	F	F
F	F	T	F	T
F	F	F	F	F

b. We are given the following:

p: I study hard. — This is true. We are told you study hard.

q: I ace the final. — This is false. We are told you do not ace the final.

r: I fail the course. — This is true. We are told you fail the course.

The given conditions, T F T, correspond to case 3 of the truth table, indicated by the voice balloon on the far left. Under these conditions, the original compound statement is true, shown by the red T in the truth table.

a. Construct a truth table for the following statement:

I study hard, and I ace the final or fail the course.

b. Suppose that you do not study hard, you ace the final, and you fail the course. Under these conditions, is the compound statement in part (a) true or false?

3 Determine the truth value of a compound statement for a specific case.

Determining Truth Values for Specific Cases

A truth table shows the truth values of a compound statement for every possible case. In our next example, we will determine the truth value of a compound statement for a specific case in which the truth values of the simple statements are known. This does not require constructing an entire truth table. By substituting the truth values of the simple statements into the symbolic form of the compound statement and using the appropriate definitions, we can determine the truth value of the compound statement.

EXAMPLE 7 Determining the Truth Value of a Compound Statement

College administrators, public health officials, and parents increasingly have become concerned about the safety of college students after highly publicized deaths on campus from alcohol abuse and other causes. The data in **Figure 2** indicate that freshmen are particularly vulnerable.

Undergraduate Enrollment and Deaths in the United States

Percentage of Undergraduate Students

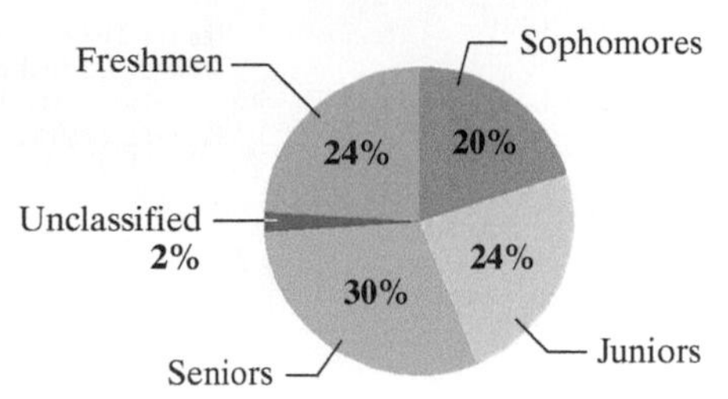

Percentage of Undergraduate Deaths

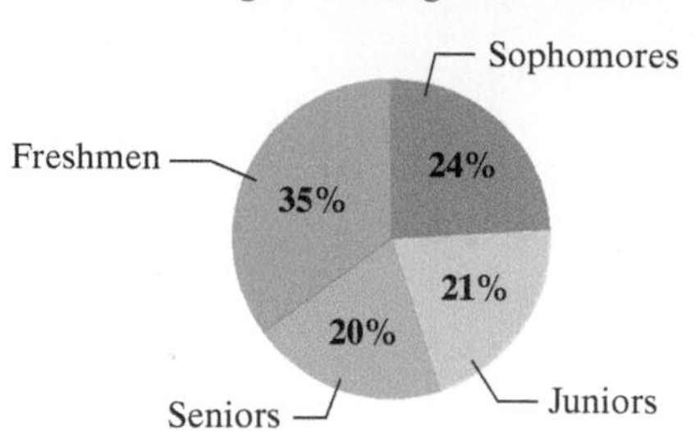

FIGURE 2
Source: USA Today

Use the information in the circle graphs to determine the truth value of the following statement:

> It is not true that freshmen make up 24% of the undergraduate college population and account for more than one-third of the undergraduate deaths, or seniors do not account for 30% of the undergraduate deaths.

Solution We begin by assigning letters to the simple statements, using the graphs to determine whether each simple statement is true or false. As always, we let these letters represent statements that are not negated.

p: Freshmen make up 24% of the undergraduate college population. — This statement is true.

q: Freshmen account for more than one-third of the undergraduate deaths. — This statement is true. They account for 35% of the deaths, which is greater than $\frac{1}{3}$: $\frac{1}{3} = 33\frac{1}{3}\%$.

r: Seniors account for 30% of the undergraduate deaths. — This statement is false. They account for 20% of the deaths.

Using these representations, the given compound statement can be expressed in symbolic form as

$$\sim(p \wedge q) \vee \sim r.$$

Now we substitute the truth values for p, q, and r that we obtained from the circle graphs to determine the truth value for the given compound statement.

$\sim(p \wedge q) \vee \sim r$	This is the given compound statement in symbolic form.
$\sim(\text{T} \wedge \text{T}) \vee \sim\text{F}$	Substitute the truth values obtained from the graph.
$\sim\text{T} \vee \sim\text{F}$	Replace $\text{T} \wedge \text{T}$ with T. Conjunction is true when both parts are true.
$\text{F} \vee \text{T}$	Replace $\sim$T with F and $\sim$F with T. Negation gives the opposite truth value.
T	Replace $\text{F} \vee \text{T}$ with T. Disjunction is true when at least one part is true.

We conclude that the given statement is true.

Use the information in the circle graphs in **Figure 2** to determine the truth value for the following statement:

> Freshmen and juniors make up the same percentage of the undergraduate college population or seniors make up 35% of the population, and freshmen and juniors do not account for the same percentage of the undergraduate deaths.

Exercise Set 3

Practice Exercises

In Exercises 1–16, let p and q represent the following statements:

$p: 4 + 6 = 10$

$q: 5 \times 8 = 80$

Determine the truth value for each statement.

1. $\sim q$
2. $\sim p$
3. $p \wedge q$
4. $q \wedge p$
5. $\sim p \wedge q$
6. $p \wedge \sim q$
7. $\sim p \wedge \sim q$
8. $q \wedge \sim q$
9. $q \vee p$
10. $p \vee q$
11. $p \vee \sim q$
12. $\sim p \vee q$
13. $p \vee \sim p$
14. $q \vee \sim q$
15. $\sim p \vee \sim q$
16. $\sim q \vee \sim p$

In Exercises 17–24, complete the truth table for the given statement by filling in the required columns.

17. $\sim p \wedge p$

p	$\sim p$	$\sim p \wedge p$
T		
F		

18. $\sim(\sim p)$

p	$\sim p$	$\sim(\sim p)$
T		
F		

19. $\sim p \wedge q$

p	q	$\sim p$	$\sim p \wedge q$
T	T		
T	F		
F	T		
F	F		

20. $\sim p \vee q$

p	q	$\sim p$	$\sim p \vee q$
T	T		
T	F		
F	T		
F	F		

21. $\sim(p \vee q)$

p	q	$p \vee q$	$\sim(p \vee q)$
T	T		
T	F		
F	T		
F	F		

22. $\sim(p \vee \sim q)$

p	q	$\sim q$	$p \vee \sim q$	$\sim(p \vee \sim q)$
T	T			
T	F			
F	T			
F	F			

23. $\sim p \wedge \sim q$

p	q	$\sim p$	$\sim q$	$\sim p \wedge \sim q$
T	T			
T	F			
F	T			
F	F			

24. $p \wedge \sim q$

p	q	$\sim q$	$p \wedge \sim q$
T	T		
T	F		
F	T		
F	F		

In Exercises 25–42, construct a truth table for the given statement.

25. $p \vee \sim q$
26. $\sim q \wedge p$
27. $\sim(\sim p \vee q)$
28. $\sim(p \wedge \sim q)$
29. $(p \vee q) \wedge \sim p$
30. $(p \wedge q) \vee \sim p$
31. $\sim p \vee (p \wedge \sim q)$
32. $\sim p \wedge (p \vee \sim q)$
33. $(p \vee q) \wedge (\sim p \vee \sim q)$
34. $(p \wedge \sim q) \vee (\sim p \wedge q)$
35. $(p \wedge \sim q) \vee (p \wedge q)$
36. $(p \vee \sim q) \wedge (p \vee q)$
37. $p \wedge (\sim q \vee r)$
38. $p \vee (\sim q \wedge r)$
39. $(r \wedge \sim p) \vee \sim q$
40. $(r \vee \sim p) \wedge \sim q$
41. $\sim(p \vee q) \wedge \sim r$
42. $\sim(p \wedge q) \vee \sim r$

In Exercises 43–52,

a. *Write each statement in symbolic form. Assign letters to simple statements that are not negated.*

b. *Construct a truth table for the symbolic statement in part (a).*

c. *Use the truth table to indicate one set of conditions that makes the compound statement true, or state that no such conditions exist.*

43. You did not do the dishes and you left the room a mess.

44. You did not do the dishes, but you did not leave the room a mess.

45. It is not true that I bought a meal ticket and did not use it.

46. It is not true that I ordered pizza while watching late-night TV and did not gain weight.

47. The student is intelligent or an overachiever, and not an overachiever.

48. You're blushing or sunburned, and you're not sunburned.

49. Married people are healthier than single people and more economically stable than single people, and children of married people do better on a variety of indicators.

50. You walk or jog, or engage in something physical.

51. I go to office hours and ask questions, or my professor does not remember me.

52. You marry the person you love, but you do not always love that person or do not always have a successful marriage.

In Exercises 53–62, determine the truth value for each statement when p is false, q is true, and r is false.

53. $p \wedge (q \vee r)$

54. $p \vee (q \wedge r)$

55. $\sim p \vee (q \wedge \sim r)$

56. $\sim p \wedge (\sim q \wedge r)$

57. $\sim(p \wedge q) \vee r$

58. $\sim(p \vee q) \wedge r$

59. $\sim(p \vee q) \wedge \sim(p \wedge r)$

60. $\sim(p \wedge q) \vee \sim(p \vee r)$

61. $(\sim p \wedge q) \vee (\sim r \wedge p)$

62. $(\sim p \vee q) \wedge (\sim r \vee p)$

Practice Plus

In Exercises 63–66, construct a truth table for each statement.

63. $\sim[\sim(p \wedge \sim q) \vee \sim(\sim p \vee q)]$

64. $\sim[\sim(p \vee \sim q) \wedge \sim(\sim p \wedge q)]$

65. $[(p \wedge \sim r) \vee (q \wedge \sim r)] \wedge \sim(\sim p \vee r)$

66. $[(p \vee \sim r) \wedge (q \vee \sim r)] \vee \sim(\sim p \vee r)$

In Exercises 67–70, write each statement in symbolic form and construct a truth table. Then indicate under what conditions, if any, the compound statement is true.

67. You notice this notice or you do not, and you notice this notice is not worth noticing.

68. You notice this notice and you notice this notice is not worth noticing, or you do not notice this notice.

69. It is not true that $x \leq 3$ or $x \geq 7$, but $x > 3$ and $x < 7$.

70. It is not true that $x < 5$ or $x > 8$, but $x \geq 5$ and $x \leq 8$.

Application Exercises

With aging, body fat increases and muscle mass declines. The line graphs show the percent body fat in adult women and men as they age from 25 to 75 years.

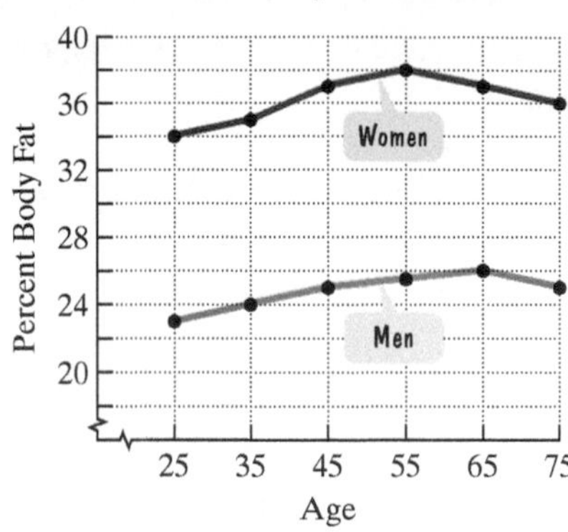

Source: Thompson et al., *The Science of Nutrition*, Benjamin Cummings, 2008.

In Exercises 71–80, let p, q, and r represent the following simple statements:

p: The percent body fat in women peaks at age 55.

q: The percent body fat in men peaks at age 65.

r: Men have more than 24% body fat at age 25.

Write each symbolic statement in words. Then use the information given by the graph to determine the truth value of the statement.

71. $p \wedge \sim q$

72. $p \wedge \sim r$

73. $\sim p \wedge r$

74. $q \wedge \sim p$

75. $p \vee \sim q$

76. $p \vee \sim r$

77. $\sim p \vee r$

78. $q \vee \sim p$

79. $(p \wedge q) \vee r$

80. $p \wedge (q \vee r)$

Completing the transition to adulthood is measured by one or more of the following: leaving home, finishing school, getting married, having a child, or being financially independent. The bar graph shows the percentage of Americans, ages 20 and 30, who had completed the transition to adulthood in 1960 and in 2000.

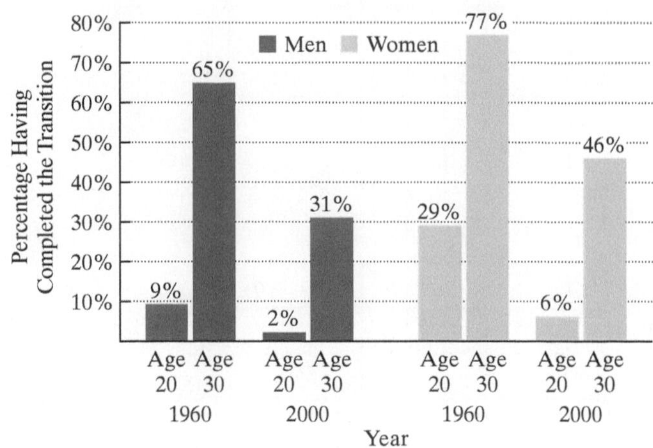

Source: James M. Henslin, *Sociology*, Eighth Edition, Allyn and Bacon, 2007.

In Exercises 81–84, write each statement in symbolic form. Then use the information in the graph at the bottom of the previous page to determine the truth value of the compound statement.

81. It is not true that in 2000, 2% of 20-year-old men and 46% of 30-year-old men had completed the transition to adulthood.

82. It is not true that in 2000, 2% of 20-year-old women and 46% of 30-year-old women had completed the transition to adulthood.

83. From 1960 through 2000, the percentage of 20-year-old women making the transition to adulthood decreased or the percentage of 30-year-old women making the transition increased, and the percentage of 30-year-old men making the transition did not decrease.

84. From 1960 through 2000, the percentage of 20-year-old men making the transition to adulthood decreased, but the percentage of 30-year-old men making the transition did not decrease or the percentage of 20-year-old women making the transition increased.

85. To qualify for the position of music professor, an applicant must have a master's degree in music, and be able to play at least three musical instruments or have at least five years' experience playing with a symphony orchestra.

There are three applicants for the position:

- *Bolero Mozart* has a master's degree in journalism and plays the piano, tuba, and violin.
- *Cha-Cha Bach* has a master's degree in music, plays the piano and the harp, and has two years' experience with a symphony orchestra.
- *Hora Gershwin* has a master's degree in music, plays 14 instruments, and has two years' experience in a symphony orchestra.

a. Which of the applicants qualifies for the position?

b. Explain why each of the other applicants does not qualify for the position.

86. To qualify for the position of art professor, an applicant must have a master's degree in art, and a body of work judged as excellent by at least two working artists or at least two works on public display in the United States.

There are three applicants for the position:

- *Adagio Picasso* needs two more courses to complete a master's degree in art, has a body of work judged as excellent by ten working artists, and has over 50 works on public display in a number of different American cities.
- *Rondo Seurat* has a master's degree in art, a body of work judged as excellent by a well-known working artist, and two works on public display in New York City.
- *Yodel Van Gogh* has a master's degree in art, is about to complete a doctorate in art history, has 20 works on public display in Paris, France, and has a body of work judged as excellent by a working artist.

a. Which of the applicants qualifies for the position?

b. Explain why each of the other applicants does not qualify for the position.

Writing in Mathematics

87. Under which conditions is a conjunction true?

88. Under which conditions is a conjunction false?

89. Under which conditions is a disjunction true?

90. Under which conditions is a disjunction false?

91. Describe how to construct a truth table for a compound statement.

92. Describe the information given by the truth values in the final column of a truth table.

93. Describe how to set up the eight different true–false combinations for a compound statement consisting of three simple statements.

94. The circle graphs in **Figure 2** indicate that college freshmen account for more than one-third of undergraduate deaths, although they comprise only 24% of the undergraduate population. What explanations can you offer for these grim statistics?

Critical Thinking Exercises

Make Sense? *In Exercises 95–98, determine whether each statement makes sense or does not make sense, and explain your reasoning.*

95. I'm filling in the truth values for a column in a truth table that requires me to look back at three columns.

96. If I know that p is true, q is false, and r is false, the most efficient way to determine the truth value of $(p \wedge \sim q) \vee r$ is to construct a truth table.

97. My truth table for $\sim(\sim p)$ has four possible combinations of truth values.

98. Using inductive reasoning, I conjecture that a truth table for a compound statement consisting of n simple statements has 2^n true–false combinations.

99. Use the bar graph for Exercises 81–84 to write a true compound statement with each of the following characteristics. Do not use any of the simple statements that appear in Exercises 81–84.

a. The statement contains three different simple statements.

b. The statement contains two different connectives.

c. The statement contains one simple statement with the word *not*.

100. If $\sim(p \vee q)$ is true, determine the truth values for p and q.

101. The truth table that defines $\vee$, the *inclusive or*, indicates that the compound statement is true if one or both of its component statements are true. The symbol for the *exclusive or* is $\underline{\vee}$. The *exclusive or* means *either p or q*, but *not both*. Use this meaning to construct the truth table that defines $p \underline{\vee} q$.

Group Exercise

102. Each member of the group should find a graph that is of particular interest to that person. Share the graphs. The group should select the three graphs that it finds most intriguing. For the graphs selected, group members should write four compound statements. Two of the statements should be true and two should be false. One of the statements should contain three different simple statements and two different connectives.

OBJECTIVES

1 Understand the logic behind the definition of the conditional.
2 Construct truth tables for conditional statements.
3 Understand the definition of the biconditional.
4 Construct truth tables for biconditional statements.
5 Determine the truth value of a compound statement for a specific case.

4 Truth Tables for the Conditional and the Biconditional

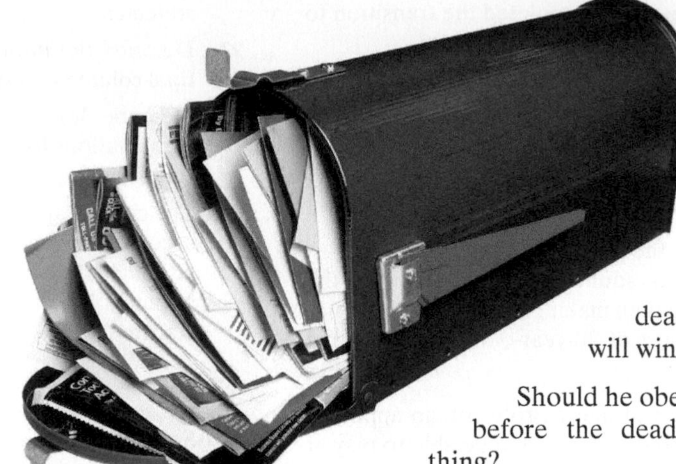

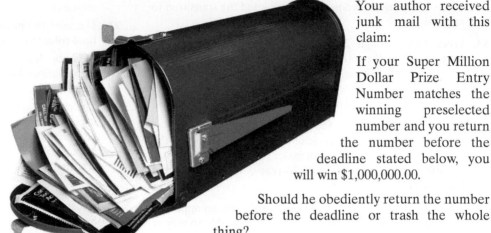

Fotolia

Your author received junk mail with this claim:

If your Super Million Dollar Prize Entry Number matches the winning preselected number and you return the number before the deadline stated below, you will win $1,000,000.00.

Should he obediently return the number before the deadline or trash the whole thing?

In this section, we will use logic to analyze the claim in the junk mail. By understanding when statements involving the conditional, $\rightarrow$ (if–then), and the biconditional, $\leftrightarrow$ (if and only if), are true and when they are false, you will be able to determine the truth value of the claim.

1 Understand the logic behind the definition of the conditional.

Conditional Statements, $\rightarrow$

We begin by looking at the truth table for conditional statements. Suppose that your professor promises you the following:

If you pass the final, then you pass the course.

Break the statement down into its two component statements:

p: You pass the final.
q: You pass the course.

Translated into symbolic form, your professor's statement is $p \rightarrow q$. We now look at the four cases shown in **Table 16**, the truth table for the conditional.

TABLE 16 Conditional

	p	q	$p \rightarrow q$
Case 1	T	T	T
Case 2	T	F	F
Case 3	F	T	T
Case 4	F	F	T

Case 1 (T, T) You do pass the final and you do pass the course. Your professor did what was promised, so the conditional statement is true.

Case 2 (T, F) You pass the final, but you do not pass the course. Your professor did not do what was promised, so the conditional statement is false.

Case 3 (F, T) You do not pass the final, but you do pass the course. Your professor's original statement talks about only what would happen if you passed the final. It says nothing about what would happen if you did not pass the final. Your professor did not break the promise of the original statement, so the conditional statement is true.

Case 4 (F, F) You do not pass the final and you do not pass the course. As with case 3, your professor's original statement talks about only what would happen if you passed the final. The promise of the original statement has not been broken. Therefore, the conditional statement is true.

Table 16 illustrates that a conditional statement is false only when the antecedent, the statement before the $\rightarrow$ connective, is true and the consequent, the statement after the $\rightarrow$ connective, is false. A conditional statement is true in all other cases.

THE DEFINITION OF THE CONDITIONAL

p	q	$p \rightarrow q$
T	T	T
T	F	F
F	T	T
F	F	T

A conditional is false only when the antecedent is true and the consequent is false.

2 Construct truth tables for conditional statements.

Constructing Truth Tables

Our first example shows how truth tables can be used to gain a better understanding of conditional statements.

EXAMPLE 1 Constructing a Truth Table

Construct a truth table for

$$\sim q \rightarrow \sim p$$

to determine when the statement is true and when the statement is false.

Solution Remember that without parentheses, the symbol ~ negates only the statement that immediately follows it. Therefore, we cannot determine the truth values for this conditional statement until we first determine the truth values for $\sim q$ and for $\sim p$, the statements before and after the $\rightarrow$ connective.

Step 1 List the simple statements on top and show the four possible cases for the truth values.

p	q	
T	T	
T	F	
F	T	
F	F	

Step 2 Make columns for $\sim q$ and for $\sim p$. Fill in the $\sim q$ column by looking back at the q column, the second column, and taking the opposite of the truth values in this column. Fill in the $\sim p$ column by taking the opposite of the truth values in the first column, the p column.

Opposite truth values

p	q	$\sim q$	$\sim p$
T	T	F	F
T	F	T	F
F	T	F	T
F	F	T	T

Opposite truth values

Step 3 Construct one more column for $\sim q \rightarrow \sim p$. Look back at the $\sim q$ column, column 3, and the $\sim p$ column, column 4. Now use the conditional definition to determine the truth values for $\sim q \rightarrow \sim p$ based on columns 3 and 4. Conditional definition: An *if–then* statement is false only when the antecedent is true and the consequent is false. This occurs only in the second row.

p	q	$\sim q$	$\sim p$	$\sim q \rightarrow \sim p$
T	T	F	F	T
T	F	T	F	F
F	T	F	T	T
F	F	T	T	T

$\sim q$ is true and $\sim p$ is false, so $\sim q \rightarrow \sim p$ is false.

column 3 → column 4

CHECK POINT 1 Construct a truth table for $\sim p \rightarrow \sim q$ to determine when the statement is true and when the statement is false.

TABLE 17

p	q	$p \rightarrow q$	$\sim q \rightarrow \sim p$
T	T	T	T
T	F	F	F
F	T	T	T
F	F	T	T

$p \rightarrow q$ and $\sim q \rightarrow \sim p$ have the same truth values.

The truth values for $p \rightarrow q$, as well as those for $\sim q \rightarrow \sim p$ from Example 1, are shown in **Table 17**. Notice that $p \rightarrow q$ and $\sim q \rightarrow \sim p$ have the same truth value in each of the four cases. What does this mean? **Every time you hear or utter a conditional statement, you can reverse and negate the antecedent and consequent, and the statement's truth value will not change.** Here's an example from a student providing advice on campus fashion:

- If you're cool, you won't wear clothing with your school name on it.
- If you wear clothing with your school name on it, you're not cool.

If the fashion tip above is true then so is this, and if it's false then this is false as well.

We'll have lots more to say about this (that is, variations of conditional statements, not tips on dressing up and down around campus) in the next section.

EXAMPLE 2 Constructing a Truth Table

Construct a truth table for

$$[(p \vee q) \wedge \sim p] \rightarrow q$$

to determine when the statement is true and when the statement is false.

Solution The statement is a conditional statement because the *if–then* symbol, →, is outside the grouping symbols. We cannot determine the truth values for this conditional until we first determine the truth values for the statements before and after the → connective.

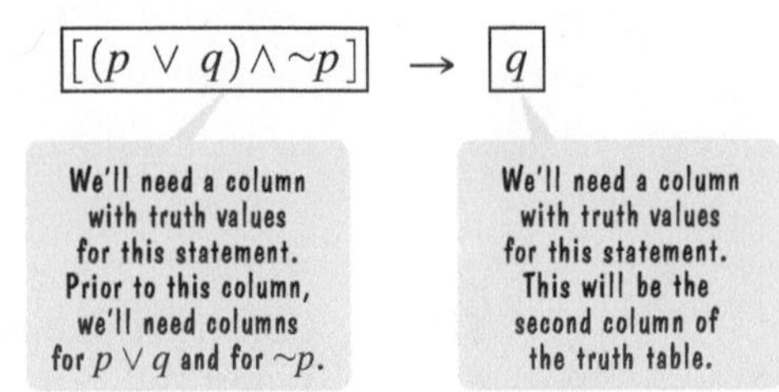

[(p ∨ q) ∧ ~p] → q
We'll need a column with truth values for this statement. Prior to this column, we'll need columns for p ∨ q and for ~p.
We'll need a column with truth values for this statement. This will be the second column of the truth table.

The disjunction, $\vee$, is false only when both component statements are false.

The truth value of $\sim p$ is opposite that of p.

The conjunction, $\wedge$, is true only when both $p \vee q$ and $\sim p$ are true.

The conditional, $\rightarrow$, is false only when $(p \vee q) \wedge \sim p$ is true and q is false.

Show four possible cases.

p	q	$p \vee q$	$\sim p$	$(p \vee q) \wedge \sim p$	$[(p \vee q) \wedge \sim p] \rightarrow q$
T	T	T	F	F	T
T	F	T	F	F	T
F	T	T	T	T	T
F	F	F	T	F	T

The completed truth table shows that the conditional statement in the last column, $[(p \vee q) \wedge \sim p] \rightarrow q$, is true in all cases.

In Section 3, we defined a **tautology** as a compound statement that is always true. Example 2 proves that the conditional statement $[(p \vee q) \wedge \sim p] \rightarrow q$ is a tautology.

Conditional statements that are tautologies are called **implications**. For the conditional statement

$$[(p \vee q) \wedge \sim p] \rightarrow q$$

we can say that

$$(p \vee q) \wedge \sim p \textit{ implies } q.$$

Using p: I am visiting London and q: I am visiting Paris, we can say that

> I am visiting London or Paris, and I am not visiting London, implies that I am visiting Paris.

Construct a truth table for $[(p \rightarrow q) \wedge \sim q] \rightarrow \sim p$ and show that the compound statement is a tautology.

Some compound statements are false in all possible cases. Such statements are called **self-contradictions**. An example of a self-contradiction is the statement $p \wedge \sim p$:

p	$\sim p$	$p \wedge \sim p$
T	F	F
F	T	F

$p \wedge \sim p$ is always false.

If p represents "I am going," then $p \wedge \sim p$ translates as "I am going and I am not going." Such a translation sounds like a contradiction.

EXAMPLE 3 Constructing a Truth Table with Eight Cases

The following is from an editorial that appeared in *The New York Times*:

> Our entire tax system depends upon the vast majority of taxpayers who attempt to pay the taxes they owe having confidence that they're being treated fairly and that their competitors and neighbors are also paying what is due. If the public concludes that the IRS cannot meet these basic expectations, the risk to the tax system will become very high and the effects very difficult to reverse.
>
> *The New York Times*, February 13, 2000

a. Construct a truth table for the underlined statement.

If the public concludes that the IRS cannot meet these basic expectations, the risk to the tax system will become very high and the effects very difficult to reverse.

The underlined statement from the previous page (repeated)

b. Suppose that the public concludes that the IRS cannot meet basic expectations, the risk to the tax system becomes very high, but the effects are not very difficult to reverse. Under these conditions, is the underlined statement true or false?

Solution

a. We begin by assigning letters to the simple statements. Use the following representations:

p: The public concludes that the IRS *can* meet basic expectations (of fair treatment and others paying what is due).

q: The risk to the tax system will become very high.

r: The effects will be very difficult to reverse.

The underlined statement in symbolic form is

$$\sim p \rightarrow (q \wedge r).$$

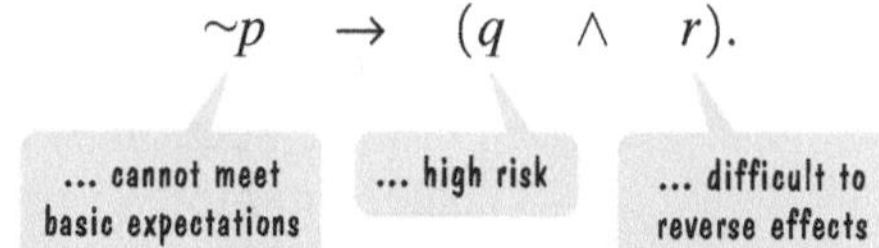

The statement $\sim p \rightarrow (q \wedge r)$ is a conditional statement because the *if–then* symbol, $\rightarrow$, is outside the parentheses. We cannot determine the truth values for this conditional until we have determined the truth values for $\sim p$ and for $q \wedge r$, the statements before and after the $\rightarrow$ connective. Because the compound statement consists of three simple statements, represented by p, q, and r, the truth table must contain eight cases. The completed truth table appears as follows:

The conjunction is true only when q, column 2, is true and r, column 3, is true.

Take the opposite of the truth values in column 1.

The conditional is false only when the $\sim p$ column is true and the $q \wedge r$ column is false.

Show eight possible cases.

p	q	r	$\sim p$	$q \wedge r$	$\sim p \rightarrow (q \wedge r)$
T	T	T	F	T	T
T	T	F	F	F	T
T	F	T	F	F	T
T	F	F	F	F	T
F	T	T	T	T	T
F	T	F	T	F	F
F	F	T	T	F	F
F	F	F	T	F	F

These are the conditions in part (b).

b. We are given that p (... can meet basic expectations) is false, q (... high risk) is true, and r (... difficult to reverse effects) is false. The given conditions, F T F, correspond to case 6 of the truth table, indicated by the voice balloon on the far left. Under these conditions, the original compound statement is false, shown by the red F in the truth table.

An advertisement makes the following claim:

If you use Hair Grow and apply it daily, then you will not go bald.

a. Construct a truth table for the claim.

b. Suppose you use Hair Grow, forget to apply it every day, and you go bald. Under these conditions, is the claim in the advertisement false?

3 Understand the definition of the biconditional.

Biconditional Statements

In Section 2, we introduced the biconditional connective, $\leftrightarrow$, translated as "if and only if." The biconditional statement $p \leftrightarrow q$ means that $p \rightarrow q$ and $q \rightarrow p$. We write this symbolically as

$$(p \rightarrow q) \wedge (q \rightarrow p).$$

To create the truth table for $p \leftrightarrow q$, we will first make a truth table for the conjunction of the two conditionals $p \rightarrow q$ and $q \rightarrow p$. The truth table for $(p \rightarrow q) \wedge (q \rightarrow p)$ is shown as follows:

The conditional is false only when p is true and q is false.

The conditional is false only when q is true and p is false.

The conjunction is true only when both $p \rightarrow q$ and $q \rightarrow p$ are true.

Show four possible cases.

p	q	$p \rightarrow q$	$q \rightarrow p$	$(p \rightarrow q) \wedge (q \rightarrow p)$
T	T	T	T	T
T	F	F	T	F
F	T	T	F	F
F	F	T	T	T

col. 1 $\rightarrow$ col. 2 | col. 2 $\rightarrow$ col. 1 | col. 3 $\wedge$ col. 4

The truth values in the column for $(p \rightarrow q) \wedge (q \rightarrow p)$ show the truth values for the biconditional statement $p \leftrightarrow q$.

THE DEFINITION OF THE BICONDITIONAL

p	q	$p \leftrightarrow q$
T	T	T
T	F	F
F	T	F
F	F	T

A biconditional is true only when the component statements have the same truth value.

Before we continue our work with truth tables, let's take a moment to summarize the basic definitions of symbolic logic.

THE DEFINITIONS OF SYMBOLIC LOGIC

1. **Negation** $\sim$: not
   The negation of a statement has the opposite meaning, as well as the opposite truth value, from the statement.
2. **Conjunction** $\wedge$: and
   The only case in which a conjunction is true is when both component statements are true.
3. **Disjunction** $\vee$: or
   The only case in which a disjunction is false is when both component statements are false.
4. **Conditional** $\rightarrow$: if–then
   The only case in which a conditional is false is when the first component statement, the antecedent, is true and the second component statement, the consequent, is false.
5. **Biconditional** $\leftrightarrow$: if and only if
   A biconditional is true only when the component statements have the same truth value.

4 Construct truth tables for biconditional statements.

EXAMPLE 4 Constructing a Truth Table

Construct a truth table for

$$(p \vee q) \leftrightarrow (\sim q \rightarrow p)$$

to determine whether the statement is a tautology.

Solution The statement is a biconditional because the biconditional symbol, $\leftrightarrow$, is outside the parentheses. We cannot determine the truth values for this biconditional until we determine the truth values for the statements in parentheses.

$$\boxed{(p \vee q)} \leftrightarrow \boxed{(\sim q \rightarrow p)}$$

We need a column with truth values for this statement.

We need a column with truth values for this statement.

The completed truth table for $(p \vee q) \leftrightarrow (\sim q \rightarrow p)$ appears as follows:

p	q	$p \vee q$	$\sim q$	$\sim q \rightarrow p$	$(p \vee q) \leftrightarrow (\sim q \rightarrow p)$
T	T	T	F	T	T
T	F	T	T	T	T
F	T	T	F	T	T
F	F	F	T	F	T

col. 1 ∨ col. 2   ~ col. 2   col. 4 → col. 1   col. 3 ↔ col. 5

We applied the definition of the biconditional to fill in the last column. In each case, the truth values of $p \vee q$ and $\sim q \rightarrow p$ are the same. Therefore, the biconditional $(p \vee q) \leftrightarrow (\sim q \rightarrow p)$ is true in each case. Because all cases are true, the biconditional is a tautology.

Construct a truth table for $(p \vee q) \leftrightarrow (\sim p \rightarrow q)$ to determine whether the statement is a tautology.

5 Determine the truth value of a compound statement for a specific case.

EXAMPLE 5 Determining the Truth Value of a Compound Statement

Your author recently received a letter from his credit card company that began as follows:

> Dear Mr. Bob Blitzer,
>
> I am pleased to inform you that a personal Super Million Dollar Prize Entry Number—665567010—has been assigned in your name as indicated above. <u>If your Super Million Dollar Prize Entry Number matches the winning preselected number and you return the number before the deadline stated below, you will win $1,000,000.00</u>. It's as simple as that.

Consider the claim in the underlined conditional statement. Suppose that your Super Million Dollar Prize Entry Number does not match the winning preselected number (those dirty rotten scoundrels!), you obediently return the number before the deadline, and you win only a free issue of a magazine (with the remaining 11 issues billed to your credit card). Under these conditions, can you sue the credit card company for making a false claim?

Solution Let's begin by assigning letters to the simple statements in the claim. We'll also indicate the truth value of each simple statement.

p: Your Super Million Dollar Prize Entry Number matches the winning preselected number. — false

q: You return the number before the stated deadline. — true

r: You win \$1,000,000.00. — false; To make matters worse, you were duped into buying a magazine subscription.

Now we can write the underlined claim in the letter to Bob in symbolic form.

If
your number matches the winning number
and
you return it before the stated deadline,
then
you win $1,000,000.00.

$$(p \quad \wedge \quad q) \quad \rightarrow \quad r$$

We substitute the truth values for p, q, and r to determine the truth value for the credit card company's claim.

$(p \wedge q) \rightarrow r$	This is the claim in symbolic form.
$(\text{F} \wedge \text{T}) \rightarrow \text{F}$	Substitute the truth values for the simple statements.
$\text{F} \rightarrow \text{F}$	Replace F $\wedge$ T with F. Conjunction is false when one part is false.
T	Replace F $\rightarrow$ F with T. The conditional is true with a false antecedent and a false consequent.

Our truth-value analysis indicates that you cannot sue the credit card company for making a false claim. Call it conditional trickery, but the company's claim is true.

CHECK POINT 5

Consider the underlined claim in the letter in Example 5. Suppose that your number actually matches the winning preselected number, you do not return the number, and you win nothing. Under these conditions, determine the claim's truth value.

BLITZER BONUS

CONDITIONAL WISHFUL THINKING

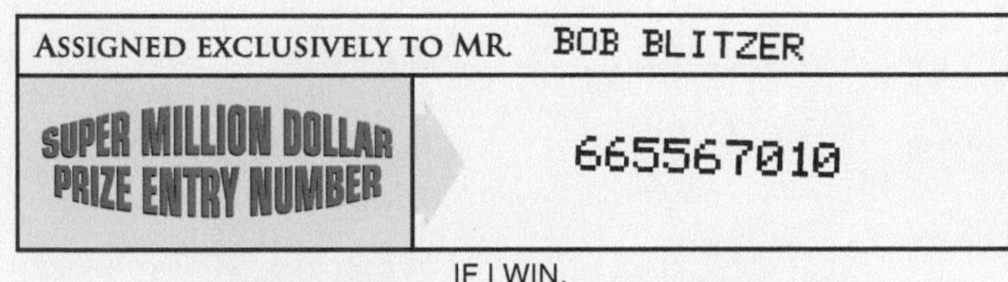

ASSIGNED EXCLUSIVELY TO MR.	BOB BLITZER
SUPER MILLION DOLLAR PRIZE ENTRY NUMBER	665567010

IF I WIN,

I PREFER MY \$1,000,000 PRIZE:

- ☐ in installments of \$33,333.34 annually until the entire \$1,000,000.00 is paid out
- ☐ lump-sum settlement of \$546,783.00

Bob's credit card company is too kind. It even offers options as to how he wants to receive his million-dollar winnings. With this lure, people who do not think carefully might interpret the conditional claim in the letter to read as follows:

If you return your winning number and do so before the stated deadline, you win \$1,000,000.00.

This misreading is wishful thinking. There is no winning number to return. What there is, of course, is a deceptive attempt to sell magazines.

Exercise Set 4

Practice Exercises

In Exercises 1–16, construct a truth table for the given statement.

1. $p \rightarrow \sim q$
2. $\sim p \rightarrow q$
3. $\sim(q \rightarrow p)$
4. $\sim(p \rightarrow q)$
5. $(p \wedge q) \rightarrow (p \vee q)$
6. $(p \vee q) \rightarrow (p \wedge q)$
7. $(p \rightarrow q) \wedge \sim q$
8. $(p \rightarrow q) \wedge \sim p$
9. $(p \vee q) \rightarrow r$
10. $p \rightarrow (q \vee r)$
11. $r \rightarrow (p \wedge q)$
12. $r \rightarrow (p \vee q)$
13. $\sim r \wedge (\sim q \rightarrow p)$
14. $\sim r \wedge (q \rightarrow \sim p)$
15. $\sim(p \wedge r) \rightarrow (\sim q \vee r)$
16. $\sim(p \vee r) \rightarrow (\sim q \wedge r)$

In Exercises 17–32, construct a truth table for the given statement.

17. $p \leftrightarrow \sim q$
18. $\sim p \leftrightarrow q$
19. $\sim(p \leftrightarrow q)$
20. $\sim(q \leftrightarrow p)$
21. $(p \leftrightarrow q) \rightarrow p$
22. $(p \leftrightarrow q) \rightarrow q$
23. $(\sim p \leftrightarrow q) \rightarrow (\sim p \rightarrow q)$
24. $(p \leftrightarrow \sim q) \rightarrow (q \rightarrow \sim p)$
25. $[(p \wedge q) \wedge (q \rightarrow p)] \leftrightarrow (p \wedge q)$
26. $[(p \rightarrow q) \vee (p \wedge \sim p)] \leftrightarrow (\sim q \rightarrow \sim p)$
27. $(p \leftrightarrow q) \rightarrow \sim r$
28. $(p \rightarrow q) \leftrightarrow \sim r$
29. $(p \wedge r) \leftrightarrow \sim(q \vee r)$
30. $(p \vee r) \leftrightarrow \sim(q \wedge r)$
31. $[r \vee (\sim q \wedge p)] \leftrightarrow \sim p$
32. $[r \wedge (q \vee \sim p)] \leftrightarrow \sim q$

In Exercises 33–56, use a truth table to determine whether each statement is a tautology, a self-contradiction, or neither.

33. $[(p \rightarrow q) \wedge q] \rightarrow p$
34. $[(p \rightarrow q) \wedge p] \rightarrow q$
35. $[(p \rightarrow q) \wedge \sim q] \rightarrow \sim p$
36. $[(p \rightarrow q) \wedge \sim p] \rightarrow \sim q$
37. $[(p \vee q) \wedge p] \rightarrow \sim q$
38. $[(p \vee q) \wedge \sim q] \rightarrow p$
39. $(p \rightarrow q) \rightarrow (\sim p \vee q)$
40. $(q \rightarrow p) \rightarrow (p \vee \sim q)$
41. $(p \wedge q) \wedge (\sim p \vee \sim q)$
42. $(p \vee q) \wedge (\sim p \wedge \sim q)$
43. $\sim(p \wedge q) \leftrightarrow (\sim p \wedge \sim q)$
44. $\sim(p \vee q) \leftrightarrow (\sim p \wedge \sim q)$
45. $(p \rightarrow q) \leftrightarrow (q \rightarrow p)$
46. $(p \rightarrow q) \leftrightarrow (\sim p \rightarrow \sim q)$
47. $(p \rightarrow q) \leftrightarrow (\sim p \vee q)$
48. $(p \rightarrow q) \leftrightarrow (p \vee \sim q)$
49. $(p \leftrightarrow q) \leftrightarrow [(q \rightarrow p) \wedge (p \rightarrow q)]$
50. $(q \leftrightarrow p) \leftrightarrow [(p \rightarrow q) \wedge (q \rightarrow p)]$
51. $(p \wedge q) \leftrightarrow (\sim p \vee r)$
52. $(p \wedge q) \rightarrow (\sim q \vee r)$
53. $[(p \rightarrow q) \wedge (q \rightarrow r)] \rightarrow (p \rightarrow r)$
54. $[(p \rightarrow q) \wedge (q \rightarrow r)] \rightarrow (\sim r \rightarrow \sim p)$
55. $[(q \rightarrow r) \wedge (r \rightarrow \sim p)] \leftrightarrow (q \wedge p)$
56. $[(q \rightarrow \sim r) \wedge (\sim r \rightarrow p)] \leftrightarrow (q \wedge \sim p)$

In Exercises 57–64,

a. *Write each statement in symbolic form. Assign letters to simple statements that are not negated.*

b. *Construct a truth table for the symbolic statement in part (a).*

c. *Use the truth table to indicate one set of conditions that makes the compound statement false, or state that no such conditions exist.*

57. If you do homework right after class then you will not fall behind, and if you do not do homework right after class then you will.
58. If you do a little bit each day then you'll get by, and if you do not do a little bit each day then you won't.
59. If you "cut-and-paste" from the Internet and do not cite the source, then you will be charged with plagiarism.
60. If you take more than one class with a lot of reading, then you will not have free time and you'll be in the library until 1 A.M.
61. You'll be comfortable in your room if and only if you're honest with your roommate, or you won't enjoy the college experience.
62. I fail the course if and only if I rely on a used book with highlightings by an idiot, or I do not buy a used book.
63. I enjoy the course if and only if I choose the class based on the professor and not the course description.
64. I do not miss class if and only if they take attendance or there are pop quizzes.

In Exercises 65–74, determine the truth value for each statement when p is false, q is true, and r is false.

65. $\sim(p \rightarrow q)$
66. $\sim(p \leftrightarrow q)$
67. $\sim p \leftrightarrow q$
68. $\sim p \rightarrow q$
69. $q \rightarrow (p \wedge r)$
70. $(p \wedge r) \rightarrow q$
71. $(\sim p \wedge q) \leftrightarrow \sim r$
72. $\sim p \leftrightarrow (\sim q \wedge r)$
73. $\sim[(p \rightarrow \sim r) \leftrightarrow (r \wedge \sim p)]$
74. $\sim[(\sim p \rightarrow r) \leftrightarrow (p \vee \sim q)]$

Practice Plus

In Exercises 75–78, use grouping symbols to clarify the meaning of each statement. Then construct a truth table for the statement.

75. $p \rightarrow q \leftrightarrow p \wedge q \rightarrow \sim p$
76. $q \rightarrow p \leftrightarrow p \vee q \rightarrow \sim p$
77. $p \rightarrow \sim q \vee r \leftrightarrow p \wedge r$
78. $\sim p \rightarrow q \wedge r \leftrightarrow p \vee r$

In Exercises 79–82, construct a truth table for each statement. Then use the table to indicate one set of conditions that make the compound statement false, or state that no such conditions exist.

79. Loving a person is necessary for marrying that person, but not loving someone is sufficient for not marrying that person.
80. Studying hard is necessary for getting an A, but not studying hard is sufficient for not getting an A.
81. It is not true that being happy and living contentedly are necessary conditions for being wealthy.
82. It is not true that being wealthy is a sufficient condition for being happy and living contentedly.

Application Exercises

The bar graph shows the percentage of American adults who believed in God, Heaven, the devil, and Hell in 2008 compared with 2003.

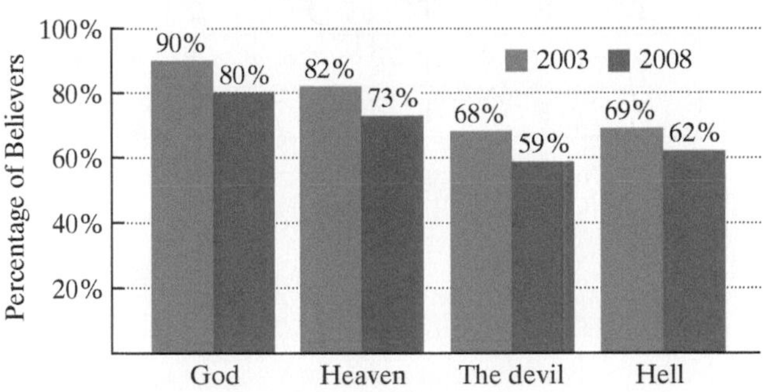

Source: Harris Interactive poll of 2201 adults Jan. 21–27, 2003, and 2126 adults Nov. 10–17, 2008

In Exercises 83–86, write each statement in symbolic form. (Increases or decreases in each simple statement refer to 2008 compared with 2003.) Then use the information in the graph to determine the truth value of each compound statement.

83. If there was an increase in the percentage who believed in God and a decrease in the percentage who believed in Heaven, then there was an increase in the percentage who believed in the devil.

84. If there was a decrease in the percentage who believed in God, then it is not the case that there was an increase in the percentage who believed in the devil or in Hell.

85. There was a decrease in the percentage who believed in God if and only if there was an increase in the percentage who believed in Heaven, or the percentage believing in the devil decreased.

86. There was an increase in the percentage who believed in God if and only if there was an increase in the percentage who believed in Heaven, and the percentage believing in Hell decreased.

Sociologists Joseph Kahl and Dennis Gilbert developed a six-tier model to portray the class structure of the United States. The bar graph gives the percentage of Americans who are members of each of the six social classes.

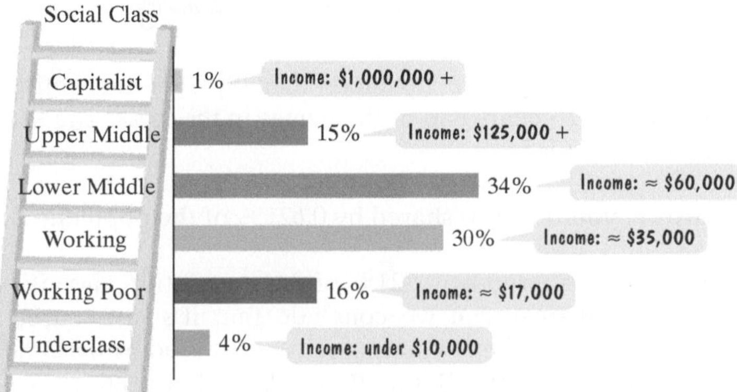

Source: James Henslin, *Sociology*, Eighth Edition, Allyn and Bacon, 2007.

In Exercises 87–90, write each statement in symbolic form. Then use the information given by the graph at the bottom of the previous column to determine the truth value of each compound statement.

87. Fifteen percent are capitalists or 34% are not members of the upper-middle class, if and only if the number of working poor exceeds the number belonging to the working class.

88. Fifteen percent are capitalists and 34% are not members of the upper-middle class, if and only if the number of working poor exceeds the number belonging to the working class.

89. If there are more people in the lower-middle class than in the capitalist and upper-middle classes combined, then 1% are capitalists and 34% belong to the upper-middle class.

90. If there are more people in the lower-middle class than in the capitalist and upper-middle classes combined, then 1% are capitalists or 34% belong to the upper-middle class.

Writing in Mathematics

91. Explain when conditional statements are true and when they are false.

92. Explain when biconditional statements are true and when they are false.

93. What is the difference between a tautology and a self-contradiction?

94. Based on the meaning of the inclusive *or*, explain why it is reasonable that if $p \vee q$ is true, then $\sim p \rightarrow q$ must also be true.

95. Based on the meaning of the inclusive *or*, explain why if $p \vee q$ is true, then $p \rightarrow \sim q$ is not necessarily true.

Critical Thinking Exercises

Make Sense? *In Exercises 96–99, determine whether each statement makes sense or does not make sense, and explain your reasoning.*

96. The statement "If $2 + 2 = 5$, then the moon is made of green cheese" is true in logic, but does not make much sense in everyday speech.

97. I'm working with a true conditional statement, but when I reverse the antecedent and the consequent, my new conditional statement is no longer true.

98. When asked the question "What is time?", the fourth-century Christian philosopher St. Augustine replied,

> "If you don't ask me, I know, but if you ask me, I don't know."

I constructed a truth table for St. Augustine's statement and discovered it is a tautology.

99. In "Computing Machines and Intelligence," the English mathematician Alan Turing (1912–1954) wrote,

> "If each man had a definite set of rules of conduct by which he regulated his life, he would be a machine, but there are no such rules, so men cannot be machines."

I constructed a truth table for Turing's statement and discovered it is a tautology.

In Exercises 100–103, determine whether each statement is true or false. If the statement is false, make the necessary change(s) to produce a true statement.

100. A conditional statement is false only when the consequent is true and the antecedent is false.

101. Some implications are not tautologies.

102. An equivalent form for a conditional statement is obtained by reversing the antecedent and consequent, and then negating the resulting statement.

103. A compound statement consisting of two simple statements that are both false can be true.

104. Consider the statement "If you get an A in the course, I'll take you out to eat." If you complete the course and I do take you out to eat, can you conclude that you got an A? Explain your answer.

In Exercises 105–106, the headings for the columns in the truth tables are missing. Fill in the statements to replace the missing headings. (More than one correct statement may be possible.)

105.

Do not repeat the statement from the third column.

p	q				
T	T	T	F	T	T
T	F	F	F	F	T
F	T	T	T	T	T
F	F	T	T	T	T

106.

Do not repeat the previous statement.

p	q				
T	T	T	T	F	F
T	F	T	F	T	T
F	T	T	F	T	T
F	F	F	F	T	T

OBJECTIVES

1 Use a truth table to show that statements are equivalent.

2 Write the contrapositive for a conditional statement.

3 Write the converse and inverse of a conditional statement.

5 Equivalent Statements and Variations of Conditional Statements

Actors Will Smith and Tommy Lee Jones

TOP U.S. LAST NAMES

Name	% of All Names
Smith	1.006%
Johnson	0.810%
Williams	0.699%
Brown	0.621%
Jones	0.621%

Source: Russell Ash, *The Top 10 of Everything*

The top U.S. last names shown above make up more than $3\frac{3}{4}\%$ of the entire population. One American in every 26 bears one of the names in the table. The list indicates that the following statement is true:

If your last name is Brown, your name is shared by 0.621% of the population.

Does this mean that if your name is shared by 0.621% of the population, then it's Brown? If your last name isn't Brown, can we conclude that it's not shared by 0.621% of the population? Furthermore, if your name is not shared by 0.621% of the population, can we conclude that it's not Brown? In this section, we will use truth tables and logic to unravel this verbal morass of conditional statements.

1 Use a truth table to show that statements are equivalent.

Equivalent Statements

Equivalent compound statements are made up of the same simple statements and have the same corresponding truth values for all true-false combinations of these simple statements. If a compound statement is true, then its equivalent statement must also be true. Likewise, if a compound statement is false, its equivalent statement must also be false.

Truth tables are used to show that two statements are equivalent. When translated into English, equivalencies can be used to gain a better understanding of English statements.

EXAMPLE 1 Showing That Statements Are Equivalent

a. Show that $p \vee \sim q$ and $\sim p \rightarrow \sim q$ are equivalent.

b. Use the result from part (a) to write a statement that is equivalent to

The bill receives majority approval or the bill does not become law.

Solution

a. Construct a truth table that shows the truth values for $p \vee \sim q$ and $\sim p \rightarrow \sim q$. The truth values for each statement are shown below.

p	q	$\sim q$	$p \vee \sim q$	$\sim p$	$\sim p \rightarrow \sim q$
T	T	F	T	F	T
T	F	T	T	F	T
F	T	F	F	T	F
F	F	T	T	T	T

Corresponding truth values are the same.

The table shows that the truth values for $p \vee \sim q$ and $\sim p \rightarrow \sim q$ are the same. Therefore, the statements are equivalent.

b. The statement

The bill receives majority approval or the bill does not become law

can be expressed in symbolic form using the following representations:

p: The bill receives majority approval.

q: The bill becomes law.

In symbolic form, the statement is $p \vee \sim q$. Based on the truth table in part (a), we know that an equivalent statement is $\sim p \rightarrow \sim q$. The equivalent statement can be expressed in words as

If the bill does not receive majority approval, then the bill does not become law.

Notice that the given statement and its equivalent are both true.

a. Show that $p \vee q$ and $\sim q \rightarrow p$ are equivalent.

b. Use the result from part (a) to write a statement that is equivalent to

I attend classes or I lose my scholarship.

A special symbol, $\equiv$, is used to show that two statements are equivalent. Because $p \vee \sim q$ and $\sim p \rightarrow \sim q$ are equivalent, we can write

$$p \vee \sim q \equiv \sim p \rightarrow \sim q \quad \text{or} \quad \sim p \rightarrow \sim q \equiv p \vee \sim q.$$

EXAMPLE 2 Showing That Statements Are Equivalent

Show that $\sim(\sim p) \equiv p$.

p	$\sim p$	$\sim(\sim p)$
T	F	T
F	T	F

Corresponding truth values are the same.

Solution Determine the truth values for $\sim(\sim p)$ and p. These are shown in the truth table at the left.

The truth values for $\sim(\sim p)$ were obtained by taking the opposite of each truth value for $\sim p$. The table shows that the truth values for $\sim(\sim p)$ and p are the same. Therefore, the statements are equivalent:

$$\sim(\sim p) \equiv p.$$

The equivalence in Example 2 illustrates that **the double negation of a statement is equivalent to the statement.** For example, the statement "It is not true that Ernest Hemingway was not a writer" means the same thing as "Ernest Hemingway was a writer."

STUDY TIP

A familiar algebraic statement should help you remember the logical equivalency

$$\sim(\sim p) \equiv p.$$

If a represents a number, then

$$-(-a) = a.$$

For example, $-(-4) = 4$.

CHECK POINT 2 Show that $\sim[\sim(\sim p)] \equiv \sim p$.

EXAMPLE 3 Equivalencies and Truth Tables

Select the statement that is not equivalent to

Miguel is blushing or sunburned.

a. If Miguel is blushing, then he is not sunburned.
b. Miguel is sunburned or blushing.
c. If Miguel is not blushing, then he is sunburned.
d. If Miguel is not sunburned, then he is blushing.

Solution To determine which of the choices is not equivalent to the given statement, begin by writing the given statement and the choices in symbolic form. Then construct a truth table and compare each statement's truth values to those of the given statement. The nonequivalent statement is the one that does not have exactly the same truth values as the given statement.

The simple statements that make up "Miguel is blushing or sunburned" can be represented as follows:

p: Miguel is blushing.
q: Miguel is sunburned.

Here are the symbolic representations for the given statement and the four choices:

Miguel is blushing or sunburned: $p \vee q$.

a. If Miguel is blushing, then he is not sunburned: $p \rightarrow \sim q$.
b. Miguel is sunburned or blushing: $q \vee p$.
c. If Miguel is not blushing, then he is sunburned: $\sim p \rightarrow q$.
d. If Miguel is not sunburned, then he is blushing: $\sim q \rightarrow p$.

Next, construct a truth table that contains the truth values for the given statement, $p \vee q$, as well as those for the four options. The truth table is shown as follows:

Equivalent (same corresponding truth values)

		Given		(a)	(b)		(c)	(d)
p	q	$p \vee q$	$\sim q$	$p \rightarrow \sim q$	$q \vee p$	$\sim p$	$\sim p \rightarrow q$	$\sim q \rightarrow p$
T	T	T	F	F	T	F	T	T
T	F	T	T	T	T	F	T	T
F	T	T	F	T	T	T	T	T
F	F	F	T	T	F	T	F	F

Not equivalent

The statement in option (a) does not have the same corresponding truth values as those for $p \vee q$. Therefore, this statement is not equivalent to the given statement.

In Example 3, we used a truth table to show that $p \vee q$ and $p \rightarrow \sim q$ are not equivalent. We can use our understanding of the inclusive *or* to see why the following English translations for these symbolic statements are not equivalent:

Miguel is blushing or sunburned.

If Miguel is blushing, then he is not sunburned.

Let us assume that the first statement is true. The inclusive *or* tells us that Miguel might be both blushing and sunburned. This means that the second statement might not be true. The fact that Miguel is blushing does not indicate that he is not sunburned; he might be both.

CHECK POINT 3 Select the statement that is not equivalent to

If it's raining, then I need a jacket.

a. It's not raining or I need a jacket.

b. I need a jacket or it's not raining.

c. If I need a jacket, then it's raining.

d. If I do not need a jacket, then it's not raining.

2 Write the contrapositive for a conditional statement.

Variations of the Conditional Statement $p \rightarrow q$

In Section 4, we learned that $p \rightarrow q$ is equivalent to $\sim q \rightarrow \sim p$. The truth value of a conditional statement does not change if the antecedent and the consequent are reversed and then both of them are negated. The **contrapositive** of a conditional statement is a statement obtained by reversing and negating the antecedent and the consequent.

p	q	$p \rightarrow q$	$\sim q \rightarrow \sim p$
T	T	T	T
T	F	F	F
F	T	T	T
F	F	T	T

$p \rightarrow q$ and $\sim q \rightarrow \sim p$ are equivalent.

A CONDITIONAL STATEMENT AND ITS EQUIVALENT CONTRAPOSITIVE

$$p \rightarrow q \equiv \sim q \rightarrow \sim p$$

The truth value of a conditional statement does not change if the antecedent and consequent are reversed and both are negated. The statement $\sim q \rightarrow \sim p$ is called the **contrapositive** of the conditional $p \rightarrow q$.

EXAMPLE 4 Writing Equivalent Contrapositives

Write the contrapositive for each of the following statements:

a. If you live in Los Angeles, then you live in California.

b. If the patient is not breathing, then the patient is dead.

c. If all people obey the law, then prisons are not needed.

d. $\sim(p \wedge q) \rightarrow r$

Solution In parts (a)–(c), we write each statement in symbolic form. Then we form the contrapositive by reversing and negating the antecedent and the consequent. Finally, we translate the symbolic form of the contrapositive back into English.

a. Use the following representations:

p: You live in Los Angeles.

q: You live in California.

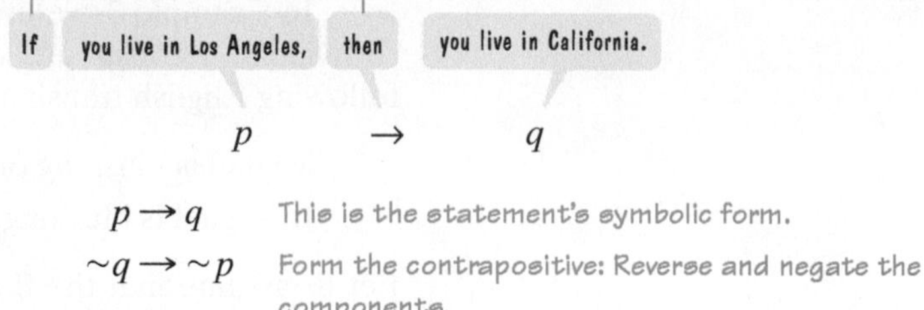

$p \rightarrow q$ This is the statement's symbolic form.

$\sim q \rightarrow \sim p$ Form the contrapositive: Reverse and negate the components.

Translating $\sim q \rightarrow \sim p$ into English, the contrapositive is

If you do not live in California, then you do not live in Los Angeles.

Notice that the given conditional statement and its contrapositive are both true.

b. Use the following representations:

p: The patient is breathing.

q: The patient is dead.

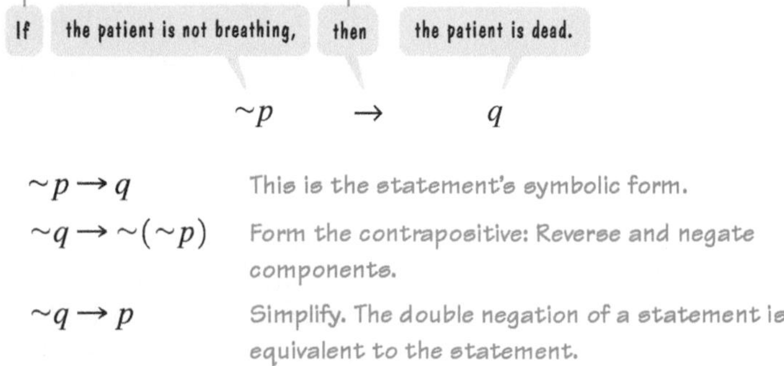

$\sim p \rightarrow q$ This is the statement's symbolic form.

$\sim q \rightarrow \sim(\sim p)$ Form the contrapositive: Reverse and negate components.

$\sim q \rightarrow p$ Simplify. The double negation of a statement is equivalent to the statement.

Translating $\sim q \rightarrow p$ into English, the contrapositive is

If the patient is not dead, then the patient is breathing.

c. Use the following representations:

p: All people obey the law.

q: Prisons are needed.

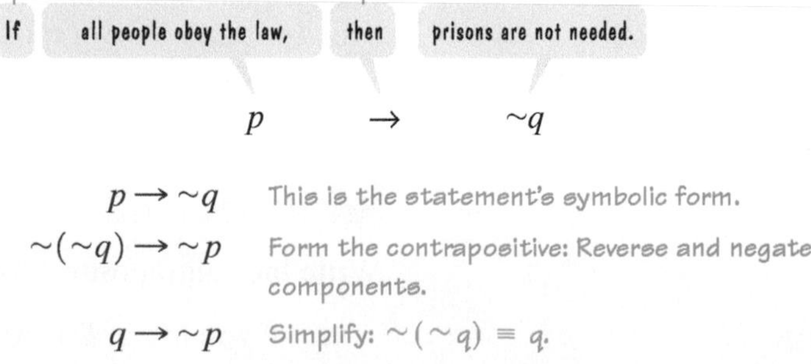

$p \rightarrow \sim q$ This is the statement's symbolic form.

$\sim(\sim q) \rightarrow \sim p$ Form the contrapositive: Reverse and negate components.

$q \rightarrow \sim p$ Simplify: $\sim(\sim q) \equiv q$.

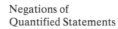

Negations of Quantified Statements

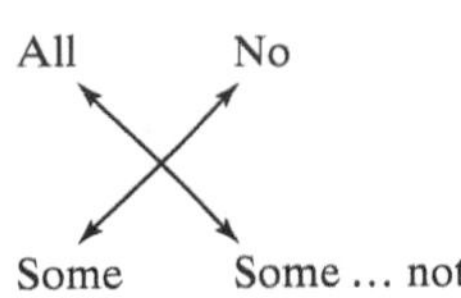

Recall, as shown in the margin, that the negation of *all* is *some ... not*. Using this negation and translating $q \rightarrow \sim p$ into English, the contrapositive is

If prisons are needed, then some people do not obey the law.

d. $\sim(p \wedge q) \rightarrow r$ This is the given symbolic statement.

$\sim r \rightarrow \sim[\sim(p \wedge q)]$ Form the contrapositive: Reverse and negate the components.

$\sim r \rightarrow (p \wedge q)$ Simplify: $\sim[\sim(p \wedge q)] \equiv p \wedge q$.

The contrapositive of $\sim(p \wedge q) \rightarrow r$ is $\sim r \rightarrow (p \wedge q)$. Using the dominance of connectives, the contrapositive can be expressed as $\sim r \rightarrow p \wedge q$.

CHECK POINT 4 Write the contrapositive for each of the following statements:

a. If you can read this, then you're driving too closely.

b. If you do not have clean underwear, it's time to do the laundry.

c. If all students are honest, then supervision during exams is not required.

d. $\sim(p \vee r) \rightarrow \sim q$

---

3 Write the converse and inverse of a conditional statement.

The truth value of a conditional statement does not change if the antecedent and the consequent are reversed and then both of them are negated. But what happens to the conditional's truth value if just one, but not both, of these changes is made? If the antecedent and the consequent are reversed but not negated, the resulting statement is called the **converse** of the conditional statement. By negating both the antecedent and the consequent but not reversing them, we obtain the **inverse** of the conditional statement.

VARIATIONS OF THE CONDITIONAL STATEMENT

Name	Symbolic Form	English Translation
Conditional	$p \rightarrow q$	If p, then q.
Converse	$q \rightarrow p$	If q, then p.
Inverse	$\sim p \rightarrow \sim q$	If not p, then not q.
Contrapositive	$\sim q \rightarrow \sim p$	If not q, then not p.

Let's see what happens to the truth value of a true conditional statement when we form its converse and its inverse.

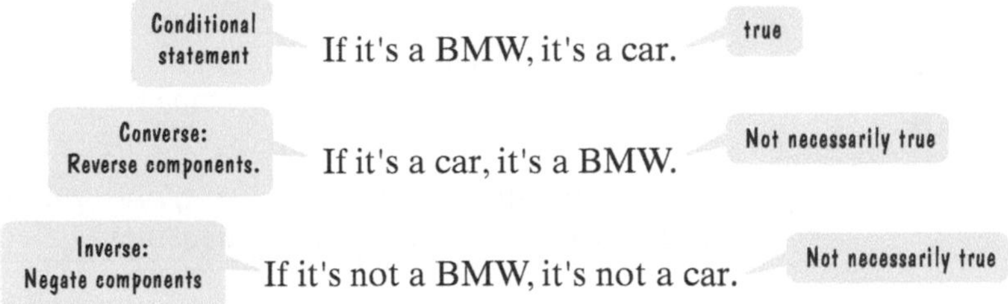

These statements illustrate that if a conditional statement is true, its converse and inverse are not necessarily true. Because the equivalent of a true statement must be true, we see that a conditional statement is not equivalent to its converse or its inverse.

The relationships among the truth values for a conditional statement, its converse, its inverse, and its contrapositive are shown in the truth table that follows:

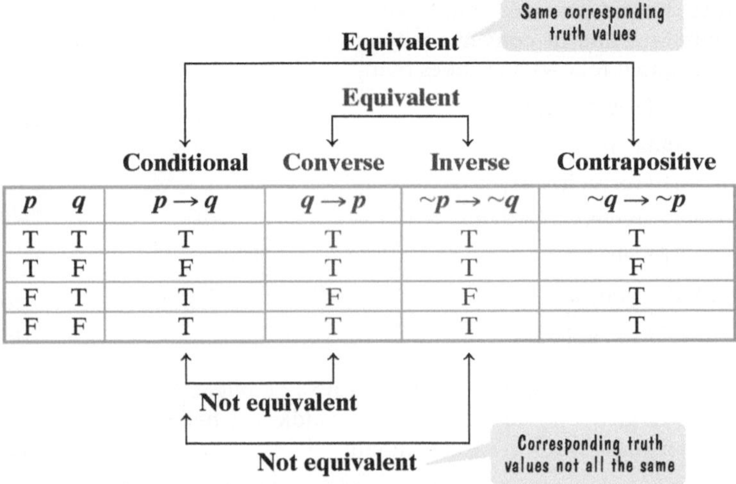

p	q	$p \rightarrow q$	$q \rightarrow p$	$\sim p \rightarrow \sim q$	$\sim q \rightarrow \sim p$
T	T	T	T	T	T
T	F	F	T	T	F
F	T	T	F	F	T
F	F	T	T	T	T

The truth table on the previous page confirms that a conditional statement is equivalent to its contrapositive. The table also shows that a conditional statement is not equivalent to its converse; in some cases they have the same truth value, but in other cases they have opposite truth values. Also, a conditional statement is not equivalent to its inverse. By contrast, the converse and the inverse are equivalent to each other.

EXAMPLE 5 Writing Variations of a Conditional Statement

The following conditional statement is surprisingly true:

If it's a lead pencil, then it does not contain lead.

(The so-called lead is actually a mixture of graphite and clay.) Write the statement's converse, inverse, and contrapositive.

Solution Use the following representations:

p: It's a lead pencil.

q: It contains lead.

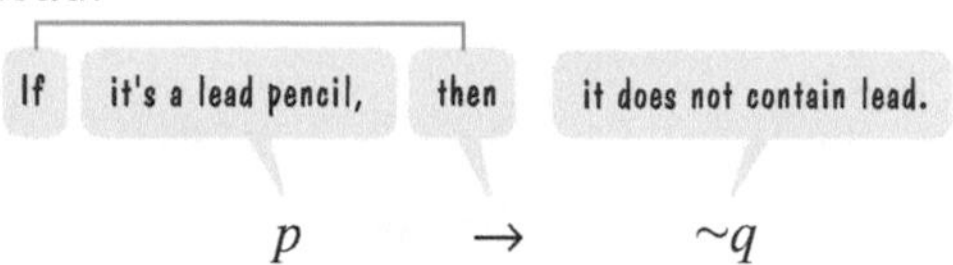

$$p \quad \rightarrow \quad {\sim}q$$

We now work with $p \rightarrow {\sim}q$ to form the converse, inverse, and contrapositive. We then translate the symbolic form of each statement back into English.

	Symbolic Statement	English Translation
Given Conditional Statement	$p \rightarrow {\sim}q$	If it's a lead pencil, then it does not contain lead. (true)
Converse: Reverse the components of $p \rightarrow {\sim}q$.	${\sim}q \rightarrow p$	If it does not contain lead, then it's a lead pencil. (not necessarily true)
Inverse: Negate the components of $p \rightarrow {\sim}q$.	${\sim}p \rightarrow {\sim}({\sim}q)$ simplifies to ${\sim}p \rightarrow q$	If it is not a lead pencil, then it contains lead. (not necessarily true)
Contrapositive: Reverse and negate the components of $p \rightarrow {\sim}q$.	${\sim}({\sim}q) \rightarrow {\sim}p$ simplifies to $q \rightarrow {\sim}p$	If it contains lead, then it's not a lead pencil. (true)

Write the converse, inverse, and contrapositive of the following statement:

If you are in Iran, then you don't see a Club Med.

BLITZER BONUS

CONVERSES IN *ALICE'S ADVENTURES IN WONDERLAND*

Alice has a problem with logic: She believes that a conditional and its converse mean the same thing. In the passage that follows, she states that

If I say it, I mean it

is the same as

If I mean it, I say it.

She is corrected, told that

If I eat it, I see it

is not the same as

If I see it, I eat it.

"Come, we shall have some fun now" thought Alice. "I'm glad they've begun asking riddles—I believe I can guess that," she added aloud.

"Do you mean that you think you can find out the answer to it?" said the March Hare.

"Exactly so." said Alice.

"Then you should say what you mean," the March Hare went on.

"I do," Alice hastily replied; "at least—at least I mean what I say—that's the same thing, you know."

"Not the same thing a bit!" said the Hatter. "Why, you might just as well say that 'I see what I eat' is the same thing as 'I eat what I see'!"

"You might just as well say," added the March Hare, "that 'I like what I get' is the same thing as 'I get what I like'!"

"You might just as well say," added the Dormouse, which seemed to be talking in its sleep, "that 'I breathe when I sleep' is the same thing as 'I sleep when I breathe'!"

Exercise Set 5

Practice Exercises

1. a. Use a truth table to show that $\sim p \rightarrow q$ and $p \vee q$ are equivalent.
   b. Use the result from part (a) to write a statement that is equivalent to

   If the United States does not energetically support the development of solar-powered cars, then it will suffer increasing atmospheric pollution.

2. a. Use a truth table to show that $p \rightarrow q$ and $\sim p \vee q$ are equivalent.
   b. Use the result from part (a) to write a statement that is equivalent to

   If a number is even, then it is divisible by 2.

In Exercises 3–14, use a truth table to determine whether the two statements are equivalent.

3. $\sim p \rightarrow q, q \rightarrow \sim p$
4. $\sim p \rightarrow q, p \rightarrow \sim q$
5. $(p \rightarrow \sim q) \wedge (\sim q \rightarrow p), p \leftrightarrow \sim q$
6. $(\sim p \rightarrow q) \wedge (q \rightarrow \sim p), \sim p \leftrightarrow q$
7. $(p \wedge q) \wedge r, p \wedge (q \wedge r)$
8. $(p \vee q) \vee r, p \vee (q \vee r)$
9. $(p \wedge q) \vee r, p \wedge (q \vee r)$
10. $(p \vee q) \wedge r, p \vee (q \wedge r)$
11. $(p \vee r) \rightarrow \sim q, (\sim p \wedge \sim r) \rightarrow q$
12. $(p \wedge \sim r) \rightarrow q, (\sim p \vee r) \rightarrow \sim q$
13. $\sim p \rightarrow (q \vee \sim r), (r \wedge \sim q) \rightarrow p$
14. $\sim p \rightarrow (\sim q \wedge r), (\sim r \vee q) \rightarrow p$
15. Select the statement that is equivalent to

    I saw the original *King Kong* or the 2005 version.

    a. If I did not see the original *King Kong*, I saw the 2005 version.
    b. I saw both the original *King Kong* and the 2005 version.
    c. If I saw the original *King Kong*, I did not see the 2005 version.
    d. If I saw the 2005 version, I did not see the original *King Kong*.
16. Select the statement that is equivalent to

    Citizen Kane or *Howard the Duck* appears in a list of greatest U.S. movies.

    a. If *Citizen Kane* appears in the list of greatest U.S. movies, *Howard the Duck* does not.
    b. If *Howard the Duck* does not appear in the list of greatest U.S. movies, then *Citizen Kane* does.
    c. Both *Citizen Kane* and *Howard the Duck* appear in a list of greatest U.S. movies.
    d. If *Howard the Duck* appears in the list of greatest U.S. movies, *Citizen Kane* does not.
17. Select the statement that is *not* equivalent to

    It is not true that Sondheim and Picasso are both musicians.

    a. Sondheim is not a musician or Picasso is not a musician.
    b. If Sondheim is a musician, then Picasso is not a musician.
    c. Sondheim is not a musician and Picasso is not a musician.
    d. If Picasso is a musician, then Sondheim is not a musician.
18. Select the statement that is *not* equivalent to

    It is not true that England and Africa are both countries.

    a. If England is a country, then Africa is not a country.
    b. England is not a country and Africa is not a country.
    c. England is not a country or Africa is not a country.
    d. If Africa is a country, then England is not a country.

In Exercises 19–30, write the converse, inverse, and contrapositive of each statement.

19. If I am in Chicago, then I am in Illinois.
20. If I am in Birmingham, then I am in the South.
21. If the stereo is playing, then I cannot hear you.
22. If it is blue, then it is not an apple.
23. "If you don't laugh, you die." (humorist Alan King)
24. "If it doesn't fit, you must acquit." (lawyer Johnnie Cochran)
25. If the president is telling the truth, then all troops were withdrawn.
26. If the review session is successful, then no students fail the test.
27. If all institutions place profit above human need, then some people suffer.
28. If all hard workers are successful, then some people are not hard workers.
29. $\sim q \rightarrow \sim r$
30. $\sim p \rightarrow r$

Practice Plus

In Exercises 31–38, express each statement in "if... then" form. (More than one correct wording in "if... then" form may be possible.) Then write the statement's converse, inverse, and contrapositive.

31. All people who diet lose weight.
32. All senators are politicians.
33. No vehicle that has no flashing light on top is an ambulance.
34. All people who are not fearful are crazy.
35. Passing the bar exam is a necessary condition for being an attorney.
36. Being a citizen is a necessary condition for voting.
37. Being a pacifist is sufficient for not being a warmonger.
38. Being a writer is sufficient for not being illiterate.

Application Exercises

The Corruption Perceptions Index uses perceptions of the general public, business people, and risk analysts to rate countries by how likely they are to accept bribes. The ratings are on a scale from 0 to 10, where higher scores represent less corruption. The graph shows the corruption ratings for the world's least corrupt and most corrupt countries. (The rating for the United States is 7.6.) Use the graph to solve Exercises 39–40.

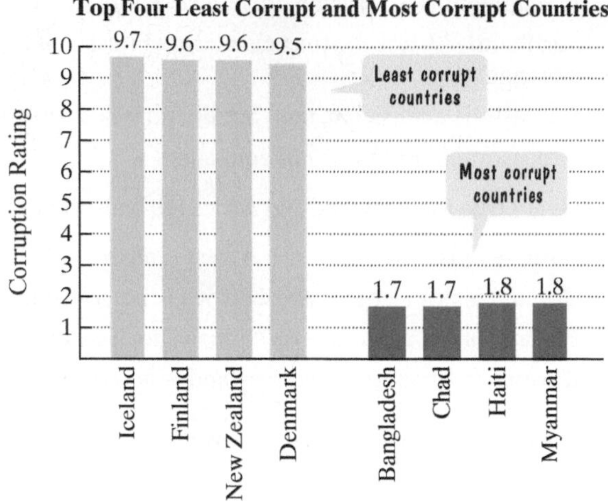

Source: Transparency International, *Corruption Perceptions Index*

39. a. Consider the statement

If the country is Finland, then the corruption rating is 9.6.

Use the information given by the graph to determine the truth value of this conditional statement.

b. Write the converse, inverse, and contrapositive of the statement in part (a). Then use the information given by the graph to determine whether each statement is true or not necessarily true.

40. a. Consider the statement

If the country is Haiti, then the corruption rating is 1.8.

Use the information given by the graph to determine the truth value of this conditional statement.

b. Write the converse, inverse, and contrapositive of the statement in part (a). Then use the information given by the graph to determine whether each statement is true or not necessarily true.

Writing in Mathematics

41. What are equivalent statements?

42. Describe how to determine if two statements are equivalent.

43. Describe how to obtain the contrapositive of a conditional statement.

44. Describe how to obtain the converse and the inverse of a conditional statement.

45. Give an example of a conditional statement that is true, but whose converse and inverse are not necessarily true. Try to make the statement somewhat different from the conditional statements that you have encountered throughout this section. Explain why the converse and the inverse that you wrote are not necessarily true.

46. Read the most recent Blitzer Bonus. The Dormouse's last statement is the setup for a joke. The punchline, delivered by the Hatter to the Dormouse, is, "For you, it's the same thing." Explain the joke. What does this punchline have to do with the difference between a conditional and a biconditional statement?

Critical Thinking Exercises

Make Sense? *In Exercises 47–50, determine whether each statement makes sense or does not make sense, and explain your reasoning.*

47. A conditional statement can sometimes be true if its contrapositive is false.

48. A conditional statement can never be false if its converse is true.

49. The inverse of a statement's converse is the statement's contrapositive.

50. Groucho Marx stated, "I cannot say that I do not disagree with you," which is equivalent to asserting that I disagree with you.

Group Exercise

51. Can you think of an advertisement in which the person using a product is extremely attractive or famous? It is true that if you are this attractive or famous person, then you use the product. (Or at least pretend, for monetary gain, that you use the product!) In order to get you to buy the product, here is what the advertisers would *like* you to believe: If I use this product, then I will be just like this attractive or famous person. This, the converse, is not necessarily true and, for most of us, is unfortunately false. Each group member should find an example of this kind of deceptive advertising to share with the other group members.

OBJECTIVES

1 Write the negation of a conditional statement.
2 Use De Morgan's laws.

6 Negations of Conditional Statements and De Morgan's Laws

It was suggested that by itemizing deductions, you would pay less in taxes. Not only did you drown in paperwork, but the suggestion turned out to be false. Your taxing situation can be summarized by negating a conditional statement.

1 Write the negation of a conditional statement.

The Negation of the Conditional Statement $p \rightarrow q$

Suppose that your accountant makes the following statement:

> If you itemize deductions, then you pay less in taxes.

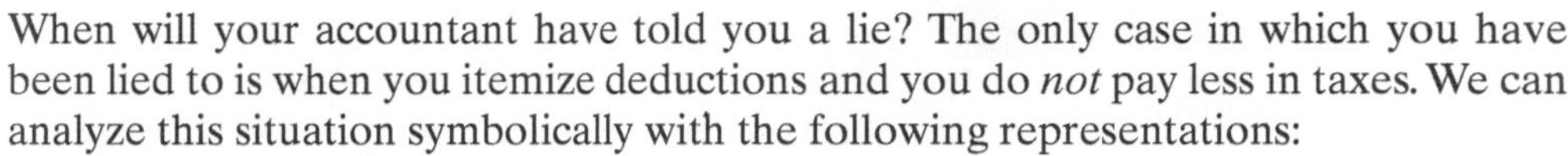

When will your accountant have told you a lie? The only case in which you have been lied to is when you itemize deductions and you do *not* pay less in taxes. We can analyze this situation symbolically with the following representations:

p: You itemize deductions.

q: You pay less in taxes.

We represent each compound statement in symbolic form.

$p \rightarrow q$: If you itemize deductions, then you pay less in taxes.

$p \wedge \sim q$: You itemize deductions and you do not pay less in taxes.

The truth table that follows shows that the negation of $p \rightarrow q$ is $p \wedge \sim q$.

p	q	$p \rightarrow q$	$\sim q$	$p \wedge \sim q$
T	T	T	F	F
T	F	F	T	T
F	T	T	F	F
F	F	T	T	F

These columns have opposite truth values, so $p \wedge \sim q$ negates $p \rightarrow q$.

THE NEGATION OF A CONDITIONAL STATEMENT

The negation of $p \rightarrow q$ is $p \wedge \sim q$. This can be expressed as

$$\sim(p \rightarrow q) \equiv p \wedge \sim q.$$

To form the negation of a conditional statement, leave the antecedent (the first part) unchanged, change the *if–then* connective to *and*, and negate the consequent (the second part).

EXAMPLE 1 Writing the Negation of a Conditional Statement

Write the negation of

If too much homework is given, a class should not be taken.

Solution Use the following representations:

p: Too much homework is given.

q: A class should be taken.

The symbolic form of the conditional statement is $p \rightarrow \sim q$.

$p \rightarrow \sim q$	This is the given statement in symbolic form.
$p \wedge \sim(\sim q)$	Form the negation: Copy the antecedent, change $\rightarrow$ to $\wedge$, and negate the consequent.
$p \wedge q$	Simplify: $\sim(\sim q) \equiv q$.

Translating $p \wedge q$ into English, the negation of the given statement is

Too much homework is given and the class should be taken.

Write the negation of

If you do not have a fever, you do not have the flu.

The box that follows summarizes what we have learned about conditional statements:

STUDY TIP

Don't confuse the inverse of $p \rightarrow q$ with the negation of $p \rightarrow q$. You obtain the inverse, $\sim p \rightarrow \sim q$, which is an *if–then* statement, by negating the two component statements. However, this process does not make the inverse the negation. The negation of $p \rightarrow q$ is $p \wedge \sim q$, which is an *and* statement.

THE CONDITIONAL STATEMENT $p \rightarrow q$

Contrapositive

$p \rightarrow q$ is equivalent to $\sim q \rightarrow \sim p$ (the contrapositive).

Converse and Inverse

1. $p \rightarrow q$ is not equivalent to $q \rightarrow p$ (the converse).
2. $p \rightarrow q$ is not equivalent to $\sim p \rightarrow \sim q$ (the inverse).

Negation

The negation of $p \rightarrow q$ is $p \wedge \sim q$.

2 Use De Morgan's laws.

De Morgan's Laws

De Morgan's laws, named after the English mathematician Augustus De Morgan (1806–1871), can be applied to sets:

$$(A \cap B)' = A' \cup B'$$
$$(A \cup B)' = A' \cap B'.$$

Similar relationships apply to the statements of symbolic logic:

$$\sim(p \wedge q) \equiv \sim p \vee \sim q$$
$$\sim(p \vee q) \equiv \sim p \wedge \sim q.$$

Here is a truth table that serves as a deductive proof for the first of these two equivalences:

p	q	$p \wedge q$	$\sim(p \wedge q)$	$\sim p$	$\sim q$	$\sim p \vee \sim q$
T	T	T	F	F	F	F
T	F	F	T	F	T	T
F	T	F	T	T	F	T
F	F	F	T	T	T	T

Corresponding truth values are the same, proving that $\sim(p \wedge q) \equiv \sim p \vee \sim q$.

We can prove that $\sim(p \vee q) \equiv \sim p \wedge \sim q$ in a similar manner. Do this now by constructing a truth table and showing that $\sim(p \vee q)$ and $\sim p \wedge \sim q$ have the same corresponding truth values.

DE MORGAN'S LAWS

1. $\sim(p \wedge q) \equiv \sim p \vee \sim q$
2. $\sim(p \vee q) \equiv \sim p \wedge \sim q$

EXAMPLE 2 Using a De Morgan Law

Write a statement that is equivalent to

It is not true that Atlanta and California are cities.

Solution Let p and q represent the following statements:

p: Atlanta is a city.

q: California is a city.

The statement is of the form $\sim(p \wedge q)$. An equivalent statement is $\sim p \vee \sim q$. We can translate this as

Atlanta is not a city or California is not a city.

CHECK POINT 2 Write a statement that is equivalent to

It is not true that Bart Simpson and Tony Soprano are cartoon characters.

EXAMPLE 3 Using a De Morgan Law

The underlined portion of the following quote is an equivalent paraphrase of the famous "I have a dream speech" given by Martin Luther King, Jr. in 1963 during the March on Washington for civil rights:

AP Wide World Photos

"I have a dream that my four little children will one day live in a nation where <u>it is not true that they will be judged by the color of their skin or not by the content of their character</u>. I have a dream today."

Write a statement that is equivalent to the underlined passage.

Solution Let p and q represent the following statements:

p: My children will be judged by the color of their skin.

q: My children will be judged by the content of their character.

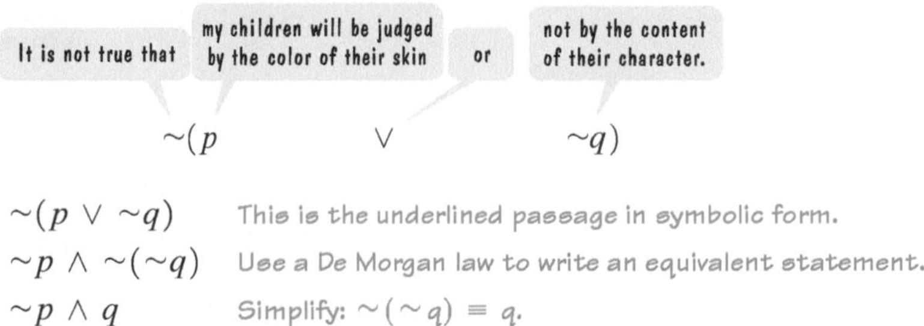

$\sim(p \vee \sim q)$ This is the underlined passage in symbolic form.

$\sim p \wedge \sim(\sim q)$ Use a De Morgan law to write an equivalent statement.

$\sim p \wedge q$ Simplify: $\sim(\sim q) \equiv q$.

Translating $\sim p \wedge q$ into English, a statement that is equivalent to the underlined passage is

My children will not be judged by the color of their skin but by the content of their character.

CHECK POINT 3 Write a statement that is equivalent to

It is not true that you leave by 5 P.M. or you do not arrive home on time.

De Morgan's laws can be used to write the negation of a compound statement that is a conjunction ($\wedge$, *and*) or a disjunction ($\vee$, *or*).

STUDY TIP

In addition to the procedures for negating conjunctions and disjunctions that are shown in the box, remember that we also have a rule for negating conditionals:

$$\sim(p \rightarrow q) \equiv p \wedge \sim q.$$

DE MORGAN'S LAWS AND NEGATIONS

1. $\sim(p \wedge q) \equiv \sim p \vee \sim q$
   The negation of $p \wedge q$ is $\sim p \vee \sim q$. To negate a conjunction, negate each component statement and change *and* to *or*.
2. $\sim(p \vee q) \equiv \sim p \wedge \sim q$
   The negation of $p \vee q$ is $\sim p \wedge \sim q$. To negate a disjunction, negate each component statement and change *or* to *and*.

We can apply these rules to English conjunctions or disjunctions and immediately obtain their negations without having to introduce symbolic representations.

EXAMPLE 4 Negating Conjunctions and Disjunctions

Write the negation for each of the following statements:

a. All students do laundry on weekends and I do not.

b. Some college professors are entertaining lecturers or I'm bored.

Negations of Quantified Statements

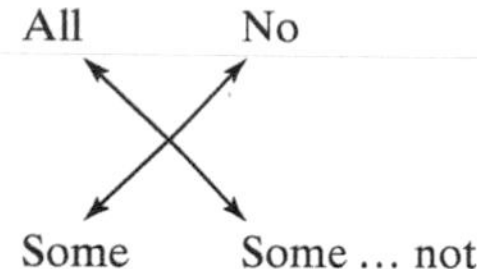

Solution To negate some of the simple statements, we use the negations of quantified statements shown in the margin.

a. Conjunction:

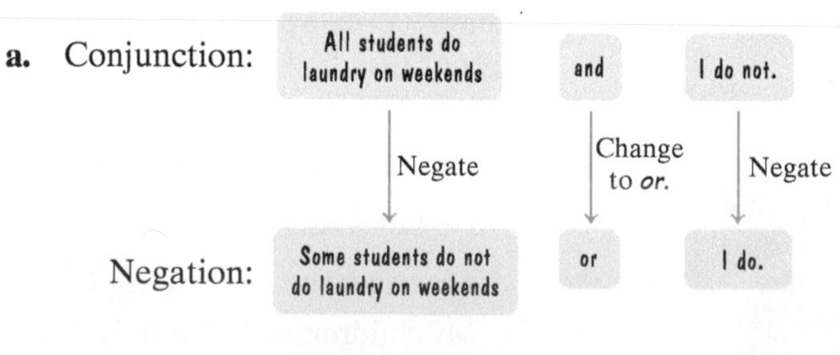

Negation:

b. Disjunction:

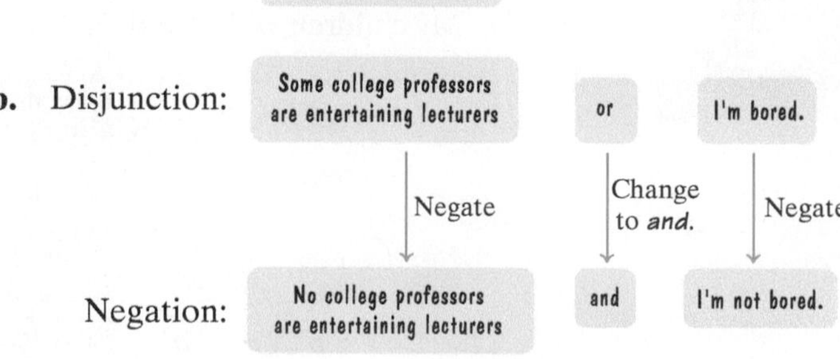

Negation:

CHECK POINT 4 Write the negation for each of the following statements:

a. All horror movies are scary and some are funny.

b. Your workouts are strenuous or you do not get stronger.

EXAMPLE 5 Using a De Morgan Law to Formulate a Contrapositive

Write a statement that is equivalent to

If it rains, I do not go outdoors and I study.

Solution We begin by writing the conditional statement in symbolic form. Let p, q, and r represent the following simple statements:

p: It rains.
q: I go outdoors.
r: I study.

Using these representations, the given conditional statement can be expressed in symbolic form as

$$p \rightarrow (\sim q \wedge r).$$ If it rains, I do not go outdoors and I study.

An equivalent statement is the contrapositive.

$$\sim(\sim q \wedge r) \rightarrow \sim p$$ Form the contrapositive: Reverse and negate the components.

$$[\sim(\sim q) \vee \sim r] \rightarrow \sim p$$ Use a De Morgan law to negate the conjunction: Negate each component and change $\wedge$ to $\vee$.

$$(q \vee \sim r) \rightarrow \sim p$$ Simplify: $\sim(\sim q) \equiv q$.

Thus,

$$p \rightarrow (\sim q \wedge r) \equiv (q \vee \sim r) \rightarrow \sim p.$$

Using the representations for p, q, and r, a statement that is equivalent to "If it rains, I do not go outdoors and I study" is

If I go outdoors or I do not study, it is not raining.

Write a statement that is equivalent to:

If it is not windy, we can swim and we cannot sail.

BLITZER BONUS

A GÖDELIAN UNIVERSE

At the age of 10, Czech mathematician Kurt Gödel (1906–1978) was studying mathematics, religion, and several languages. By age 25 he had produced what many mathematicians consider the most important result of twentieth-century mathematics: Gödel proved that all deductive systems eventually give rise to statements that cannot be proved to be either true or false within that system. Take someone who says "I am lying." If he is then he isn't, and if he isn't then he is. There is no way to determine whether the statement is true or false. There are similar undecidable statements in every branch of mathematics, from number theory to algebra.

Gödel's Theorem suggests infinitely many layers, none of which are capable of capturing all truth in one logical system. Gödel showed that statements arise in a system that cannot be proved or disproved within that system. To prove them, one must ascend to a "richer" system in which the previous undecidable statement can now be proved, but this richer system will in turn lead to new statements that cannot be proved, and so on. The process goes on forever.

Is the universe Gödelian in the sense there is no end to the discovery of its mathematical laws and in which the ultimate reality is always out of reach? The situation is echoed in the painting *The Two Mysteries* by René Magritte. A small picture of a pipe is shown with a caption that asserts (to translate from the French) "This is not a pipe." Above the fake pipe is a presumably genuine larger pipe, but it too is painted on the canvas. In Magritte's Gödelian universe, reality is infinitely layered, and it is impossible to say what reality really is.

René Magritte (1898–1967) *Les Deux Mystères (The Two Mysteries)*, 1966, oil on canvas, 65 × 80 cm. Private Collection. Phototheque R. Magritte–ADAGP/Art Resource, NY. © 2008 C. Herscovici, Brussels/Artists Rights Society (ARS), New York.

Exercise Set 6

Practice Exercises

In Exercises 1–10, write the negation of each conditional statement.

1. If I am in Los Angeles, then I am in California.
2. If I am in Houston, then I am in Texas.
3. If it is purple, then it is not a carrot.
4. If the TV is playing, then I cannot concentrate.
5. If he doesn't, I will.
6. If she says yes, he says no.
7. If there is a blizzard, then all schools are closed.
8. If there is a tax cut, then all people have extra spending money.
9. $\sim q \rightarrow \sim r$
10. $\sim p \rightarrow r$

In Exercises 11–26, use De Morgan's laws to write a statement that is equivalent to the given statement.

11. It is not true that Australia and China are both islands.
12. It is not true that Florida and California are both peninsulas.
13. It is not the case that my high school encouraged creativity and diversity.
14. It is not the case that the course covers logic and dream analysis.
15. It is not the case that Jewish scripture gives a clear indication of a heaven or an afterlife.
16. It is not true that Martin Luther King, Jr. supported violent protest or the Vietnam war.
17. It is not the case that the United States has eradicated poverty or racism.
18. It is not the case that the movie is interesting or entertaining.
19. $\sim(\sim p \wedge q)$
20. $\sim(p \vee \sim q)$
21. If you attend lecture and study, you succeed.
22. If you suffer from synesthesia, you can literally taste music and smell colors.
23. If he does not cook, his wife or child does.
24. If it is Saturday or Sunday, I do not work.
25. $p \rightarrow (q \vee \sim r)$
26. $p \rightarrow (\sim q \wedge \sim r)$

In Exercises 27–38, write the negation of each statement.

27. I'm going to Seattle or San Francisco.
28. This course covers logic or statistics.
29. I study or I do not pass.
30. I give up tobacco or I am not healthy.
31. I am not going and he is going.
32. I do not apply myself and I succeed.
33. A bill becomes law and it does not receive majority approval.
34. They see the show and they do not have tickets.
35. $p \vee \sim q$
36. $\sim p \vee q$
37. $p \wedge (q \vee r)$
38. $p \vee (q \wedge r)$

In Exercises 39–46, determine which, if any, of the three given statements are equivalent. You may use information about a conditional statement's converse, inverse, or contrapositive, De Morgan's laws, or truth tables.

39. **a.** If he is guilty, then he does not take a lie-detector test.
    b. He is not guilty or he takes a lie-detector test.
    c. If he is not guilty, then he takes a lie-detector test.
40. **a.** If the train is late, then I am not in class on time.
    b. The train is late or I am in class on time.
    c. If I am in class on time, then the train is not late.
41. **a.** It is not true that I have a ticket and cannot go.
    b. I do not have a ticket and can go.
    c. I have a ticket or I cannot go.
42. **a.** I work hard or I do not succeed.
    b. It is not true that I do not work hard and succeed.
    c. I do not work hard and I do succeed.
43. **a.** If the grass turns yellow, you did not use fertilizer or water.
    b. If you use fertilizer and water, the grass will not turn yellow.
    c. If the grass does not turn yellow, you used fertilizer and water.
44. **a.** If you do not file or provide fraudulent information, you will be prosecuted.
    b. If you file and do not provide fraudulent information, you will not be prosecuted.
    c. If you are not prosecuted, you filed or did not provide fraudulent information.
45. **a.** I'm leaving, and Tom is relieved or Sue is relieved.
    b. I'm leaving, and it is false that Tom and Sue are not relieved.
    c. If I'm leaving, then Tom is relieved or Sue is relieved.
46. **a.** You play at least three instruments, and if you have a master's degree in music then you are eligible.
    b. You are eligible, if and only if you have a master's degree in music and play at least three instruments.
    c. You play at least three instruments, and if you are not eligible then you do not have a master's degree in music.

Practice Plus

In Exercises 47–50, express each statement in "if ... then" form. (More than one correct wording in "if ... then" form is possible.) Then write the statement's converse, inverse, contrapositive, and negation.

47. No pain is sufficient for no gain.
48. Not observing the speed limit is necessary for getting a speeding ticket.

49. Being neither hedonistic nor ascetic is necessary for following Buddha's "Middle Way."

50. Going into heat and not finding a mate are sufficient for a female ferret's death.

In Exercises 51–54, write the negation of each statement. Express each negation in a form such that the symbol ~ negates only simple statements.

51. $p \rightarrow (r \wedge \sim s)$

52. $p \rightarrow (\sim r \vee s)$

53. $p \wedge (r \rightarrow \sim s)$

54. $p \vee (\sim r \rightarrow s)$

Application Exercises

The bar graph shows ten leading causes of death in the United States, along with the average number of days of life lost for each hazard.

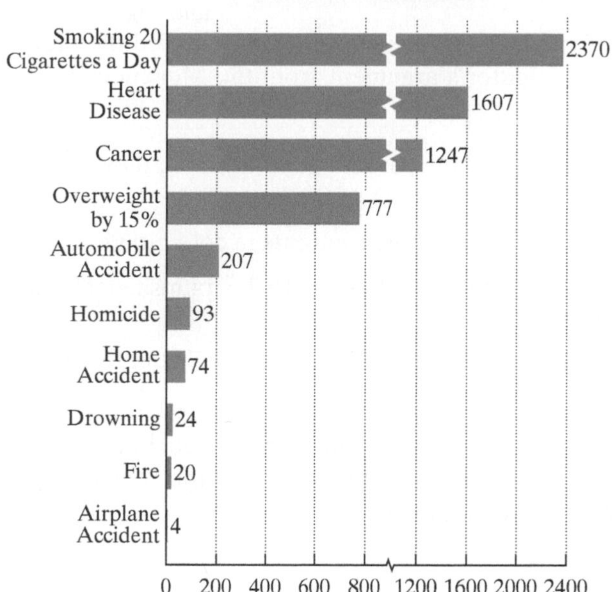

Source: Withgott and Brennan, *Essential Environment*, Third Edition, Pearson, 2009.

In Exercises 55–60,

a. *Use the information given by the graph to determine the truth value of the compound statement.*

b. *Write the compound statement's negation.*

c. *Use the information given by the graph to determine the truth value of the negation in part (b).*

55. Smoking reduces life expectancy by 2370 days and heart disease reduces life expectancy by 1247 days.

56. Cancer reduces life expectancy by 1607 days and being overweight reduces life expectancy by 777 days.

57. Homicide reduces life expectancy by 74 days or fire does not reduce life expectancy by 25 days.

58. Automobile accidents reduce life expectancy by 500 days or drowning does not reduce life expectancy by 30 days.

59. If drowning reduces life expectancy by ten times the number of days as airplane accidents, then drowning does not reduce life expectancy by 24 days.

60. If fire reduces life expectancy by ten times the number of days as airplane accidents, then fire does not reduce life expectancy by 20 days.

Writing in Mathematics

61. Explain how to write the negation of a conditional statement.

62. Explain how to write the negation of a conjunction.

63. Give an example of a disjunction that is true, even though one of its component statements is false. Then write the negation of the disjunction and explain why the negation is false.

Critical Thinking Exercises

Make Sense? *In Exercises 64–67, determine whether each statement makes sense or does not make sense, and explain your reasoning.*

64. Too much time was spent explaining how to negate $p \rightarrow q$, $p \wedge q$, and $p \vee q$, when all I have to do is to negate p and negate q.

65. If I know that a conditional statement is false, I can obtain a true statement by taking the conjunction of its antecedent and negated consequent.

66. I took the contrapositive of $\sim q \rightarrow (p \wedge r)$ and obtained $\sim(p \vee r) \rightarrow q$.

67. The Chinese Taoist philosopher Lao Tzu (*The Way of Life*) wrote, "If one man leads, another must follow. How silly that is and how false!" Based on my understanding of the conditional and its negation, I concluded that Lao Tzu is saying that one man leads and another need not follow.

68. Write the negation for the following conjunction:

We will neither replace nor repair the roof, and we will sell the house.

69. Write the contrapositive and the negation for the following statement:

Some people eating turkey is necessary for it to be Thanksgiving.

OBJECTIVES

1 Use truth tables to determine validity.

2 Recognize and use forms of valid and invalid arguments.

7 Arguments and Truth Tables

Ted Soqui\CORBIS- NY

A noted criminal case in 1995 involved Lyle and Erik Menendez, who shot and killed their parents. Although everyone agreed that the brothers committed the crime, it took two trials before they were convicted. The *arguments* in the trial centered around the boys' motivation: Was the killing a premeditated act by two children hoping to receive an inheritance, or was it an act motivated by years of abuse and a desperate sense of helplessness and rage?

1 Use truth tables to determine validity.

An **argument** consists of two parts: the given statements, called the **premises**, and a **conclusion**. Here's the prosecutor's argument from the Menendez brothers' criminal case:

Premise 1: If children murder their parents in cold blood, they deserve to be punished to the full extent of the law.

Premise 2: These children murdered their parents in cold blood.

Conclusion: Therefore, these children deserve to be punished to the full extent of the law.

(*Source:* Sherry Diestler, *Becoming a Critical Thinker*, Fourth Edition, Prentice Hall, 2005.)

It appears that if the premises are true, then the jurors must decide to punish the brothers to the full extent of the law. The true premises force the conclusion to be true, making this an example of a *valid argument.*

DEFINITION OF A VALID ARGUMENT

An argument is **valid** if the conclusion is true whenever the premises are assumed to be true. An argument that is not valid is said to be an **invalid argument**, also called a **fallacy**.

Truth tables can be used to test validity. We begin by writing the argument in symbolic form. Let's do this for the prosecutor's argument in the Menendez case. Represent each simple statement with a letter:

p: Children murder their parents in cold blood.

q: They deserve to be punished to the full extent of the law.

Now we write the two premises and the conclusion in symbolic form:

Premise 1:	$p \rightarrow q$	If children murder their parents in cold blood, they deserve to be punished to the full extent of the law.
Premise 2:	$\underline{p}$	These children murdered their parents in cold blood.
Conclusion:	$\therefore q$	Therefore, these children need to be punished to the full extent of the law.

(The three-dot triangle, $\therefore$, is read "therefore.")

To decide whether this argument is valid, we rewrite it as a conditional statement that has the following form:

$$[(p \rightarrow q) \wedge p] \rightarrow q.$$

If premise 1 and premise 2, then conclusion.

At this point, we can determine whether the conjunction of the premises implies that the conclusion is true for all possible truth values for p and q. We construct a truth table for the statement

$$[(p \rightarrow q) \wedge p] \rightarrow q.$$

If the final column in the truth table for $[(p \rightarrow q) \wedge p] \rightarrow q$ is true in every case, then the statement is a tautology and the argument is valid. If the conditional statement in the last column is false in at least one case, then the statement is not a tautology, and the argument is invalid. The truth table is shown below.

p	q	$p \rightarrow q$	$(p \rightarrow q) \wedge p$	$[(p \rightarrow q) \wedge p] \rightarrow q$
T	T	T	T	T
T	F	F	F	T
F	T	T	F	T
F	F	T	F	T

The final column in the table is true in every case. The conditional statement is a tautology. This means that the premises imply the conclusion. The conclusion necessarily follows from the premises. Therefore, the argument is valid.

The form of the prosecutor's argument in the Menendez case

$$\begin{array}{l} p \rightarrow q \\ \underline{p \quad\quad} \\ \therefore q \end{array}$$

is called **direct reasoning**. All arguments that have the direct reasoning form are valid regardless of the English statements that p and q represent.

Here's a step-by-step procedure to test the validity of an argument using truth tables:

TESTING THE VALIDITY OF AN ARGUMENT WITH A TRUTH TABLE

1. Use a letter to represent each simple statement in the argument.
2. Express the premises and the conclusion symbolically.
3. Write a symbolic conditional statement of the form

   $$[(\text{premise } 1) \wedge (\text{premise } 2) \wedge \cdots \wedge (\text{premise } n)] \rightarrow \text{conclusion},$$

   where n is the number of premises.
4. Construct a truth table for the conditional statement in step 3.
5. If the final column of the truth table has all trues, the conditional statement is a tautology and the argument is valid. If the final column does not have all trues, the conditional statement is not a tautology and the argument is invalid.

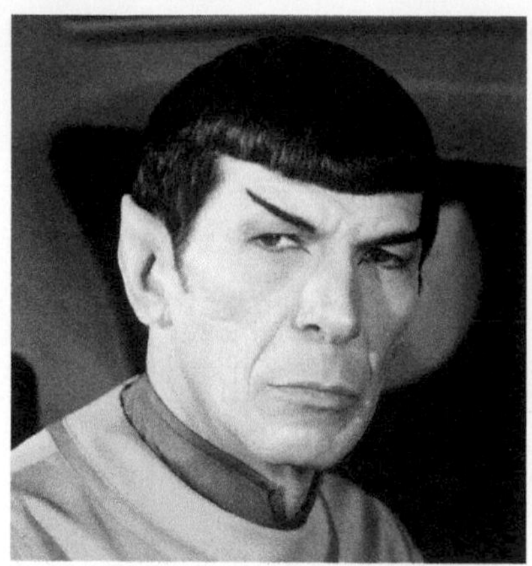

Paramount / The Kobal Collection

EXAMPLE 1 Did the Pickiest Logician in the Galaxy Foul Up?

In an episode of the television series *Star Trek,* the starship *Enterprise* is hit by an ion storm, causing the power to go out. Captain Kirk wonders if Mr. Scott, the engineer, is aware of the problem. Mr. Spock, the paragon of extraterrestrial intelligence, replies, "If Mr. Scott is still with us, the power should be on momentarily." Moments later, the ship's power comes on and Spock arches his Vulcan brow: "Ah, Mr. Scott is still with us."

Spock's logic can be expressed in the form of an argument:

If Mr. Scott is still with us, then the power will come on.
The power comes on.
____
Therefore, Mr. Scott is still with us.

Determine whether this argument is valid or invalid.

Solution

Step 1 Use a letter to represent each simple statement in the argument. We introduce the following representations:

p: Mr. Scott is still with us.
q: The power will come on.

Step 2 Express the premises and the conclusion symbolically.

$p \rightarrow q$	If Mr. Scott is still with us, then the power will come on.
q	The power comes on.
$\therefore p$	Mr. Scott is still with us.

Step 3 Write a symbolic statement of the form

$$[(\textbf{premise 1}) \wedge (\textbf{premise 2})] \rightarrow \textbf{conclusion.}$$

The symbolic statement is

$$[(p \rightarrow q) \wedge q] \rightarrow p.$$

Step 4 Construct a truth table for the conditional statement in step 3.

p	q	$p \rightarrow q$	$(p \rightarrow q) \wedge q$	$[(p \rightarrow q) \wedge q] \rightarrow p$
T	T	T	T	T
T	F	F	F	T
F	T	T	T	F
F	F	T	F	T

Step 5 Use the truth values in the final column to determine if the argument is valid or invalid. The entries in the final column of the truth table are not all true, so the conditional statement is not a tautology. Spock's argument is invalid, or a fallacy.

STUDY TIP

If Spock's fallacious reasoning represents television writers' best efforts at being logical, do not expect much from their commercials.

The form of the argument in Spock's logical foul-up

$$\begin{array}{l} p \rightarrow q \\ \underline{q \quad\quad} \\ \therefore p \end{array}$$

is called the **fallacy of the converse**. It should remind you that a conditional statement is not equivalent to its converse. All arguments that have this form are invalid regardless of the English statements that p and q represent.

You may also recall that a conditional statement is not equivalent to its inverse. Another common invalid form of argument is called the **fallacy of the inverse**:

$$\begin{array}{l} p \rightarrow q \\ \underline{\sim p \quad\quad} \\ \therefore \sim q. \end{array}$$

An example of the fallacy of the inverse is "If I study, I pass. I do not study. Therefore, I do not pass." For most students, the conclusion is true, but it does not have to be. If an argument is invalid, then the conclusion is not necessarily true. This, however, does not mean that the conclusion must be false.

CHECK POINT 1 Use a truth table to determine whether the following argument is valid or invalid:

> The United States must energetically support the development of solar-powered cars or suffer increasing atmospheric pollution.
> The United States must not suffer increasing atmospheric pollution.
> Therefore, the United States must energetically support the development of solar-powered cars.

EXAMPLE 2 Determining Validity with a Truth Table

Determine whether the following argument is valid or invalid:

> *"I can't have anything more to do with the operation. If I did, I'd have to lie to the Ambassador. And I can't do that."*
>
> — Henry Bromell, "I Know Your Heart, Marco Polo," *The New Yorker*

Solution We can express the argument as follows:

> If I had anything more to do with the operation, I'd have to lie to the Ambassador.
> I can't lie to the Ambassador.
> Therefore, I can't have anything more to do with the operation.

Step 1 Use a letter to represent each statement in the argument. We introduce the following representations:

p: I have more to do with the operation.

q: I have to lie to the Ambassador.

Step 2 Express the premises and the conclusion symbolically.

$p \to q$	If I had anything more to do with the operation, I'd have to lie to the Ambassador.
$\sim q$	I can't lie to the Ambassador.
$\therefore \sim p$	Therefore, I can't have anything more to do with the operation.

Step 3 Write a symbolic statement of the form

$$[(\textbf{premise 1}) \land (\textbf{premise 2})] \to \textbf{conclusion.}$$

The symbolic statement is

$$[(p \to q) \land \sim q] \to \sim p.$$

Step 4 Construct a truth table for the conditional statement in step 3.

p	q	$p \to q$	$\sim q$	$(p \to q) \land \sim q$	$\sim p$	$[(p \to q) \land \sim q] \to \sim p$
T	T	T	F	F	F	T
T	F	F	T	F	F	T
F	T	T	F	F	T	T
F	F	T	T	T	T	T

Step 5 Use the truth values in the final column to determine if the argument is valid or invalid. The entries in the final column of the truth table at the bottom of the previous page are all true, so the conditional statement is a tautology. The given argument is valid.

The form of the argument in Example 2

$$\begin{array}{l} p \rightarrow q \\ \underline{\sim q \quad} \\ \therefore \sim p \end{array}$$

should remind you that a conditional statement is equivalent to its contrapositive:

$$p \rightarrow q \equiv \sim q \rightarrow \sim p.$$

The form of this argument is called **contrapositive reasoning**.

Use a truth table to determine whether the following argument is valid or invalid:

I study for 5 hours or I fail.
I did not study for 5 hours.
Therefore, I failed.

EXAMPLE 3 The Defense Attorney's Argument at the Menendez Trial

The defense attorney at the Menendez trial admitted that the brothers murdered their parents. However, she presented the following argument that resulted in a different conclusion about sentencing:

If children murder parents because they fear abuse, there are mitigating circumstances to the murder.
If there are mitigating circumstances, then children deserve a lighter sentence.
Therefore, if children murder parents because they fear abuse, they deserve a lighter sentence.

(*Source*: Sherry Diestler, *Becoming a Critical Thinker*, Fourth Edition, Prentice Hall, 2005.)

Determine whether this argument is valid or invalid.

Solution

Step 1 Use a letter to represent each statement in the argument. We introduce the following representations:

p: Children murder parents because they fear abuse.

q: There are mitigating circumstances to the murder.

r: Children deserve a lighter sentence.

Step 2 Express the premises and the conclusion symbolically.

$p \rightarrow q$	If children murder parents because they fear abuse, there are mitigating circumstances to the murder.
$q \rightarrow r$	If there are mitigating circumstances, then children deserve a lighter sentence.
$\therefore p \rightarrow r$	Therefore, if children murder parents because they fear abuse, they deserve a lighter sentence.

Step 3 Write a symbolic statement of the form

$$[(\textbf{premise 1}) \wedge (\textbf{premise 2})] \rightarrow \textbf{conclusion.}$$

The symbolic statement is

$$[(p \rightarrow q) \wedge (q \rightarrow r)] \rightarrow (p \rightarrow r).$$

Step 4 Construct a truth table for the conditional statement in step 3.

p	q	r	$p \to q$	$q \to r$	$p \to r$	$(p \to q) \wedge (q \to r)$	$[(p \to q) \wedge (q \to r)] \to (p \to r)$
T	T	T	T	T	T	T	T
T	T	F	T	F	F	F	T
T	F	T	F	T	T	F	T
T	F	F	F	T	F	F	T
F	T	T	T	T	T	T	T
F	T	F	T	F	T	F	T
F	F	T	T	T	T	T	T
F	F	F	T	T	T	T	T

Step 5 Use the truth values in the final column to determine if the argument is valid or invalid. The entry in each of the eight rows in the final column of the truth table is true, so the conditional statement is a tautology. The defense attorney's argument is valid.

The form of the defense attorney's argument

$$\begin{array}{l} p \to q \\ \underline{q \to r} \\ \therefore\ p \to r \end{array}$$

is called **transitive reasoning**. If p implies q and q implies r, then p must imply r. Because $p \to r$ is a valid conclusion, the contrapositive, $\sim r \to \sim p$, is also a valid conclusion. Not necessarily true are the converse, $r \to p$, and the inverse, $\sim p \to \sim r$.

Use a truth table to determine whether the following argument is valid or invalid:

If you lower the fat in your diet, you lower your cholesterol.
If you lower your cholesterol, you reduce the risk of heart disease.
Therefore, if you do not lower the fat in your diet, you do not reduce the risk of heart disease.

We have seen two valid arguments that resulted in very different conclusions. The prosecutor in the Menendez case concluded that the brothers needed to be punished to the full extent of the law. The defense attorney concluded that they deserved a lighter sentence. This illustrates that the conclusion of a valid argument is true *relative to the premises*. The conclusion may follow from the premises, although one or more of the premises may not be true.

A valid argument with true premises is called a **sound argument**. The conclusion of a sound argument is true relative to the premises, but it is also true as a separate statement removed from the premises. When an argument is sound, its conclusion represents perfect certainty. Knowing how to assess the validity and soundness of arguments is a very important skill that will enable you to avoid being fooled into thinking that something is proven with certainty when it is not.

2 Recognize and use forms of valid and invalid arguments.

Table 18 contains the standard forms of commonly used valid and invalid arguments. If an English argument translates into one of these forms, you can immediately determine whether or not it is valid without using a truth table.

TABLE 18 Standard Forms of Arguments

Valid Arguments			
Direct Reasoning	**Contrapositive Reasoning**	**Disjunctive Reasoning**	**Transitive Reasoning**
$p \rightarrow q$ $\underline{p}$ $\therefore q$	$p \rightarrow q$ $\underline{\sim q}$ $\therefore \sim p$	$p \vee q$ $p \vee q$ $\underline{\sim p}$ $\underline{\sim q}$ $\therefore q$ $\therefore p$	$p \rightarrow q$ $\underline{q \rightarrow r}$ $\therefore p \rightarrow r$ $\therefore \sim r \rightarrow \sim p$
Invalid Arguments			
Fallacy of the Converse	**Fallacy of the Inverse**	**Misuse of Disjunctive Reasoning**	**Misuse of Transitive Reasoning**
$p \rightarrow q$ $\underline{q}$ $\therefore p$	$p \rightarrow q$ $\underline{\sim p}$ $\therefore \sim q$	$p \vee q$ $p \vee q$ $\underline{p}$ $\underline{q}$ $\therefore \sim q$ $\therefore \sim p$	$p \rightarrow q$ $\underline{q \rightarrow r}$ $\therefore r \rightarrow p$ $\therefore \sim p \rightarrow \sim r$

EXAMPLE 4 Determining Validity without Truth Tables

Determine whether each argument is valid or invalid. Identify any sound arguments.

a. There is no need for surgery. I know this because if there is a tumor then there is need for surgery, but there is no tumor.

b. The emergence of democracy is a cause for hope or environmental problems will overshadow any promise of a bright future. Because environmental problems will overshadow any promise of a bright future, it follows that the emergence of democracy is not a cause for hope.

c. If evidence of the defendant's DNA is found at the crime scene, we can connect him with the crime. If we can connect him with the crime, we can have him stand trial. Therefore, if the defendant's DNA is found at the crime scene, we can have him stand trial.

Solution

a. We introduce the following representations:

p: There is a tumor.

q: There is need for surgery.

We express the premises and conclusion symbolically.

If there is a tumor then there is need for surgery.	$p \rightarrow q$
<u>There is no tumor.</u>	$\underline{\sim p}$
Therefore, there is no need for surgery.	$\therefore \sim q$

The argument is in the form of the fallacy of the inverse. Therefore, the argument is invalid.

b. We introduce the following representations:

p: The emergence of democracy is a cause for hope.

q: Environmental problems will overshadow any promise of a bright future.

We express the premises and conclusion symbolically.

The emergence of democracy is a cause for hope or environmental problems will overshadow any promise of a bright future.	$p \lor q$
Environmental problems will overshadow any promise of a bright future.	q
Therefore, the emergence of democracy is not a cause for hope.	$\therefore \sim p$

The argument is in a form that represents a misuse of disjunctive reasoning. Therefore, the argument is invalid.

c. We introduce the following representations:

p: Evidence of the defendant's DNA is found at the crime scene.

q: We can connect him with the crime.

r: We can have him stand trial.

The argument can now be expressed symbolically.

If evidence of the defendant's DNA is found at the crime scene, we can connect him with the crime.	$p \rightarrow q$
If we can connect him with the crime, we can have him stand trial.	$q \rightarrow r$
Therefore, if the defendant's DNA is found at the crime scene, we can have him stand trial.	$\therefore p \rightarrow r$

The argument is in the form of transitive reasoning. Therefore, the argument is valid. Furthermore, the premises appear to be true statements, so this is a sound argument.

Determine whether each argument is valid or invalid.

a. The emergence of democracy is a cause for hope or environmental problems will overshadow any promise of a bright future. Environmental problems will not overshadow any promise of a bright future. Therefore, the emergence of democracy is a cause for hope.

b. If the defendant's DNA is found at the crime scene, then we can have him stand trial. He is standing trial. Consequently, we found evidence of his DNA at the crime scene.

c. If you mess up, your self-esteem goes down. If your self-esteem goes down, everything else falls apart. So, if you mess up, everything else falls apart.

EXAMPLE 5 Nixon's Resignation

"The decision of the Supreme Court in U.S. v. Nixon *(1974), handed down the first day of the Judiciary Committee's final debate, was critical. If the President defied the order, he would be impeached. If he obeyed the order, it was increasingly apparent he would be impeached on the evidence."*

—Victoria Schuck, "Watergate," *The Key Reporter*

Richard Nixon's resignation on August 8, 1974, was the sixth anniversary of the day he had triumphantly accepted his party's nomination for his first term as president.
AP Wide World Photos

Based on the paragraph at the bottom of the previous page, we can formulate the following argument:

If Nixon did not obey the Supreme Court order, he would be impeached.
If Nixon obeyed the Supreme Court order, he would be impeached.
Therefore, Nixon's impeachment was certain.

Determine whether this argument is valid or invalid.

Solution

Step 1 Use a letter to represent each simple statement in the argument. We introduce the following representations:

p: Nixon obeys the Supreme Court order.
q: Nixon is impeached.

Step 2 Express the premises and the conclusion symbolically.

$\sim p \rightarrow q$ If Nixon did not obey the Supreme Court order, he would be impeached.
$p \rightarrow q$ If Nixon obeyed the Supreme Court order, he would be impeached.
$\therefore q$ Therefore, Nixon's impeachment was certain.

Because this argument is not in the form of a recognizable valid or invalid argument, we will use a truth table to determine validity.

Step 3 Write a symbolic statement of the form

$$[(\textbf{premise 1}) \wedge (\textbf{premise 2})] \rightarrow \textbf{conclusion}.$$

The symbolic statement is

$$[(\sim p \rightarrow q) \wedge (p \rightarrow q)] \rightarrow q.$$

Step 4 Construct a truth table for the conditional statement in step 3.

p	q	$\sim p$	$\sim p \rightarrow q$	$p \rightarrow q$	$(\sim p \rightarrow q) \wedge (p \rightarrow q)$	$[(\sim p \rightarrow q) \wedge (p \rightarrow q)] \rightarrow q$
T	T	F	T	T	T	T
T	F	F	T	F	F	T
F	T	T	T	T	T	T
F	F	T	F	T	F	T

Step 5 Use the truth values in the final column to determine if the argument is valid or invalid. The entries in the final column of the truth table are all true, so the conditional statement is a tautology. Thus, the given argument is valid. Because the premises are true statements, this is a sound argument, with impeachment a certainty. In a 16-minute broadcast on August 8, 1974, Richard Nixon yielded to the inevitability of the argument's conclusion and, staring sadly into the cameras, announced his resignation.

Determine whether the following argument is valid or invalid:

If people are good, laws are not needed to prevent wrongdoing.
If people are not good, laws will not succeed in preventing wrongdoing.
Therefore, laws are not needed to prevent wrongdoing or laws will not succeed in preventing wrongdoing.

A **logical** or **valid conclusion** is one that forms a valid argument when it follows a given set of premises. Suppose that the premises of an English argument translate into any one of the symbolic forms of premises for the valid arguments in **Table 18**. The symbolic conclusion can be used to find a valid English conclusion. Example 6 shows how this is done.

EXAMPLE 6 Drawing a Logical Conclusion

Draw a valid conclusion from the following premises:

If all students get requirements out of the way early, then no students take required courses in their last semester. Some students take required courses in their last semester.

Solution

Let p be: All students get requirements out of the way early.

Let q be: No students take required courses in their last semester.

The form of the premises is

$p \rightarrow q$	If all students get requirements out of the way early, then no students take required courses in their last semester.
$\underline{\sim q}$	Some students take required courses in their last semester. (Recall that the negation of *no* is *some*.)
$\therefore ?$	

The conclusion $\sim p$ is valid because it forms the contrapositive reasoning of a valid argument when it follows the given premises. The conclusion $\sim p$ translates as

Not all students get requirements out of the way early.

Because the negation of *all* is *some ... not*, we can equivalently conclude that

Some students do not get requirements out of the way early.

Draw a valid conclusion from the following premises:

If all people lead, then no people follow. Some people follow.

Exercise Set 7

Practice Exercises

In Exercises 1–14, use a truth table to determine whether the symbolic form of the argument is valid or invalid.

1. $p \rightarrow q$
$\underline{\sim p}$
$\therefore \sim q$

2. $p \rightarrow q$
$\underline{\sim p}$
$\therefore q$

3. $p \rightarrow \sim q$
$\underline{q}$
$\therefore \sim p$

4. $\sim p \rightarrow q$
$\underline{\sim q}$
$\therefore p$

5. $p \wedge \sim q$
$\underline{p}$
$\therefore \sim q$

6. $\sim p \vee q$
$\underline{p}$
$\therefore q$

7. $p \rightarrow q$
$\underline{q \rightarrow p}$
$\therefore p \wedge q$

8. $(p \rightarrow q) \wedge (q \rightarrow p)$
$\underline{p}$
$\therefore p \vee q$

9. $p \rightarrow q$
$\underline{q \rightarrow r}$
$\therefore r \rightarrow p$

10. $p \rightarrow q$
$\underline{q \rightarrow r}$
$\therefore \sim p \rightarrow \sim r$

11. $p \rightarrow q$
$\underline{q \wedge r}$
$\therefore p \vee r$

12. $\sim p \wedge q$
$\underline{p \leftrightarrow r}$
$\therefore p \wedge r$

13. $p \leftrightarrow q$
$\underline{q \rightarrow r}$
$\therefore \sim r \rightarrow \sim p$

14. $q \rightarrow \sim p$
$\underline{q \wedge r}$
$\therefore r \rightarrow p$

In Exercises 15–42, translate each argument into symbolic form. Then determine whether the argument is valid or invalid. You may use a truth table or, if applicable, compare the argument's symbolic form to a standard valid or invalid form. (You can ignore differences in past, present, and future tense.)

15. If it is cold, my motorcycle will not start.
<u>My motorcycle started.</u>
$\therefore$ It is not cold.

16. If a metrorail system is not in operation, there are traffic delays.
Over the past year there have been no traffic delays.
∴ Over the past year a metrorail system has been in operation.

17. There must be a dam or there is flooding.
This year there is flooding.
∴ This year there is no dam.

18. You must eat well or you will not be healthy.
I eat well.
∴ I am healthy.

19. If we close the door, then there is less noise.
There is less noise.
∴ We closed the door.

20. If an argument is in the form of the fallacy of the inverse, then it is invalid.
This argument is invalid.
∴ This argument is in the form of the fallacy of the inverse.

21. If he was disloyal, his dismissal was justified.
If he was loyal, his dismissial was justified.
∴ His dismissal was justified.

22. If I tell you I cheated, I'm miserable.
If I don't tell you I cheated, I'm miserable.
∴ I'm miserable.

23. We criminalize drugs or we damage the future of young people.
We will not damage the future of young people.
∴ We criminalize drugs.

24. He is intelligent or an overachiever.
He is not intelligent.
∴ He is an overachiever.

25. If all people obey the law, then no jails are needed.
Some people do not obey the law.
∴ Some jails are needed.

26. If all people obey the law, then no jails are needed.
Some jails are needed.
∴ Some people do not obey the law.

27. If I'm tired, I'm edgy.
If I'm edgy, I'm nasty.
∴ If I'm tired, I'm nasty.

28. If I am at the beach, then I swim in the ocean.
If I swim in the ocean, then I feel refreshed.
∴ If I am at the beach, then I feel refreshed.

29. If I'm tired, I'm edgy.
If I'm edgy, I'm nasty.
∴ If I'm nasty, I'm tired.

30. If I'm at the beach, then I swim in the ocean.
If I swim in the ocean, then I feel refreshed.
∴ If I'm not at the beach, then I don't feel refreshed.

31. If Tim and Janet play, then the team wins.
Tim played and the team did not win.
∴ Janet did not play.

32. If *The Graduate* and *Midnight Cowboy* are shown, then the performance is sold out.
Midnight Cowboy was shown and the performance was not sold out.
∴ *The Graduate* was not shown.

33. If it rains or snows, then I read.
I am not reading.
∴ It is neither raining nor snowing.

34. If I am tired or hungry, I cannot concentrate.
I can concentrate.
∴ I am neither tired nor hungry.

35. If it rains or snows, then I read.
I am reading.
∴ It is raining or snowing.

36. If I am tired or hungry, I cannot concentrate.
I cannot concentrate.
∴ I am tired or hungry.

37. If it is hot and humid, I complain.
It is not hot or it is not humid.
∴ I am not complaining.

38. If I watch *Schindler's List* and *Milk*, I am aware of the destructive nature of intolerance.
Today I did not watch *Schindler's List* or I did not watch *Milk*.
∴ Today I am not aware of the destructive nature of intolerance.

39. If you tell me what I already understand, you do not enlarge my understanding.
If you tell me something that I do not understand, then your remarks are unintelligible to me.
∴ Whatever you tell me does not enlarge my understanding or is unintelligible to me.

40. If we are to have peace, we must not encourage the competitive spirit.
If we are to make progress, we must encourage the competitive spirit.
∴ We do not have peace and we do not make progress.

41. If some journalists learn about the invasion, the newspapers will print the news.
If the newspapers print the news, the invasion will not be a secret.
The invasion was a secret.
∴ No journalists learned about the invasion.

42. If some journalists learn about the invasion, the newspapers will print the news.
If the newspapers print the news, the invasion will not be a secret.
No journalists learned about the invasion.
∴ The invasion was a secret.

In Exercises 43–50, use the standard forms of valid arguments to draw a valid conclusion from the given premises.

43. If a person is a chemist, then that person has a college degree.
My best friend does not have a college degree.
Therefore, . . .

44. If the Westway Expressway is not in operation, automobile traffic makes the East Side Highway look like a parking lot.

On June 2, the Westway Expressway was completely shut down because of an overturned truck.

Therefore, . . .

45. The writers of *My Mother the Car* were told by the network to improve their scripts or be dropped from prime time.

The writers of *My Mother the Car* did not improve their scripts.

Therefore, . . .

46. You exercise or you do not feel energized.

I do not exercise.

Therefore, . . .

47. If all electricity is off, then no lights work.

Some lights work.

Therefore, . . .

48. If all houses meet the hurricane code, then none of them are destroyed by a category 4 hurricane.

Some houses were destroyed by Andrew, a category 4 hurricane.

Therefore, . . .

49. If I vacation in Paris, I eat French pastries.

If I eat French pastries, I gain weight.

Therefore, . . .

50. If I am a full-time student, I cannot work.

If I cannot work, I cannot afford a rental apartment costing more than \$500 per month.

Therefore, . . .

Practice Plus

In Exercises 51–58, translate each argument into symbolic form. Then determine whether the argument is valid or invalid.

51. If it was any of your business, I would have invited you. It is not, and so I did not.

52. If it was any of your business, I would have invited you. I did, and so it is.

53. It is the case that $x < 5$ or $x > 8$, but $x \geq 5$, so $x > 8$.

54. It is the case that $x < 3$ or $x > 10$, but $x \leq 10$, so $x < 3$.

55. Having a college degree is necessary for obtaining a teaching position. You have a college degree, so you have a teaching position.

56. Having a college degree is necessary for obtaining a teaching position. You do not obtain a teaching position, so you do not have a college degree.

57. "I do know that this pencil exists; but I could not know this if Hume's principles were true. Therefore, Hume's principles, one or both of them, are false."

— G. E. Moore, *Some Main Problems of Philosophy*

58. (In this exercise, determine if the argument is sound, valid but not sound, or invalid.)

If an argument is invalid, it does not produce truth, whereas a valid unsound argument also does not produce truth. Arguments are invalid or they are valid but unsound. Therefore, no arguments produce truth.

Application Exercises

Exercises 59–60 illustrate arguments that have appeared in cartoons. Each argument is restated below the cartoon. Translate the argument into symbolic form and then determine whether it is valid or invalid.

59.

Peanuts reprinted by permission of United Feature Syndicate, Inc.

If you do not know how to read, you cannot read *War and Peace*. If you cannot read *War and Peace*, then Leo Tolstoy will hate you. Therefore, if you do not know how to read, Leo Tolstoy will hate you.

60.

Betty by Gary Delainey and Gery Rasmussen.
Reprinted by permission of Newspaper Enterprise Association, Inc.

If I say I'm in denial, then I'm not in denial. I am saying that I'm in denial, so I'm not in denial at all.

61. Conservative commentator Rush Limbaugh directed this passage at liberals and the way they think about crime.

Of course, liberals will argue that these actions [contemporary youth crime] can be laid at the foot of socioeconomic inequities, or poverty. However, the Great Depression caused a level of poverty unknown to exist in America today, and yet I have been unable to find any accounts of crime waves sweeping our large cities. Let the liberals chew on that.

(*See, I Told You So*, p. 83)

Limbaugh's passage can be expressed in the form of an argument:

If poverty causes crime, then crime waves would have swept American cities during the Great Depression.
Crime waves did not sweep American cities during the Great Depression.
$\therefore$ Poverty does not cause crime. (Liberals are wrong.)

Translate this argument into symbolic form and determine whether it is valid or invalid.

62. In the following passage, Martin Luther King, Jr. presents an argument with the conclusion "Segregation statutes are unjust." Use two premises, one a conditional statement and the other a simple statement, to rewrite King's argument in the format used throughout this section. Then determine if the argument is sound, valid but not sound, or invalid.

> *"Any law that uplifts human personality is just. Any law that degrades human personality is unjust. All segregation statutes are unjust because segregation distorts the soul and damages the personality. It gives the segregator a false sense of superiority, and the segregated a false sense of inferiority."*
>
> —Martin Luther King, Jr., "Letter from a Birmingham Jail"

In addition to the forms of invalid arguments, fallacious reasoning occurs in everyday logic. Some people use the fallacies described below to intentionally deceive. Others use fallacies innocently; they are not even aware they are using them. Match each description below with the example from Exercises 63–74 that illustrates the fallacy. The matching is one-to-one.

Common Fallacies in Everyday Reasoning

- **a.** *The* **fallacy of emotion** *consists of appealing to emotion (pity, force, etc.) in an argument.*
- **b.** *The* **fallacy of inappropriate authority** *consists of claiming that a statement is true because a person cited as an authority says it's true or because most people believe it's true.*
- **c.** *The* **fallacy of hasty generalization** *occurs when an inductive generalization is made on the basis of a few observations or an unrepresentative sample.*
- **d.** *The* **fallacy of questionable cause** *consists of claiming that A caused B when it is known that A occurred before B.*
- **e.** *The* **fallacy of ambiguity** *occurs when the conclusion of an argument is based on a word or phrase that is used in two different ways in the premises.*
- **f.** *The* **fallacy of ignorance** *consists of claiming that a statement is true simply because it has not been proven false, or vice versa.*
- **g.** *The* **mischaracterization fallacy** *consists of misrepresenting an opponent's position or attacking the opponent rather than that person's ideas in order to refute his or her argument.*
- **h.** *The* **slippery slope fallacy** *occurs when an argument reasons without justification that an event will set off a series of events leading to an undesirable consequence.*
- **i.** *The* **either/or fallacy** *mistakenly presents only two solutions to a problem, negates one of these either/or alternatives, and concludes that the other must be true.*
- **j.** *The* **fallacy of begging the question** *assumes that the conclusion is true within the premises.*
- **k.** *The* **fallacy of composition** *occurs when an argument moves from premises about the parts of a group to a conclusion about the whole group. It also occurs when characteristics of an entire group are mistakenly applied to parts of the group.*
- **l.** *The* **fallacy of the complex question** *consists of drawing a conclusion from a self-incriminating question.*

63. If we allow physician-assisted suicide for those who are terminally ill and request it, it won't be long before society begins pressuring the old and infirm to get out of the way and make room for the young. Before long the government will be deciding who should live and who should die.

64. Of course there are extraterrestrials. Haven't you read that article in the *National Enquirer* about those UFOs spotted in Texas last month?

65. Either you go to college and make something of yourself, or you'll end up as an unhappy street person. You cannot be an unhappy street person, so you should go to college.

66. Scientists have not proved that AIDS cannot be transmitted through casual contact. Therefore, we should avoid casual contact with suspected AIDS carriers.

67. Each of my three uncles smoked two packs of cigarettes every day and they all lived into their 90s. Smoking can't be that bad for your health.

68. You once cheated on tests. I know this because when I asked you if you had stopped cheating on tests, you said yes.

69. My paper is late, but I know you'll accept it because I've been sick and my parents will kill me if I flunk this course.

70. We've all heard Professor Jones tell us about how economic systems should place human need above profit. But I'm not surprised that he neglected to tell you that he's a communist who has visited Cuba twice. How can he possibly speak the truth about economic systems?

71. It's easy to see that suicide is wrong. After all, no one is ever justified in taking his or her own life.

72. The reason I hurt your arm is because you hurt me just as much by telling Dad.

73. Statistics show that nearly every heroin user started out by using marijuana. It's reasonable to conclude that smoking marijuana leads to harder drugs.

74. I know, without even looking, that question #17 on this test is difficult. This is the case because the test was made up by Professor Flunkem and Flunkem's exams are always difficult.

Writing in Mathematics

75. Describe what is meant by a valid argument.

76. If you are given an argument in words that contains two premises and a conclusion, describe how to determine if the argument is valid or invalid.

77. Write an original argument in words for the direct reasoning form.

78. Write an original argument in words for the contrapositive reasoning form.

79. Write an original argument in words for the transitive reasoning form.

80. What is a valid conclusion?

81. Write a valid argument on one of the following questions. If you can, write valid arguments on both sides.

a. Should the death penalty be abolished?

b. Should *Roe v. Wade* be overturned?

c. Should women be allowed combat roles in the military?

d. Should marijuana be legalized?

e. Should grades be abolished?

f. Should same-sex marriage be legalized?

Critical Thinking Exercises

Make Sense? *Exercises 82–85 are based on the following argument by conservative radio talk show host Rush Limbaugh and directed at former vice president Al Gore.*

> You would think that if Al Gore and company believe so passionately in their environmental crusading that [sic] they would first put these ideas to work in their own lives, right? ... Al Gore thinks the automobile is one of the greatest threats to the planet, but he sure as heck still travels in one of them—a gas guzzler too.
>
> (*See, I Told You So*, p. 168)

Limbaugh's passage can be expressed in the form of an argument:

> If Gore really believed that the automobile were a threat to the planet, he would not travel in a gas guzzler.
>
> Gore does travel in a gas guzzler.
>
> Therefore, Gore does not really believe that the automobile is a threat to the planet.

In Exercises 82–85, use Limbaugh's argument to determine whether each statement makes sense or does not make sense, and explain your reasoning.

82. I know for a fact that Al Gore does not travel in a gas guzzler, so Limbaugh's argument is invalid.

83. I think Limbaugh is a fanatic and all his arguments are invalid.

84. In order to avoid a long truth table and instead use a standard form of an argument, I tested the validity of Limbaugh's argument using the following representations:

> p: Gore really believes that the automobile is a threat to the planet.
>
> q: He does not travel in a gas guzzler.

85. Using my representations in Exercise 84, I determined that Limbaugh's argument is invalid.

86. Write an original argument in words that has a true conclusion, yet is invalid.

87. Draw a valid conclusion from the given premises. Then use a truth table to verify your answer.

> If you only spoke when spoken to and I only spoke when spoken to, then nobody would ever say anything. Some people do say things. Therefore, ...

88. Translate the argument below into symbolic form. Then use a truth table to determine if the argument is valid or invalid.

> It's wrong to smoke in public if secondary cigarette smoke is a health threat. If secondary cigarette smoke were not a health threat, the American Lung Association would not say that it is. The American Lung Association says that secondary cigarette smoke is a health threat. Therefore, it's wrong to smoke in public.

89. Draw what you believe is a valid conclusion in the form of a disjunction for the following argument. Then verify that the argument is valid for your conclusion.

> "Inevitably, the use of the placebo involved built-in contradictions. A good patient–doctor relationship is essential to the process, but what happens to that relationship when one of the partners conceals important information from the other? If the doctor tells the truth, he destroys the base on which the placebo rests. If he doesn't tell the truth, he jeopardizes a relationship built on trust."
>
> —Norman Cousins, *Anatomy of an Illness*

Group Exercise

90. In this section, we used a variety of examples, including arguments from the Menendez trial, the inevitability of Nixon's impeachment, Spock's (fallacious) logic on *Star Trek*, and even two cartoons, to illustrate symbolic arguments.

a. From any source that is of particular interest to you (these can be the words of someone you truly admire or a person who really gets under your skin), select a paragraph or two in which the writer argues a particular point. (An intriguing source is *What Is Your Dangerous Idea?*, edited by John Brockman, published by Harper Perennial, 2007.) Rewrite the reasoning in the form of an argument using words. Then translate the argument into symbolic form and use a truth table to determine if it is valid or invalid.

b. Each group member should share the selected passage with other people in the group. Explain how it was expressed in argument form. Then tell why the argument is valid or invalid.

OBJECTIVE

1 | Use Euler diagrams to determine validity.

8 Arguments and Euler Diagrams

William Shakespeare Martin Droeshout (British) "William Shakespeare" (1564-1616). National Portrait Gallery, London/SuperStock

Leonhard Euler Image Works/Mary Evans Picture Library Ltd.

He is the Shakespeare of mathematics, yet he is unknown by the general public. Most people cannot even correctly pronounce his name. The Swiss mathematician Leonhard Euler (1707–1783), whose last name rhymes with *boiler*, not *ruler*, is the most prolific mathematician in history. His collected books and papers fill some 80 volumes; Euler published an average of 800 pages of new mathematics per year over a career that spanned six decades. Euler was also an astronomer, botanist, chemist, physicist, and linguist. His productivity was not at all slowed down by the total blindness he experienced the last 17 years of his life. An equation discovered by Euler, $e^{\pi i} + 1 = 0$, connected five of the most important numbers in mathematics in a totally unexpected way.

1 | Use Euler diagrams to determine validity.

Euler invented an elegant way to determine the validity of arguments whose premises contain the words *all, some*, and *no*. The technique for doing this uses geometric ideas and involves four basic diagrams, known as **Euler diagrams**. **Figure 3** illustrates how Euler diagrams represent four quantified statements.

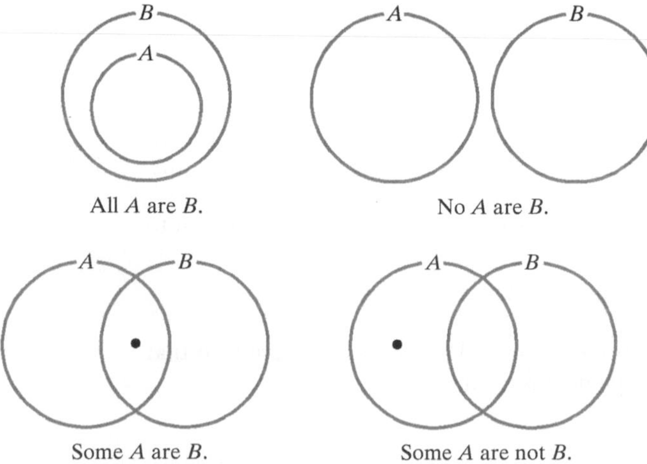

FIGURE 3 Euler diagrams for quantified statements

The Euler diagrams in **Figure 3** are just like the Venn diagrams that we used in studying sets. However, there is no need to enclose the circles inside a rectangle representing a universal set. In these diagrams, circles are used to indicate relationships of premises to conclusions.

Here's a step-by-step procedure for using Euler diagrams to determine whether or not an argument is valid:

EULER DIAGRAMS AND ARGUMENTS

1. Make an Euler diagram for the first premise.
2. Make an Euler diagram for the second premise on top of the one for the first premise.
3. The argument is valid if and only if every possible diagram illustrates the conclusion of the argument. If there is even *one* possible diagram that contradicts the conclusion, this indicates that the conclusion is not true in every case, so the argument is invalid.

The goal of this procedure is to produce, if possible, *a diagram that does* **not** *illustrate the argument's conclusion*. The method of Euler diagrams boils down to determining whether such a diagram is possible. If it is, this serves as a counterexample to the argument's conclusion, and the argument is immediately declared invalid. By contrast, if no such counterexample can be drawn, the argument is valid.

The technique of using Euler diagrams is illustrated in Examples 1–6.

EXAMPLE 1 Arguments and Euler Diagrams

Use Euler diagrams to determine whether the following argument is valid or invalid:

All people who arrive late cannot perform.
All people who cannot perform are ineligible for scholarships.
Therefore, all people who arrive late are ineligible for scholarships.

STUDY TIP

When making Euler diagrams, remember that the size of a circle is not relevant. It is the circle's location that counts.

Solution

Step 1 Make an Euler diagram for the first premise. We begin by diagramming the premise

All people who arrive late cannot perform.

The region inside the smaller circle represents people who arrive late. The region inside the larger circle represents people who cannot perform.

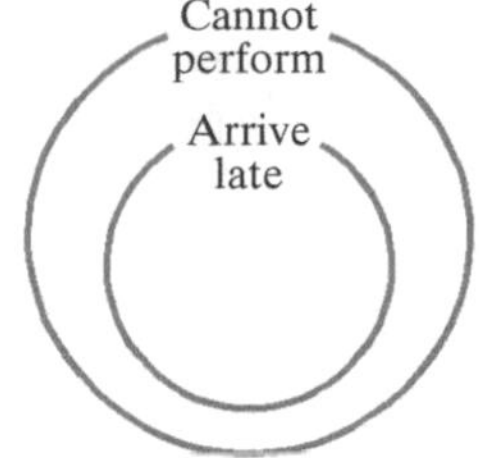

Step 2 Make an Euler diagram for the second premise on top of the one for the first premise. We add to our previous figure the diagram for the second premise:

All people who cannot perform are ineligible for scholarships.

A third, larger, circle representing people who are ineligible for scholarships is drawn surrounding the circle representing people who cannot perform.

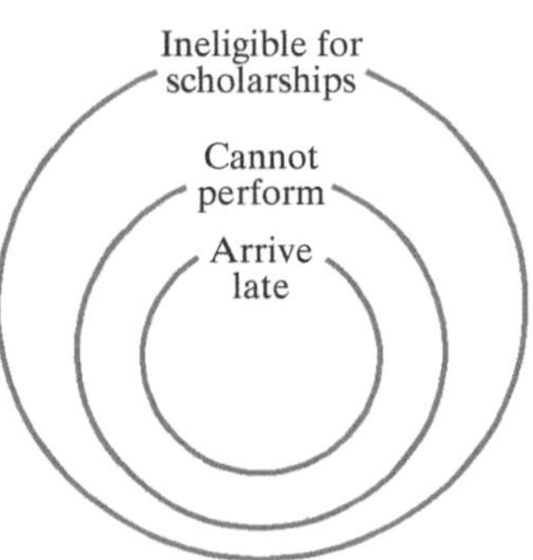

Step 3 The argument is valid if and only if every possible diagram illustrates the argument's conclusion. There is only one possible diagram. Let's see if this diagram illustrates the argument's conclusion, namely

All people who arrive late are ineligible for scholarships.

This is indeed the case because the Euler diagram shows the circle representing the people who arrive late contained within the circle of people who are ineligible for scholarships. The Euler diagram supports the conclusion and the given argument is valid.

Use Euler diagrams to determine whether the following argument is valid or invalid:

All U.S. voters must register.
All people who register must be U.S. citizens.
Therefore, all U.S. voters are U.S. citizens.

EXAMPLE 2 Arguments and Euler Diagrams

Use Euler diagrams to determine whether the following argument is valid or invalid:

All poets appreciate language.
All writers appreciate language.
Therefore, all poets are writers.

Solution

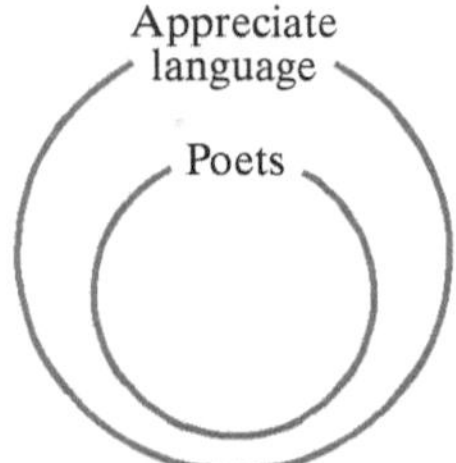

Step 1 Make an Euler diagram for the first premise. We begin by diagramming the premise

All poets appreciate language.

Up to this point, our work is similar to what we did in Example 1.

Step 2 Make an Euler diagram for the second premise on top of the one for the first premise. We add to our previous figure the diagram for the second premise:

All writers appreciate language.

A third circle representing writers must be drawn inside the circle representing people who appreciate language. There are four ways to do this.

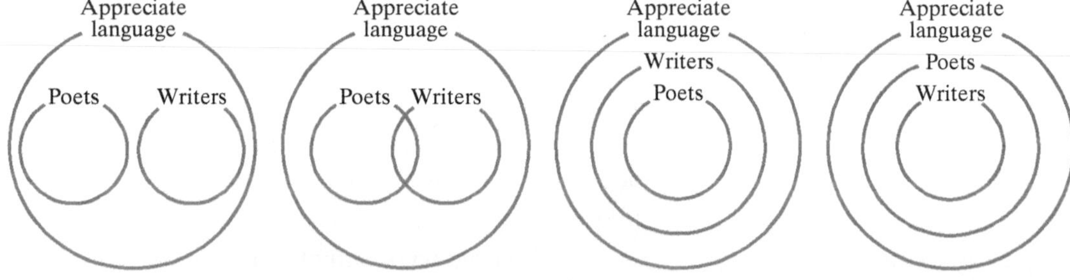

Step 3 The argument is valid if and only if every possible diagram illustrates the argument's conclusion. The argument's conclusion is

All poets are writers.

This conclusion is not illustrated by every possible diagram shown above. One of these diagrams is repeated in the margin. This diagram shows "no poets are writers." There is no need to examine the other three diagrams.

The diagram on the left serves as a counterexample to the argument's conclusion. This means that the given argument is invalid. It would have sufficed to draw only the counterexample on the left to determine that the argument is invalid.

CHECK POINT 2 Use Euler diagrams to determine whether the following argument is valid or invalid:

All baseball players are athletes.
<u>All ballet dancers are athletes.</u>
Therefore, no baseball players are ballet dancers.

EXAMPLE 3 Arguments and Euler Diagrams

Use Euler diagrams to determine whether the following argument is valid or invalid:

All freshmen live on campus.
<u>No people who live on campus can own cars.</u>
Therefore, no freshmen can own cars.

Solution

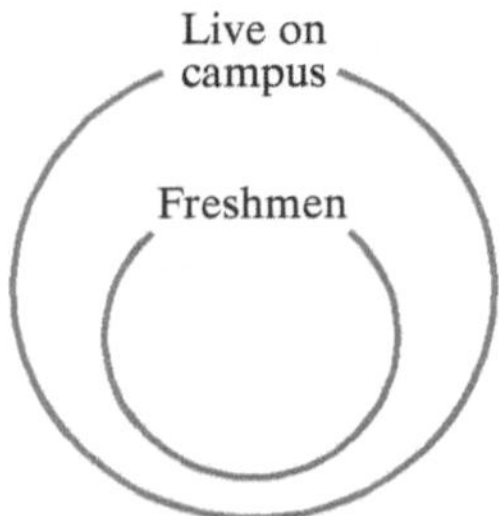

Step 1 Make an Euler diagram for the first premise. The diagram for

All freshmen live on campus

is shown on the right. The region inside the smaller circle represents freshmen. The region inside the larger circle represents people who live on campus.

Step 2 Make an Euler diagram for the second premise on top of the one for the first premise. We add to our previous figure the diagram for the second premise:

No people who live on campus can own cars.

A third circle representing people who own cars is drawn outside the circle representing people who live on campus.

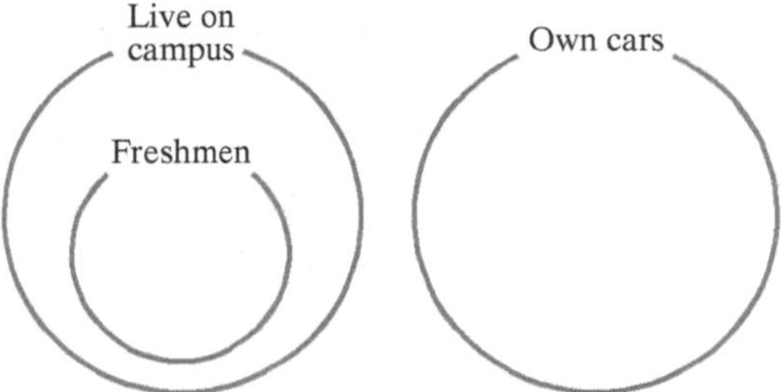

Step 3 The argument is valid if and only if every possible diagram illustrates the argument's conclusion. There is only one possible diagram. The argument's conclusion is

No freshmen can own cars.

This is supported by the diagram shown above because it shows the circle representing freshmen drawn outside the circle representing people who own cars. The Euler diagram supports the conclusion, and it is impossible to find a counterexample that does not. The given argument is valid.

Use Euler diagrams to determine whether the following argument is valid or invalid:

All mathematicians are logical.
<u>No poets are logical.</u>
Therefore, no poets are mathematicians.

Let's see what happens to the validity if we reverse the second premise and the conclusion of the argument in Example 3.

EXAMPLE 4 Euler Diagrams and Validity

Use Euler diagrams to determine whether the following argument is valid or invalid:

All freshmen live on campus.
No freshmen can own cars.
Therefore, no people who live on campus can own cars.

Solution

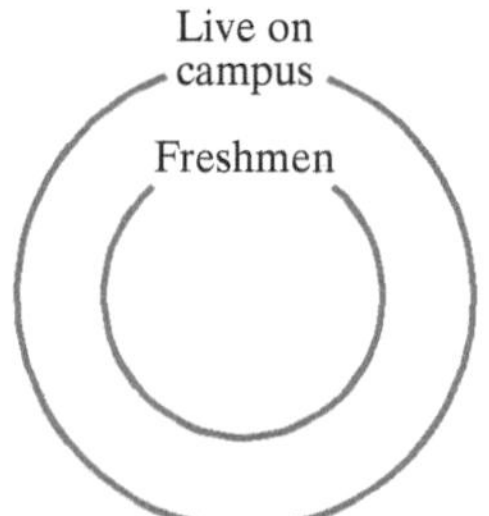

Step 1 Make an Euler diagram for the first premise. We once again begin with the diagram for

All freshmen live on campus.

So far, our work is exactly the same as in the previous example.

Step 2 Make an Euler diagram for the second premise on top of the one for the first premise. We add to our previous figure the diagram for the second premise:

No freshmen can own cars.

The circle representing people who own cars is drawn outside the freshmen circle. At least two Euler diagrams are possible.

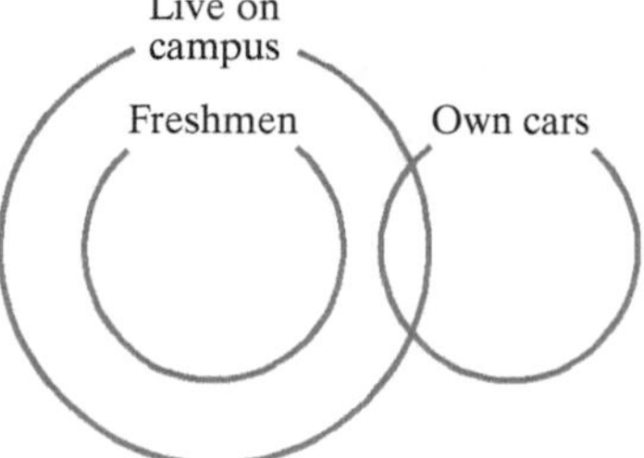

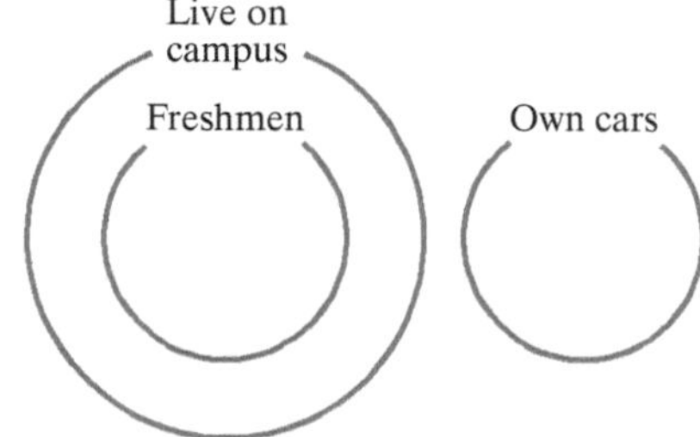

Step 3 The argument is valid if and only if every possible diagram illustrates the argument's conclusion. The argument's conclusion is

No people who live on campus can own cars.

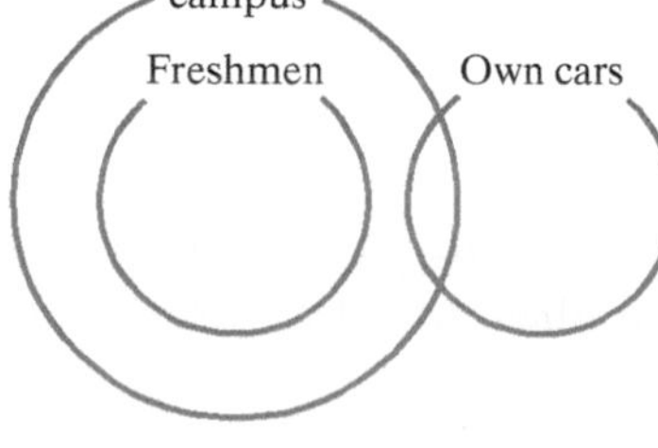

This conclusion is not supported by both diagrams shown above. The diagram that does not support the conclusion is repeated in the margin. Notice that the "live on campus" circle and the "own cars" circle intersect. This diagram serves as a counterexample to the argument's conclusion. This means that the argument is invalid. Once again, only the counterexample on the left is needed to conclude that the argument is invalid.

CHECK POINT 4 Use Euler diagrams to determine whether the following argument is valid or invalid:

All mathematicians are logical.
No poets are mathematicians.
Therefore, no poets are logical.

So far, the arguments that we have looked at have contained "all" or "no" in the premises and conclusions. The quantifier "some" is a bit trickier to work with. Because the statement "Some A are B" means there exists at least one A that is a B,

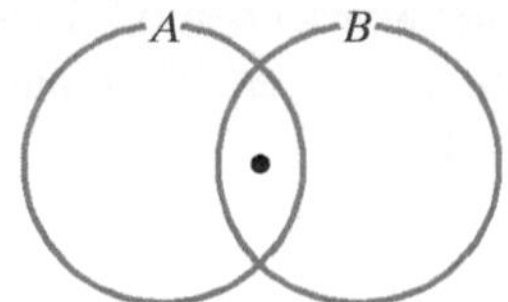

FIGURE 4 Some A are B.

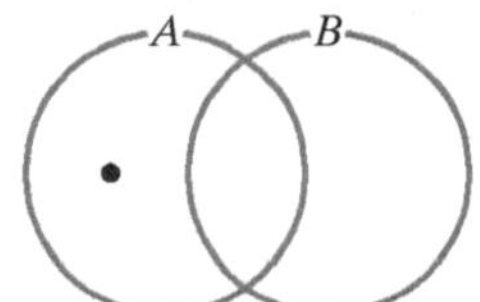

FIGURE 5 Illustrated by the dot is some A are not B. We cannot validly conclude that some B are not A.

we diagram this existence by showing a dot in the region where A and B intersect, illustrated in **Figure 4**.

Suppose that it is true that "Some A are not B," illustrated by the dot in **Figure 5**. This Euler diagram does not let us conclude that "Some B are not A" because there is not a dot in the part of the B circle that is not in the A circle. Conclusions with the word "some" must be shown by existence of at least one element represented by a dot in an Euler diagram.

Here is an example that shows the premise "Some A are not B" does not enable us to logically conclude that "Some B are not A."

Some U.S. citizens are not U.S. senators. (true)

$\therefore$ Some U.S. senators are not U.S. citizens. (false)

EXAMPLE 5 Euler Diagrams and the Quantifier "Some"

Use Euler diagrams to determine whether the following argument is valid or invalid:

All people are mortal.

<u>Some mortals are students.</u>

Therefore, some people are students.

Solution

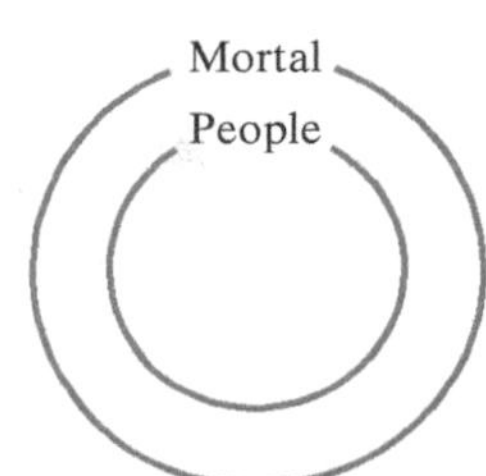

Step 1 Make an Euler diagram for the first premise. Begin with the premise.

All people are mortal.

The Euler diagram is shown on the right.

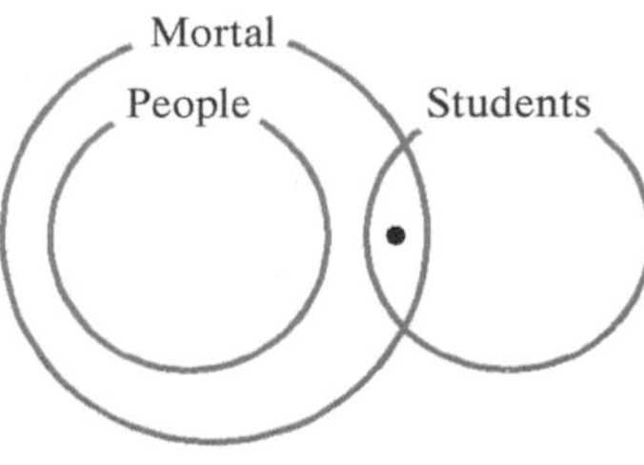

Step 2 Make an Euler diagram for the second premise on top of the one for the first premise. We add to our previous figure the diagram for the second premise:

Some mortals are students.

The circle representing students intersects the circle representing mortals. The dot in the region of intersection shows that at least one mortal is a student. Another diagram is possible, but if this serves as a counterexample then it is all we need. Let's check if it is a counterexample.

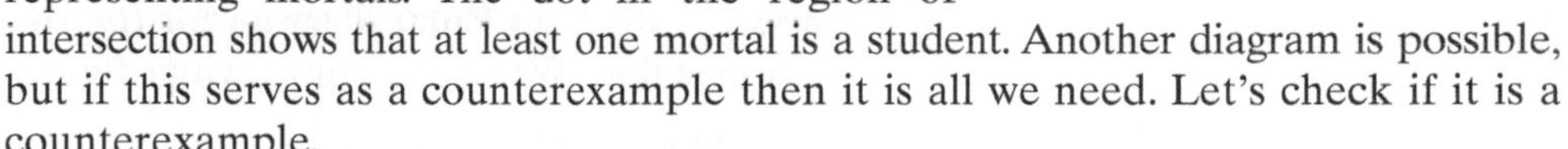

Step 3 The argument is valid if and only if every possible diagram illustrates the conclusion of the argument. The argument's conclusion is

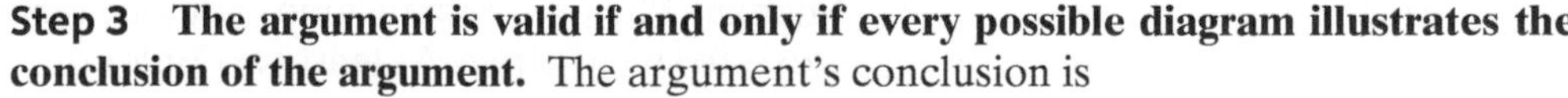

Some people are students.

This conclusion is not supported by the Euler diagram. The diagram does not show the "people" circle and the "students" circle intersecting with a dot in the region of intersection. Although this conclusion is true in the real world, the Euler diagram serves as a counterexample that shows it does not follow from the premises. Therefore, the argument is invalid.

Use Euler diagrams to determine whether the following argument is valid or invalid:

All mathematicians are logical.

<u>Some poets are logical.</u>

Therefore, some poets are mathematicians.

Some arguments show existence without using the word "some." Instead, a particular person or thing is mentioned in one of the premises. This particular person or thing is represented by a dot. Here is an example:

All men are mortal.
Aristotle is a man.
Therefore, Aristotle is mortal.

The two premises can be represented by the following Euler diagrams:

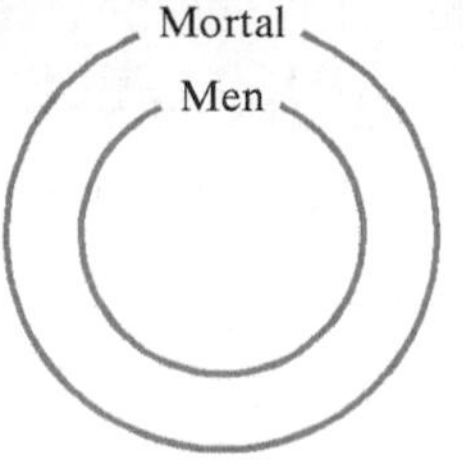

All men are mortal.

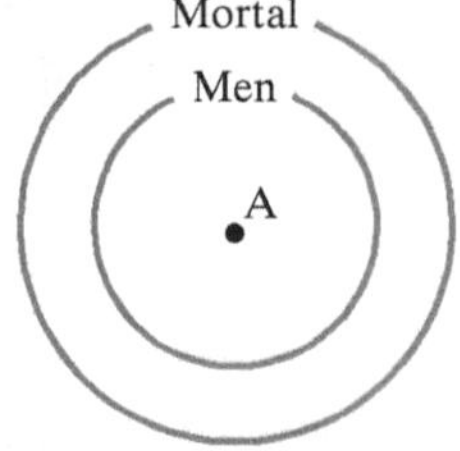

Aristotle (•) is a man.

The Euler diagram on the right uses a dot labeled A (for Aristotle). The diagram shows Aristotle (•) winding up in the "mortal" circle. The diagram supports the conclusion that Aristotle is mortal. This argument is valid.

EXAMPLE 6 An Argument Mentioning One Person

Use Euler diagrams to determine whether the following argument is valid or invalid:

All children love to swim.
Michael Phelps loves to swim.
Therefore, Michael Phelps is a child.

Solution

Step 1 Make an Euler diagram for the first premise. Begin with the premise

All children love to swim.

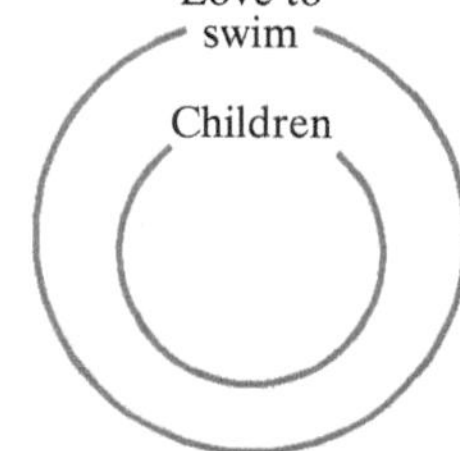

The Euler diagram is shown on the right.

Step 2 Make an Euler diagram for the second premise on top of the one for the first premise. We add to our previous figure the diagram for the second premise:

Michael Phelps loves to swim.

Michael Phelps is represented by a dot labeled M. The dot must be placed in the "love to swim" circle. At least two Euler diagrams are possible.

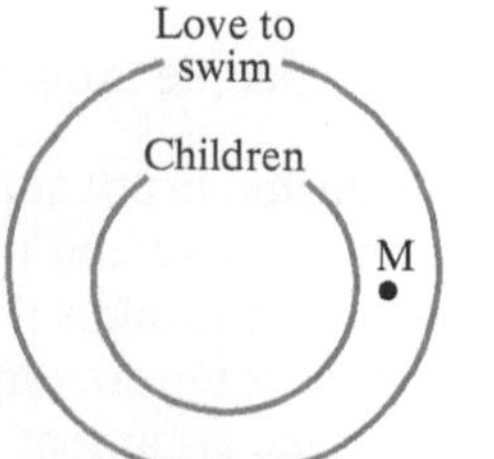

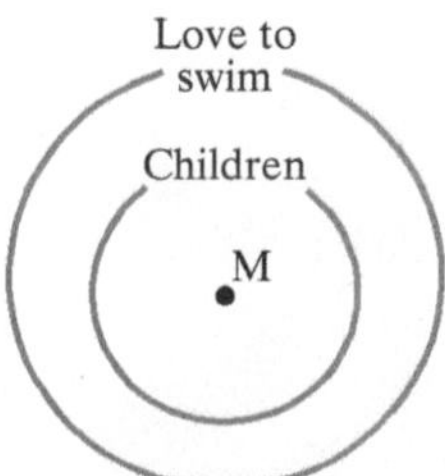

Step 3 The argument is valid if and only if every possible diagram illustrates the conclusion of the argument. The argument's conclusion is

Michael Phelps is a child.

This conclusion is not supported by the Euler diagram shown above on the left. The dot representing Michael Phelps is outside the "children" circle. Michael Phelps might not be a child. This diagram serves as a counterexample to the argument's conclusion. The argument is invalid.

Use Euler diagrams to determine whether the following argument is valid or invalid:

All mathematicians are logical.
Euclid was logical.
Therefore, Euclid was a mathematician.

BLITZER BONUS

ARISTOTLE 384–322 B.C.

The first systematic attempt to describe the logical rules that may be used to arrive at a valid conclusion was made by the ancient Greeks, in particular Aristotle. Aristotelian forms of valid arguments are built into the ways that Westerners think and view the world. In this detail of Raphael's painting *The School of Athens*, Aristotle (on the left) is debating with his teacher and mentor, Plato.

Raphael (1483–1520). *School of Athens*, Stanza della Segnatura, Vatican Palace, Vatican State. © Scala/Art Resource.

Exercise Set 8

Practice Exercises

In Exercises 1–24, use Euler diagrams to determine whether each argument is valid or invalid.

1. All writers appreciate language.
All poets are writers.
Therefore, all poets appreciate language.

2. All physicists are scientists.
All scientists attended college.
Therefore, all physicists attended college.

3. All clocks keep time accurately.
All time-measuring devices keep time accurately.
Therefore, all clocks are time-measuring devices.

4. All cowboys live on ranches.
All cowherders live on ranches.
Therefore, all cowboys are cowherders.

5. All insects have six legs.
No spiders have six legs.
Therefore, no spiders are insects.

6. All humans are warm-blooded.
No reptiles are warm-blooded.
Therefore, no reptiles are human.

7. All insects have six legs.
No spiders are insects.
Therefore, no spiders have six legs.

8. All humans are warm-blooded.
No reptiles are human.
Therefore, no reptiles are warm-blooded.

9. All professors are wise people.
Some wise people are actors.
Therefore, some professors are actors.

10. All comedians are funny people.
Some funny people are professors.
Therefore, some comedians are professors.

11. All professors are wise people.
Some professors are actors.
Therefore, some wise people are actors.

12. All comedians are funny people.
Some comedians are professors.
Therefore, some funny people are professors.

13. All dancers are athletes.
Savion Glover is a dancer.
Therefore, Savion Glover is an athlete.

14. All actors are artists.
Tom Hanks is an actor.
Therefore, Tom Hanks is an artist.

15. All dancers are athletes.
Savion Glover is an athlete.
Therefore, Savion Glover is a dancer.

16. All actors are artists.
Tom Hanks is an artist.
Therefore, Tom Hanks is an actor.

17. Some people enjoy reading.
Some people enjoy TV.
Therefore, some people who enjoy reading enjoy TV.

18. All thefts are immoral acts.
Some thefts are justifiable.
Therefore, some immoral acts are justifiable.

19. All dogs have fleas.
Some dogs have rabies.
Therefore, all dogs with rabies have fleas.

20. All logic problems make sense.
Some jokes make sense.
Therefore, some logic problems are jokes.

21. No blank disks contain data.
Some blank disks are formatted.
Therefore, some formatted disks do not contain data.

22. Some houses have two stories.
Some houses have air conditioning.
Therefore, some houses with air conditioning have two stories.

23. All multiples of 6 are multiples of 3.
Eight is not a multiple of 3.
Therefore, 8 is not a multiple of 6.

24. All multiples of 6 are multiples of 3.
Eight is not a multiple of 6.
Therefore, 8 is not a multiple of 3.

Practice Plus

In Exercises 25–36, determine whether each argument is valid or invalid.

25. All natural numbers are whole numbers, all whole numbers are integers, and -4006 is not a whole number. Thus, -4006 is not an integer.

26. Some natural numbers are even, all natural numbers are whole numbers, and all whole numbers are integers. Thus, some integers are even.

27. All natural numbers are real numbers, all real numbers are complex numbers, but some complex numbers are not real numbers. The number $19 + 0i$ is a complex number, so it is not a natural number.

28. All rational numbers are real numbers, all real numbers are complex numbers, but some complex numbers are not real numbers. The number $\frac{1}{2} + 0i$ is a complex number, so it is not a rational number.

29. All A are B, all B are C, and all C are D. Thus, all A are D.

30. All A are B, no C are B, and all D are C. Thus, no A are D.

31. No A are B, some A are C, and all C are D. Thus, some D are B.

32. No A are B, some A are C, and all C are D. Thus, some D are C.

33. No A are B, no B are C, and no C are D. Thus, no A are D.

34. Some A are B, some B are C, and some C are D. Thus, some A are D.

35. All A are B, all A are C, and some B are D. Thus, some A are D.

36. Some A are B, all B are C, and some C are D. Thus, some A are D.

Application Exercises

37. This is an excerpt from a 1967 speech in the U.S. House of Representatives by Representative Adam Clayton Powell:

> He who is without sin should cast the first stone. There is no one here who does not have a skeleton in his closet. I know, and I know them by name.

Powell's argument can be expressed as follows:

> No sinner is one who should cast the first stone.
> All people here are sinners.
> Therefore, no person here is one who should cast the first stone.

Use an Euler diagram to determine whether the argument is valid or invalid.

38. In the *Sixth Meditation*, Descartes writes

> I first take notice here that there is a great difference between the mind and the body, in that the body, from its nature, is always divisible and the mind is completely indivisible.

Descartes's argument can be expressed as follows:

> All bodies are divisible.
> No minds are divisible.
> Therefore, no minds are bodies.

Use an Euler diagram to determine whether the argument is valid or invalid.

39. In *Symbolic Logic*, Lewis Carroll presents the following argument:

> Babies are illogical. (All babies are illogical persons.)
> Illogical persons are despised. (All illogical persons are despised persons.)
> Nobody is despised who can manage a crocodile. (No persons who can manage crocodiles are despised persons.)
> Therefore, babies cannot manage crocodiles.

Use an Euler diagram to determine whether the argument is valid or invalid.

Writing in Mathematics

40. Explain how to use Euler diagrams to determine whether or not an argument is valid.

41. Under what circumstances should Euler diagrams rather than truth tables be used to determine whether or not an argument is valid?

Critical Thinking Exercises

Make Sense? *In Exercises 42–45, determine whether each statement makes sense or does not make sense, and explain your reasoning.*

42. I made Euler diagrams for the premises of an argument and one of my possible diagrams illustrated the conclusion, so the argument is valid.

43. I made Euler diagrams for the premises of an argument and one of my possible diagrams did not illustrate the conclusion, so the argument is invalid.

44. I used Euler diagrams to determine that an argument is valid, but when I reverse one of the premises and the conclusion, this new argument is invalid.

45. I can't use Euler diagrams to determine the validity of an argument if one of the premises is false.

46. Write an example of an argument with two quantified premises that is invalid but that has a true conclusion.

47. No animals that eat meat are vegetarians.
No cat is a vegetarian.
Felix is a cat.
Therefore, . . .

a. Felix is a vegetarian.
b. Felix is not a vegetarian.
c. Felix eats meat.
d. All animals that do not eat meat are vegetarians.

48. Supply the missing first premise that will make this argument valid.

Some opera singers are terrible actors.
Therefore, some people who take voice lessons are terrible actors.

49. Supply the missing first premise that will make this argument valid.

All amusing people are entertaining.
Therefore, some teachers are entertaining.

Chapter Summary, Review, and Test

Summary – Definitions and Concepts — Examples

1 Statements, Negations, and Quantified Statements

2 Compound Statements and Connectives

a. A statement is a sentence that is either true or false, but not both simultaneously.

b. Negations and equivalences of quantified statements are given in the following diagram. Each quantified statement's equivalent is written in parentheses below the statement. The statements diagonally opposite each other are negations. Table 2, Ex. 4

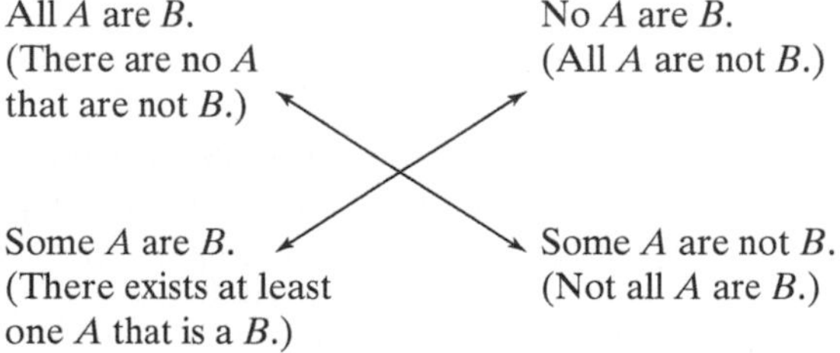
All A are B.
(There are no A that are not B.)
No A are B.
(All A are not B.)
Some A are B.
(There exists at least one A that is a B.)
Some A are not B.
(Not all A are B.)

c. The statements of symbolic logic and their translations are given as follows: Ex. 1, Ex. 2, Ex. 3, Ex. 4, Ex. 5

- Negation
  $\sim p$: Not p. It is not true that p.
- Conjunction
  $p \wedge q$: p and q. p but q. p yet q. p nevertheless q.
- Disjunction
  $p \vee q$: p or q.
- Conditional
  $p \rightarrow q$: If p, then q. q if p. p is sufficient for q. q is necessary for p. p only if q. Only if q, p.
- Biconditional
  $p \leftrightarrow q$: p if and only if q. q if and only if p. If p then q, and if q then p. p is necessary and sufficient for q. q is necessary and sufficient for p.

d. Groupings in symbolic statements are determined as follows: Ex. 6 Ex. 7 Ex. 8

- Unless parentheses follow the negation symbol, ~, only the statement that immediately follows it is negated.
- When translating symbolic statements into English, the simple statements in parentheses appear on the same side of the comma.
- If a symbolic statement appears without parentheses, group statements before and after the most dominant connective, where dominance is defined as follows:

1. Negation 2. Conjunction Disjunction 3. Conditional 4. Biconditional.

Least dominant — Most dominant

3 Truth Tables for Negation, Conjunction, and Disjunction

4 Truth Tables for the Conditional and the Biconditional

a. The definitions of symbolic logic are given by the truth values in the following table: Table 12 Table 14

p	q	Negation $\sim p$	Conjunction $p \wedge q$	Disjunction $p \vee q$	Conditional $p \rightarrow q$	Biconditional $p \leftrightarrow q$
T	T	F	T	T	T	T
T	F	F	F	T	F	F
F	T	T	F	T	T	F
F	F	T	F	F	T	T
		Opposite truth values from p	True only when both component statements are true	False only when both component statements are false	False only when the antecedent is true and the consequent is false	True only when the component statements have the same truth value

b. A truth table for a compound statement shows when the statement is true and when it is false. The first few columns show the simple statements that comprise the compound statement and their possible truth values. The final column heading is the given compound statement. The truth values in each column are determined by looking back at appropriate columns and using one of the five definitions of symbolic logic. If a compound statement is always true, it is called a tautology. Ex. 2 Ex. 3 Ex. 4 Ex. 5 Ex. 6 Ex. 1 Ex. 2 Ex. 3 Ex. 4

c. To determine the truth value of a compound statement for a specific case, substitute the truth values of the simple statements into the symbolic form of the compound statement and then use the appropriate definitions. Ex. 7 Ex. 5

5 Equivalent Statements and Variations of Conditional Statements

6 Negations of Conditional Statements and De Morgan's Laws

a. Two statements are equivalent, symbolized by $\equiv$, if they have the same truth value in every possible case. Ex. 1 Ex. 2

b. Variations of the Conditional Statement $p \rightarrow q$ Ex. 4 Ex. 5 Ex. 1

- $p \rightarrow q$ is equivalent to $\sim q \rightarrow \sim p$, the contrapositive: $p \rightarrow q \equiv \sim q \rightarrow \sim p$.
- $p \rightarrow q$ is not equivalent to $q \rightarrow p$, the converse.
- $p \rightarrow q$ is not equivalent to $\sim p \rightarrow \sim q$, the inverse.
- The negation of $p \rightarrow q$ is $p \wedge \sim q$: $\sim(p \rightarrow q) \equiv p \wedge \sim q$.

c. De Morgan's Laws
- $\sim(p \wedge q) \equiv \sim p \vee \sim q$: The negation of $p \wedge q$ is $\sim p \vee \sim q$.
- $\sim(p \vee q) \equiv \sim p \wedge \sim q$: The negation of $p \vee q$ is $\sim p \wedge \sim q$.

Ex. 2
Ex. 3
Ex. 4

7 Arguments and Truth Tables

a. An argument consists of two parts: the given statements, called the premises, and a conclusion. An argument is valid if the conclusion is true whenever the premises are assumed to be true. An argument that is not valid is called an invalid argument or a fallacy. A valid argument with true premises is called a sound argument.

b. A procedure to test the validity of an argument using a truth table is described in the box near the beginning of this section. If the argument contains n premises, write a conditional statement of the form

$$[(\text{premise } 1) \wedge (\text{premise } 2) \wedge \cdots \wedge (\text{premise } n)] \rightarrow \text{conclusion}$$

and construct a truth table. If the conditional statement is a tautology, the argument is valid; if not, the argument is invalid.

Ex. 1
Ex. 2
Ex. 3
Ex. 5

c. Table 18 contains the standard forms of commonly used valid and invalid arguments.

Ex. 4
Ex. 6

8 Arguments and Euler Diagrams

a. Euler diagrams for quantified statements are given as follows:

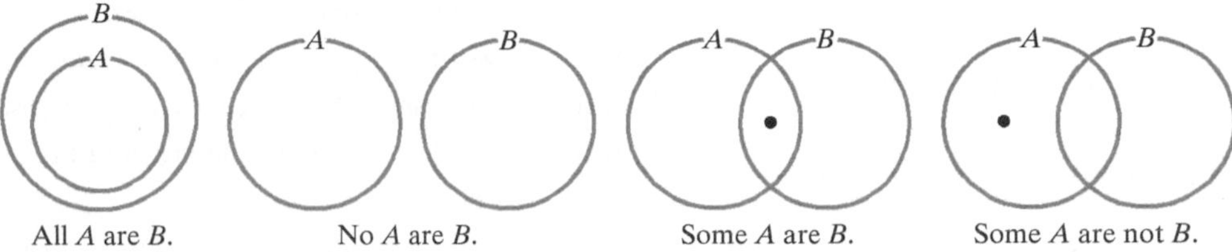

All A are B. No A are B. Some A are B. Some A are not B.

b. To test the validity of an argument with an Euler diagram,
1. Make an Euler diagram for the first premise.
2. Make an Euler diagram for the second premise on top of the one for the first premise.
3. The argument is valid if and only if every possible diagram illustrates the conclusion of the argument.

Ex. 1
Ex. 2
Ex. 3
Ex. 4
Ex. 5
Ex. 6

Review Exercises

1 and 2

In Exercises 1–6, let p, q, and r represent the following simple statements:

p: The temperature is below 32°.

q: We finished studying.

r: We go to the movies.

Express each symbolic compound statement in English. If a symbolic statement is given without parentheses, place them, as needed, before and after the most dominant connective and then translate into English.

1. $p \wedge q \rightarrow r$

2. $\sim r \rightarrow \sim p \vee \sim q$

3. $p \wedge (q \rightarrow r)$

4. $r \leftrightarrow (p \wedge q)$

5. $\sim(p \wedge q)$

6. $\sim r \leftrightarrow (\sim p \vee \sim q)$

In Exercises 7–12, let p, q, and r represent the following simple statements:

p: The outside temperature is at least 80°.

q: The air conditioner is working.

r: The house is hot.

Express each English statement in symbolic form.

7. The outside temperature is at least 80° and the air conditioner is working, or the house is hot.

8. If the outside temperature is at least 80° or the air conditioner is not working, then the house is hot.

9. If the air conditioner is working, then the outside temperature is at least 80° if and only if the house is hot.

10. The house is hot, if and only if the outside temperature is at least 80° and the air conditioner is not working.

11. Having an outside temperature of at least 80° is sufficient for having a hot house.
12. Not having a hot house is necessary for the air conditioner to be working.

In Exercises 13–16, write the negation of each statement.

13. All houses are made with wood.
14. No students major in business.
15. Some crimes are motivated by passion.
16. Some Democrats are not registered voters.
17. The speaker stated that, "All new taxes are for education." We later learned that the speaker was not telling the truth. What can we conclude about new taxes and education?

3 and 4

In Exercises 18–25, construct a truth table for each statement. Then indicate whether the statement is a tautology, a self-contradiction, or neither.

18. $p \vee (\sim p \wedge q)$
19. $\sim p \vee \sim q$
20. $p \rightarrow (\sim p \vee q)$
21. $p \leftrightarrow \sim q$
22. $\sim(p \vee q) \rightarrow (\sim p \wedge \sim q)$
23. $(p \vee q) \rightarrow \sim r$
24. $(p \wedge q) \leftrightarrow (p \wedge r)$
25. $p \wedge [q \vee (r \rightarrow p)]$

In Exercises 26–27,

a. *Write each statement in symbolic form. Assign letters to simple statements that are not negated.*

b. *Construct a truth table for the symbolic statement in part (a).*

c. *Use the truth table to indicate one set of conditions that make the compound statement true, or state that no such conditions exist.*

26. I'm in class or I'm studying, and I'm not in class.
27. If you spit from a truck then it's legal, but if you spit from a car then it's not. (This law is still on the books in Georgia!)

In Exercises 28–31, determine the truth value for each statement when p is true, q is false, and r is false.

28. $\sim(q \leftrightarrow r)$
29. $(p \wedge q) \rightarrow (p \vee r)$
30. $(\sim q \rightarrow p) \vee (r \wedge \sim p)$
31. $\sim[(\sim p \vee r) \rightarrow (q \wedge r)]$

The circle graph shows the percentage of American adults who consider various subjects the most taboo to discuss at work.

What Is the Most Taboo Topic to Discuss at Work?

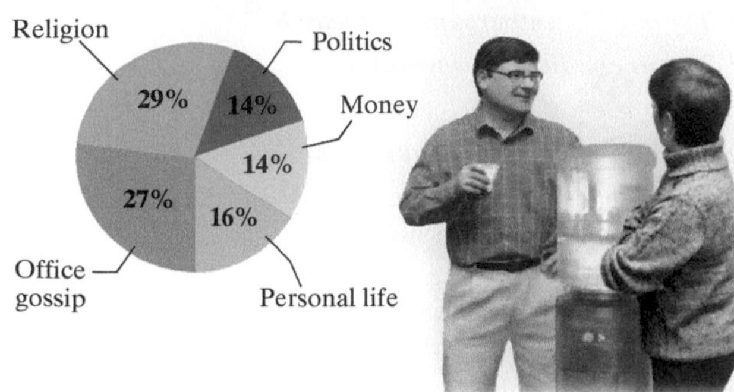

Source: Adecco survey of 1807 workers

In Exercises 32–34, write each statement in symbolic form. Then use the information displayed by the graph at the bottom of the previous column to determine the truth value of the compound statement.

32. Twenty-nine percent consider religion the most taboo topic and it is not true that 14% consider politics the most taboo topic.
33. If a greater percentage of people consider money a more taboo topic than personal life, then 16% consider money the most taboo topic and 14% consider personal life the most taboo topic.
34. Fourteen percent consider money the most taboo topic if and only if 14% consider politics the most taboo topic, or it is not true that the greatest percentage consider religion the most taboo topic.

5 and 6

35. **a.** Use a truth table to show that $\sim p \vee q$ and $p \rightarrow q$ are equivalent.
    b. Use the result from part (a) to write a statement that is equivalent to
    The triangle is not isosceles or it has two equal sides.
36. Select the statement that is equivalent to
    Joe grows mangos or oranges.
    a. If Joe grows mangos, he does not grow oranges.
    b. If Joe grows oranges, he does not grow mangos.
    c. If Joe does not grow mangos, he grows oranges.
    d. Joe grows both mangos and oranges.

In Exercises 37–38, use a truth table to determine whether the two statements are equivalent.

37. $\sim(p \leftrightarrow q), \sim p \vee \sim q$
38. $\sim p \wedge (q \vee r), (\sim p \wedge q) \vee (\sim p \wedge r)$

In Exercises 39–42, write the converse, inverse, and contrapositive of each statement.

39. If I am in Atlanta, then I am in the South.
40. If I am in class, then today is not a holiday.
41. If I work hard, then I pass all courses.
42. $\sim p \rightarrow \sim q$

In Exercises 43–45, write the negation of each conditional statement.

43. If an argument is sound, then it is valid.
44. If I do not work hard, then I do not succeed.
45. $\sim r \rightarrow p$

In Exercises 46–48, use De Morgan's laws to write a statement that is equivalent to each statement.

46. It is not true that both Chicago and Maine are cities.
47. It is not true that Ernest Hemingway was a musician or an actor.
48. If a number is not positive and not negative, the number is 0.

In Exercises 49–51, use De Morgan's laws to write the negation of each statement.

49. I work hard or I do not succeed.

50. She is not using her car and she is taking a bus.

51. $\sim p \vee q$

In Exercises 52–55, determine which, if any, of the three given statements are equivalent.

52. **a.** If it is hot, then I use the air conditioner.

b. If it is not hot, then I do not use the air conditioner.

c. It is not hot or I use the air conditioner.

53. **a.** If she did not play, then we lost.

b. If we did not lose, then she played.

c. She did not play and we did not lose.

54. **a.** He is here or I'm not.

b. If I'm not here, he is.

c. It is not true that he isn't here and I am.

55. **a.** If the class interests me and I like the teacher, then I enjoy studying.

b. If the class interests me, then I like the teacher and I enjoy studying.

c. The class interests me, or I like the teacher and I enjoy studying.

7

In Exercises 56–57, use a truth table to determine whether the symbolic form of the argument is valid or invalid.

56. $p \rightarrow q$
$\underline{\sim q}$
$\therefore p$

57. $p \wedge q$
$\underline{q \rightarrow r}$
$\therefore p \rightarrow r$

In Exercises 58–63, translate each argument into symbolic form. Then determine whether the argument is valid or invalid. You may use a truth table or, if applicable, compare the argument's symbolic form to a standard valid or invalid form.

58. If Tony plays, the team wins.
The team won.
∴ Tony played.

59. My plant is fertilized or it turns yellow.
My plant is turning yellow.
∴ My plant is not fertilized.

60. A majority of legislators vote for a bill or that bill does not become law.
A majority of legislators did not vote for bill x.
∴ Bill x did not become law.

61. Having good eye–hand coordination is necessary for being a good baseball player.
Todd does not have good eye–hand coordination.
∴ Todd is not a good baseball player.

62. If you love the person you marry, you can fall out of love with that person.
If you do not love the person you marry, you can fall in love with that person.
∴ You love the person you marry if and only if you can fall out of love with that person.

63. If I purchase season tickets to the football games, then I do not attend all lectures.
If I do well in school, then I attend all lectures.
∴ If I do not do well in school, then I purchased season tickets to the football games.

8

In Exercises 64–69, use Euler diagrams to determine whether each argument is valid or invalid.

64. All birds have feathers.
All parrots have feathers.
∴ All parrots are birds.

65. All botanists are scientists.
All scientists have college degrees.
∴ All botanists have college degrees.

66. All native desert plants can withstand severe drought.
No tree ferns can withstand severe drought.
∴ No tree ferns are native desert plants.

67. All native desert plants can withstand severe drought.
No tree ferns are native desert plants.
∴ No tree ferns can withstand severe drought.

68. All poets are writers.
Some writers are wealthy.
∴ Some poets are wealthy.

69. Some people enjoy reading.
All people who enjoy reading appreciate language.
∴ Some people appreciate language.

Chapter Test

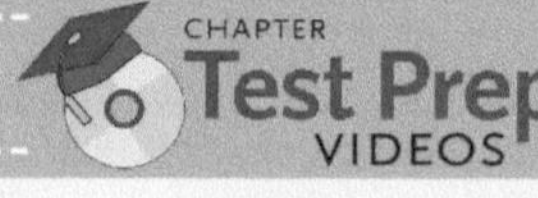

Step-by-step test solutions are found on the Chapter Test Prep Videos available on YouTube (search "Blitzer, Thinking Mathematically" and click on "Channels").

Use the following representations in Exercises 1–6:

p: I'm registered.
q: I'm a citizen.
r: I vote.

Express each compound statement in English.

1. $(p \wedge q) \rightarrow r$

2. $\sim r \leftrightarrow (\sim p \vee \sim q)$

3. $\sim(p \vee q)$

Express each English statement in symbolic form.

4. I am registered and a citizen, or I do not vote.

5. If I am not registered or not a citizen, then I do not vote.

6. Being a citizen is necessary for voting.

In Exercises 7–8, write the negation of the statement.

7. All numbers are divisible by 5.

8. Some people wear glasses.

In Exercises 9–11, construct a truth table for the statement.

9. $p \wedge (\sim p \vee q)$

10. $\sim(p \wedge q) \leftrightarrow (\sim p \vee \sim q)$

11. $p \leftrightarrow q \vee r$

12. Write the following statement in symbolic form and construct a truth table. Then indicate one set of conditions that makes, the compound statement false.

    If you break the law and change the law, then you have not broken the law.

In Exercises 13–14, determine the truth value for each statement when p is false, q is true, and r is false.

13. $\sim(q \rightarrow r)$

14. $(p \vee r) \leftrightarrow (\sim r \wedge p)$

15. The following statement pertains to support for the death penalty in the United States in 2008 compared to 1997:

    There was no increase in the percentage of Americans who supported the death penalty, or there was an increase in the percentage who opposed the death penalty and those who were not sure about the death penalty.

    a. Write the statement in symbolic form.

    b. Use the information in the following graph to determine the truth value of the statement in part (a).

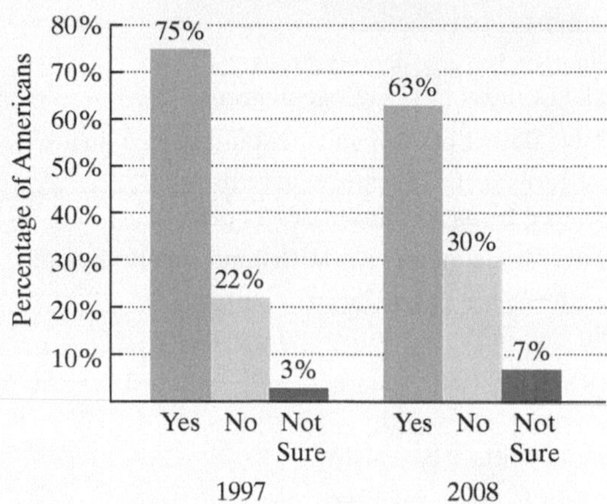

Source: Harris Interactive

16. Select the statement below that is equivalent to

    Gene is an actor or a musician.

    a. If Gene is an actor, then he is not a musician.

    b. If Gene is not an actor, then he is a musician.

    c. It is false that Gene is not an actor or not a musician.

    d. If Gene is an actor, then he is a musician.

17. Write the contrapositive of
    If it is August, it does not snow.

18. Write the converse and the inverse of the following statement:
    If the radio is playing, then I cannot concentrate.

19. Write the negation of the following statement:
    If it is cold, we do not use the pool.

20. Write a statement that is equivalent to
    It is not true that the test is today or the party is tonight.

21. Write the negation of the following statement:
    The banana is green and it is not ready to eat.

In Exercises 22–23, determine which, if any, of the three given statements are equivalent.

22. **a.** If I'm not feeling well, I'm grouchy.

    b. I'm feeling well or I'm grouchy.

    c. If I'm feeling well, I'm not grouchy.

23. **a.** It is not true that today is a holiday or tomorrow is a holiday.

    b. If today is not a holiday, then tomorrow is not a holiday.

    c. Today is not a holiday and tomorrow is not a holiday.

Determine whether each argument in Exercises 24–29 is valid or invalid.

24. If a parrot talks, it is intelligent.
    This parrot is intelligent.
    ∴ This parrot talks.

25. I am sick or I am tired.
    I am not tired.
    ∴ I am sick.

26. I am going if and only if you are not.
    You are going.
    ∴ I'm going.

27. All mammals are warm-blooded.
    All dogs are warm-blooded.
    ∴ All dogs are mammals.

28. All conservationists are advocates of solar-powered cars.
    No oil company executives are advocates of solar-powered cars.
    ∴ No conservationists are oil company executives.

29. All rabbis are Jewish.
    Some Jews observe kosher dietary traditions.
    ∴ Some rabbis observe kosher dietary traditions.

Answers to Selected Exercises

Section 1

Check Point Exercises

1. a. Paris is not the capital of Spain. **b.** July is a month. **2. a.** $\sim p$ **b.** $\sim q$ **3.** Chicago O'Hare is not the world's busiest airport. **4.** Some new tax dollars will not be used to improve education.; At least one new tax dollar will not be used to improve education.

Exercise Set 1

1. statement **3.** statement **5.** not a statement **7.** statement **9.** not a statement **11.** statement **13.** statement **15.** It is not raining. **17.** The Dallas Cowboys are the team with the most Super Bowl wins. **19.** Chocolate in moderation is good for the heart. **21.** $\sim p$ **23.** $\sim r$ **25.** Listening to classical music does not make infants smarter. **27.** Sigmund Freud's father was 20 years older than his mother. **29. a.** There are no whales that are not mammals. **b.** Some whales are not mammals. **31. a.** At least one student is a business major. **b.** No students are business majors. **33. a.** At least one thief is not a criminal. **b.** All thieves are criminals. **35. a.** All Democratic presidents have not been impeached. **b.** Some Democratic presidents have been impeached. **37. a.** All seniors graduated. **b.** Some seniors did not graduate. **39. a.** Some parrots are not pets. **b.** All parrots are pets. **41. a.** No atheist is a churchgoer. **b.** Some atheists are churchgoers. **43.** Some Africans have Jewish ancestry. **45.** Some rap is not hip-hop. **47. a.** All birds are parrots. **b.** false; Some birds are not parrots. **49. a.** No college students are business majors. **b.** false; Some college students are business majors. **51. a.** All people like Sara Lee. **b.** Some people don't like Sara Lee. **53. a.** No safe thing is exciting. **b.** Some safe things are exciting. **55. a.** Some great actors are not a Tom Hanks. **b.** All great actors are a Tom Hanks. **57.** b **59.** true **61.** false; Some college students in the United States are willing to marry without romantic love. **63.** true **65.** false; The sentence "5% of college students in Australia are willing to marry without romantic love" is a statement. **75.** does not make sense **77.** does not make sense

Section 2

Check Point Exercises

1. a. $q \wedge p$ **b.** $\sim p \wedge q$ **2. a.** $p \vee q$ **b.** $q \vee \sim p$ **3. a.** $\sim p \rightarrow \sim q$ **b.** $q \rightarrow \sim p$ **4.** $\sim q \rightarrow p$ **5. a.** $q \leftrightarrow p$ **b.** $\sim p \leftrightarrow \sim q$ **6. a.** It is not true that he earns $105,000 yearly and that he is often happy. **b.** He is not often happy and he earns $105,000 yearly. **c.** It is not true that if he is often happy then he earns $105,000 yearly. **7. a.** If the plant is fertilized and watered, then it will not wilt. **b.** The plant is fertilized, and if it is watered then it will not wilt. **8.** p: There is too much homework.; q: A teacher is boring.; r: I take the class. **a.** $(p \vee q) \rightarrow \sim r$ **b.** $p \vee (q \rightarrow \sim r)$

Exercise Set 2

1. $p \wedge q$ **3.** $q \wedge \sim p$ **5.** $\sim q \wedge p$ **7.** $p \vee q$ **9.** $p \vee \sim q$ **11.** $p \rightarrow q$ **13.** $\sim p \rightarrow \sim q$ **15.** $\sim q \rightarrow \sim p$ **17.** $p \rightarrow q$ **19.** $p \rightarrow \sim q$ **21.** $q \rightarrow \sim p$ **23.** $p \rightarrow \sim q$ **25.** $q \rightarrow \sim p$ **27.** $p \leftrightarrow q$ **29.** $\sim q \leftrightarrow \sim p$ **31.** $q \leftrightarrow p$ **33.** The heater is not working and the house is cold. **35.** The heater is working or the house is not cold. **37.** If the heater is working, then the house is not cold. **39.** The heater is working if and only if the house is not cold. **41.** It is July 4th and we are not having a barbecue. **43.** It is not July 4th or we are having a barbecue. **45.** If we are having a barbecue, then it is not July 4th. **47.** It is not July 4th if and only if we are having a barbecue. **49.** It is not true that Romeo loves Juliet and Juliet loves Romeo. **51.** Romeo does not love Juliet and Juliet loves Romeo. **53.** It is not true that Juliet loves Romeo or Romeo loves Juliet; Neither Juliet loves Romeo nor Romeo loves Juliet. **55.** Juliet does not love Romeo or Romeo loves Juliet. **57.** Romeo does not love Juliet and Juliet does not love Romeo. **59.** $(p \wedge q) \vee r$ **61.** $(p \vee \sim q) \rightarrow r$ **63.** $r \leftrightarrow (p \wedge \sim q)$ **65.** $(p \wedge \sim q) \rightarrow r$ **67.** If the temperature is above 85° and we have finished studying, then we will go to the beach. **69.** The temperature is above 85°, and if we have finished studying then we will go to the beach. **71.** $\sim r \rightarrow (\sim p \vee \sim q)$; If we do not go to the beach, then the temperature is not above 85° or we have not finished studying. **73.** If we do not go to the beach then we have not finished studying, or the temperature is above 85°. **75.** $r \leftrightarrow (p \wedge q)$; We will go to the beach if and only if the temperature is above 85° and we have finished studying. **77.** The temperature is above 85° if and only if we have finished studying, and we go to the beach. **79.** If we do not go to the beach, then it is not true that both the temperature is above 85° and we have finished studying. **81.** p: I like the teacher.; q: The course is interesting.; r: I miss class.; $(p \vee q) \rightarrow \sim r$ **83.** p: I like the teacher.; q: The course is interesting.; r: I miss class.; $p \vee (q \rightarrow \sim r)$ **85.** p: I like the teacher.; q: The course is interesting.; r: I miss class.; $r \leftrightarrow \sim(p \wedge q)$ **87.** p: I like the teacher.; q: The course is interesting.; r: I miss class.; $(p \rightarrow \sim r) \leftrightarrow q$ **89.** p: I like the teacher.; q: The course is interesting.; r: I miss class.; s: I spend extra time reading the book.; $(\sim p \wedge r) \rightarrow (\sim q \vee s)$ **91.** p: Being French is necessary for being a Parisian.; q: Being German is necessary for being a Berliner.; $\sim p \rightarrow \sim q$ **93.** p: You file an income tax report.; q: You file a complete statement of earnings.; r: You are a taxpayer.; s: You are an authorized tax preparer.; $(r \vee s) \rightarrow (p \wedge q)$ **95.** p: You are wealthy.; q: You are happy.; r: You live contentedly.; $\sim(p \rightarrow (q \wedge r))$ **97.** $[p \rightarrow (q \vee r)] \leftrightarrow (p \wedge r)$ **99.** $(p \rightarrow p) \leftrightarrow [(p \wedge p) \rightarrow \sim p]$ **101.** $\sim p \rightarrow q$ **103.** $(p \rightarrow q) \wedge \sim q$ **105.** $((p \rightarrow q) \wedge \sim p) \rightarrow \sim q$ **115.** makes sense **117.** does not make sense **119.** p: Shooting unarmed citizens is morally justifiable.; q: Bombing unarmed citizens is morally justifiable.; $((p \leftrightarrow q) \wedge \sim p) \rightarrow \sim q$

Section 3

Check Point Exercises

1. a. false **b.** true **c.** false **d.** true

2.

p	q	$p \vee q$	$\sim(p \vee q)$
T	T	T	F
T	F	T	F
F	T	T	F
F	F	F	T

$\sim(p \vee q)$ is true when both p and q are false; otherwise, $\sim(p \vee q)$ is false.

3.

p	q	$\sim p$	$\sim q$	$\sim p \wedge \sim q$
T	T	F	F	F
T	F	F	T	F
F	T	T	F	F
F	F	T	T	T

$\sim p \wedge \sim q$ is true when both p and q are false; otherwise, $\sim p \wedge \sim q$ is false.

4.

p	q	$\sim q$	$p \wedge \sim q$	$\sim p$	$(p \wedge \sim q) \vee \sim p$
T	T	F	F	F	F
T	F	T	T	F	T
F	T	F	F	T	T
F	F	T	F	T	T

$(p \wedge \sim q) \vee \sim p$ is false when both p and q are true; otherwise, $(p \wedge \sim q) \vee \sim p$ is true.

5.

p	$\sim p$	$p \wedge \sim p$
T	F	F
F	T	F

$p \wedge \sim p$ is false in all cases.

6. p: I study hard.; q: I ace the final.; r: I fail the course.

a.

p	q	r	$q \vee r$	$p \wedge (q \vee r)$
T	T	T	T	T
T	T	F	T	T
T	F	T	T	T
T	F	F	F	F
F	T	T	T	F
F	T	F	T	F
F	F	T	T	F
F	F	F	F	F

b. false **7.** true

Exercise Set 3

1. true **3.** false **5.** false **7.** false **9.** true **11.** true **13.** true **15.** true

17.

p	$\sim p$	$\sim p \wedge p$
T	F	F
F	T	F

19.

p	q	$\sim p$	$\sim p \wedge q$
T	T	F	F
T	F	F	F
F	T	T	T
F	F	T	F

21.

p	q	$p \vee q$	$\sim(p \vee q)$
T	T	T	F
T	F	T	F
F	T	T	F
F	F	F	T

23.

p	q	$\sim p$	$\sim q$	$\sim p \wedge \sim q$
T	T	F	F	F
T	F	F	T	F
F	T	T	F	F
F	F	T	T	T

25.

p	q	$\sim q$	$p \vee \sim q$
T	T	F	T
T	F	T	T
F	T	F	F
F	F	T	T

27.

p	q	$\sim p$	$\sim p \vee q$	$\sim(\sim p \vee q)$
T	T	F	T	F
T	F	F	F	T
F	T	T	T	F
F	F	T	T	F

29.

p	q	$\sim p$	$p \vee q$	$(p \vee q) \wedge \sim p$
T	T	F	T	F
T	F	F	T	F
F	T	T	T	T
F	F	T	F	F

31.

p	q	$\sim p$	$\sim q$	$p \wedge \sim q$	$\sim p \vee (p \wedge \sim q)$
T	T	F	F	F	F
T	F	F	T	T	T
F	T	T	F	F	T
F	F	T	T	F	T

33.

p	q	$\sim p$	$\sim q$	$p \vee q$	$\sim p \vee \sim q$	$(p \vee q) \wedge (\sim p \vee \sim q)$
T	T	F	F	T	F	F
T	F	F	T	T	T	T
F	T	T	F	T	T	T
F	F	T	T	F	T	F

35.

p	q	$\sim q$	$p \wedge \sim q$	$p \wedge q$	$(p \wedge \sim q) \vee (p \wedge q)$
T	T	F	F	T	T
T	F	T	T	F	T
F	T	F	F	F	F
F	F	T	F	F	F

37.

p	q	r	$\sim q$	$\sim q \vee r$	$p \wedge (\sim q \vee r)$
T	T	T	F	T	T
T	T	F	F	F	F
T	F	T	T	T	T
T	F	F	T	T	T
F	T	T	F	T	F
F	T	F	F	F	F
F	F	T	T	T	F
F	F	F	T	T	F

39.

p	q	r	$\sim p$	$\sim q$	$r \wedge \sim p$	$(r \wedge \sim p) \vee \sim q$
T	T	T	F	F	F	F
T	T	F	F	F	F	F
T	F	T	F	T	F	T
T	F	F	F	T	F	T
F	T	T	T	F	T	T
F	T	F	T	F	F	F
F	F	T	T	T	T	T
F	F	F	T	T	F	T

41.

p	q	r	$p \vee q$	$\sim(p \vee q)$	$\sim r$	$\sim(p \vee q) \wedge \sim r$
T	T	T	T	F	F	F
T	T	F	T	F	T	F
T	F	T	T	F	F	F
T	F	F	T	F	T	F
F	T	T	T	F	F	F
F	T	F	T	F	T	F
F	F	T	F	T	F	F
F	F	F	F	T	T	T

43. a. p: You did the dishes.; q: You left the room a mess.; $\sim p \wedge q$ **b.** See truth table for Exercise 19. **c.** The statement is true when p is false and q is true. **45. a.** p: I bought a meal ticket.; q: I used it.; $\sim(p \wedge \sim q)$

b.

p	q	$\sim q$	$p \wedge \sim q$	$\sim(p \wedge \sim q)$
T	T	F	F	T
T	F	T	T	F
F	T	F	F	T
F	F	T	F	T

c. Answers will vary; an example is: The statement is true when p and q are true.

47. a. p: The student is intelligent.; q: The student is an overachiever.; $(p \vee q) \wedge \sim q$

b.

p	q	$\sim q$	$p \vee q$	$(p \vee q) \wedge \sim q$
T	T	F	T	F
T	F	T	T	T
F	T	F	T	F
F	F	T	F	F

c. The statement is true when p is true and q is false.

49. a. p: Married people are healthier than single people.; q: Married people are more economically stable than single people.; r: Children of married people do better on a variety of indicators.; $(p \wedge q) \wedge r$

b.

p	q	r	$p \wedge q$	$(p \wedge q) \wedge r$
T	T	T	T	T
T	T	F	T	F
T	F	T	F	F
T	F	F	F	F
F	T	T	F	F
F	T	F	F	F
F	F	T	F	F
F	F	F	F	F

c. The statement is true when p, q, and r are all true.

51. a. p: I go to office hours.; q: I ask questions.; r: My professor remembers me.; $(p \wedge q) \vee \sim r$

b.

p	q	r	$\sim r$	$p \wedge q$	$(p \wedge q) \vee \sim r$
T	T	T	F	T	T
T	T	F	T	T	T
T	F	T	F	F	F
T	F	F	T	F	T
F	T	T	F	F	F
F	T	F	T	F	T
F	F	T	F	F	F
F	F	F	T	F	T

c. Answers will vary; an example is: The statement is true when p, q, and r are all true.

53. false **55.** true **57.** true **59.** false **61.** true

63.

p	q	$\sim[\sim(p \wedge \sim q) \vee \sim(\sim p \vee q)]$
T	T	F
T	F	F
F	T	F
F	F	F

65.

p	q	r	$[(p \wedge \sim r) \vee (q \wedge \sim r)] \wedge \sim(\sim p \vee r)$
T	T	T	F
T	T	F	T
T	F	T	F
T	F	F	T
F	T	T	F
F	T	F	F
F	F	T	F
F	F	F	F

67. p: You notice this notice.; q: You notice this notice is not worth noticing.; $(p \vee \sim p) \wedge q$

p	q	$\sim p$	$p \vee \sim p$	$(p \vee \sim p) \wedge q$
T	T	F	T	T
T	F	F	T	F
F	T	T	T	T
F	F	T	T	F

The statement is true when q is true.

69. p: $x \leq 3$; q: $x \geq 7$; $\sim(p \vee q) \wedge (\sim p \wedge \sim q)$

p	q	$\sim p$	$\sim q$	$p \vee q$	$\sim(p \vee q)$	$\sim p \wedge \sim q$	$\sim(p \vee q) \wedge (\sim p \wedge \sim q)$
T	T	F	F	T	F	F	F
T	F	F	T	T	F	F	F
F	T	T	F	T	F	F	F
F	F	T	T	F	T	T	T

The statement is true when both p and q are false.

71. The percent body fat in women peaks at age 55 and the percent body fat in men does not peak at age 65.; false **73.** The percent body fat in women does not peak at age 55 and men have more than 24% body fat at age 25.; false **75.** The percent body fat in women peaks at age 55 or the percent body fat in men does not peak at age 65.; true **77.** The percent body fat in women does not peak at age 55 or men have more than 24% body fat at age 25.; false **79.** The percent body fat in women peaks at age 55 and the percent body fat in men peaks at age 65, or men have more than 24% body fat at age 25.; true **81.** p: In 2000, 2% of 20-year-old men had completed the transition to adulthood.; q: In 2000, 46% of 30-year-old men had completed the transition to adulthood.; $\sim(p \wedge q)$; true **83.** p: From 1960 through 2000, the percentage of 20-year-old women making the transition to adulthood decreased.; q: From 1960 through 2000, the percentage of 30-year-old women making the transition increased.; r: From 1960 through 2000, the percentage of 30-year-old men making the transition decreased.; $(p \vee q) \wedge \sim r$; false **85. a.** Hora Gershwin **b.** Bolera Mozart does not have a master's degree in music. Cha-Cha Bach does not either play three instruments or have five years experience playing with a symphony orchestra. **95.** does not make sense **97.** does not make sense

101.

p	q	$p \veebar q$
T	T	F
T	F	T
F	T	T
F	F	F

Section 4

Check Point Exercises

1.

p	q	$\sim p$	$\sim q$	$\sim p \rightarrow \sim q$
T	T	F	F	T
T	F	F	T	T
F	T	T	F	F
F	F	T	T	T

2. The table shows that $[(p \rightarrow q) \wedge \sim q] \rightarrow \sim p$ is always true; therefore, it is a tautology.

p	q	$\sim p$	$\sim q$	$p \rightarrow q$	$(p \rightarrow q) \wedge \sim q$	$[(p \rightarrow q) \wedge \sim q] \rightarrow \sim p$
T	T	F	F	T	F	T
T	F	F	T	F	F	T
F	T	T	F	T	F	T
F	F	T	T	T	T	T

3. a. p: You use Hair Grow.; q: You apply it daily.; r: You go bald.

p	q	r	$\sim r$	$p \wedge q$	$(p \wedge q) \rightarrow \sim r$
T	T	T	F	T	F
T	T	F	T	T	T
T	F	T	F	F	T
T	F	F	T	F	T
F	T	T	F	F	T
F	T	F	T	F	T
F	F	T	F	F	T
F	F	F	T	F	T

b. no

4.

p	q	$p \vee q$	$\sim p$	$\sim p \rightarrow q$	$(p \vee q) \leftrightarrow (\sim p \rightarrow q)$
T	T	T	F	T	T
T	F	T	F	T	T
F	T	T	T	T	T
F	F	F	T	F	T

Because all cases are true, the statement is a tautology.

5. true

Exercise Set 4

1.

p	q	$\sim q$	$p \rightarrow \sim q$
T	T	F	F
T	F	T	T
F	T	F	T
F	F	T	T

3.

p	q	$q \rightarrow p$	$\sim(q \rightarrow p)$
T	T	T	F
T	F	T	F
F	T	F	T
F	F	T	F

5.

p	q	$p \wedge q$	$p \vee q$	$(p \wedge q) \rightarrow (p \vee q)$
T	T	T	T	T
T	F	F	T	T
F	T	F	T	T
F	F	F	F	T

7.

p	q	$p \rightarrow q$	$\sim q$	$(p \rightarrow q) \wedge \sim q$
T	T	T	F	F
T	F	F	T	F
F	T	T	F	F
F	F	T	T	T

9.

p	q	r	$p \vee q$	$(p \vee q) \rightarrow r$
T	T	T	T	T
T	T	F	T	F
T	F	T	T	T
T	F	F	T	F
F	T	T	T	T
F	T	F	T	F
F	F	T	F	T
F	F	F	F	T

11.

p	q	r	$p \wedge q$	$r \rightarrow (p \wedge q)$
T	T	T	T	T
T	T	F	T	T
T	F	T	F	F
T	F	F	F	T
F	T	T	F	F
F	T	F	F	T
F	F	T	F	F
F	F	F	F	T

13.

p	q	r	$\sim q$	$\sim r$	$\sim q \rightarrow p$	$\sim r \wedge (\sim q \rightarrow p)$
T	T	T	F	F	T	F
T	T	F	F	T	T	T
T	F	T	T	F	T	F
T	F	F	T	T	T	T
F	T	T	F	F	T	F
F	T	F	F	T	T	T
F	F	T	T	F	F	F
F	F	F	T	T	F	T

15.

p	q	r	$\sim q$	$p \wedge r$	$\sim(p \wedge r)$	$\sim q \vee r$	$\sim(p \wedge r) \rightarrow (\sim q \vee r)$
T	T	T	F	T	F	T	T
T	T	F	F	F	T	F	F
T	F	T	T	T	F	T	T
T	F	F	T	F	T	T	T
F	T	T	F	F	T	T	T
F	T	F	F	F	T	F	F
F	F	T	T	F	T	T	T
F	F	F	T	F	T	T	T

17.

p	q	$\sim q$	$p \leftrightarrow \sim q$
T	T	F	F
T	F	T	T
F	T	F	T
F	F	T	F

19.

p	q	$p \leftrightarrow q$	$\sim(p \leftrightarrow q)$
T	T	T	F
T	F	F	T
F	T	F	T
F	F	T	F

21.

p	q	$p \leftrightarrow q$	$(p \leftrightarrow q) \rightarrow p$
T	T	T	T
T	F	F	T
F	T	F	T
F	F	T	F

23.

p	q	$\sim p$	$\sim p \leftrightarrow q$	$\sim p \rightarrow q$	$(\sim p \leftrightarrow q) \rightarrow (\sim p \rightarrow q)$
T	T	F	F	T	T
T	F	F	T	T	T
F	T	T	T	T	T
F	F	T	F	F	T

25.

p	q	$p \wedge q$	$q \rightarrow p$	$(p \wedge q) \wedge (q \rightarrow p)$	$[(p \wedge q) \wedge (q \rightarrow p)] \leftrightarrow (p \wedge q)$
T	T	T	T	T	T
T	F	F	T	F	T
F	T	F	F	F	T
F	F	F	T	F	T

27.

p	q	r	$\sim r$	$p \leftrightarrow q$	$(p \leftrightarrow q) \rightarrow \sim r$
T	T	T	F	T	F
T	T	F	T	T	T
T	F	T	F	F	T
T	F	F	T	F	T
F	T	T	F	F	T
F	T	F	T	F	T
F	F	T	F	T	F
F	F	F	T	T	T

29.

p	q	r	$p \wedge r$	$q \vee r$	$\sim(q \vee r)$	$(p \wedge r) \leftrightarrow \sim(q \vee r)$
T	T	T	T	T	F	F
T	T	F	F	T	F	T
T	F	T	T	T	F	F
T	F	F	F	F	T	F
F	T	T	F	T	F	T
F	T	F	F	T	F	T
F	F	T	F	T	F	T
F	F	F	F	F	T	F

31.

p	q	r	$\sim q$	$\sim q \wedge p$	$r \vee (\sim q \wedge p)$	$\sim p$	$[r \vee (\sim q \wedge p)] \leftrightarrow \sim p$
T	T	T	F	F	T	F	F
T	T	F	F	F	F	F	T
T	F	T	T	T	T	F	F
T	F	F	T	T	T	F	F
F	T	T	F	F	T	T	T
F	T	F	F	F	F	T	F
F	F	T	T	F	T	T	T
F	F	F	T	F	F	T	F

33. neither

p	q	$p \rightarrow q$	$(p \rightarrow q) \wedge q$	$[(p \rightarrow q) \wedge q] \rightarrow p$
T	T	T	T	T
T	F	F	F	T
F	T	T	T	F
F	F	T	F	T

35. tautology

p	q	$\sim p$	$\sim q$	$p \rightarrow q$	$(p \rightarrow q) \wedge \sim q$	$[(p \rightarrow q) \wedge \sim q] \rightarrow \sim p$
T	T	F	F	T	F	T
T	F	F	T	F	F	T
F	T	T	F	T	F	T
F	F	T	T	T	T	T

37. neither

p	q	$\sim q$	$p \vee q$	$(p \vee q) \wedge p$	$[(p \vee q) \wedge p] \rightarrow \sim q$
T	T	F	T	T	F
T	F	T	T	T	T
F	T	F	T	F	T
F	F	T	F	F	T

39. tautology

p	q	$\sim p$	$p \rightarrow q$	$\sim p \vee q$	$(p \rightarrow q) \rightarrow (\sim p \vee q)$
T	T	F	T	T	T
T	F	F	F	F	T
F	T	T	T	T	T
F	F	T	T	T	T

41. self-contradiction

p	q	$\sim p$	$\sim q$	$p \wedge q$	$\sim p \vee \sim q$	$(p \wedge q) \wedge (\sim p \vee \sim q)$
T	T	F	F	T	F	F
T	F	F	T	F	T	F
F	T	T	F	F	T	F
F	F	T	T	F	T	F

43. neither

p	q	$\sim p$	$\sim q$	$p \wedge q$	$\sim(p \wedge q)$	$\sim p \wedge \sim q$	$\sim(p \wedge q) \leftrightarrow (\sim p \wedge \sim q)$
T	T	F	F	T	F	F	T
T	F	F	T	F	T	F	F
F	T	T	F	F	T	F	F
F	F	T	T	F	T	T	T

45. neither

p	q	$p \rightarrow q$	$q \rightarrow p$	$(p \rightarrow q) \leftrightarrow (q \rightarrow p)$
T	T	T	T	T
T	F	F	T	F
F	T	T	F	F
F	F	T	T	T

47. tautology

p	q	$\sim p$	$p \rightarrow q$	$\sim p \vee q$	$(p \rightarrow q) \leftrightarrow (\sim p \vee q)$
T	T	F	T	T	T
T	F	F	F	F	T
F	T	T	T	T	T
F	F	T	T	T	T

49. tautology

p	q	$p \leftrightarrow q$	$p \rightarrow q$	$q \rightarrow p$	$(q \rightarrow p) \wedge (p \rightarrow q)$	$(p \leftrightarrow q) \leftrightarrow [(q \rightarrow p) \wedge (p \rightarrow q)]$
T	T	T	T	T	T	T
T	F	F	F	T	F	T
F	T	F	T	F	F	T
F	F	T	T	T	T	T

51. neither

p	q	r	$\sim p$	$p \wedge q$	$\sim p \vee r$	$(p \wedge q) \leftrightarrow (\sim p \vee r)$
T	T	T	F	T	T	T
T	T	F	F	T	F	F
T	F	T	F	F	T	F
T	F	F	F	F	F	T
F	T	T	T	F	T	F
F	T	F	T	F	T	F
F	F	T	T	F	T	F
F	F	F	T	F	T	F

53. tautology

p	q	r	$p \to q$	$q \to r$	$(p \to q) \wedge (q \to r)$	$p \to r$	$[(p \to q) \wedge (q \to r)] \to (p \to r)$
T	T	T	T	T	T	T	T
T	T	F	T	F	F	F	T
T	F	T	F	T	F	T	T
T	F	F	F	T	F	F	T
F	T	T	T	T	T	T	T
F	T	F	T	F	F	T	T
F	F	T	T	T	T	T	T
F	F	F	T	T	T	T	T

55. neither

p	q	r	$[(q \to r) \wedge (r \to \sim p)] \leftrightarrow (q \wedge p)$
T	T	T	F
T	T	F	F
T	F	T	T
T	F	F	F
F	T	T	F
F	T	F	T
F	F	T	F
F	F	F	F

57. a. p: You do homework right after class.; q: You fall behind.; $(p \to \sim q) \wedge (\sim p \to q)$

b.

p	q	$\sim p$	$\sim q$	$p \to \sim q$	$\sim p \to q$	$(p \to \sim q) \wedge (\sim p \to q)$
T	T	F	F	F	T	F
T	F	F	T	T	T	T
F	T	T	F	T	T	T
F	F	T	T	T	F	F

c. Answers will vary; an example is: The statement is true when p and q have opposite truth values.

59. a. p: You cut and paste from the Internet.; q: You cite the source.; r: You are charged with plagiarism.; $(p \wedge \sim q) \to r$

b.

p	q	r	$\sim q$	$p \wedge \sim q$	$(p \wedge \sim q) \to r$
T	T	T	F	F	T
T	T	F	F	F	T
T	F	T	T	T	T
T	F	F	T	T	F
F	T	T	F	F	T
F	T	F	F	F	T
F	F	T	T	F	T
F	F	F	T	F	T

c. Answers will vary; an example is: The statement is true when p, q, and r are all true.

61. a. p: You are comfortable in your room.; q: You are honest with your roommate.; r: You enjoy the college experience.; $(p \leftrightarrow q) \vee \sim r$

b.

p	q	r	$\sim r$	$p \leftrightarrow q$	$(p \leftrightarrow q) \vee \sim r$
T	T	T	F	T	T
T	T	F	T	T	T
T	F	T	F	F	F
T	F	F	T	F	T
F	T	T	F	F	F
F	T	F	T	F	T
F	F	T	F	T	T
F	F	F	T	T	T

c. Answers will vary; an example is: The statement is true when p, q, and r are all true.

63. a. p: I enjoy the course.; q: I choose the class based on the professor.; r: I choose the class based on the course description.; $p \leftrightarrow (q \wedge \sim r)$

b.

p	q	r	$\sim r$	$q \wedge \sim r$	$p \leftrightarrow (q \wedge \sim r)$
T	T	T	F	F	F
T	T	F	T	T	T
T	F	T	F	F	F
T	F	F	T	F	F
F	T	T	F	F	T
F	T	F	T	T	F
F	F	T	F	F	T
F	F	F	T	F	T

c. Answers will vary; an example is: The statement is true when p, q, and r are all false.
65. false **67.** true **69.** false **71.** true **73.** true
75. $(p \rightarrow q) \leftrightarrow [(p \wedge q) \rightarrow \sim p]$

p	q	$(p \rightarrow q) \leftrightarrow [(p \wedge q) \rightarrow \sim p]$
T	T	F
T	F	F
F	T	T
F	F	T

77. $[p \rightarrow (\sim q \vee r)] \leftrightarrow (p \wedge r)$

p	q	r	$[p \rightarrow (\sim q \vee r)] \leftrightarrow (p \wedge r)$
T	T	T	T
T	T	F	T
T	F	T	T
T	F	F	F
F	T	T	F
F	T	F	F
F	F	T	F
F	F	F	F

79. p: You love a person.; q: You marry that person.; $(q \rightarrow p) \wedge (\sim p \rightarrow \sim q)$

p	q	$\sim p$	$\sim q$	$q \rightarrow p$	$\sim p \rightarrow \sim q$	$(q \rightarrow p) \wedge (\sim p \rightarrow \sim q)$
T	T	F	F	T	T	T
T	F	F	T	T	T	T
F	T	T	F	F	F	F
F	F	T	T	T	T	T

Answers will vary; an example is: The statement is false when p is false and q is true.
81. p: You are happy.; q: You live contentedly.; r: You are wealthy.; $\sim[r \rightarrow (p \wedge q)]$

p	q	r	$p \wedge q$	$r \rightarrow (p \wedge q)$	$\sim[r \rightarrow (p \wedge q)]$
T	T	T	T	T	F
T	T	F	T	T	F
T	F	T	F	F	T
T	F	F	F	T	F
F	T	T	F	F	T
F	T	F	F	T	F
F	F	T	F	F	T
F	F	F	F	T	F

Answers will vary; an example is: The statement is false when p, q, and r are all true.
83. p: There was an increase in the percentage who believed in God.; q: There was a decrease in the percentage who believed in Heaven.; r: There was an increase in the percentage who believed in the devil.; $(p \wedge q) \rightarrow r$; true **85.** p: There was a decrease in the percentage who believed in God.; q: There was an increase in the percentage who believed in Heaven.; r: The percentage believing in the devil decreased.; $(p \leftrightarrow q) \vee r$; true
87. p: Fifteen percent are capitalists.; q: Thirty-four percent are members of the upper-middle class.; r: The number of working poor exceeds the number belonging to the working class.; $(p \vee \sim q) \leftrightarrow r$; false **89.** p: There are more people in the lower-middle class than in the capitalist and upper-middle classes combined.; q: One percent are capitalists.; r: Thirty-four percent belong to the upper-middle class.; $p \rightarrow (q \wedge r)$; false
97. makes sense **99.** makes sense **101.** false **103.** true **105.** Answers will vary; examples are $p \rightarrow q$, $\sim p$, $(p \rightarrow q) \vee \sim p$, and $\sim p \rightarrow [(p \rightarrow q) \vee \sim p]$.

Section 5

Check Point Exercises

1. a.

p	q	$\sim q$	$p \vee q$	$\sim q \rightarrow p$
T	T	F	T	T
T	F	T	T	T
F	T	F	T	T
F	F	T	F	F

The statements are equivalent since their truth values are the same.

b. If I don't lose my scholarship, then I attend classes.

2.

p	$\sim p$	$\sim(\sim p)$	$\sim[\sim(\sim p)]$
T	F	T	F
F	T	F	T

Since the truth values are the same, $\sim[\sim(\sim p)] \equiv \sim p$.

3. c **4. a.** If you're not driving too closely, then you can't read this. **b.** If it's not time to do the laundry, then you have clean underwear. **c.** If supervision during exams is required, then some students are not honest. **d.** $q \rightarrow (p \vee r)$ **5.** Converse: If you don't see a Club Med, then you are in Iran.; Inverse: If you are not in Iran, then you see a Club Med.; Contrapositive: If you see a Club Med, then you are not in Iran.

Exercise Set 5

1. a.

p	q	$\sim p$	$p \vee q$	$\sim p \rightarrow q$
T	T	F	T	T
T	F	F	T	T
F	T	T	T	T
F	F	T	F	F

b. The United States supports the development of solar-powered cars or it will suffer increasing atmospheric pollution.
3. not equivalent **5.** equivalent **7.** equivalent **9.** not equivalent **11.** not equivalent **13.** equivalent **15.** a **17.** c
19. Converse: If I am in Illinois, then I am in Chicago.; Inverse: If I am not in Chicago, then I am not in Illinois.; Contrapositive: If I am not in Illinois, then I am not in Chicago. **21.** Converse: If I cannot hear you, then the stereo is playing.; Inverse: If the stereo is not playing, then I can hear you.; Contrapositive: If I can hear you, then the stereo is not playing. **23.** Converse: If you die, you don't laugh.; Inverse: If you laugh, you don't die.; Contrapositive: If you don't die, you laugh. **25.** Converse: If all troops were withdrawn, then the president is telling the truth.; Inverse: If the president is not telling the truth, then some troops were not withdrawn.; Contrapositive: If some troops were not withdrawn, then the president was not telling the truth. **27.** Converse: If some people suffer, then all institutions place profit above human need.; Inverse: If some institutions do not place profit above human need, then no people suffer.; Contrapositive: If no people suffer, then some institutions do not place profit above human need.
29. Converse: $\sim r \rightarrow \sim q$; Inverse: $q \rightarrow r$; Contrapositive: $r \rightarrow q$ **31.** If a person diets, then he or she loses weight.; Converse: If a person loses weight, then he or she is dieting.; Inverse: If a person is not dieting, then he or she is not losing weight.; Contrapositive: If a person is not losing weight, then he or she is not dieting. **33.** If a vehicle has no flashing light on top, then it is not an ambulance.; Converse: If a vehicle is not an ambulance, then it has no flashing light on top.; Inverse: If a vehicle has a flashing light on top, then it is an ambulance.; Contrapositive: If a vehicle is an ambulance, then it has a flashing light on top. **35.** If a person is an attorney, then he or she has passed the bar exam.; Converse: If a person has passed the bar exam, then he or she is an attorney.; Inverse: If a person is not an attorney, then he or she has not passed the bar exam.; Contrapositive: If a person has not passed the bar exam, then he or she is not an attorney. **37.** If a person is a pacifist, then he or she is not a warmonger.; Converse: If a person is not a warmonger, then he or she is a pacifist.; Inverse: If a person is not a pacifist, then he or she is a warmonger.; Contrapositive: If a person is a warmonger, then he or she is not a pacifist. **39. a.** true **b.** Converse: If the corruption rating is 9.6, then the country is Finland.; Inverse: If the country is not Finland, then the corruption rating is not 9.6.; Contrapositive: If the corruption rating is not 9.6, then the country is not Finland.; The contrapositive is true. The converse and inverse are not necessarily true. **47.** does not make sense **49.** makes sense

Section 6

Check Point Exercises

1. You do not have a fever and you have the flu. **2.** Bart Simpson is not a cartoon character or Tony Soprano is not a cartoon character.
3. You do not leave by 5 P.M. and you arrive home on time. **4. a.** Some horror movies are not scary or none are funny. **b.** Your workouts are not strenuous and you get stronger. **5.** If we cannot swim or we can sail, it is windy.

Exercise Set 6

1. I am in Los Angeles and not in California. **3.** It is purple and it is a carrot. **5.** He doesn't and I won't. **7.** There is a blizzard and some schools are not closed. **9.** $\sim q \wedge r$ **11.** Australia is not an island or China is not an island. **13.** My high school did not encourage creativity or it did not encourage diversity. **15.** Jewish scripture does not give a clear indication of a heaven and it does not give a clear indication of an afterlife. **17.** The United States has eradicated neither poverty nor racism. **19.** $p \vee \sim q$ **21.** If you do not succeed, you did not attend lecture or did not study. **23.** If his wife does not cook and his child does not cook, then he does. **25.** $(\sim q \wedge r) \rightarrow \sim p$ **27.** I'm going to neither Seattle nor San Francisco. **29.** I do not study and I pass. **31.** I am going or he is not going. **33.** A bill does not become law or it receives majority approval. **35.** $\sim p \wedge q$ **37.** $\sim p \vee (\sim q \wedge \sim r)$ **39.** none **41.** none **43.** a and b **45.** a and b **47.** If there is no pain, there is no gain.; Converse: If there is no gain, then there is no pain.; Inverse: If there is pain, then there is gain.; Contrapositive: If there is gain, then there is pain.; Negation: There is no pain and there is gain. **49.** If you follow Buddha's "Middle Way," then you are neither hedonistic nor ascetic.; Converse: If you are neither hedonistic nor ascetic, then you follow Buddha's "Middle Way."; Inverse: If you do not follow Buddha's "Middle Way," then you are either hedonistic or ascetic.; Contrapositive: If you are either hedonistic or ascetic, then you do not follow Buddha's "Middle Way."; Negation: You follow Buddha's "Middle Way" and you are either hedonistic or ascetic. **51.** $p \wedge (\sim r \vee s)$ **53.** $\sim p \vee (r \wedge s)$ **55. a.** false
b. Smoking does not reduce life expectancy by 2370 days or heart disease does not reduce life expectancy by 1247 days. **c.** true **57. a.** true
b. Homicide does not reduce life expectancy by 74 days and fire reduces life expectancy by 25 days. **c.** false **59. a.** true **b.** Drowning reduces life expectancy by ten times the number of days as airplane accidents and drowning reduces life expectancy by 24 days. **c.** false
65. makes sense **67.** makes sense **69.** Contrapositive: If no one is eating turkey, then it is not Thanksgiving.; Negation: It is Thanksgiving and no one is eating turkey.

Section 7

Check Point Exercises

1. valid **2.** valid **3.** invalid **4. a.** valid **b.** invalid **c.** valid **5.** valid **6.** Some people do not lead.

Exercise Set 7

1. invalid **3.** valid **5.** valid **7.** invalid **9.** invalid **11.** valid **13.** valid

15. $\begin{array}{r} p \rightarrow \sim q \\ q \\ \hline \therefore \sim p \end{array}$ valid **17.** $\begin{array}{r} p \vee q \\ q \\ \hline \therefore \sim p \end{array}$ invalid **19.** $\begin{array}{r} p \rightarrow q \\ q \\ \hline \therefore p \end{array}$ invalid **21.** $\begin{array}{r} p \rightarrow q \\ \sim p \rightarrow q \\ \hline \therefore q \end{array}$ valid **23.** $\begin{array}{r} p \vee q \\ \sim q \\ \hline \therefore p \end{array}$ valid **25.** $\begin{array}{r} p \rightarrow q \\ \sim p \\ \hline \therefore \sim q \end{array}$ invalid **27.** $\begin{array}{r} p \rightarrow q \\ q \rightarrow r \\ \hline \therefore p \rightarrow r \end{array}$ valid **29.** $\begin{array}{r} p \rightarrow q \\ q \rightarrow r \\ \hline \therefore r \rightarrow p \end{array}$ invalid

31. $\begin{array}{r} (p \wedge q) \rightarrow r \\ p \wedge \sim r \\ \hline \therefore \sim q \end{array}$ valid **33.** $\begin{array}{r} (p \vee q) \rightarrow r \\ \sim r \\ \hline \therefore \sim p \wedge \sim q \end{array}$ valid **35.** $\begin{array}{r} (p \vee q) \rightarrow r \\ r \\ \hline \therefore p \vee q \end{array}$ invalid **37.** $\begin{array}{r} (p \wedge q) \rightarrow r \\ \sim p \vee \sim q \\ \hline \therefore \sim r \end{array}$ invalid **39.** $\begin{array}{r} p \rightarrow q \\ \sim p \rightarrow r \\ \hline \therefore q \vee r \end{array}$ valid **41.** $\begin{array}{r} p \rightarrow q \\ q \rightarrow \sim r \\ r \\ \hline \therefore \sim p \end{array}$ valid

43. My best friend is not a chemist. **45.** They were dropped from prime time. **47.** Some electricity is not off.
49. If I vacation in Paris, I gain weight.

51. $\begin{array}{r} p \rightarrow q \\ \sim p \\ \hline \therefore \sim q \end{array}$ invalid **53.** $\begin{array}{r} p \vee q \\ \sim p \\ \hline \therefore q \end{array}$ valid **55.** $\begin{array}{r} p \rightarrow q \\ q \\ \hline \therefore p \end{array}$ invalid **57.** $\begin{array}{r} p \rightarrow q \\ \sim q \\ \hline \therefore \sim p \end{array}$ valid **59.** $\begin{array}{r} p \rightarrow q \\ q \rightarrow r \\ \hline \therefore p \rightarrow r \end{array}$ valid **61.** $\begin{array}{r} p \rightarrow q \\ \sim q \\ \hline \therefore \sim p \end{array}$ valid **63.** h **65.** i **67.** c **69.** a **71.** j

73. d **83.** does not make sense **85.** does not make sense **87.** People sometimes speak without being spoken to. **89.** The doctor either destroys the base on which the placebo rests or jeopardizes a relationship built on trust.

Section 8

Check Point Exercises

1. valid **2.** invalid **3.** valid **4.** invalid **5.** invalid **6.** invalid

Exercise Set 8

1. valid **3.** invalid **5.** valid **7.** invalid **9.** invalid **11.** valid **13.** valid **15.** invalid **17.** invalid **19.** valid **21.** valid **23.** valid **25.** invalid **27.** invalid **29.** valid **31.** invalid **33.** invalid **35.** invalid **37.** valid **39.** valid **43.** makes sense **45.** does not make sense **47.** b **49.** Some teachers are amusing people.

Chapter Review Exercises

1. $(p \wedge q) \rightarrow r$; If the temperature is below 32° and we have finished studying, we will go to the movies. **2.** $\sim r \rightarrow (\sim p \vee \sim q)$; If we do not go to the movies, then the temperature is not below 32° or we have not finished studying. **3.** The temperature is below 32°, and if we finish studying, we will go to the movies. **4.** We will go to the movies if and only if the temperature is below 32° and we have finished studying. **5.** It is not true that both the temperature is below 32° and we have finished studying. **6.** We will not go to the movies if and only if the temperature is not below 32° or we have not finished studying. **7.** $(p \wedge q) \vee r$ **8.** $(p \vee \sim q) \rightarrow r$ **9.** $q \rightarrow (p \leftrightarrow r)$ **10.** $r \leftrightarrow (p \wedge \sim q)$ **11.** $p \rightarrow r$ **12.** $q \rightarrow \sim r$ **13.** Some houses are not made with wood. **14.** Some students major in business. **15.** No crimes are motivated by passion. **16.** All Democrats are registered voters. **17.** Some new taxes will not be used for education.

18. neither

p	q	$\sim p$	$\sim p \wedge q$	$p \wedge (\sim p \wedge q)$
T	T	F	F	T
T	F	F	F	T
F	T	T	T	T
F	F	T	F	F

19. neither

p	q	$\sim p$	$\sim q$	$\sim p \vee \sim q$
T	T	F	F	F
T	F	F	T	T
F	T	T	F	T
F	F	T	T	T

20. neither

p	q	$\sim p$	$\sim p \vee q$	$p \rightarrow (\sim p \vee q)$
T	T	F	T	T
T	F	F	F	F
F	T	T	T	T
F	F	T	T	T

21. neither

p	q	$\sim q$	$p \leftrightarrow \sim q$
T	T	F	F
T	F	T	T
F	T	F	T
F	F	T	F

22. tautology

p	q	$\sim p$	$\sim q$	$p \vee q$	$\sim(p \vee q)$	$\sim p \wedge \sim q$	$\sim(p \vee q) \rightarrow (\sim p \wedge \sim q)$
T	T	F	F	T	F	F	T
T	F	F	T	T	F	F	T
F	T	T	F	T	F	F	T
F	F	T	T	F	T	T	T

23. neither

p	q	r	$\sim r$	$p \vee q$	$(p \vee q) \rightarrow \sim r$
T	T	T	F	T	F
T	T	F	T	T	T
T	F	T	F	T	F
T	F	F	T	T	T
F	T	T	F	T	F
F	T	F	T	T	T
F	F	T	F	F	T
F	F	F	T	F	T

24. neither

p	q	r	$p \wedge q$	$p \wedge r$	$(p \wedge q) \leftrightarrow (p \wedge r)$
T	T	T	T	T	T
T	T	F	T	F	F
T	F	T	F	T	F
T	F	F	F	F	T
F	T	T	F	F	T
F	T	F	F	F	T
F	F	T	F	F	T
F	F	F	F	F	T

25. neither

p	q	r	$r \rightarrow p$	$q \vee (r \rightarrow p)$	$p \wedge [q \vee (r \rightarrow p)]$
T	T	T	T	T	T
T	T	F	T	T	T
T	F	T	T	T	T
T	F	F	T	T	T
F	T	T	F	T	F
F	T	F	T	T	F
F	F	T	F	F	F
F	F	F	T	T	F

26. **a.** p: I'm in class.; q: I'm studying.; $(p \vee q) \wedge \sim p$
b.

p	q	$\sim p$	$p \vee q$	$(p \vee q) \wedge \sim p$
T	T	F	T	F
T	F	F	T	F
F	T	T	T	T
F	F	T	F	F

c. The statement is true when p is false and q is true.

27. **a.** p: You spit from a truck.; q: It's legal.; r: You spit from a car.; $(p \to q) \wedge (r \to \sim q)$
b.

p	q	r	$\sim q$	$p \to q$	$r \to \sim q$	$(p \to q) \wedge (r \to \sim q)$
T	T	T	F	T	F	F
T	T	F	F	T	T	T
T	F	T	T	F	T	F
T	F	F	T	F	T	F
F	T	T	F	T	F	F
F	T	F	F	T	T	T
F	F	T	T	T	T	T
F	F	F	T	T	T	T

c. The statement is true when p and q are both false.

28. false **29.** true **30.** true **31.** false **32.** p: Twenty-nine percent consider religion the most taboo topic.; q: Fourteen percent consider politics the most taboo topic.; $p \wedge \sim q$; false **33.** p: A greater percentage of people consider money a more taboo topic than personal life.; q: Sixteen percent consider money the most taboo topic.; r: Fourteen percent consider personal life the most taboo topic.; $p \to (q \wedge r)$; true **34.** p: Fourteen percent consider money the most taboo topic.; q: Fourteen percent consider politics the most taboo topic.; r: The greatest percentage consider religion the most taboo topic.; $(p \leftrightarrow q) \vee \sim r$; true

35. **a.**

p	q	$\sim p$	$\sim p \vee q$	$p \to q$
T	T	F	T	T
T	F	F	F	F
F	T	T	T	T
F	F	T	T	T

b. If the triangle is isosceles, then it has two equal sides.

36. c **37.** not equivalent **38.** equivalent **39.** Converse: If I am in the South, then I am in Atlanta.; Inverse: If I am not in Atlanta, then I am not in the South.; Contrapositive: If I am not in the South, then I am not in Atlanta. **40.** Converse: If today is not a holiday, then I am in class.; Inverse: If I am not in class, then today is a holiday.; Contrapositive: If today is a holiday, then I am not in class. **41.** Converse: If I pass all courses, then I worked hard.; Inverse: If I don't work hard, then I don't pass some courses.; Contrapositive: If I do not pass some course, then I did not work hard. **42.** Converse: $\sim q \to \sim p$; Inverse: $p \to q$.; Contrapositive: $q \to p$ **43.** An argument is sound and it is not valid. **44.** I do not work hard and I succeed. **45.** $\sim r \wedge \sim p$ **46.** Chicago is not a city or Maine is not a city. **47.** Ernest Hemingway was neither a musician nor an actor. **48.** If a number is not 0, the number is positive or negative. **49.** I do not work hard and I succeed. **50.** She is using her car or she is not taking a bus. **51.** $p \wedge \sim q$ **52.** a and c **53.** a and b **54.** a and c **55.** none **56.** invalid **57.** valid

58. $p \to q$; q; $\therefore p$ — invalid
59. $p \vee q$; q; $\therefore \sim p$ — invalid
60. $p \vee q$; $\sim p$; $\therefore q$ — valid
61. $p \to q$; $\sim q$; $\therefore \sim p$ — valid
62. $p \to \sim q$; $\sim p \to q$; $\therefore p \leftrightarrow \sim q$ — valid
63. $p \to \sim q$; $r \to q$; $\therefore \sim r \to p$ — invalid

64. invalid **65.** valid **66.** valid **67.** invalid **68.** invalid **69.** valid

Chapter Test

1. If I'm registered and I'm a citizen, then I vote. **2.** I don't vote if and only if I'm not registered or I'm not a citizen. **3.** I'm neither registered nor a citizen. **4.** $(p \wedge q) \vee \sim r$ **5.** $(\sim p \vee \sim q) \to \sim r$ **6.** $r \to q$ **7.** Some numbers are not divisible by 5. **8.** No people wear glasses.

9.

p	q	$\sim p$	$\sim p \vee q$	$p \wedge (\sim p \vee q)$
T	T	F	T	T
T	F	F	F	F
F	T	T	T	F
F	F	T	T	F

10.

p	q	$\sim p$	$\sim q$	$p \wedge q$	$\sim(p \wedge q)$	$(\sim p \vee \sim q)$	$\sim(p \wedge q) \leftrightarrow (\sim p \vee \sim q)$
T	T	F	F	T	F	F	T
T	F	F	T	F	T	T	T
F	T	T	F	F	T	T	T
F	F	T	T	F	T	T	T

11.

p	q	r	$q \vee r$	$p \leftrightarrow (q \vee r)$
T	T	T	T	T
T	T	F	T	T
T	F	T	T	T
T	F	F	F	F
F	T	T	T	F
F	T	F	T	F
F	F	T	T	F
F	F	F	F	T

12. p: You break the law.; q: You change the law.; $(p \wedge q) \rightarrow \sim p$

p	q	$\sim p$	$p \wedge q$	$(p \wedge q) \rightarrow \sim p$
T	T	F	T	F
T	F	F	F	T
F	T	T	F	T
F	F	T	F	T

Answers will vary; an example is: The statement is false when p and q are both true.

13. true **14.** true **15. a.** p: There was an increase in the percentage of Americans who supported the death penalty.; q: There was an increase in the percentage who opposed the death penalty.; r: There was an increase in the percentage who were not sure about the death penalty.; $\sim p \vee (q \wedge r)$ **b.** true **16.** b **17.** If it snows, then it is not August. **18.** Converse: If I cannot concentrate, then the radio is playing.; Inverse: If the radio is not playing, then I can concentrate. **19.** It is cold and we use the pool. **20.** The test is not today and the party is not tonight. **21.** The banana is not green or it is ready to eat. **22.** a and b **23.** a and c **24.** invalid **25.** valid **26.** invalid **27.** invalid **28.** valid **29.** invalid

Consumer Mathematics and Financial Management

"I realize, of course, that it's no shame to be poor, but it's no great honor either. So what would have been so terrible if I had a small fortune?"

-Tevye, a poor dairyman, in the musical *Fiddler on the Roof*

We all want a wonderful life with fulfilling work, good health, and loving relationships. And let's be honest: Financial security, or even a small fortune, wouldn't hurt! Achieving this goal depends on understanding basic ideas about savings, loans, and investments. A solid understanding of the topics in this chapter can pay, literally, by making your financial goals a reality.

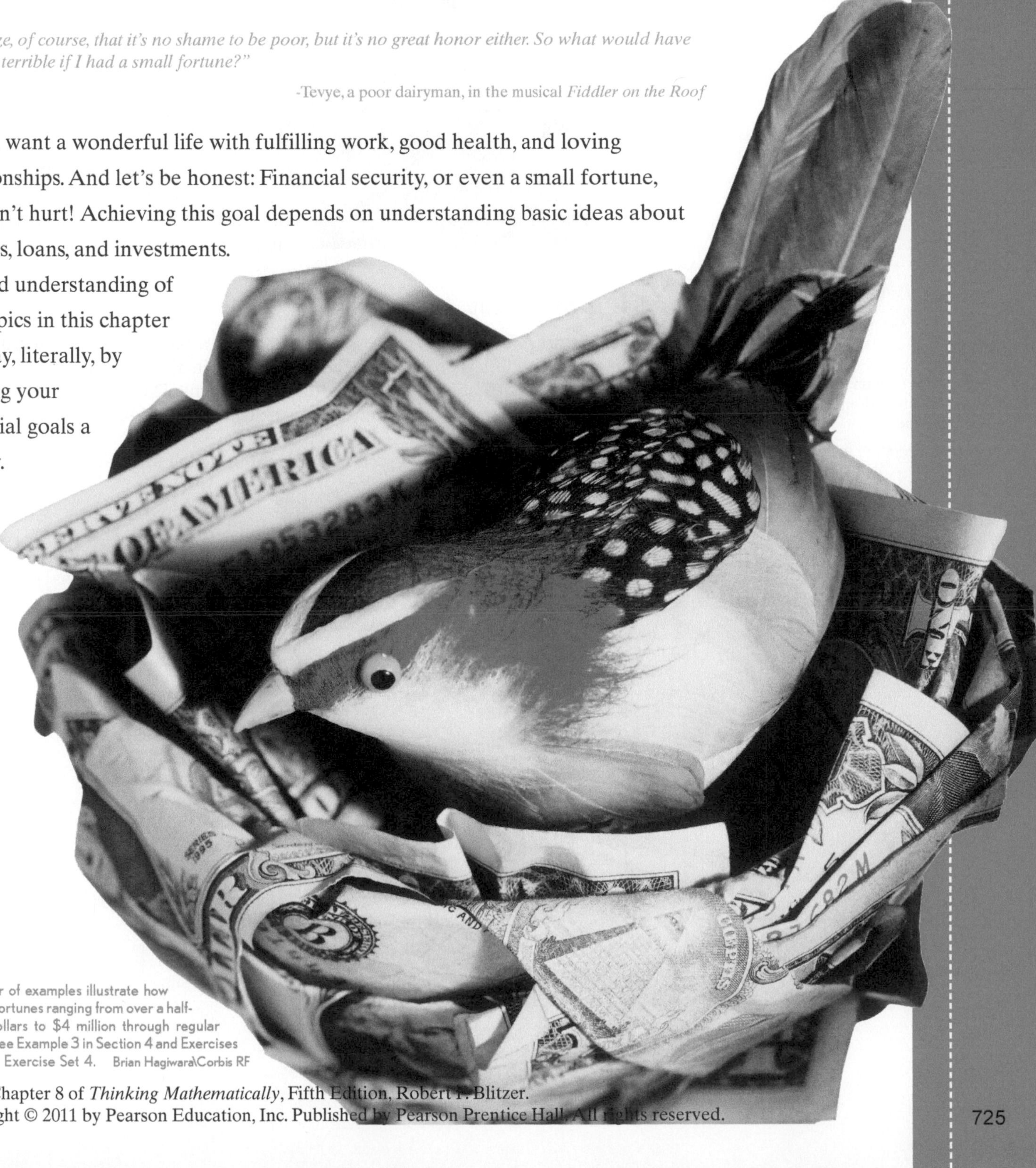

A number of examples illustrate how to attain fortunes ranging from over a half-million dollars to $4 million through regular savings. See Example 3 in Section 4 and Exercises 35–36 in Exercise Set 4. Brian Hagiwara\Corbis RF

From Chapter 8 of *Thinking Mathematically*, Fifth Edition, Robert F. Blitzer.

OBJECTIVES

1 Express a fraction as a percent.
2 Express a decimal as a percent.
3 Express a percent as a decimal.
4 Solve applied problems involving sales tax and discounts.
5 Compute income tax.
6 Determine percent increase or decrease.
7 Investigate some of the ways percent can be abused.

1 Percent, Sales Tax, and Income Tax

Charles Rex Arbogast\AP Wide World Photos

"And if elected, it is my solemn pledge to cut your taxes by 10% for each of my first three years in office, for a total cut of 30%."

Did you know that one of the most common ways that you are given numerical information is with percents? This section will provide you with the tools to make sense of the politician's promise, as we present the uses, and abuses, of percent.

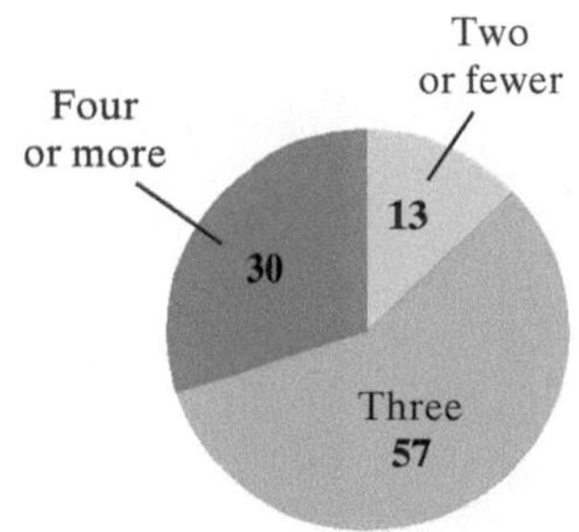

FIGURE 1 Number of bedrooms in privately owned single-family U.S. houses per 100 houses

Source: U.S. Census Bureau and HUD

Basics of Percent

Percents are the result of expressing numbers as a part of 100. The word *percent* means *per hundred*. For example, the circle graph in **Figure 1** shows that 57 out of every 100 single-family homes have three bedrooms. Thus, $\frac{57}{100} = 57\%$, indicating that 57% of the houses have three bedrooms. The percent sign, %, is used to indicate the number of parts out of one hundred parts.

A fraction can be expressed as a percent using the following procedure:

EXPRESSING A FRACTION AS A PERCENT

1. Divide the numerator by the denominator.
2. Multiply the quotient by 100. This is done by moving the decimal point in the quotient two places to the right.
3. Add a percent sign.

1 Express a fraction as a percent.

EXAMPLE 1 Expressing a Fraction as a Percent

Express $\frac{5}{8}$ as a percent.

Solution

Step 1 Divide the numerator by the denominator.

$$5 \div 8 = 0.625$$

Step 2 Multiply the quotient by 100.

$$0.625 \times 100 = 62.5$$

Step 3 Add a percent sign.

$$62.5\%$$

Thus, $\frac{5}{8} = 62.5\%$.

CHECK POINT 1 Express $\frac{1}{8}$ as a percent.

2 Express a decimal as a percent.

Our work in Example 1 shows that $0.625 = 62.5\%$. This illustrates the procedure for expressing a decimal number as a percent.

STUDY TIP

Dictionaries indicate that the word *percentage* has the same meaning as the word *percent*. Use the word that sounds better in the circumstance.

EXPRESSING A DECIMAL NUMBER AS A PERCENT

1. Move the decimal point two places to the right.
2. Attach a percent sign.

EXAMPLE 2 Expressing a Decimal as a Percent

Express 0.47 as a percent.

Solution

Move decimal point two places right.

0.47 %

Add a percent sign.

Thus, $0.47 = 47\%$.

CHECK POINT 2 Express 0.023 as a percent.

---

3 Express a percent as a decimal.

We reverse the procedure of Example 2 to express a percent as a decimal number.

EXPRESSING A PERCENT AS A DECIMAL NUMBER

1. Move the decimal point two places to the left.
2. Remove the percent sign.

EXAMPLE 3 Expressing Percents as Decimals

Express each percent as a decimal:

a. 19% **b.** 180%.

Solution Use the two steps in the box.

a.

$19\% = 19.\% = 0.19\%$

The percent sign is removed.

The decimal point starts at the far right.

The decimal point is moved two places to the left.

Thus, $19\% = 0.19$.

b. $180\% = 1.80\% = 1.80$ or 1.8

CHECK POINT 3 Express each percent as a decimal:

a. 67% **b.** 250%.

If a fraction is part of a percent, as in $\frac{1}{4}\%$, begin by expressing the fraction as a decimal, retaining the percent sign. Then, express the percent as a decimal number. For example,

$$\tfrac{1}{4}\% = 0.25\% = 00.25\% = 0.0025.$$

4 Solve applied problems involving sales tax and discounts.

Percent, Sales Tax, and Discounts

Many applications involving percent are based on the following formula:

A is P percent of B.

$$A = P \cdot B.$$

Note that the word *of* implies multiplication.

We can use this formula to determine the **sales tax** collected by states, counties, and cities on sales of items to customers. The sales tax is a percent of the cost of an item.

$$\text{Sales tax amount} = \text{tax rate} \times \text{item's cost}$$

EXAMPLE 4 Percent and Sales Tax

Suppose that the local sales tax rate is 7.5% and you purchase a bicycle for \$894.

a. How much tax is paid?

b. What is the bicycle's total cost?

Solution

a. Sales tax amount = tax rate × item's cost

$$= 7.5\% \times \$894 = 0.075 \times \$894 = \$67.05$$

7.5% of the item's cost, or 7.5% of \$894

The tax paid is \$67.05.

b. The bicycle's total cost is the purchase price, \$894, plus the sales tax, \$67.05.

$$\text{Total cost} = \$894.00 + \$67.05 = \$961.05$$

The bicycle's total cost is \$961.05.

Suppose that the local sales tax rate is 6% and you purchase a computer for \$1260.

a. How much tax is paid?

b. What is the computer's total cost?

None of us is thrilled about sales tax, but we do like buying things that are *on sale*. Businesses reduce prices, or **discount**, to attract customers and to reduce inventory. The discount rate is a percent of the original price.

$$\text{Discount amount} = \text{discount rate} \times \text{original price}$$

EXAMPLE 5 Percent and Sales Price

A computer with an original price of \$1460 is on sale at 15% off.

a. What is the discount amount?

b. What is the computer's sale price?

TECHNOLOGY

A calculator is useful, and sometimes essential, in this chapter. The keystroke sequence that gives the sale price in Example 5 is

1460 [−] .15 [×] 1460.

Press [=] or [ENTER] to display the answer, 1241.

Solution

a. Discount amount = discount rate × original price
= 15% × \$1460 = 0.15 × \$1460 = \$219

15% of the original price, or 15% of \$1460

The discount amount is \$219.

b. The computer's sale price is the original price, \$1460, minus the discount amount, \$219.

Sale price = \$1460 − \$219 = \$1241

The computer's sale price is \$1241.

CHECK POINT 5 A CD player with an original price of \$380 is on sale at 35% off.

a. What is the discount amount?

b. What is the CD player's sale price?

5 Compute income tax.

Percent and Income Tax

We have seen how tax rates determine the amount of sales tax on an item. They also determine the amount that we must each pay in income tax.

CALCULATING INCOME TAX

1. Determine your adjusted gross income:

Adjusted gross income = Gross income − Adjustments.

Gross income: All income for the year, including wages, tips, earnings from investments, and unemployment compensation

Adjustments: Includes payments to tax-deferred savings plans

2. Determine your taxable income:

Taxable income = Adjusted gross income − (Exemptions + Deductions).

Exemptions: A fixed amount for yourself (\$3500 in 2008) and the same amount for each dependent

Deductions: Choose the greater of a standard deduction or an itemized deduction, which includes interest on home mortgages, state income taxes, property taxes, charitable contributions, and medical expenses exceeding 7.5% of adjusted gross income.

3. Determine the income tax:

Income tax = Tax computation − Tax credits.

Tax computation: Use your taxable income and tax rates for your filing status (single, married, etc.) to determine this amount.

Tax credits: May include up to \$1000 per child, the cost of child care so a parent can work, and adoption credits for qualified expenses.

Tax Rate	Single
10%	up to \$8025
15%	\$8026 to \$32,550

A portion of Table 1
(The complete table appears on the next page.)

Table 1 on the next page shows 2008 tax rates, standard deductions, and exemptions for the four **filing status** categories described in the voice balloons. The tax rates in the left column, called **marginal tax rates**, are assigned to various income ranges, called **margins.** For example, suppose you are single and your taxable income is \$25,000. The singles column of the table shows that you must pay 10% tax on the first \$8025, which is

10% of \$8025 = 0.10 × \$8025 = \$802.50.

You must also pay 15% tax on the remaining \$16,975 (\$25,000 − \$8025 = \$16,975), which is

$$15\% \text{ of } \$16{,}975 = 0.15 \times \$16{,}975 = \$2546.25.$$

Your total tax is \$802.50 + \$2546.25 = \$3348.75. In this scenario, your *marginal rate* is 15% and you are in the 15% *tax bracket.*

TABLE 1 2008 Marginal Tax Rates, Standard Deductions, and Exemptions

	Unmarried, divorced, or legally separated	Married and each partner files a separate tax return	Married and both partners file a single tax return	Unmarried and paying more than half the cost of supporting a child or parent
Tax Rate	**Single**	**Married Filing Separately**	**Married Filing Jointly**	**Head of Household**
10%	up to \$8025	up to \$8025	up to \$16,050	up to \$11,450
15%	\$8026 to \$32,550	\$8026 to \$32,550	\$16,051 to \$65,100	\$11,451 to \$43,650
25%	\$32,551 to \$78,850	\$32,551 to \$65,725	\$65,101 to \$131,450	\$43,651 to \$112,650
28%	\$78,851 to \$164,550	\$65,726 to \$100,150	\$131,451 to \$200,300	\$112,651 to \$182,400
33%	\$164,551 to \$357,700	\$100,151 to \$178,850	\$200,301 to \$357,700	\$182,401 to \$357,700
35%	more than \$357,700	more than \$178,850	more than \$357,700	more than \$357,700
Standard Deduction	\$5450	\$5450	\$10,900	\$8000
Exemptions (per person)	\$3500	\$3500	\$3500	\$3500

SINGLE WOMAN WITH NO DEPENDENTS

Gross income: \$62,000

Adjustments: \$4000 paid to a tax-deferred IRA (Individual Retirement Account)

Deductions:

- \$7500: mortgage interest
- \$2200: property taxes
- \$2400: charitable contributions
- \$1500: medical expenses not covered by insurance

Tax credit: \$500

EXAMPLE 6 Computing Income Tax

Calculate the income tax owed by a single woman with no dependents whose gross income, adjustments, deductions, and credits are given in the margin. Use the 2008 marginal tax rates in **Table 1**.

Solution

Step 1 Determine the adjusted gross income.

$$\begin{aligned}\text{Adjusted gross income} &= \text{Gross income} - \text{Adjustments}\\ &= \$62{,}000 - \$4000\\ &= \$58{,}000\end{aligned}$$

Step 2 Determine the taxable income.

$$\begin{aligned}\text{Taxable income} &= \text{Adjusted gross income} - (\text{Exemptions} + \text{Deductions})\\ &= \$58{,}000 - (\$3500 + \text{Deductions})\end{aligned}$$

The singles column in **Table 8.1** shows a personal exemption of \$3500.

The singles column in **Table 8.1** shows a \$5450 standard deduction. A greater deduction can be obtained by itemizing.

Itemized Deductions

\$7500 : mortgage interest
\$2200 : property taxes
\$2400 : charitable contributions
~~\$1500 : medical expenses~~
\$12,100 : total of deductible expenditures

Can only deduct amount in excess of 7.5% of adjusted gross income: 0.075 × \$58,000 = \$4350

We substitute \$12,100 for deductions in the formula for taxable income.

$$\begin{aligned}\text{Taxable income} &= \text{Adjusted gross income} - (\text{Exemptions} + \text{Deductions})\\ &= \$58{,}000 - (\$3500 + \$12{,}100)\\ &= \$58{,}000 - \$15{,}600\\ &= \$42{,}400\end{aligned}$$

Step 3 Determine the income tax.

$$\begin{aligned}\text{Income tax} &= \text{Tax computation} - \text{Tax credits}\\ &= \text{Tax computation} - \$500\end{aligned}$$

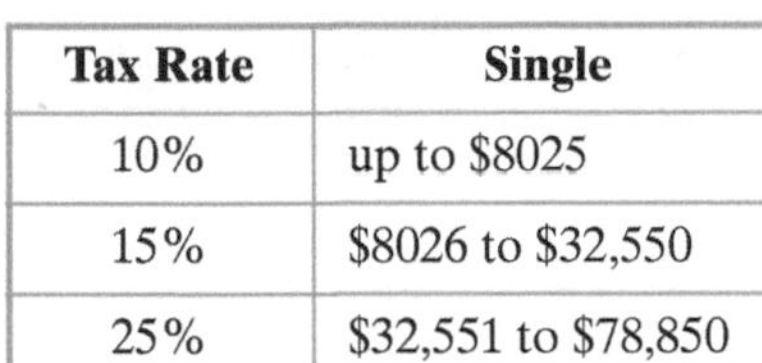

Tax Rate	Single
10%	up to \$8025
15%	\$8026 to \$32,550
25%	\$32,551 to \$78,850

A portion of Table 1 (repeated)

We perform the tax computation using the singles rates in **Table 1**. Our taxpayer is in the 25% tax bracket because her taxable income, \$42,400, is in the \$32,551 to \$78,850 income range. This means that she owes 10% on the first \$8025 of her taxable income, 15% on her taxable income between \$8026 and \$32,550, inclusive, and 25% on her taxable income above \$32,550.

10% marginal rate on first \$8025 of taxable income

15% marginal rate on taxable income between \$8026 and \$32,550

25% marginal rate on taxable income above \$32,550

$$\begin{aligned}\text{Tax computation} &= 0.10 \times \$8025 + 0.15 \times (\$32{,}550 - \$8025) + 0.25 \times (\$42{,}400 - \$32{,}550)\\ &= 0.10 \times \$8025 + 0.15 \times \$24{,}525 + 0.25 \times \$9850\\ &= \$802.50 + \$3678.75 + \$2462.50\\ &= \$6943.75\end{aligned}$$

We substitute \$6943.75 for the tax computation in the formula for income tax.

$$\begin{aligned}\text{Income tax} &= \text{Tax computation} - \text{Tax credits}\\ &= \$6943.75 - \$500\\ &= \$6443.75\end{aligned}$$

The income tax owed is \$6443.75.

STUDY TIP

A tax credit is not the same thing as a tax deduction. The *tax credit* of \$500 in Example 6 *reduces the income tax owed by the full dollar-for-dollar amount,* namely, \$500. The *tax deduction* of \$12,100 *reduces the taxable income* by \$12,100, thereby saving only a percentage of \$12,100 in taxes.

CHECK POINT 6 Use the 2008 marginal tax rates in **Table 1** to calculate the tax owed by a single man with no dependents whose gross income, adjustments, deductions, and credits are given as follows:

Gross income: \$40,000
Adjustments: \$1000
Deductions: \$3000: charitable contributions
\$1500: theft loss
\$300: cost of tax preparation
Tax credit: none.

6 Determine percent increase or decrease.

Percent and Change

Percents are used for comparing changes, such as increases or decreases in sales, population, prices, and production. If a quantity changes, its **percent increase** or its **percent decrease** can be found as follows:

FINDING PERCENT INCREASE OR PERCENT DECREASE

1. Find the fraction for the percent increase or the percent decrease:

$$\frac{\text{amount of increase}}{\text{original amount}} \quad \text{or} \quad \frac{\text{amount of decrease}}{\text{original amount}}.$$

2. Find the percent increase or the percent decrease by expressing the fraction in step 1 as a percent.

EXAMPLE 7 Finding Percent Increase and Decrease

In 2000, world population was approximately 6 billion. **Figure 2** shows world population projections through the year 2150. The data are from the United Nations Family Planning Program and are based on optimistic or pessimistic expectations for successful control of human population growth.

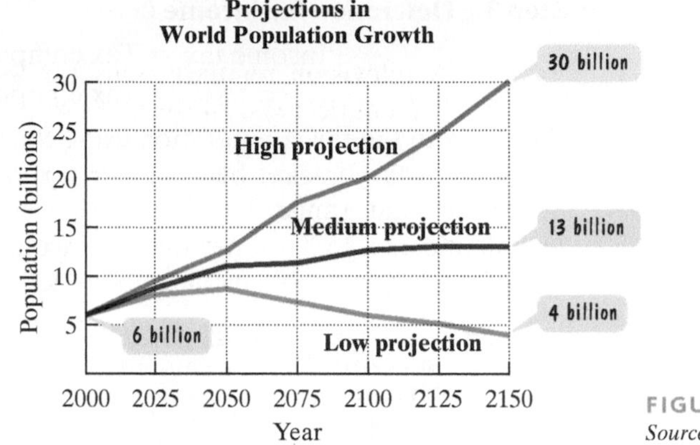

FIGURE 2
Source: United Nations

a. Find the percent increase in world population from 2000 to 2150 using the high projection data.

b. Find the percent decrease in world population from 2000 to 2150 using the low projection data.

Solution

a. Use the data shown on the blue, high-projection, graph.

$$\text{Percent increase} = \frac{\text{amount of increase}}{\text{original amount}}$$

$$= \frac{30 - 6}{6} = \frac{24}{6} = 4 = 400\%$$

The projected percent increase in world population is 400%.

b. Use the data shown on the green, low-projection, graph.

$$\text{Percent decrease} = \frac{\text{amount of decrease}}{\text{original amount}}$$

$$= \frac{6 - 4}{6} = \frac{2}{6} = \frac{1}{3} = 0.33\frac{1}{3} = 33\frac{1}{3}\%$$

The projected percent decrease in world population is $33\frac{1}{3}\%$.

In Example 7, we expressed the percent decrease as $33\frac{1}{3}\%$ because of the familiar conversion $\frac{1}{3} = 0.33\frac{1}{3}$. However, in many situations, rounding is needed. We suggest that you round to the nearest tenth of a percent. Carry the division in the fraction for percent increase or decrease to four places after the decimal point. Then round the decimal to three places, or to the nearest thousandth. Expressing this rounded decimal as a percent gives percent increase or decrease to the nearest tenth of a percent.

CHECK POINT 7

a. If 6 is increased to 10, find the percent increase.

b. If 10 is decreased to 6, find the percent decrease.

EXAMPLE 8 Finding Percent Decrease

A jacket regularly sells for \$135.00. The sale price is \$60.75. Find the percent decrease of the sale price from the regular price.

Solution

$$\text{Percent decrease} = \frac{\text{amount of decrease}}{\text{original amount}}$$

$$= \frac{135.00 - 60.75}{135} = \frac{74.25}{135} = 0.55 = 55\%$$

The percent decrease of the sale price from the regular price is 55%. This means that the sale price of the jacket is 55% lower than the regular price.

CHECK POINT 8 A television regularly sells for \$940. The sale price is \$611. Find the percent decrease of the sale price from the regular price.

7 Investigate some of the ways percent can be abused.

Abuses of Percent

In our next examples, we look at a few of the many ways that percent can be used incorrectly. Confusion often arises when percent increase (or decrease) refers to a changing quantity that is itself a percent.

EXAMPLE 9 Percents of Percents

John Tesh, while he was still coanchoring *Entertainment Tonight*, reported that the PBS series *The Civil War* had an audience of 13% versus the usual 4% PBS audience, "an increase of more than 300%." Did Tesh report the percent increase correctly?

Solution We begin by finding the percent increase.

$$\text{Percent increase} = \frac{\text{amount of increase}}{\text{original amount}}$$

$$= \frac{13\% - 4\%}{4\%} = \frac{9\%}{4\%} = \frac{9}{4} = 2.25 = 225\%$$

The percent increase for PBS was 225%. This is not more than 300%, so Tesh did not report the percent increase correctly.

CHECK POINT 9 An episode of a television series had an audience of 12% versus its usual 10%. What was the percent increase for this episode?

EXAMPLE 10 Promises of a Politician

A politician states, "If you elect me to office, I promise to cut your taxes for each of my first three years in office by 10% each year, for a total reduction of 30%." Evaluate the accuracy of the politician's statement.

Solution To make things simple, let's assume that a taxpayer paid \$100 in taxes in the year previous to the politician's election. A 10% reduction during year 1 is 10% of \$100.

$$10\% \text{ of previous year tax} = 10\% \text{ of } \$100 = 0.10 \times \$100 = \$10$$

With a 10% reduction the first year, the taxpayer will pay only \$100 − \$10, or \$90, in taxes during the politician's first year in office.

The following table shows how we calculate the new, reduced tax for each of the first three years in office:

Year	Tax Paid the Year Before	10% Reduction	Taxes Paid This Year
1	\$100	0.10 × \$100 = \$10	\$100 − \$10 = \$90
2	\$90	0.10 × \$90 = \$9	\$90 − \$9 = \$81
3	\$81	0.10 × \$81 = \$8.10	\$81 − \$8.10 = \$72.90

BLITZER BONUS

SuperStock, Inc.

PERCENTS AND TAX RATES

In 1944 and 1945, the highest marginal tax rate in the United States was a staggering 94%. The tax rate on the highest-income Americans remained at approximately 90% throughout the 1950s, decreased to 70% in the 1960s and 1970s, and to 50% in the early 1980s before reaching a post–World War II low of 28% in 1998. (*Source*: IRS) In 2008, Denmark had the world's highest tax rate, starting at 42% and climbing to 68% for its wealthiest taxpayers.

Now, we determine the percent decrease in taxes over the three years.

$$\text{Percent decrease} = \frac{\text{amount of decrease}}{\text{original amount}}$$

$$= \frac{\$100 - \$72.90}{\$100} = \frac{\$27.10}{\$100} = \frac{27.1}{100} = 0.271 = 27.1\%$$

The taxes decline by 27.1%, not by 30%. The politician is ill-informed in saying that three consecutive 10% cuts add up to a total tax cut of 30%. In our calculation, which serves as a counterexample to the promise, the total tax cut is only 27.1%.

Suppose you paid \$1200 in taxes. During year 1, taxes decrease by 20%. During year 2, taxes increase by 20%.

a. What do you pay in taxes for year 2?

b. How do your taxes for year 2 compare with what you originally paid, namely \$1200? If the taxes are not the same, find the percent increase or decrease.

Exercise Set 1

Practice Exercises

In Exercises 1–10, express each fraction as a percent.

1. $\frac{2}{5}$ **2.** $\frac{3}{5}$ **3.** $\frac{1}{4}$ **4.** $\frac{3}{4}$

5. $\frac{3}{8}$ **6.** $\frac{7}{8}$ **7.** $\frac{1}{40}$ **8.** $\frac{3}{40}$

9. $\frac{9}{80}$ **10.** $\frac{13}{80}$

In Exercises 11–20, express each decimal as a percent.

11. 0.59 **12.** 0.96 **13.** 0.3844

14. 0.003 **15.** 2.87 **16.** 9.83

17. 14.87 **18.** 19.63

19. 100 **20.** 95

In Exercises 21–34, express each percent as a decimal.

21. 72% **22.** 38% **23.** 43.6%

24. 6.25% **25.** 130% **26.** 260%

27. 2% **28.** 6% **29.** $\frac{1}{2}\%$

30. $\frac{3}{4}\%$ **31.** $\frac{5}{8}\%$ **32.** $\frac{1}{8}\%$

33. $62\frac{1}{2}\%$ **34.** $87\frac{1}{2}\%$

Use the percent formula, $A = PB$: A is P percent of B, to solve Exercises 35–38.

35. What is 3% of 200? **36.** What is 8% of 300?

37. What is 18% of 40? **38.** What is 16% of 90?

Practice Plus

There are three basic types of percent problems that can be solved using the percent formula $A = PB$.

Question	Given	Percent Formula
What is P percent of B?	P and B	Solve for A.
A is P percent of what?	A and P	Solve for B.
A is what percent of B?	A and B	Solve for P.

Exercises 35–38 involved using the formula to answer the first question. In Exercises 39–46, use the percent formula to answer the second or third question.

39. 3 is 60% of what?

40. 8 is 40% of what?

41. 24% of what number is 40.8?

42. 32% of what number is 51.2?

43. 3 is what percent of 15?

44. 18 is what percent of 90?

45. What percent of 2.5 is 0.3?

46. What percent of 7.5 is 0.6?

Application Exercises

47. Suppose that the local sales tax rate is 6% and you purchase a car for \$32,800.

a. How much tax is paid?

b. What is the car's total cost?

48. Suppose that the local sales tax rate is 7% and you purchase a graphing calculator for \$96.

a. How much tax is paid?

b. What is the calculator's total cost?

49. An exercise machine with an original price of \$860 is on sale at 12% off.

a. What is the discount amount?

b. What is the exercise machine's sale price?

50. A dictionary that normally sells for \$16.50 is on sale at 40% off.

a. What is the discount amount?

b. What is the dictionary's sale price?

*In Exercises 51–54, use the 2008 marginal tax rates in **Table 1** to calculate the income tax owed by each person.*

51. Single male, no dependents

Gross income: $75,000
Adjustments: $4000
Deductions:
$28,000 mortgage interest
$4200 property taxes
$3000 charitable contributions
Tax credit: none

52. Single female, no dependents

Gross income: $70,000
Adjustments: $2000
Deductions:
$10,000 mortgage interest
$2500 property taxes
$1200 charitable contributions
Tax credit: none

53. Unmarried head of household with two dependent children

Gross income: $50,000
Adjustments: none
Deductions:
$4500 state taxes
$2000 theft loss
Tax credit: $2000

54. Unmarried head of household with one dependent child

Gross income: $40,000
Adjustments: $1500
Deductions:
$3600 state taxes
$800 charitable contributions
Tax credit: $2500

In addition to income tax, we are required to pay the federal government FICA (Federal Insurance Contribution Act) taxes that are used for Social Security and Medicare benefits. For people who are not self-employed, the 2008 FICA tax rates were as follows:

- *7.65% on the first $102,000 from wages and tips*
- *1.45% on income in excess of $102,000.*

The individual's employer must also pay matching amounts of FICA taxes. People who are self-employed pay double the rates shown above. Taxpayers are not permitted to subtract adjustments, exemptions, or deductions when determining FICA taxes. Use this information to solve Exercises 55–60.

55. If you are not self-employed and earn $120,000 what are your FICA taxes?

56. If you are not self-employed and earn $140,000 what are your FICA taxes?

57. If you are self-employed and earn $150,000, what are your FICA taxes?

58. If you are self-employed and earn $160,000, what are your FICA taxes?

59. In 2008, to help pay for college, you worked part-time at a local restaurant, earning $20,000 in wages and tips.

a. Calculate your FICA taxes.

b. Use **Table 1** to calculate your income tax. Assume you are single with no dependents, have no adjustments or tax credit, and you take the standard deduction.

c. Including both FICA and income tax, what percent of your gross income are your federal taxes? Round to the nearest tenth of a percent.

60. In 2008, to help pay for college, you worked part-time at a local restaurant, earning $18,000 in wages and tips.

a. Calculate your FICA taxes.

b. Use **Table 1** to calculate your income tax. Assume you are single with no dependents, have no adjustments or tax credit, and take the standard deduction.

c. Including both FICA and income tax, what percent of your gross income are your federal taxes? Round to the nearest tenth of a percent.

Exams are administered every four years by the Trends in International Mathematics and Science Study to assess global differences among fourth-grade students. The bar graph shows average math scores in 1995 and 2007 for five selected countries. Use this information to solve Exercises 61–64. Round all answers to the nearest tenth of a percent.

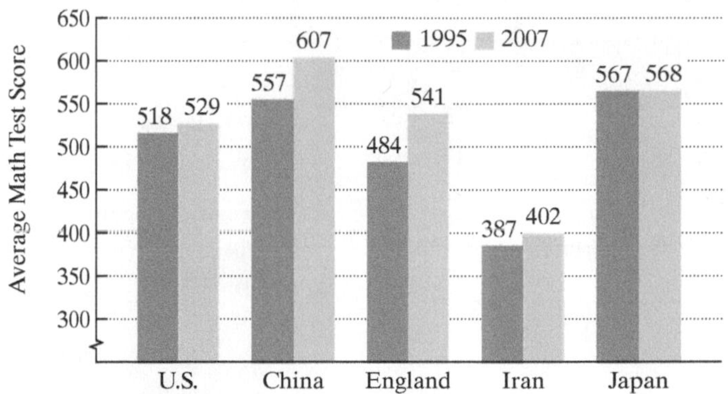

Source: National Center for Education Services

61. Find the percent increase in the average math scores from 1995 to 2007 for the country with the highest average score in 2007.

62. Find the percent increase in the average math scores from 1995 to 2007 for the country with the lowest average score in 2007.

63. Find the percent increase in the average math scores from 1995 to 2007 for the country with the least increase in average scores.

64. Find the percent increase in the average math scores from 1995 to 2007 for the country with the greatest increase in average scores.

65. A sofa regularly sells for $840. The sale price is $714. Find the percent decrease of the sale price from the regular price.

66. A FAX machine regularly sells for \$380. The sale price is \$266. Find the percent decrease of the sale price from the regular price.

67. Suppose that you have \$10,000 in a rather risky investment recommended by your financial advisor. During the first year, your investment decreases by 30% of its original value. During the second year, your investment increases by 40% of its first-year value. Your advisor tells you that there must have been a 10% overall increase of your original \$10,000 investment. Is your financial advisor using percentages properly? If not, what is your actual percent gain or loss of your original \$10,000 investment?

68. The price of a color printer is reduced by 30% of its original price. When it still does not sell, its price is reduced by 20% of the reduced price. The salesperson informs you that there has been a total reduction of 50%. Is the salesperson using percentages properly? If not, what is the actual percent reduction from the original price?

Writing in Mathematics

69. What is a percent?

70. Describe how to express a decimal number as a percent and give an example.

71. Describe how to express a percent as a decimal number and give an example.

72. Explain how to use the sales tax rate to determine an item's total cost.

73. A common complaint about income tax is "I can't afford to work more because it will put me in a higher tax bracket." Is it possible that being in a higher bracket means you actually lose money? Explain your answer.

74. Because of the mortgage interest tax deduction, is it possible to save money buying a house rather than renting, even though rent payments are lower than mortgage payments? Explain your answer.

75. Describe how to find percent increase and give an example.

Critical Thinking Exercises

Make Sense? *In Exercises 76–79, determine whether each statement makes sense or does not make sense, and explain your reasoning.*

76. I have \$100 and my restaurant bill comes to \$80, which is not enough to leave a 20% tip.

77. I found the percent decrease in a jacket's price to be 120%.

78. My weight increased by 1% in January and 1% in February, so my increase in weight over the two months is 2%.

79. My rent increased from 20% to 30% of my income, so the percent increase is 10%.

80. A condominium is taxed based on its \$78,500 value. The tax rate is \$3.40 for every \$100 of value. If the tax is paid before March 1, 3% of the normal tax is given as a discount. How much tax is paid if the condominium owner takes advantage of the discount?

81. In January, each of 60 people purchased a \$500 washing machine. In February, 10% fewer customers purchased the same washing machine that had increased in price by 20%. What was the change in sales from January to February?

OBJECTIVES

1. Calculate simple interest.
2. Use the future value formula.
3. Use the simple interest formula on discounted loans.

2 Simple Interest

The Granger Collection, New York

In 1626, Peter Minuit convinced the Wappinger Indians to sell him Manhattan Island for \$24. If the native Americans had put the \$24 into a bank account at a 5% interest rate compounded monthly, by the year 2010 there would be well over \$5 billion in the account!

Although you may not yet understand terms such as *interest rate* and *compounded monthly,* one thing seems clear: Money in certain savings accounts grows in remarkable ways. You, too, can take advantage of such accounts with astonishing results. In the next two sections, we will show you how.

1 Calculate simple interest.

Simple Interest

Interest is the amount of money that we get paid for lending or investing money, or that we pay for borrowing money. When we deposit money in a savings institution, the institution pays us interest for its use. When we borrow money, interest is the price we pay for the privilege of using the money until we repay it.

The amount of money that we deposit or borrow is called the **principal**. For example, if you deposit $2000 in a savings account, then $2000 is the principal. The amount of interest depends on the principal, the interest **rate**, which is given as a percent and varies from bank to bank, and the length of time for which the money is deposited. In this section, the rate is assumed to be annual (per year).

Simple interest involves interest calculated only on the principal. The following formula is used to find simple interest:

CALCULATING SIMPLE INTEREST

$$\text{Interest} = \text{principal} \times \text{rate} \times \text{time}$$
$$I = Prt$$

The rate, r, is expressed as a decimal when calculating simple interest.

STUDY TIP

Throughout this section and the chapter, keep in mind that all given rates are assumed to be *per year,* unless otherwise stated.

EXAMPLE 1 Calculating Simple Interest for a Year

You deposit $2000 in a savings account at Hometown Bank, which has a rate of 6%. Find the interest at the end of the first year.

Solution To find the interest at the end of the first year, we use the simple interest formula.

$$I = Prt = (2000)(0.06)(1) = 120$$

Principal, or amount deposited, is $2000. Rate is 6% = 0.06. Time is 1 year.

At the end of the first year, the interest is $120. You can withdraw the $120 interest and you still have $2000 in the savings account.

CHECK POINT 1 You deposit $3000 in a savings account at Yourtown Bank, which has a rate of 5%. Find the interest at the end of the first year.

EXAMPLE 2 Calculating Simple Interest for More Than a Year

A student took out a simple interest loan for $1800 for two years at a rate of 8% to purchase a used car. What is the interest on the loan?

Solution To find the interest on the loan, we use the simple interest formula.

$$I = Prt = (1800)(0.08)(2) = 288$$

Principal, or amount borrowed, is $1800. Rate is 8% = 0.08. Time is 2 years.

The interest on the loan is $288.

CHECK POINT 2 A student took out a simple interest loan for $2400 for two years at a rate of 7%. What is the interest on the loan?

Simple interest is used for many short-term loans, including automobile and consumer loans. Imagine that a short-term loan is taken for 125 days. The time of the loan is $\frac{125}{365}$ because there are 365 days in a year. However, before the modern use of calculators and computers, the **Banker's rule** allowed financial institutions to use 360 in the denominator of such a fraction because this simplified the interest calculation. Using the Banker's rule, the time, *t*, for a 125-day short-term loan is

$$\frac{125 \cancel{\text{days}}}{360 \cancel{\text{days}}} = \frac{125}{360}.$$

Compare the values for time, *t*, for a 125-day short-term loan using denominators of 360 and 365.

$$\frac{125}{360} \approx 0.347 \qquad \frac{125}{365} \approx 0.342$$

The denominator of 360 benefits the bank by resulting in a greater period of time for the loan, and consequently more interest.

With the widespread use of calculators and computers, government agencies and the Federal Reserve Bank calculate simple interest using 365 days in a year, as do many credit unions and banks. However, there are still some financial institutions that use the Banker's rule with 360 days in a year because it produces a greater amount of interest.

2 Use the future value formula.

Future Value: Principal Plus Interest

When a loan is repaid, the interest is added to the original principal to find the total amount due. In Example 2, at the end of two years, the student will have to repay

$$\text{principal} + \text{interest} = \$1800 + \$288 = \$2088.$$

In general, if a principal P is borrowed at a simple interest rate r, then after t years the amount due, A, can be determined as follows:

$$A = P + I = P + Prt = P(1 + rt).$$

The amount due, A, is called the **future value** of the loan. The principal borrowed now, P, is also known as the loan's **present value**.

CALCULATING FUTURE VALUE FOR SIMPLE INTEREST

The future value, A, of P dollars at simple interest rate r (as a decimal) for t years is given by

$$A = P(1 + rt).$$

EXAMPLE 3 Calculating Future Value

A loan of $1060 has been made at 6.5% for three months. Find the loan's future value.

Solution The amount borrowed, or principal, P, is $1060. The rate, r, is 6.5%, or 0.065. The time, t, is given as 3 months. We need to express the time in years because the rate is understood to be 6.5% per year. Because 3 months is $\frac{3}{12}$ of a year, $t = \frac{3}{12} = \frac{1}{4} = 0.25$.

The loan's future value, or the total amount due after three months, is

$$A = P(1 + rt) = 1060[1 + (0.065)(0.25)] \approx \$1077.23.$$

Rounded to the nearest cent, the loan's future value is $1077.23.

TECHNOLOGY

1060 [1 + (0.065)(0.25)]

On a Scientific Calculator:

1060 [×] [(] 1 [+] .065 [×] .25 [)] [=]

CHECK POINT 3 A loan of $2040 has been made at 7.5% for four months. Find the loan's future value.

The formula for future value, $A = P(1 + rt)$, has four variables. If we are given values for any three of these variables, we can solve for the fourth.

EXAMPLE 4 Determining a Simple Interest Rate

You borrow \$2500 from a friend and promise to pay back \$2655 in six months. What simple interest rate will you pay?

Solution We use the formula for future value, $A = P(1 + rt)$. You borrow \$2500: $P = 2500$. You will pay back \$2655, so this is the future value: $A = 2655$. You will do this in six months, which must be expressed in years: $t = \frac{6}{12} = \frac{1}{2} = 0.5$. To determine the simple interest rate you will pay, we solve the future value formula for r.

$$A = P(1 + rt) \quad \text{This is the formula for future value.}$$

$$2655 = 2500[1 + r(0.5)] \quad \text{Substitute the given values.}$$

$$2655 = 2500 + 1250r \quad \text{Use the distributive property.}$$

$$155 = 1250r \quad \text{Subtract 2500 from both sides.}$$

$$\frac{155}{1250} = \frac{1250r}{1250} \quad \text{Divide both sides by 1250.}$$

$$r = 0.124 = 12.4\% \quad \text{Express } \frac{155}{1250} \text{ as a percent.}$$

You will pay a simple interest rate of 12.4%.

CHECK POINT 4 You borrow \$5000 from a friend and promise to pay back \$6800 in two years. What simple interest rate will you pay?

EXAMPLE 5 Determining a Present Value

You plan to save \$2000 for a trip to Europe in two years. You decide to purchase a certificate of deposit (CD) from your bank that pays a simple interest rate of 4%. How much must you put in this CD now in order to have the \$2000 in two years?

Solution We use the formula for future value, $A = P(1 + rt)$. We are interested in finding the principal, P, or the present value.

$$A = P(1 + rt) \quad \text{This is the formula for future value.}$$

$$2000 = P[1 + (0.04)(2)] \quad A\text{(future value)} = \$2000,\ r\text{(interest rate)} = 0.04, \text{ and } t = 2 \text{ (you want \$2000 in two years).}$$

$$2000 = 1.08P \quad \text{Simplify: } 1 + (0.04)(2) = 1.08.$$

$$\frac{2000}{1.08} = \frac{1.08P}{1.08} \quad \text{Divide both sides by 1.08.}$$

$$P \approx 1851.852 \quad \text{Simplify.}$$

To make sure you will have enough money for the vacation, let's round this principal *up* to \$1851.86. Thus, you should put \$1851.86 in the CD now to have \$2000 in two years.

STUDY TIP

When computing present value, round the principal, or present value, *up*. To round up to the nearest cent, add 1 to the hundredths digit, regardless of the digit to the right. In this way, you'll be sure to have enough money to meet future goals.

CHECK POINT 5 How much should you put in an investment paying a simple interest rate of 8% if you need \$4000 in six months?

3 Use the simple interest formula on discounted loans.

Discounted Loans

Some lenders collect the interest from the amount of the loan at the time that the loan is made. This type of loan is called a **discounted loan**. The interest that is deducted from the loan is the **discount**.

EXAMPLE 6 A Discounted Loan

You borrow \$10,000 on a 10% discounted loan for a period of 8 months.

a. What is the loan's discount?

b. Determine the net amount of money you receive.

c. What is the loan's actual interest rate?

Solution

a. Because the loan's discount is the deducted interest, we use the simple interest formula.

$$I = Prt = (10{,}000)(0.10)\left(\tfrac{2}{3}\right) \approx 666.67$$

Principal is \$10,000. Rate is 10% = 0.10. Time is 8 months $= \frac{8}{12} = \frac{2}{3}$ year.

The loan's discount is \$666.67.

b. The net amount that you receive is the amount of the loan, \$10,000, minus the discount, \$666.67:

$$10{,}000 - 666.67 = 9333.33.$$

Thus, you receive \$9333.33.

c. We can calculate the loan's actual interest rate, rather than the stated 10%, by using the simple interest formula.

$$I = Prt$$ This is the simple interest formula.

$$666.67 = (9333.33)r\left(\frac{2}{3}\right)$$ I(interest) = \$666.67, P(principal, or the net amount received) = \$9333.33, and $t = \frac{2}{3}$ year.

$$666.67 = 6222.22r$$ Simplify: $9333.33\left(\frac{2}{3}\right) = 6222.22$.

$$r = \frac{666.67}{6222.22} \approx 0.107 = 10.7\%$$ Solve for r and express r to the nearest tenth of a percent.

The actual rate of interest on the 10% discounted loan is approximately 10.7%.

You borrow \$5000 on a 12% discounted loan for a period of two years. Determine: **a.** the loan's discount; **b.** the net amount you receive; **c.** the actual interest rate.

Exercise Set 2

Practice Exercises

In Exercises 1–8, the principal P is borrowed at simple interest rate r for a period of time t. Find the simple interest owed for the use of the money. Assume 360 days in a year.

1. $P = \$4000, r = 6\%, t = 1$ year
2. $P = \$7000, r = 5\%, t = 1$ year
3. $P = \$180, r = 3\%, t = 2$ years
4. $P = \$260, r = 4\%, t = 3$ years
5. $P = \$5000, r = 8.5\%, t = 9$ months
6. $P = \$18{,}000, r = 7.5\%, t = 18$ months
7. $P = \$15{,}500, r = 11\%, t = 90$ days
8. $P = \$12{,}600, r = 9\%, t = 60$ days

In Exercises 9–14, the principal P is borrowed at simple interest rate r for a period of time t. Find the loan's future value, A, or the total amount due at time t.

9. $P = \$3000, r = 7\%, t = 2$ years
10. $P = \$2000, r = 6\%, t = 3$ years
11. $P = \$26{,}000, r = 9.5\%, t = 5$ years
12. $P = \$24{,}000, r = 8.5\%, t = 6$ years
13. $P = \$9000, r = 6.5\%, t = 8$ months
14. $P = \$6000, r = 4.5\%, t = 9$ months

In Exercises 15–20, the principal P is borrowed and the loan's future value, A, at time t is given. Determine the loan's simple interest rate, r, to the nearest tenth of a percent.

15. $P = \$2000$, $A = \$2150$, $t = 1$ year

16. $P = \$3000$, $A = \$3180$, $t = 1$ year

17. $P = \$5000$, $A = \$5900$, $t = 2$ years

18. $P = \$10{,}000$, $A = \$14{,}060$, $t = 2$ years

19. $P = \$2300$, $A = \$2840$, $t = 9$ months

20. $P = \$1700$, $A = \$1820$, $t = 6$ months

In Exercises 21–26, determine the present value, P, you must invest to have the future value, A, at simple interest rate r after time t. Round answers up to the nearest cent.

21. $A = \$6000$, $r = 8\%$, $t = 2$ years

22. $A = \$8500$, $r = 7\%$, $t = 3$ years

23. $A = \$14{,}000$, $r = 9.5\%$, $t = 6$ years

24. $A = \$16{,}000$, $r = 11.5\%$, $t = 5$ years

25. $A = \$5000$, $r = 14.5\%$, $t = 9$ months

26. $A = \$2000$, $r = 12.6\%$, $t = 8$ months

Exercises 27–30 involve discounted loans. In each exercise, determine

a. *the loan's discount.*

b. *the net amount of money you receive.*

c. *the loan's actual interest rate, to the nearest tenth of a percent.*

27. You borrow \$2000 on a 7% discounted loan for a period of 8 months.

28. You borrow \$3000 on an 8% discounted loan for a period of 9 months.

29. You borrow \$12,000 on a 6.5% discounted loan for a period of two years.

30. You borrow \$20,000 on an 8.5% discounted loan for a period of three years.

Practice Plus

31. Solve for r: $A = P(1 + rt)$.

32. Solve for t: $A = P(1 + rt)$.

33. Solve for P: $A = P(1 + rt)$.

34. Solve for P: $A = P\left(1 + \frac{r}{n}\right)^{nt}$. (We will be using this formula in the next section.)

Application Exercises

35. In order to start a small business, a student takes out a simple interest loan for \$4000 for 9 months at a rate of 8.25%.

a. How much interest must the student pay?

b. Find the future value of the loan.

36. In order to pay for baseball uniforms, a school takes out a simple interest loan for \$20,000 for 7 months at a rate of 12%.

a. How much interest must the school pay?

b. Find the future value of the loan.

37. You borrow \$1400 from a friend and promise to pay back \$2000 in two years. What simple interest rate, to the nearest tenth of a percent, will you pay?

38. Treasury bills (T-bills) can be purchased from the U.S. Treasury Department. You buy a T-bill for \$981.60 that pays \$1000 in 13 weeks. What simple interest rate, to the nearest tenth of a percent, does this T-bill earn?

39. To borrow money, you pawn your guitar. Based on the value of the guitar, the pawnbroker loans you \$960. One month later, you get the guitar back by paying the pawnbroker \$1472. What annual interest rate did you pay?

40. To borrow money, you pawn your mountain bike. Based on the value of the bike, the pawnbroker loans you \$552. One month later, you get the bike back by paying the pawnbroker \$851. What annual interest rate did you pay?

41. A bank offers a CD that pays a simple interest rate of 6.5%. How much must you put in this CD now in order to have \$3000 for a home-entertainment center in two years?

42. A bank offers a CD that pays a simple interest rate of 5.5%. How much must you put in this CD now in order to have \$8000 for a kitchen remodeling project in two years?

43. In order to pay for dental work, you borrow \$8000 on an 8% discounted loan for a period of three years.

a. What is the loan's discount?

b. Determine the net amount of money you receive.

c. What is the loan's actual interest rate?

44. In order to pay for wedding expenses, you borrow \$20,000 on a 6% discounted loan for a period of four years.

a. What is the loan's discount?

b. Determine the net amount of money you receive.

c. What is the loan's actual interest rate?

Writing in Mathematics

45. Explain how to calculate simple interest.

46. What is the future value of a loan and how is it determined?

47. What is a discounted loan? How is the net amount of money received from such a loan determined?

Critical Thinking Exercises

Make Sense? *In Exercises 48–51, determine whether each statement makes sense or does not make sense, and explain your reasoning.*

48. After depositing \$1500 in an account at a rate of 4%, my balance at the end of the first year was \$(1500)(0.04).

49. I saved money on my short-term loan for 90 days by finding a financial institution that used the Banker's rule rather than one that calculated interest using 365 days in a year.

50. I planned to save \$5000 in four years, computed the present value to be \$3846.153, so I rounded the principal to \$3846.15.

51. When I borrowed money on a discounted loan, the amount of money I received was less than the amount I wanted to borrow.

52. Use the future value formula to show that the time required for an amount of money P to double in value to $2P$ is given by

$$t = \frac{1}{r}.$$

53. You deposit \$5000 in an account that earns 5.5% simple interest.

a. Express the future value in the account as a linear function of time, t.

b. Determine the slope of the function in part (a) and describe what this means. Use the phrase "rate of change" in your description.

OBJECTIVES

1 Use compound interest formulas.
2 Calculate present value.
3 Understand and compute effective annual yield.

3 Compound Interest

pal PV

So, how did the present value of Manhattan in 1626—that is, the \$24 paid to the native Americans—attain a future value of over \$5 billion in 2010, 384 years later, at a mere 5% interest rate? After all, the future value on \$24 for 384 years at 5% simple interest is

$$A = P(1 + rt)$$
$$= 24[1 + (0.05)(384)] = 484.8,$$

or a paltry \$484.80, compared to over \$5 billion. To understand this dramatic difference in future value, we turn to the concept of *compound interest.*

1 Use compound interest formulas.

Compound Interest

Compound interest is interest computed on the original principal as well as on any accumulated interest. Many savings accounts pay compound interest. For example, suppose you deposit \$1000 in a savings account at a rate of 5%. **Table 2** shows how the investment grows if the interest earned is automatically added on to the principal.

TABLE 2 Calculating the Amount in an Account Subject to Compound Interest

Use $A = P(1 + rt)$ with $r = 0.05$ and $t = 1$, or $A = P(1 + 0.05)$.

Year	Starting Balance	Amount in the Account at Year's End
1	\$1000	$A = \$1000(1 + 0.05) = \$1050$
2	\$1050 or $\$1000(1 + 0.05)$	$A = \$1050(1 + 0.05) = \$1102.50$ or $A = \$1000(1 + 0.05)(1 + 0.05) = \$1000(1 + 0.05)^2$
3	\$1102.50 or $\$1000(1 + 0.05)^2$	$A = \$1102.50(1 + 0.05) \approx \$1157.63$ or $A = \$1000(1 + 0.05)^2(1 + 0.05) = \$1000(1 + 0.05)^3$

Using inductive reasoning, the amount, A, in the account after t years is the original principal, \$1000, times $(1 + 0.05)^t$: $A = 1000(1 + 0.05)^t$.

If the original principal is P and the interest rate is r, we can use this same approach to determine the amount, A, in an account subject to compound interest.

CALCULATING THE AMOUNT IN AN ACCOUNT FOR COMPOUND INTEREST PAID ONCE A YEAR

If you deposit P dollars at rate r, in decimal form, subject to compound interest, then the amount, A, of money in the account after t years is given by

$$A = P(1 + r)^t.$$

The amount A is called the account's **future value** and the principal P is called its **present value.**

EXAMPLE 1 Using the Compound Interest Formula

You deposit \$2000 in a savings account at Hometown Bank, which has a rate of 6%.

a. Find the amount, A, of money in the account after 3 years subject to interest compounded once a year.

b. Find the interest.

Solution

a. The amount deposited, or principal, P, is \$2000. The rate, r, is 6%, or 0.06. The time of the deposit, t, is three years. The amount in the account after three years is

$$A = P(1 + r)^t = 2000(1 + 0.06)^3 = 2000(1.06)^3 \approx 2382.03.$$

Rounded to the nearest cent, the amount in the savings account after three years is \$2382.03.

b. Because the amount in the account is \$2382.03 and the original principal is \$2000, the interest is \$2382.03 − \$2000, or \$382.03.

TECHNOLOGY

Here are the calculator keystrokes to compute $2000(1.06)^3$:

Many Scientific Calculators

2000 [×] 1.06 [y^x] 3 [=]

Many Graphing Calculators

2000 [×] 1.06 [∧] 3 [ENTER]

CHECK POINT 1 You deposit \$1000 in a savings account at a bank that has a rate of 4%.

a. Find the amount, A, of money in the account after 5 years subject to interest compounded once a year. Round to the nearest cent.

b. Find the interest.

Compound Interest Paid More Than Once a Year

The period of time between two interest payments is called the **compounding period**. When compound interest is paid once per year, the compounding period is one year. We say that the interest is **compounded annually**.

Most savings institutions have plans in which interest is paid more than once per year. If compound interest is paid twice per year, the compounding period is six months. We say that the interest is **compounded semiannually**. When compound interest is paid four times per year, the compounding period is three months and the interest is said to be **compounded quarterly**. Some plans allow for monthly compounding or daily compounding.

In general, when compound interest is paid n times per year, we say that there are ***n* compounding periods per year**. The following formula is used to calculate the amount in an account subject to compound interest with n compounding periods per year:

CALCULATING THE AMOUNT IN AN ACCOUNT FOR COMPOUND INTEREST PAID *n* TIMES A YEAR

If you deposit P dollars at rate r, in decimal form, subject to compound interest paid n times per year, then the amount, A, of money in the account after t years is given by

$$A = P\left(1 + \frac{r}{n}\right)^{nt}.$$

A is the account's **future value** and the principal P is its **present value**.

STUDY TIP

If $n = 1$ (interest paid once a year), the formula in the box becomes

$$A = P\left(1 + \frac{r}{1}\right)^{1t}, \text{ or}$$

$$A = P(1 + r)^t.$$

This shows that the amount in an account subject to annual compounding is just one application of the general formula in the box. With this general formula, you no longer need a separate formula for annual compounding.

EXAMPLE 2 Using the Compound Interest Formula

You deposit \$7500 in a savings account that has a rate of 6%. The interest is compounded monthly.

a. How much money will you have after five years?

b. Find the interest after five years.

TECHNOLOGY

Here are the calculator keystrokes to compute

$$7500\left(1+\frac{0.06}{12}\right)^{12\cdot 5}:$$

Many Scientific Calculators

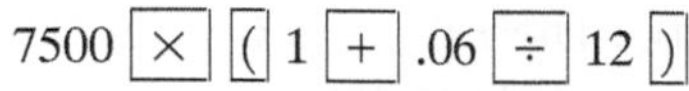

7500 [×] [(] 1 [+] .06 [÷] 12 [)] [y^x] [(] 12 [×] 5 [)] [=]

Many Graphing Calculators

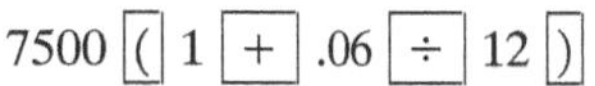

7500 [(] 1 [+] .06 [÷] 12 [)] [∧] [(] 12 [×] 5 [)] [ENTER]

Solution

a. The amount deposited, or principal, P, is \$7500. The rate, r, is 6%, or 0.06. Because interest is compounded monthly, there are 12 compounding periods per year, so $n = 12$. The time of the deposit, t, is five years. The amount in the account after five years is

$$A = P\left(1+\frac{r}{n}\right)^{nt} = 7500\left(1+\frac{0.06}{12}\right)^{12\cdot 5} = 7500(1.005)^{60} \approx 10{,}116.38.$$

Rounded to the nearest cent, you will have \$10,116.38 after five years.

b. Because the amount in the account is \$10,116.38 and the original principal is \$7500, the interest after five years is \$10,116.38 − \$7500, or \$2616.38.

CHECK POINT 2 You deposit \$4200 in a savings account that has a rate of 4%. The interest is compounded quarterly.

a. How much money will you have after ten years? Round to the nearest cent.

b. Find the interest after ten years.

Continuous Compounding

Some banks use **continuous compounding**, where the compounding periods increase infinitely (compounding interest every trillionth of a second, every quadrillionth of a second, etc.). As n, the number of compounding periods in a year, increases without bound, the expression $\left(1+\frac{1}{n}\right)^n$ approaches the irrational number e: $e \approx 2.71828$. This is illustrated in **Table 3**. As a result, the formula for the balance in an account with n compounding periods per year, $A = P\left(1+\frac{r}{n}\right)^{nt}$, becomes $A = Pe^{rt}$ with continuous compounding. Although continuous compounding sounds terrific, it yields only a fraction of a percent more interest over a year than daily compounding.

TABLE 3 As n Takes on Increasingly Large Values, the Expression $\left(1+\frac{1}{n}\right)^n$ Approaches the Irrational Number e.

n	$\left(1+\frac{1}{n}\right)^n$
1	2
2	2.25
5	2.48832
10	2.59374246
100	2.704813829
1000	2.716923932
10,000	2.718145927
100,000	2.718268237
1,000,000	2.718280469
1,000,000,000	2.718281827

FORMULAS FOR COMPOUND INTEREST

After t years, the balance, A, in an account with principal P and annual interest rate r (in decimal form) is given by the following formulas:

1. For n compounding periods per year: $A = P\left(1+\frac{r}{n}\right)^{nt}$
2. For continuous compounding: $A = Pe^{rt}$.

TECHNOLOGY

You can compute e to a power using the [e^x] key on your calculator. Use the key to enter e^1 and verify that e is approximately equal to 2.71828.

Scientific Calculators	Graphing Calculators
1 [e^x]	[e^x] 1 [ENTER]

EXAMPLE 3 Choosing between Investments

You decide to invest \$8000 for 6 years and you have a choice between two accounts. The first pays 7% per year, compounded monthly. The second pays 6.85% per year, compounded continuously. Which is the better investment?

Solution The better investment is the one with the greater balance in the account after 6 years. Let's begin with the account with monthly compounding. We use the compound interest formula with $P = 8000$, $r = 7\% = 0.07$, $n = 12$ (monthly compounding means 12 compounding periods per year), and $t = 6$.

$$A = P\left(1 + \frac{r}{n}\right)^{nt} = 8000\left(1 + \frac{0.07}{12}\right)^{12\cdot 6} \approx 12{,}160.84$$

The balance in this account after 6 years would be $12,160.84.

For the second investment option, we use the formula for continuous compounding with $P = 8000$, $r = 6.85\% = 0.0685$, and $t = 6$.

$$A = Pe^{rt} = 8000e^{0.0685(6)} \approx 12{,}066.60$$

The balance in this account after 6 years would be $12,066.60, slightly less than the previous amount. Thus, the better investment is the 7% monthly compounding option.

TECHNOLOGY

Here are the calculator keystrokes to compute

$8000e^{0.0685(6)}$:

Many Scientific Calculators

8000 [×] [(] .0685 [×] 6 [)] [e^x] [=]

Many Graphing Calculators

8000 [e^x] [(] .0685 [×] 6 [)] [ENTER]

CHECK POINT 3 A sum of $10,000 is invested at an annual rate of 8%. Find the balance in the account after 5 years subject to **a.** quarterly compounding and **b.** continuous compounding.

2 Calculate present value.

Planning for the Future with Compound Interest

Just as we did in Section 2, we can determine P, the principal or present value, that should be deposited now in order to have a certain amount, A, in the future. If an account earns compound interest, the amount of money that should be invested today to obtain a future value of A dollars can be determined by solving the compound interest formula for P:

CALCULATING PRESENT VALUE

If A dollars are to be accumulated in t years in an account that pays rate r compounded n times per year, then the present value, P, that needs to be invested now is given by

$$P = \frac{A}{\left(1 + \frac{r}{n}\right)^{nt}}.$$

Remember to round the principal *up* to the nearest cent when computing present value so there will be enough money to meet future goals.

EXAMPLE 4 Calculating Present Value

How much money should be deposited today in an account that earns 6% compounded monthly so that it will accumulate to $20,000 in five years?

Solution The amount we need today, or the present value, is determined by the present value formula. Because the interest is compounded monthly, $n = 12$. Furthermore, A (the future value) $= \$20{,}000$, r (the rate) $= 6\% = 0.06$, and t (time in years) $= 5$.

$$P = \frac{A}{\left(1 + \frac{r}{n}\right)^{nt}} = \frac{20{,}000}{\left(1 + \frac{0.06}{12}\right)^{12\cdot 5}} \approx 14{,}827.4439$$

To make sure there will be enough money, we round the principal *up* to $14,827.45. Approximately $14,827.45 should be invested today in order to accumulate to $20,000 in five years.

TECHNOLOGY

Here are the keystrokes for Example 4:

Many Scientific Calculators

20000 [÷] [(] 1 [+] .06 [÷] 12 [)]

[y^x] [(] 12 [×] 5 [)] [=]

Many Graphing Calculators

20000 [÷] [(] 1 [+] .06 [÷] 12 [)]

[∧] [(] 12 [×] 5 [)] [ENTER]

CHECK POINT 4 How much money should be deposited today in an account that earns 7% compounded weekly so that it will accumulate to $10,000 in eight years?

3 Understand and compute effective annual yield.

Effective Annual Yield

As we've seen before, a common problem in financial planning is selecting the best investment from two or more investments. For example, is an investment that pays 8.25% interest compounded quarterly better than one that pays 8.3% interest compounded semiannually? Another way to answer the question is to compare the *effective rates* of the investments, also called their *effective annual yields*.

BLITZER BONUS

DOUBLING YOUR MONEY: THE RULE OF 72

Here's a shortcut for estimating the number of years it will take for your investment to double: Divide 72 by the effective annual yield without the percent sign. For example, if the effective annual yield is 6%, your money will double in approximately

$$\frac{72}{6}$$

years, or in 12 years.

EFFECTIVE ANNUAL YIELD

The **effective annual yield**, or the **effective rate**, is the simple interest rate that produces the same amount of money in an account at the end of one year as when the account is subjected to compound interest at a stated rate.

EXAMPLE 5 Understanding Effective Annual Yield

You deposit $4000 in an account that pays 8% interest compounded monthly.

a. Find the future value after one year.

b. Use the future value formula for simple interest to determine the effective annual yield.

Solution

a. We use the compound interest formula to find the account's future value after one year.

$$A = P\left(1 + \frac{r}{n}\right)^{nt} = 4000\left(1 + \frac{0.08}{12}\right)^{12\cdot 1} \approx \$4332.00$$

Principal is $4000. Stated rate is 8% = 0.08. Monthly compounding: $n = 12$ Time is one year: $t = 1$.

Rounded to the nearest cent, the future value after one year is $4332.00.

b. **The effective annual yield, or effective rate, is a simple interest rate.** We use the future value formula for simple interest to determine the simple interest rate that produces a future value of $4332 for a $4000 deposit after one year.

$$A = P(1 + rt)$$ This is the future value formula for simple interest.

$$4332 = 4000(1 + r\cdot 1)$$ Substitute the given values.

$$4332 = 4000 + 4000r$$ Use the distributive property.

$$332 = 4000r$$ Subtract 4000 from both sides.

$$\frac{332}{4000} = \frac{4000r}{4000}$$ Divide both sides by 4000.

$$r = \frac{332}{4000} = 0.083 = 8.3\%$$ Express r as a percent.

The effective annual yield, or effective rate, is 8.3%. This means that money invested at 8.3% simple interest earns the same amount in one year as money invested at 8% interest compounded monthly.

BLITZER BONUS

HIGH-YIELD SAVINGS

Online banks can afford to pay the best rates on savings accounts by avoiding the expense of managing a brick-and-mortar bank. To search for the best deals, go to BankRate.com for bank accounts and iMoneyNet.com for money-market funds.

In Example 5, the stated 8% rate is called the **nominal rate**. The 8.3% rate is the effective rate and is a simple interest rate.

You deposit $6000 in an account that pays 10% interest compounded monthly.

a. Find the future value after one year.

b. Determine the effective annual yield.

Generalizing the procedure of Example 5 and Check Point 5 gives a formula for effective annual yield:

CALCULATING EFFECTIVE ANNUAL YIELD

Suppose that an investment has a nominal interest rate, r, in decimal form, and pays compound interest n times per year. The investment's effective annual yield, Y, in decimal form, is given by

$$Y = \left(1 + \frac{r}{n}\right)^n - 1.$$

The decimal form of Y given by the formula should then be converted to a percent.

TECHNOLOGY

Here are the keystrokes for Example 6:

Many Scientific Calculators

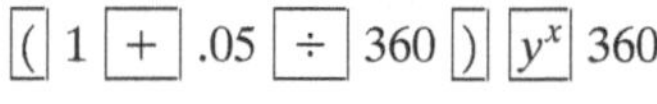

Many Graphing Calculators

(1 + .05 ÷ 360) ^ 360

− 1 ENTER.

Given the nominal rate and the number of compounding periods per year, some graphing calculators display the effective annual yield. The screen shows the calculation of the effective rate in Example 6 on the TI-84 Plus.

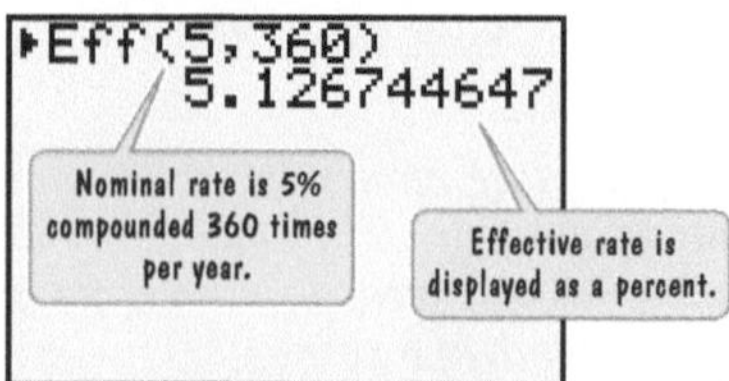
▸Eff(5,360)
5.126744647
Nominal rate is 5% compounded 360 times per year.
Effective rate is displayed as a percent.

EXAMPLE 6 Calculating Effective Annual Yield

A passbook savings account has a nominal rate of 5%. The interest is compounded daily. Find the account's effective annual yield. (Assume 360 days in a year.)

Solution The rate, r, is 5%, or 0.05. Because interest is compounded daily and we assume 360 days in a year, $n = 360$. The account's effective annual yield is

$$Y = \left(1 + \frac{r}{n}\right)^n - 1 = \left(1 + \frac{0.05}{360}\right)^{360} - 1 \approx 0.0513 = 5.13\%.$$

The effective annual yield is 5.13%. Thus, money invested at 5.13% simple interest earns the same amount of interest in one year as money invested at 5% interest, the nominal rate, compounded daily.

What is the effective annual yield of an account paying 8% compounded quarterly?

The effective annual yield is often included in the information about investments or loans. Because it's the true interest rate you're earning or paying, it's the number you should pay attention to. **If you are selecting the best investment from two or more investments, the best choice is the account with the greatest effective annual yield.** However, there are differences in the types of accounts that you need to take into consideration. Some pay interest from the day of deposit to the day of withdrawal. Other accounts start paying interest the first day of the month that follows the day of deposit. Some savings institutions stop paying interest if the balance in the account falls below a certain amount.

When *borrowing money,* the effective rate or effective annual yield is usually called the **annual percentage rate**. If all other factors are equal and you are borrowing money, select the option with the least annual percentage rate.

Exercise Set 3

Here is a list of formulas needed to solve the exercises. Be sure you understand what each formula describes and the meaning of the variables in the formulas.

$$A = P\left(1 + \frac{r}{n}\right)^{nt} \qquad P = \frac{A}{\left(1 + \frac{r}{n}\right)^{nt}}$$

$$A = Pe^{rt} \qquad Y = \left(1 + \frac{r}{n}\right)^{n} - 1$$

Practice Exercises

In Exercises 1–12, the principal represents an amount of money deposited in a savings account subject to compound interest at the given rate.

a. *Find how much money there will be in the account after the given number of years. (Assume 360 days in a year.)*

b. *Find the interest earned.*

Round answers to the nearest cent.

Principal	Rate	Compounded	Time
1. $10,000	4%	annually	2 years
2. $8000	6%	annually	3 years
3. $3000	5%	semiannually	4 years
4. $4000	4%	semiannually	5 years
5. $9500	6%	quarterly	5 years
6. $2500	8%	quarterly	6 years
7. $4500	4.5%	monthly	3 years
8. $2500	6.5%	monthly	4 years
9. $1500	8.5%	daily	2.5 years
10. $1200	8.5%	daily	3.5 years
11. $20,000	4.5%	daily	20 years
12. $25,000	5.5%	daily	20 years

Solve Exercises 13–16 using appropriate compound interest formulas. Round answers to the nearest cent.

13. Find the accumulated value of an investment of $10,000 for 5 years at an interest rate of 5.5% if the money is **a.** compounded semiannually; **b.** compounded quarterly; **c.** compounded monthly; **d.** compounded continuously.

14. Find the accumulated value of an investment of $5000 for 10 years at an interest rate of 6.5% if the money is **a.** compounded semiannually; **b.** compounded quarterly; **c.** compounded monthly; **d.** compounded continuously.

15. Suppose that you have $12,000 to invest. Which investment yields the greater return over 3 years: 7% compounded monthly or 6.85% compounded continuously?

16. Suppose that you have $6000 to invest. Which investment yields the greater return over 4 years: 8.25% compounded quarterly or 8.3% compounded semiannually?

In Exercises 17–20, round answers up to the nearest cent.

17. How much money should be deposited today in an account that earns 6% compounded semiannually so that it will accumulate to $10,000 in three years?

18. How much money should be deposited today in an account that earns 7% compounded semiannually so that it will accumulate to $12,000 in four years?

19. How much money should be deposited today in an account that earns 9.5% compounded monthly so that it will accumulate to $10,000 in three years?

20. How much money should be deposited today in an account that earns 10.5% compounded monthly so that it will accumulate to $22,000 in four years?

21. You deposit $10,000 in an account that pays 4.5% interest compounded quarterly.

a. Find the future value after one year.

b. Use the future value formula for simple interest to determine the effective annual yield.

22. You deposit $12,000 in an account that pays 6.5% interest compounded quarterly.

a. Find the future value after one year.

b. Use the future value formula for simple interest to determine the effective annual yield.

In Exercises 23–28, a passbook savings account has a rate of 6%. Find the effective annual yield, rounded to the nearest tenth of a percent, if the interest is compounded

23. semiannually.

24. quarterly.

25. monthly.

26. daily. (Assume 360 days in a year.)

27. 1000 times per year.

28. 100,000 times per year.

In Exercises 29–32, determine the effective annual yield for each investment. Then select the better investment. Assume 360 days in a year. If rounding is required, round to the nearest tenth of a percent.

29. 8% compounded monthly; 8.25% compounded annually

30. 5% compounded monthly; 5.25% compounded quarterly

31. 5.5% compounded semiannually; 5.4% compounded daily

32. 7% compounded annually; 6.85% compounded daily

Practice Plus

In Exercises 33–38, assume that you place money in an account subject to interest compounded annually. Use the formula $A = P(1 + r)^t$, a calculator, and trial and error to answer each question. Give answers to the nearest tenth of a year.

33. How long will it take for the investment to triple at an interest rate of 5%?

34. How long will it take for the investment to triple at an interest rate of 10%?

35. How long will it take for the investment to increase by 50% at an interest rate of 10%?

36. How long will it take for the investment to increase by 50% at an interest rate of 5%?

37. How long will it take for the investment to increase by 90% at an interest rate of 8%?

38. How long will it take for the investment to increase by 90% at an interest rate of 12%?

Application Exercises

Assume that the accounts described in the exercises have no other deposits or withdrawals except for what is stated. Round all answers to the nearest dollar, rounding up to the nearest dollar in present-value problems. Assume 360 days in a year.

39. At the time of a child's birth, $12,000 was deposited in an account paying 6% interest compounded semiannually. What will be the value of the account at the child's twenty-first birthday?

40. At the time of a child's birth, $10,000 was deposited in an account paying 5% interest compounded semiannually. What will be the value of the account at the child's twenty-first birthday?

41. You deposit $2600 in an account that pays 4% interest compounded once a year. Your friend deposits $2200 in an account that pays 5% interest compounded monthly.
    a. Who will have more money in their account after one year? How much more?
    b. Who will have more money in their account after five years? How much more?
    c. Who will have more money in their account after 20 years? How much more?

42. You deposit $3000 in an account that pays 3.5% interest compounded once a year. Your friend deposits $2500 in an account that pays 4.8% interest compounded monthly.
    a. Who will have more money in their account after one year? How much more?
    b. Who will have more money in their account after five years? How much more?
    c. Who will have more money in their account after 20 years? How much more?

43. You deposit $3000 in an account that pays 7% interest compounded semiannually. After ten years, the interest rate is increased to 7.25% compounded quarterly. What will be the value of the account after 16 years?

44. You deposit $6000 in an account that pays 5.25% interest compounded semiannually. After ten years, the interest rate is increased to 5.4% compounded quarterly. What will be the value of the account after 18 years?

45. In 1626, Peter Minuit convinced the Wappinger Indians to sell him Manhattan Island for $24. If the Native Americans had put the $24 into a bank account paying compound interest at a 5% rate, how much would the investment be worth in the year 2010 ($t = 384$ years) if interest were compounded **a.** monthly? **b.** 360 times per year?

46. In 1777, Jacob DeHaven loaned George Washington's army $450,000 in gold and supplies. Due to a disagreement over the method of repayment (gold versus Continental money), DeHaven was never repaid, dying penniless. In 1989, his descendants sued the U.S. government over the 212-year-old debt. If the DeHavens used an interest rate of 6% and daily compounding (the rate offered by the Continental Congress in 1777), how much money did the DeHaven family demand in their suit? (*Hint:* Use the compound interest formula with $n = 360$ and $t = 212$ years.)

47. Will you earn more interest in one year by depositing $2000 in a simple interest account that pays 6% or in an account that pays 5.9% interest compounded daily? How much more interest will you earn?

48. Will you earn more interest in one year by depositing $1000 in a simple interest account that pays 7% or in an account that pays 6.9% interest compounded daily? How much more interest will you earn?

49. Two accounts each begin with a deposit of $5000. Both accounts have rates of 5.5%, but one account compounds interest once a year while the other account compounds interest continuously. Make a table that shows the amount in each account and the interest earned after one year, five years, ten years, and 20 years.

50. Two accounts each begin with a deposit of $10,000. Both accounts have rates of 6.5%, but one account compounds interest once a year while the other account compounds interest continuously. Make a table that shows the amount in each account and the interest earned after one year, five years, ten years, and 20 years.

51. Parents wish to have $80,000 available for a child's education. If the child is now 5 years old, how much money must be set aside at 6% compounded semiannually to meet their financial goal when the child is 18?

52. A 30-year-old worker plans to retire at age 65. He believes that $500,000 is needed to retire comfortably. How much should be deposited now at 7% compounded monthly to meet the $500,000 retirement goal?

53. You would like to have $75,000 available in 15 years. There are two options. Account A has a rate of 4.5% compounded once a year. Account B has a rate of 4% compounded daily. How much would you have to deposit in each account to reach your goal?

54. You would like to have $150,000 available in 20 years. There are two options. Account A has a rate of 5.5% compounded once a year. Account B has a rate of 5% compounded daily. How much would you have to deposit in each account to reach your goal?

55. You invest $1600 in an account paying 5.4% interest compounded daily. What is the account's effective annual yield? Round to the nearest hundredth of a percent.

56. You invest $3700 in an account paying 3.75% interest compounded daily. What is the account's effective annual yield? Round to the nearest hundredth of a percent.

57. An account has a nominal rate of 4.2%. Find the effective annual yield, rounded to the nearest tenth of a percent, with quarterly compounding, monthly compounding, and daily compounding. How does changing the compounding period affect the effective annual yield?

58. An account has a nominal rate of 4.6%. Find the effective annual yield, rounded to the nearest tenth of a percent, with quarterly compounding, monthly compounding, and daily compounding. How does changing the compounding period affect the effective annual yield?

59. A bank offers a money market account paying 4.5% interest compounded semiannually. A competing bank offers a money market account paying 4.4% interest compounded daily. Which account is the better investment?

60. A bank offers a money market account paying 4.9% interest compounded semiannually. A competing bank offers a money market account paying 4.8% interest compounded daily. Which account is the better investment?

Writing in Mathematics

61. Describe the difference between simple and compound interest.
62. Give two examples that illustrate the difference between a compound interest problem involving future value and a compound interest problem involving present value.
63. What is effective annual yield?
64. Explain how to select the best investment from two or more investments.

Critical Thinking Exercises

Make Sense? *In Exercises 65–68, determine whether each statement makes sense or does not make sense, and explain your reasoning.*

65. My bank provides simple interest at 3.25% per year, but I can't determine if this is a better deal than a competing bank offering 3.25% compound interest without knowing the compounding period.
66. When choosing between two accounts, the one with the greater annual interest rate is always the better deal.
67. A bank can't increase compounding periods indefinitely without owing its customers an infinite amount of money.
68. My bank advertises a compound interest rate of 2.4%, although, without making deposits or withdrawals, the balance in my account increased by 2.43% in one year.
69. A depositor opens a new savings account with $6000 at 5% compounded semiannually. At the beginning of year 3, an additional $4000 is deposited. At the end of six years, what is the balance in the account?
70. A depositor opens a money market account with $5000 at 8% compounded monthly. After two years, $1500 is withdrawn from the account to buy a new computer. A year later, $2000 is put in the account. What will be the ending balance if the money is kept in the account for another three years?
71. Use the future value formulas for simple and compound interest in one year to derive the formula for effective annual yield.

Group Exercise

72. This activity is a group research project intended for four or five people. Present your research in a seminar on the history of interest and banking. The seminar should last about 30 minutes. Address the following questions:

When was interest first charged on loans? How was lending money for a fee opposed historically? What is usury? What connection did banking and interest rates play in the historic European rivalries between Christians and Jews? When and where were some of the highest interest rates charged? What were the rates? Where does the word *interest* come from? What is the origin of the word *shylock*? What is the difference between usury and interest in modern times? What is the history of a national bank in the United States?

OBJECTIVES

1. Determine the value of an annuity.
2. Determine regular annuity payments needed to achieve a financial goal.
3. Understand stocks and bonds as investments.
4. Read stock tables.

4 Annuities, Stocks, and Bonds

"Good Times Are Predicted in 1929"

—*The Washington Post*, JAN. 1, 1929

"In a few months, I expect to see the stock market much higher than today."

—ESTEEMED ECONOMIST IRVING FISHER: OCT. 14, 1929

Date on which the stock market crashed and began the Great Depression: Oct. 29, 1929

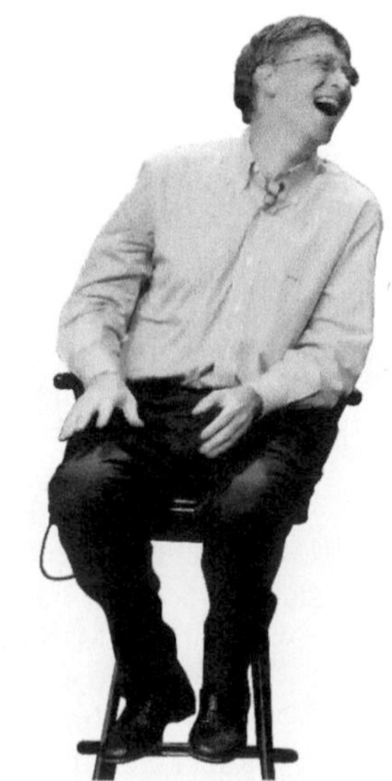

Nati Harnik\AP Wide World Photos

According to the *Forbes Billionaires List*, in 2009 the two richest Americans were Bill Gates (net worth: $40 billion) and Warren Buffett (net worth: $37 billion). In May 1965, Buffett's new company, Berkshire Hathaway, was selling one share of stock for $18. By the end of 2008, the price of a share had increased to $96,600. If you had purchased one share in May 1965, your **return**, or percent increase, would be

$$\frac{\text{amount of increase}}{\text{original amount}} = \frac{\$96{,}600 - \$18}{\$18} \approx 5365.67 = 536{,}567\%.$$

What does a return of nearly 540,000% mean? If you had invested \$250 in Warren Buffett's company in May 1965, your shares would have been worth over \$1.3 million by December 2008.

Of course, investments that potentially offer outrageous returns come with great risk of losing part or all of the principal. The bottom line: Is there a safe way to save regularly and have an investment worth one million dollars or more? In this section, we consider such savings plans, some of which come with special tax treatment, as well as riskier investments in stocks and bonds.

1 Determine the value of an annuity.

Annuities

The compound interest formula

$$A = P(1 + r)^t$$

gives the future value, A, after t years, when a fixed amount of money, P, the principal, is deposited in an account that pays an annual interest rate r (in decimal form) compounded once a year. However, money is often invested in small amounts at periodic intervals. For example, to save for retirement, you might decide to place \$1000 into an Individual Retirement Account (IRA) at the end of each year until you retire. An **annuity** is a sequence of equal payments made at equal time periods. An IRA is an example of an annuity.

The **value of an annuity** is the sum of all deposits plus all interest paid. Our first example illustrates how to find this value.

EXAMPLE 1 Determining the Value of an Annuity

You deposit \$1000 into a savings plan at the end of each year for three years. The interest rate is 8% per year compounded annually.

a. Find the value of the annuity after three years.

b. Find the interest.

Solution

a. The value of the annuity after three years is the sum of all deposits made plus all interest paid over three years.

This is the \$1000 deposit at year's end.

Value at end of year 1 $= \$1000$

This is the first-year deposit with interest earned for a year. This is the \$1000 deposit at year's end.

Value at end of year 2 $= \$1000(1 + 0.08) + \$1000$

$= \$1080 + \$1000 = \$2080$

Use $A = P(1 + r)^t$ with $r = 0.08$ and $t = 1$, or $A = P(1 + 0.08)$.

This is the second-year balance, \$2080, with interest earned for a year. This is the \$1000 deposit at year's end.

Value at end of year 3 $= \$2080(1 + 0.08) + \$1000$

$= \$2246.40 + \$1000 = \$3246.40$

The value of the annuity at the end of three years is \$3246.40.

b. You made three payments of \$1000 each, depositing a total of $3 \times \$1000$, or \$3000. Because the value of the annuity is \$3246.40, the interest is $\$3246.40 - \$3000$, or \$246.40.

You deposit \$2000 into a savings plan at the end of each year for three years. The interest rate is 10% per year compounded annually.

a. Find the value of the annuity after three years.

b. Find the interest.

Suppose that you deposit P dollars into an account at the end of each year. The account pays an annual interest rate, r, compounded annually. At the end of the first year, the account contains P dollars. At the end of the second year, P dollars is deposited again. At the time of this deposit, the first deposit has received interest earned during the second year. Thus, the value of the annuity after two years is

$$P + P(1 + r).$$

Deposit of P dollars at end of second year

First-year deposit of P dollars with interest earned for a year

The value of the annuity after three years is

$$P \quad + \quad P(1 + r) \quad + \quad P(1 + r)^2.$$

Deposit of P dollars at end of third year

Second-year deposit of P dollars with interest earned for a year

First-year deposit of P dollars with interest earned over two years

The value of the annuity after t years is

$$P + P(1 + r) + P(1 + r)^2 + P(1 + r)^3 + \cdots + P(1 + r)^{t-1}.$$

Deposit of P dollars at end of year t

First-year deposit of P dollars with interest earned over $t - 1$ years

Each term in this sum is obtained by multiplying the preceding term by $(1 + r)$. Thus, the terms form a geometric sequence. Using a formula for the sum of the terms of a geometric sequence, we can obtain the following formula that gives the value of this annuity:

VALUE OF AN ANNUITY: INTEREST COMPOUNDED ONCE A YEAR

If P is the deposit made at the end of each year for an annuity that pays an annual interest rate r (in decimal form) compounded once a year, the value, A, of the annuity after t years is

$$A = \frac{P[(1 + r)^t - 1]}{r}.$$

EXAMPLE 2 Determining the Value of an Annuity

To save for retirement, you decide to deposit \$1000 into an IRA at the end of each year for the next 30 years. If you can count on an interest rate of 10% per year compounded annually,

a. How much will you have from the IRA after 30 years?

b. Find the interest.

Round answers to the nearest dollar.

TECHNOLOGY

Here are the calculator keystrokes to compute

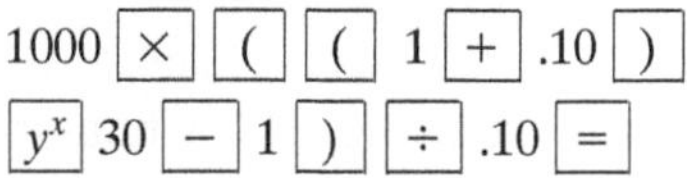

$$\frac{1000[(1+0.10)^{30}-1]}{0.10}:$$

Many Scientific Calculators

1000 [×] [(] [(] 1 [+] .10 [)] [y^x] 30 [−] 1 [)] [÷] .10 [=]

Observe that the part of the numerator in brackets is entered as $((1 + 0.10)^{30} - 1)$ to maintain the order of operations.

Many Graphing Calculators

1000 [(] [(] 1 [+] .10 [)] [∧] 30 [−] 1 [)] [÷] .10 [ENTER]

Solution

a. The amount that you will have from the IRA is its value after 30 years.

$$A = \frac{P[(1+r)^t - 1]}{r}$$ Use the formula for the value of an annuity.

$$A = \frac{1000[(1+0.10)^{30} - 1]}{0.10}$$ The annuity involves year-end deposits of \$1000: $P = 1000$. The interest rate is 10%: $r = 0.10$. The number of years is 30: $t = 30$. The Technology box shows how this computation can be done in a single step using parentheses keys.

$$= \frac{1000[(1.10)^{30} - 1]}{0.10}$$ Add in parentheses: $1 + 0.10 = 1.10$.

$$\approx \frac{1000(17.4494 - 1)}{0.10}$$ Use a calculator to find $(1.10)^{30}$: 1.1 [y^x] 30 [=].

$$= \frac{1000(16.4494)}{0.10}$$ Simplify in parentheses: $17.4494 - 1 = 16.4494$.

$$= 164{,}494$$ Use a calculator: 1000 [×] 16.4494 [÷] .10 [=].

After 30 years, you will have approximately \$164,494 from the IRA.

b. You made 30 payments of \$1000 each, depositing a total of 30 × \$1000, or \$30,000. Because the value of the annuity is approximately \$164,494, the interest is approximately

$$\$164{,}494 - \$30{,}000, \text{ or } \$134{,}494.$$

The interest is nearly $4\frac{1}{2}$ times the amount of your payments, illustrating the power of compounding.

CHECK POINT 2 You deposit \$3000 into an IRA at the end of each year for the next 40 years. If you can count on an interest rate of 8% per year compounded annually,

a. How much will you have from the IRA after 40 years?

b. Find the interest.

Round answers to the nearest dollar.

STUDY TIP

If $n = 1$ (interest compounded once a year), the formula in the box becomes

$$A = \frac{P\left[\left(1+\frac{r}{1}\right)^{1t} - 1\right]}{\left(\frac{r}{1}\right)}, \text{ or}$$

$$A = \frac{P\left[(1+r)^t - 1\right]}{r}.$$

This was the boxed formula from earlier in this chapter, showing that the value of an annuity with interest compounded once a year is just one application of the general formula in the box on the right. With this general formula, you no longer need a separate formula for annual compounding.

We can adjust the formula for the value of an annuity if equal payments are made at the end of each of n yearly compounding periods.

VALUE OF AN ANNUITY: INTEREST COMPOUNDED n TIMES PER YEAR

If P is the deposit made at the end of each compounding period for an annuity that pays an annual interest rate r (in decimal form) compounded n times per year, the value, A, of the annuity after t years is

$$A = \frac{P\left[\left(1+\frac{r}{n}\right)^{nt} - 1\right]}{\left(\frac{r}{n}\right)}.$$

BLITZER BONUS

STASHING CASH AND MAKING TAXES LESS TAXING

As you prepare for your future career, retirement probably seems very far away. Making regular deposits into an IRA may not be fun, but there is a special incentive from Uncle Sam that makes it far more appealing. Traditional IRAs are **tax-deferred savings plans**. This means that you do not pay taxes on deposits and interest until you begin withdrawals, typically at retirement. Before then, yearly deposits count as adjustments to gross income and are not part of your taxable income. Not only do you get a tax break now, but you ultimately earn more. This is because you do not pay taxes on interest from year to year, allowing earnings to accumulate until you start withdrawals. With a tax code that encourages long-term savings, opening an IRA early in your career is a smart way to gain more control over how you will spend a large part of your life.

EXAMPLE 3 Determining the Value of an Annuity

At age 25, to save for retirement, you decide to deposit \$200 at the end of each month into an IRA that pays 7.5% compounded monthly.

a. How much will you have from the IRA when you retire at age 65?

b. Find the interest.

Round answers to the nearest dollar.

Solution

a. Because you are 25, the amount that you will have from the IRA when you retire at 65 is its value after 40 years.

$$A = \frac{P\left[\left(1+\frac{r}{n}\right)^{nt}-1\right]}{\left(\frac{r}{n}\right)}$$

Use the formula for the value of an annuity.

$$A = \frac{200\left[\left(1+\frac{0.075}{12}\right)^{12\cdot 40}-1\right]}{\left(\frac{0.075}{12}\right)}$$

The annuity involves month-end deposits of \$200: $P = 200$. The interest rate is 7.5%: $r = 0.075$. The interest is compounded monthly: $n = 12$. The number of years is 40: $t = 40$.

$$= \frac{200[(1+0.00625)^{480}-1]}{0.00625}$$

Using parentheses keys, this calculation or the previous calculation can be performed in a single step on a calculator.

$$= \frac{200[(1.00625)^{480}-1]}{0.00625}$$

Add in parentheses: $1 + 0.00625 = 1.00625$.

$$\approx \frac{200(19.8989-1)}{0.00625}$$

Use a calculator to find $(1.00625)^{480}$: 1.00625 [y^x] 480 [=].

$$\approx 604{,}765$$

After 40 years, you will have approximately \$604,765 when retiring at age 65.

b. Interest = Value of the IRA − Total deposits

$\approx \$604{,}765 - \$200 \cdot 12 \cdot 40$

(\$200 per month × 12 months per year × 40 years)

$= \$604{,}765 - \$96{,}000 = \$508{,}765$

The interest is approximately \$508,765, more than five times the amount of your contributions to the IRA.

Annuities can be categorized by when payments are made. The formula used to solve Example 3 describes **ordinary annuities**, where payments are made at the end of each period. The formula assumes the same number of yearly payments and yearly compounding periods. An annuity plan in which payments are made at the beginning of each period is called an **annuity due**. The formula for the value of this type of annuity is slightly different than the one used in Example 3.

At age 30, to save for retirement, you decide to deposit \$100 at the end of each month into an IRA that pays 9.5% compounded monthly.

a. How much will you have from the IRA when you retire at age 65?

b. Find the interest.

Round answers to the nearest dollar.

2 Determine regular annuity payments needed to achieve a financial goal.

Planning for the Future with an Annuity

By solving the annuity formula for P, we can determine the amount of money that should be deposited at the end of each compounding period so that an annuity has a future value of A dollars. The following formula gives the regular payments, P, needed to reach a financial goal, A:

REGULAR PAYMENTS NEEDED TO ACHIEVE A FINANCIAL GOAL

The deposit, P, that must be made at the end of each compounding period into an annuity that pays an annual interest rate r (in decimal form) compounded n times per year in order to achieve a value of A dollars after t years is

$$P = \frac{A\left(\frac{r}{n}\right)}{\left[\left(1+\frac{r}{n}\right)^{nt} - 1\right]}.$$

When computing regular payments needed to achieve a financial goal, round the deposit made at the end of each compounding period *up*. In this way, you won't fall slightly short of being able to meet future goals. In this section, we will round annuity payments up to the nearest dollar.

EXAMPLE 4 Achieving a Financial Goal

You would like to have \$20,000 to use as a down payment for a home in five years by making regular, end-of-month deposits in an annuity that pays 6% compounded monthly.

a. How much should you deposit each month? Round up to the nearest dollar.

b. How much of the \$20,000 down payment comes from deposits and how much comes from interest?

Solution

a. $$P = \frac{A\left(\frac{r}{n}\right)}{\left[\left(1+\frac{r}{n}\right)^{nt} - 1\right]}$$

Use the formula for regular payments, P, needed to achieve a financial goal, A.

$$P = \frac{20{,}000\left(\frac{0.06}{12}\right)}{\left[\left(1+\frac{0.06}{12}\right)^{12\cdot 5} - 1\right]}$$

Your goal is to accumulate \$20,000 ($A = 20{,}000$) over five years ($t = 5$). The interest rate is 6% ($r = 0.06$) compounded monthly ($n = 12$).

$$\approx 287$$

Use a calculator and round up to the nearest dollar to be certain you do not fall short of your goal.

You should deposit \$287 each month to be certain of having \$20,000 for a down payment on a home.

b. Total deposits $= \$287 \cdot 12 \cdot 5 = \$17{,}220$

\$287 per month × 12 months per year × 5 years

Interest $= \$20{,}000 - \$17{,}220 = \$2780$

We see that \$17,220 of the \$20,000 comes from your deposits and the remainder, \$2780, comes from interest.

STUDY TIP

In Example 4 of Section 3, we saw that a lump-sum deposit of approximately \$14,828 at 6% compounded monthly would accumulate to \$20,000 in five years. In Example 4 on the right, we see that total deposits of \$17,220 are required to reach the same goal. With the same interest rate, compounding period, and time period, a lump-sum deposit will generate more interest than an annuity. If you don't have a large sum of money to open an account, an annuity is a realistic, although more expensive, option to a lump-sum deposit for achieving the same financial goal.

Parents of a baby girl are in a financial position to begin saving for her college education. They plan to have \$100,000 in a college fund in 18 years by making regular, end-of-month deposits in an annuity that pays 9% compounded monthly.

a. How much should they deposit each month? Round up to the nearest dollar.

b. How much of the \$100,000 college fund comes from deposits and how much comes from interest?

3 Understand stocks and bonds as investments.

Investments

When you deposit money into a bank account, you are making a **cash investment**. Bank accounts up to \$250,000 are insured by the federal government, so there is no risk of losing the principal you've invested. The account's interest rate guarantees a certain percent increase in your investment, called its **return**. For example, if you deposit \$7500 in a savings account that has a rate of 4% compounded annually, the annual return is 4%. There are other kinds of investments that are riskier, meaning that it is possible to lose all or part of your principal. These investments include **stocks** and **bonds**.

Stocks

Investors purchase **stock**, shares of ownership in a company. The shares indicate the percent of ownership. For example, if a company has issued a total of one million shares and an investor owns 20,000 of these shares, that investor owns

$$\frac{20{,}000 \cancel{\text{ shares}}}{1{,}000{,}000 \cancel{\text{ shares}}} = 0.02$$

or 2% of the company. Any investor who owns some percentage of the company is called a **shareholder**.

Buying or selling stock is referred to as **trading**. Shares of stock need both a seller and a buyer to be traded. Stocks are traded on a **stock exchange**. The price of a share of stock is determined by the law of supply and demand. If a company is prospering, investors will be willing to pay a good price for its stock, and so the stock price goes up. If the company does not do well, investors may decide to sell, and the stock price goes down. Stock prices indicate the performance of the companies they represent, as well as the state of the national and global economies.

There are two ways to make money by investing in stock:

- You sell the shares for more money than what you paid for them, in which case you have a **capital gain** on the sale of stock. (There can also be a capital loss by selling for less than what you paid, or if the company goes bankrupt.)
- While you own the stock, the company distributes all or part of its profits to shareholders as **dividends**. Each share is paid the same dividend, so the amount you receive depends on the number of shares owned. (Some companies reinvest all profits and do not distribute dividends.)

When more and more average Americans began investing and making money in stocks in the 1990s, the federal government cut the capital-gains tax rate in 1997. Long-term capital gains (profits on items held for more than a year before being sold) and dividends are taxed at lower rates than wages and interest earnings.

Bonds

People who buy stock become part owners in a company. In order to raise money and not dilute the ownership of current stockholders, companies sell **bonds**. People who buy a bond are **lending money** to the company from which they buy the bond. Bonds are a commitment from a company to pay the price an investor pays for the bond at the time it was purchased, called the **face value**, along with interest payments at a given rate.

There are many reasons for issuing bonds. A company might need to raise money for research on a drug that has the potential for curing AIDS, so it issues bonds. The U.S. Treasury Department issues 30-year bonds at a fixed 7% annual rate to borrow money to cover possible federal deficits. Local governments often issue bonds to borrow money to build schools, parks, and libraries.

Bonds are traded like stock, and their price is a function of supply and demand. If a company goes bankrupt, bondholders are the first to claim the company's assets. They make their claims before the stockholders, even though (unlike stockholders) they do not own a share of the company. Buying and selling bonds is frequently done through online investing.

Generally speaking, investing in bonds is less risky than investing in stocks, although the return is lower. A listing of all the investments that a person holds is called a **financial portfolio**. Most financial advisors recommend a portfolio with a mixture of low-risk and high-risk investments, called a **diversified portfolio**.

4 Read stock tables.

Reading Stock Tables

Daily newspapers and online services give current stock prices and other information about stocks. We will use FedEx (Federal Express) stock to learn how to read these daily stock tables. Look at the following newspaper listing of FedEx stock.

52-Week High	52-Week Low	Stock	SYM	Div	Yld %	PE	Vol 100s	Hi	Lo	Close	Net Chg
99.46	34.02	FedEx	FDX	.44	1.0	19	37701	45	43.47	44.08	−1.60

The headings indicate the meanings of the numbers across the row.

52-Week High
99.46

The heading **52-Week High** refers to the *highest price* at which FedEx stock traded during the past 52 weeks. The highest price was $99.46 per share. This means that during the past 52 weeks at least one investor was willing to pay $99.46 for a share of FedEx stock. Notice that 99.46 represents a quantity in dollars, although the stock table does not show the dollar sign.

52-Week Low
34.02

The heading **52-Week Low** refers to the *lowest price* at which FedEx stock traded during the past 52 weeks. This price is $34.02.

Stock	SYM
FedEx	FDX

The heading **Stock** is the *company name*, FedEx. The heading **SYM** is the *symbol* the company uses for trading. FedEx uses the symbol FDX.

Div
.44

The heading **Div** refers to *dividends* paid per share to stockholders last year. FedEx paid a dividend of $0.44 per share. Once again, the dollar symbol does not appear in the table. Thus, if you owned 100 shares, you received a dividend of $0.44 × 100, or $44.00.

Yld %
1.0

The heading **Yld %** stands for *percent yield*. In this case, the percent yield is 1.0%. (The stock table does not show the percent sign.) This means that the dividends alone give investors an annual return of 1.0%. This is much lower than interest rates offered by most banks. However, this percent does not take into account the fact that FedEx stock prices might rise. If an investor sells shares for more than what they were paid for, the gain will probably make FedEx stock a much better investment than a bank account.

In order to understand the meaning of the heading PE, we need to understand some of the other numbers in the table. We will return to this column.

Vol 100s
37701

The heading **Vol 100s** stands for *sales volume in hundreds*. This is the number of shares traded yesterday, in hundreds. The number in the table is 37,701. This means that yesterday, a total of 37,701 × 100, or 3,770,100 shares of FedEx were traded.

Hi
45

The heading **Hi** stands for the *highest price* at which FedEx stock traded *yesterday*. This number is 45. Yesterday, FedEx's highest trading price was $45 a share.

Lo
43.47

The heading **Lo** stands for the *lowest price* at which FedEx stock traded *yesterday*. This number is 43.47. Yesterday, FedEx's lowest trading price was $43.47 a share.

Close
44.08

The heading **Close** stands for the *price* at which shares traded *when the stock exchange closed yesterday*. This number is 44.08. Thus, the price at which shares of FedEx traded when the stock exchange closed yesterday was $44.08 per share. This is called yesterday's **closing price**.

Net Chg
−1.60

The heading **Net Chg** stands for *net change*. This is the change in price from the market close two days ago to yesterday's market close. This number is −1.60. Thus, the price of a share of FedEx stock went down by $1.60. For some stock listings, the notation . . . appears under Net Chg. This means that there was *no change in price* for a share of stock from the market close two days ago to yesterday's market close.

PE
19

Now, we are ready to return to the heading **PE,** standing for the *price-to-earnings ratio*.

$$\text{PE ratio} = \frac{\text{Yesterday's closing price per share}}{\text{Annual earnings per share}}$$

This can be expressed as

$$\text{Annual earnings per share} = \frac{\text{Yesterday's closing price per share}}{\text{PE ratio}}.$$

The PE ratio for FedEx is given to be 19. Yesterday's closing price per share was 44.08. We can substitute these numbers into the formula to find annual earnings per share:

Close	PE
44.08	19

$$\text{Annual earnings per share} = \frac{44.08}{19} = 2.32.$$

The annual earnings per share for FedEx are $2.32. The PE ratio, 19, tells us that yesterday's closing price per share, $44.08, is 19 times greater than the earnings per share, $2.32.

EXAMPLE 5 Reading Stock Tables

52-Week High	52-Week Low	Stock	SYM	Div	Yld %	PE	Vol 100s	Hi	Lo	Close	Net Chg
42.38	22.50	Disney	DIS	.21	.6	43	115900	32.50	31.25	32.50	. . .

Use the stock table for Disney to answer the following questions.

a. What were the high and low prices for the past 52 weeks?

b. If you owned 3000 shares of Disney stock last year, what dividend did you receive?

c. What is the annual return for dividends alone? How does this compare to a bank account offering a 3.5% interest rate?

d. How many shares of Disney were traded yesterday?

e. What were the high and low prices for Disney shares yesterday?

f. What was the price at which Disney shares traded when the stock exchange closed yesterday?

g. What does the value or symbol in the net change column mean?

h. Compute Disney's annual earnings per share using

$$\text{Annual earnings per share} = \frac{\text{Yesterday's closing price per share}}{\text{PE ratio}}.$$

Solution

a. We find the high price for the past 52 weeks by looking under the heading **High**. The price is listed in dollars, given as 42.38. Thus, the high price for a share of stock for the past 52 weeks was $42.38. We find the low price for the past 52 weeks by looking under the heading **Low**. This price is also listed in dollars, given as 22.50. Thus, the low price for a share of Disney stock for the past 52 weeks was $22.50.

b. We find the dividend paid for a share of Disney stock last year by looking under the heading **Div**. The price is listed in dollars, given as .21. Thus, Disney paid a dividend of \$0.21 per share to stockholders last year. If you owned 3000 shares, you received a dividend of \$0.21 × 3000, or \$630.

c. We find the annual return for dividends alone by looking under the heading **Yld %**, standing for percent yield. The number in the table, .6, is a percent. This means that the dividends alone give Disney investors an annual return of 0.6%. This is much lower than a bank account paying a 3.5% interest rate. However, if Disney shares increase in value, the gain might make Disney stock a better investment than the bank account.

d. We find the number of shares of Disney traded yesterday by looking under the heading **Vol 100s**, standing for sales volume in hundreds. The number in the table is 115900. This means that yesterday, a total of 115,900 × 100, or 11,590,000 shares, were traded.

e. We find the high and low prices for Disney shares yesterday by looking under the headings **Hi** and **Lo**. Both prices are listed in dollars, given as 32.50 and 31.25. Thus, the high and low prices for Disney shares yesterday were \$32.50 and \$31.25, respectively.

f. We find the price at which Disney shares traded when the stock exchange closed yesterday by looking under the heading **Close**. The price is listed in dollars, given as 32.50. Thus, when the stock exchange closed yesterday, the price of a share of Disney stock was \$32.50.

g. The ... under **Net Chg** means that there was no change in price in Disney stock from the market close two days ago to yesterday's market close. In part (f), we found that the price of a share of Disney stock at yesterday's close was \$32.50, so the price at the market close two days ago was also \$32.50.

h. We are now ready to use

$$\text{Annual earnings per share} = \frac{\text{Yesterday's closing price per share}}{\text{PE ratio}}$$

to compute Disney's annual earnings per share. We found that yesterday's closing price per share was \$32.50. We find the PE ratio under the heading **PE**. The given number is 43. Thus,

$$\text{Annual earnings per share} = \frac{\$32.50}{43} \approx \$0.76.$$

The annual earnings per share for Disney are \$0.76. The PE ratio, 43, tells us that yesterday's closing price per share, \$32.50, is 43 times greater than the earnings per share, approximately \$0.76.

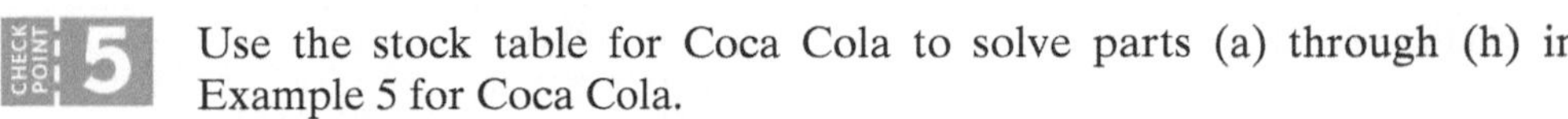

CHECK POINT 5 Use the stock table for Coca Cola to solve parts (a) through (h) in Example 5 for Coca Cola.

52-Week High	52-Week Low	Stock	SYM	Div	Yld %	PE	Vol 100s	Hi	Lo	Close	Net Chg
63.38	42.37	Coca Cola	CocaCl	.72	1.5	37	72032	49.94	48.33	49.50	+0.03

Ways to Invest in Annuities, Stocks, and Bonds

Investments in annuities, stocks, and bonds can be bought directly, which means making these investments on your own. You can open an IRA at a bank, purchase stock through stockbrokers, who charge a commission for their services, or buy bonds from the government.

It is not an easy job to determine which stocks and bonds to buy or sell, or when to do so. Even IRAs can be funded by mixing stocks and bonds. Many small investors have decided that they do not have the time to stay informed about the progress of corporations, even with the help of online industry research. Instead, they invest in a **mutual fund**. A mutual fund is a group of stocks and/or bonds managed by a professional investor. When you purchase shares in a mutual fund, you give your money to the **fund manager**. Your money is combined with the money of other investors in the mutual fund. The fund manager invests this pool of money, buying and selling shares of stocks and bonds to obtain the maximum possible returns.

Investors in mutual funds own a small portion of many different companies, which may protect them against the poor performance of a single company. When comparing mutual funds, consider both the fees charged for investing and how well the fund manager is doing with the fund's money. Newspapers publish ratings from 1 (worst) to 5 (best) of mutual fund performance based on whether the manager is doing a good job with its investors' money. Two numbers are given. The first number compares the performance of the mutual fund to a large group of similar funds. The second number compares the performance to funds that are nearly identical. The best rating a fund manager can receive is 5/5; the worst is 1/1.

Exercise Set 4

Here are the formulas needed to solve the exercises. Be sure you understand what each formula describes and the meaning of the variables in the formulas.

$$A = \frac{P\left[\left(1+\frac{r}{n}\right)^{nt}-1\right]}{\left(\frac{r}{n}\right)} \qquad P = \frac{A\left(\frac{r}{n}\right)}{\left[\left(1+\frac{r}{n}\right)^{nt}-1\right]}$$

Practice Exercises

In Exercises 1–10,

a. *Find the value of each annuity. Round to the nearest dollar.*

b. *Find the interest.*

Periodic Deposit	Rate	Time
1. \$2000 at the end of each year	5% compounded annually	20 years
2. \$3000 at the end of each year	4% compounded annually	20 years
3. \$4000 at the end of each year	6.5% compounded annually	40 years
4. \$4000 at the end of each year	5.5% compounded annually	40 years
5. \$50 at the end of each month	6% compounded monthly	30 years
6. \$60 at the end of each month	5% compounded monthly	30 years
7. \$100 at the end of every six months	4.5% compounded semiannually	25 years
8. \$150 at the end of every six months	6.5% compounded semiannually	25 years
9. \$1000 at the end of every three months	6.25% compounded quarterly	6 years
10. \$1200 at the end of every three months	3.25% compounded quarterly	6 years

In Exercises 11–18,

a. *Determine the periodic deposit. Round up to the nearest dollar.*

b. *How much of the financial goal comes from deposits and how much comes from interest?*

Periodic Deposit	Rate	Time	Financial Goal
11. $? at the end of each year	6% compounded annually	18 years	$140,000
12. $? at the end of each year	5% compounded annually	18 years	$150,000
13. $? at the end of each month	4.5% compounded monthly	10 years	$200,000
14. $? at the end of each month	7.5% compounded monthly	10 years	$250,000
15. $? at the end of each month	7.25% compounded monthly	40 years	$1,000,000
16. $? at the end of each month	8.25% compounded monthly	40 years	$1,500,000
17. $? at the end of every three months	3.5% compounded quarterly	5 years	$20,000
18. $? at the end of every three months	4.5% compounded quarterly	5 years	$25,000

Exercises 19 and 20 refer to the stock tables for Goodyear (the tire company) and JC Penney (the department store) given below. In each exercise, use the stock table to answer the following questions. Where necessary, round dollar amounts to the nearest cent.

a. *What were the high and low prices for a share for the past 52 weeks?*

b. *If you owned 700 shares of this stock last year, what dividend did you receive?*

c. *What is the annual return for the dividends alone? How does this compare to a bank offering a 3% interest rate?*

d. *How many shares of this company's stock were traded yesterday?*

e. *What were the high and low prices for a share yesterday?*

f. *What was the price at which a share traded when the stock exchange closed yesterday?*

g. *What was the change in price for a share of stock from the market close two days ago to yesterday's market close?*

h. *Compute the company's annual earnings per share using*

$$\text{Annual earnings per share} = \frac{\text{Yesterday's closing price per share}}{\text{PE ratio}}.$$

19.

52-Week High	52-Week Low	Stock	SYM	Div	Yld %	PE	Vol 100s	Hi	Lo	Close	Net Chg
73.25	45.44	Goodyear	GT	1.20	2.2	17	5915	56.38	54.38	55.50	+1.25

20.

52-Week High	52-Week Low	Stock	SYM	Div	Yld %	PE	Vol 100s	Hi	Lo	Close	Net Chg
78.34	35.38	Penney JC	JCP	2.18	4.7	22	7473	48.19	46.63	46.88	−1.31

Practice Plus

In Exercises 21–22, round all answers to the nearest dollar.

21. Here are two ways of investing $30,000 for 20 years.

Lump-Sum Deposit	Rate	Time
$30,000	5% compounded annually	20 years

Periodic Deposit	Rate	Time
$1500 at the end of each year	5% compounded annually	20 years

a. After 20 years, how much more will you have from the lump-sum investment than from the annuity?

b. After 20 years, how much more interest will be earned from the lump-sum investment than from the annuity?

22. Here are two ways of investing $40,000 for 25 years.

Lump-Sum Deposit	Rate	Time
$40,000	6.5% compounded annually	25 years

Periodic Deposit	Rate	Time
$1600 at the end of each year	6.5% compounded annually	25 years

a. After 25 years, how much more will you have from the lump-sum investment than from the annuity?

b. After 25 years, how much more interest will be earned from the lump-sum investment than from the annuity?

In Exercises 23–24,

a. *Determine the deposit at the end of each month. Round up to the nearest dollar.*

b. *Assume that the annuity in part (a) is a tax-deferred IRA belonging to a man whose gross income in 2008 was $50,000. Use* ***Table 1*** *to calculate his 2008 taxes first with and then without the IRA. Assume the man is single with no dependents, has no tax credits, and takes the standard deduction.*

c. *What percent of his gross income are the man's federal taxes with and without the IRA? Round to the nearest tenth of a percent.*

	Periodic Deposit	Rate	Time	Financial Goal
23.	$? at the end of each month	8% compounded monthly	40 years	$1,000,000
24.	$? at the end of each month	7% compounded monthly	40 years	$650,000

25. Solve for P:

$$A = \frac{P[(1 + r)^t - 1]}{r}.$$

What does the resulting formula describe?

26. Solve for P:

$$A = \frac{P\left[\left(1 + \frac{r}{n}\right)^{nt} - 1\right]}{\left(\frac{r}{n}\right)}.$$

What does the resulting formula describe?

Application Exercises

In Exercises 27–32, round to the nearest dollar.

27. To save money for a sabbatical to earn a master's degree, you deposit $2000 at the end of each year in an annuity that pays 7.5% compounded annually.

a. How much will you have saved at the end of five years?

b. Find the interest.

28. To save money for a sabbatical to earn a master's degree, you deposit $2500 at the end of each year in an annuity that pays 6.25% compounded annually.

a. How much will you have saved at the end of five years?

b. Find the interest.

29. At age 25, to save for retirement, you decide to deposit $50 at the end of each month in an IRA that pays 5.5% compounded monthly.

a. How much will you have from the IRA when you retire at age 65?

b. Find the interest.

30. At age 25, to save for retirement, you decide to deposit $75 at the end of each month in an IRA that pays 6.5% compounded monthly.

a. How much will you have from the IRA when you retire at age 65?

b. Find the interest.

31. To offer scholarship funds to children of employees, a company invests $10,000 at the end of every three months in an annuity that pays 10.5% compounded quarterly.

a. How much will the company have in scholarship funds at the end of ten years?

b. Find the interest.

32. To offer scholarship funds to children of employees, a company invests $15,000 at the end of every three months in an annuity that pays 9% compounded quarterly.

a. How much will the company have in scholarship funds at the end of ten years?

b. Find the interest.

In Exercises 33–36, round up to the nearest dollar.

33. You would like to have $3500 in four years for a special vacation following graduation by making deposits at the end of every six months in an annuity that pays 5% compounded semiannually.

a. How much should you deposit at the end of every six months?

b. How much of the $3500 comes from deposits and how much comes from interest?

34. You would like to have $4000 in four years for a special vacation following graduation by making deposits at the end of every six months in an annuity that pays 7% compounded semiannually.

a. How much should you deposit at the end of every six months?

b. How much of the $4000 comes from deposits and how much comes from interest?

35. How much should you deposit at the end of each month into an IRA that pays 6.5% compounded monthly to have $2 million when you retire in 45 years? How much of the $2 million comes from interest?

36. How much should you deposit at the end of each month into an IRA that pays 8.5% compounded monthly to have $4 million when you retire in 45 years? How much of the $4 million comes from interest?

Writing in Mathematics

37. What is an annuity?

38. What is meant by the value of an annuity?

39. Write a problem involving the formula for regular payments needed to achieve a financial goal. The problem should be similar to Example 4. However, the problem should be unique to your situation. Include something for which you would like to save, how much you need to save, and how long it will take to achieve your goal. Then solve the problem.

40. What is stock?

41. Describe how to find the percent ownership that a shareholder has in a company.

42. Describe the two ways that investors make money with stock.

43. What is a bond? Describe the difference between a stock and a bond.

44. Using a recent newspaper, copy the stock table for a company of your choice. Then explain the meaning of the numbers in the columns.

45. If an investor sees that the return from dividends for a stock is lower than the return for a no-risk bank account, should the stock be sold and the money placed in the bank account? Explain your answer.

Use the following investments to answer Exercises 46–49.

Investment 1: 1000 shares of IBM stock

Investment 2: A 5-year bond with a 22% interest rate issued by a small company that is testing and planning to sell delicious, nearly zero-calorie desserts

Investment 3: A 30-year U.S. treasury bond at a fixed 7% annual rate

46. Which of these investments has the greatest risk? Explain why.
47. Which of these investments has the least risk? Explain why.
48. Which of these investments has the possibility of the greatest return? Explain why.
49. If you could be given one of these investments as a gift, which one would you choose? Explain why.

Critical Thinking Exercises

Make Sense? *In Exercises 50–53, determine whether each statement makes sense or does not make sense, and explain your reasoning.*

50. With the same interest rate, compounding period, and time period, an annuity will generate more interest than a lump-sum deposit.
51. By putting $20 at the end of each month into an IRA that pays 3.5% compounded monthly, I'll be able to retire comfortably in just 30 years.
52. Even though my IRA is a tax-deferred savings plan, I have no idea what tax rates will be 30 years from now, so my retirement income from my annuity could be taxed quite heavily at the time it is withdrawn.
53. At the end of each month, I'm better off investing a fixed amount into stocks rather than making a regular payment into an annuity because stocks offer me the greater return on my money.
54. How much should you deposit at the end of each month in an IRA that pays 8% compounded monthly to earn $60,000 per year from interest alone, while leaving the principal untouched, when you retire in 30 years?

Group Exercises

55. Each group should have a newspaper with current stock quotations. Choose nine stocks that group members think would make good investments. Imagine that you invest $10,000 in each of these nine investments. Check the value of your stock each day over the next five weeks and then sell the nine stocks after five weeks. What is the group's profit or loss over the five-week period? Compare this figure with the profit or loss of other groups in your class for this activity.
56. This activity is a group research project intended for four or five people. Use the research to present a seminar on investments. The seminar is intended to last about 30 minutes and should result in an interesting and informative presentation to the entire class. The seminar should include investment considerations, how to read the bond section of the newspaper, how to read the mutual fund section, and higher-risk investments.
57. Group members have inherited $1 million. However, the group cannot spend any of the money for ten years. As a group, determine how to invest this money in order to maximize the money you will make over ten years. The money can be invested in as many ways as the group decides. Explain each investment decision. What are the risks involved in each investment plan?

OBJECTIVES

1. Compute the monthly payment and interest costs for a mortgage.
2. Prepare a partial loan amortization schedule.
3. Compute payments and interest for other kinds of fixed installment loans.
4. Find the interest, the balance due, and the minimum monthly payment for credit card loans.

5 Installment Loans, Amortization, and Credit Cards

Do you buy products with a credit card? Although your card lets you use a product while paying for it, the costs associated with such cards, including their high interest rates, fees, and penalties, stack the odds in favor of your getting hurt by them. In 2008, the average credit-card debt per U.S. household was $11,211. If you use a credit card, you are engaging in **installment buying**, in which you repay a loan for the cost of a product on a monthly basis. A loan that you pay off with weekly or monthly payments, or payments in some other time period, is called an **installment loan**. The advantage of an installment loan is that the consumer gets to use a product immediately. In this section, we will see that the disadvantage is that it can add a substantial amount to the cost of a purchase. When it comes to installment buying, consumer beware!

Corbis RF

BLITZER BONUS

AN EASY WAY TO FIND THE CHEAPEST MORTGAGE

When people learn all the major costs of getting a mortgage, they often feel like they're drowning in an ocean of rates, points, and formulas. Assume you'll be in your new home for five years, the average length of time most people stay. An easy way to shop for the best mortgage is to ask six different lenders for the total *dollar costs* of

1. up-front fees (such as appraisal and credit reports)
2. closing costs, including points
3. interest for the first five years.

Then add up the total cost of these three items at each lender and compare the various deals. Don't let lenders get away with saying, "Then, of course, there are certain other fees and charges." You want them all now—period.

Mortgages

A **mortgage** is a long-term installment loan (perhaps up to 30, 40, or even 50 years) for the purpose of buying a home, and for which the property is pledged as security for payment. If payments are not made on the loan, the lender may take possession of the property. The **down payment** is the portion of the sale price of the home that the buyer initially pays to the seller. The minimum required down payment is computed as a percentage of the sale price. For example, suppose you decide to buy a \$220,000 home that requires you to pay the seller 10% of the sale price. You must pay 10% of \$220,000, which is $0.10 \times \$220,000$, or \$22,000, to the seller. Thus, \$22,000 is the down payment. The **amount of the mortgage** is the difference between the sale price and the down payment. For your \$220,000 home, the amount of the mortgage is $\$220,000 - \$22,000$, or \$198,000.

Monthly payments for a mortgage depend on the amount of the mortgage, or the principal, the interest rate, and the time of the mortgage. Mortgages can have a fixed interest rate or a variable interest rate. **Fixed-rate mortgages** have the same monthly payment during the entire time of the loan. A loan like this that has a schedule for paying a fixed amount each period is called a **fixed installment loan.** **Variable-rate mortgages**, also known as **adjustable-rate mortgages** (ARMs), have payment amounts that change from time to time depending on changes in the interest rate. ARMS are less predictable than fixed-rate mortgages. They start out at lower rates than fixed-rate mortgages. Caps limit how high rates can go over the term of the loan.

1 Compute the monthly payment and interest costs for a mortgage.

Computation Involved with Buying a Home

Although monthly payments for a mortgage depend on the amount of the mortgage, the time of the loan, and the interest rate, the rate is not the only cost of a mortgage. Most lending institutions require the buyer to pay one or more **points** at the time of closing—that is, the time at which the mortgage begins. A point is a one-time charge that equals 1% of the loan amount. For example, two points means that the buyer must pay 2% of the loan amount at closing. Often, a buyer can pay fewer points in exchange for a higher interest rate or more points for a lower rate. A document, called the **Truth-in-Lending Disclosure Statement**, shows the buyer the APR for the mortgage. The APR takes into account the interest rate and points.

A monthly mortgage payment is used to repay the principal plus interest. In addition, lending institutions can require monthly deposits into an **escrow account**, an account used by the lender to pay real estate taxes and insurance. These deposits increase the amount of the monthly payment.

We can use formulas for compound interest and the value of an annuity to determine the amount of mortgage payments for fixed-rate mortgages. Suppose that you borrow P dollars at interest rate r over t years.

The lender expects A dollars at the end of t years.

$$A = P\left(1 + \frac{r}{n}\right)^{nt}$$

You save the A dollars in an annuity by paying PMT dollars n times per year.

$$A = \frac{PMT\left[\left(1 + \frac{r}{n}\right)^{nt} - 1\right]}{\left(\frac{r}{n}\right)}$$

To find your regular payment amount, PMT, we set the amount the lender expects to receive equal to the amount you will save in the annuity:

$$P\left(1 + \frac{r}{n}\right)^{nt} = \frac{PMT\left[\left(1 + \frac{r}{n}\right)^{nt} - 1\right]}{\left(\frac{r}{n}\right)}.$$

Solving this equation for PMT, we obtain a formula for the loan payment for any installment loan, including payments on fixed-rate mortgages.

STUDY TIP

Because the formula in the box assumes the same number of yearly payments and yearly compounding periods, the actual payments may differ slightly from those calculated using the formula.

LOAN PAYMENT FORMULA FOR FIXED INSTALLMENT LOANS

The regular payment amount, PMT, required to repay a loan of P dollars paid n times per year over t years at an annual rate r is given by

$$PMT = \frac{P\left(\frac{r}{n}\right)}{\left[1 - \left(1 + \frac{r}{n}\right)^{-nt}\right]}.$$

EXAMPLE 1 Computing the Monthly Payment and Interest Costs for a Mortgage

The price of a home is \$195,000. The bank requires a 10% down payment and two points at the time of closing. The cost of the home is financed with a 30-year fixed-rate mortgage at 7.5%.

a. Find the required down payment.
b. Find the amount of the mortgage.
c. How much must be paid for the two points at closing?
d. Find the monthly payment (excluding escrowed taxes and insurance).
e. Find the total interest paid over 30 years.

Solution

a. The required down payment is 10% of \$195,000 or

$$0.10 \times \$195{,}000 = \$19{,}500.$$

b. The amount of the mortgage is the difference between the price of the home and the down payment.

$$\text{Amount of the mortgage} = \text{sale price} - \text{down payment}$$
$$= \$195{,}000 - \$19{,}500$$
$$= \$175{,}500$$

c. To find the cost of two points on a mortgage of \$175,500, find 2% of \$175,500.

$$0.02 \times \$175{,}500 = \$3510$$

The down payment (\$19,500) is paid to the seller and the cost of two points (\$3510) is paid to the lending institution.

d. We are interested in finding the monthly payment for a \$175,500 mortgage at 7.5% for 30 years. We use the loan payment formula for installment loans.

P, the mortgage amount, is \$175,500.
Fixed rate, r, is 7.5%.
12 payments per year
The mortgage time, t, is 30 years.

$$PMT = \frac{P\left(\frac{r}{n}\right)}{\left[1 - \left(1 + \frac{r}{n}\right)^{-nt}\right]} = \frac{175{,}500\left(\frac{0.075}{12}\right)}{\left[1 - \left(1 + \frac{0.075}{12}\right)^{-12(30)}\right]}$$

$$= \frac{1096.875}{1 - (1.00625)^{-360}} \approx 1227$$

The monthly mortgage payment for principal and interest is approximately \$1227.00. (Keep in mind that this payment does not include escrowed taxes and insurance.)

BLITZER BONUS

THE MORTGAGE CRISIS

In 2006, the median U.S. home price jumped to \$206,000, up a stunning 15% in a year and 55% over five years. This rise in home values made property an attractive investment to many people, including those with poor credit records and low incomes. Credit standards for mortgages were lowered and loans were made to high-risk borrowers. By 2008, America's raucous house party was over. A brief period of easy lending, especially lax mortgage practices from 2002 through 2006, exploded into the worst financial crisis since the Great Depression. The price plunge in home prices wiped out trillions of dollars in home equity, setting off fears that foreclosures and tight credit could send home prices falling to the point that millions of families and thousands of banks might be thrust into insolvency.

e. The total cost of interest over 30 years is equal to the difference between the total of all monthly payments and the amount of the mortgage. The total of all monthly payments is equal to the amount of the monthly payment multiplied by the number of payments. We found the amount of each monthly payment in (d): \$1227. The number of payments is equal to the number of months in a year, 12, multiplied by the number of years in the mortgage, 30: $12 \times 30 = 360$. Thus, the total of all monthly payments = $\$1227 \times 360$.
Now we can calculate the interest over 30 years.

Total interest paid = total of all monthly payments minus amount of the mortgage.

$$= \$1227 \times 360 - \$175{,}500$$

$$= \$441{,}720 - \$175{,}500 = \$266{,}220$$

The total interest paid over 30 years is approximately \$266,220.

In Example 1, the \$175,500 mortgage was financed with a 30-year fixed rate at 7.5%. The total interest paid over 30 years was approximately \$266,220.

a. Use the loan payment formula for installment loans to find the monthly payment if the time of the mortgage is reduced to 15 years. Round to the nearest dollar.

b. Find the total interest paid over 15 years.

c. How much interest is saved by reducing the mortgage from 30 to 15 years?

2 Prepare a partial loan amortization schedule.

Loan Amortization Schedules

When a loan is paid off through a series of regular payments, it is said to be **amortized**, which literally means "killed off." In working Check Point 1(c), were you surprised that nearly \$150,000 was saved when the mortgage was amortized over 15 years rather than over 30 years? What adds to the interest cost is the long period over which the loan is financed. **Although each payment is the same, with each successive payment the interest portion decreases and the portion applied toward paying off the principal increases.** The interest is computed using the simple interest formula $I = Prt$. The principal, P, is equal to the balance of the loan, which changes each month. The rate, r, is the annual interest rate of the mortgage loan. Because a payment is made each month, the time, t, is

$$\frac{1 \text{ month}}{12 \text{ months}} = \frac{1 \cancel{\text{month}}}{12 \cancel{\text{months}}}$$

or $\frac{1}{12}$ of a year.

A document showing how the payment each month is split between interest and principal is called a **loan amortization schedule**. Typically, this document includes the number of the most recent payment and those of any previous monthly payments, the interest for each payment, the amount of each payment applied to the principal, and the balance of the loan.

EXAMPLE 2 Preparing a Loan Amortization Schedule

Prepare a loan amortization schedule for the first two months of the mortgage loan shown in the table at the top of the next page.

LOAN AMORTIZATION SCHEDULE

Annual % rate: 9.5% **Amount of Mortgage: $130,000** **Number of Monthly Payments: 180**		**Monthly payment: $1357.50** **Term: Years 15, Months 0**	
Payment Number	**Interest Payment**	**Principal Payment**	**Balance of Loan**
1			
2			

Solution We begin with payment number 1.

$$\text{Interest for the month} = Prt = \$130{,}000 \times 0.095 \times \frac{1}{12} \approx \$1029.17$$

$$\begin{aligned}\text{Principal payment} &= \text{Monthly payment} - \text{Interest payment}\\ &= \$1357.50 - \$1029.17 = \$328.33\end{aligned}$$

$$\begin{aligned}\text{Balance of loan} &= \text{Principal balance} - \text{Principal payment}\\ &= \$130{,}000 - \$328.33 = \$129{,}671.67\end{aligned}$$

Now, starting with a loan balance of $129,671.67, we repeat these computations for the second month.

$$\text{Interest for the month} = Prt = \$129{,}671.67 \times 0.095 \times \frac{1}{12} \approx \$1026.57$$

$$\begin{aligned}\text{Principal payment} &= \text{Monthly payment} - \text{Interest payment}\\ &= \$1357.50 - \$1026.57 = \$330.93\end{aligned}$$

$$\begin{aligned}\text{Balance of loan} &= \text{Principal balance} - \text{Principal payment}\\ &= \$129{,}671.67 - \$330.93 = \$129{,}340.74\end{aligned}$$

The results of these computations are included in **Table 4**, a partial loan amortization schedule. By using the simple interest formula month-to-month on the loan's balance, a complete loan amortization schedule for all 180 payments can be calculated.

TABLE 4 Loan Amortization Schedule

Annual % rate: 9.5% **Amount of Mortgage: $130,000** **Number of Monthly Payments: 180**		**Monthly payment: $1357.50** **Term: Years 15, Months 0**	
Payment Number	**Interest Payment**	**Principal Payment**	**Balance of Loan**
1	$1029.17	$328.33	$129,671.67
2	1026.57	330.93	129,340.74
3	1023.96	333.54	129,007.22
4	1021.32	336.18	128,671.04
30	944.82	412.68	118,931.35
31	941.55	415.95	118,515.52
125	484.62	872.88	60,340.84
126	477.71	879.79	59,461.05
179	21.26	1336.24	1347.74
180	9.76	1347.74	

BLITZER BONUS

BITTERSWEET INTEREST

Mel Yates\Getty Images, Inc– Taxi

Early mortgage payments illustrate that it can be discouraging to realize how much goes toward interest and how little goes toward paying off the principal. Although you get socked with tons of interest in the early years of a loan, the one bright side to the staggering cost of a mortgage is the **mortgage interest tax deduction**. To make the cost of owning a home more affordable, the tax code permits deducting all the mortgage interest (but not the principal) that you pay per year on the loan. **Table 5** illustrates how this tax loophole reduces the cost of the mortgage.

TABLE 5 Tax Deductions for a $100,000 Mortgage at 7% for a Taxpayer in the 28% Tax Bracket

Year	Interest	Tax Savings	Net Cost of Mortgage
1	$6968	$1951	$5017
2	$6895	$1931	$4964
3	$6816	$1908	$4908
4	$6732	$1885	$4847
5	$6641	$1859	$4782

Many lenders supply a loan amortization schedule like the one in Example 2 at the time of closing. Such a schedule shows how the buyer pays slightly less in interest and more in principal for each payment over the entire life of the loan.

CHECK POINT 2 Prepare a loan amortization schedule for the first two months of the mortgage loan shown in the following table:

Annual % rate: 7.0% **Amount of Mortgage: $200,000** **Number of Monthly Payments: 240**		**Monthly payment: $1550.00** **Term: Years 20, Months 0**	
Payment Number	**Interest Payment**	**Principal Payment**	**Balance of Loan**
1			
2			

3 Compute payments and interest for other kinds of fixed installment loans.

Monthly Payments and Interest Costs for Other Kinds of Fixed Installment Loans

The loan payment formula can be used to determine how much your regular payments will be on fixed installment loans other than mortgages, including car loans and student loans. The portions of each payment going toward the principal and toward the interest will vary as the loan balance declines. Near the beginning of the loan term, the portion going toward the interest will be relatively high and the portion going toward the principal will be relatively low. As the loan term continues, the principal portion will gradually increase and the interest portion will gradually decrease.

BLITZER BONUS

CHECKING OUT FINANCING OPTIONS

It's a good idea to get preapproved for a car loan through a bank or credit union before going to the dealer. You can then compare the loan offered by the dealer to your preapproved loan. Furthermore, with more money in hand, you'll have more negotiating power.

EXAMPLE 3 Comparing Car Loans

You decide to borrow $20,000 for a new car. You can select one of the following loans, each requiring regular monthly payments:

Installment Loan A: 3-year loan at 7%

Installment Loan B: 5-year loan at 9%.

a. Find the monthly payments and the total interest for Loan A.

b. Find the monthly payments and the total interest for Loan B.

c. Compare the monthly payments and total interest for the two loans.

Solution For each loan, we use the loan payment formula to compute the monthly payments.

a. We first determine monthly payments and total interest for Loan A.

$$PMT = \frac{P\left(\frac{r}{n}\right)}{\left[1-\left(1+\frac{r}{n}\right)^{-nt}\right]} = \frac{20{,}000\left(\frac{0.07}{12}\right)}{\left[1-\left(1+\frac{0.07}{12}\right)^{-12(3)}\right]} \approx 618$$

P, the loan amount, is $20,000. Rate, *r*, is 7%. 12 payments per year. The loan is for 3 years.

The monthly payments are approximately $618.

Now we calculate the interest over 3 years, or 36 months.

$$\underbrace{\text{Total interest over 3 years}} = \underbrace{\text{Total of all monthly payments}} \text{ minus } \underbrace{\text{amount of the loan.}}$$

$$= \$618 \times 36 - \$20{,}000$$

$$= \$2248$$

The total interest paid over 3 years is approximately \$2248.

b. Next, we determine monthly payments and total interest for Loan B.

P, the loan amount, is \$20,000. Rate, r, is 9%. 12 payments per year. The loan is for 5 years.

$$PMT = \frac{P\left(\frac{r}{n}\right)}{\left[1 - \left(1 + \frac{r}{n}\right)^{-nt}\right]} = \frac{20{,}000\left(\frac{0.09}{12}\right)}{\left[1 - \left(1 + \frac{0.09}{12}\right)^{-12(5)}\right]} \approx 415$$

The monthly payments are approximately \$415.
Now we calculate the interest over 5 years, or 60 months.

$$\underbrace{\text{Total interest over 5 years}} = \underbrace{\text{Total of all monthly payments}} \text{ minus } \underbrace{\text{amount of the loan.}}$$

$$= \$415 \times 60 - \$20{,}000$$

$$= \$4900$$

The total interest paid over 5 years is approximately \$4900.

c. **Table 6** compares the monthly payments and total interest for the two loans.

TABLE 6 Comparing Car Loans

\$20,000 loan	Monthly Payment	Total Interest
3-year loan at 7%	\$618	\$2248
5-year loan at 9%	\$415	\$4900

Monthly payments are less with the longer-term loan.

Interest is more with the longer-term loan.

BLITZER BONUS

THE DARK SIDE OF STUDENT LOANS

Exercises 17 and 18 in the Exercise Set that follows apply the loan payment formula to determine regular payments and interest on student loans. Sallie Mae, the private company that makes, holds, and buys the most student loans, has been criticized as being a moneymaker for its executives rather than an agency designed to help students without the means to finance a college education. Initially a government agency, Sallie Mae has been profiting mightily since it was privatized in 1997. It earned an average of 48% annual return in 2008, three times the return of commercial banks. Students who sign up for loans with what appear to be low fixed rates may discover upon graduating that they face an 18% rate. If they make a single late payment, late fees will be tacked on *every month* until the debt is paid off. Albert Lord, Sallie Mae's chief executive, has become so rich from student lending that he built his own private golf course just outside Washington, D.C.

Getting money to pay for college may be tough, but paying it back can break you. Visit the Web site of Student Loan Justice, where borrowers tell how their lives have been ruined by the burden of debts and harsh treatment by lenders.

Sources: 60 Minutes, May 14, 2006, *Consumer Reports Money Adviser,* March 2006, *Mother Jones*, January 2009

CHECK POINT 3 You decide to borrow \$15,000 for a new car. You can select one of the following loans, each requiring regular monthly payments:

Installment Loan A: 4-year loan at 8%

Installment Loan B: 6-year loan at 10%

a. Find the monthly payments and the total interest for Loan A.

b. Find the monthly payments and the total interest for Loan B.

c. Compare the monthly payments and total interest for the two loans.

Open-End Installment Loans

Using a credit card is an example of an open-end installment loan, commonly called **revolving credit**. Open-end loans differ from fixed installment loans such as the car loans in Example 3 in that there is no schedule for paying a fixed amount each period. Credit card loans require users to make only a minimum monthly payment that depends on the unpaid balance and the interest rate. Credit cards have high interest rates compared to other kinds of loans. The interest on credit cards is computed using the simple interest formula $I = Prt$. However, r represents the *monthly* interest rate and t is time in months rather than in years. A typical interest rate is 1.57% monthly. This is equivalent to a yearly rate of $12 \times 1.57\%$, or 18.84%. With such a high annual percentage rate, credit card balances should be paid off as quickly as possible.

Most credit card customers are billed every month. A typical billing period is May 1 through May 31, but it can also run from, say, May 5 through June 4. Customers receive a statement, called an **itemized billing**, that includes the unpaid balance on the first day of the billing period, the total balance owed on the last day of the billing period, a list of purchases and cash advances made during the billing period, any finance charges or other fees incurred, the date of the last day of the billing period, the payment due date, and the minimum payment required.

Customers who make a purchase during the billing period and pay the entire amount of the purchase by the payment due date are not charged interest. By contrast, customers who make cash advances using their credit cards must pay interest from the day the money is advanced until the day it is repaid.

4 Find the interest, the balance due, and the minimum monthly payment for credit card loans.

Interest on Credit Cards: The Average Daily Balance Method

Methods for calculating interest, or finance charges, on credit cards may vary and the interest can differ on credit cards that show the same annual percentage rate, or APR. The method used for calculating interest on most credit cards is called the *average daily balance method.*

THE AVERAGE DAILY BALANCE METHOD

Interest is calculated using $I = Prt$, where r is the monthly rate and t is one month. The principal, P, is the average daily balance. The **average daily balance** is the sum of the unpaid balances for each day in the billing period divided by the number of days in the billing period.

$$\text{Average daily balance} = \frac{\text{Sum of the unpaid balances for each day in the billing period}}{\text{Number of days in the billing period}}$$

In Example 4, we illustrate how to determine the average daily balance. At the conclusion of the example, we summarize the steps used in the computation.

EXAMPLE 4 Balance Due on a Credit Card

A particular VISA card calculates interest using the average daily balance method. The monthly interest rate is 1.3% of the average daily balance. The following transactions occurred during the May 1–May 31 billing period.

BLITZER BONUS

THE MINIMUM-PAYMENT TRAP

Credit-card debt is made worse by paying only the required minimum, a mistake made by 11% of credit-card debtors. Pay the minimum and most of it goes to interest charges.

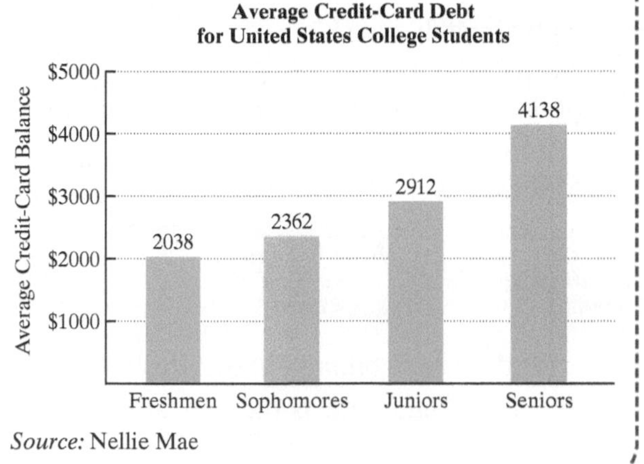

Source: Nellie Mae

Transaction Description	Transaction Amount
Previous balance, $1350.00	
May 1 Billing date	
May 8 Payment	$250.00 Credit
May 10 Charge: Airline Tickets	$375.00
May 20 Charge: Books	$ 57.50
May 28 Charge: Restaurant	$ 65.30
May 31 End of billing period	
Payment Due Date: June 9	

a. Find the average daily balance for the billing period. Round to the nearest cent.

b. Find the interest to be paid on June 1, the next billing date. Round to the nearest cent.

c. Find the balance due on June 1.

d. This credit card requires a $10 minimum monthly payment if the balance due at the end of the billing period is less than $360. Otherwise, the minimum monthly payment is $\frac{1}{36}$ of the balance due at the end of the billing period, rounded up to the nearest whole dollar. What is the minimum monthly payment due by June 9?

Solution

a. We begin by finding the average daily balance for the billing period. First make a table that shows the beginning date of the billing period, each transaction date, and the unpaid balance for each date.

Date	Unpaid Balance	
May 1	$1350.00	previous balance
May 8	$1350.00 − $250.00 = $1100.00	$250.00 payment
May 10	$1100.00 + $375.00 = $1475.00	$375.00 charge
May 20	$1475.00 + $57.50 = $1532.50	$57.50 charge
May 28	$1532.50 + $65.30 = $1597.80	$65.30 charge

We now extend our table by adding two columns. One column shows the number of days at each unpaid balance. The final column shows each unpaid balance multiplied by the number of days that the balance is outstanding.

Date	Unpaid Balance	Number of Days at Each Unpaid Balance	(Unpaid Balance) · (Number of Days)
May 1	$1350.00	7	($1350.00)(7) = $9450.00
May 8	$1100.00	2	($1100.00)(2) = $2200.00
May 10	$1475.00	10	($1475.00)(10) = $14,750.00
May 20	$1532.50	8	($1532.50)(8) = $12,260.00
May 28	$1597.80	4	($1597.80)(4) = $6391.20
		Total: 31	Total: $45,051.20

There are 4 days at this unpaid balance, May 28, 29, 30, and 31 before the beginning of the next billing period, June 1.

This is the number of days in the billing period.

This is the sum of the unpaid balances for each day in the billing period.

Notice that we found the sum of the products in the final column of the table. This dollar amount, $45,051.20, gives the sum of the unpaid balances for each day in the billing period.

Now we divide the sum of the unpaid balances for each day in the billing period, \$45,051.20, by the number of days in the billing period, 31. This gives the average daily balance.

Average daily balance

$$= \frac{\text{Sum of the unpaid balances for each day in the billing period}}{\text{Number of days in the billing period}}$$

$$= \frac{\$45{,}051.20}{31} \approx \$1453.26$$

The average daily balance is approximately \$1453.26.

b. Now we find the interest to be paid on June 1, the next billing date. The monthly interest rate is 1.3% of the average daily balance. The interest due is computed using $I = Prt$.

$$I = Prt = (\$1453.26)(0.013)(1) \approx \$18.89$$

The average daily balance serves as the principal.

Time, t, is measured in months, and $t = 1$ month.

The interest, or finance charge, for the June 1 billing will be \$18.89.

c. The balance due on June 1, the next billing date, is the unpaid balance on May 31 plus the interest.

$$\text{Balance due} = \$1597.80 + \$18.89 = \$1616.69$$

Unpaid balance on May 31, obtained from the table at the bottom of the previous page

Interest, or finance charge, obtained from part (b)

The balance due on June 1 is \$1616.69.

d. Because the balance due, \$1616.69, exceeds \$360, the customer must pay a minimum of $\frac{1}{36}$ of the balance due.

$$\text{Minimum monthly payment} = \frac{\text{balance due}}{36} = \frac{\$1616.69}{36} \approx \$45$$

Rounded up to the nearest whole dollar, the minimum monthly payment due by June 9 is \$45.

STUDY TIP

The quotient in part (d) is approximately 44.908, which rounds to 45. Because the minimum monthly payment is rounded up, \$45 would still be the payment if the approximate quotient had been 44.098.

The following box summarizes the steps used in Example 4 to determine the average daily balance. Calculating the average daily balance can be quite tedious when there are numerous transactions during a billing period.

DETERMINING THE AVERAGE DAILY BALANCE

Step 1 Make a table that shows the beginning date of the billing period, each transaction date, and the unpaid balance for each date.

Step 2 Add a column to the table that shows the number of days at each unpaid balance.

Step 3 Add a final column to the table that shows each unpaid balance multiplied by the number of days that the balance is outstanding.

Step 4 Find the sum of the products in the final column of the table. This dollar amount is the sum of the unpaid balances for each day in the billing period.

Step 5 Compute the average daily balance.

Average daily balance

$$= \frac{\text{Sum of the unpaid balances for each day in the billing period}}{\text{Number of days in the billing period}}$$

BLITZER BONUS

THE CHANGING-TERMS TRAP

Consumer Reports (October 2008) cited a credit card with an enticing 9.9% annual interest rate. But the fine print revealed a \$29 account-setup fee, a \$95 program fee, a \$48 annual fee, and a \$7 monthly servicing fee. Nearly 40% of the \$40 billion in profits that U.S. card issuers earned in 2008 came from fees. Furthermore, issuers can hike interest rates and fees at any time, for any reason. In 2009, these abuses had Congress listening, with proposed reforms that would bring sweeping changes to the lightly regulated, \$160 billion credit-card industry.

A credit card calculates interest using the average daily balance method. The monthly interest rate is 1.6% of the average daily balance. The following transactions occurred during the May 1–May 31 billing period.

Transaction Description	Transaction Amount
Previous balance, $8240.00	
May 1 Billing date	
May 7 Payment	$ 350.00 Credit
May 15 Charge: Computer	$1405.00
May 17 Charge: Restaurant	$ 45.20
May 30 Charge: Clothing	$ 180.72
May 31 End of billing period	
Payment Due Date: June 9	

Answer parts (a) through (d) in Example 4 using this information.

Exercise Set 5

Practice and Application Exercises

In Exercises 1–18, use

$$PMT = \frac{P\left(\frac{r}{n}\right)}{\left[1 - \left(1 + \frac{r}{n}\right)^{-nt}\right]}$$

to determine the regular payment amount, rounded to the nearest dollar.

Exercises 1–8 involve home mortgages.

1. The price of a home is $220,000. The bank requires a 20% down payment and three points at the time of closing. The cost of the home is financed with a 30-year fixed-rate mortgage at 7%.
   a. Find the required down payment.
   b. Find the amount of the mortgage.
   c. How much must be paid for the three points at closing?
   d. Find the monthly payment (excluding escrowed taxes and insurance).
   e. Find the total cost of interest over 30 years.
2. The price of a condominium is $180,000. The bank requires a 5% down payment and one point at the time of closing. The cost of the condominium is financed with a 30-year fixed-rate mortgage at 8%.
   a. Find the required down payment.
   b. Find the amount of the mortgage.
   c. How much must be paid for the one point at closing?
   d. Find the monthly payment (excluding escrowed taxes and insurance).
   e. Find the total cost of interest over 30 years.
3. The price of a small cabin is $100,000. The bank requires a 5% down payment. The buyer is offered two mortgage options: 20-year fixed at 8% or 30-year fixed at 8%. Calculate the amount of interest paid for each option. How much does the buyer save in interest with the 20-year option?
4. The price of a home is $160,000. The bank requires a 15% down payment. The buyer is offered two mortgage options: 15-year fixed at 8% or 30-year fixed at 8%. Calculate the amount of interest paid for each option. How much does the buyer save in interest with the 15-year option?
5. In terms of paying less in interest, which is more economical for a $150,000 mortgage: a 30-year fixed-rate at 8% or a 20-year fixed-rate at 7.5%? How much is saved in interest?
6. In terms of paying less in interest, which is more economical for a $90,000 mortgage: a 30-year fixed-rate at 8% or a 15-year fixed-rate at 7.5%? How much is saved in interest?

In Exercises 7–8, which mortgage loan has the greater total cost (closing costs + the amount paid for points + total cost of interest)? By how much?

7. A $120,000 mortgage with two loan options:

   Mortgage A: 30-year fixed at 7% with closing costs of $2000 and one point

   Mortgage B: 30-year fixed at 6.5% with closing costs of $1500 and four points
8. A $250,000 mortgage with two loan options:

   Mortgage A: 30-year fixed at 7.25% with closing costs of $2000 and one point

   Mortgage B: 30-year fixed at 6.25% with closing costs of costs of $350 and four points

Exercises 9–18 involve installment loans other than mortgages.

9. Your credit card has a balance of \$4200 and an annual interest rate of 18%. You decide to pay off the balance over two years. If there are no further purchases charged to the card,

a. How much must you pay each month?

b. How much total interest will you pay?

10. Your credit card has a balance of \$3600 and an annual interest rate of 16.5%. You decide to pay off the balance over two years. If there are no further purchases charged to the card,

a. How much must you pay each month?

b. How much total interest will you pay?

11. To pay off the \$4200 credit-card balance in Exercise 9, you can get a bank loan at 10.5% with a term of three years.

a. How much will you pay each month? How does this compare with your credit-card payment in Exercise 9?

b. How much total interest will you pay? How does this compare with your total credit-card interest in Exercise 9?

12. To pay off the \$3600 credit-card balance in Exercise 10, you can get a bank loan at 9.5% with a term of three years.

a. How much will you pay each month? How does this compare with your credit-card payment in Exercise 10?

b. How much total interest will you pay? How does this compare with your total credit-card interest in Exercise 10?

13. Rework Exercise 9 if you decide to pay off the balance over one year rather than two. How much more must you pay each month and how much less will you pay in total interest?

14. Rework Exercise 10 if you decide to pay off the balance over one year rather than two. How much more must you pay each month and how much less will you pay in total interest?

In Exercises 15–18, round to the nearest cent.

15. You borrow \$10,000 for four years at 8% toward the purchase of a car.

a. Find the monthly payments and the total interest for the loan.

b. Prepare a loan amortization schedule for the first three months of the car loan. Round entries to the nearest cent.

Payment Number	Interest	Principal	Loan Balance
1			
2			
3			

16. You borrow \$30,000 for four years at 8% toward the purchase of a car.

a. Find the monthly payments and the total interest for the loan.

b. Prepare a loan amortization schedule for the first three months of the car loan. Use the table in Exercise 15(b) and round entries to the nearest cent.

17. A student graduates from college with a loan of \$40,000. The interest rate is 8.5% and the loan term is 20 years.

a. Find the monthly payments and the total interest for the loan.

b. Prepare a loan amortization schedule for the first three months of the student loan. Use the table in Exercise 15(b) and round entries to the nearest cent.

c. If the interest rate remains at 8.5% and the loan term is reduced to ten years, how much more must the student pay each month and how much less will be paid in total interest?

18. A student graduates from college with a loan of \$50,000. The interest rate is 7.5% and the loan term is 20 years.

a. Find the monthly payments and the total interest for the loan.

b. Prepare a loan amortization schedule for the first three months of the student loan. Use the table in Exercise 15(b) and round entries to the nearest cent.

c. If the interest rate remains at 7.5% and the loan term is reduced to ten years, how much more must the student pay each month and how much less will be paid in total interest?

Exercises 19–20 involve credit cards that calculate interest using the average daily balance method. The monthly interest rate is 1.5% of the average daily balance. Each exercise shows transactions that occurred during the March 1–March 31 billing period. In each exercise,

a. Find the average daily balance for the billing period. Round to the nearest cent.

b. Find the interest to be paid on April 1, the next billing date. Round to the nearest cent.

c. Find the balance due on April 1.

d. This credit card requires a \$10 minimum monthly payment if the balance due at the end of the billing period is less than \$360. Otherwise, the minimum monthly payment is $\frac{1}{36}$ of the balance due at the end of the billing period, rounded up to the nearest whole dollar. What is the minimum monthly payment due by April 9?

19.

Transaction Description	Transaction Amount
Previous balance, \$6240.00	
March 1 Billing date	
March 5 Payment	\$300.00 credit
March 7 Charge: Restaurant	\$ 40.00
March 12 Charge: Groceries	\$ 90.00
March 21 Charge: Car Repairs	\$230.00
March 31 End of billing period	
Payment Due Date: April 9	

20.

Transaction Description	Transaction Amount
Previous balance, $7150.00	
March 1 Billing date	
March 4 Payment	$ 400.00 credit
March 6 Charge: Furniture	$1200.00
March 15 Charge: Gas	$ 40.00
March 30 Charge: Groceries	$ 50.00
March 31 End of billing period	
Payment Due Date: April 9	

Exercises 21–22 involve credit cards that calculate interest using the average daily balance method. The monthly interest rate is 1.2% of the average daily balance. Each exercise shows transactions that occurred during the June 1-June 30 billing period. In each exercise,

a. Find the average daily balance for the billing period. Round to the nearest cent.

b. Find the interest to be paid on July 1, the next billing date. Round to the nearest cent.

c. Find the balance due on July 1.

d. This credit card requires a $30 minimum monthly payment if the balance due at the end of the billing period is less than $400. Otherwise, the minimum monthly payment is $\frac{1}{25}$ of the balance due at the end of the billing period, rounded up to the nearest whole dollar. What is the minimum monthly payment due by July 9?

21.

Transaction Description	Transaction Amount
Previous balance, $2653.48	
June 1 Billing date	
June 6 Payment	$1000.00 credit
June 8 Charge: Gas	$ 36.25
June 9 Charge: Groceries	$ 138.43
June 17 Charge: Gas	$ 42.36
Charge: Groceries	$ 127.19
June 27 Charge: Clothing	$ 214.83
June 30 End of billing period	
Payment Due Date: July 9	

22.

Transaction Description	Transaction Amount
Previous balance, $4037.93	
June 1 Billing date	
June 5 Payment	$350.00 credit
June 10 Charge: Gas	$ 31.17
June 15 Charge: Prescriptions	$ 42.50
June 22 Charge: Gas Charge: Groceries	$ 43.86 $112.91
June 29 Charge: Clothing	$ 96.73
June 30 End of billing period	
Payment Due Date: July 9	

Writing in Mathematics

23. What is a mortgage?

24. What is a down payment?

25. How is the amount of a mortgage determined?

26. Describe why a buyer would select a 30-year fixed-rate mortgage instead of a 15-year fixed-rate mortgage if interest rates are $\frac{1}{4}$% to $\frac{1}{2}$% lower on a 15-year mortgage.

27. Describe one advantage and one disadvantage of an adjustable-rate mortgage over a fixed-rate mortgage.

28. What is a loan amortization schedule?

29. Describe what happens to the portions of payments going to principal and interest over the life of an installment loan.

30. Describe one advantage and one disadvantage of home ownership over renting.

31. Describe the difference between a fixed installment loan and an open-end installment loan.

32. For a credit card billing period, describe how the average daily balance is determined. Why is this computation somewhat tedious when done by hand?

Critical Thinking Exercises

Make Sense? *In Exercises 33–36, determine whether each statement makes sense or does not make sense, and explain your reasoning.*

33. There must be an error in the loan amortization schedule for my mortgage because the annual interest rate is only 3.5%, yet the schedule shows that I'm paying more on interest than on the principal for many of my payments.

34. Assuming that a 3-year car loan has a lower interest rate than a 5-year car loan, people should always select the 3-year loan.

35. I like to keep all my money, so I pay only the minimum required payment on my credit card.

36. I used the formula

$$PMT = \frac{P\left(\frac{r}{n}\right)}{\left[1 - \left(1 + \frac{r}{n}\right)^{-nt}\right]}$$

to determine the payment due on my credit card.

37. Use the discussion on home buying to prove the loan payment formula shown in the box containing the loan payment formula for fixed installment loans. Work with the equation in which the amount the lender expects to receive is equal to the amount saved in the annuity. Multiply both sides of this equation by $\frac{r}{n}$ and then solve for PMT by dividing both sides by the appropriate expression. Finally, divide the numerator and the denominator of the resulting formula for PMT by $\left(1 + \frac{r}{n}\right)^{nt}$ to obtain the form of the loan payment formula shown in the box.

38. The unpaid balance of an installment loan is equal to the present value of the remaining payments. The unpaid balance, P, is given by

$$P = PMT\frac{\left[1 - \left(1 + \frac{r}{n}\right)^{-nt}\right]}{\left(\frac{r}{n}\right)},$$

where PMT is the regular payment amount, r is the annual interest rate, n is the number of payments per year, and t is the number of years remaining in the mortgage.

a. Use the loan payment formula to derive the unpaid balance formula.

b. The price of a home is $180,000. The bank requires a 10% down payment. After the down payment, the balance is financed with a 30-year fixed-rate mortgage at 6.3%. Determine the unpaid balance after ten years. Round all calculations to the nearest cent.

39. A bank bills its credit card holders on the first of each month for each itemized billing. The card provides a 20-day period in which to pay the bill before charging interest. If the card holder wants to buy an expensive gift for a September 30 wedding but can't pay for it until November 5, explain how this can be done without adding an interest charge.

Group Exercise

40. Group members should go to the Internet and select a car that they might like to buy. Price the car and its options. Then find two loans with the best rates, but with different terms. For each loan, calculate the monthly payments and total interest. Select one of the loans and prepare a partial or complete amortization schedule.

Chapter Summary, Review, and Test

Summary – Definitions and Concepts

Examples

1 Percent, Sales Tax, and Income Tax

a. Percent means per hundred. Thus, $97\% = \frac{97}{100}$.

b. To express a fraction as a percent, divide the numerator by the denominator, move the decimal point in the quotient two places to the right, and add a percent sign. Ex. 1

c. To express a decimal number as a percent, move the decimal point two places to the right and add a percent sign. Ex. 2

d. To express a percent as a decimal number, move the decimal point two places to the left and remove the percent sign. Ex. 3

e. The percent formula, $A = PB$, means A is P percent of B.

f. Sales tax amount = tax rate × item's cost Ex. 4

g. Discount amount = discount rate × original price Ex. 5

h. Calculating Income Tax Ex. 6

1. Determine adjusted gross income:

Adjusted gross income = Gross income − Adjustments.

2. Determine taxable income:

Taxable income = Adjusted gross income − (Exemptions + Deductions).

3. Determine the income tax:

Income tax = Tax computation − Tax credits.

See details in the box.

i. The fraction for percent increase (or decrease) is

$$\frac{\text{amount of increase (or decrease)}}{\text{original amount}}.$$

Find the percent increase (or decrease) by expressing this fraction as a percent. Ex. 7, Ex. 8, Ex. 9, Ex. 10

2 Simple Interest

a. Interest is the amount of money that we get paid for lending or investing money, or that we pay for borrowing money. The amount deposited or borrowed is the principal. The charge for interest, given as a percent, is the rate, assumed to be per year.

b. Simple interest involves interest calculated only on the principal and is computed using $I = Prt$. Ex. 1, Ex. 2

c. The future value, A, of P dollars at simple interest rate r for t years is $A = P(1 + rt)$. Ex. 3 Ex. 4 Ex. 5

d. Discounted loans deduct the interest, called the discount, from the loan amount at the time the loan is made. Ex. 6

3 Compound Interest

a. Compound interest involves interest computed on the original principal as well as on any accumulated interest. The amount in an account for one compounding period per year is $A = P(1 + r)^t$. For n compounding periods per year, the amount is $A = P\left(1 + \frac{r}{n}\right)^{nt}$. For continuous compounding, the amount is $A = Pe^{rt}$, where $e \approx 2.72$. Ex. 1 Ex. 2 Ex. 3

b. Calculating Present Value Ex. 4

If A dollars are to be accumulated in t years in an account that pays rate r compounded n times per year, then the present value, P, that needs to be invested now is given by

$$P = \frac{A}{\left(1 + \frac{r}{n}\right)^{nt}}.$$

c. Effective Annual Yield Ex. 5 Ex. 6

Effective annual yield is defined in the box. The effective annual yield, Y, for an account that pays rate r compounded n times per year is given by

$$Y = \left(1 + \frac{r}{n}\right)^{n} - 1.$$

4 Annuities, Stocks, and Bonds

a. An annuity is a sequence of equal payments made at equal time periods. The value of an annuity is the sum of all deposits plus all interest paid. Ex. 1

b. The value of an annuity after t years is Ex. 2 Ex. 3

$$A = \frac{P\left[\left(1 + \frac{r}{n}\right)^{nt} - 1\right]}{\left(\frac{r}{n}\right)},$$

where interest is compounded n times per year. See the box.

c. The formula Ex. 4

$$P = \frac{A\left(\frac{r}{n}\right)}{\left[\left(1 + \frac{r}{n}\right)^{nt} - 1\right]}$$

gives the deposit, P, into an annuity at the end of each compounding period needed to achieve a value of A dollars after t years. See the box.

d. The return on an investment is the percent increase in the investment.

e. Investors purchase stock, shares of ownership in a company. The shares indicate the percent of ownership. Trading refers to buying and selling stock. Investors make money by selling a stock for more money than they paid for it. They can also make money while they own stock if a company distributes all or part of its profits as dividends. Each share of stock is paid the same dividend.

f. Investors purchase a bond, lending money to the company from which they purchase the bond. The company commits itself to pay the price an investor pays for the bond at the time it was purchased, called its face value, along with interest payments at a given rate.

g. Reading stock tables is explained in this section. Ex. 5

5 Installment Loans, Amortization, and Credit Cards

a. A fixed installment loan is paid off with a series of equal periodic payments. An open-end installment loan is paid off with variable monthly payments. Credit card loans are open-end installment loans.

b. A mortgage is a long-term loan for the purpose of buying a home, and for which the property is pledged as security for payment. The term of the mortgage is the number of years until final payoff. The down payment is the portion of the sale price of the home that the buyer initially pays. The amount of the mortgage is the difference between the sale price and the down payment.

c. Fixed-rate mortgages have the same monthly payment during the entire time of the loan. Variable-rate mortgages, or adjustable-rate mortgages, have payment amounts that change from time to time depending on changes in the interest rate.

d. A point is a one-time charge that equals 1% of the amount of a mortgage loan.

e. Loan Payment Formula for Fixed Installment Loans Ex. 1 Ex. 3

$$PMT = \frac{P\left(\frac{r}{n}\right)}{\left[1 - \left(1 + \frac{r}{n}\right)^{-nt}\right]}$$

PMT is the regular payment amount required to repay a loan of P dollars paid n times per year over t years at an annual interest rate r.

f. Amortizing a loan is the process of making regular payments on the principal and interest until the loan is paid off. A document containing the payment number, payment toward the interest, payment toward the principal, and balance of the loan is called a loan amortization schedule. Such a schedule shows how the buyer pays slightly less in interest and more in principal for each payment over the entire life of the loan. Ex. 2

g. Most credit cards calculate interest using the average daily balance method. Interest is calculated using $I = Prt$, where P is the average daily balance, r is the monthly rate, and t is one month. Ex. 4

Average daily balance

$$= \frac{\text{Sum of the unpaid balances for each day in the billing period}}{\text{Number of days in the billing period}}$$

The steps needed to determine the average daily balance are given in the box.

SUMMARY OF FINANCIAL MANAGEMENT FORMULAS

Simple Interest

$$I = Prt$$
$$A = P(1 + rt)$$

Compound Interest

$$A = P\left(1 + \frac{r}{n}\right)^{nt}$$

$$P = \frac{A}{\left(1 + \frac{r}{n}\right)^{nt}}$$

$$Y = \left(1 + \frac{r}{n}\right)^{n} - 1$$

Annuities

$$A = \frac{P\left[\left(1 + \frac{r}{n}\right)^{nt} - 1\right]}{\left(\frac{r}{n}\right)}$$

$$P = \frac{A\left(\frac{r}{n}\right)}{\left[\left(1 + \frac{r}{n}\right)^{nt} - 1\right]}$$

Amortization

$$PMT = \frac{P\left(\frac{r}{n}\right)}{\left[1 - \left(1 + \frac{r}{n}\right)^{-nt}\right]}$$

Be sure you understand what each formula in the box describes and the meaning of the variables in the formulas. Select the appropriate formula or formulas as you work the exercises in the Review Exercises and the Chapter Test.

Review Exercises

1

In Exercises 1–3, express each fraction as a percent.

1. $\frac{4}{5}$ **2.** $\frac{1}{8}$ **3.** $\frac{3}{4}$

In Exercises 4–6, express each decimal as a percent.

4. 0.72 **5.** 0.0035

6. 4.756

In Exercises 7–12, express each percent as a decimal.

7. 65% **8.** 99.7%

9. 150% **10.** 3%

11. 0.65% **12.** $\frac{1}{4}$%

13. What is 8% of 120?

14. Suppose that the local sales tax rate is 6% and you purchase a backpack for $24.

a. How much tax is paid?

b. What is the backpack's total cost?

15. A television with an original price of $850 is on sale at 35% off.

a. What is the discount amount?

b. What is the television's sale price?

16. Use the 2008 marginal tax rates in **Table 1** to calculate the income tax owed by the following person:

- Single, no dependents
- Gross income: $40,000
- $2500 paid to a tax-deferred IRA
- $6500 mortgage interest
- $1800 property taxes
- No tax credits

17. A college that had 40 students for each lecture course increased the number to 45 students. What is the percent increase in the number of students in a lecture course?

18. A dictionary regularly sells for $56.00. The sale price is $36.40. Find the percent decrease of the sale price from the regular price.

19. Consider the following statement:

My portfolio fell 10% last year, but then it rose 10% this year, so at least I recouped my losses.

Is this statement true? In particular, suppose you invested $10,000 in the stock market last year. How much money would be left in your portfolio with a 10% fall and then a 10% rise? If there is a loss, what is the percent decrease, to the nearest tenth of a percent, in your portfolio?

2

In Exercises 20–23, find the simple interest. (Assume 360 days in a year.)

	Principal	Rate	Time
20.	$6000	3%	1 year
21.	$8400	5%	6 years
22.	$20,000	8%	9 months
23.	$36,000	15%	60 days

24. In order to pay for tuition and books, a student borrows $3500 for four months at 10.5% interest.

a. How much interest must the student pay?

b. Find the future value of the loan.

In Exercises 25–29, use the formula for future value with simple interest to find the missing quantity. Round dollar amounts to the nearest cent and rates to the nearest tenth of a percent.

25. $A = ?$, $P = \$12{,}000$, $r = 8.2\%$, $t = 9$ months

26. $A = \$5750$, $P = \$5000$, $r = ?$, $t = 2$ years

27. $A = \$16{,}000$, $P = ?$, $r = 6.5\%$, $t = 3$ years

28. You plan to buy a $12,000 sailboat in four years. How much should you invest now, at 7.3% simple interest, to have enough for the boat in four years? (Round up to the nearest cent.)

29. You borrow $1500 from a friend and promise to pay back $1800 in six months. What simple interest rate will you pay?

30. You borrow $1800 on a 7% discounted loan for a period of 9 months.

a. What is the loan's discount?

b. Determine the net amount of money you will receive.

c. What is the loan's actual interest rate, to the nearest tenth of a percent?

3

In Exercises 31–33, the principal represents an amount of money deposited in a savings account that provides the lender compound interest at the given rate.

a. *Find how much money, to the nearest cent, there will be in the account after the given number of years.*

b. *Find the interest earned.*

	Principal	Rate	Compounding Periods per Year	Time
31.	$7000	3%	1	5 years
32.	$30,000	2.5%	4	10 years
33.	$2500	4%	12	20 years

34. Suppose that you have $14,000 to invest. Which investment yields the greater return over 10 years: 7% compounded monthly or 6.85% compounded continuously? How much more (to the nearest dollar) is yielded by the better investment?

In Exercises 35–36, round answers up to the nearest cent.

35. How much money should parents deposit today in an account that earns 7% compounded monthly so that it will accumulate to $100,000 in 18 years for their child's college education?

36. How much money should be deposited today in an account that earns 5% compounded quarterly so that it will accumulate to $75,000 in 35 years for retirement?

37. You deposit \$2000 in an account that pays 6% interest compounded quarterly.

a. Find the future value, to the nearest cent, after one year.

b. Use the future value formula for simple interest to determine the effective annual yield. Round to the nearest tenth of a percent.

38. What is the effective annual yield, to the nearest hundredth of a percent, of an account paying 5.5% compounded quarterly? What does your answer mean?

39. Which investment is the better choice: 6.25% compounded monthly or 6.3% compounded annually?

4

In Exercises 40–41, round the value of each annuity to the nearest dollar.

40. You spend \$10 per week on lottery tickets, averaging \$520 per year. Instead of buying tickets, if you deposited the \$520 at the end of each year in an annuity paying 6% compounded annually,

a. How much would you have after 20 years?

b. Find the interest.

41. To save for retirement, you decide to deposit \$100 at the end of each month in an IRA that pays 5.5% compounded monthly.

a. How much will you have from the IRA after 30 years?

b. Find the interest.

42. You would like to have \$25,000 to use as a down payment for a home in five years by making regular deposits at the end of every three months in an annuity that pays 7.25% compounded quarterly.

a. Determine the amount of each deposit. Round up to the nearest dollar.

b. How much of the \$25,000 comes from deposits and how much comes from interest?

For Exercises 43–50, refer to the stock table for Harley Davidson (the motorcycle company). Where necessary, round dollar amounts to the nearest cent.

52-Week High	52-Week Low	Stock	SYM	Div	Yld %	PE
64.06	26.13	Harley Dav	HDI	.16	.3	41

Vol 100s	Hi	Lo	Close	Net Chg
5458	61.25	59.25	61	+1.75

43. What were the high and low prices for a share for the past 52 weeks?

44. If you owned 900 shares of this stock last year, what dividend did you receive?

45. What is the annual return for the dividends alone?

46. How many shares of this company's stock were traded yesterday?

47. What were the high and low prices for a share yesterday?

48. What was the price at which a share traded when the stock exchange closed yesterday?

49. What was the change in price for a share of stock from the market close two days ago to yesterday's market close?

50. Compute the company's annual earnings per share using

$$\text{Annual earnings per share} = \frac{\text{Yesterday's closing price per share}}{\text{PE ratio}}.$$

51. Explain the difference between investing in a stock and investing in a bond.

5

In Exercises 52–55, round to the nearest dollar.

52. The price of a home is \$240,000. The bank requires a 20% down payment and two points at the time of closing. The cost of the home is financed with a 30-year fixed-rate mortgage at 7%.

a. Find the required down payment.

b. Find the amount of the mortgage.

c. How much must be paid for the two points at closing?

d. Find the monthly payment (excluding escrowed taxes and insurance).

e. Find the total cost of interest over 30 years.

53. In terms of paying less in interest, which is more economical for a \$70,000 mortgage: a 30-year fixed-rate at 8.5% or a 20-year fixed-rate at 8%? How much is saved in interest? Discuss one advantage and one disadvantage for each mortgage option.

54. You need a loan of \$100,000 to buy a home. Here are your options:

Option A: 30-year fixed-rate at 8.5% with no closing costs and no points

Option B: 30-year fixed-rate at 7.5% with closing costs of \$1300 and three points.

a. Determine your monthly payments for each option and discuss how you would decide between the two options.

b. Which mortgage loan has the greater total cost (closing costs + the amount paid for points + total cost of interest)? By how much?

55. You decide to take a $15,000 loan for a new car. You can select one of the following loans, each requiring regular monthly payments:

Loan A: 3-year loan at 7.2%

Loan B: 5-year loan at 8.1%.

a. Find the monthly payments and the total interest for Loan A.

b. Find the monthly payments and the total interest for Loan B.

c. Compare the monthly payments and interest for the longer-term loan to the monthly payments and interest for the shorter-term loan.

56. (In this exercise, round answers to the nearest cent.) In 2008, the average credit-card debt was $11,211. Suppose your card has this balance and an annual interest rate of 18%. You decide to pay off the balance over two years. If there are no further purchases charged to the card,

a. How much must you pay each month?

b. How much total interest will you pay?

c. Prepare an amortization schedule for the first three months of payments.

Payment Number	Interest	Principal	Balance
1			
2			
3			

57. A credit card calculates interest using the average daily balance method. The monthly interest rate is 1.1% of the average daily balance. The following transactions occurred during the November 1–November 30 billing period.

Transaction Description		Transaction Amount
Previous balance, $4620.80		
November 1	Billing date	
November 7	Payment	$650.00 credit
November 11	Charge: Airline Tickets	$350.25
November 25	Charge: Groceries	$125.70
November 28	Charge: Gas	$ 38.25
November 30	End of billing period	
Payment Due Date: December 9		

a. Find the average daily balance for the billing period. Round to the nearest cent.

b. Find the interest to be paid on December 1, the next billing date. Round to the nearest cent.

c. Find the balance due on December 1.

d. This credit card requires a $10 minimum monthly payment if the balance due at the end of the billing period is less than $360. Otherwise, the minimum monthly payment is $\frac{1}{36}$ of the balance due at the end of the billing period, rounded up to the nearest whole dollar. What is the minimum monthly payment due by December 9?

Chapter Test

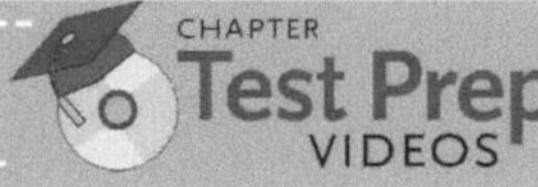

Step-by-step test solutions are found on the Chapter Test Prep Videos available on YouTube (search "Blitzer, Thinking Mathematically" and click on "Channels").

The box in the chapter summary summarizes the financial management formulas you have worked with throughout the chapter. Where applicable, use the appropriate formula to solve an exercise in this test. Unless otherwise stated, round dollar amounts to the nearest cent and rates to the nearest tenth of a percent.

1. A CD player with an original price of $120 is on sale at 15% off.

a. What is the amount of the discount?

b. What is the sale price of the CD player?

2. Use the 2008 marginal tax rates in **Table 1** to calculate the income tax owed by the following person:

- Single, no dependents
- Gross income: $36,500
- $2000 paid to a tax-deferred IRA
- $4700 mortgage interest
- $1300 property taxes
- No tax credits

3. You purchased shares of stock for $2000 and sold them for $3500. Find the percent increase, or your return, on this investment.

4. You borrow $2400 for three months at 12% simple interest. Find the amount of interest paid and the future value of the loan.

5. You borrow $2000 from a friend and promise to pay back $3000 in two years. What simple interest rate will you pay?

6. In six months, you want to have $7000 worth of remodeling done to your home. How much should you invest now, at 9% simple interest, to have enough money for the project? (Round up to the nearest cent.)

7. Find the effective annual yield, to the nearest hundredth of a percent, of an account paying 4.5% compounded quarterly. What does your answer mean?

8. To save money to use as a down payment for a home in five years, you deposit $6000 in an account that pays 6.5% compounded monthly.

a. How much, to the nearest dollar, will you have as a down payment after five years?

b. Find the interest.

9. Instead of making the lump-sum deposit of $6000 described in Exercise 8, you decide to deposit $100 at the end of each month in an annuity that pays 6.5% compounded monthly.

a. How much, to the nearest dollar, will you have as a down payment after five years?

b. Find the interest.

c. Why is less interest earned from this annuity than from the lump-sum deposit in Exercise 8? With less interest earned, why would one select the annuity rather than the lump-sum deposit?

10. You would like to have $3000 in four years for a special vacation by making a lump-sum investment in an account that pays 9.5% compounded semiannually. How much should you deposit now? Round up to the nearest dollar.

11. How much should you deposit at the end of each month in an IRA that pays 6.25% compounded monthly to have $1,500,000 when you retire in 40 years? Round up to the nearest dollar. How much of the $1.5 million comes from interest?

Use the stock table for AT&T to solve Exercises 12–14.

52-Week High	52-Week Low	Stock	SYM	Div	Yld %	PE
26.50	24.25	AT & T	PNS	2.03	7.9	18

Vol 100s	Hi	Lo	Close	Net Chg
961	25.75	25.50	25.75	+0.13

12. What were the high and low prices for a share yesterday?

13. If you owned 1000 shares of this stock last year, what dividend did you receive?

14. Suppose that you bought 600 shares of AT&T, paying the price per share at which a share traded when the stock exchange closed yesterday. If the broker charges 2.5% of the price paid for all 600 shares, find the broker's commission.

Use this information to solve Exercises 15–20. The price of a home is $120,000. The bank requires a 10% down payment and two points at the time of closing. The cost of the home is financed with a 30-year fixed-rate mortgage at 8.5%.

15. Find the required down payment.

16. Find the amount of the mortgage.

17. How much must be paid for the two points at closing?

18. Find the monthly payment (excluding escrowed taxes and insurance). Round to the nearest dollar.

19. Find the total cost of interest over 30 years.

20. A student graduates from college with a loan of $20,000. The interest rate is 6.8% and the loan term is ten years.

    a. Find the monthly payments, rounded to the nearest dollar, and the total interest for the loan.

    b. Prepare a loan amortization schedule for the first two months of the student loan. Round entries to the nearest cent.

Payment Number	Interest	Principal	Balance
1			
2			

21. A credit card calculates interest using the average daily balance method. The monthly interest rate is 2% of the average daily balance. The following transactions occurred during the September 1–September 30 billing period.

Transaction Description	Transaction Amount
Previous balance, $3800.00	
September 1 Billing date	
September 5 Payment	$800.00 credit
September 9 Charge: Gas	$ 40.00
September 19 Charge: Clothing	$160.00
September 27 Charge: Airline Ticket	$200.00
September 30 End of billing period	
Payment Due Date: October 9	

a. Find the average daily balance for the billing period. Round to the nearest cent.

b. Find the interest to be paid on October 1, the next billing date. Round to the nearest cent.

c. Find the balance due on October 1.

d. Terms for the credit card require a $10 minimum monthly payment if the balance due is less than $360. Otherwise, the minimum monthly payment is $\frac{1}{36}$ of the balance due, rounded up to the nearest whole dollar. What is the minimum monthly payment due by October 9?

Answers to Selected Exercises

Section 1

Check Point Exercises

1. 12.5% **2.** 2.3% **3. a.** 0.67 **b.** 2.5 **4. a.** $75.60 **b.** $1335.60 **5. a.** $133 **b.** $247 **6.** $4106.25 **7. a.** $66\frac{2}{3}\%$ **b.** 40% **8.** 35% **9.** 20% **10. a.** $1152 **b.** 4% decrease

Exercise Set 1

1. 40% **3.** 25% **5.** 37.5% **7.** 2.5% **9.** 11.25% **11.** 59% **13.** 38.44% **15.** 287% **17.** 1487% **19.** 10,000% **21.** 0.72 **23.** 0.436 **25.** 1.3 **27.** 0.02 **29.** 0.005 **31.** 0.00625 **33.** 0.625 **35.** 6 **37.** 7.2 **39.** 5 **41.** 170 **43.** 20% **45.** 12% **47. a.** $1968 **b.** $34,768 **49. a.** $103.20 **b.** $756.80 **51.** $4443.75 **53.** $2152.50 **55.** $8064 **57.** $16,998 **59. a.** $1530 **b.** $1256.25 **c.** 13.9% **61.** 9.0% **63.** 0.2% **65.** 15% **67.** no; 2% loss **77.** does not make sense **79.** does not make sense **81.** $2400 increase

Section 2

Check Point Exercises

1. $150 **2.** $336 **3.** $2091 **4.** 18% **5.** $3846.16 **6. a.** $1200 **b.** $3800 **c.** 15.8%

Exercise Set 2

1. $240 **3.** $10.80 **5.** $318.75 **7.** $426.25 **9.** $3420 **11.** $38,350 **13.** $9390 **15.** 7.5% **17.** 9% **19.** 31.3% **21.** $5172.42 **23.** $8917.20 **25.** $4509.59 **27. a.** $93.33 **b.** $1906.67 **c.** 7.3% **29. a.** $1560 **b.** $10,440 **c.** 7.5% **31.** $r = \frac{A - P}{Pt}$ **33.** $P = \frac{A}{1 + rt}$ **35. a.** $247.50 **b.** $4247.50 **37.** 21.4% **39.** 640% **41.** $2654.87 **43. a.** $1920 **b.** $6080 **c.** 10.5% **49.** does not make sense **51.** makes sense **53. a.** $A = 275t + 5000$ **b.** Answers will vary; an example is: The rate of change of the future value per year is $275.

Section 3

Check Point Exercises

1. a. $1216.65 **b.** $216.65 **2. a.** $6253.23 **b.** $2053.23 **3. a.** $14,859.47 **b.** $14,918.25 **4.** $5714.25 **5. a.** $6628.28 **b.** 10.5% **6.** $\approx$ 8.24%

Exercise Set 3

1. a. $10,816 **b.** $816 **3. a.** $3655.21 **b.** $655.21 **5. a.** $12,795.12 **b.** $3295.12 **7. a.** $5149.12 **b.** $649.12 **9. a.** $1855.10 **b.** $355.10 **11. a.** $49,189.30 **b.** $29,189.30 **13. a.** $13,116.51 **b.** $13,140.67 **c.** $13,157.04 **d.** $13,165.31 **15.** 7% compounded monthly **17.** $8374.85 **19.** $7528.59 **21. a.** $10,457.65 **b.** 4.6% **23.** 6.1% **25.** 6.2% **27.** 6.2% **29.** 8.3%; 8.25%; 8% compounded monthly **31.** 5.6%; 5.5%; 5.5% compounded semiannually **33.** 22.5 yr **35.** 4.3 yr **37.** 8.3 yr **39.** $41,528 **41. a.** you; $391 **b.** you; $340 **c.** your friend; $271 **43.** $9187 **45. a.** $\approx$ $5,027,400,000 **b.** $\approx$ $5,225,000,000 **47.** 5.9% compounded daily; $2

49.

	Once a Year		Continuous	
Years	Amount	Interest	Amount	Interest
1	$5275	$275	$5283	$283
5	$6535	$1535	$6583	$1583
10	$8541	$3541	$8666	$3666
20	$14,589	$9589	$15,021	$10,021

51. $37,096 **53.** A: $38,755; B: $41,163 **55.** 5.55% **57.** 4.3%; 4.3%; 4.3%; As the number of compounding periods increases, the effective annual yield increases slightly. However, with the rates rounded to the nearest tenth of a percent, this increase is not evident. **59.** 4.5% compounded semiannually **65.** does not make sense **67.** does not make sense **69.** $12,942.94 **71.** $A = P\left(1 + \frac{r}{n}\right)^{nt}$

Substitute this value of A into the future value formula for simple interest. Since the interest rates are two different values, use Y, the effective yield, for the interest rate on the right side of the equation.

$$P\left(1 + \frac{r}{n}\right)^{nt} = P(1 + Yt)$$

$$\left(1 + \frac{r}{n}\right)^{nt} = (1 + Yt) \qquad \text{Divide each side by } P.$$

$$\left(1 + \frac{r}{n}\right)^{n} = 1 + Y \qquad \text{Let } t = 1.$$

$$Y = \left(1 + \frac{r}{n}\right)^{n} - 1 \qquad \text{Subtract 1 from each side and interchange the sides.}$$

Section 4

Check Point Exercises

1. a. \$6620 **b.** \$620 **2. a.** \$777,170 **b.** \$657,170 **3. a.** \$333,946 **b.** \$291,946 **4. a.** \$187 **b.** deposits: \$40,392; interest: \$59,608 **5. a.** high: \$63.38; low: \$42.37 **b.** \$2160 **c.** 1.5%; This is much lower than a bank account paying 3.5%. **d.** 7,203,200 shares **e.** high: \$49.94; low: \$48.33 **f.** \$49.50 **g.** The closing price is up \$0.03 from the previous day's closing price. **h.** $\approx$ \$1.34

Exercise Set 4

1. a. \$66,132 **b.** \$26,132 **3. a.** \$702,528 **b.** \$542,528 **5. a.** \$50,226 **b.** \$32,226 **7. a.** \$9076 **b.** \$4076 **9. a.** \$28,850 **b.** \$4850 **11. a.** \$4530 **b.** deposits: \$81,540; interest: \$58,460 **13. a.** \$1323 **b.** deposits: \$158,760; interest: \$41,240 **15. a.** \$356 **b.** deposits: \$170,880; interest: \$829,120 **17. a.** \$920 **b.** deposits: \$18,400; interest: \$1600 **19. a.** high: \$73.25; low: \$45.44 **b.** \$840 **c.** 2.2%; Answers will vary. **d.** 591,500 shares **e.** high: \$56.38; low: \$54.38 **f.** \$55.50 **g.** \$1.25 increase **h.** $\approx$ \$3.26 **21. a.** \$30,000 **b.** \$30,000 **23. a.** \$287 **b.** with: \$5745.25; without: \$6606.25 **c.** with: 11.5%; without: 13.2% **25.** $P = \dfrac{Ar}{[(1+r)^t - 1]}$; the deposit at the end of each year that yields A dollars after t years with interest rate r compounded annually **27. a.** \$11,617 **b.** \$1617 **29. a.** \$87,052 **b.** \$63,052 **31. a.** \$693,031 **b.** \$293,031 **33. a.** \$401 **b.** deposits: \$3208; interest: \$292 **35.** \$620; \$1,665,200 **51.** does not make sense **53.** does not make sense

Section 5

Check Point Exercises

1. a. \$1627 **b.** \$117,360 **c.** \$148,860

2.

Payment Number	Interest Payment	Principal Payment	Balance of Loan
1	\$1166.67	\$383.33	\$199,616.67
2	\$1164.43	\$385.57	\$199,231.10

3. a. payment: \$366; interest: \$2568 **b.** payment: \$278; interest: \$5016 **c.** Monthly payments are less with the longer-term loan, but there is more interest with this loan. **4. a.** \$8761.76 **b.** \$140.19 **c.** \$9661.11 **d.** \$269

Exercise Set 5

1. a. \$44,000 **b.** \$176,000 **c.** \$5280 **d.** \$1171 **e.** \$245,560 **3.** \$60,120 **5.** 20-year at 7.5%; \$106,440 **7.** Mortgage A; \$11,300 **9. a.** \$210 **b.** \$840 **11. a.** \$137; lower monthly payment **b.** \$732; less interest **13.** monthly payment: \$385; total interest: \$420; \$175 more each month; \$420 less interest

15. a. monthly payment: \$244.13; total interest: \$1718.24

b.

Payment Number	Interest	Principal	Loan Balance
1	\$66.67	\$177.46	\$9822.54
2	\$65.48	\$178.65	\$9643.89
3	\$64.29	\$179.84	\$9464.05

17. a. monthly payment: \$347.13; total interest: \$43,311.20

b.

Payment Number	Interest	Principal	Loan Balance
1	\$283.33	\$63.80	\$39,936.20
2	\$282.88	\$64.25	\$39,871.95
3	\$282.43	\$64.70	\$39,807.25

c. \$148.81 more each month; \$23,798.40 less interest

19. a. \$6150.65 **b.** \$92.26 **c.** \$6392.26 **d.** \$178 **21. a.** \$2057.22 **b.** \$24.69 **c.** \$2237.23 **d.** \$90 **33.** does not make sense **35.** does not make sense

37.

$$P\left(1+\frac{r}{n}\right)^{nt} = \frac{PMT\left[\left(1+\frac{r}{n}\right)^{nt}-1\right]}{\left(\frac{r}{n}\right)}$$

$$P\left(\frac{r}{n}\right)\left(1+\frac{r}{n}\right)^{nt} = PMT\left[\left(1+\frac{r}{n}\right)^{nt}-1\right]$$

$$\frac{P\left(\frac{r}{n}\right)\left(1+\frac{r}{n}\right)^{nt}}{\left[\left(1+\frac{r}{n}\right)^{nt}-1\right]} = PMT$$

$$\frac{P\left(\frac{r}{n}\right)}{\left[1 - \left(1 + \frac{r}{n}\right)^{-nt}\right]} = PMT$$

Review Exercises

1. 80% **2.** 12.5% **3.** 75% **4.** 72% **5.** 0.35% **6.** 475.6% **7.** 0.65 **8.** 0.997 **9.** 1.50 **10.** 0.03 **11.** 0.0065 **12.** 0.0025 **13.** 9.6 **14. a.** $1.44 **b.** $25.44 **15. a.** $297.50 **b.** $552.50 **16.** $3453.75 **17.** 12.5% increase **18.** 35% decrease **19.** no; $9900; 1% decrease **20.** $180 **21.** $2520 **22.** $1200 **23.** $900 **24. a.** $122.50 **b.** $3622.50 **25.** $12,738 **26.** 7.5% **27.** $13,389.12 **28.** $9287.93 **29.** 40% **30. a.** $94.50 **b.** $1705.50 **c.** 7.4% **31. a.** $8114.92 **b.** $1114.92 **32. a.** $38,490.80 **b.** $8490.80 **33. a.** $5556.46 **b.** $3056.46 **34.** 7% compounded monthly; $362 **35.** $28,469,44 **36.** $13,175.19 **37. a.** $2122.73 **b.** 6.1% **38.** 5.61%; Answers will vary; an example is: The same amount of money would earn 5.61% in a simple interest account for a year. **39.** 6.25% compounded monthly **40. a.** $19,129 **b.** $8729 **41. a.** $91,361 **b.** $55,361 **42. a.** $1049 **b.** $20,980; $4020 **43.** high: $64.06; low: $26.13 **44.** $144 **45.** 0.3% **46.** 545,800 shares **47.** high: $61.25; low: $59.25 **48.** $61.00 **49.** $1.75 increase **50.** $1.49 **52. a.** $48,000 **b.** $192,000 **c.** $3840 **d.** $1277 **e.** $267,720 **53.** 20-year at 8%; $53,040; Answers will vary. **54. a.** option A: $769; option B: $699; Answers will vary. **b.** Mortgage A: $20,900 **55. a.** monthly payment: $465; total interest: $1740 **b.** monthly payment: $305; total interest: $3300 **c.** Longer term has lower monthly payment but greater total interest.

56. a. $559.70 **b.** $2221.80

c.

Payment Number	Interest	Principal	Loan Balance
1	$168.17	$391.53	$10,819.47
2	$162.29	$397.41	$10,422.06
3	$156.33	$403.37	$10,018,69

57. a. $4363.27 **b.** $48.00 **c.** $4533.00 **d.** $126

Chapter Test

1. a. $18 **b.** $102 **2.** $3348.75 **3.** 75% **4.** $72; $2472 **5.** 25% **6.** $6698.57 **7.** 4.58%; Answers will vary; an example is: The same amount of money would earn 4.58% in a simple interest account for a year. **8. a.** $8297 **b.** $2297 **9. a.** $7067 **b.** $1067 **c.** Only part of the $6000 is invested for the entire five years.; Answers will vary. **10.** $2070 **11.** $704 per month; $1,162,080 interest **12.** high: $25.75; low: $25.50 **13.** $2030 **14.** $386.25 **15.** $12,000 **16.** $108,000 **17.** $2160 **18.** $830 **19.** $190,800 **20. a.** monthly payment: $230; total interest: $7600

b.

Payment Number	Interest	Principal	Loan Balance
1	$113.33	$116.67	$19,883.33
2	$112.67	$117.33	$19,766.00

21. a. $3226.67 **b.** $64.53 **c.** $3464.53 **d.** $97

Counting Methods and Probability Theory

Two of America's best-loved presidents, Abraham Lincoln and John F. Kennedy, are linked by a bizarre series of coincidences:

- Lincoln was elected president in 1860. Kennedy was elected president in 1960.
- Lincoln's assassin, John Wilkes Booth, was born in 1839. Kennedy's assassin, Lee Harvey Oswald, was born in 1939.
- Lincoln's secretary, named Kennedy, warned him not to go to the theater on the night he was shot. Kennedy's secretary, named Lincoln, warned him not to go to Dallas on the day he was shot.
- Booth shot Lincoln in a theater and ran into a warehouse. Oswald shot Kennedy from a warehouse and ran into a theater.
- Both Lincoln and Kennedy were shot from behind, with their wives present.
- Andrew Johnson, who succeeded Lincoln, was born in 1808. Lyndon Johnson, who succeeded Kennedy, was born in 1908.

Source: Edward Burger and Michael Starbird, *Coincidences, Chaos, and All That Math Jazz,* W. W. Norton and Company, 2005.

Amazing coincidences? A cosmic conspiracy? Not really. In this chapter, you will see how the mathematics of uncertainty and risk, called probability theory, numerically describes situations in which to expect the unexpected. By assigning numbers to things that are extraordinarily unlikely, we can logically analyze coincidences without erroneous beliefs that strange and mystical events are occurring. We'll even see how wildly inaccurate our intuition can be about the likelihood of an event by examining an "amazing" coincidence that is nearly certain.

Coincidences are discussed in a Blitzer Bonus. Coincidences that are nearly certain are developed in Exercise 87 of Exercise Set 7.

From Chapter 11 of *Thinking Mathematically*, Fifth Edition, Robert F. Blitzer.

OBJECTIVE

1 | Use the Fundamental Counting Principle to determine the number of possible outcomes in a given situation.

1 The Fundamental Counting Principle

Chet Brokaw\AP Wide World Photos

Have you ever imagined what your life would be like if you won the lottery? What changes would you make? Before you fantasize about becoming a person of leisure with a staff of obedient elves, think about this: The probability of winning top prize in the lottery is about the same as the probability of being struck by lightning. There are millions of possible number combinations in lottery games and only one way of winning the grand prize. Determining the probability of winning involves calculating the chance of getting the winning combination from all possible outcomes. In this section, we begin preparing for the surprising world of probability by looking at methods for counting possible outcomes.

1 | Use the Fundamental Counting Principle to determine the number of possible outcomes in a given situation.

The Fundamental Counting Principle with Two Groups of Items

It's early morning, you're groggy, and you have to select something to wear for your 8 A.M. class. (What *were* you thinking when you signed up for a class at that hour?!) Fortunately, your "lecture wardrobe" is rather limited—just two pairs of jeans to choose from (one blue, one black) and three T-shirts to choose from (one beige, one yellow, and one blue). Your early-morning dilemma is illustrated in **Figure 1**.

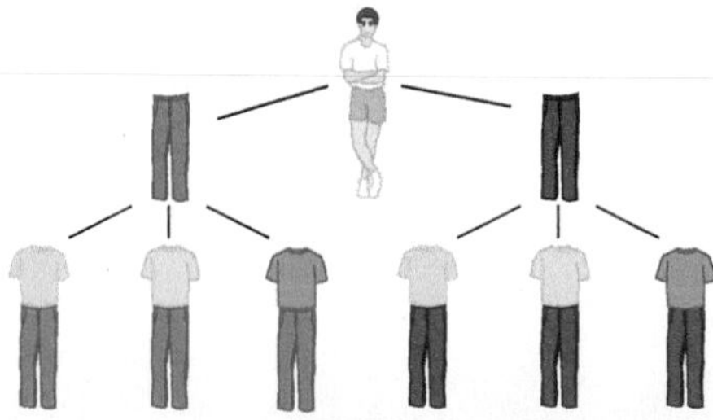

FIGURE 1 Selecting a wardrobe

The **tree diagram**, so named because of its branches, shows that you can form six different outfits from your two pairs of jeans and three T-shirts. Each pair of jeans can be combined with one of three T-shirts. Notice that the total number of outfits can be obtained by multiplying the number of choices for the jeans, 2, by the number of choices for the T-shirts, 3:

$$2 \cdot 3 = 6.$$

We can generalize this idea to any two groups of items—not just jeans and T-shirts—with the **Fundamental Counting Principle**.

THE FUNDAMENTAL COUNTING PRINCIPLE

If you can choose one item from a group of M items and a second item from a group of N items, then the total number of two-item choices is $M \cdot N$.

EXAMPLE 1 Applying the Fundamental Counting Principle

The Greasy Spoon Restaurant offers 6 appetizers and 14 main courses. In how many ways can a person order a two-course meal?

Solution Choosing from one of 6 appetizers and one of 14 main courses, the total number of two-course meals is

$$6 \cdot 14 = 84.$$

A person can order a two-course meal in 84 different ways.

A restaurant offers 10 appetizers and 15 main courses. In how many ways can you order a two-course meal?

EXAMPLE 2 Applying the Fundamental Counting Principle

This is the semester that you will take your required psychology and social science courses. Because you decide to register early, there are 15 sections of psychology from which you can choose. Furthermore, there are 9 sections of social science that are available at times that do not conflict with those for psychology. In how many ways can you create two-course schedules that satisfy the psychology–social science requirement?

Solution The number of ways that you can satisfy the requirement is found by multiplying the number of choices for each course. You can choose your psychology course from 15 sections and your social science course from 9 sections. For both courses you have

$$15 \cdot 9, \text{ or } 135$$

choices. Thus, you can satisfy the psychology–social science requirement in 135 ways.

Rework Example 2 given that the number of sections of psychology and nonconflicting sections of social science each decrease by 5.

The Fundamental Counting Principle with More Than Two Groups of Items

Whoops! You forgot something in choosing your lecture wardrobe—shoes! You have two pairs of sneakers to choose from—one black and one red, for that extra fashion flair! Your possible outfits including sneakers are shown in **Figure 2**.

The number of possible ways of playing the first four moves on each side in a game of chess is 318,979,564,000. SuperStock, Inc.

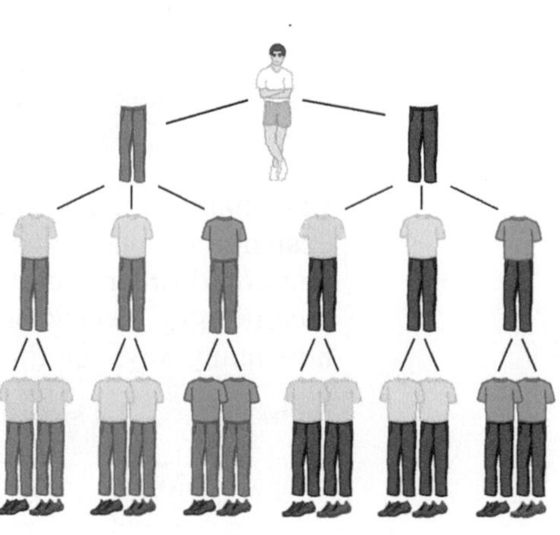

FIGURE 2 Increasing wardrobe selections

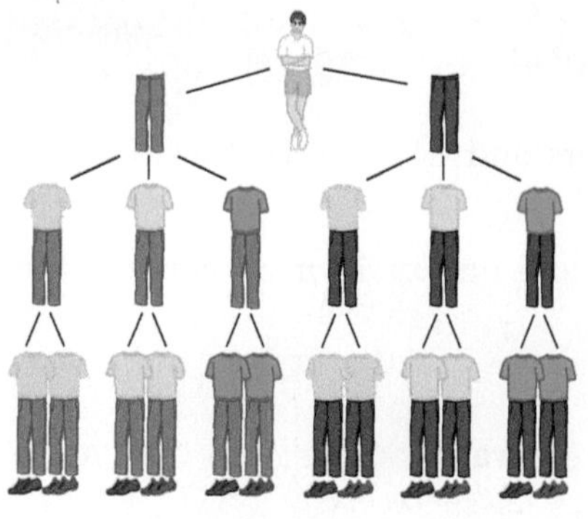
FIGURE 2 (repeated)

The tree diagram shows that you can form 12 outfits from your two pairs of jeans, three T-shirts, and two pairs of sneakers. Notice that the number of outfits can be obtained by multiplying the number of choices for jeans, 2, the number of choices for T-shirts, 3, and the number of choices for sneakers, 2:

$$2 \cdot 3 \cdot 2 = 12.$$

Unlike your earlier dilemma, you are now dealing with *three* groups of items. The Fundamental Counting Principle can be extended to determine the number of possible outcomes in situations in which there are three or more groups of items.

THE FUNDAMENTAL COUNTING PRINCIPLE

The number of ways in which a series of successive things can occur is found by multiplying the number of ways in which each thing can occur.

For example, if you own 30 pairs of jeans, 20 T-shirts, and 12 pairs of sneakers, you have

$$30 \cdot 20 \cdot 12 = 7200$$

choices for your wardrobe.

EXAMPLE 3 Options in Planning a Course Schedule

Next semester you are planning to take three courses—math, English, and humanities. Based on time blocks and highly recommended professors, there are 8 sections of math, 5 of English, and 4 of humanities that you find suitable. Assuming no scheduling conflicts, how many different three-course schedules are possible?

Solution This situation involves making choices with three groups of items.

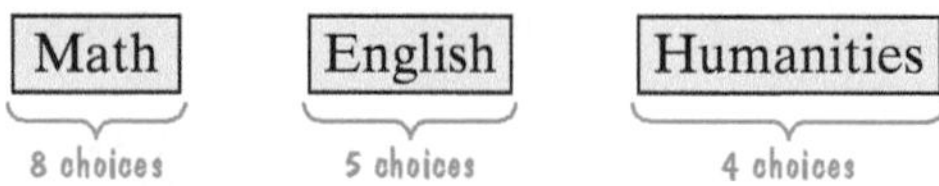

We use the Fundamental Counting Principle to find the number of three-course schedules. Multiply the number of choices for each of the three groups.

$$8 \cdot 5 \cdot 4 = 160$$

Thus, there are 160 different three-course schedules.

CHECK POINT 3 A pizza can be ordered with two choices of size (medium or large), three choices of crust (thin, thick, or regular), and five choices of toppings (ground beef, sausage, pepperoni, bacon, or mushrooms). How many different one-topping pizzas can be ordered?

EXAMPLE 4 Car of the Future

Car manufacturers are now experimenting with lightweight three-wheel cars, designed for one person, and considered ideal for city driving. Intrigued? Suppose you could order such a car with a choice of 9 possible colors, with or without air conditioning, electric or gas powered, and with or without an onboard computer. In how many ways can this car be ordered with regard to these options?

Solution This situation involves making choices with four groups of items.

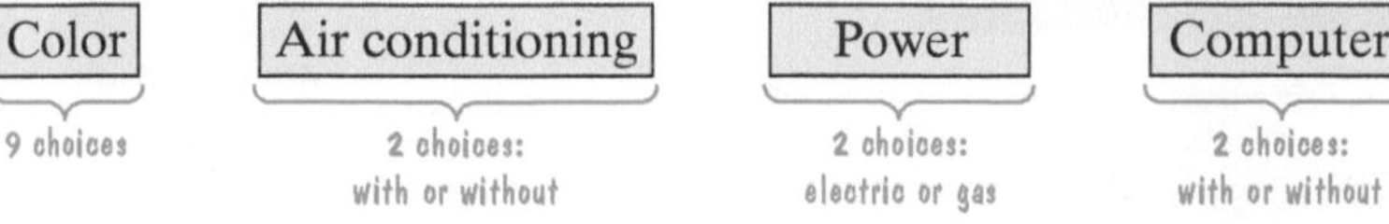

We use the Fundamental Counting Principle to find the number of ordering options. Multiply the number of choices for each of the four groups.

$$9 \cdot 2 \cdot 2 \cdot 2 = 72$$

Thus, the car can be ordered in 72 different ways.

The car in Example 4 is now available in 10 possible colors. The options involving air conditioning, power, and an onboard computer still apply. Furthermore, the car is available with or without a global positioning system (for pinpointing your location at every moment). In how many ways can this car be ordered in terms of these options?

EXAMPLE 5 A Multiple-Choice Test

You are taking a multiple-choice test that has ten questions. Each of the questions has four answer choices, with one correct answer per question. If you select one of these four choices for each question and leave nothing blank, in how many ways can you answer the questions?

Solution This situation involves making choices with ten questions.

We use the Fundamental Counting Principle to determine the number of ways that you can answer the questions on the test. Multiply the number of choices, 4, for each of the ten questions.

$$4 \cdot 4 \cdot 4 \cdot 4 \cdot 4 \cdot 4 \cdot 4 \cdot 4 \cdot 4 \cdot 4 = 4^{10} = 1{,}048{,}576$$ *Use a calculator: 4 y^x 10 =.*

Thus, you can answer the questions in 1,048,576 different ways.

Are you surprised that there are over one million ways of answering a ten-question multiple-choice test? Of course, there is only one way to answer the test and receive a perfect score. The probability of guessing your way into a perfect score involves calculating the chance of getting a perfect score, just one way, from all 1,048,576 possible outcomes. In short, prepare for the test and do not rely on guessing!

CHECK POINT 5 You are taking a multiple-choice test that has six questions. Each of the questions has three answer choices, with one correct answer per question. If you select one of these three choices for each question and leave nothing blank, in how many ways can you answer the questions?

EXAMPLE 6 Telephone Numbers in the United States

Telephone numbers in the United States begin with three-digit area codes followed by seven-digit local telephone numbers. Area codes and local telephone numbers cannot begin with 0 or 1. How many different telephone numbers are possible?

Solution This situation involves making choices with ten groups of items.

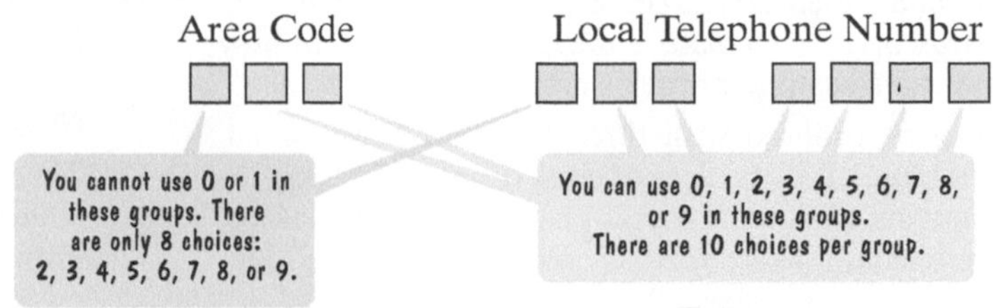

BLITZER BONUS

RUNNING OUT OF TELEPHONE NUMBERS

Apple / Splash News\Newscom

By the year 2020, portable telephones used for business and pleasure will all be videophones. At that time, U.S. population is expected to be 323 million. Faxes, beepers, cell phones, computer phone lines, and business lines may result in certain areas running out of phone numbers. Solution: Add more digits!

With or without extra digits, we expect that the 2020 videophone greeting will still be "hello," a word created by Thomas Edison in 1877. Phone inventor Alexander Graham Bell preferred "ahoy," but "hello" won out, appearing in the *Oxford English Dictionary* in 1883.

(*Source: New York Times*)

Here are the choices for each of the ten groups of items:

Area Code	Local Telephone Number
8 10 10	8 10 10 10 10 10 10

We use the Fundamental Counting Principle to determine the number of different telephone numbers that are possible. The total number of telephone numbers possible is

$$8 \cdot 10 \cdot 10 \cdot 8 \cdot 10 \cdot 10 \cdot 10 \cdot 10 \cdot 10 \cdot 10 = 6{,}400{,}000{,}000.$$

There are six billion four hundred million different telephone numbers that are possible.

An electronic gate can be opened by entering five digits on a keypad containing the digits $0, 1, 2, 3, \ldots, 8, 9$. How many different keypad sequences are possible if the digit 0 cannot be used as the first digit?

Exercise Set 1

Practice and Application Exercises

1. A restaurant offers 8 appetizers and 10 main courses. In how many ways can a person order a two-course meal?
2. The model of the car you are thinking of buying is available in nine different colors and three different styles (hatchback, sedan, or station wagon). In how many ways can you order the car?
3. A popular brand of pen is available in three colors (red, green, or blue) and four writing tips (bold, medium, fine, or micro). How many different choices of pens do you have with this brand?
4. In how many ways can a casting director choose a female lead and a male lead from five female actors and six male actors?
5. A student is planning a two-part trip. The first leg of the trip is from San Francisco to New York, and the second leg is from New York to Paris. From San Francisco to New York, travel options include airplane, train, or bus. From New York to Paris, the options are limited to airplane or ship. In how many ways can the two-part trip be made?
6. For a temporary job between semesters, you are painting the parking spaces for a new shopping mall with a letter of the alphabet and a single digit from 1 to 9. The first parking space is A1 and the last parking space is Z9. How many parking spaces can you paint with distinct labels?
7. An ice cream store sells two drinks (sodas or milk shakes), in four sizes (small, medium, large, or jumbo), and five flavors (vanilla, strawberry, chocolate, coffee, or pistachio). In how many ways can a customer order a drink?
8. A pizza can be ordered with three choices of size (small, medium, or large), four choices of crust (thin, thick, crispy, or regular), and six choices of toppings (ground beef, sausage, pepperoni, bacon, mushrooms, or onions). How many one-topping pizzas can be ordered?
9. A restaurant offers the following limited lunch menu.

Main Course	Vegetables	Beverages	Desserts
Ham	Potatoes	Coffee	Cake
Chicken	Peas	Tea	Pie
Fish	Green beans	Milk	Ice cream
Beef		Soda	

If one item is selected from each of the four groups, in how many ways can a meal be ordered? Describe two such orders.

10. An apartment complex offers apartments with four different options, designated by A through D.

A	B	C	D
one bedroom	one bathroom	first floor	lake view
two bedrooms	two bathrooms	second floor	golf course view
three bedrooms			no special view

How many apartment options are available? Describe two such options.

11. Shoppers in a large shopping mall are categorized as male or female, over 30 or 30 and under, and cash or credit card shoppers. In how many ways can the shoppers be categorized?
12. There are three highways from city A to city B, two highways from city B to city C, and four highways from city C to city D. How many different highway routes are there from city A to city D?

13. A person can order a new car with a choice of six possible colors, with or without air conditioning, with or without automatic transmission, with or without power windows, and with or without a CD player. In how many different ways can a new car be ordered with regard to these options?
14. A car model comes in nine colors, with or without air conditioning, with or without a sun roof, with or without automatic transmission, and with or without antilock brakes. In how many ways can the car be ordered with regard to these options?
15. You are taking a multiple-choice test that has five questions. Each of the questions has three answer choices, with one correct answer per question. If you select one of these three choices for each question and leave nothing blank, in how many ways can you answer the questions?
16. You are taking a multiple-choice test that has eight questions. Each of the questions has three answer choices, with one correct answer per question. If you select one of these three choices for each question and leave nothing blank, in how many ways can you answer the questions?
17. In the original plan for area codes in 1945, the first digit could be any number from 2 through 9, the second digit was either 0 or 1, and the third digit could be any number except 0. With this plan, how many different area codes are possible?
18. The local seven-digit telephone numbers in Inverness, California, have 669 as the first three digits. How many different telephone numbers are possible in Inverness?
19. License plates in a particular state display two letters followed by three numbers, such as AT-887 or BB-013. How many different license plates can be manufactured for this state?
20. How many different four-letter radio station call letters can be formed if the first letter must be W or K?
21. A stock can go up, go down, or stay unchanged. How many possibilities are there if you own seven stocks?
22. A social security number contains nine digits, such as 074-66-7795. How many different social security numbers can be formed?

Writing in Mathematics

23. Explain the Fundamental Counting Principle.
24. **Figure 2** shows that a tree diagram can be used to find the total number of outfits. Describe one advantage of using the Fundamental Counting Principle rather than a tree diagram.
25. Write an original problem that can be solved using the Fundamental Counting Principle. Then solve the problem.

Critical Thinking Exercises

Make Sense? *In Exercises 26–29, determine whether each statement makes sense or does not make sense, and explain your reasoning.*

26. I used the Fundamental Counting Principle to determine the number of five-digit ZIP codes that are available to the U.S. Postal Service.
27. The Fundamental Counting Principle can be used to determine the number of ways of arranging the numbers 1, 2, 3, 4, 5, . . . , 98, 99, 100.
28. I estimate there are approximately 10,000 ways to arrange the letters A, B, C, D, E, . . . , X, Y, Z.
29. The statement in the last frame of this cartoon is highly unlikely because there are 2048 possible sets of answers on an eleven-item true/false test.

Peanuts: © United Feature Syndicate, Inc.

30. How many four-digit odd numbers are there? Assume that the digit on the left cannot be 0.
31. In order to develop a more appealing hamburger, a franchise uses taste tests with 12 different buns, 30 sauces, 4 types of lettuce, and 3 types of tomatoes. If the taste tests were done at one restaurant by one tester who takes 10 minutes to eat each hamburger, approximately how long would it take the tester to eat all possible hamburgers?

OBJECTIVES

1 | Use the Fundamental Counting Principle to count permutations.
2 | Evaluate factorial expressions.
3 | Use the permutations formula.
4 | Find the number of permutations of duplicate items.

2 Permutations

"Read the book!" "See the movie!"

We open this section with six jokes about books. (Stay with us on this one.)

- *"Outside of a dog, a book is man's best friend. Inside of a dog, it's too dark to read."—Groucho Marx*
- *"I recently bought a book of free verse. For \$12."—George Carlin*
- *"If a word in the dictionary was misspelled, how would we know?"—Steven Wright*
- *"I wrote a book under a pen name: 'Bic.'" —Henny Youngman*
- *"A bookstore is one of the only pieces of evidence we have that people are still thinking."—Jerry Seinfeld*
- *"I honestly believe there is absolutely nothing like going to bed with a good book. Or a friend who's read one."—Phyllis Diller*

1 | Use the Fundamental Counting Principle to count permutations.

We can use the Fundamental Counting Principle to determine the number of ways these jokes can be delivered. You can choose any one of the six jokes as the first one told. Once this joke is delivered, you'll have five jokes to choose from for the second joke told. You'll then have four jokes left to choose from for the third delivery. Continuing in this manner, the situation can be shown as follows:

First Joke Delivered	Second Joke Delivered	Third Joke Delivered	Fourth Joke Delivered	Fifth Joke Delivered	Sixth Joke Delivered
6 choices	5 choices	4 choices	3 choices	2 choices	1 choice

Using the Fundamental Counting Principle, we multiply the choices:

$$6 \cdot 5 \cdot 4 \cdot 3 \cdot 2 \cdot 1 = 720.$$

Thus, there are 720 different ways to deliver the six jokes about books. One of the 720 possible arrangements is

Seinfeld joke—Youngman joke—Carlin joke—Marx joke—Wright joke—Diller joke.

Such an ordered arrangement is called a *permutation* of the six jokes.

A **permutation** is an ordered arrangement of items that occurs when

- No item is used more than once. (Each joke is told exactly once.)
- The order of arrangement makes a difference. (The order in which these jokes are told makes a difference in terms of how they are received.)

EXAMPLE 1 Counting Permutations

How many ways can the six jokes about books be delivered if George Carlin's joke is delivered first and Jerry Seinfeld's joke is told last?

Solution The conditions of Carlin's joke first and Seinfeld's joke last can be shown as follows:

First Joke Delivered	Second Joke Delivered	Third Joke Delivered	Fourth Joke Delivered	Fifth Joke Delivered	Sixth Joke Delivered
1 choice: Carlin					1 choice: Seinfeld

Now let's fill in the number of choices for positions two through five. You can choose any one of the four remaining jokes for the second delivery. Once you've chosen this joke, you'll have three jokes to choose from for the third delivery. This leaves only two jokes to choose from for the fourth delivery. Once this choice is made, there is just one joke left to choose for the fifth delivery.

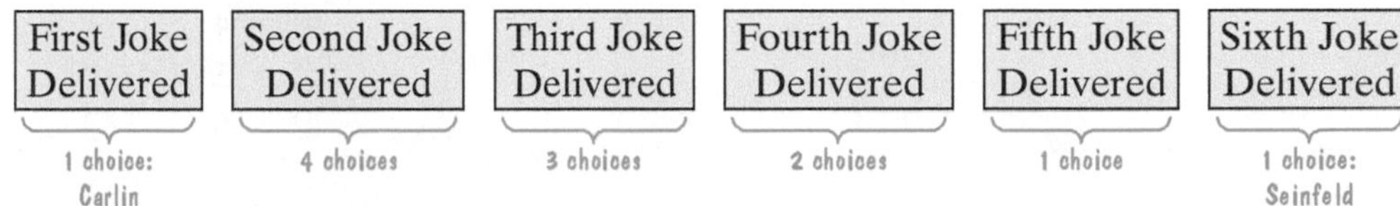

We use the Fundamental Counting Principle to find the number of ways the six jokes can be delivered. Multiply the choices:

$$1 \cdot 4 \cdot 3 \cdot 2 \cdot 1 \cdot 1 = 24.$$

Thus, there are 24 different ways the jokes can be delivered if Carlin's joke is told first and Seinfeld's joke is told last.

CHECK POINT 1 How many ways can the six jokes about books be delivered if a man's joke is told first?

EXAMPLE 2 Counting Permutations

You need to arrange seven of your favorite books along a small shelf. How many different ways can you arrange the books, assuming that the order of the books makes a difference to you?

Solution You may choose any of the seven books for the first position on the shelf. This leaves six choices for second position. After the first two positions are filled, there are five books to choose from for third position, four choices left for the fourth position, three choices left for the fifth position, then two choices for the sixth position, and only one choice for the last position. This situation can be shown as follows:

First Shelf Position	Second Shelf Position	Third Shelf Position	Fourth Shelf Position	Fifth Shelf Position	Sixth Shelf Position	Seventh Shelf Position
7 choices	6 choices	5 choices	4 choices	3 choices	2 choices	1 choice

We use the Fundamental Counting Principle to find the number of ways you can arrange the seven books along the shelf. Multiply the choices:

$$7 \cdot 6 \cdot 5 \cdot 4 \cdot 3 \cdot 2 \cdot 1 = 5040.$$

Thus, you can arrange the books in 5040 ways. There are 5040 different possible permutations.

CHECK POINT 2 In how many ways can you arrange five books along a shelf, assuming that the order of the books makes a difference?

BLITZER BONUS

HOW TO PASS THE TIME FOR $2\frac{1}{2}$ MILLION YEARS

If you were to arrange 15 different books on a shelf and it took you one minute for each permutation, the entire task would take 2,487,965 years.

Source: Isaac Asimov's Book of Facts

2 Evaluate factorial expressions.

FACTORIALS: 0 THROUGH 20

0!	1
1!	1
2!	2
3!	6
4!	24
5!	120
6!	720
7!	5040
8!	40,320
9!	362,880
10!	3,628,800
11!	39,916,800
12!	479,001,600
13!	6,227,020,800
14!	87,178,291,200
15!	1,307,674,368,000
16!	20,922,789,888,000
17!	355,687,428,096,000
18!	6,402,373,705,728,000
19!	121,645,100,408,832,000
20!	2,432,902,008,176,640,000

Factorial Notation

The product in Example 2,

$$7 \cdot 6 \cdot 5 \cdot 4 \cdot 3 \cdot 2 \cdot 1$$

is given a special name and symbol. It is called 7 **factorial**, and written 7!. Thus,

$$7! = 7 \cdot 6 \cdot 5 \cdot 4 \cdot 3 \cdot 2 \cdot 1.$$

In general, if n is a positive integer, then $n!$ (*n factorial*) is the product of all positive integers from n down through 1. For example,

$$\begin{aligned} 1! &= 1 \\ 2! &= 2 \cdot 1 = 2 \\ 3! &= 3 \cdot 2 \cdot 1 = 6 \\ 4! &= 4 \cdot 3 \cdot 2 \cdot 1 = 24 \\ 5! &= 5 \cdot 4 \cdot 3 \cdot 2 \cdot 1 = 120 \\ 6! &= 6 \cdot 5 \cdot 4 \cdot 3 \cdot 2 \cdot 1 = 720. \end{aligned}$$

FACTORIAL NOTATION

If n is a positive integer, the notation $n!$ (read "n factorial") is the product of all positive integers from n down through 1.

$$n! = n(n-1)(n-2) \cdots (3)(2)(1)$$

0! (zero factorial), by definition, is 1.

$$0! = 1$$

EXAMPLE 3 Using Factorial Notation

Evaluate the following factorial expressions without using the factorial key on your calculator:

a. $\frac{8!}{5!}$ **b.** $\frac{26!}{21!}$ **c.** $\frac{500!}{499!}$.

Solution

a. We can evaluate the numerator and the denominator of $\frac{8!}{5!}$. However, it is easier to use the following simplification:

$$\frac{8!}{5!} = \frac{8 \cdot 7 \cdot 6 \cdot \boxed{5 \cdot 4 \cdot 3 \cdot 2 \cdot 1}}{\boxed{5 \cdot 4 \cdot 3 \cdot 2 \cdot 1}} = \frac{8 \cdot 7 \cdot 6 \cdot \boxed{5!}}{\boxed{5!}} = \frac{8 \cdot 7 \cdot 6 \cdot \cancel{5!}}{\cancel{5!}} = 8 \cdot 7 \cdot 6 = 336.$$

b. Rather than write out 26!, the numerator of $\frac{26!}{21!}$, as the product of all integers from 26 down to 1, we can express 26! as

$$26! = 26 \cdot 25 \cdot 24 \cdot 23 \cdot 22 \cdot 21!.$$

In this way, we can cancel 21! in the numerator and the denominator of the given expression.

$$\frac{26!}{21!} = \frac{26 \cdot 25 \cdot 24 \cdot 23 \cdot 22 \cdot 21!}{21!} = \frac{26 \cdot 25 \cdot 24 \cdot 23 \cdot 22 \cdot \cancel{21!}}{\cancel{21!}}$$
$$= 26 \cdot 25 \cdot 24 \cdot 23 \cdot 22 = 7{,}893{,}600$$

c. In order to cancel identical factorials in the numerator and the denominator of $\frac{500!}{499!}$, we can express 500! as $500 \cdot 499!$.

$$\frac{500!}{499!} = \frac{500 \cdot 499!}{499!} = \frac{500 \cdot \cancel{499!}}{\cancel{499!}} = 500$$

CHECK POINT 3 Evaluate without using a calculator's factorial key:

a. $\frac{9!}{6!}$ **b.** $\frac{16!}{11!}$ **c.** $\frac{100!}{99!}$.

TECHNOLOGY

Most calculators have a key or menu item for calculating factorials. Here are the keystrokes for finding 9!:

Many Scientific Calculators:

9 [x!] [=]

Many Graphing Calculators:

9 [!] [ENTER]

On TI graphing calculators, this is selected using the MATH PRB menu.

Because $n!$ becomes quite large as n increases, your calculator will display these larger values in scientific notation.

3 Use the permutations formula.

A Formula for Permutations

You are the coach of a little league baseball team. There are 13 players on the team (and lots of parents hovering in the background, dreaming of stardom for their little "Derek Jeter"). You need to choose a batting order having 9 players. The order makes a difference, because, for instance, if bases are loaded and "Little Derek" is fourth or fifth at bat, his possible home run will drive in three additional runs. How many batting orders can you form?

You can choose any of 13 players for the first person at bat. Then you will have 12 players from which to choose the second batter, then 11 from which to choose the third batter, and so on. The situation can be shown as follows:

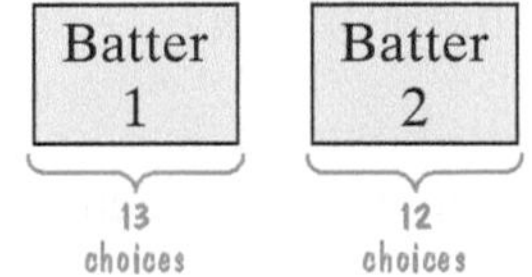
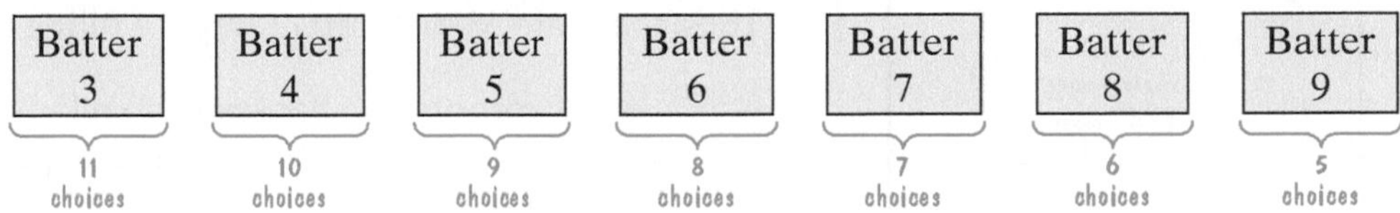

Batter 1	Batter 2	Batter 3	Batter 4	Batter 5	Batter 6	Batter 7	Batter 8	Batter 9
13 choices	12 choices	11 choices	10 choices	9 choices	8 choices	7 choices	6 choices	5 choices

The total number of batting orders is

$$13 \cdot 12 \cdot 11 \cdot 10 \cdot 9 \cdot 8 \cdot 7 \cdot 6 \cdot 5 = 259{,}459{,}200.$$

Nearly 260 million batting orders are possible for your 13-player little league team. Each batting order is a permutation because the order of the batters makes a difference. The number of permutations of 13 players taken 9 at a time is 259,459,200.

We can obtain a formula for finding the number of permutations by rewriting our computation:

$$13 \cdot 12 \cdot 11 \cdot 10 \cdot 9 \cdot 8 \cdot 7 \cdot 6 \cdot 5$$

$$= \frac{13 \cdot 12 \cdot 11 \cdot 10 \cdot 9 \cdot 8 \cdot 7 \cdot 6 \cdot 5 \cdot \boxed{4 \cdot 3 \cdot 2 \cdot 1}}{\boxed{4 \cdot 3 \cdot 2 \cdot 1}} = \frac{13!}{4!} = \frac{13!}{(13-9)!}.$$

Thus, the number of permutations of 13 things taken 9 at a time is $\frac{13!}{(13-9)!}$. The special notation ${}_{13}P_9$ is used to replace the phrase "the number of permutations of 13 things taken 9 at a time." Using this new notation, we can write

$${}_{13}P_9 = \frac{13!}{(13-9)!}.$$

The numerator of this expression is the factorial of the number of items, 13 team members: 13!. The denominator is also a factorial. It is the factorial of the difference between the number of items, 13, and the number of items in each permutation, 9 batters: $(13 - 9)!$.

The notation ${}_nP_r$ means the **number of permutations of n things taken r at a time**. We can generalize from the situation in which 9 batters were taken from 13 players. By generalizing, we obtain the following formula for the number of permutations if r items are taken from n items:

STUDY TIP

Because all permutation problems are also Fundamental Counting problems, they can be solved using the formula for ${}_nP_r$ or using the Fundamental Counting Principle.

PERMUTATIONS OF n THINGS TAKEN r AT A TIME

The number of possible permutations if r items are taken from n items is

$${}_nP_r = \frac{n!}{(n-r)!}.$$

EXAMPLE 4 Using the Formula for Permutations

You and 19 of your friends have decided to form an Internet marketing consulting firm. The group needs to choose three officers—a CEO, an operating manager, and a treasurer. In how many ways can those offices be filled?

TECHNOLOGY

Graphing calculators have a menu item for calculating permutations, usually labeled $\boxed{{}_nP_r}$. For example, to find ${}_{20}P_3$, the keystrokes are

20 $\boxed{{}_nP_r}$ 3 $\boxed{\text{ENTER}}$.

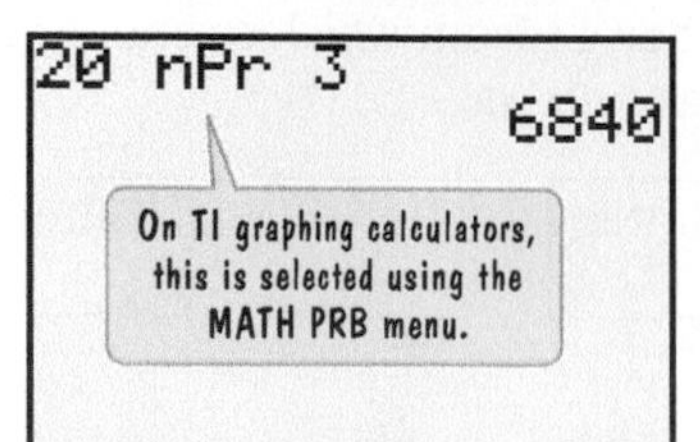

If you are using a scientific calculator, check your manual for the location of the menu item for calculating permutations and the required keystrokes.

Solution Your group is choosing $r = 3$ officers from a group of $n = 20$ people (you and 19 friends). The order in which the officers are chosen matters because the CEO, the operating manager, and the treasurer each have different responsibilities. Thus, we are looking for the number of permutations of 20 things taken 3 at a time. We use the formula

$${}_nP_r = \frac{n!}{(n-r)!}$$

with $n = 20$ and $r = 3$.

$${}_{20}P_3 = \frac{20!}{(20-3)!} = \frac{20!}{17!} = \frac{20 \cdot 19 \cdot 18 \cdot 17!}{17!} = \frac{20 \cdot 19 \cdot 18 \cdot \cancel{17!}}{\cancel{17!}} = 20 \cdot 19 \cdot 18 = 6840$$

Thus, there are 6840 different ways of filling the three offices.

CHECK POINT 4 A corporation has seven members on its board of directors. In how many different ways can it elect a president, vice-president, secretary, and treasurer?

EXAMPLE 5 Using the Formula for Permutations

You are working for The Sitcom Television Network. Your assignment is to help set up the television schedule for Monday evenings between 7 and 10 P.M. You need to schedule a show in each of six 30-minute time blocks, beginning with 7 to 7:30 and ending with 9:30 to 10:00. You can select from among the following situation comedies: *Home Improvement, Seinfeld, Mad About You, Cheers, Friends, Frasier, All in the Family, I Love Lucy, M* A* S* H, The Larry Sanders Show, The Jeffersons, Married with Children,* and *Happy Days*. How many different programming schedules can be arranged?

Solution You are choosing $r = 6$ situation comedies from a collection of $n = 13$ classic sitcoms. The order in which the programs are aired matters. Family-oriented comedies have higher ratings when aired in earlier time blocks, such as 7 to 7:30. By contrast, comedies with adult themes do better in later time blocks. In short, we are looking for the number of permutations of 13 things taken 6 at a time. We use the formula

$${}_nP_r = \frac{n!}{(n-r)!}$$

with $n = 13$ and $r = 6$.

$${}_{13}P_6 = \frac{13!}{(13-6)!} = \frac{13!}{7!} = \frac{13 \cdot 12 \cdot 11 \cdot 10 \cdot 9 \cdot 8 \cdot \cancel{7!}}{\cancel{7!}} = 13 \cdot 12 \cdot 11 \cdot 10 \cdot 9 \cdot 8 = 1{,}235{,}520$$

There are 1,235,520 different programming schedules that can be arranged.

CHECK POINT 5 How many different programming schedules can be arranged by choosing 5 situation comedies from a collection of 9 classic sitcoms?

Find the number of permutations of duplicate items.

Permutations of Duplicate Items

The number of permutations of the letters in the word SET is 3!, or 6. The six permutations are

SET, STE, EST, ETS, TES, TSE.

Are there also six permutations of the letters in the name ANA? The answer is no. Unlike SET, with three distinct letters, ANA contains three letters, of which the two As are duplicates. If we rearrange the letters just as we did with SET, we obtain

ANA, AAN, NAA, NAA, ANA, AAN.

Without the use of color to distinguish between the two As, there are only three distinct permutations: ANA, AAN, NAA.

There is a formula for finding the number of distinct permutations when duplicate items exist:

PERMUTATIONS OF DUPLICATE ITEMS

The number of permutations of n items, where p items are identical, q items are identical, r items are identical, and so on, is given by

$$\frac{n!}{p!\,q!\,r!\ldots}.$$

For example, ANA contains three letters ($n = 3$), where two of the letters are identical ($p = 2$). The number of distinct permutations is

$$\frac{n!}{p!} = \frac{3!}{2!} = \frac{3 \cdot \cancel{2!}}{\cancel{2!}} = 3.$$

We saw that the three distinct permutations are ANA, AAN, and NAA.

TECHNOLOGY

Parentheses are necessary to enclose the factorials in the denominator when using a calculator to find

$$\frac{11!}{4!\,4!\,2!}.$$

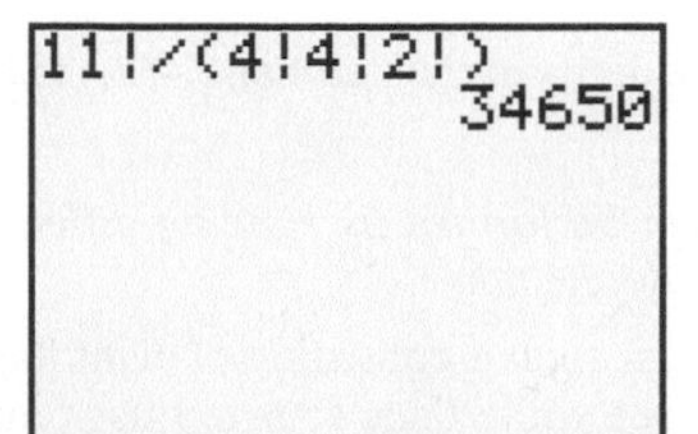

EXAMPLE 6 Using the Formula for Permutations of Duplicate Items

In how many distinct ways can the letters of the word MISSISSIPPI be arranged?

Solution The word contains 11 letters ($n = 11$), where four Is are identical ($p = 4$), four Ss are identical ($q = 4$), and 2 Ps are identical ($r = 2$). The number of distinct permutations is

$$\frac{n!}{p!\,q!\,r!} = \frac{11!}{4!\,4!\,2!} = \frac{11 \cdot 10 \cdot 9 \cdot 8 \cdot 7 \cdot 6 \cdot 5 \cdot \cancel{4!}}{\cancel{4!}\,4 \cdot 3 \cdot 2 \cdot 1 \cdot 2 \cdot 1} = 34{,}650$$

There are 34,650 distinct ways the letters in the word MISSISSIPPI can be arranged.

CHECK POINT 6 In how many ways can the letters of the word OSMOSIS be arranged?

Exercise Set 2

Practice and Application Exercises

Use the Fundamental Counting Principle to solve Exercises 1–12.

1. Six performers are to present their comedy acts on a weekend evening at a comedy club. How many different ways are there to schedule their appearances?
2. Five singers are to perform on a weekend evening at a night club. How many different ways are there to schedule their appearances?
3. In the *Cambridge Encyclopedia of Language* (Cambridge University Press, 1987), author David Crystal presents five sentences that make a reasonable paragraph regardless of their order. The sentences are as follows:
   - Mark had told him about the foxes.
   - John looked out of the window.
   - Could it be a fox?
   - However, nobody had seen one for months.
   - He thought he saw a shape in the bushes.

   In how many different orders can the five sentences be arranged?
4. In how many different ways can a police department arrange eight suspects in a police lineup if each lineup contains all eight people?
5. As in Exercise 1, six performers are to present their comedy acts on a weekend evening at a comedy club. One of the performers insists on being the last stand-up comic of the evening. If this performer's request is granted, how many different ways are there to schedule the appearances?
6. As in Exercise 2, five singers are to perform at a night club. One of the singers insists on being the last performer of the evening. If this singer's request is granted, how many different ways are there to schedule the appearances?
7. You need to arrange nine of your favorite books along a small shelf. How many different ways can you arrange the books, assuming that the order of the books makes a difference to you?
8. You need to arrange ten of your favorite photographs on the mantle above a fireplace. How many ways can you arrange the photographs, assuming that the order of the pictures makes a difference to you?

In Exercises 9–10, use the five sentences that are given in Exercise 3.

9. How many different five-sentence paragraphs can be formed if the paragraph begins with "He thought he saw a shape in the bushes" and ends with "John looked out of the window"?

10. How many different five-sentence paragraphs can be formed if the paragraph begins with "He thought he saw a shape in the bushes" followed by "Mark had told him about the foxes"?

11. A television programmer is arranging the order that five movies will be seen between the hours of 6 P.M. and 4 A.M. Two of the movies have a G rating, and they are to be shown in the first two time blocks. One of the movies is rated NC-17, and it is to be shown in the last of the time blocks, from 2 A.M. until 4 A.M. Given these restrictions, in how many ways can the five movies be arranged during the indicated time blocks?

12. A camp counselor and six campers are to be seated along a picnic bench. In how many ways can this be done if the counselor must be seated in the middle and a camper who has a tendency to engage in food fights must sit to the counselor's immediate left?

In Exercises 13–32, evaluate each factorial expression.

13. $\frac{9!}{6!}$ **14.** $\frac{12!}{10!}$ **15.** $\frac{29!}{25!}$

16. $\frac{31!}{28!}$ **17.** $\frac{19!}{11!}$ **18.** $\frac{17!}{9!}$

19. $\frac{600!}{599!}$ **20.** $\frac{700!}{699!}$ **21.** $\frac{104!}{102!}$

22. $\frac{106!}{104!}$ **23.** $7! - 3!$ **24.** $6! - 3!$

25. $(7 - 3)!$ **26.** $(6 - 3)!$ **27.** $\left(\frac{12}{4}\right)!$

28. $\left(\frac{45}{9}\right)!$ **29.** $\frac{7!}{(7-2)!}$ **30.** $\frac{8!}{(8-5)!}$

31. $\frac{13!}{(13-3)!}$ **32.** $\frac{17!}{(17-3)!}$

In Exercises 33–40, use the formula for ${}_nP_r$ to evaluate each expression.

33. ${}_9P_4$ **34.** ${}_7P_3$ **35.** ${}_8P_5$

36. ${}_{10}P_4$ **37.** ${}_6P_6$ **38.** ${}_9P_9$

39. ${}_8P_0$ **40.** ${}_6P_0$

Use an appropriate permutations formula to solve Exercises 41–56.

41. A club with ten members is to choose three officers—president, vice-president, and secretary-treasurer. If each office is to be held by one person and no person can hold more than one office, in how many ways can those offices be filled?

42. A corporation has seven members on its board of directors. In how many different ways can it elect a president, vice-president, secretary, and treasurer?

43. For a segment of a radio show, a disc jockey can play 7 records. If there are 13 records to select from, in how many ways can the program for this segment be arranged?

44. Suppose you are asked to list, in order of preference, the three best movies you have seen this year. If you saw 20 movies during the year, in how many ways can the three best be chosen and ranked?

45. In a race in which six automobiles are entered and there are no ties, in how many ways can the first three finishers come in?

46. In a production of *West Side Story,* eight actors are considered for the male roles of Tony, Riff, and Bernardo. In how many ways can the director cast the male roles?

47. Nine bands have volunteered to perform at a benefit concert, but there is only enough time for five of the bands to play. How many lineups are possible?

48. How many arrangements can be made using four of the letters of the word COMBINE if no letter is to be used more than once?

49. In how many distinct ways can the letters of the word DALLAS be arranged?

50. In how many distinct ways can the letters of the word SCIENCE be arranged?

51. How many distinct permutations can be formed using the letters of the word TALLAHASSEE?

52. How many distinct permutations can be formed using the letters of the word TENNESSEE?

53. In how many ways can the digits in the number 5,446,666 be arranged?

54. In how many ways can the digits in the number 5,432,435 be arranged?

In Exercises 55–56, a signal can be formed by running different colored flags up a pole, one above the other.

55. Find the number of different signals consisting of eight flags that can be made using three white flags, four red flags, and one blue flag.

56. Find the number of different signals consisting of nine flags that can be made using three white flags, five red flags, and one blue flag.

Writing in Mathematics

57. What is a permutation?

58. Explain how to find $n!$, where n is a positive integer.

59. Explain the best way to evaluate $\frac{900!}{899!}$ without a calculator.

60. Describe what ${}_nP_r$ represents.

61. Write a word problem that can be solved by evaluating 5!.

62. Write a word problem that can be solved by evaluating ${}_7P_3$.

63. If 24 permutations can be formed using the letters in the word BAKE, why can't 24 permutations also be formed using the letters in the word BABE? How is the number of permutations in BABE determined?

Critical Thinking Exercises

Make Sense? *In Exercises 64–67, determine whether each statement makes sense or does not make sense, and explain your reasoning.*

64. I used the formula for ${}_nP_r$ to determine the number of ways the manager of a baseball team can form a 9-player batting order from a team of 25 players.

65. I used the Fundamental Counting Principle to determine the number of permutations of the letters of the word ENGLISH.

66. I used the formula for ${}_nP_r$ to determine the number of ways people can select their 9 favorite baseball players from a team of 25 players.
67. I used the Fundamental Counting Principle to determine the number of permutations of the letters of the word SUCCESS.
68. Ten people board an airplane that has 12 aisle seats. In how many ways can they be seated if they all select aisle seats?
69. Six horses are entered in a race. If two horses are tied for first place and there are no ties among the other four horses, in how many ways can the six horses cross the finish line?
70. Performing at a concert are eight rock bands and eight jazz groups. How many ways can the program be arranged if the first, third, and eighth performers are jazz groups?
71. Five men and five women line up at a checkout counter in a store. In how many ways can they line up if the first person in line is a woman, and the people in line alternate woman, man, woman, man, and so on?
72. How many four-digit odd numbers less than 6000 can be formed using the digits 2, 4, 6, 7, 8, and 9?
73. Express ${}_nP_{n-2}$ without using factorials.

OBJECTIVES

1 Distinguish between permutation and combination problems.

2 Solve problems involving combinations using the combinations formula.

3 Combinations

Discussing the tragic death of actor Heath Ledger at age 28, *USA Today* (Jan. 30, 2008) cited five people who had achieved cult-figure status after death. Made iconic by death: Marilyn Monroe (actress, 1927–1962), James Dean (actor, 1931–1955), Jim Morrison (musician and lead singer of The Doors, 1943–1971), Janis Joplin (blues/rock singer, 1943–1970), and Jimi Hendrix (guitar virtuoso, 1943–1970).

(**Marilyn Monroe**) Picture Desk, Inc./Kobal Collection; (**James Dean**) Imapress/Globe Photos, Inc.; (**Jim Morrison**) Michael Ochs Archives Ltd./Getty Images Inc.-Los Angeles; (**Janis Joplin**) AP Wide World Photos; (**Jimi Hendrix**) Pictorial Press Ltd./Alamy Images.

Imagine that you ask your friends the following question: "Of these five people, which three would you select to be included in a documentary featuring the best of their work?" You are not asking your friends to rank their three favorite artists in any kind of order—they should merely select the three to be included in the documentary.

One friend answers, "Jim Morrison, Janis Joplin, and Jimi Hendrix." Another responds, "Jimi Hendrix, Janis Joplin, and Jim Morrison." These two people have the same artists in their group of selections, even if they are named in a different order. We are interested *in which artists are named, not the order in which they are named,* for the documentary. Because the items are taken without regard to order, this is not a permutation problem. No ranking of any sort is involved.

Later on, you ask your roommate which three artists she would select for the documentary. She names Marilyn Monroe, James Dean, and Jimi Hendrix. Her selection is different from those of your two other friends because different entertainers are cited.

Mathematicians describe the group of artists given by your roommate as a *combination*. A **combination** of items occurs when

- The items are selected from the same group (the five stars who were made iconic by death).
- No item is used more than once. (You may view Jimi Hendrix as a guitar god, but your three selections cannot be Jimi Hendrix, Jimi Hendrix, and Jimi Hendrix.)
- The order of the items makes no difference. (Morrison, Joplin, Hendrix is the same group in the documentary as Hendrix, Joplin, Morrison.)

1 Distinguish between permutation and combination problems.

Do you see the difference between a permutation and a combination? A permutation is an ordered arrangement of a given group of items. A combination is a group of items taken without regard to their order. **Permutation** problems involve situations in which **order matters**. **Combination** problems involve situations in which the **order** of the items **makes no difference**.

EXAMPLE 1 Distinguishing between Permutations and Combinations

For each of the following problems, determine whether the problem is one involving permutations or combinations. (It is not necessary to solve the problem.)

a. Six students are running for student government president, vice-president, and treasurer. The student with the greatest number of votes becomes the president, the second highest vote-getter becomes vice-president, and the student who gets the third largest number of votes will be treasurer. How many different outcomes are possible for these three positions?

b. Six people are on the board of supervisors for your neighborhood park. A three-person committee is needed to study the possibility of expanding the park. How many different committees could be formed from the six people?

c. Baskin-Robbins offers 31 different flavors of ice cream. One of its items is a bowl consisting of three scoops of ice cream, each a different flavor. How many such bowls are possible?

Solution

a. Students are choosing three student government officers from six candidates. The order in which the officers are chosen makes a difference because each of the offices (president, vice-president, treasurer) is different. Order matters. This is a problem involving permutations.

b. A three-person committee is to be formed from the six-person board of supervisors. The order in which the three people are selected does not matter because they are not filling different roles on the committee. Because order makes no difference, this is a problem involving combinations.

c. A three-scoop bowl of three different flavors is to be formed from Baskin-Robbins's 31 flavors. The order in which the three scoops of ice cream are put into the bowl is irrelevant. A bowl with chocolate, vanilla, and strawberry is exactly the same as a bowl with vanilla, strawberry, and chocolate. Different orderings do not change things, and so this is a problem involving combinations.

For each of the following problems, determine whether the problem is one involving permutations or combinations. (It is not necessary to solve the problem.)

a. How many ways can you select 6 free DVDs from a list of 200 DVDs?

b. In a race in which there are 50 runners and no ties, in how many ways can the first three finishers come in?

2 Solve problems involving combinations using the combinations formula.

A Formula for Combinations

We have seen that the notation ${}_nP_r$ means the number of permutations of n things taken r at a time. Similarly, the notation ${}_nC_r$ **means the number of combinations of** n **things taken** r **at a time.**

We can develop a formula for ${}_nC_r$ by comparing permutations and combinations. Consider the letters A, B, C, and D. The number of permutations of these four letters taken three at a time is

$${}_4P_3 = \frac{4!}{(4-3)!} = \frac{4!}{1!} = \frac{4 \cdot 3 \cdot 2 \cdot 1}{1} = 24.$$

Here are the 24 permutations:

ABC,	ABD,	ACD,	BCD,
ACB,	ADB,	ADC,	BDC,
BAC,	BAD,	CAD,	CBD,
BCA,	BDA,	CDA,	CDB,
CAB,	DAB,	DAC,	DBC,
CBA,	DBA,	DCA,	DCB.
This column contains only one combination, ABC.	This column contains only one combination, ABD.	This column contains only one combination, ACD.	This column contains only one combination, BCD.

Because the order of items makes no difference in determining combinations, each column of six permutations represents one combination. There is a total of four combinations:

ABC, ABD, ACD, BCD.

Thus, ${}_4C_3 = 4$: The number of combinations of 4 things taken 3 at a time is 4. With 24 permutations and only four combinations, there are 6, or 3!, times as many permutations as there are combinations.

In general, there are $r!$ times as many permutations of n things taken r at a time as there are combinations of n things taken r at a time. Thus, we find the number of combinations of n things taken r at a time by dividing the number of permutations of n things taken r at a time by $r!$.

$${}_nC_r = \frac{{}_nP_r}{r!} = \frac{\frac{n!}{(n-r)!}}{r!} = \frac{n!}{(n-r)!\,r!}$$

STUDY TIP

The number of combinations if r items are taken from n items cannot be found using the Fundamental Counting Principle and requires the use of the formula shown in the green box.

COMBINATIONS OF n THINGS TAKEN r AT A TIME

The number of possible combinations if r items are taken from n items is

$${}_nC_r = \frac{n!}{(n-r)!\,r!}.$$

TECHNOLOGY

Graphing calculators have a menu item for calculating combinations, usually labeled ${}_nC_r$. (On TI graphing calculators, ${}_nC_r$ is selected using the MATH PRB menu.) For example, to find ${}_8C_3$, the keystrokes on most graphing calculators are

8 [${}_nC_r$] 3 [ENTER].

If you are using a scientific calculator, check your manual to see whether there is a menu item for calculating combinations.

If you use your calculator's factorial key to find $\frac{8!}{5!3!}$, be sure to enclose the factorials in the denominator with parentheses

8 [!] [÷] [(] 5 [!] [×] 3 [!] [)]

pressing [=] or [ENTER] to obtain the answer.

EXAMPLE 2 Using the Formula for Combinations

A three-person committee is needed to study ways of improving public transportation. How many committees could be formed from the eight people on the board of supervisors?

Solution The order in which the three people are selected does not matter. This is a problem of selecting $r = 3$ people from a group of $n = 8$ people. We are looking for the number of combinations of eight things taken three at a time. We use the formula

$${}_nC_r = \frac{n!}{(n-r)!\,r!}$$

with $n = 8$ and $r = 3$.

$${}_8C_3 = \frac{8!}{(8-3)!\,3!} = \frac{8!}{5!\,3!} = \frac{8 \cdot 7 \cdot 6 \cdot 5!}{5! \cdot 3 \cdot 2 \cdot 1} = \frac{8 \cdot 7 \cdot 6 \cdot \cancel{5!}}{\cancel{5!} \cdot 3 \cdot 2 \cdot 1} = 56$$

Thus, 56 committees of three people each can be formed from the eight people on the board of supervisors.

You volunteer to pet-sit for your friend who has seven different animals. How many different pet combinations are possible if you take three of the seven pets?

EXAMPLE 3 Using the Formula for Combinations

In poker, a person is dealt 5 cards from a standard 52-card deck. The order in which the 5 cards are received does not matter. How many different 5-card poker hands are possible?

Solution Because the order in which the 5 cards are received does not matter, this is a problem involving combinations. We are looking for the number of combinations of $n = 52$ cards drawn $r = 5$ at a time. We use the formula

$$_nC_r = \frac{n!}{(n-r)!\,r!}$$

with $n = 52$ and $r = 5$.

$$_{52}C_5 = \frac{52!}{(52-5)!\,5!} = \frac{52!}{47!\,5!} = \frac{52\cdot 51\cdot 50\cdot 49\cdot 48\cdot \cancel{47!}}{\cancel{47!}\cdot 5\cdot 4\cdot 3\cdot 2\cdot 1} = 2{,}598{,}960$$

Thus, there are 2,598,960 different 5-card poker hands possible. It surprises many people that more than 2.5 million 5-card hands can be dealt from a mere 52 cards.

FIGURE 3 A royal flush

If you are a card player, it does not get any better than to be dealt the 5-card poker hand shown in **Figure 3**. This hand is called a *royal flush*. It consists of an ace, king, queen, jack, and 10, all of the same suit: all hearts, all diamonds, all clubs, or all spades. The probability of being dealt a royal flush involves calculating the number of ways of being dealt such a hand: just 4 of all 2,598,960 possible hands. In the next section, we move from counting possibilities to computing probabilities.

How many different 4-card hands can be dealt from a deck that has 16 different cards?

EXAMPLE 4 Using the Formula for Combinations and the Fundamental Counting Principle

In December 2009, the U.S. Senate consisted of 60 Democrats and 40 Republicans. How many distinct five-person committees can be formed if each committee must have 3 Democrats and 2 Republicans?

Solution The order in which the members are selected does not matter. Thus, this is a problem involving combinations.

We begin with the number of ways of selecting 3 Democrats out of 60 Democrats without regard to order. We are looking for the number of combinations of $n = 60$ people taken $r = 3$ people at a time. We use the formula

$$_nC_r = \frac{n!}{(n-r)!\,r!}$$

with $n = 60$ and $r = 3$.

We are picking 3 Democrats out of 60 Democrats.

$$_{60}C_3 = \frac{60!}{(60-3)!\,3!} = \frac{60!}{57!\,3!} = \frac{60\cdot 59\cdot 58\cdot \cancel{57!}}{\cancel{57!}\,3\cdot 2\cdot 1} = \frac{60\cdot 59\cdot 58}{3\cdot 2\cdot 1} = 34{,}220$$

There are 34,220 ways to choose three Democrats for a committee.

Next, we find the number of ways of selecting 2 Republicans out of 40 Republicans without regard to order. We are looking for the number of combinations of $n = 40$ people taken $r = 2$ people at a time. Once again, we use the formula

$$_nC_r = \frac{n!}{(n - r)!\,r!}.$$

This time, $n = 40$ and $r = 2$.

We are picking 2 Republicans out of 40 Republicans.

$$_{40}C_2 = \frac{40!}{(40-2)!\,2!} = \frac{40!}{38!\,2!} = \frac{40 \cdot 39 \cdot \cancel{38!}}{\cancel{38!}\,2 \cdot 1} = \frac{40 \cdot 39}{2 \cdot 1} = 780$$

There are 780 ways to choose two Republicans for a committee.

We use the Fundamental Counting Principle to find the number of committees that can be formed:

$$_{60}C_3 \cdot {}_{40}C_2 = 34{,}220 \cdot 780 = 26{,}691{,}600.$$

Thus, 26,691,600 distinct committees can be formed.

CHECK POINT 4 A zoo has six male bears and seven female bears. Two male bears and three female bears will be selected for an animal exchange program with another zoo. How many five-bear collections are possible?

Exercise Set 3

Practice Exercises

In Exercises 1–4, does the problem involve permutations or combinations? Explain your answer. (It is not necessary to solve the problem.)

1. A medical researcher needs 6 people to test the effectiveness of an experimental drug. If 13 people have volunteered for the test, in how many ways can 6 people be selected?
2. Fifty people purchase raffle tickets. Three winning tickets are selected at random. If first prize is \$1000, second prize is \$500, and third prize is \$100, in how many different ways can the prizes be awarded?
3. How many different four-letter passwords can be formed from the letters A, B, C, D, E, F, and G if no repetition of letters is allowed?
4. Fifty people purchase raffle tickets. Three winning tickets are selected at random. If each prize is \$500, in how many different ways can the prizes be awarded?

In Exercises 5–20, use the formula for $_nC_r$ to evaluate each expression.

5. $_6C_5$
6. $_8C_7$
7. $_9C_5$
8. $_{10}C_6$
9. $_{11}C_4$
10. $_{12}C_5$
11. $_8C_1$
12. $_7C_1$
13. $_7C_7$
14. $_4C_4$
15. $_{30}C_3$
16. $_{25}C_4$
17. $_5C_0$
18. $_6C_0$
19. $\dfrac{_7C_3}{_5C_4}$
20. $\dfrac{_{10}C_3}{_6C_4}$

Practice Plus

In Exercises 21–28, evaluate each expression.

21. $\dfrac{_7P_3}{3!} - {}_7C_3$
22. $\dfrac{_{20}P_2}{2!} - {}_{20}C_2$
23. $1 - \dfrac{_3P_2}{_4P_3}$
24. $1 - \dfrac{_5P_3}{_{10}P_4}$
25. $\dfrac{_7C_3}{_5C_4} - \dfrac{98!}{96!}$
26. $\dfrac{_{10}C_3}{_6C_4} - \dfrac{46!}{44!}$
27. $\dfrac{_4C_2 \cdot {}_6C_1}{_{18}C_3}$
28. $\dfrac{_5C_1 \cdot {}_7C_2}{_{12}C_3}$

Application Exercises

Use the formula for $_nC_r$ to solve Exercises 29–40.

29. An election ballot asks voters to select three city commissioners from a group of six candidates. In how many ways can this be done?
30. A four-person committee is to be elected from an organization's membership of 11 people. How many different committees are possible?
31. Of 12 possible books, you plan to take 4 with you on vacation. How many different collections of 4 books can you take?
32. There are 14 standbys who hope to get seats on a flight, but only 6 seats are available on the plane. How many different ways can the 6 people be selected?
33. You volunteer to help drive children at a charity event to the zoo, but you can fit only 8 of the 17 children present in your van. How many different groups of 8 children can you drive?
34. Of the 100 people in the U.S. Senate, 18 serve on the Foreign Relations Committee. How many ways are there to select Senate members for this committee (assuming party affiliation is not a factor in the selection)?
35. To win at LOTTO in the state of Florida, one must correctly select 6 numbers from a collection of 53 numbers (1 through 53). The order in which the selection is made does not matter. How many different selections are possible?

36. To win in the New York State lottery, one must correctly select 6 numbers from 59 numbers. The order in which the selection is made does not matter. How many different selections are possible?
37. In how many ways can a committee of four men and five women be formed from a group of seven men and seven women?
38. How many different committees can be formed from 5 professors and 15 students if each committee is made up of 2 professors and 10 students?
39. The U.S. Senate of the 109th Congress consisted of 55 Republicans, 44 Democrats, and 1 Independent. How many committees can be formed if each committee must have 4 Republicans and 3 Democrats?
40. A mathematics exam consists of 10 multiple-choice questions and 5 open-ended problems in which all work must be shown. If an examinee must answer 8 of the multiple-choice questions and 3 of the open-ended problems, in how many ways can the questions and problems be chosen?

In Exercises 41–60, solve by the method of your choice.

41. In a race in which six automobiles are entered and there are no ties, in how many ways can the first four finishers come in?
42. A book club offers a choice of 8 books from a list of 40. In how many ways can a member make a selection?
43. A medical researcher needs 6 people to test the effectiveness of an experimental drug. If 13 people have volunteered for the test, in how many ways can 6 people be selected?
44. Fifty people purchase raffle tickets. Three winning tickets are selected at random. If first prize is \$1000, second prize is \$500, and third prize is \$100, in how many different ways can the prizes be awarded?
45. From a club of 20 people, in how many ways can a group of three members be selected to attend a conference?
46. Fifty people purchase raffle tickets. Three winning tickets are selected at random. If each prize is \$500, in how many different ways can the prizes be awarded?
47. How many different four-letter passwords can be formed from the letters A, B, C, D, E, F, and G if no repetition of letters is allowed?
48. Nine comedy acts will perform over two evenings. Five of the acts will perform on the first evening. How many ways can the schedule for the first evening be made?
49. Using 15 flavors of ice cream, how many cones with three different flavors can you create if it is important to you which flavor goes on the top, middle, and bottom?
50. Baskin-Robbins offers 31 different flavors of ice cream. One of its items is a bowl consisting of three scoops of ice cream, each a different flavor. How many such bowls are possible?
51. A restaurant lunch special allows the customer to choose two vegetables from this list: okra, corn, peas, carrots, and squash. How many outcomes are possible if the customer chooses two different vegetables?
52. There are six employees in the stock room at an appliance retail store. The manager will choose three of them to deliver a refrigerator. How many three-person groups are possible?
53. You have three dress shirts, two ties, and two jackets. You need to select a dress shirt, a tie, and a jacket for work today. How many outcomes are possible?
54. You have four flannel shirts. You are going to choose two of them to take on a camping trip. How many outcomes are possible?
55. A chef has five brands of hot sauce. Three of the brands will be chosen to mix into gumbo. How many outcomes are possible?
56. In the Mathematics Department, there are four female professors and six male professors. Three female professors will be chosen to serve as mentors for a special program designed to encourage female students to pursue careers in mathematics. In how many ways can the professors be chosen?
57. There are four Democrats and five Republicans on the county commission. From among their group they will choose a committee of two Democrats and two Republicans to examine a proposal to purchase land for a new county park. How many four-person groups are possible?
58. An office employs six customer service representatives. Each day, two of them are randomly selected and their customer interactions are monitored for the purposes of improving customer relations. In how many ways can the representatives be chosen?
59. A group of campers is going to occupy five campsites at a campground. There are 12 campsites from which to choose. In how many ways can the campsites be chosen?
60. Your mom and dad have driven to work in separate cars. When they arrive, there are seven empty spaces in the parking lot. They each choose a parking space. How many outcomes are possible?

(*Source* for Exercises 51–60: James Wooland, *CLAST Manual for Thinking Mathematically*)

Thousands of jokes have been told about marriage and divorce. Exercises 61–68 are based on the following observations:

- *"By all means, marry; if you get a good wife, you'll be happy. If you get a bad one, you'll become a philosopher."—Socrates*
- *"My wife and I were happy for 20 years. Then we met."—Rodney Dangerfield*
- *"Whatever you may look like, marry a man your own age. As your beauty fades, so will his eyesight."—Phyllis Diller*
- *"Why do Jewish divorces cost so much? Because they're worth it."—Henny Youngman*
- *"I think men who have a pierced ear are better prepared for marriage. They've experienced pain and bought jewelry."—Rita Rudner*
- *"For a while we pondered whether to take a vacation or get a divorce. We decided that a trip to Bermuda is over in two weeks, but a divorce is something you always have."—Woody Allen*

61. In how many ways can these six jokes be ranked from best to worst?
62. If Socrates's thoughts about marriage are excluded, in how many ways can the remaining five jokes be ranked from best to worst?
63. In how many ways can people select their three favorite jokes from these thoughts about marriage and divorce?
64. In how many ways can people select their two favorite jokes from these thoughts about marriage and divorce?
65. If the order in which these jokes are told makes a difference in terms of how they are received, how many ways can they be delivered if Socrates's comments are scheduled first and Dangerfield's joke is told last?

66. If the order in which these jokes are told makes a difference in terms of how they are received, how many ways can they be delivered if a joke by a woman (Rudner or Diller) is told first?
67. In how many ways can people select their favorite joke told by a woman (Rudner or Diller) and their two favorite jokes told by a man?
68. In how many ways can people select their favorite joke told by a woman (Rudner or Diller) and their three favorite jokes told by a man?

Writing in Mathematics

69. What is a combination?
70. Explain how to distinguish between permutation and combination problems.
71. Write a word problem that can be solved by evaluating ${}_7C_3$.

Critical Thinking Exercises

Make Sense? *In Exercises 72–76, determine whether each statement makes sense or does not make sense, and explain your reasoning.*

72. I used the formula for ${}_nC_r$ to determine the number of possible outcomes when ranking five politicians from most admired to least admired.
73. I used the formula for ${}_nC_r$ to determine how many four-letter passwords with no repeated letters can be formed using a, d, h, n, p, and w.
74. I solved a problem involving the number of possible outcomes when selecting from two groups, which required me to use both the formula for ${}_nC_r$ and the Fundamental Counting Principle.
75. I used the formula for ${}_nC_r$ to determine how many outcomes are possible when choosing four letters from a, d, h, n, p, and w.
76. Write a word problem that can be solved by evaluating to ${}_{10}C_3 \cdot {}_7C_2$.
77. A 6/53 lottery involves choosing 6 of the numbers from 1 through 53 and a 5/36 lottery involves choosing 5 of the numbers from 1 through 36. The order in which the numbers are chosen does not matter. Which lottery is easier to win? Explain your answer.
78. If the number of permutations of n objects taken r at a time is six times the number of combinations of n objects taken r at a time, determine the value of r. Is there enough information to determine the value of n? Why or why not?
79. In a group of 20 people, how long will it take each person to shake hands with each of the other persons in the group, assuming that it takes three seconds for each shake and only 2 people can shake hands at a time? What if the group is increased to 40 people?
80. A sample of 4 telephones is selected from a shipment of 20 phones. There are 5 defective telephones in the shipment. How many of the samples of 4 phones do not include any of the defective ones?

OBJECTIVES

1. Compute theoretical probability.
2. Compute empirical probability.

4 Fundamentals of Probability

TABLE 1 The Hours of Sleep Americans Get on a Typical Night

Hours of Sleep	Number of Americans, in millions
4 or less	12
5	27
6	75
7	90
8	81
9	9
10 or more	6

Total: 300

Source: Discovery Health Media

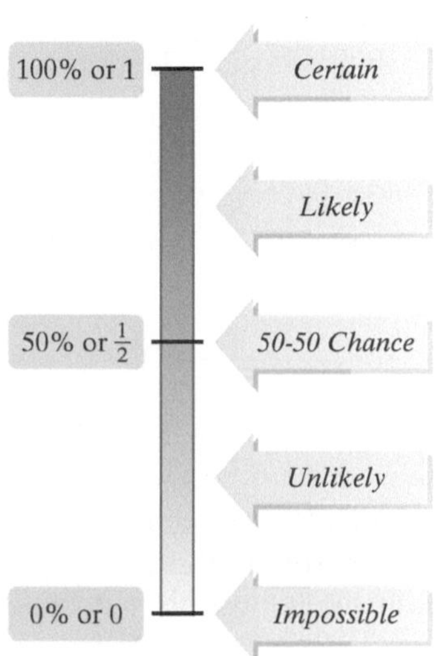

Possible Values for Probabilities

How many hours of sleep do you typically get each night? **Table 1** indicates that 75 million out of 300 million Americans are getting six hours of sleep on a typical night. The *probability* of an American getting six hours of sleep on a typical night is $\frac{75}{300}$. This fraction can be reduced to $\frac{1}{4}$, or expressed as 0.25, or 25%. Thus, 25% of Americans get six hours of sleep each night.

We find a probability by dividing one number by another. Probabilities are assigned to an *event*, such as getting six hours of sleep on a typical night. Events that are certain to occur are assigned probabilities of 1, or 100%. For example, the probability that a given individual will eventually die is 1. Although Woody Allen whined, "I don't want to achieve immortality through my work. I want to achieve it through not dying," death (and taxes) are always certain. By contrast, if an event cannot occur, its probability is 0. Regrettably, the probability that Elvis will return and serenade us with one final reprise of "Don't Be Cruel" (and we hope we're not) is 0.

Probabilities of events are expressed as numbers ranging from 0 to 1, or 0% to 100%. The closer the probability of a given event is to 1, the more likely it is that the event will occur. The closer the probability of a given event is to 0, the less likely it is that the event will occur.

1 Compute theoretical probability.

Theoretical Probability

You toss a coin. Although it is equally likely to land either heads up, denoted by H, or tails up, denoted by T, the actual outcome is uncertain. Any occurrence for which the outcome is uncertain is called an **experiment**. Thus, tossing a coin is an example of an experiment. The set of all possible outcomes of an experiment is the **sample space** of the experiment, denoted by S. The sample space for the coin-tossing experiment is

$$S = \{H, T\}.$$

Lands heads up — Lands tails up

An **event**, denoted by E, is any subset of a sample space. For example, the subset $E = \{T\}$ is the event of landing tails up when a coin is tossed.

Theoretical probability applies to situations like this, in which the sample space only contains equally likely outcomes, all of which are known. To calculate the theoretical probability of an event, we divide the number of outcomes resulting in the event by the total number of outcomes in the sample space.

COMPUTING THEORETICAL PROBABILITY

If an event E has $n(E)$ equally likely outcomes and its sample space S has $n(S)$ equally likely outcomes, the **theoretical probability** of event E, denoted by $P(E)$, is

$$P(E) = \frac{\text{number of outcomes in event } E}{\text{total number of possible outcomes}} = \frac{n(E)}{n(S)}.$$

How can we use this formula to compute the probability of a coin landing tails up? We use the following sets:

$$E = \{T\} \qquad S = \{H, T\}.$$

This is the event of landing tails up. — This is the sample space with all equally likely outcomes.

The probability of a coin landing tails up is

$$P(E) = \frac{\text{number of outcomes that result in tails up}}{\text{total number of possible outcomes}} = \frac{n(E)}{n(S)} = \frac{1}{2}.$$

Theoretical probability applies to many games of chance, including dice rolling, lotteries, card games, and roulette. We begin with rolling a die. **Figure 4** illustrates that when a die is rolled, there are six equally likely possible outcomes. The sample space can be shown as

$$S = \{1, 2, 3, 4, 5, 6\}.$$

FIGURE 4 Outcomes when a die is rolled

EXAMPLE 1 Computing Theoretical Probability

A die is rolled once. Find the probability of rolling

a. a 3. **b.** an even number. **c.** a number less than 5.
d. a number less than 10. **e.** a number greater than 6.

Solution The sample space is $S = \{1, 2, 3, 4, 5, 6\}$ with $n(S) = 6$. We will use 6, the total number of possible outcomes, in the denominator of each probability fraction.

a. The phrase "rolling a 3" describes the event $E = \{3\}$. This event can occur in one way: $n(E) = 1$.

$$P(3) = \frac{\text{number of outcomes that result in 3}}{\text{total number of possible outcomes}} = \frac{n(E)}{n(S)} = \frac{1}{6}$$

The probability of rolling a 3 is $\frac{1}{6}$.

b. The phrase "rolling an even number" describes the event $E = \{2, 4, 6\}$. This event can occur in three ways: $n(E) = 3$.

$$P(\text{even number}) = \frac{\text{number of outcomes that result in an even number}}{\text{total number of possible outcomes}} = \frac{n(E)}{n(S)} = \frac{3}{6} = \frac{1}{2}$$

The probability of rolling an even number is $\frac{1}{2}$.

c. The phrase "rolling a number less than 5" describes the event $E = \{1, 2, 3, 4\}$. This event can occur in four ways: $n(E) = 4$.

$$P(\text{less than } 5) = \frac{\text{number of outcomes that are less than 5}}{\text{total number of possible outcomes}} = \frac{n(E)}{n(S)} = \frac{4}{6} = \frac{2}{3}$$

The probability of rolling a number less than 5 is $\frac{2}{3}$.

d. The phrase "rolling a number less than 10" describes the event $E = \{1, 2, 3, 4, 5, 6\}$. This event can occur in six ways: $n(E) = 6$. Can you see that all of the possible outcomes are less than 10? This event is certain to occur.

$$P(\text{less than } 10) = \frac{\text{number of outcomes that are less than 10}}{\text{total number of possible outcomes}} = \frac{n(E)}{n(S)} = \frac{6}{6} = 1$$

The probability of any certain event is 1.

e. The phrase "rolling a number greater than 6" describes an event that cannot occur, or the empty set. Thus, $E = \varnothing$ and $n(E) = 0$.

$$P(\text{greater than } 6) = \frac{\text{number of outcomes that are greater than 6}}{\text{total number of possible outcomes}} = \frac{n(E)}{n(S)} = \frac{0}{6} = 0$$

The probability of an event that cannot occur is 0.

In Example 1, there are six possible outcomes, each with a probability of $\frac{1}{6}$:

$$P(1) = \frac{1}{6} \quad P(2) = \frac{1}{6} \quad P(3) = \frac{1}{6} \quad P(4) = \frac{1}{6} \quad P(5) = \frac{1}{6} \quad P(6) = \frac{1}{6}.$$

The sum of these probabilities is 1: $\frac{1}{6} + \frac{1}{6} + \frac{1}{6} + \frac{1}{6} + \frac{1}{6} + \frac{1}{6} = 1$. In general, **the sum of the theoretical probabilities of all possible outcomes in the sample space is 1.**

CHECK POINT 1

A die is rolled once. Find the probability of rolling

a. a 2. **b.** a number less than 4.

c. a number greater than 7. **d.** a number less than 7.

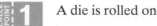

Our next example involves a standard 52-card bridge deck, illustrated in **Figure 5**. The deck has four suits: Hearts and diamonds are red, and clubs and spades are black. Each suit has 13 different face values—A(ace), 2, 3, 4, 5, 6, 7, 8, 9, 10, J(jack), Q(queen), and K(king). Jacks, queens, and kings are called **picture cards** or **face cards**.

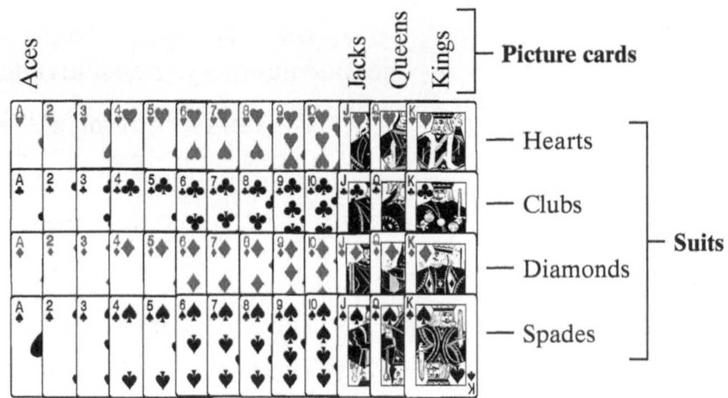

FIGURE 5 A standard 52-card bridge deck

EXAMPLE 2 Probability and a Deck of 52 Cards

You are dealt one card from a standard 52-card deck. Find the probability of being dealt

a. a king. **b.** a heart. **c.** the king of hearts.

Solution Because there are 52 cards in the deck, the total number of possible ways of being dealt a single card is 52. The number of outcomes in the sample space is 52: $n(S) = 52$. We use 52 as the denominator of each probability fraction.

a. Let E be the event of being dealt a king. Because there are four kings in the deck, this event can occur in four ways: $n(E) = 4$.

$$P(\text{king}) = \frac{\text{number of outcomes that result in a king}}{\text{total number of possible outcomes}} = \frac{n(E)}{n(S)} = \frac{4}{52} = \frac{1}{13}$$

The probability of being dealt a king is $\frac{1}{13}$.

b. Let E be the event of being dealt a heart. Because there are 13 hearts in the deck, this event can occur in 13 ways: $n(E) = 13$.

$$P(\text{heart}) = \frac{\text{number of outcomes that result in a heart}}{\text{total number of possible outcomes}} = \frac{n(E)}{n(S)} = \frac{13}{52} = \frac{1}{4}$$

The probability of being dealt a heart is $\frac{1}{4}$.

c. Let E be the event of being dealt the king of hearts. Because there is only one card in the deck that is the king of hearts, this event can occur in just one way: $n(E) = 1$.

$$P(\text{king of hearts}) = \frac{\text{number of outcomes that result in the king of hearts}}{\text{total number of possible outcomes}} = \frac{n(E)}{n(S)} = \frac{1}{52}$$

The probability of being dealt the king of hearts is $\frac{1}{52}$.

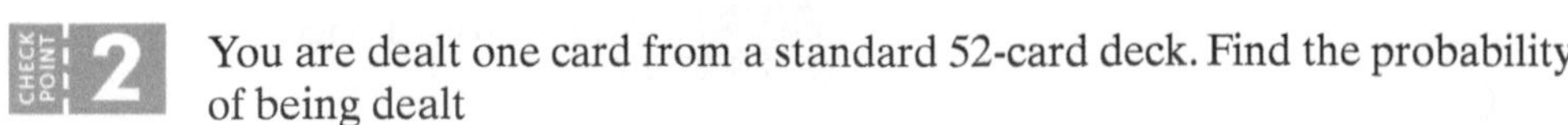

CHECK POINT 2 You are dealt one card from a standard 52-card deck. Find the probability of being dealt

a. an ace. **b.** a red card. **c.** a red king.

BLITZER BONUS

TRY TO BENCH PRESS THIS AT THE GYM

You have a deck of cards for every permutation of the 52 cards. If each deck weighed only as much as a single hydrogen atom, all the decks together would weigh a billion times as much as the sun.

Source: Isaac Asimov's Book of Facts

Probabilities play a valuable role in the science of genetics. Example 3 deals with cystic fibrosis, an inherited lung disease occurring in about 1 out of every 2000 births among Caucasians and in about 1 out of every 250,000 births among non-Caucasians.

EXAMPLE 3 Probabilities in Genetics

Each person carries two genes that are related to the absence or presence of the disease cystic fibrosis. Most Americans have two normal genes for this trait and are unaffected by cystic fibrosis. However, 1 in 25 Americans carries one normal gene and one defective gene. If we use c to represent a defective gene and C a normal gene, such a carrier can be designated as Cc. Thus, CC is a person who neither carries nor has cystic fibrosis, Cc is a carrier who is not actually sick, and cc is a person sick with the disease. **Table 2** shows the four equally likely outcomes for a child's genetic inheritance from two parents who are both carrying one cystic fibrosis gene. One copy of each gene is passed on to the child from the parents.

TABLE 2 Cystic Fibrosis and Genetic Inheritance

		Second Parent	
		C	c
First Parent	C	CC	Cc
	c	cC	cc

Shown in the table are the four possibilities for a child whose parents each carry one cystic fibrosis gene.

If each parent carries one cystic fibrosis gene, what is the probability that their child will have cystic fibrosis?

Solution **Table 2** shows that there are four equally likely outcomes. The sample space is $S = \{CC, Cc, cC, cc\}$ and $n(S) = 4$. The phrase "will have cystic fibrosis" describes only the cc child. Thus, $E = \{cc\}$ and $n(E) = 1$.

$$P(\text{cystic fibrosis}) = \frac{\text{number of outcomes that result in cystic fibrosis}}{\text{total number of possible outcomes}} = \frac{n(E)}{n(S)} = \frac{1}{4}$$

If each parent carries one cystic fibrosis gene, the probability that their child will have cystic fibrosis is $\frac{1}{4}$.

Use **Table 2** in Example 3 to solve this exercise. If each parent carries one cystic fibrosis gene, find the probability that their child will be a carrier of the disease who is not actually sick.

2 Compute empirical probability.

Empirical Probability

Theoretical probability is based on a set of equally likely outcomes and the number of elements in the set. By contrast, *empirical probability* applies to situations in which we observe how frequently an event occurs. We use the following formula to compute the empirical probability of an event:

COMPUTING EMPIRICAL PROBABILITY

The empirical probability of event E is

$$P(E) = \frac{\text{observed number of times } E \text{ occurs}}{\text{total number of observed occurrences}}.$$

EXAMPLE 4 Computing Empirical Probability

In 2007, there were approximately 235.8 million Americans ages 18 or older. **Table 3** shows the distribution, by marital status and gender, of this population.

TABLE 3 Marital Status of the U.S. Population, Ages 18 or Older, in Millions

	Never Married	Married	Widowed	Divorced	Total
Male	37.5	64.7	2.7	9.6	114.5
Female	31.7	65.2	11.2	13.2	121.3
Total	69.2	129.9	13.9	22.8	235.8

Total male: $37.5 + 64.7 + 2.7 + 9.6 = 114.5$

Total female: $31.7 + 65.2 + 11.2 + 13.2 = 121.3$

Total never married: $37.5 + 31.7 = 69.2$

Total widowed: $2.7 + 11.2 = 13.9$

Total adult population: $114.5 + 121.3 = 235.8$

Total married: $64.7 + 65.2 = 129.9$

Total divorced: $9.6 + 13.2 = 22.8$

Source: U.S. Census Bureau

STUDY TIP

Our selection from the U.S. adult population is *random*. This means that every person in the population has an equal chance of being chosen.

If one person is randomly selected from the population described in **Table 3**, find the probability, to the nearest hundredth, that the person

a. is divorced. **b.** is female.

Solution

a. The probability of selecting a divorced person is the observed number of divorced people, 22.8 (million), divided by the total number of U.S. adults, 235.8 (million).

$$P(\text{selecting a divorced person from the U.S. adult population})$$
$$= \frac{\text{number of divorced people}}{\text{total number of U.S. adults}} = \frac{22.8}{235.8} \approx 0.10$$

The empirical probability of selecting a divorced person from the U.S. adult population is approximately 0.10.

b. The probability of selecting a female is the observed number of females, 121.3 (million), divided by the total number of U.S. adults, 235.8 (million).

$$P(\text{selecting a female from the U.S. adult population})$$
$$= \frac{\text{number of females}}{\text{total number of U.S. adults}} = \frac{121.3}{235.8} \approx 0.51$$

The empirical probability of selecting a female from the U.S. adult population is approximately 0.51.

If one person is randomly selected from the population described in **Table 3**, find the probability, expressed as a decimal rounded to the nearest hundredth, that the person

a. has never been married.

b. is male.

In certain situations, we can establish a relationship between the two kinds of probability. Consider, for example, a coin that is equally likely to land heads or tails. Such a coin is called a **fair coin**. Empirical probability can be used to determine whether a coin is fair. Suppose we toss a coin 10, 50, 100, 1000, 10,000, and 100,000 times. We record the number of heads observed, shown in **Table 4** at the top of the next page. For each of the six cases in the table, the empirical probability of heads is determined by dividing the number of heads observed by the number of tosses.

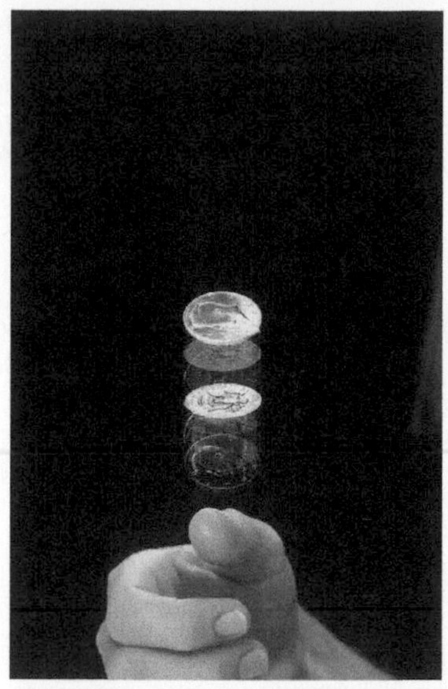
Ron Avery\SuperStock, Inc.

TABLE 4 Empirical Probabilities of Heads as the Number of Tosses Increases		
Number of Tosses	**Number of Heads Observed**	**Empirical Probability of Heads, or $P(H)$**
10	4	$P(H) = \frac{4}{10} = 0.4$
50	27	$P(H) = \frac{27}{50} = 0.54$
100	44	$P(H) = \frac{44}{100} = 0.44$
1000	530	$P(H) = \frac{530}{1000} = 0.53$
10,000	4851	$P(H) = \frac{4851}{10,000} = 0.4851$
100,000	49,880	$P(H) = \frac{49,880}{100,000} = 0.4988$

A pattern is exhibited by the empirical probabilities in the right-hand column of **Table 4**. As the number of tosses increases, the empirical probabilities tend to get closer to 0.5, the theoretical probability. These results give us no reason to suspect that the coin is not fair.

Table 4 illustrates an important principle when observing uncertain outcomes such as the event of a coin landing on heads. As an experiment is repeated more and more times, the empirical probablity of an event tends to get closer to the theoretical probability of that event. This principle is known as the **law of large numbers**.

Exercise Set 4

Practice and Application Exercises

In Exercises 1–54, express each probability as a fraction reduced to lowest terms.

In Exercises 1–10, a die is rolled. The set of equally likely outcomes is {1, 2, 3, 4, 5, 6}. Find the probability of rolling

1. a 4.

2. a 5.

3. an odd number.

4. a number greater than 3.

5. a number less than 3.

6. a number greater than 4.

7. a number less than 20.

8. a number less than 8.

9. a number greater than 20.

10. a number greater than 8.

In Exercises 11–20, you are dealt one card from a standard 52-card deck. Find the probability of being dealt

11. a queen.

12. a jack.

13. a club.

14. a diamond.

15. a picture card.

16. a card greater than 3 and less than 7.

17. the queen of spades.

18. the ace of clubs.

19. a diamond and a spade.

20. a card with a green heart.

In Exercises 21–26, a fair coin is tossed two times in succession. The set of equally likely outcomes is {HH, HT, TH, TT}. Find the probability of getting

21. two heads.

22. two tails.

23. the same outcome on each toss.

24. different outcomes on each toss.

25. a head on the second toss.

26. at least one head.

In Exercises 27–34, you select a family with three children. If M represents a male child and F a female child, the set of equally likely outcomes for the children's genders is {MMM, MMF, MFM, MFF, FMM, FMF, FFM, FFF}. Find the probability of selecting a family with

27. exactly one female child.

28. exactly one male child.

29. exactly two male children.

30. exactly two female children.

31. at least one male child.

32. at least two female children.

33. four male children.

34. fewer than four female children.

In Exercises 35–40, a single die is rolled twice. The 36 equally likely outcomes are shown as follows:

		Second Roll					
		⚀	⚁	⚂	⚃	⚄	⚅
First Roll	⚀	(1, 1)	(1, 2)	(1, 3)	(1, 4)	(1, 5)	(1, 6)
	⚁	(2, 1)	(2, 2)	(2, 3)	(2, 4)	(2, 5)	(2, 6)
	⚂	(3, 1)	(3, 2)	(3, 3)	(3, 4)	(3, 5)	(3, 6)
	⚃	(4, 1)	(4, 2)	(4, 3)	(4, 4)	(4, 5)	(4, 6)
	⚄	(5, 1)	(5, 2)	(5, 3)	(5, 4)	(5, 5)	(5, 6)
	⚅	(6, 1)	(6, 2)	(6, 3)	(6, 4)	(6, 5)	(6, 6)

Find the probability of getting

35. two even numbers.

36. two odd numbers.

37. two numbers whose sum is 5.

38. two numbers whose sum is 6.

39. two numbers whose sum exceeds 12.

40. two numbers whose sum is less than 13.

Use the spinner shown to answer Exercises 41–48. Assume that it is equally probable that the pointer will land on any one of the ten colored regions. If the pointer lands on a borderline, spin again.

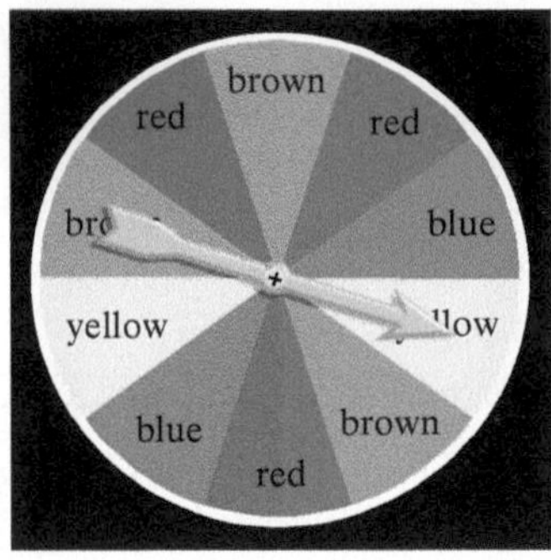

Find the probability that the spinner lands in

41. a red region.

42. a yellow region.

43. a blue region.

44. a brown region.

45. a region that is red or blue.

46. a region that is yellow or brown.

47. a region that is red and blue.

48. a region that is yellow and brown.

Exercises 49–54 deal with sickle cell anemia, an inherited disease in which red blood cells become distorted and deprived of oxygen. Approximately 1 in every 500 African-American infants is born with the disease; only 1 in 160,000 white infants has the disease. A person with two sickle cell genes will have the disease, but a person with only one sickle cell gene will have a mild, nonfatal anemia called sickle cell trait. (Approximately 8%–10% of the African-American population has this trait.)

		Second Parent	
		S	***s***
First	***S***	*SS*	*Ss*
Parent	***s***	*sS*	*ss*

If we use s to represent a sickle cell gene and S a healthy gene, the table at the bottom of the previous column shows the four possibilities for the children of two Ss parents. Each parent has only one sickle cell gene, so each has the relatively mild sickle cell trait. Find the probability that these parents give birth to a child who

49. has sickle cell anemia.

50. has sickle cell trait.

51. is healthy.

In Exercises 52–54, use the following table that shows the four possibilities for the children of one healthy, SS, parent, and one parent with sickle cell trait, Ss.

		Second Parent (with Sickle Cell Trait)	
		S	***s***
Healthy	***S***	*SS*	*Ss*
First Parent	***S***	*SS*	*Ss*

Find the probability that these parents give birth to a child who

52. has sickle cell anemia.

53. has sickle cell trait.

54. is healthy.

The table shows the distribution, by age and gender, of the 29.3 million Americans who live alone. Use the data in the table to solve Exercises 55–60.

NUMBER OF PEOPLE IN THE UNITED STATES LIVING ALONE, IN MILLIONS

	Ages 15–24	Ages 25–34	Ages 35–44	Ages 45–64	Ages 65–74	Ages ≥ 75	Total
Male	0.7	2.2	2.6	4.3	1.3	1.4	12.5
Female	0.8	1.6	1.6	5.0	2.9	4.9	16.8
Total	1.5	3.8	4.2	9.3	4.2	6.3	29.3

Source: U.S. Census Bureau

Find the probability, expressed as a decimal rounded to the nearest hundredth, that a randomly selected American living alone is

55. male.

56. female.

57. in the 25–34 age range.

58. in the 35–44 age range.

59. a woman in the 15–24 age range.

60. a man in the 45–64 age range.

The table shows the number of Americans who moved in a recent year, categorized by where they moved and whether they were an owner or a renter. Use the data in the table, expressed in millions, to solve Exercises 61–66.

NUMBER OF PEOPLE IN THE UNITED STATES WHO MOVED, IN MILLIONS

	Moved to Same State	Moved to Different State	Moved to Different Country
Owner	11.7	2.8	0.3
Renter	18.7	4.5	1.0

Source: U.S. Census Bureau

Use the table on the previous page to find the probability, expressed as a decimal rounded to the nearest hundredth, that a randomly selected American who moved was

61. an owner.

62. a renter.

63. a person who moved within the same state.

64. a person who moved to a different country.

65. a renter who moved to a different state.

66. an owner who moved to a different state.

The table shows the educational attainment of the U.S. population, ages 65 and over, in 2007. Use the data in the table, expressed in millions, to solve Exercises 67–70.

EDUCATIONAL ATTAINMENT OF THE U.S. POPULATION, AGES 65 AND OVER, IN MILLIONS

	Less Than 4 Years High School	4 Years High School Only	Some College (Less Than 4 years)	4 Years College (or More)
Male	3.6	5.0	2.6	3.9
Female	5.2	8.0	4.1	3.0

Source: U.S. Census Bureau

Find the probability, expressed as a decimal rounded to the nearest hundredth, that a randomly selected American in 2007, aged 65 or over,

67. had less than 4 years of high school.

68. had 4 years of high school only.

69. was a woman with 4 years of college or more.

70. was a man with 4 years of college or more.

Writing in Mathematics

71. What is the sample space of an experiment? What is an event?

72. How is the theoretical probability of an event computed?

73. Describe the difference between theoretical probability and empirical probability.

74. Give an example of an event whose probability must be determined empirically rather than theoretically.

75. Use the definition of theoretical probability to explain why the probability of an event that cannot occur is 0.

76. Use the definition of theoretical probability to explain why the probability of an event that is certain to occur is 1.

77. Write a probability word problem whose answer is one of the following fractions: $\frac{1}{6}$ or $\frac{1}{4}$ or $\frac{1}{3}$.

78. The president of a large company with 10,000 employees is considering mandatory cocaine testing for every employee. The test that would be used is 90% accurate, meaning that it will detect 90% of the cocaine users who are tested, and that 90% of the nonusers will test negative. This also means that the test gives 10% false positive. Suppose that 1% of the employees actually use cocaine. Find the probability that someone who tests positive for cocaine use is, indeed, a user.

Hint: Find the following probability fraction:

$$\frac{\text{the number of employees who test positive and are cocaine users}}{\text{the number of employes who test positive}}.$$

This fraction is given by

$$\frac{90\% \text{ of } 1\% \text{ of } 10{,}000}{\text{the number who test positive who actually use cocaine plus the number who test positive who do not use cocaine}}.$$

What does this probability indicate in terms of the percentage of employees who test positive who are not actually users? Discuss these numbers in terms of the issue of mandatory drug testing. Write a paper either in favor of or against mandatory drug testing, incorporating the actual percentage accuracy for such tests.

Critical Thinking Exercises

Make Sense? *In Exercises 79–82, determine whether each statement makes sense or does not make sense, and explain your reasoning.*

79. Assuming the next U.S. president will be a Democrat or a Republican, the probability of a Republican president is 0.5.

80. The probability that I will go to graduate school is 1.5.

81. When I toss a coin, the probability of getting heads *or* tails is 1, but the probability of getting heads *and* tails is 0.

82. When I am dealt one card from a standard 52-card deck, the probability of getting a red card *or* a black card is 1, but the probability of getting a red card *and* a black card is 0.

83. The target in the figure shown contains four squares. If a dart thrown at random hits the target, find the probability that it will land in an orange region.

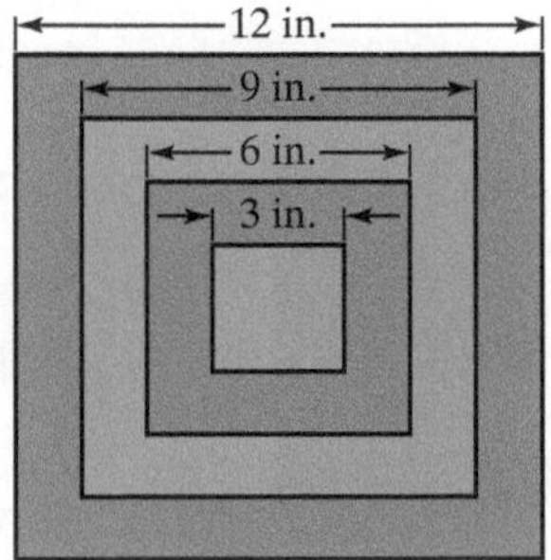

84. Some three-digit numbers, such as 101 and 313, read the same forward and backward. If you select a number from all three-digit numbers, find the probability that it will read the same forward and backward.

OBJECTIVES

1 | Compute probabilities with permutations.
2 | Compute probabilities with combinations.

5 Probability with the Fundamental Counting Principle, Permutations, and Combinations

PROBABILITY OF DYING AT ANY GIVEN AGE

Age	Probability of Male Death	Probability of Female Death
10	0.00013	0.00010
20	0.00140	0.00050
30	0.00153	0.00050
40	0.00193	0.00095
50	0.00567	0.00305
60	0.01299	0.00792
70	0.03473	0.01764
80	0.07644	0.03966
90	0.15787	0.11250
100	0.26876	0.23969
110	0.39770	0.39043

Source: George Shaffner, *The Arithmetic of Life and Death*

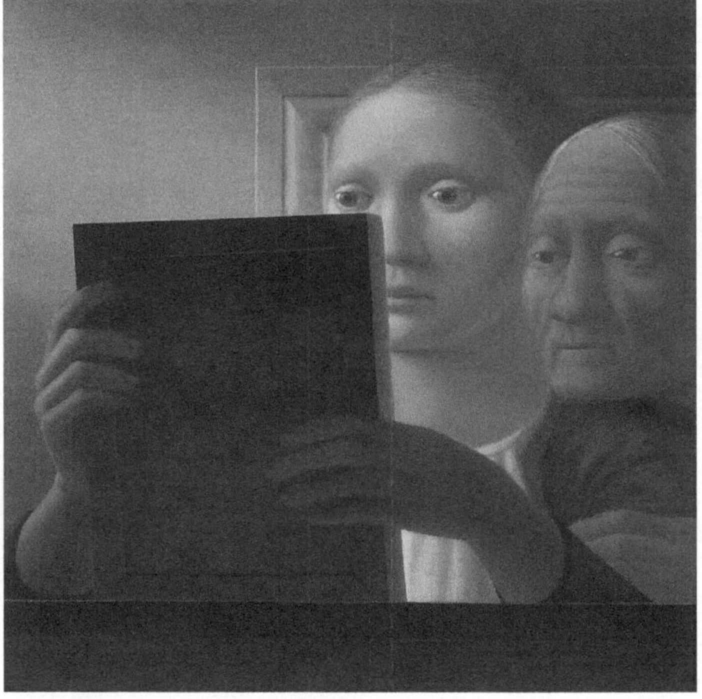

George Tooker (b. 1920) *"Mirror II"* 1963, egg tempera on gesso panel, 20 × 20 in., 1968. Gift of R. H. Donnelley Erdman (PA 1956). Addison Gallery of American Art, Phillips Academy, Andover, Massachusetts.

According to actuarial tables, there is no year in which death is as likely as continued life, at least until the age of 115. Until that age, the probability of dying in any one year ranges from a low of 0.00009 for a girl at age 11 to a high of 0.465 for either gender at age 114. For a healthy 30-year-old, how does the probability of dying this year compare to the probability of winning the top prize in a state lottery game? In this section, we provide the surprising answer to this question, as we study probability with the Fundamental Counting Principle, permutations, and combinations.

1 | Compute probabilities with permutations.

Probability with Permutations

Groucho Marx Getty Images Inc. - Hulton Archive Photos

EXAMPLE 1 Probability and Permutations

We return to the six jokes about books by Groucho Marx, George Carlin, Steven Wright, Henny Youngman, Jerry Seinfeld, and Phyllis Diller that opened Section 2. Suppose that each joke is written on one of six cards. The cards are placed in a hat and then six cards are drawn, one at a time. The order in which the cards are drawn determines the order in which the jokes are delivered. What is the probability that a man's joke will be delivered first and a man's joke will be delivered last?

Solution We begin by applying the definition of probability to this situation.

$$P(\text{man's joke first, man's joke last}) = \frac{\text{number of permutations with man's joke first, man's joke last}}{\text{total number of possible permutations}}$$

George Carlin Paul Drinkwater / NBCU Photo Bank\AP Wide World Photos

Steven Wright ©Neal Preston/CORBIS All Rights Reserved.

Henny Youngman CBS Photo Archive\ Getty Images

Jerry Seinfeld ©David Turnley/CORBIS All Rights Reserved.

Phyllis Diller Getty Images Inc. - Hulton Archive Photos

We can use the Fundamental Counting Principle to find the total number of possible permutations. This represents the number of ways the six jokes can be delivered.

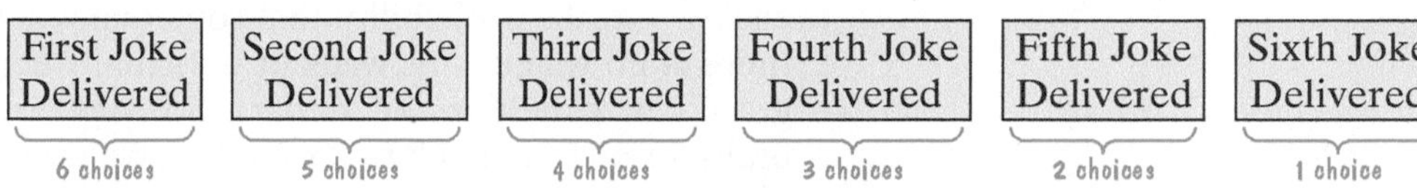

There are $6 \cdot 5 \cdot 4 \cdot 3 \cdot 2 \cdot 1$, or 720 possible permutations. Equivalently, there are 720 different ways to deliver the six jokes about books.

We can also use the Fundamental Counting Principle to find the number of permutations with a man's joke delivered first and a man's joke delivered last. These conditions can be shown as follows:

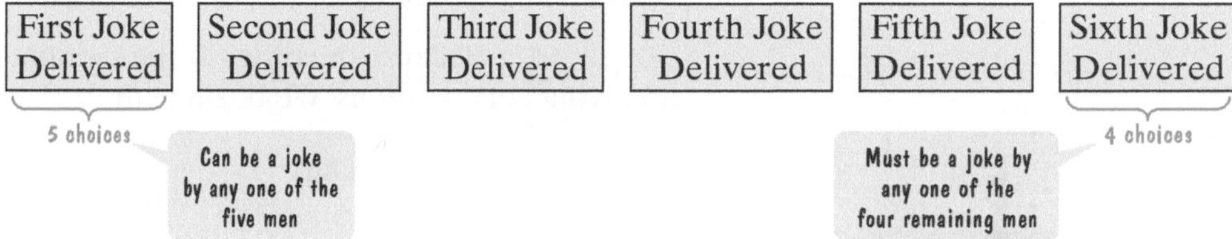

Now let's fill in the number of choices for positions two through five.

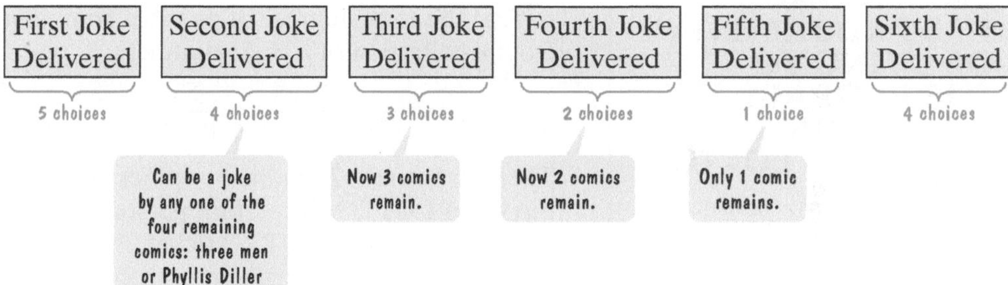

Thus, there are $5 \cdot 4 \cdot 3 \cdot 2 \cdot 1 \cdot 4$, or 480 possible permutations. Equivalently, there are 480 ways to deliver the jokes with a man's joke told first and a man's joke delivered last.

Now we can return to our probability fraction.

P (man's joke first, man's joke last)

$$= \frac{\text{number of permutations with man's joke first, man's joke last}}{\text{total number of possible permutations}}$$

$$= \frac{480}{720} = \frac{2}{3}$$

The probability of a man's joke delivered first and a man's joke told last is $\frac{2}{3}$.

Consider the six jokes about books by Groucho Marx, George Carlin, Steven Wright, Henny Youngman, Jerry Seinfeld, and Phyllis Diller. As in Example 1, each joke is written on one of six cards which are randomly drawn one card at a time. The order in which the cards are drawn determines the order in which the jokes are delivered. What is the probability that a joke by a comic whose first name begins with G is told first and a man's joke is delivered last?

2 Compute probabilities with combinations.

Probability with Combinations

In 2008, Americans spent approximately $60 billion on lotteries set up by 42 revenue-hungry states and Washington, D.C. If your state has a lottery drawing each week, the probability that someone will win the top prize is relatively high. If there is no winner this week, it is virtually certain that eventually someone will be graced with millions of dollars. So, why are you so unlucky compared to this undisclosed someone? In Example 2, we provide an answer to this question.

EXAMPLE 2 Probability and Combinations: Winning the Lottery

Florida's lottery game, LOTTO, is set up so that each player chooses six different numbers from 1 to 53. If the six numbers chosen match the six numbers drawn randomly, the player wins (or shares) the top cash prize. (As of this writing, the top cash prize has ranged from $7 million to $106.5 million.) With one LOTTO ticket, what is the probability of winning this prize?

Solution Because the order of the six numbers does not matter, this is a situation involving combinations. We begin with the formula for probability.

$$P(\text{winning}) = \frac{\text{number of ways of winning}}{\text{total number of possible combinations}}$$

We can use the combinations formula

$$_nC_r = \frac{n!}{(n-r)!\,r!}$$

to find the total number of possible combinations. We are selecting $r = 6$ numbers from a collection of $n = 53$ numbers.

$$_{53}C_6 = \frac{53!}{(53-6)!\,6!} = \frac{53!}{47!\,6!} = \frac{53 \cdot 52 \cdot 51 \cdot 50 \cdot 49 \cdot 48 \cdot \cancel{47!}}{\cancel{47!} \cdot 6 \cdot 5 \cdot 4 \cdot 3 \cdot 2 \cdot 1} = 22{,}957{,}480$$

There are nearly 23 million number combinations possible in LOTTO. If a person buys one LOTTO ticket, that person has selected only one combination of the six numbers. With one LOTTO ticket, there is only one way of winning.

Now we can return to our probability fraction.

$$P(\text{winning}) = \frac{\text{number of ways of winning}}{\text{total number of possible combinations}} = \frac{1}{22{,}957{,}480} \approx 0.0000000436$$

The probability of winning the top prize with one LOTTO ticket is $\frac{1}{22{,}957{,}480}$, or about 1 in 23 million.

Suppose that a person buys 5000 different tickets in Florida's LOTTO. Because that person has selected 5000 different combinations of the six numbers, the probability of winning is

$$\frac{5000}{22{,}957{,}480} \approx 0.000218.$$

The chances of winning the top prize are about 218 in a million. At $1 per LOTTO ticket, it is highly probable that our LOTTO player will be $5000 poorer. Knowing a little probability helps a lotto.

BLITZER BONUS

COMPARING THE PROBABILITY OF DYING TO THE PROBABILITY OF WINNING FLORIDA'S LOTTO

As a healthy nonsmoking 30-year-old, your probability of dying this year is approximately 0.001. Divide this probability by the probability of winning LOTTO with one ticket:

$$\frac{0.001}{0.0000000436} \approx 22{,}936.$$

A healthy 30-year-old is nearly 23,000 times more likely to die this year than to win Florida's lottery.

CHECK POINT 2 People lose interest when they do not win at games of chance, including Florida's LOTTO. With drawings twice weekly instead of once, the game described in Example 2 was brought in to bring back lost players and increase ticket sales. The original LOTTO was set up so that each player chose six different numbers from 1 to 49, rather than from 1 to 53, with a lottery drawing only once a week. With one LOTTO ticket, what was the probability of winning the top cash prize in Florida's original LOTTO? Express the answer as a fraction and as a decimal correct to ten places.

EXAMPLE 3 Probability and Combinations

A club consists of five men and seven women. Three members are selected at random to attend a conference. Find the probability that the selected group consists of

a. three men.

b. one man and two women.

Solution The order in which the three people are selected does not matter, so this is a problem involving combinations.

12 Club Members

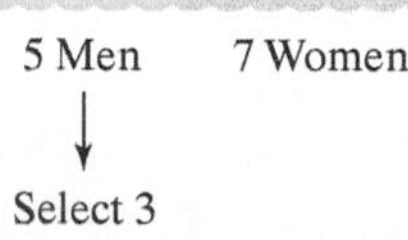

a. We begin with the probability of selecting three men.

$$P(3 \text{ men}) = \frac{\text{number of ways of selecting 3 men}}{\text{total number of possible combinations}}$$

First, we consider the denominator of the probability fraction. We are selecting $r = 3$ people from a total group of $n = 12$ people (five men and seven women). The total number of possible combinations is

$$_{12}C_3 = \frac{12!}{(12-3)!\,3!} = \frac{12!}{9!\,3!} = \frac{12 \cdot 11 \cdot 10 \cdot \cancel{9!}}{\cancel{9!} \cdot 3 \cdot 2 \cdot 1} = 220.$$

Thus, there are 220 possible three-person selections.

Next, we consider the numerator of the probability fraction. We are interested in the number of ways of selecting three men from five men. We are selecting $r = 3$ men from a total group of $n = 5$ men. The number of possible combinations of three men is

$$_5C_3 = \frac{5!}{(5-3)!\,3!} = \frac{5!}{2!\,3!} = \frac{5 \cdot 4 \cdot \cancel{3!}}{2 \cdot 1 \cdot \cancel{3!}} = 10.$$

Thus, there are 10 ways of selecting three men from five men. Now we can fill in the numbers in the numerator and the denominator of our probability fraction.

$$P(3 \text{ men}) = \frac{\text{number of ways of selecting 3 men}}{\text{total number of possible combinations}} = \frac{10}{220} = \frac{1}{22}$$

The probability that the group selected to attend the conference consists of three men is $\frac{1}{22}$.

12 Club Members

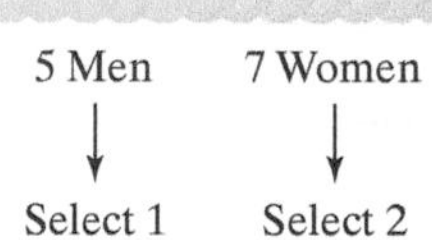

b. We set up the fraction for the probability that the selected group consists of one man and two women.

$$P(1 \text{ man, } 2 \text{ women}) = \frac{\text{number of ways of selecting 1 man and 2 women}}{\text{total number of possible combinations}}$$

The denominator of this fraction is the same as the denominator in part (a). The total number of possible combinations is found by selecting $r = 3$ people from $n = 12$ people: $_{12}C_3 = 220$.

Next, we move to the numerator of the probability fraction. The number of ways of selecting $r = 1$ man from $n = 5$ men is

$$_5C_1 = \frac{5!}{(5-1)!\,1!} = \frac{5!}{4!\,1!} = \frac{5 \cdot \cancel{4!}}{\cancel{4!} \cdot 1} = 5.$$

The number of ways of selecting $r = 2$ women from $n = 7$ women is

$$_7C_2 = \frac{7!}{(7-2)!\,2!} = \frac{7!}{5!\,2!} = \frac{7 \cdot 6 \cdot \cancel{5!}}{\cancel{5!} \cdot 2 \cdot 1} = 21.$$

By the Fundamental Counting Principle, the number of ways of selecting 1 man and 2 women is

$$_5C_1 \cdot {_7C_2} = 5 \cdot 21 = 105.$$

Now we can fill in the numbers in the numerator and the denominator of our probability fraction.

$$P(1\text{ man, }2\text{ women}) = \frac{\text{number of ways of selecting 1 man and 2 women}}{\text{total number of possible combinations}} = \frac{{}_5C_1 \cdot {}_7C_2}{{}_{12}C_3} = \frac{105}{220} = \frac{21}{44}$$

The probability that the group selected to attend the conference consists of one man and two women is $\frac{21}{44}$.

A club consists of six men and four women. Three members are selected at random to attend a conference. Find the probability that the selected group consists of

a. three men.

b. two men and one woman.

Exercise Set 5

Practice and Application Exercises

1. Martha, Lee, Nancy, Paul, and Armando have all been invited to a dinner party. They arrive randomly and each person arrives at a different time.

a. In how many ways can they arrive?

b. In how many ways can Martha arrive first and Armando last?

c. Find the probability that Martha will arrive first and Armando last.

2. Three men and three women line up at a checkout counter in a store.

a. In how many ways can they line up?

b. In how many ways can they line up if the first person in line is a woman, and then the line alternates by gender—that is a woman, a man, a woman, a man, and so on?

c. Find the probability that the first person in line is a woman and the line alternates by gender.

3. Six stand-up comics, A, B, C, D, E, and F, are to perform on a single evening at a comedy club. The order of performance is determined by random selection. Find the probability that

a. Comic E will perform first.

b. Comic C will perform fifth and comic B will perform last.

c. The comedians will perform in the following order: D, E, C, A, B, F.

d. Comic A or comic B will perform first.

4. Seven performers, A, B, C, D, E, F, and G, are to appear in a fund raiser. The order of performance is determined by random selection. Find the probability that

a. D will perform first.

b. E will perform sixth and B will perform last.

c. They will perform in the following order: C, D, B, A, G, F, E.

d. F or G will perform first.

5. A group consists of four men and five women. Three people are selected to attend a conference.

a. In how many ways can three people be selected from this group of nine?

b. In how many ways can three women be selected from the five women?

c. Find the probability that the selected group will consist of all women.

6. A political discussion group consists of five Democrats and six Republicans. Four people are selected to attend a conference.

a. In how many ways can four people be selected from this group of eleven?

b. In how many ways can four Republicans be selected from the six Republicans?

c. Find the probability that the selected group will consist of all Republicans.

7. To play the California lottery, a person has to correctly select 6 out of 51 numbers, paying $1 for each six-number selection. If the six numbers picked are the same as the ones drawn by the lottery, mountains of money are bestowed. What is the probability that a person with one combination of six numbers will win? What is the probability of winning if 100 different lottery tickets are purchased?

8. A state lottery is designed so that a player chooses five numbers from 1 to 30 on one lottery ticket. What is the probability that a player with one lottery ticket will win? What is the probability of winning if 100 different lottery tickets are purchased?

9. A box contains 25 transistors, 6 of which are defective. If 6 are selected at random, find the probability that

a. all are defective. **b.** none are defective.

10. A committee of five people is to be formed from six lawyers and seven teachers. Find the probability that

a. all are lawyers.

b. none are lawyers.

11. A city council consists of six Democrats and four Republicans. If a committee of three people is selected, find the probability of selecting one Democrat and two Republicans.

12. A parent-teacher committee consisting of four people is to be selected from fifteen parents and five teachers. Find the probability of selecting two parents and two teachers.

Exercises 13–18 involve a deck of 52 cards. If necessary, refer to the picture of a deck of cards, **Figure 5**.

13. A poker hand consists of five cards.
   a. Find the total number of possible five-card poker hands.
   b. A diamond flush is a five-card hand consisting of all diamonds. Find the number of possible diamond flushes.
   c. Find the probability of being dealt a diamond flush.

14. A poker hand consists of five cards.
   a. Find the total number of possible five-card poker hands.
   b. Find the number of ways in which four aces can be selected.
   c. Find the number of ways in which one king can be selected.
   d. Use the Fundamental Counting Principle and your answers from parts (b) and (c) to find the number of ways of getting four aces and one king.
   e. Find the probability of getting a poker hand consisting of four aces and one king.

15. If you are dealt 3 cards from a shuffled deck of 52 cards, find the probability that all 3 cards are picture cards.

16. If you are dealt 4 cards from a shuffled deck of 52 cards, find the probability that all 4 are hearts.

17. If you are dealt 4 cards from a shuffled deck of 52 cards, find the probability of getting two queens and two kings.

18. If you are dealt 4 cards from a shuffled deck of 52 cards, find the probability of getting three jacks and one queen.

Writing in Mathematics

19. If people understood the mathematics involving probabilities and lotteries, as you now do, do you think they would continue to spend hundreds of dollars per year on lottery tickets? Explain your answer.

20. Write and solve an original problem involving probability and permutations.

21. Write and solve an original problem involving probability and combinations whose solution requires $\frac{_{14}C_{10}}{_{20}C_{10}}$.

Critical Thinking Exercises

Make Sense? *In Exercises 22–25, determine whether each statement makes sense or does not make sense, and explain your reasoning.*

22. When solving probability problems using the Fundamental Counting Principle, I find it easier to reduce the probability fraction if I leave the numerator and denominator as products of numbers.

23. I would never choose the lottery numbers 1, 2, 3, 4, 5, 6 because the probability of winning with six numbers in a row is less than winning with six random numbers.

24. From an investment point of view, a state lottery is a very poor place to put my money.

25. When finding the probability of randomly selecting two men and one woman from a group of ten men and ten women, I used the formula for $_nC_r$ three times.

26. An apartment complex offers apartments with four different options, designated by A through D. There are an equal number of apartments with each combination of options.

A	B	C	D
one bedroom two bedrooms three bedrooms	one bathroom two bathrooms	first floor second floor	lake view golf course view no special view

If there is only one apartment left, what is the probability that it is precisely what a person is looking for, namely two bedrooms, two bathrooms, first floor, and a lake or golf course view?

27. Reread Exercise 7. How much must a person spend so that the probability of winning the California lottery is $\frac{1}{2}$?

28. Suppose that it is a week in which the cash prize in Florida's LOTTO is promised to exceed \$50 million. If a person purchases 22,957,480 tickets in LOTTO at \$1 per ticket (all possible combinations), isn't this a guarantee of winning the lottery? Because the probability in this situation is 1, what's wrong with doing this?

29. The digits 1, 2, 3, 4, and 5 are randomly arranged to form a three-digit number. (Digits are not repeated.) Find the probability that the number is even and greater than 500.

30. In a five-card poker hand, what is the probability of being dealt exactly one ace and no picture cards?

Group Exercise

31. Research and present a group report on state lotteries. Include answers to some or all of the following questions. As always, make the report interesting and informative. Which states do not have lotteries? Why not? How much is spent per capita on lotteries? What are some of the lottery games? What is the probability of winning top prize in these games? What income groups spend the greatest amount of money on lotteries? If your state has a lottery, what does it do with the money it makes? Is the way the money is spent what was promised when the lottery first began?

OBJECTIVES

1 Find the probability that an event will not occur.
2 Find the probability of one event or a second event occurring.
3 Understand and use odds.

6 Events Involving *Not* and *Or*; Odds

You take your first trip to London. You are surprised to learn that the British gamble on everything. Shops with bookmakers are available everywhere for placing bets. In such a shop, you overhear a conversation about turning up the king of hearts in a deck of cards. You are expecting to hear something about a probability of $\frac{1}{52}$. Instead, you hear the phrase "51 to 1 against." Are you having difficulty understanding the British accents or did you miss something in your liberal arts math course? Whatever happened to probability?

No, it's not the accent. There are several ways to express the likelihood of an event. For example, we can discuss the probability of an event. We can also discuss *odds against* an event and *odds in favor* of an event. In this section, we expand our knowledge of probability and explain the meaning of odds.

Simon Wilkinson\Alamy Images

1 Find the probability that an event will not occur.

Probability of an Event Not Occurring

If we know $P(E)$, the probability of an event E, we can determine the probability that the event will not occur, denoted by $P(\text{not } E)$. The event *not* E is the **complement** of E because it is the set of all outcomes in the sample space S that are not outcomes in the event E. In any experiment, an event must occur or its complement must occur. Thus, the sum of the probability that an event will occur and the probability that it will not occur is 1:

$$P(E) + P(\text{not } E) = 1.$$

Solving for $P(E)$ or for $P(\text{not } E)$, we obtain the following formulas:

COMPLEMENT RULES OF PROBABILITY

- The probability that an event E will not occur is equal to 1 minus the probability that it will occur.
$$P(\text{not } E) = 1 - P(E)$$
- The probability that an event E will occur is equal to 1 minus the probability that it will not occur.
$$P(E) = 1 - P(\text{not } E)$$

Using set notation, if E' is the complement of E, then $P(E') = 1 - P(E)$ and $P(E) = 1 - P(E')$.

EXAMPLE 1 The Probability of an Event Not Occurring

If you are dealt one card from a standard 52-card deck, find the probability that you are not dealt a queen.

STUDY TIP

You can work Example 1 without using the formula for $P(\text{not } E)$. Here is how it's done:

$$P(\text{not a queen}) = \frac{\text{number of ways a non-queen can occur}}{\text{total number of outcomes}}$$

$$= \frac{48}{52}$$

With 4 queens, 52 4 = 48 cards are not queens.

$$= \frac{4 \cdot 12}{4 \cdot 13} = \frac{12}{13}.$$

Solution Because

$$P(\text{not } E) = 1 - P(E)$$

then

$$P(\text{not a queen}) = 1 - P(\text{queen}).$$

There are four queens in a deck of 52 cards. The probability of being dealt a queen is $\frac{4}{52} = \frac{1}{13}$. Thus.

$$P(\text{not a queen}) = 1 - P(\text{queen}) = 1 - \frac{1}{13} = \frac{13}{13} - \frac{1}{13} = \frac{12}{13}.$$

The probability that you are not dealt a queen is $\frac{12}{13}$.

If you are dealt one card from a standard 52-card deck, find the probability that you are not dealt a diamond.

EXAMPLE 2 Using the Complement Rules

The circle graph in **Figure 6** shows the distribution, by age group, of the 191 million car drivers in the United States, with all numbers rounded to the nearest million. If one driver is randomly selected from this population, find the probability that the person

a. is not in the 20–29 age group.

b. is less than 80 years old.

Express probabilities as simplified fractions.

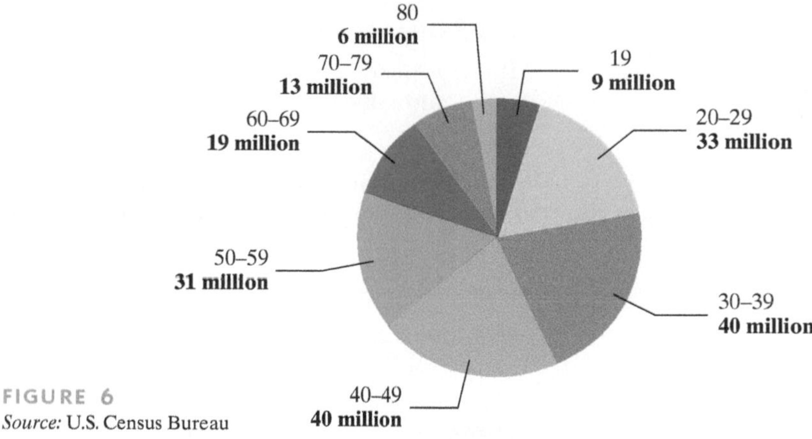

FIGURE 6
Source: U.S. Census Bureau

Solution

a. We begin with the probability that a randomly selected driver is not in the 20–29 age group.

$$P(\text{not in 20–29 age group}) = 1 - P(\text{in 20–29 age group})$$

$$= 1 - \frac{33}{191}$$

The graph shows 33 million drivers in the 20–29 age group.

This number, 191 million drivers, was given, but can be obtained by adding the numbers in the eight sectors.

$$= \frac{191}{191} - \frac{33}{191} = \frac{158}{191}$$

The probability that a randomly selected driver is not in the 20–29 age group is $\frac{158}{191}$.

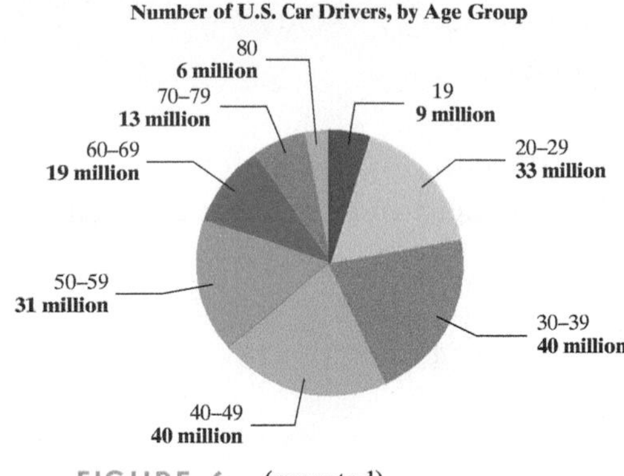

FIGURE 6 (repeated)

b. We could compute the probability that a randomly selected driver is less than 80 years old by adding the numbers in each of the seven sectors representing drivers less than 80 and dividing this sum by 191 (million). However, it is easier to use complements. The complement of selecting a driver less than 80 years old is selecting a driver 80 or older.

$$P(\text{less than 80 years old}) = 1 - P(\text{80 or older})$$

$$= 1 - \frac{6}{191}$$ The graph shows 6 million drivers 80 or older.

$$= \frac{191}{191} - \frac{6}{191} = \frac{185}{191}$$

The probability that a randomly selected driver is less than 80 years old is $\frac{185}{191}$.

CHECK POINT 2 If one driver is randomly selected from the population represented in **Figure 6**, find the probability, expressed as a simplified fraction, that the person

a. is not in the 50–59 age group.

b. is at least 20 years old.

2 Find the probability of one event or a second event occurring.

Or Probabilities with Mutually Exclusive Events

Suppose that you randomly select one card from a deck of 52 cards. Let A be the event of selecting a king and B be the event of selecting a queen. Only one card is selected, so it is impossible to get both a king and a queen. The events of selecting a king and a queen cannot occur simultaneously. They are called *mutually exclusive events.*

MUTUALLY EXCLUSIVE EVENTS

If it is impossible for events A and B to occur simultaneously, the events are said to be **mutually exclusive**.

In general, if A and B are mutually exclusive events, the probability that either A or B will occur is determined by adding their individual probabilities.

Or PROBABILITIES WITH MUTUALLY EXCLUSIVE EVENTS

If A and B are mutually exclusive events, then

$$P(A \text{ or } B) = P(A) + P(B).$$

Using set notation, $P(A \cup B) = P(A) + P(B)$.

EXAMPLE 3 The Probability of Either of Two Mutually Exclusive Events Occurring

If one card is randomly selected from a deck of cards, what is the probability of selecting a king or a queen?

Solution We find the probability that either of these mutually exclusive events will occur by adding their individual probabilities.

$$P(\text{king or queen}) = P(\text{king}) + P(\text{queen}) = \frac{4}{52} + \frac{4}{52} = \frac{8}{52} = \frac{2}{13}$$

The probability of selecting a king or a queen is $\frac{2}{13}$.

CHECK POINT 3 If you roll a single, six-sided die, what is the probability of getting either a 4 or a 5?

Or Probabilities with Events That Are Not Mutually Exclusive

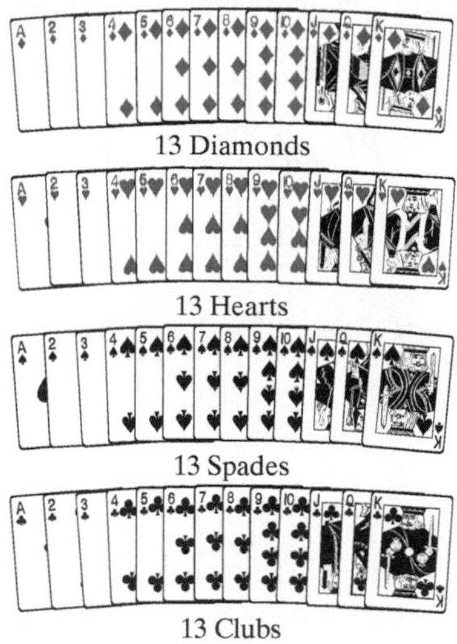

FIGURE 7 A deck of 52 cards

Consider the deck of 52 cards shown in **Figure 7**. Suppose that these cards are shuffled and you randomly select one card from the deck. What is the probability of selecting a diamond or a picture card (jack, queen, king)? Begin by adding their individual probabilities.

$$P(\text{diamond}) + P(\text{picture card}) = \frac{13}{52} + \frac{12}{52}$$

There are 13 diamonds in the deck of 52 cards.

There are 12 picture cards in the deck of 52 cards.

However, this sum is not the probability of selecting a diamond or a picture card. The problem is that there are three cards that are *simultaneously* diamonds and picture cards, shown in **Figure 8**. The events of selecting a diamond and selecting a picture card are not mutually exclusive. It is possible to select a card that is both a diamond and a picture card.

FIGURE 8 Three diamonds are picture cards.

The situation is illustrated in the Venn diagram in **Figure 9**. Why can't we find the probability of selecting a diamond or a picture card by adding their individual probabilities? The Venn diagram shows that three of the cards, the three diamonds that are picture cards, get counted twice when we add the individual probabilities. First the three cards get counted as diamonds and then they get counted as picture cards. In order to avoid the error of counting the three cards twice, we need to subtract the probability of getting a diamond and a picture card, $\frac{3}{52}$, as follows:

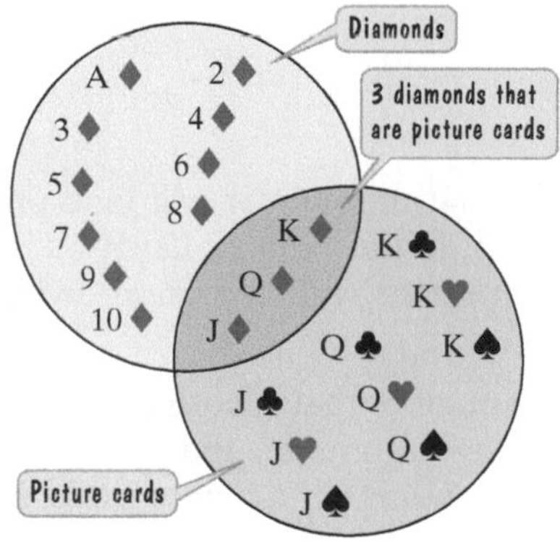

FIGURE 9

P(diamond or picture card)

$$= P(\text{diamond}) + P(\text{picture card}) - P(\text{diamond and picture card})$$

$$= \frac{13}{52} + \frac{12}{52} - \frac{3}{52} = \frac{13 + 12 - 3}{52} = \frac{22}{52} = \frac{11}{26}.$$

Thus, the probability of selecting a diamond or a picture card is $\frac{11}{26}$.

In general, if A and B are events that are not mutually exclusive, the probability that A or B will occur is determined by adding their individual probabilities and then subtracting the probability that A and B occur simultaneously.

Or PROBABILITIES WITH EVENTS THAT ARE NOT MUTUALLY EXCLUSIVE

If A and B are not mutually exclusive events, then

$$P(A \text{ or } B) = P(A) + P(B) - P(A \text{ and } B).$$

Using set notation,

$$P(A \cup B) = P(A) + P(B) - P(A \cap B).$$

EXAMPLE 4 An *Or* Probability with Events That Are Not Mutually Exclusive

In a group of 25 baboons, 18 enjoy grooming their neighbors, 16 enjoy screeching wildly, while 10 enjoy grooming their neighbors and screeching wildly. If one baboon is selected at random from the group, find the probability that it enjoys grooming its neighbors or screeching wildly.

Manoj Shah\Getty Images Inc. - Stone Allstock

Solution It is possible for a baboon in the group to enjoy both grooming its neighbors and screeching wildly. Ten of the brutes are given to engage in both activities. These events are not mutually exclusive.

$$P\left(\begin{matrix}\text{grooming}\\ \text{or screeching}\end{matrix}\right) = P(\text{grooming}) + P(\text{screeching}) - P\left(\begin{matrix}\text{grooming}\\ \text{and screeching}\end{matrix}\right)$$

$$= \frac{18}{25} + \frac{16}{25} - \frac{10}{25}$$

18 of the 25 baboons enjoy grooming.

16 of the 25 baboons enjoy screeching.

10 of the 25 baboons enjoy both.

$$= \frac{18 + 16 - 10}{25} = \frac{24}{25}$$

The probability that a baboon in the group enjoys grooming its neighbors or screeching wildly is $\frac{24}{25}$.

CHECK POINT 4 In a group of 50 students, 23 take math, 11 take psychology, and 7 take both math and psychology. If one student is selected at random, find the probability that the student takes math or psychology.

EXAMPLE 5 An *Or* Probability with Events That Are Not Mutually Exclusive

1
2
3
4
5
6
7
8

FIGURE 10 It is equally probable that the pointer will land on any one of the eight regions.

Figure 10 illustrates a spinner. It is equally probable that the pointer will land on any one of the eight regions, numbered 1 through 8. If the pointer lands on a borderline, spin again. Find the probability that the pointer will stop on an even number or on a number greater than 5.

Solution It is possible for the pointer to land on a number that is both even and greater than 5. Two of the numbers, 6 and 8, are even and greater than 5. These events are not mutually exclusive. The probability of landing on a number that is even or greater than 5 is calculated as follows:

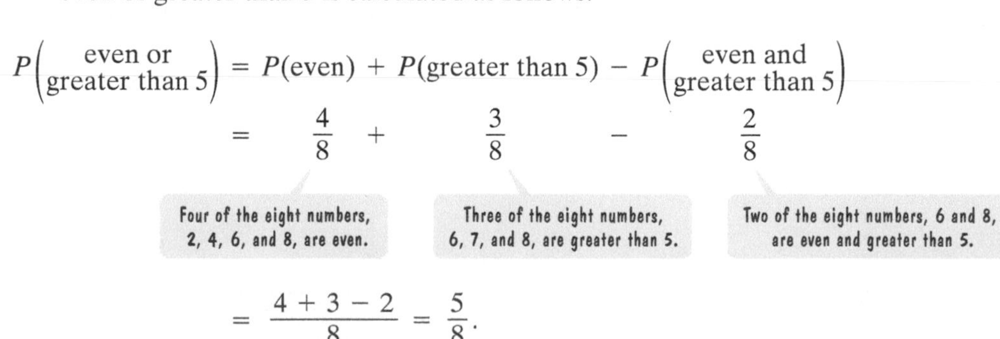

$$P\left(\begin{matrix}\text{even or}\\ \text{greater than 5}\end{matrix}\right) = P(\text{even}) + P(\text{greater than 5}) - P\left(\begin{matrix}\text{even and}\\ \text{greater than 5}\end{matrix}\right)$$

$$= \frac{4}{8} + \frac{3}{8} - \frac{2}{8}$$

Four of the eight numbers, 2, 4, 6, and 8, are even.
Three of the eight numbers, 6, 7, and 8, are greater than 5.
Two of the eight numbers, 6 and 8, are even and greater than 5.

$$= \frac{4 + 3 - 2}{8} = \frac{5}{8}.$$

The probability that the pointer will stop on an even number or a number greater than 5 is $\frac{5}{8}$.

CHECK POINT 5 Use **Figure 10** to find the probability that the pointer will stop on an odd number or a number less than 5.

EXAMPLE 6 *Or* Probabilities with Real-World Data

Each year the Internal Revenue Service audits a sample of tax forms to verify their accuracy. **Table 5** at the top of the next page shows the number of tax returns filed and audited in 2006, by taxable income.

TABLE 5 Tax Returns Filed and Audited, by Taxable Income, 2006

	< $25,000	$25,000–$49,999	$50,000–$99,999	≥ $100,000	Total
Audit	461,729	191,150	163,711	166,839	983,429
No audit	51,509,900	30,637,782	26,300,262	12,726,963	121,174,907
Total	51,971,629	30,828,932	26,463,973	12,893,802	122,158,336

Source: Internal Revenue Service

If one person is randomly selected from the population represented in **Table 5**, find the probability that

a. the taxpayer had a taxable income less than $25,000 or was audited.
b. the taxpayer had a taxable income less than $25,000 or at least $100,000.

Express probabilities as decimals rounded to the nearest hundredth.

Solution

a. It is possible to select a taxpayer who both earned less than $25,000 and was audited. Thus, these events are not mutually exclusive.

$P(\text{less than \$25,000 or audited})$

$$= P(\text{less than \$25,000}) + P(\text{audited}) - P(\text{less than \$25,000 and audited})$$

$$= \frac{51{,}971{,}629}{122{,}158{,}336} + \frac{983{,}429}{122{,}158{,}336} - \frac{461{,}729}{122{,}158{,}336}$$

Of the 122,158,336 taxpayers, 51,971,629 had taxable incomes less than $25,000.

Of the 122,158,336 taxpayers, 983,429 were audited.

Of the 122,158,336 taxpayers, 461,729 earned less than $25,000 and were audited.

$$= \frac{52{,}493{,}329}{122{,}158{,}336} \approx 0.43$$

The probability that a taxpayer had a taxable income less than $25,000 or was audited is approximately 0.43.

b. A taxable income of *at least* $100,000 means $100,000 or more. Thus, it is not possible to select a taxpayer with both a taxable income of less than $25,000 and at least $100,000. These events are mutually exclusive.

$P(\text{less than \$25,000 or at least \$100,000})$

$$= P(\text{less than \$25,000}) + P(\text{at least \$100,000})$$

$$= \frac{51{,}971{,}629}{122{,}158{,}336} + \frac{12{,}893{,}802}{122{,}158{,}336}$$

Of the 122,158,336 taxpayers, 51,971,629 had taxable incomes less than $25,000.

Of the 122,158,336 taxpayers, 12,893,802 had taxable incomes of $100,000 or more.

$$= \frac{64{,}865{,}431}{122{,}158{,}336} \approx 0.53$$

The probability that a taxpayer had a taxable income less than $25,000 or at least $100,000 is approximately 0.53.

If one person is randomly selected from the population represented in **Table 5**, find the probability, expressed as a decimal rounded to the nearest hundredth, that

a. the taxpayer had a taxable income of at least $100,000 or was not audited.
b. the taxpayer had a taxable income less than $25,000 or between $50,000 and $99,999, inclusive.

3 | Understand and use odds.

Odds

If we know the probability of an event E, we can also speak of the *odds in favor*, or the *odds against*, the event. The following definitions link together the concepts of odds and probabilities:

PROBABILITY TO ODDS

If $P(E)$ is the probability of an event E occurring, then

1. The **odds in favor of E** are found by taking the probability that E will occur and dividing by the probability that E will not occur.

$$\text{Odds in favor of } E = \frac{P(E)}{P(\text{not } E)}$$

2. The **odds against E** are found by taking the probability that E will not occur and dividing by the probability that E will occur.

$$\text{Odds against } E = \frac{P(\text{not } E)}{P(E)}$$

The odds against E can also be found by reversing the ratio representing the odds in favor of E.

EXAMPLE 7 From Probability to Odds

You roll a single, six-sided die.

a. Find the odds in favor of rolling a 2.

b. Find the odds against rolling a 2.

Solution Let E represent the event of rolling a 2. In order to determine odds, we must first find the probability of E occurring and the probability of E not occurring. With $S = \{1, 2, 3, 4, 5, 6\}$ and $E = \{2\}$, we see that

$$P(E) = \frac{1}{6}$$

$$\text{and } P(\text{not } E) = 1 - \frac{1}{6} = \frac{6}{6} - \frac{1}{6} = \frac{5}{6}.$$

Now we are ready to construct the ratios for the odds in favor of E and the odds against E.

a. $$\text{Odds in favor of } E \text{ (rolling a 2)} = \frac{P(E)}{P(\text{not } E)} = \frac{\frac{1}{6}}{\frac{5}{6}} = \frac{1}{6}\cdot\frac{6}{5} = \frac{1}{5}$$

The odds in favor of rolling a 2 are $\frac{1}{5}$. The ratio $\frac{1}{5}$ is usually written 1:5 and is read "1 to 5." Thus, the odds in favor of rolling a 2 are 1 to 5.

b. Now that we have the odds in favor of rolling a 2, namely $\frac{1}{5}$ or 1:5, we can find the odds against rolling a 2 by reversing this ratio. Thus,

$$\text{Odds against } E \text{ (rolling a 2)} = \frac{5}{1} \text{ or } 5{:}1.$$

The odds against rolling a 2 are 5 to 1.

> **STUDY TIP**
>
> When computing odds, the denominators of the two probabilities will always divide out.

You are dealt one card from a 52-card deck.

a. Find the odds in favor of getting a red queen.

b. Find the odds against getting a red queen.

EXAMPLE 8 From Probability to Odds

The winner of a raffle will receive a new sports utility vehicle. If 500 raffle tickets were sold and you purchased ten tickets, what are the odds against your winning the car?

Solution Let E represent the event of winning the SUV. Because you purchased ten tickets and 500 tickets were sold,

$$P(E) = \frac{10}{500} = \frac{1}{50} \text{ and } P(\text{not } E) = 1 - \frac{1}{50} = \frac{50}{50} - \frac{1}{50} = \frac{49}{50}.$$

Now we are ready to construct the ratio for the odds against E (winning the SUV).

$$\text{Odds against } E = \frac{P(\text{not } E)}{P(E)} = \frac{\frac{49}{50}}{\frac{1}{50}} = \frac{49}{50} \cdot \frac{50}{1} = \frac{49}{1}$$

The odds against winning the SUV are 49 to 1, written 49:1.

CHECK POINT 8 The winner of a raffle will receive a two-year scholarship to the college of his or her choice. If 1000 raffle tickets were sold and you purchased five tickets, what are the odds against your winning the scholarship?

BLITZER BONUS

HOUSE ODDS

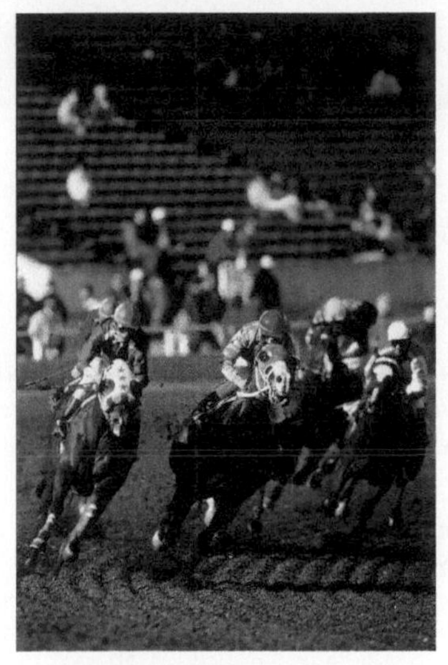

Alec Pytlowany\Masterfile Corporation

The odds given at horse races and at all games of chance are usually *odds against*. If the odds in favor of a particular horse winning a race are 2 to 5, then the odds against winning are 5 to 2. At a horse race, the odds on this horse are given simply as 5 to 2. These **house odds** tell a gambler what the payoff is on a bet. For every \$2 bet on the horse, the gambler would win \$5 if the horse won, in addition to having the \$2 bet returned.

Odds enable us to play and bet fairly on games. For example, we have seen that the odds in favor of getting 2 when you roll a die are 1 to 5. Suppose this is a gaming situation and you bet \$1 on a 2 turning up. In terms of your bet, there is one favorable outcome, rolling 2, and five unfavorable outcomes, rolling 1, 3, 4, 5, or 6. The odds in favor of getting 2, 1 to 5, compares the number of favorable outcomes, one, to the number of unfavorable outcomes, five.

Using odds in a gaming situation where money is waged, we can determine if the game is *fair*. If the odds in favor of an event E are a to b, the **game is fair** if a bet of \$$a$ is lost if event E does not occur, but a win of \$$b$ (as well as returning the bet of \$$a$) is realized if event E does occur. For example, the odds in favor of getting 2 on a die roll are 1 to 5. If you bet \$1 on a 2 turning up and the game is fair, you should win \$5 (and have your bet of \$1 returned) if a 2 turns up.

Now that we know how to convert from probability to odds, let's see how to convert from odds to probability. Suppose that the odds in favor of event E occurring are a to b. This means that

$$\frac{P(E)}{P(\text{not } E)} = \frac{a}{b} \quad \text{or} \quad \frac{P(E)}{1 - P(E)} = \frac{a}{b}.$$

By solving the equation on the right for $P(E)$, we obtain a formula for converting from odds to probability.

ODDS TO PROBABILITY

If the odds in favor of event E are a to b, then the probability of the event is given by

$$P(E) = \frac{a}{a + b}.$$

EXAMPLE 9 From Odds to Probability

The odds in favor of a particular horse winning a race are 2 to 5. What is the probability that this horse will win the race?

Solution Because odds in favor, a to b, means a probability of $\frac{a}{a+b}$, then odds in favor, 2 to 5, means a probability of

$$\frac{2}{2 + 5} = \frac{2}{7}.$$

The probability that this horse will win the race is $\frac{2}{7}$.

The odds against a particular horse winning a race are 15 to 1. Find the odds in favor of the horse winning the race and the probability of the horse winning the race.

Exercise Set 6

Practice and Application Exercises

In Exercises 1–6, you are dealt one card from a 52-card deck. Find the probability that you are not dealt

1. an ace. **2.** a 3. **3.** a heart. **4.** a club. **5.** a picture card. **6.** a red picture card.

In 5-card poker, played with a standard 52-card deck, ${}_{52}C_5$, or 2,598,960, different hands are possible. The probability of being dealt various hands is the number of different ways they can occur divided by 2,598,960. Shown in Exercises 7–10 are various types of poker hands and their probabilities. In each exercise, find the probability of not being dealt this type of hand.

Type of Hand	Illustration	Number of Ways the Hand Can Occur	Probability
7. Straight flush: 5 cards with consecutive numbers, all in the same suit (excluding royal flush)		36	$\frac{36}{2,598,960}$
8. Four of a kind: 4 cards with the same number, plus 1 additional card		624	$\frac{624}{2,598,960}$
9. Full house: 3 cards of one number and 2 cards of a second number		3744	$\frac{3744}{2,598,960}$
10. Flush: 5 cards of the same suit (excluding royal flush and straight flush)		5108	$\frac{5108}{2,598,960}$

The graph shows the probability of cardiovascular disease, by age and gender. Use the information in the graph to solve Exercises 11–12. Express all probabilities as decimals, estimated to two decimal places.

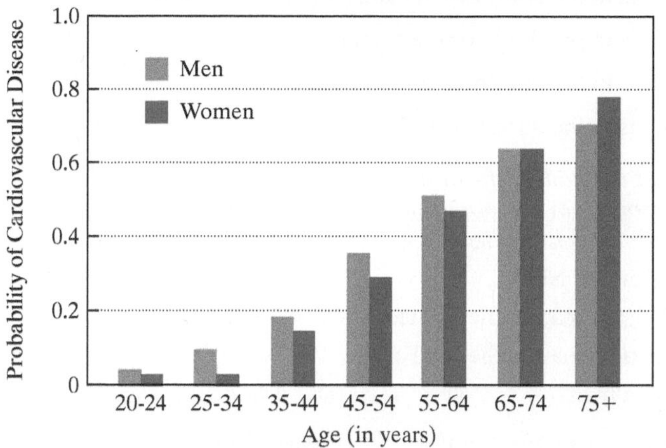

Source: American Heart Association

11. a. What is the probability that a randomly selected man between the ages of 25 and 34 has cardiovascular disease?

b. What is the probability that a randomly selected man between the ages of 25 and 34 does not have cardiovascular disease?

12. a. What is the probability that a randomly selected woman, 75 or older, has cardiovascular disease?

b. What is the probability that a randomly selected woman, 75 or older, does not have cardiovascular disease?

The table shows the distribution, by annual income, of the 118 million households in the United States in 2007, with all numbers rounded to the nearest million. Use this distribution to solve Exercises 13–16.

INCOME DISTRIBUTION OF U.S. HOUSEHOLDS, IN MILLIONS

Annual Income	Number
Less than $10,000	8
$10,000–$14,999	7
$15,000–$24,999	14
$25,000–$34,999	13
$35,000–$49,999	17
$50,000–$74,999	21
$75,000–$99,999	14
$100,000 or more	24

Source: U.S. Census Bureau

If one household is randomly selected from this population, find the probability, expressed as a simplified fraction, that

13. the household income is not in the $50,000–$74,999 range.

14. the household income is not in the $15,000–$24,999 range.

15. the household income is less than $100,000.

16. the household income is at least $10,000.

In Exercises 17–22, you randomly select one card from a 52-card deck. Find the probability of selecting

17. a 2 or a 3.

18. a 7 or an 8.

19. a red 2 or a black 3.

20. a red 7 or a black 8.

21. the 2 of hearts or the 3 of spades.

22. the 7 of hearts or the 8 of spades.

23. The mathematics faculty at a college consists of 8 professors, 12 associate professors, 14 assistant professors, and 10 instructors. If one faculty member is randomly selected, find the probability of choosing a professor or an instructor.

24. A political discussion group consists of 30 Republicans, 25 Democrats, 8 Independents, and 4 members of the Green party. If one person is randomly selected from the group, find the probability of choosing an Independent or a Green.

In Exercises 25–26, a single die is rolled. Find the probability of rolling

25. an even number or a number less than 5.

26. an odd number or a number less than 4.

In Exercises 27–30, you are dealt one card from a 52-card deck. Find the probability that you are dealt

27. a 7 or a red card.

28. a 5 or a black card.

29. a heart or a picture card.

30. a card greater than 2 and less than 7, or a diamond.

In Exercises 31–34, it is equally probable that the pointer on the spinner shown will land on any one of the eight regions, numbered 1 through 8. If the pointer lands on a borderline, spin again.

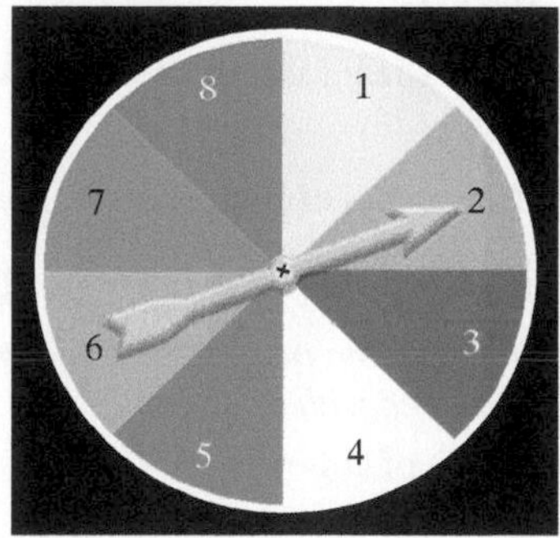

Find the probability that the pointer will stop on

31. an odd number or a number less than 6.

32. an odd number or a number greater than 3.

33. an even number or a number greater than 5.

34. an even number or a number less than 4.

Use this information to solve Exercises 35–38. The mathematics department of a college has 8 male professors, 11 female professors, 14 male teaching assistants, and 7 female teaching assistants. If a person is selected at random from the group, find the probability that the selected person is

35. a professor or a male.

36. a professor or a female.

37. a teaching assistant or a female.

38. a teaching assistant or a male.

39. In a class of 50 students, 29 are Democrats, 11 are business majors, and 5 of the business majors are Democrats. If one student is randomly selected from the class, find the probability of choosing a Democrat or a business major.

40. A student is selected at random from a group of 200 students in which 135 take math, 85 take English, and 65 take both math and English. Find the probability that the selected student takes math or English.

The table shows the educational attainment of the U.S. population, ages 25 and over, in 2007. Use the data in the table, expressed in millions, to solve Exercises 41–48.

EDUCATIONAL ATTAINMENT OF THE U.S. POPULATION, AGES 25 AND OVER, IN MILLIONS

	Less Than 4 Years High School	4 Years High School Only	Some College (Less than 4 years)	4 Years College (or More)	Total
Male	14	25	20	23	82
Female	15	31	24	22	92
Total	29	56	44	45	174

Source: U.S. Census Bureau

Find the probability, expressed as a simplified fraction, that a randomly selected American, aged 25 or over,

41. has not completed four years (or more) of college.

42. has not completed four years of high school.

43. has completed four years of high school only or less than four years of college.

44. has completed less than four years of high school or four years of high school only.

45. has completed four years of high school only or is a man.

46. has completed four years of high school only or is a woman.

Find the odds in favor and the odds against a randomly selected American, aged 25 and over, with

47. four years (or more) of college.

48. less than four years of high school.

The graph shows the distribution, by branch and gender, of the 1.38 million, or 1380 thousand, active-duty personnel in the U.S. military in 2007. Numbers are given in thousands and rounded to the nearest ten thousand. Use the data to solve Exercises 49–60.

Active Duty U.S. Military Personnel

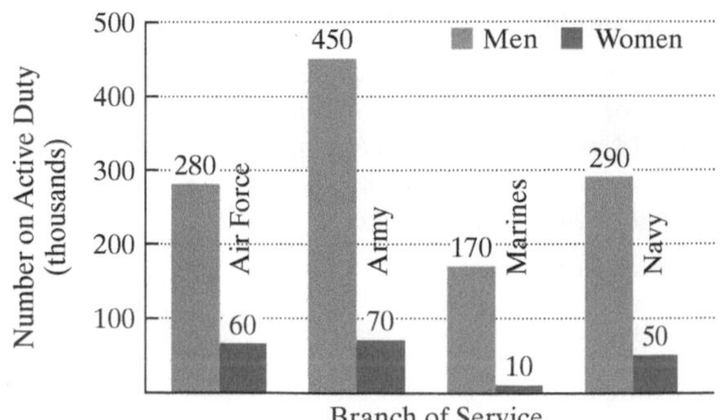

Source: U.S. Defense Department

If one person is randomly selected from the population represented in the bar graph in the previous column, find the probability, expressed as a simplified fraction, that the person

49. is not in the Army.

50. is not in the Marines.

51. is in the Navy or is a man.

52. is in the Army or is a woman.

53. is in the Air Force or the Marines.

54. is in the Army or the Navy.

Find the odds in favor and the odds against a randomly selected person from the population represented in the bar graph in the previous column being

55. in the Navy.

56. in the Army.

57. a woman in the Marines.

58. a woman in the Air Force.

59. a man.

60. a woman.

In Exercises 61–64, a single die is rolled. Find the odds

61. in favor of rolling a number greater than 2.

62. in favor of rolling a number less than 5.

63. against rolling a number greater than 2.

64. against rolling a number less than 5.

The circle graphs show the percentage of children in the United States whose parents are college graduates in one-parent households and two-parent households. Use the information shown to solve Exercises 65–66.

Percentage of U.S. Children Whose Parents Are College Graduates

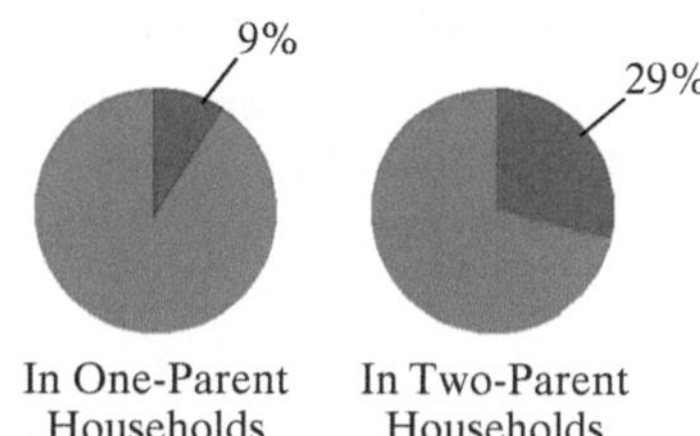

Source: U.S. Census Bureau

65. a. What are the odds in favor of a child in a one-parent household having a parent who is a college graduate?

b. What are the odds against a child in a one-parent household having a parent who is a college graduate?

66. a. What are the odds in favor of a child in a two-parent household having parents who are college graduates?

b. What are the odds against a child in a two-parent household having parents who are college graduates?

In Exercises 67–76, one card is randomly selected from a deck of cards. Find the odds

67. in favor of drawing a heart.

68. in favor of drawing a picture card.

69. in favor of drawing a red card.

70. in favor of drawing a black card.

71. against drawing a 9.

72. against drawing a 5.

73. against drawing a black king.

74. against drawing a red jack.

75. against drawing a spade greater than 3 and less than 9.

76. against drawing a club greater than 4 and less than 10.

77. The winner of a raffle will receive a 21-foot outboard boat. If 1000 raffle tickets were sold and you purchased 20 tickets, what are the odds against your winning the boat?

78. The winner of a raffle will receive a 30-day all-expense-paid trip throughout Europe. If 5000 raffle tickets were sold and you purchased 30 tickets, what are the odds against your winning the trip?

Of the 38 plays attributed to Shakespeare, 18 are comedies, 10 are tragedies, and 10 are histories. In Exercises 79–86, one play is randomly selected from Shakespeare's 38 plays. Find the odds

79. in favor of selecting a comedy.

80. in favor of selecting a tragedy.

81. against selecting a history.

82. against selecting a comedy.

83. in favor of selecting a comedy or a tragedy.

84. in favor of selecting a tragedy or a history.

85. against selecting a tragedy or a history.

86. against selecting a comedy or a history.

87. If you are given odds of 3 to 4 in favor of winning a bet, what is the probability of winning the bet?

88. If you are given odds of 3 to 7 in favor of winning a bet, what is the probability of winning the bet?

89. Based on his skills in basketball, it was computed that when Michael Jordan shot a free throw, the odds in favor of his making it were 21 to 4. Find the probability that when Michael Jordan shot a free throw, he missed it. Out of every 100 free throws he attempted, on the average how many did he make?

90. The odds in favor of a person who is alive at age 20 still being alive at age 70 are 193 to 270. Find the probability that a person who is alive at age 20 will still be alive at age 70.

Exercises 91–92 give the odds against various flight risks. Use these odds to determine the probability of the underlined event for those in flight. (Source: Men's Health)

91. odds against contracting an airborne disease: 999 to 1

92. odds against deep-vein thrombosis (blood clot in the leg): 28 to 1

Writing in Mathematics

93. Explain how to find the probability of an event not occurring. Give an example.

94. What are mutually exclusive events? Give an example of two events that are mutually exclusive.

95. Explain how to find *or* probabilities with mutually exclusive events. Give an example.

96. Give an example of two events that are not mutually exclusive.

97. Explain how to find *or* probabilities with events that are not mutually exclusive. Give an example.

98. Explain how to find the odds in favor of an event if you know the probability that the event will occur.

99. Explain how to find the probability of an event if you know the odds in favor of that event.

Critical Thinking Exercises

Make Sense? *In Exercises 100–103, determine whether each statement makes sense or does not make sense, and explain your reasoning.*

100. The probability that Jill will win the election is 0.7 and the probability that she will not win is 0.4.

101. The probability of selecting a king from a deck of 52 cards is $\frac{4}{52}$ and the probability of selecting a heart is $\frac{13}{52}$, so the probability of selecting a king or a heart is $\frac{4}{52} + \frac{13}{52}$.

102. The probability of selecting a king or a heart from a deck of 52 cards is the same as the probability of selecting the king of hearts.

103. I estimate that the odds in favor of most students getting married before receiving an undergraduate degree are 9:1.

104. In Exercise 39, find the probability of choosing **a.** a Democrat who is not a business major; **b.** a student who is neither a Democrat nor a business major.

105. On New Year's Eve, the probability of a person driving while intoxicated or having a driving accident is 0.35. If the probability of driving while intoxicated is 0.32 and the probability of having a driving accident is 0.09, find the probability of a person having a driving accident while intoxicated.

106. The formula for converting from odds to probability is given in the box at the end of this section. Read the paragraph that precedes this box and derive the formula.

OBJECTIVES

1 Find the probability of one event and a second event occurring.
2 Compute conditional probabilities.

7 Events Involving *And*; Conditional Probability

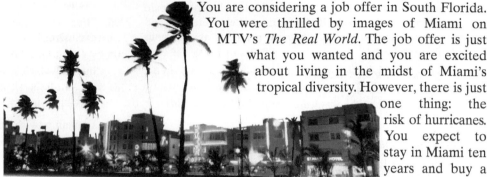

Angelo Cavalli/Age Fotostock\SuperStock, Inc.

You are considering a job offer in South Florida. You were thrilled by images of Miami on MTV's *The Real World*. The job offer is just what you wanted and you are excited about living in the midst of Miami's tropical diversity. However, there is just one thing: the risk of hurricanes. You expect to stay in Miami ten years and buy a home. What is the probability that South Florida will be hit by a hurricane at least once in the next ten years?

In this section, we look at the probability that an event occurs at least once by expanding our discussion of probability to events involving *and*.

1 Find the probability of one event and a second event occurring.

And Probabilities with Independent Events

Consider tossing a fair coin two times in succession. The outcome of the first toss, heads or tails, does not affect what happens when you toss the coin a second time. For example, the occurrence of tails on the first toss does not make tails more likely or less likely to occur on the second toss. The repeated toss of a coin produces *independent events* because the outcome of one toss does not affect the outcome of others.

STUDY TIP

Do not confuse *independent events* and *mutually exclusive events*. Mutually exclusive events cannot occur at the same time. Independent events occur at different times, although they have no effect on each other.

INDEPENDENT EVENTS

Two events are **independent events** if the occurrence of either of them has no effect on the probability of the other.

When a fair coin is tossed two times in succession, the set of equally likely outcomes is

$$\{\text{heads heads, heads tails, tails heads, tails tails}\}.$$

We can use this set to find the probability of getting heads on the first toss and heads on the second toss:

$$P(\text{heads and heads}) = \frac{\text{number of ways two heads can occur}}{\text{total number of possible outcomes}} = \frac{1}{4}.$$

We can also determine the probability of two heads, $\frac{1}{4}$, without having to list all the equally likely outcomes. The probability of heads on the first toss is $\frac{1}{2}$. The probability of heads on the second toss is also $\frac{1}{2}$. The product of these probabilities, $\frac{1}{2} \cdot \frac{1}{2}$, results in the probability of two heads, namely $\frac{1}{4}$. Thus,

$$P(\text{heads and heads}) = P(\text{heads}) \cdot P(\text{heads}).$$

In general, if two events are independent, we can calculate the probability of the first occurring and the second occurring by multiplying their probabilities.

***And* PROBABILITIES WITH INDEPENDENT EVENTS**

If A and B are independent events, then

$$P(A \text{ and } B) = P(A) \cdot P(B).$$

EXAMPLE 1 Independent Events on a Roulette Wheel

FIGURE 11 A U.S. roulette wheel

Figure 11 shows a U.S. roulette wheel that has 38 numbered slots (1 through 36, 0, and 00). Of the 38 compartments, 18 are black, 18 are red, and 2 are green. A play has the dealer spin the wheel and a small ball in opposite directions. As the ball slows to a stop, it can land with equal probability on any one of the 38 numbered slots. Find the probability of red occurring on two consecutive plays.

Solution The wheel has 38 equally likely outcomes and 18 are red. Thus, the probability of red occurring on a play is $\frac{18}{38}$, or $\frac{9}{19}$. The result that occurs on each play is independent of all previous results. Thus,

$$P(\text{red and red}) = P(\text{red}) \cdot P(\text{red}) = \frac{9}{19} \cdot \frac{9}{19} = \frac{81}{361} \approx 0.224.$$

The probability of red occurring on two consecutive plays is $\frac{81}{361}$.

Some roulette players incorrectly believe that if red occurs on two consecutive plays, then another color is "due." Because the events are independent, the outcomes of previous spins have no effect on any other spins.

Find the probability of green occurring on two consecutive plays on a roulette wheel.

The *and* rule for independent events can be extended to cover three or more independent events. Thus, if A, B, and C are independent events, then

$$P(A \text{ and } B \text{ and } C) = P(A) \cdot P(B) \cdot P(C).$$

EXAMPLE 2 Independent Events in a Family

The picture in the margin shows a family that had nine girls in a row. Find the probability of this occurrence.

UPI\CORBIS-NY

Solution If two or more events are independent, we can find the probability of them all occurring by multiplying their probabilities. The probability of a baby girl is $\frac{1}{2}$, so the probability of nine girls in a row is $\frac{1}{2}$ used as a factor nine times.

$$P(\text{nine girls is a row}) = \frac{1}{2} \cdot \frac{1}{2} \cdot \frac{1}{2} \cdot \frac{1}{2} \cdot \frac{1}{2} \cdot \frac{1}{2} \cdot \frac{1}{2} \cdot \frac{1}{2} \cdot \frac{1}{2}$$
$$= \left(\frac{1}{2}\right)^9 = \frac{1}{512}$$

The probability of a run of nine girls in a row is $\frac{1}{512}$. (If another child is born into the family, this event is independent of the other nine and the probability of a girl is still $\frac{1}{2}$.)

Find the probability of a family having four boys in a row.

TABLE 6 The Saffir/Simpson Hurricane Scale

Category	Winds (Miles per Hour)
1	74–95
2	96–110
3	111–130
4	131–155
5	> 155

Now let us return to the hurricane problem that opened this section. The Saffir/Simpson scale assigns numbers 1 through 5 to measure the disaster potential of a hurricane's winds. **Table 6** describes the scale. According to the National Hurricane Center, the probability that South Florida will be hit by a category 1 hurricane or higher in any single year is $\frac{5}{19}$, or approximately 0.26. In Example 3, we explore the risks of living in "Hurricane Alley."

EXAMPLE 3 Hurricanes and Probabilities

If the probability that South Florida will be hit by a hurricane in any single year is $\frac{5}{19}$,

a. What is the probability that South Florida will be hit by a hurricane in three consecutive years?

b. What is the probability that South Florida will not be hit by a hurricane in the next ten years?

Solution

a. The probability that South Florida will be hit by a hurricane in three consecutive years is

$$P(\text{hurricane and hurricane and hurricane})$$
$$= P(\text{hurricane}) \cdot P(\text{hurricane}) \cdot P(\text{hurricane}) = \frac{5}{19} \cdot \frac{5}{19} \cdot \frac{5}{19} = \frac{125}{6859} \approx 0.018.$$

b. We will first find the probability that South Florida will not be hit by a hurricane in any single year.

$$P(\text{no hurricane}) = 1 - P(\text{hurricane}) = 1 - \frac{5}{19} = \frac{14}{19} \approx 0.737$$

The probability of not being hit by a hurricane in a single year is $\frac{14}{19}$. Therefore, the probability of not being hit by a hurricane ten years in a row is $\frac{14}{19}$ used as a factor ten times.

$$P(\text{no hurricanes for ten years})$$
$$= P\begin{pmatrix}\text{no hurricane}\\ \text{for year 1}\end{pmatrix} \cdot P\begin{pmatrix}\text{no hurricane}\\ \text{for year 2}\end{pmatrix} \cdot P\begin{pmatrix}\text{no hurricane}\\ \text{for year 3}\end{pmatrix} \cdot \cdots \cdot P\begin{pmatrix}\text{no hurricane}\\ \text{for year 10}\end{pmatrix}$$
$$= \frac{14}{19} \cdot \frac{14}{19} \cdot \frac{14}{19} \cdot \cdots \cdot \frac{14}{19}$$
$$= \left(\frac{14}{19}\right)^{10} \approx (0.737)^{10} \approx 0.047$$

The probability that South Florida will not be hit by a hurricane in the next ten years is approximately 0.047.

STUDY TIP

When solving probability problems, begin by deciding whether to use the *or* formulas or the *and* formulas.

- *Or* problems usually have the word *or* in the statement of the problem. These problems involve only one selection.

Example:
If one person is selected, find the probability of selecting a man or a Canadian.

- *And* problems often do not have the word *and* in the statement of the problem. These problems involve more than one selection.

Example:
If two people are selected, find the probability that both are men.

Now we are ready to answer your question:

What is the probability that South Florida will be hit by a hurricane at least once in the next ten years?

Because $P(\text{not } E) = 1 - P(E)$,

$$P(\text{no hurricane for ten years}) = 1 - P(\text{at least one hurricane in ten years}).$$

In our logic chapter, we saw that the negation of "at least one" is "no."

Equivalently,

$$P(\text{at least one hurricane in ten years}) = 1 - P(\text{no hurricane for ten years})$$
$$= 1 - 0.047 = 0.953.$$

With a probability of 0.953, it is nearly certain that South Florida will be hit by a hurricane at least once in the next ten years.

THE PROBABILITY OF AN EVENT HAPPENING AT LEAST ONCE

$P(\text{event happening at least once}) = 1 - P(\text{event does not happen})$

If the probability that South Florida will be hit by a hurricane in any single year is $\frac{5}{19}$,

a. What is the probability that South Florida will be hit by a hurricane in four consecutive years?

b. What is the probability that South Florida will not be hit by a hurricane in the next four years?

c. What is the probability that South Florida will be hit by a hurricane at least once in the next four years?

Express all probabilities as fractions and as decimals rounded to three places.

And Probabilities with Dependent Events

5 chocolate-covered cherries lie within the 20 pieces.

Chocolate lovers, please help yourselves! There are 20 mouth-watering tidbits to select from. What's that? You want 2? And you prefer chocolate-covered cherries? The problem is that there are only 5 chocolate-covered cherries and it's impossible to tell what is inside each piece. They're all shaped exactly alike. At any rate, reach in, select a piece, enjoy, choose another piece, eat, and be well. There is nothing like savoring a good piece of chocolate in the midst of all this chit-chat about probability and hurricanes.

Another question? You want to know what your chances are of selecting 2 chocolate-covered cherries? Well, let's see. Five of the 20 pieces are chocolate-covered cherries, so the probability of getting one of them on your first selection is $\frac{5}{20}$, or $\frac{1}{4}$. Now, suppose that you did choose a chocolate-covered cherry on your first pick. Eat it slowly; there's no guarantee that you'll select your favorite on the second selection. There are now only 19 pieces of chocolate left. Only 4 are chocolate-covered cherries. The probability of getting a chocolate-covered cherry on your second try is 4 out of 19, or $\frac{4}{19}$. This is a different probability than the $\frac{1}{4}$ probability on your first selection. Selecting a chocolate-covered cherry the first time changes what is in the candy box. The probability of what you select the second time *is* affected by the outcome of the first event. For this reason, we say that these are *dependent events*.

DEPENDENT EVENTS

Two events are **dependent events** if the occurrence of one of them has an effect on the probability of the other.

Once a chocolate-covered cherry is selected, only 4 chocolate-covered cherries lie within the remaining 19 pieces.

The probability of selecting two chocolate-covered cherries in a row can be found by multiplying the $\frac{1}{4}$ probability on the first selection by the $\frac{4}{19}$ probability on the second selection:

$$P(\text{chocolate-covered cherry and chocolate-covered cherry})$$
$$= P(\text{chocolate-covered cherry}) \cdot P\begin{pmatrix}\text{chocolate-covered cherry}\\ \text{given that one was selected}\end{pmatrix}$$
$$= \frac{1}{4} \cdot \frac{4}{19} = \frac{1}{19}.$$

The probability of selecting two chocolate-covered cherries in a row is $\frac{1}{19}$. This is a special case of finding the probability that each of two dependent events occurs.

***And* PROBABILITIES WITH DEPENDENT EVENTS**

If A and B are dependent events, then

$$P(A \text{ and } B) = P(A) \cdot P(B \text{ given that } A \text{ has occurred}).$$

EXAMPLE 4 An *And* Probability with Dependent Events

Good news: You won a free trip to Madrid and can take two people with you, all expenses paid. Bad news: Ten of your cousins have appeared out of nowhere and are begging you to take them. You write each cousin's name on a card, place the cards in a hat, and select one name. Then you select a second name without replacing the first card. If three of your ten cousins speak Spanish, find the probability of selecting two Spanish-speaking cousins.

STUDY TIP

Example 4 can also be solved using the combinations formula.

$$P(\text{two Spanish speakers}) = \frac{\text{number of ways of selecting 2 Spanish-speaking cousins}}{\text{number of ways of selecting 2 cousins}}$$

$$= \frac{_3C_2}{_{10}C_2}$$

2 Spanish speakers selected from 3 Spanish-speaking cousins (numerator)

2 cousins selected from 10 cousins (denominator)

$$= \frac{3}{45} = \frac{1}{15}$$

Solution Because $P(A \text{ and } B) = P(A) \cdot P(B \text{ given that } A \text{ has occurred})$, then

$P(\text{two Spanish-speaking cousins})$

$= P(\text{speaks Spanish and speaks Spanish})$

$= P(\text{speaks Spanish}) \cdot P\left(\begin{array}{c}\text{speaks Spanish given that a Spanish-speaking}\\ \text{cousin was selected first}\end{array}\right)$

$= \dfrac{3}{10} \cdot \dfrac{2}{9}$

There are ten cousins, three of whom speak Spanish.

After picking a Spanish-speaking cousin, there are nine cousins left, two of whom speak Spanish.

$= \dfrac{6}{90} = \dfrac{1}{15} \approx 0.067.$

The probability of selecting two Spanish-speaking cousins is $\frac{1}{15}$.

CHECK POINT 4 You are dealt two cards from a 52-card deck. Find the probability of getting two kings.

The multiplication rule for dependent events can be extended to cover three or more dependent events. For example, in the case of three such events,

$P(A \text{ and } B \text{ and } C)$

$= P(A) \cdot P(B \text{ given that } A \text{ occurred}) \cdot P(C \text{ given that } A \text{ and } B \text{ occurred}).$

EXAMPLE 5 An *And* Probability with Three Dependent Events

Three people are randomly selected, one person at a time, from five freshmen, two sophomores, and four juniors. Find the probability that the first two people selected are freshmen and the third is a junior.

Solution

$P(\text{first two are freshmen and the third is a junior})$

$= P(\text{freshman}) \cdot P\left(\begin{array}{c}\text{freshman given that a}\\ \text{freshman was selected first}\end{array}\right) \cdot P\left(\begin{array}{c}\text{junior given that a freshman was}\\ \text{selected first and a freshman was}\\ \text{selected second}\end{array}\right)$

$= \dfrac{5}{11} \cdot \dfrac{4}{10} \cdot \dfrac{4}{9}$

There are 11 people, five of whom are freshmen.

After picking a freshman, there are 10 people left, four of whom are freshmen.

After the first two selections, 9 people are left, four of whom are juniors.

$= \dfrac{8}{99}$

The probability that the first two people selected are freshmen and the third is a junior is $\frac{8}{99}$.

CHECK POINT 5 You are dealt three cards from a 52-card deck. Find the probability of getting three hearts.

2 Compute conditional probabilities.

Conditional Probability

We have seen that for any two dependent events A and B,

$$P(A \text{ and } B) = P(A) \cdot P(B \text{ given that } A \text{ occurs}).$$

The probability of B given that A occurs is called *conditional probability,* denoted by $P(B|A)$.

CONDITIONAL PROBABILITY

The probability of event B, assuming that the event A has already occurred, is called the **conditional probability** of B, given A. This probability is denoted by $P(B|A)$.

It is helpful to think of the conditional probability $P(B|A)$ as the **probability that event B occurs if the sample space is restricted to the outcomes associated with event A.**

EXAMPLE 6 Finding Conditional Probability

A letter is randomly selected from the letters of the English alphabet. Find the probability of selecting a vowel, given that the outcome is a letter that precedes h.

Solution We are looking for

$$P(\text{vowel}|\text{letter precedes h}).$$

This is the probability of a vowel if the sample space is restricted to the set of letters that precede h. Thus, the sample space is given by

$$S = \{a, b, c, d, e, f, g\}.$$

There are seven possible outcomes in the sample space. We can select a vowel from this set in one of two ways: a or e. Therefore, the probability of selecting a vowel, given that the outcome is a letter that precedes h, is $\frac{2}{7}$.

$$P(\text{vowel}|\text{letter precedes h}) = \frac{2}{7}$$

A letter is randomly selected from the letters of the English alphabet. Find the probability of selecting a letter that precedes h, given that the outcome is a vowel. (Do not include the letter y among the vowels.)

EXAMPLE 7 Finding Conditional Probability

You are dealt one card from a 52-card deck.

a. Find the probability of getting a heart, given that the card you were dealt is a red card.

b. Find the probability of getting a red card, given that the card you were dealt is a heart.

BLITZER BONUS

COINCIDENCES

The phone rings and it's the friend you were just thinking of. You're driving down the road and a song you were humming in your head comes on the radio. Although these coincidences seem strange, perhaps even mystical, they're not. Coincidences are bound to happen. Ours is a world in which there are a great many potential coincidences, each with a low probability of occurring. When these surprising coincidences happen, we are amazed and remember them. However, we pay little attention to the countless number of non-coincidences: How often do you think of your friend and she doesn't call, or how often does she call when you're not thinking about her? By noticing the hits and ignoring the misses, we incorrectly perceive that there is a relationship between the occurrence of two independent events.

Another problem is that we often underestimate the probabilities of coincidences in certain situations, acting with more surprise than we should when they occur. For example, in a group of only 23 people, the probability that two individuals share a birthday (same month and day) is greater than $\frac{1}{2}$. Above 50 people, the probability of any two people sharing a birthday approaches certainty. You can verify the probabilities behind the coincidence of shared birthdays in relatively small groups by working Exercise 87 in Exercise Set 7.

Solution

a. We begin with

$$P(\text{heart} \mid \text{red card}).$$

Probability of getting a heart if the sample space is restricted to the set of red cards

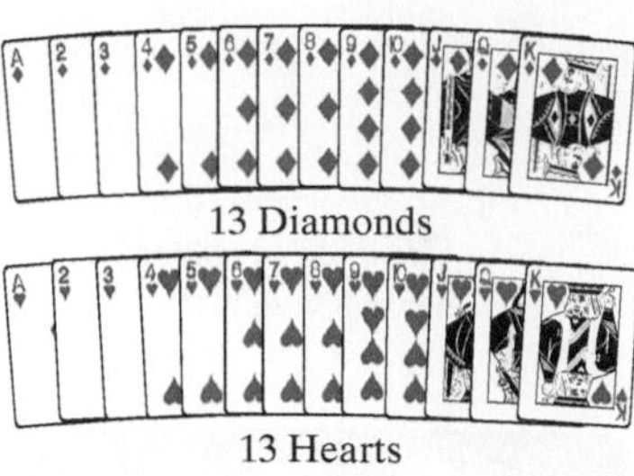

FIGURE 12

The sample space is shown in **Figure 12**. There are 26 outcomes in the sample space. We can get a heart from this set in 13 ways. Thus,

$$P(\text{heart}|\text{red card}) = \frac{13}{26} = \frac{1}{2}.$$

b. We now find

$$P(\text{red card} \mid \text{heart}).$$

Probability of getting a red card if the sample space is restricted to the set of hearts

FIGURE 13

The sample space is shown in **Figure 13**. There are 13 outcomes in the sample space. All of the outcomes are red. We can get a red card from this set in 13 ways. Thus,

$$P(\text{red card}|\text{heart}) = \frac{13}{13} = 1.$$

Example 7 illustrates that $P(\text{heart}|\text{red card})$ is not equal to $P(\text{red card}|\text{heart})$. In general, $P(B|A) \neq P(A|B)$.

You are dealt one card from a 52-card deck.

a. Find the probability of getting a black card, given the card you were dealt is a spade.

b. Find the probability of getting a spade, given the card you were dealt is a black card.

EXAMPLE 8 Conditional Probabilities with Real-World Data

When women turn 40, their gynecologists typically remind them that it is time to undergo mammography screening for breast cancer. The data in **Table 7** are based on 100,000 U.S. women, ages 40 to 50, who participated in mammography screening.

TABLE 7 Mammography Screening on 100,000 U.S. Women, Ages 40 to 50

	Breast Cancer	No Breast Cancer	Total
Positive Mammogram	720	6944	7664
Negative Mammogram	80	92,256	92,336
Total	800	99,200	100,000

Source: Gerd Gigerenzer, *Calculated Risks*. Simon and Schuster, 2002.

Assuming that these numbers are representative of all U.S. women ages 40 to 50, find the probability that a woman in this age range

a. has a positive mammogram, given that she does not have breast cancer.

b. does not have breast cancer, given that she has a positive mammogram.

Solution

a. We begin with the probability that a U.S. woman aged 40 to 50 has a positive mammogram, given that she does not have breast cancer:

$$P(\text{positive mammogram}|\text{no breast cancer}).$$

This is the probability of a positive mammogram if the data are restricted to women without breast cancer:

	No Breast Cancer
Positive Mammogram	6944
Negative Mammogram	92,256
Total	99,200

Within the restricted data, there are 6944 women with positive mammograms and 6944 + 92,256, or 99,200 women without breast cancer. Thus,

$$P(\text{positive mammogram}|\text{no breast cancer}) = \frac{6944}{99{,}200} = 0.07.$$

Among women without breast cancer, the probability of a positive mammogram is 0.07.

b. Now, we find the probability that a U.S. woman aged 40 to 50 does not have breast cancer, given that she has a positive mammogram:

$$P(\text{no breast cancer}|\text{positive mammogram}).$$

This is the probability of not having breast cancer if the data are restricted to women with positive mammograms:

	Breast Cancer	**No Breast Cancer**	**Total**
Positive Mammogram	720	6944	7664

Within the restricted data, there are 6944 women without breast cancer and 720 + 6944, or 7664 women with positive mammograms. Thus,

$$P(\text{no breast cancer} \mid \text{positive mammogram}) = \frac{6944}{7664} \approx 0.906.$$

Among women with positive mammograms, the probability of not having breast cancer is $\frac{6944}{7664}$, or approximately 0.906.

STUDY TIP

Example 8 shows that the probability of a positive mammogram among women without breast cancer, 0.07, is not the same as the probability of not having breast cancer among women with positive mammograms, approximately 0.9. We have seen that the conditional probability of *B*, given *A*, is not the same as the conditional probability of *A*, given *B*:

$$P(B|A) \neq P(A|B).$$

Use the data in **Table 7** at the bottom of the previous page to find the probability that a U.S. woman aged 40 to 50

a. has a positive mammogram, given that she has breast cancer.

b. has breast cancer, given that she has a positive mammogram.

Express probabilities as decimals and, if necessary, round to three decimal places.

We have seen that $P(B|A)$ is the probability that event B occurs if the sample space is restricted to event A. Thus,

$$P(B|A) = \frac{\text{number of outcomes of } B \text{ that are in the restricted sample space } A}{\text{number of outcomes in the restricted sample space } A}.$$

This can be stated in terms of the following formula:

A FORMULA FOR CONDITIONAL PROBABILITY

$$P(B|A) = \frac{n(B \cap A)}{n(A)} = \frac{\text{number of outcomes common to } B \text{ and } A}{\text{number of outcomes in } A}$$

Exercise Set 7

Practice and Application Exercises

Exercises 1–26 involve probabilities with independent events.

Use the spinner shown to solve Exercises 1–10. It is equally probable that the pointer will land on any one of the six regions. If the pointer lands on a borderline, spin again. If the pointer is spun twice, find the probability it will land on

1. green and then red.
2. yellow and then green.
3. yellow and then yellow.
4. red and then red.
5. a color other than red each time.
6. a color other than green each time.

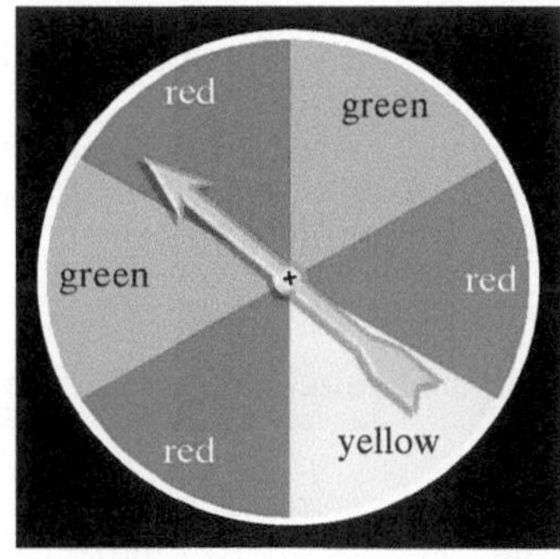

If the pointer is spun three times, find the probability it will land on

7. green and then red and then yellow.
8. red and then red and then green.
9. red every time.
10. green every time.

In Exercises 11–14, a single die is rolled twice. Find the probability of rolling

11. a 2 the first time and a 3 the second time.
12. a 5 the first time and a 1 the second time.
13. an even number the first time and a number greater than 2 the second time.
14. an odd number the first time and a number less than 3 the second time.

In Exercises 15–20, you draw one card from a 52-card deck. Then the card is replaced in the deck, the deck is shuffled, and you draw again. Find the probability of drawing

15. a picture card the first time and a heart the second time.
16. a jack the first time and a club the second time.
17. a king each time.
18. a 3 each time.
19. a red card each time.
20. a black card each time.
21. If you toss a fair coin six times, what is the probability of getting all heads?
22. If you toss a fair coin seven times, what is the probability of getting all tails?

In Exercises 23–24, a coin is tossed and a die is rolled. Find the probability of getting

23. a head and a number greater than 4.
24. a tail and a number less than 5.
25. The probability that South Florida will be hit by a major hurricane (category 4 or 5) in any single year is $\frac{1}{16}$. (*Source:* National Hurricane Center)
    a. What is the probability that South Florida will be hit by a major hurricane two years in a row?
    b. What is the probability that South Florida will be hit by a major hurricane in three consecutive years?
    c. What is the probability that South Florida will not be hit by a major hurricane in the next ten years?
    d. What is the probability that South Florida will be hit by a major hurricane at least once in the next ten years?
26. The probability that a region prone to flooding will flood in any single year is $\frac{1}{10}$.
    a. What is the probability of a flood two years in a row?
    b. What is the probability of flooding in three consecutive years?
    c. What is the probability of no flooding for ten consecutive years?
    d. What is the probability of flooding at least once in the next ten years?

The graph shows that U.S. adults dependent on tobacco have a greater probability of suffering from some ailments than the general adult population. When making two or more selections from populations with large numbers, such as the U.S. adult population or the population dependent on tobacco, we assume that each selection is independent of every other selection. In Exercises 27–32, assume that the selections are independent events.

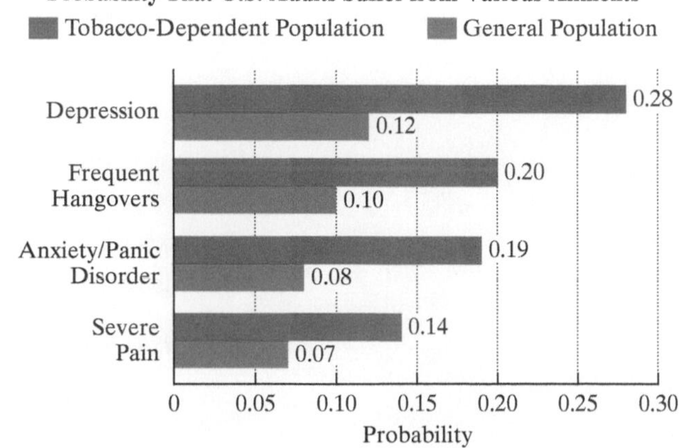

Source: MARS 2005 OTC/DTC

27. If two adults are randomly selected from the general population, what is the probability that they both suffer from depression?

28. It two adults are randomly selected from the population of cigarette smokers, what is the probability that they both suffer from depression?

29. If three adults are randomly selected from the population of cigarette smokers, what is the probability that they all suffer from frequent hangovers?

30. If three adults are randomly selected from the general population, what is the probability that they all suffer from frequent hangovers?

31. If three adults are randomly selected from the population of cigarette smokers, what is the probability, expressed as a decimal correct to four places, that at least one person suffers from anxiety/panic disorder?

32. If three adults are randomly selected from the population of cigarette smokers, what is the probability, expressed as a decimal correct to four places, that at least one person suffers from severe pain?

Exercises 33–48 involve probabilities with dependent events.

In Exercises 33–36, we return to our box of chocolates. There are 30 chocolates in the box, all identically shaped. Five are filled with coconut, 10 with caramel, and 15 are solid chocolate. You randomly select one piece, eat it, and then select a second piece. Find the probability of selecting

33. two solid chocolates in a row.

34. two caramel-filled chocolates in a row.

35. a coconut-filled chocolate followed by a caramel-filled chocolate.

36. a coconut-filled chocolate followed by a solid chocolate.

In Exercises 37–42, consider a political discussion group consisting of 5 Democrats, 6 Republicans, and 4 Independents. Suppose that two group members are randomly selected, in succession, to attend a political convention. Find the probability of selecting

37. two Democrats.

38. two Republicans.

39. an Independent and then a Republican.

40. an Independent and then a Democrat.

41. no Independents.

42. no Democrats.

In Exercises 43–48, an ice chest contains six cans of apple juice, eight cans of grape juice, four cans of orange juice, and two cans of mango juice. Suppose that you reach into the container and randomly select three cans in succession. Find the probability of selecting

43. three cans of apple juice.

44. three cans of grape juice.

45. a can of grape juice, then a can of orange juice, then a can of mango juice.

46. a can of apple juice, then a can of grape juice, then a can of orange juice.

47. no grape juice.

48. no apple juice.

In Exercises 49–56, the numbered disks shown are placed in a box and one disk is selected at random.

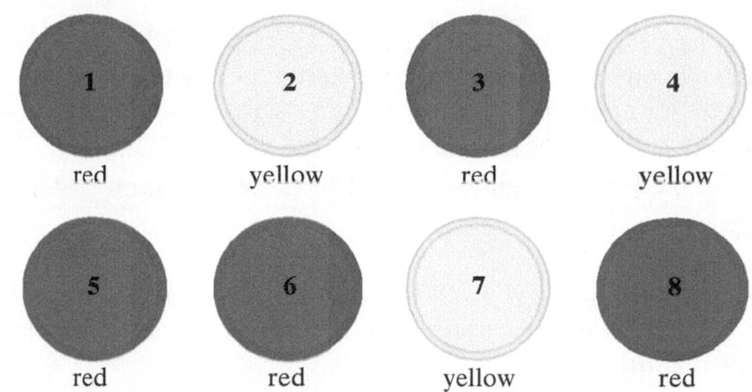

Find the probability of selecting

49. a 3, given that a red disk is selected.

50. a 7, given that a yellow disk is selected.

51. an even number, given that a yellow disk is selected.

52. an odd number, given that a red disk is selected.

53. a red disk, given that an odd number is selected.

54. a yellow disk, given that an odd number is selected.

55. a red disk, given that the number selected is at least 5.

56. a yellow disk, given that the number selected is at most 3.

The table shows the outcome of car accidents in Florida for a recent year by whether or not the driver wore a seat belt. Use the data to solve Exercises 57–60. Express probabilities as fractions and as decimals rounded to three places.

CAR ACCIDENTS IN FLORIDA

	Wore Seat Belt	No Seat Belt	Total
Driver Survived	412,368	162,527	574,895
Driver Died	510	1601	2111
Total	412,878	164,128	577,006

Source: Alan Agresti and Christine Franklin, *Statistics*, Prentice Hall, 2007

57. Find the probability of surviving a car accident, given that the driver wore a seat belt.

58. Find the probability of not surviving a car accident, given that the driver did not wear a seat belt.

59. Find the probability of wearing a seat belt, given that a driver survived a car accident.

60. Find the probability of not wearing a seat belt, given that a driver did not survive a car accident.

In Exercises 61–72, we return to the table showing the distribution, by marital status and gender, of the 235.8 million Americans ages 18 or older.

MARITAL STATUS OF THE U.S. POPULATION, AGES 18 OR OLDER, IN MILLIONS

	Never Married	Married	Widowed	Divorced	Total
Male	37.5	64.7	2.7	9.6	114.5
Female	31.7	65.2	11.2	13.2	121.3
Total	69.2	129.9	13.9	22.8	235.8

Source: U.S. Census Bureau

If one person is selected from the population described in the table, find the probability, expressed as a decimal rounded to three places, that the person

61. is not divorced.

62. is not widowed.

63. is widowed or divorced.

64. has never been married or is divorced.

65. is male or divorced.

66. is female or divorced.

67. is male, given that this person is divorced.

68. is female, given that this person is divorced.

69. is widowed, given that this person is a woman.

70. is divorced, given that this person is a man.

71. has never been married or is married, given that this person is a man.

72. has never been married or is married, given that this person is a woman.

Writing in Mathematics

73. Explain how to find *and* probabilities with independent events. Give an example.

74. Explain how to find *and* probabilities with dependent events. Give an example.

75. What does $P(B|A)$ mean? Give an example.

In Exercises 76–80, write a probability problem involving the word "and" whose solution results in the probability fractions shown.

76. $\frac{1}{2} \cdot \frac{1}{2}$ **77.** $\frac{1}{6} \cdot \frac{1}{6} \cdot \frac{1}{6}$ **78.** $\frac{1}{2} \cdot \frac{1}{6}$

79. $\frac{13}{52} \cdot \frac{12}{51}$ **80.** $\frac{1}{4} \cdot \frac{3}{5}$

Critical Thinking Exercises

Make Sense? *In Exercises 81–84, determine whether each statement makes sense or does not make sense, and explain your reasoning.*

81. If a fourth child is born into a family with three boys, the odds in favor of a girl are better than 1:1.

82. In a group of five men and five women, the probability of randomly selecting a man is $\frac{1}{2}$, so if I select two people from the group, the probability that both are men is $\frac{1}{2} \cdot \frac{1}{2}$.

83. I found the probability of getting rain at least once in ten days by calculating the probability that none of the days have rain and subtracting this probability from 1.

84. I must have made an error calculating probabilities because $P(A|B)$ is not the same as $P(B|A)$.

85. If the probability of being hospitalized during a year is 0.1, find the probability that no one in a family of five will be hospitalized in a year.

86. If a single die is rolled five times, what is the probability it lands on 2 on the first, third, and fourth rolls, but not on either of the other rolls?

87. Probabilities and Coincidence of Shared Birthdays

a. If two people are selected at random, the probability that they do not have the same birthday (day and month) is $\frac{365}{365} \cdot \frac{364}{365}$. Explain why this is so. (Ignore leap years and assume 365 days in a year.)

b. If three people are selected at random, find the probability that they all have different birthdays.

c. If three people are selected at random, find the probability that at least two of them have the same birthday.

d. If 20 people are selected at random, find the probability that at least 2 of them have the same birthday.

e. How large a group is needed to give a 0.5 chance of at least two people having the same birthday?

88. Nine cards numbered from 1 through 9 are placed into a box and two cards are selected without replacement. Find the probability that both numbers selected are odd, given that their sum is even.

89. If a single die is rolled twice, find the probability of rolling an odd number and a number greater than 4 in either order.

Group Exercises

90. Do you live in an area prone to catastrophes, such as earthquakes, fires, tornados, hurricanes, or floods? If so, research the probability of this catastrophe occurring in a single year. Group members should then use this probability to write and solve a problem similar to Exercise 25 in this exercise set.

91. Group members should use the table for Exercises 61–72 to write and solve four probability problems different than those in the exercises. Two should involve *or* (one with events that are mutually exclusive and one with events that are not), one should involve *and*—that is, events in succession—and one should involve conditional probability.

OBJECTIVES

1 Compute expected value.
2 Use expected value to solve applied problems.
3 Use expected value to determine the average payoff or loss in a game of chance.

8 Expected Value

Blend Images\Getty Images - Blend Images

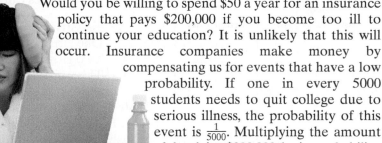

Would you be willing to spend \$50 a year for an insurance policy that pays \$200,000 if you become too ill to continue your education? It is unlikely that this will occur. Insurance companies make money by compensating us for events that have a low probability. If one in every 5000 students needs to quit college due to serious illness, the probability of this event is $\frac{1}{5000}$. Multiplying the amount of the claim, \$200,000, by its probability, $\frac{1}{5000}$, tells the insurance company what to expect to pay out on average for each policy:

$$\$200{,}000 \times \frac{1}{5000} = \$40.$$

Amount of the claim (\$200,000); Probability of paying the claim ($\frac{1}{5000}$)

Over the long run, the insurance company can expect to pay \$40 for each policy it sells. By selling the policy for \$50, the expected profit is \$10 per policy. If 400,000 students choose to take out this insurance, the company can expect to make 400,000 × \$10, or \$4,000,000.

Expected value is a mathematical way to use probabilities to determine what to expect in various situations over the long run. Expected value is used to determine premiums on insurance policies, weigh the risks versus the benefits of alternatives in business ventures, and indicate to a player of any game of chance what will happen if the game is played repeatedly.

The standard way to find expected value is to multiply each possible outcome by its probability, and then add these products. We use the letter E to represent expected value.

1 Compute expected value.

EXAMPLE 1 Computing Expected Value

Find the expected value for the outcome of the roll of a fair die.

Solution The outcomes are 1, 2, 3, 4, 5, and 6, each with a probability of $\frac{1}{6}$. The expected value, E, is computed by multiplying each outcome by its probability and then adding these products.

$$E = 1\cdot\frac{1}{6} + 2\cdot\frac{1}{6} + 3\cdot\frac{1}{6} + 4\cdot\frac{1}{6} + 5\cdot\frac{1}{6} + 6\cdot\frac{1}{6}$$

$$= \frac{1+2+3+4+5+6}{6} = \frac{21}{6} = 3.5$$

The expected value of the roll of a fair die is 3.5. This means that if the die is rolled repeatedly, there is an average of 3.5 dots per roll over the long run. This expected value cannot occur on a single roll of the die. However, it is a long-run average of the various outcomes that can occur when a fair die is rolled.

It is equally probable that a pointer will land on any one of four regions, numbered 1 through 4. Find the expected value for where the pointer will stop.

EXAMPLE 2 Computing Expected Value

Find the expected value for the number of girls for a family with three children.

Solution A family with three children can have 0, 1, 2, or 3 girls. There are eight ways these outcomes can occur.

No girls : Boy Boy Boy — One way
One girl : Girl Boy Boy, Boy Girl Boy, Boy Boy Girl — Three ways
Two girls : Girl Girl Boy, Girl Boy Girl, Boy Girl Girl — Three ways
Three girls : Girl Girl Girl — One way

TABLE 8 Outcomes and Probabilities for the Number of Girls in a Three-Child Family

Outcome: Number of Girls	Probability
0	$\frac{1}{8}$
1	$\frac{3}{8}$
2	$\frac{3}{8}$
3	$\frac{1}{8}$

Table 8 shows the probabilities for 0, 1, 2, and 3 girls.

The expected value, E, is computed by multiplying each outcome by its probability and then adding these products.

$$E = 0\cdot\frac{1}{8} + 1\cdot\frac{3}{8} + 2\cdot\frac{3}{8} + 3\cdot\frac{1}{8} = \frac{0+3+6+3}{8} = \frac{12}{8} = \frac{3}{2} = 1.5$$

The expected value is 1.5. This means that if we record the number of girls in many different three-child families, the average number of girls for all these families will be 1.5. In a three-child family, half the children are expected to be girls, so the expected value of 1.5 is consistent with this observation.

TABLE 9

Number of Heads	Probability
0	$\frac{1}{16}$
1	$\frac{4}{16}$
2	$\frac{6}{16}$
3	$\frac{4}{16}$
4	$\frac{1}{16}$

A fair coin is tossed four times in succession. **Table 9** shows the probabilities for the different number of heads that can arise. Find the expected value for the number of heads.

2 Use expected value to solve applied problems.

Applications of Expected Value

Empirical probabilities can be determined in many situations by examining what has occurred in the past. For example, an insurance company can tally various claim amounts over many years. If 15% of these amounts are for a \$2000 claim, then the probability of this claim amount is 0.15. By studying sales of similar houses in a particular area, a realtor can determine the probability that he or she will sell a listed house, another agent will sell the house, or the listed house will remain unsold. Once probabilities have been assigned to all possible outcomes, expected value can indicate what is expected to happen in the long run. These ideas are illustrated in Examples 3 and 4.

EXAMPLE 3 Determining an Insurance Premium

An automobile insurance company has determined the probabilities for various claim amounts for drivers ages 16 through 21, shown in **Table 10**.

TABLE 10 Probabilities for Auto Claims

Amount of Claim (to the nearest \$2000)	Probability
\$0	0.70
\$2000	0.15
\$4000	0.08
\$6000	0.05
\$8000	0.01
\$10,000	0.01

a. Calculate the expected value and describe what this means in practical terms.

b. How much should the company charge as an average premium so that it does not lose or gain money on its claim costs?

Solution

a. The expected value, E, is computed by multiplying each outcome by its probability and then adding these products.

$$\begin{aligned} E &= \$0(0.70) + \$2000(0.15) + \$4000(0.08) + \$6000(0.05) \\ &\quad + \$8000(0.01) + \$10{,}000(0.01) \\ &= \$0 + \$300 + \$320 + \$300 + \$80 + \$100 \\ &= \$1100 \end{aligned}$$

The expected value is \$1100. This means that in the long run the average cost of a claim is \$1100. The insurance company should expect to pay \$1100 per car insured to people in the 16–21 age group.

b. At the very least, the amount that the company should charge as an average premium for each person in the 16–21 age group is $1100. In this way, it will not lose or gain money on its claims costs. It's quite probable that the company will charge more, moving from break-even to profit.

Work Example 3 again if the probabilities for claims of $0 and $10,000 are reversed. Thus, the probability of a $0 claim is 0.01 and the probability of a $10,000 claim is 0.70.

Business decisions are interpreted in terms of dollars and cents. In these situations, **expected value is calculated by multiplying the gain or loss for each possible outcome by its probability. The sum of these products is the expected value.**

EXAMPLE 4 Expectation in a Business Decision

You are a realtor considering listing a $500,000 house. The cost of advertising and providing food for other realtors during open showings is anticipated to cost you $5000. The house is quite unusual and you are given a four-month listing. If the house is unsold after four months, you lose the listing and receive nothing. You anticipate that the probability you sell your own listed house is 0.3, the probability that another agent sells your listing is 0.2, and the probability that the house is unsold after 4 months is 0.5. If you sell your own listed house, the commission is a hefty $30,000. If another realtor sells your listing, the commission is $15,000. The bottom line: You will not take the listing unless you anticipate earning at least $6000. Should you list the house?

THE REALTOR'S SUMMARY SHEET

My Cost:	$5000
My Possible Income:	
I sell house:	$30,000
Another agent sells house:	$15,000
House unsold after 4 months:	$0
The Probabilities:	
I sell house:	0.3
Another agent sells house:	0.2
House unsold after 4 months:	0.5
My Bottom Line: I take the listing only if I anticipate earning at least $6000.	

Solution Shown in the margin is a summary of the amounts of money and probabilities that will determine your decision. The expected value in this situation is the sum of each income possibility times its probability. The expected value represents the amount you can anticipate earning if you take the listing. If the expected value is not at least $6000, you should not list the house.

The possible incomes listed in the margin, $30,000, $15,000, and $0, do not take into account your $5000 costs. Because of these costs, each amount needs to be reduced by $5000. Thus, you can gain $30,000 − $5000, or $25,000, or you can gain $15,000 − $5000, or $10,000. Because $0 − $5000 = −$5000, you can also lose $5000. **Table 11** summarizes possible outcomes if you take the listing, and their respective probabilities.

TABLE 11 Gains, Losses, and Probabilities for Listing a $500,000 House

Outcome	Gain or Loss	Probability
Sells house	$25,000	0.3
Another agent sells house	$10,000	0.2
House doesn't sell	−$5000	0.5

The expected value, E, is computed by multiplying each gain or loss in **Table 11** by its probability and then adding these results.

$$E = \$25{,}000(0.3) + \$10{,}000(0.2) + (-\$5000)(0.5)$$
$$= \$7500 + \$2000 + (-\$2500) = \$7000$$

You can expect to earn $7000 by listing the house. Because the expected value exceeds $6000, you should list the house.

3 Use expected value to determine the average payoff or loss in a game of chance.

The SAT is a multiple-choice test. Each question has five possible answers. The test taker must select one answer for each question or not answer the question. One point is awarded for each correct response and $\frac{1}{4}$ point is subtracted for each wrong answer. No points are added or subtracted for answers left blank. **Table 12** summarizes the information for the outcomes of a random guess on an SAT question. Find the expected point value of a random guess. Is there anything to gain or lose on average by guessing? Explain your answer.

TABLE 12 Gains and Losses for Guessing on the SAT

Outcome	Gain or Loss	Probability
Guess correctly	1	$\frac{1}{5}$
Guess incorrectly	$-\frac{1}{4}$	$\frac{4}{5}$

Expected Value and Games of Chance

Expected value can be interpreted as the average payoff in a contest or game when either is played a large number of times. **To find the expected value of a game, multiply the gain or loss for each possible outcome by its probability. Then add the products.**

EXAMPLE 5 Expected Value as Average Payoff

A game is played using one die. If the die is rolled and shows 1, 2, or 3, the player wins nothing. If the die shows 4 or 5, the player wins \$3. If the die shows 6, the player wins \$9. If there is a charge of \$1 to play the game, what is the game's expected value? Describe what this means in practical terms.

Solution Because there is a charge of \$1 to play the game, a player who wins \$9 gains \$9 − \$1, or \$8. A player who wins \$3 gains \$3 − \$1, or \$2. If the player gets \$0, there is a loss of \$1 because \$0 − \$1 = −\$1. The outcomes for the die, with their respective gains, losses, and probabilities, are summarized in **Table 13**.

TABLE 13 Gains, Losses, and Probabilities in a Game of Chance

Outcome	Gain or Loss	Probability
1, 2, or 3	−\$1	$\frac{3}{6}$
4 or 5	\$2	$\frac{2}{6}$
6	\$8	$\frac{1}{6}$

Expected value, *E*, is computed by multiplying each gain or loss in **Table 13** by its probability and then adding these results.

$$E = (-\$1)\left(\frac{3}{6}\right) + \$2\left(\frac{2}{6}\right) + \$8\left(\frac{1}{6}\right)$$
$$= \frac{-\$3 + \$4 + \$8}{6} = \frac{\$9}{6} = \$1.50$$

The expected value is \$1.50. This means that in the long run, a player can expect to win an average of \$1.50 for each game played. However, this does not mean that the player will win \$1.50 on any single game. It does mean that if the game is played repeatedly, then, in the long run, the player should expect to win about \$1.50 per play on the average. If 1000 games are played, one could expect to win \$1500. However, if only three games are played, one's net winnings can range between −\$3 and \$24, even though the expected winnings are \$1.50(3), or \$4.50.

BLITZER BONUS

GAMBLING IT AWAY

Miro Vintoniv\Stock Boston

Games in gambling casinos have probabilities and payoffs that result in negative expected values. This means that players will lose money in the long run. With no clocks on the walls or windows to look out of, casinos bet that players will forget about time and play longer. This brings casino owners closer to what they can expect to earn, while negative expected values sneak up on losing patrons. (No wonder they provide free beverages!)

A Potpourri of Gambling-Related Data

- Population of Las Vegas: 535,000
- Slot Machines in Las Vegas: 150,000
- Average Earnings per Slot Machine per Year: \$100,000
- Average Amount Lost per Hour in Las Vegas Casinos: \$696,000
- Average Amount an American Adult Loses Gambling per Year: \$350
- Average Amount a Nevada Resident Loses Gambling per Year: \$1000

Source: Paul Grobman, *Vital Statistics,* Plume, 2005.

CHECK POINT 5 A charity is holding a raffle and sells 1000 raffle tickets for $2 each. One of the tickets will be selected to win a grand prize of $1000. Two other tickets will be selected to win consolation prizes of $50 each. Fill in the missing column in **Table 14**. Then find the expected value if you buy one raffle ticket. Describe what this means in practical terms. What can you expect to happen if you purchase five tickets?

TABLE 14 Gains, Losses, and Probabilities in a Raffle

Outcome	Gain or Loss	Probability
Win Grand Prize		$\frac{1}{1000}$
Win Consolation Prize		$\frac{2}{1000}$
Win Nothing		$\frac{997}{1000}$

FIGURE 14 A U.S. roulette wheel

Unlike the game in Example 5, games in gambling casinos are set up so that players will lose in the long run. These games have negative expected values. Such a game is roulette, French for "little wheel." We first saw the roulette wheel in Section 7. It is shown again in **Figure 14**. Recall that the wheel has 38 numbered slots (1 through 36, 0, and 00). In each play of the game, the dealer spins the wheel and a small ball in opposite directions. The ball is equally likely to come to rest in any one of the slots, which are colored black, red, or green. Gamblers can place a number of different bets in roulette. Example 6 illustrates one gambling option.

EXAMPLE 6 Expected Value and Roulette

One way to bet in roulette is to place $1 on a single number. If the ball lands on that number, you are awarded $35 and get to keep the $1 that you paid to play the game. If the ball lands on any one of the other 37 slots, you are awarded nothing and the $1 that you bet is collected. Find the expected value for playing roulette if you bet $1 on number 20. Describe what this means.

Solution **Table 15** contains the two outcomes of interest: the ball landing on your number, 20, and the ball landing elsewhere (in any one of the other 37 slots). The outcomes, their respective gains, losses, and probabilities, are summarized in the table.

TABLE 15 Playing One Number with a 35 to 1 Payoff in Roulette

Outcome	Gain or Loss	Probability
Ball lands on 20	$35	$\frac{1}{38}$
Ball does not land on 20	−$1	$\frac{37}{38}$

Expected value, E, is computed by multiplying each gain or loss in **Table 15** by its probability and then adding these results.

$$E = \$35\left(\frac{1}{38}\right) + (-\$1)\left(\frac{37}{38}\right) = \frac{\$35 - \$37}{38} = \frac{-\$2}{38} \approx -\$0.05$$

The expected value is approximately −$0.05. This means that in the long run, a player can expect to lose about 5¢ for each game played. If 2000 games are played, one could expect to lose $100.

BLITZER BONUS

HOW TO WIN AT ROULETTE

Bob Daemmrich\Stock Boston

A player may win or lose at roulette, but in the long run the casino always wins. Casinos make an average of three cents on every dollar spent by gamblers. There *is* a way to win at roulette in the long run: Own the casino.

CHECK POINT 6 In the game of one-spot keno, a card is purchased for $1. It allows a player to choose one number from 1 to 80. A dealer then chooses twenty numbers at random. If the player's number is among those chosen, the player is paid $3.20, but does not get to keep the $1 paid to play the game. Find the expected value of a $1 bet. Describe what this means.

Exercise Set 8

Practice and Application Exercises

In Exercises 1–2, the numbers that each pointer can land on and their respective probabilities are shown. Compute the expected value for the number on which each pointer lands.

1.

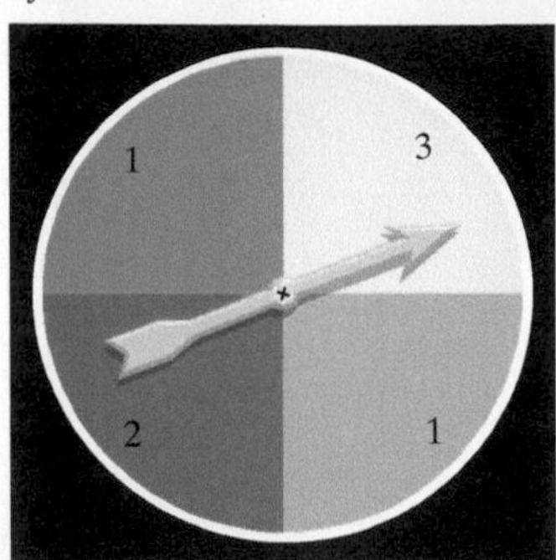

Outcome	Probability
1	$\frac{1}{2}$
2	$\frac{1}{4}$
3	$\frac{1}{4}$

2.

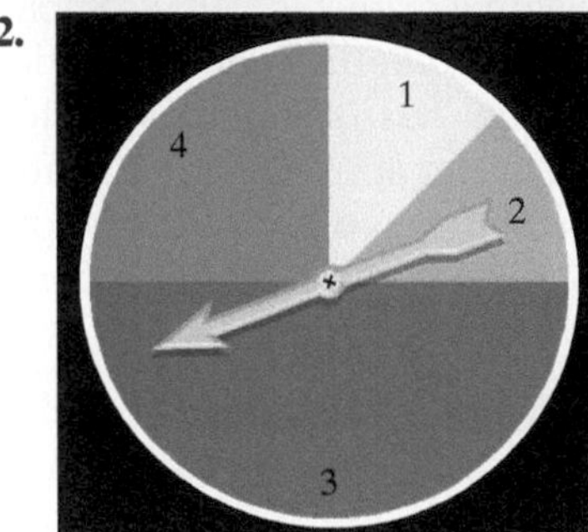

Outcome	Probability
1	$\frac{1}{8}$
2	$\frac{1}{8}$
3	$\frac{1}{2}$
4	$\frac{1}{4}$

The tables in Exercises 3–4 show claims and their probabilities for an insurance company.

a. *Calculate the expected value and describe what this means in practical terms.*

b. *How much should the company charge as an average premium so that it breaks even on its claim costs?*

c. *How much should the company charge to make a profit of $50 per policy?*

3. PROBABILITIES FOR HOMEOWNERS' INSURANCE CLAIMS

Amount of Claim (to the nearest $50,000)	Probability
$0	0.65
$50,000	0.20
$100,000	0.10
$150,000	0.03
$200,000	0.01
$250,000	0.01

4. PROBABILITIES FOR MEDICAL INSURANCE CLAIMS

Amount of Claim (to the nearest $20,000)	Probability
$0	0.70
$20,000	0.20
$40,000	0.06
$60,000	0.02
$80,000	0.01
$100,000	0.01

5. An architect is considering bidding for the design of a new museum. The cost of drawing plans and submitting a model is $10,000. The probability of being awarded the bid is 0.1, and anticipated profits are $100,000, resulting in a possible gain of this amount minus the $10,000 cost for plans and a model. What is the expected value in this situation? Describe what this value means.

6. A construction company is planning to bid on a building contract. The bid costs the company $1500. The probability that the bid is accepted is $\frac{1}{5}$. If the bid is accepted, the company will make $40,000 minus the cost of the bid. Find the expected value in this situation. Describe what this value means.

7. It is estimated that there are 27 deaths for every 10 million people who use airplanes. A company that sells flight insurance provides $100,000 in case of death in a plane crash. A policy can be purchased for $1. Calculate the expected value and thereby determine how much the insurance company can make over the long run for each policy that it sells.

8. A 25-year-old can purchase a one-year life insurance policy for $10,000 at a cost of $100. Past history indicates that the probability of a person dying at age 25 is 0.002. Determine the company's expected gain per policy.

Exercises 9–10 are related to the SAT, described in Check Point 4.

9. Suppose that you can eliminate one of the possible five answers. Modify the two probabilities shown in the final column in **Table 12** by finding the probabilities of guessing correctly and guessing incorrectly under these circumstances. What is the expected point value of a random guess? Is it advantageous to guess under these circumstances?

10. Suppose that you can eliminate two of the possible five answers. Modify the two probabilities shown in the final column in **Table 12** by finding the probabilities of guessing correctly and guessing incorrectly under these circumstances. What is the expected point value of a random guess? Is it advantageous to guess under these circumstances?

11. A store specializing in mountain bikes is to open in one of two malls. If the first mall is selected, the store anticipates a yearly profit of $300,000 if successful and a yearly loss of $100,000 otherwise. The probability of success is $\frac{1}{2}$. If the second mall is selected, it is estimated that the yearly profit will be $200,000 if successful; otherwise, the annual loss will be $60,000. The probability of success at the second mall is $\frac{3}{4}$. Which mall should be chosen in order to maximize the expected profit?

12. An oil company is considering two sites on which to drill, described as follows:

Site A: Profit if oil is found: $80 million
Loss if no oil is found: $10 million
Probability of finding oil: 0.2

Site B: Profit if oil is found: $120 million
Loss if no oil is found: $18 million
Probability of finding oil: 0.1

Which site has the larger expected profit? By how much?

13. In a product liability case, a company can settle out of court for a loss of \$350,000, or go to trial, losing \$700,000 if found guilty and nothing if found not guilty. Lawyers for the company estimate the probability of a not-guilty verdict to be 0.8.
    a. Find the expected value of the amount the company can lose by taking the case to court.
    b. Should the company settle out of court?
14. A service that repairs air conditioners sells maintenance agreements for \$80 a year. The average cost for repairing an air conditioner is \$350 and 1 in every 100 people who purchase maintenance agreements have air conditioners that require repair. Find the service's expected profit per maintenance agreement.

Exercises 15–19 involve computing expected values in games of chance.

15. A game is played using one die. If the die is rolled and shows 1, the player wins \$5. If the die shows any number other than 1, the player wins nothing. If there is a charge of \$1 to play the game, what is the game's expected value? What does this value mean?
16. A game is played using one die. If the die is rolled and shows 1, the player wins \$1; if 2, the player wins \$2; if 3, the player wins \$3. If the die shows 4, 5, or 6, the player wins nothing. If there is a charge of \$1.25 to play the game, what is the game's expected value? What does this value mean?
17. Another option in a roulette game (see Example 6) is to bet \$1 on red. (There are 18 red compartments, 18 black compartments, and 2 compartments that are neither red nor black.) If the ball lands on red, you get to keep the \$1 that you paid to play the game and you are awarded \$1. If the ball lands elsewhere, you are awarded nothing and the \$1 that you bet is collected. Find the expected value for playing roulette if you bet \$1 on red. Describe what this number means.
18. The spinner on a wheel of fortune can land with an equal chance on any one of ten regions. Three regions are red, four are blue, two are yellow, and one is green. A player wins \$4 if the spinner stops on red and \$2 if it stops on green. The player loses \$2 if it stops on blue and \$3 if it stops on yellow. What is the expected value? What does this mean if the game is played ten times?
19. For many years, organized crime ran a numbers game that is now run legally by many state governments. The player selects a three-digit number from 000 to 999. There are 1000 such numbers. A bet of \$1 is placed on a number, say number 115. If the number is selected, the player wins \$500. If any other number is selected, the player wins nothing. Find the expected value for this game and describe what this means.

Writing in Mathematics

20. What does the expected value for the outcome of the roll of a fair die represent?
21. Explain how to find the expected value for the number of girls for a family with two children. What is the expected value?
22. How do insurance companies use expected value to determine what to charge for a policy?
23. Describe a situation in which a business can use expected value.
24. If the expected value of a game is negative, what does this mean? Also describe the meaning of a positive and a zero expected value.
25. The expected value for purchasing a ticket in a raffle is −\$0.75. Describe what this means. Will a person who purchases a ticket lose \$0.75?

Critical Thinking Exercises

Make Sense? *In Exercises 26–29, determine whether each statement makes sense or does not make sense, and explain your reasoning.*

26. I found the expected value for the number of boys for a family with five children to be 2.5. I must have made an error because a family with 2.5 boys cannot occur.
27. Here's my dilemma: I can accept a \$1000 bill or play a dice game ten times. For each roll of the single die,
    - I win \$500 for rolling 1 or 2.
    - I win \$200 for rolling 3.
    - I lose \$300 for rolling 4, 5, or 6.

    Based on expected value, I should accept the \$1000 bill.
28. I've lost a fortune playing roulette, so I'm bound to reduce my losses if I play the game a little longer.
29. My expected value in a state lottery game is \$7.50.
30. A popular state lottery is the 5/35 lottery, played in Arizona, Connecticut, Illinois, Iowa, Kentucky, Maine, Massachusetts, New Hampshire, South Dakota, and Vermont. In Arizona's version of the game, prizes are set: First prize is \$50,000, second prize is \$500, and third prize is \$5. To win first prize, you must select all five of the winning numbers, numbered from 1 to 35. Second prize is awarded to players who select any four of the five winning numbers, and third prize is awarded to players who select any three of the winning numbers. The cost to purchase a lottery ticket is \$1. Find the expected value of Arizona's "Fantasy Five" game, and describe what this means in terms of buying a lottery ticket over the long run.
31. Refer to the probabilities of dying at any given age on page 630 to solve this exercise. A 20-year-old woman wants to purchase a \$200,000 one-year life insurance policy. What should the insurance company charge the woman for the policy if it wants an expected profit of \$60?

Group Exercise

32. This activity is a group research project intended for people interested in games of chance at casinos. The research should culminate in a seminar on games of chance and their expected values. The seminar is intended to last about 30 minutes and should result in an interesting and informative presentation made to the entire class.

    Each member of the group should research a game available at a typical casino. Describe the game to the class and compute its expected value. After each member has done this, so that class members now have an idea of those games with the greatest and smallest house advantages, a final group member might want to research and present ways for currently treating people whose addiction to these games has caused their lives to swirl out of control.

Chapter Summary, Review, and Test

Summary – Definitions and Concepts

Examples

1 The Fundamental Counting Principle

The number of ways in which a series of successive things can occur is found by multiplying the number of ways in which each thing can occur. Ex. 1, Ex. 2, Ex. 3, Ex. 4, Ex. 5, Ex. 6

2 Permutations

a. A permutation from a group of items occurs when no item is used more than once and the order of arrangement makes a difference. The Fundamental Counting Principle can be used to determine the number of permutations possible. Ex. 1, Ex. 2

b. Factorial Notation Ex. 3

$$n! = n(n-1)(n-2)\cdots(3)(2)(1) \text{ and } 0! = 1$$

c. Permutations Formula Ex. 4, Ex. 5

The number of permutations possible if r items are taken from n items is ${}_nP_r = \frac{n!}{(n-r)!}$.

d. Permutations of Duplicate Items Ex. 6

The number of permutations of n items, where p items are identical, q items are identical, r items are identical, and so on, is

$$\frac{n!}{p!\,q!\,r!\ldots}.$$

3 Combinations

a. A combination from a group of items occurs when no item is used more than once and the order of items makes no difference. Ex. 1

b. Combinations Formula Ex. 2, Ex. 3, Ex. 4

The number of combinations possible if r items are taken from n items is ${}_nC_r = \frac{n!}{(n-r)!\,r!}$.

4 Fundamentals of Probability

a. Theoretical probability applies to experiments in which the set of all equally likely outcomes, called the sample space, is known. An event is any subset of the sample space.

b. The theoretical probability of event E with sample space S is Ex. 1, Ex. 2, Ex. 3

$$P(E) = \frac{\text{number of outcomes in } E}{\text{total number of possible outcomes}} = \frac{n(E)}{n(S)}.$$

c. Empirical probability applies to situations in which we observe the frequency of the occurrence of an event.

d. The empirical probability of event E is Ex. 4

$$P(E) = \frac{\text{observed number of times } E \text{ occurs}}{\text{total number of observed occurrences}}.$$

5 Probability with the Fundamental Counting Principle, Permutations, and Combinations

a. Probability of a permutation Ex. 1

$$= \frac{\text{the number of ways the permutation can occur}}{\text{total number of possible permutations}}.$$

b. Probability of a combination Ex. 2 Ex. 3

$$= \frac{\text{the number of ways the combination can occur}}{\text{total number of possible combinations}}.$$

6 Events Involving *Not* and *Or*; Odds

a. Complement Rules of Probability Ex. 1 Ex. 2

$$P(\text{not } E) = 1 - P(E) \quad \text{and} \quad P(E) = 1 - P(\text{not } E)$$

b. If it is impossible for events A and B to occur simultaneously, the events are mutually exclusive.

c. If A and B are mutually exclusive events, then $P(A \text{ or } B) = P(A) + P(B)$. Ex. 3 Ex. 6(b)

d. If A and B are not mutually exclusive events, then Ex. 4 Ex. 5 Ex. 6(a)

$$P(A \text{ or } B) = P(A) + P(B) - P(A \text{ and } B).$$

e. Probability to Odds Ex. 7 Ex. 8

1. Odds in favor of $E = \dfrac{P(E)}{P(\text{not } E)}$ **2.** Odds against $E = \dfrac{P(\text{not } E)}{P(E)}$

f. Odds to Probability Ex. 9

If odds in favor of E are a to b, then $P(E) = \dfrac{a}{a+b}$.

7 Events Involving *And*; Conditional Probability

a. Two events are independent if the occurrence of either of them has no effect on the probability of the other.

b. If A and B are independent events, Ex. 1

$$P(A \text{ and } B) = P(A) \cdot P(B).$$

c. The probability of a succession of independent events is the product of each of their probabilities. Ex. 2 Ex. 3

d. Two events are dependent if the occurrence of one of them has an effect on the probability of the other.

e. If A and B are dependent events, Ex. 4

$$P(A \text{ and } B) = P(A) \cdot P(B \text{ given that } A \text{ has occurred}).$$

f. The multiplication rule for dependent events can be extended to cover three or more dependent events. In the case of three such events, Ex. 5

$$P(A \text{ and } B \text{ and } C)$$
$$= P(A) \cdot P(B \text{ given } A \text{ occurred}) \cdot P(C \text{ given } A \text{ and } B \text{ occurred}).$$

g. The conditional probability of B, given A, written $P(B|A)$, is the probability of B if the sample space is restricted to A. Ex. 6 Ex. 7 Ex. 8

$$P(B|A) = \frac{n(B \cap A)}{n(A)} = \frac{\text{number of outcomes common to } B \text{ and } A}{\text{number of outcomes in } A}$$

8 Expected Value

a. Expected value, E, is found by multiplying every possible outcome by its probability and then adding these products. Ex. 1 Ex. 2 Ex. 3

b. In situations involving business decisions, expected value is calculated by multiplying the gain or loss for each possible outcome by its probability. The sum of these products is the expected value. Ex. 4

c. In a game of chance, expected value is the average payoff when the game is played a large number of times. To find the expected value of a game, multiply the gain or loss for each possible outcome by its probability. Then add the products. Ex. 5 Ex. 6

Review Exercises

1

1. A restaurant offers 20 appetizers and 40 main courses. In how many ways can a person order a two-course meal?
2. A popular brand of pen comes in red, green, blue, or black ink. The writing tip can be chosen from extra bold, bold, regular, fine, or micro. How many different choices of pens do you have with this brand?
3. In how many ways can first and second prize be awarded in a contest with 100 people, assuming that each prize is awarded to a different person?
4. You are answering three multiple-choice questions. Each question has five answer choices, with one correct answer per question. If you select one of these five choices for each question and leave nothing blank, in how many ways can you answer the questions?
5. A stock can go up, go down, or stay unchanged. How many possibilities are there if you own five stocks?
6. A person can purchase a condominium with a choice of five kinds of carpeting, with or without a pool, with or without a porch, and with one, two, or three bedrooms. How many different options are there for the condominium?

2 and 3

In Exercises 7–10, evaluate each factorial expression.

7. $\frac{16!}{14!}$
8. $\frac{800}{799!}$
9. $5! - 3!$
10. $\frac{11!}{(11-3)!}$

In Exercises 11–12, use the formula for ${}_nP_r$ to evaluate each expression.

11. ${}_{10}P_6$
12. ${}_{100}P_2$

In Exercises 13–14, use the formula for ${}_nC_r$ to evaluate each expression.

13. ${}_{11}C_7$
14. ${}_{14}C_5$

In Exercises 15–17, does the problem involve permutations or combinations? Explain your answer. (It is not necessary to solve the problem.)

15. How many different 4-card hands can be dealt from a 52-card deck?
16. How many different ways can a director select from 20 male actors to cast the roles of Mark, Roger, Angel, and Collins in the musical *Rent?*
17. How many different ways can a director select 4 actors from a group of 20 actors to attend a workshop on performing in rock musicals?

In Exercises 18–28, solve each problem using an appropriate method.

18. Six acts are scheduled to perform in a variety show. How many different ways are there to schedule their appearances?
19. A club with 15 members is to choose four officers—president, vice-president, secretary, and treasurer. In how many ways can these offices be filled?
20. An election ballot asks voters to select four city commissioners from a group of ten candidates. In how many ways can this be done?
21. In how many distinct ways can the letters of the word TORONTO be arranged?
22. From the 20 CDs that you've bought during the past year, you plan to take 3 with you on vacation. How many different sets of three CDs can you take?
23. You need to arrange seven of your favorite books along a small shelf. Although you are not arranging the books by height, the tallest of the books is to be placed at the left end and the shortest of the books at the right end. How many different ways can you arrange the books?
24. Suppose you are asked to list, in order of preference, the five favorite CDs you purchased in the past 12 months. If you bought 20 CDs over this time period, in how many ways can the five favorite be ranked?
25. In how many ways can five airplanes line up for departure on a runway?
26. How many different 5-card hands can be dealt from a deck that has only hearts (13 different cards)?
27. A political discussion group consists of 12 Republicans and 8 Democrats. In how many ways can 5 Republicans and 4 Democrats be selected to attend a conference on politics and social issues?
28. In how many ways can the digits in the number 335,557 be arranged?

4

In Exercises 29–32, a die is rolled. Find the probability of rolling

29. a 6.
30. a number less than 5.
31. a number less than 7.
32. a number greater than 6.

In Exercises 33–37, you are dealt one card from a 52-card deck. Find the probability of being dealt

33. a 5.
34. a picture card.
35. a card greater than 4 and less than 8.
36. a 4 of diamonds.
37. a red ace.

In Exercises 38–40, suppose that you reach into a bag and randomly select one piece of candy from 15 chocolates, 10 caramels, and 5 peppermints. Find the probability of selecting

38. a chocolate.
39. a caramel.
40. a peppermint.
41. Tay-Sachs disease occurs in 1 of every 3600 births among Jews from central and eastern Europe, and in 1 in 600,000 births in other populations. The disease causes abnormal accumulation of certain fat compounds in the spinal cord and brain, resulting in paralysis, blindness, and mental impairment. Death generally occurs before the age of five. If we use *t* to represent a Tay-Sachs gene and *T* a healthy gene, the table at the top of the next page shows the four possibilities for the children of one healthy, *TT*, parent, and one parent who carries the disease, *Tt*, but is not sick.

		Second Parent	
		T	*t*
First	*T*	*TT*	*Tt*
Parent	*T*	*TT*	*Tt*

a. Find the probability that a child of these parents will be a carrier without the disease.

b. Find the probability that a child of these parents will have the disease.

The table shows the employment status of the U.S. civilian labor force, by gender, for a recent year. Use the data in the table, expressed in millions, to solve Exercises 42–44.

EMPLOYMENT STATUS OF THE U.S. LABOR FORCE, IN MILLIONS

	Employed	Unemployed	Total
Male	74.5	33.2	107.7
Female	64.7	51.0	115.7
Total	139.2	84.2	223.4

Source: U.S. Bureau of Labor Statistics

Find the probability, expressed as a decimal rounded to three places, that a randomly selected person from the civilian labor force represented in the table

42. is employed.

43. is female.

44. is an unemployed male.

5

45. If cities A, B, C, and D are visited in random order, each city visited once, find the probability that city D will be visited first, city B second, city A third, and city C last.

In Exercises 46–49, suppose that six singers are being lined up to perform at a charity. Call the singers A, B, C, D, E, and F. The order of performance is determined by writing each singer's name on one of six cards, placing the cards in a hat, and then drawing one card at a time. The order in which the cards are drawn determines the order in which the singers perform. Find the probability that

46. singer C will perform last.

47. singer B will perform first and singer A will perform last.

48. the singers will perform in the following order: F, E, A, D, C, B.

49. the performance will begin with singer A or C.

50. A lottery game is set up so that each player chooses five different numbers from 1 to 20. If the five numbers match the five numbers drawn in the lottery, the player wins (or shares) the top cash prize. What is the probability of winning the prize

a. with one lottery ticket?

b. with 100 different lottery tickets?

51. A committee of four people is to be selected from six Democrats and four Republicans. Find the probability that

a. all are Democrats.

b. two are Democrats and two are Republicans.

52. If you are dealt 3 cards from a shuffled deck of red cards (26 different cards), find the probability of getting exactly 2 picture cards.

6

In Exercises 53–57, a die is rolled. Find the probability of

53. not rolling a 5.

54. not rolling a number less than 4.

55. rolling a 3 or a 5.

56. rolling a number less than 3 or greater than 4.

57. rolling a number less than 5 or greater than 2.

In Exercises 58–63, you draw one card from a 52-card deck. Find the probability of

58. not drawing a picture card.

59. not drawing a diamond.

60. drawing an ace or a king.

61. drawing a black 6 or a red 7.

62. drawing a queen or a red card.

63. drawing a club or a picture card.

In Exercises 64–69, it is equally probable that the pointer on the spinner shown will land on any one of the six regions, numbered 1 through 6, and colored as shown. If the pointer lands on a borderline, spin again. Find the probability of

64. not stopping on 4.

65. not stopping on yellow.

66. not stopping on red.

67. stopping on red or yellow.

68. stopping on red or an even number.

69. stopping on red or a number greater than 3.

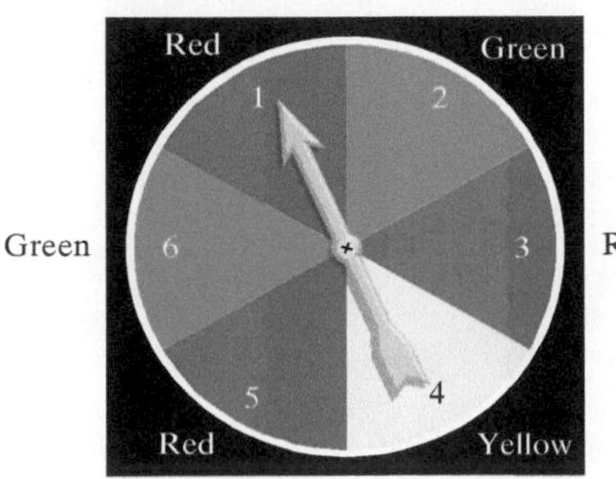

Use this information to solve Exercises 70–71. At a workshop on police work and the African-American community, there are 50 African-American male police officers, 20 African-American female police officers, 90 white male police officers, and 40 white female police officers. If one police officer is selected at random from the people at the workshop, find the probability that the selected person is

70. African American or male.

71. female or white.

Suppose that a survey of 350 college students is taken. Each student is asked the type of college attended (public or private) and the family's income level (low, middle, high). Use the data in the table to solve Exercises 72–75. Express probabilities as simplified fractions.

	Public	Private	Total
Low	120	20	140
Middle	110	50	160
High	22	28	50
Total	252	98	350

Find the probability that a randomly selected student in the survey

72. attends a public college.

73. is not from a high-income family.

74. is from a middle-income or a high-income family.

75. attends a private college or is from a high-income family.

76. One card is randomly selected from a deck of 52 cards. Find the odds in favor and the odds against getting a queen.

77. The winner of a raffle will receive a two-year scholarship to any college of the winner's choice. If 2000 raffle tickets were sold and you purchased 20 tickets, what are the odds against your winning the scholarship?

78. The odds in favor of a candidate winning an election are given at 3 to 1. What is the probability that this candidate will win the election?

7

Use the spinner shown to solve Exercises 79–83. It is equally likely that the pointer will land on any one of the six regions, numbered 1 through 6, and colored as shown. If the pointer lands on a borderline, spin again. If the pointer is spun twice, find the probability it will land on

79. yellow and then red. **80.** 1 and then 3.

81. yellow both times.

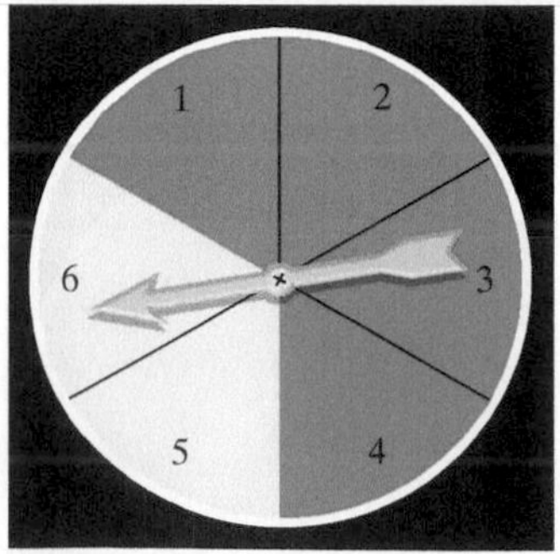

If the pointer is spun three times, find the probability it will land on

82. yellow and then 4 and then an odd number.

83. red every time.

84. What is the probability of a family having five boys born in a row?

85. The probability of a flood in any given year in a region prone to flooding is 0.2.

a. What is the probability of a flood two years in a row?

b. What is the probability of a flood for three consecutive years?

c. What is the probability of no flooding for four consecutive years?

d. What is the probability of a flood at least once in the next four years?

In Exercises 86–87, two students are selected from a group of four psychology majors, three business majors, and two music majors. The two students are to meet with the campus cafeteria manager to voice the group's concerns about food prices and quality. One student is randomly selected and leaves for the cafeteria manager's office. Then, a second student is selected. Find the probability of selecting

86. a music major and then a psychology major.

87. two business majors.

88. A final visit to the box of chocolates: It's now grown to a box of 50, of which 30 are solid chocolate, 15 are filled with jelly, and 5 are filled with cherries. The story is still the same: They all look alike. You select a piece, eat it, select a second piece, eat it, and help yourself to a final sugar rush. Find the probability of selecting a solid chocolate followed by two cherry-filled chocolates.

89. A single die is tossed. Find the probability that the tossed die shows 5, given that the outcome is an odd number.

90. A letter is randomly selected from the letters of the English alphabet. Find the probability of selecting a vowel, given that the outcome is a letter that precedes k.

91. The numbers shown below are each written on a colored chip. The chips are placed into a bag and one chip is selected at random. Find the probability of selecting

a. an odd number, given that a red chip is selected.

b. a yellow chip, given that the number selected is at least 3.

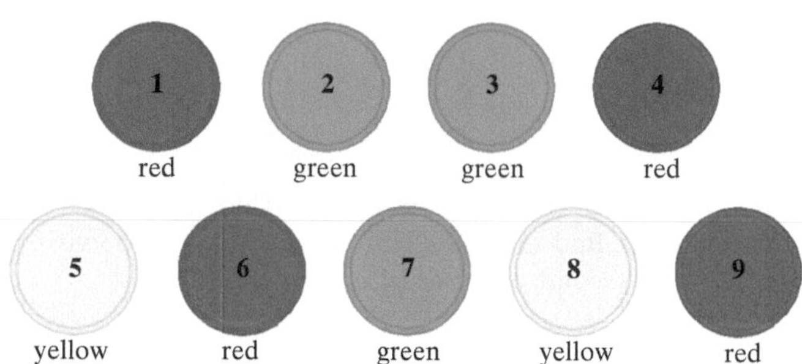

The data in the table are based on 145 Americans tested for tuberculosis. Use the data to solve Exercises 92–99. Express probabilities as simplified fractions.

	TB	No TB
Positive Screening Test	9	11
Negative Screening Test	1	124

Source: Deborah J. Bennett, *Randomness*, Harvard University Press, 1998.

Find the probability that a randomly selected person from this group

92. does not have TB.

93. tests positive.

94. does not have TB or tests positive.

95. does not have TB, given a positive test.

96. has a positive test, given no TB.

97. has TB, given a negative test.

Suppose that two people are randomly selected, in succession, from this group. Find the probability of selecting

98. two people with TB.

99. two people with positive screening tests.

4 and 6–7

The table shows the distribution, by age and gender, of the 29,625 deaths in the United States involving firearms in 2004.

DEATHS IN THE UNITED STATES INVOLVING FIREARMS, 2004

	Under Age 5	Ages 5–14	Ages 15–19	Ages 20–24	Ages 25–44	Ages 45–64	Ages 65–74	Age ≥ 75	Total
Male	31	231	2206	3700	9463	6127	1665	2123	25,546
Female	27	69	293	353	1581	1323	222	211	4079
Total	58	300	2499	4053	11,044	7450	1887	2334	29,625

Source: National Safety Council

In Exercises 100–106, use the data in the table to find the probability, expressed as a fraction and as a decimal rounded to three places, that a firearm death in the United States

100. involved a male.

101. involved a person in the 25–44 age range.

102. involved a person less than 75 years old.

103. involved a person in the 20–24 age range or in the 25–44 age range.

104. involved a female or a person younger than 5.

105. involved a person in the 20–24 age range, given that this person was a male.

106. involved a male, given that this person was at least 75.

8

107. The numbers that the pointer can land on and their respective probabilities are shown below.

Outcome	Probability
1	$\frac{1}{4}$
2	$\frac{1}{8}$
3	$\frac{1}{8}$
4	$\frac{1}{4}$
5	$\frac{1}{4}$

Compute the expected value for the number on which the pointer lands.

108. The table shows claims and their probabilities for an insurance company.

LIFE INSURANCE FOR AN AIRLINE FLIGHT

Amount of Claim	Probability
$0	0.9999995
$1,000,000	0.0000005

a. Calculate the expected value and describe what this value means.

b. How much should the company charge to make a profit of $9.50 per policy?

109. A construction company is planning to bid on a building contract. The bid costs the company $3000. The probability that the bid is accepted is $\frac{1}{4}$. If the bid is accepted, the company will make $30,000 minus the cost of the bid. Find the expected value in this situation. Describe what this value means.

110. A game is played using a fair coin that is tossed twice. The sample space is {*HH, HT, TH, TT*}. If exactly one head occurs, the player wins $5, and if exactly two tails occur, the player also wins $5. For any other outcome, the player receives nothing. There is a $4 charge to play the game. What is the expected value? What does this value mean?

Chapter Test

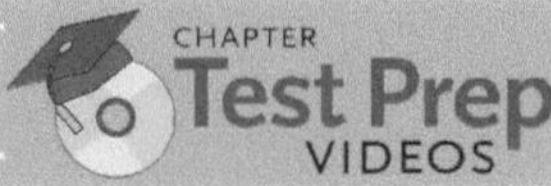

Step-by-step test solutions are found on the Chapter Test Prep Videos available on YouTube (search "Blitzer, Thinking Mathematically" and click on "Channels").

1. A person can purchase a particular model of a new car with a choice of ten colors, with or without automatic transmission, with or without four-wheel drive, with or without air conditioning, and with two, three, or four radio-CD speakers. How many different options are there for this model of the car?
2. Four acts are scheduled to perform in a variety show. How many different ways are there to schedule their appearances?
3. In how many ways can seven airplanes line up for a departure on a runway if the plane with the greatest number of passengers must depart first?
4. A human resource manager has 11 applicants to fill three different positions. Assuming that all applicants are equally qualified for any of the three positions, in how many ways can this be done?
5. From the ten books that you've recently bought but not read, you plan to take four with you on vacation. How many different sets of four books can you take?
6. In how many distinct ways can the letters of the word ATLANTA be arranged?

In Exercises 7–9, one student is selected at random from a group of 12 freshmen, 16 sophomores, 20 juniors, and 2 seniors. Find the probability that the person selected is

7. a freshman.
8. not a sophomore.
9. a junior or a senior.
10. If you are dealt one card from a 52-card deck, find the probability of being dealt a card greater than 4 and less than 10.
11. Seven movies (A, B, C, D, E, F, and G) are being scheduled for showing. The order of showing is determined by random selection. Find the probability that film C will be shown first, film A next-to-last, and film E last.
12. A lottery game is set up so that each player chooses six different numbers from 1 to 15. If the six numbers match the six numbers drawn in the lottery, the player wins (or shares) the top cash prize. What is the probability of winning the prize with 50 different lottery tickets?

In Exercises 13–14, it is equally probable that the pointer on the spinner shown will land on any one of the eight colored regions. If the pointer lands on a borderline, spin again.

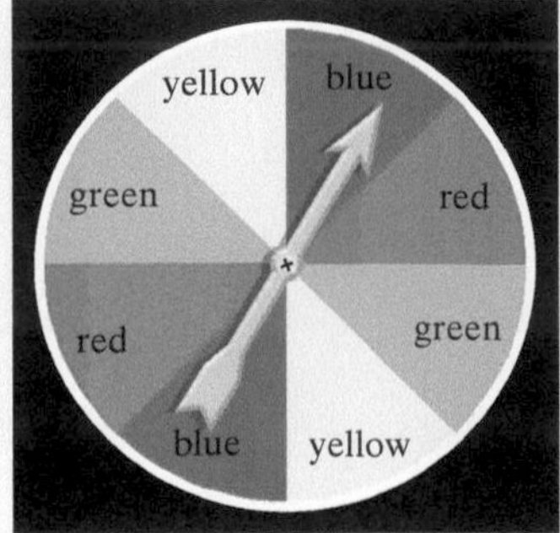

13. If the spinner is spun once, find the probability that the pointer will land on red or blue.
14. If the spinner is spun twice, find the probability that the pointer lands on red on the first spin and blue on the second spin.
15. A region is prone to flooding once every 20 years. The probability of flooding in any one year is $\frac{1}{20}$. What is the probability of flooding for three consecutive years?
16. One card is randomly selected from a deck of 52 cards. Find the probability of selecting a black card or a picture card.
17. A group of students consists of 10 male freshmen, 15 female freshmen, 20 male sophomores, and 5 female sophomores. If one person is randomly selected from the group, find the probability of selecting a freshman or a female.
18. A box contains five red balls, six green balls, and nine yellow balls. Suppose you select one ball at random from the box and do not replace it. Then you randomly select a second ball. Find the probability that both balls selected are red.
19. A quiz consisting of four multiple-choice questions has four available options (a, b, c, or d) for each question. If a person guesses at every question, what is the probability of answering *all* questions correctly?
20. A group is comprised of 20 men and 15 women. If one person is randomly selected from the group, find the odds against the person being a man.
21. The odds against a candidate winning an election are given at 1 to 4.
    a. What are the odds in favor of the candidate winning?
    b. What is the probability that the candidate will win the election?

A class is collecting data on eye color and gender. They organize the data they collected into the table shown. Numbers in the table represent the number of students from the class that belong to each of the categories. Use the data to solve Exercises 22–26. Express probabilities as simplified fractions.

	Brown	Blue	Green
Male	22	18	10
Female	18	20	12

Find the probability that a randomly selected student from this class

22. does not have brown eyes.
23. has brown eyes or blue eyes.
24. is female or has green eyes.
25. is male, given the student has blue eyes.
26. If two people are randomly selected, in succession, from the students in this class, find the probability that they both have green eyes.
27. An architect is considering bidding for the design of a new theater. The cost of drawing plans and submitting a model is \$15,000. The probability of being awarded the bid is 0.2, and anticipated profits are \$80,000, resulting in a possible gain of this amount minus the \$15,000 cost for plans and models. What is the expected value if the architect decides to bid for the design? Describe what this value means.
28. A game is played by selecting one bill at random from a bag that contains ten \$1 bills, five \$2 bills, three \$5 bills, one \$10 bill, and one \$100 bill. The player gets to keep the selected bill. There is a \$20 charge to play the game. What is the expected value? What does this value mean?

Answers to Selected Exercises

Section 1

Check Point Exercises

1. 150 **2.** 40 **3.** 30 **4.** 160 **5.** 729 **6.** 90,000

Exercise Set 1

1. 80 **3.** 12 **5.** 6 **7.** 40 **9.** 144; Answers will vary. **11.** 8 **13.** 96 **15.** 243 **17.** 144 **19.** 676,000 **21.** 2187 **27.** makes sense **29.** makes sense **31.** 720 hr

Section 2

Check Point Exercises

1. 600 **2.** 120 **3. a.** 504 **b.** 524,160 **c.** 100 **4.** 840 **5.** 15,120 **6.** 420

Exercise Set 2

1. 720 **3.** 120 **5.** 120 **7.** 362,880 **9.** 6 **11.** 4 **13.** 504 **15.** 570,024 **17.** 3,047,466,240 **19.** 600 **21.** 10,712 **23.** 5034 **25.** 24 **27.** 6 **29.** 42 **31.** 1716 **33.** 3024 **35.** 6720 **37.** 720 **39.** 1 **41.** 720 **43.** 8,648,640 **45.** 120 **47.** 15,120 **49.** 180 **51.** 831,600 **53.** 105 **55.** 280 **65.** makes sense **67.** does not make sense **69.** 360 **71.** 14,400 **73.** $\frac{n(n-1)\cdots 3\cdot 2\cdot 1}{2} = n(n-1)\cdots 3$

Section 3

Check Point Exercises

1. a. combinations **b.** permutations **2.** 35 **3.** 1820 **4.** 525

Exercise Set 3

1. combinations **3.** permutations **5.** 6 **7.** 126 **9.** 330 **11.** 8 **13.** 1 **15.** 4060 **17.** 1 **19.** 7 **21.** 0 **23.** $\frac{3}{4}$ **25.** −9499 **27.** $\frac{3}{68}$ **29.** 20 **31.** 495 **33.** 24,310 **35.** 22,957,480 **37.** 735 **39.** 4,516,932,420 **41.** 360 **43.** 1716 **45.** 1140 **47.** 840 **49.** 2730 **51.** 10 **53.** 12 **55.** 10 **57.** 60 **59.** 792 **61.** 720 **63.** 20 **65.** 24 **67.** 12 **73.** does not make sense **75.** makes sense **77.** The 5/36 lottery is easier to win.; Answers will vary. **79.** 570 sec or 9.5 min; 2340 sec or 39 min

Section 4

Check Point Exercises

1. a. $\frac{1}{6}$ **b.** $\frac{1}{2}$ **c.** 0 **d.** 1 **2. a.** $\frac{1}{13}$ **b.** $\frac{1}{2}$ **c.** $\frac{1}{26}$ **3.** $\frac{1}{2}$ **4. a.** 0.29 **b.** 0.49

Exercise Set 4

1. $\frac{1}{6}$ **3.** $\frac{1}{2}$ **5.** $\frac{1}{3}$ **7.** 1 **9.** 0 **11.** $\frac{1}{13}$ **13.** $\frac{1}{4}$ **15.** $\frac{3}{13}$ **17.** $\frac{1}{52}$ **19.** 0 **21.** $\frac{1}{4}$ **23.** $\frac{1}{2}$ **25.** $\frac{1}{2}$ **27.** $\frac{3}{8}$ **29.** $\frac{3}{8}$ **31.** $\frac{7}{8}$ **33.** 0 **35.** $\frac{1}{4}$ **37.** $\frac{1}{9}$ **39.** 0 **41.** $\frac{3}{10}$ **43.** $\frac{1}{5}$ **45.** $\frac{1}{2}$ **47.** 0 **49.** $\frac{1}{4}$ **51.** $\frac{1}{4}$ **53.** $\frac{1}{2}$ **55.** 0.43 **57.** 0.13 **59.** 0.03 **61.** 0.38 **63.** 0.78 **65.** 0.12 **67.** 0.25 **69.** 0.08 **79.** does not make sense **81.** makes sense **83.** $\frac{3}{8} = 0.375$

Section 5

Check Point Exercises

1. $\frac{4}{15}$ **1.** $\frac{1}{13{,}983{,}816} \approx 0.0000000715$ **3. a.** $\frac{1}{6}$ **b.** $\frac{1}{2}$

Exercise Set 5

1. a. 120 **b.** 6 **c.** $\frac{1}{20}$ **3. a.** $\frac{1}{6}$ **b.** $\frac{1}{30}$ **c.** $\frac{1}{720}$ **d.** $\frac{1}{3}$ **5. a.** 84 **b.** 10 **c.** $\frac{5}{42}$ **7.** $\frac{1}{18{,}009{,}460} \approx 0.0000000555$; $\frac{100}{18{,}009{,}460} \approx 0.00000555$ **9. a.** $\frac{1}{177{,}100} \approx 0.00000565$ **b.** $\frac{27{,}132}{177{,}100} \approx 0.153$ **11.** $\frac{3}{10} = 0.3$ **13. a.** 2,598,960 **b.** 1287 **c.** $\frac{1287}{2{,}598{,}960} \approx 0.000495$ **15.** $\frac{11}{1105} \approx 0.00995$ **17.** $\frac{36}{270{,}725} \approx 0.000133$ **23.** does not make sense **25.** makes sense **27.** $9,004,730 **29.** $\frac{1}{10}$

Section 6

Check Point Exercises

1. $\frac{3}{4}$ **2. a.** $\frac{160}{191}$ **b.** $\frac{182}{191}$ **3.** $\frac{1}{3}$ **4.** $\frac{27}{50}$ **5.** $\frac{3}{4}$ **6. a.** 0.99 **b.** 0.64 **7. a.** 2:50 or 1:25 **b.** 50:2 or 25:1 **8.** 199:1 **9.** 1:15; $\frac{1}{16}$

Exercise Set 6

1. $\frac{12}{13}$ **3.** $\frac{3}{4}$ **5.** $\frac{10}{13}$ **7.** $\frac{2,598,924}{2,598,960} \approx 0.999986$ **9.** $\frac{2,595,216}{2,598,960} \approx 0.998559$ **11. a.** 0.10 **b.** 0.90 **13.** $\frac{97}{118}$ **15.** $\frac{47}{59}$ **17.** $\frac{2}{13}$ **19.** $\frac{1}{13}$ **21.** $\frac{1}{26}$ **23.** $\frac{9}{22}$ **25.** $\frac{5}{6}$ **27.** $\frac{7}{13}$ **29.** $\frac{11}{26}$ **31.** $\frac{3}{4}$ **33.** $\frac{5}{8}$ **35.** $\frac{33}{40}$ **37.** $\frac{4}{5}$ **39.** $\frac{7}{10}$ **41.** $\frac{43}{58}$ **43.** $\frac{50}{87}$ **45.** $\frac{113}{174}$ **47.** 15:43; 43:15 **49.** $\frac{43}{69}$ **51.** $\frac{62}{69}$ **53.** $\frac{26}{69}$ **55.** 17:52; 52:17 **57.** 1:137; 137:1 **59.** 119:19; 19:119 **61.** 2:1 **63.** 1:2 **65. a.** 9:91 **b.** 91:9 **67.** 1:3 **69.** 1:1 **71.** 12:1 **73.** 25:1 **75.** 47:5 **77.** 49:1 **79.** 9:10 **81.** 14:5 **83.** 14:5 **85.** 9:10 **87.** $\frac{3}{7}$ **89.** $\frac{4}{25}$; 84 **91.** $\frac{1}{1000}$ **101.** does not make sense **103.** does not make sense **105.** 0.06

Section 7

Check Point Exercises

1. $\frac{1}{361} \approx 0.00277$ **2.** $\frac{1}{16}$ **3. a.** $\frac{625}{130,321} \approx 0.005$ **b.** $\frac{38,416}{130,321} \approx 0.295$ **c.** $\frac{91,905}{130,321} \approx 0.705$ **4.** $\frac{1}{221} \approx 0.00452$ **5.** $\frac{11}{850} \approx 0.0129$ **6.** $\frac{2}{5}$ **7. a.** 1 **b.** $\frac{1}{2}$ **8. a.** $\frac{9}{10} = 0.9$ **b.** $\frac{45}{479} \approx 0.094$

Exercise Set 7

1. $\frac{1}{6}$ **3.** $\frac{1}{36}$ **5.** $\frac{1}{4}$ **7.** $\frac{1}{36}$ **9.** $\frac{1}{8}$ **11.** $\frac{1}{36}$ **13.** $\frac{1}{3}$ **15.** $\frac{3}{52}$ **17.** $\frac{1}{169}$ **19.** $\frac{1}{4}$ **21.** $\frac{1}{64}$ **23.** $\frac{1}{6}$ **25. a.** $\frac{1}{256} \approx 0.00391$ **b.** $\frac{1}{4096} \approx 0.000244$ **c.** ≈ 0.524 **d.** ≈ 0.476 **27.** 0.0144 **29.** 0.008 **31.** 0.4686 **33.** $\frac{7}{29}$ **35.** $\frac{5}{87}$ **37.** $\frac{2}{21}$ **39.** $\frac{4}{35}$ **41.** $\frac{11}{21}$ **43.** $\frac{1}{57}$ **45.** $\frac{8}{855}$ **47.** $\frac{11}{57}$ **49.** $\frac{1}{5}$ **51.** $\frac{2}{3}$ **53.** $\frac{3}{4}$ **55.** $\frac{3}{4}$ **57.** $\frac{412,368}{412,878} \approx 0.999$ **59.** $\frac{412,368}{574,895} \approx 0.717$ **61.** 0.903 **63.** 0.156 **65.** 0.542 **67.** 0.421 **69.** 0.092 **71.** 0.893 **81.** does not make sense **83.** makes sense **85.** 0.59049 **87. a.** Answers will vary. **b.** $\frac{365}{365} \cdot \frac{364}{365} \cdot \frac{363}{365} \approx 0.992$ **c.** ≈ 0.008 **d.** 0.411 **e.** 23 people **89.** $\frac{11}{36}$

Section 8

Check Point Exercises

1. 2.5 **2.** 2 **3. a.** \$8000; In the long run, the average cost of a claim is \$8000. **b.** \$8000 **4.** 0; no; Answers will vary. **5.** table entries: \$998, \$48, and −\$2; expected value: −\$0.90; In the long run, a person can expect to lose an average of \$0.90 for each ticket purchased.; Answers will vary. **6.** −\$0.20; In the long run, a person can expect to lose an average of \$0.20 for each card purchased.

Exercise Set 8

1. 1.75 **3. a.** \$29,000; In the long run, the average cost of a claim is \$29,000. **b.** \$29,000 **c.** \$29,050 **5.** \$0; Answers will vary. **7.** ≈\$0.73 **9.** $\frac{1}{16} = 0.0625$; yes **11.** the second mall **13. a.** \$140,000 **b.** no **15.** ≈ − \$0.17; In the long run, a person can expect to lose an average of about \$0.17 for each game played. **17.** ≈ − \$0.05; In the long run, a person can expect to lose an average of about \$0.05 for each game played. **19.** −\$0.50; In the long run, a person can expect to lose an average of \$0.50 for each game played. **27.** makes sense **29.** does not make sense **31.** \$160

Chapter Review Exercises

1. 800 **2.** 20 **3.** 9900 **4.** 125 **5.** 243 **6.** 60 **7.** 240 **8.** 800 **9.** 114 **10.** 990 **11.** 151,200 **12.** 9900 **13.** 330 **14.** 2002 **15.** combinations **16.** permutations **17.** combinations **18.** 720 **19.** 32,760 **20.** 210 **21.** 420 **22.** 1140 **23.** 120 **24.** 1,860,480 **25.** 120 **26.** 1287 **27.** 55,440 **28.** 60 **29.** $\frac{1}{6}$ **30.** $\frac{2}{3}$ **31.** 1 **32.** 0 **33.** $\frac{1}{13}$ **34.** $\frac{3}{13}$ **35.** $\frac{3}{13}$ **36.** $\frac{1}{52}$ **37.** $\frac{1}{26}$ **38.** $\frac{1}{2}$ **39.** $\frac{1}{3}$ **40.** $\frac{1}{6}$ **41. a.** $\frac{1}{2}$ **b.** 0 **42.** 0.623 **43.** 0.518 **44.** 0.149 **45.** $\frac{1}{24}$ **46.** $\frac{1}{6}$ **47.** $\frac{1}{30}$ **48.** $\frac{1}{720}$ **49.** $\frac{1}{3}$ **50. a.** $\frac{1}{15,504} \approx 0.0000645$ **b.** $\frac{100}{15,504} \approx 0.00645$ **51. a.** $\frac{1}{14}$ **b.** $\frac{3}{7}$ **52.** $\frac{3}{26}$ **53.** $\frac{5}{6}$ **54.** $\frac{1}{2}$ **55.** $\frac{1}{3}$ **56.** $\frac{2}{3}$ **57.** 1 **58.** $\frac{10}{13}$ **59.** $\frac{3}{4}$ **60.** $\frac{2}{13}$ **61.** $\frac{1}{13}$ **62.** $\frac{7}{13}$ **63.** $\frac{11}{26}$ **64.** $\frac{5}{6}$ **65.** $\frac{5}{6}$ **66.** $\frac{1}{2}$ **67.** $\frac{2}{3}$ **68.** 1 **69.** $\frac{5}{6}$ **70.** $\frac{4}{5}$ **71.** $\frac{3}{4}$ **72.** $\frac{18}{25}$ **73.** $\frac{6}{7}$ **74.** $\frac{3}{5}$ **75.** $\frac{12}{35}$ **76.** in favor: 1:12; against: 12:1 **77.** 99:1 **78.** $\frac{3}{4}$ **79.** $\frac{2}{9}$ **80.** $\frac{1}{36}$ **81.** $\frac{1}{9}$ **82.** $\frac{1}{36}$ **83.** $\frac{8}{27}$ **84.** $\frac{1}{32}$ **85. a.** 0.04 **b.** 0.008 **c.** 0.4096 **d.** 0.5904 **86.** $\frac{1}{9}$ **87.** $\frac{1}{12}$ **88.** $\frac{1}{196}$ **89.** $\frac{1}{3}$ **90.** $\frac{3}{10}$ **91. a.** $\frac{1}{2}$

b. $\frac{2}{7}$ **92.** $\frac{27}{29}$ **93.** $\frac{4}{29}$ **94.** $\frac{144}{145}$ **95.** $\frac{11}{20}$ **96.** $\frac{11}{135}$ **97.** $\frac{1}{125}$ **98.** $\frac{1}{232}$ **99.** $\frac{19}{1044}$ **100.** $\frac{25{,}546}{29{,}625} \approx 0.862$
101. $\frac{11{,}044}{29{,}625} \approx 0.373$ **102.** $\frac{27{,}291}{29{,}625} \approx 0.921$ **103.** $\frac{15{,}097}{29{,}625} \approx 0.510$ **104.** $\frac{4110}{29{,}625} \approx 0.139$ **105.** $\frac{3700}{25{,}546} \approx 0.145$ **106.** $\frac{2123}{2334} \approx 0.910$
107. 3.125 **108. a.** \$0.50; In the long run, the average cost of a claim is \$0.50. **b.** \$10.00 **109.** \$4500; Answers will vary. **110.** −\$0.25; In the long run, a person can expect to lose an average of \$0.25 for each game played.

Chapter Test

1. 240 **2.** 24 **3.** 720 **4.** 990 **5.** 210 **6.** 420 **7.** $\frac{6}{25}$ **8.** $\frac{17}{25}$ **9.** $\frac{11}{25}$ **10.** $\frac{5}{13}$ **11.** $\frac{1}{210}$ **12.** $\frac{10}{1001} \approx 0.00999$ **13.** $\frac{1}{2}$
14. $\frac{1}{16}$ **15.** $\frac{1}{8000} = 0.000125$ **16.** $\frac{8}{13}$ **17.** $\frac{3}{5}$ **18.** $\frac{1}{19}$ **19.** $\frac{1}{256}$ **20.** 3:4 **21. a.** 4:1 **b.** $\frac{4}{5}$ **22.** $\frac{3}{5}$ **23.** $\frac{39}{50}$ **24.** $\frac{3}{5}$
25. $\frac{9}{19}$ **26.** $\frac{7}{150}$ **27.** \$1000; Answers will vary. **28.** −\$12.75; In the long run, a person can expect to lose an average of \$12.75 for each game played.

Statistics

Some random statistical factoids:

- 28% of liberals have insomnia, compared with 16% of conservatives. (*Mother Jones*)
- The French spend twice as much time enjoying meals each day as do Americans and they get an hour more sleep per night than do South Koreans. (OECD)
- 25% of college freshmen come to class without completing reading or assignments. (National Survey of Student Engagement)
- 47% of Internet users have looked for themselves on a search engine. (Pew)
- 34% of American adults believe in ghosts. (AP/Ipsos)
- 23% of high school students don't know how to write a check. (Huntington)

Statisticians collect numerical data from subgroups of populations to find out everything imaginable about the population as a whole, including whom they favor in an election, what they watch on TV, how much money they make, or what worries them. Comedians and statisticians joke that 62.38% of all statistics are made up on the spot. Because statisticians both record and influence our behavior, it is important to distinguish between good and bad methods for collecting, presenting, and interpreting data. In this chapter, you will gain an understanding of where data come from and how these numbers are used to make decisions.

Ivan Lee Sanford, *Diverse Cross-Section*, 1991 Ivan Lee Sanford\Stock Illustration Images.com

From Chapter 12 of *Thinking Mathematically*, Fifth Edition, Robert F. Blitzer.

OBJECTIVES

1 | Describe the population whose properties are to be analyzed.
2 | Select an appropriate sampling technique.
3 | Organize and present data.
4 | Identify deceptions in visual displays of data.

1 Sampling, Frequency Distributions, and Graphs

*M*A*S*H* took place in the early 1950s, during the Korean War. By the final episode, the show had lasted four times as long as the Korean War.

At the end of the twentieth century, there were 94 million households in the United States with television sets. The television program viewed by the greatest percentage of such households in that century was the final episode of *M*A*S*H*. Over 50 million American households watched this program.

Numerical information, such as the information about the top three TV shows of the twentieth century, shown in **Table 1**, is called **data**. The word **statistics** is often used when referring to data. However, statistics has a second meaning: Statistics is also a method for collecting, organizing, analyzing, and interpreting data, as well as drawing conclusions based on the data. This methodology divides statistics into two main areas. **Descriptive statistics** is concerned with collecting, organizing, summarizing, and presenting data. **Inferential statistics** has to do with making generalizations about and drawing conclusions from the data collected.

TABLE 1 TV Programs with the Greatest U.S. Audience Viewing Percentage of the Twentieth Century

Program	Total Households	Viewing Percentage
1. *M*A*S*H* Feb. 28, 1983	50,150,000	60.2%
2. *Dallas* Nov. 21, 1980	41,470,000	53.3%
3. *Roots Part 8* Jan. 30, 1977	36,380,000	51.1%

Source: Nielsen Media Research

1 | Describe the population whose properties are to be analyzed.

Populations and Samples

Consider the set of all American TV households. Such a set is called the *population*. In general, a **population** is the set containing all the people or objects whose properties are to be described and analyzed by the data collector.

The population of American TV households is huge. At the time of the *M*A*S*H* conclusion, there were nearly 84 million such households. Did over 50 million American TV households really watch the final episode of *M*A*S*H*? A friendly phone call to each household ("So, how are you? What's new? Watch any good television last night? If so, what?") is, of course, absurd. A **sample**, which is a

BLITZER BONUS

A SAMPLING FIASCO

Cover of the *Literary Digest*, October 31, 1936. General Research Division, The New York Public Library, Astor, Lenox and Tilden Foundations. The New York Public Library/Art Resource, NY

In 1936, the *Literary Digest* mailed out over ten million ballots to voters throughout the country. The results poured in, and the magazine predicted a landslide victory for Republican Alf Landon over Democrat Franklin Roosevelt. However, the prediction of the *Literary Digest* was wrong. Why? The mailing lists the editors used included people from their own subscriber list, directories of automobile owners, and telephone books. As a result, its sample was anything but random. It excluded most of the poor, who were unlikely to subscribe to the *Literary Digest,* or to own a car or telephone in the heart of the Depression. Prosperous people in 1936 were more likely to be Republican than the poor. Thus, although the sample was massive, it included a higher percentage of affluent individuals than the population as a whole did. A victim of both the Depression and the 1936 sampling fiasco, the *Literary Digest* folded in 1937.

subset or subgroup of the population, is needed. In this case, it would be appropriate to have a sample of a few thousand TV households to draw conclusions about the population of all TV households.

EXAMPLE 1 Populations and Samples

A group of hotel owners in a large city decide to conduct a survey among citizens of the city to discover their opinions about casino gambling.

a. Describe the population.

b. One of the hotel owners suggests obtaining a sample by surveying all the people at six of the largest nightclubs in the city on a Saturday night. Each person will be asked to express his or her opinion on casino gambling. Does this seem like a good idea?

Solution

a. The population is the set containing all the citizens of the city.

b. Questioning people at six of the city's largest nightclubs is a terrible idea. The nightclub subset is probably more likely to have a positive attitude toward casino gambling than the population of all the city's citizens.

A city government wants to conduct a survey among the city's homeless to discover their opinions about required residence in city shelters from midnight until 6 A.M.

a. Describe the population.

b. A city commissioner suggests obtaining a sample by surveying all the homeless people at the city's largest shelter on a Sunday night. Does this seem like a good idea? Explain your answer.

Random Sampling

There is a way to use a small sample to make generalizations about a large population: Guarantee that every member of the population has an equal chance to be selected for the sample. Surveying people at six of the city's largest nightclubs does not provide this guarantee. Unless it can be established that all citizens of the city frequent these clubs, which seems unlikely, this sampling scheme does not permit each citizen an equal chance of selection.

RANDOM SAMPLES

A **random sample** is a sample obtained in such a way that every element in the population has an equal chance of being selected for the sample.

Suppose that you are elated with the quality of one of your courses. Although it's an auditorium section with 120 students, you feel that the professor is lecturing right to you. During a wonderful lecture, you look around the auditorium to see if any of the other students are sharing your enthusiasm. Based on body language, it's hard to tell. You really want to know the opinion of the population of 120 students taking this course. You think about asking students to grade the course on an A to F scale, anticipating a unanimous A. You cannot survey everyone. Eureka! Suddenly you have an idea on how to take a sample. Place cards numbered from 1 through 120, one number per card, in a box. Because the course has assigned seating by number, each numbered card corresponds to a student in the class. Reach in and randomly select six cards. Each card, and therefore each student, has an equal chance of being selected. Then use the opinions about the course from the six randomly selected students to generalize about the course opinion for the entire 120-student population.

2 Select an appropriate sampling technique.

Your idea is precisely how random samples are obtained. In random sampling, each element in the population must be identified and assigned a number. The numbers are generally assigned in order. The way to sample from the larger numbered population is to generate random numbers using a computer or calculator. Each numbered element from the population that corresponds to one of the generated random numbers is selected for the sample.

Call-in polls on radio and television are not reliable because those polled do not represent the larger population. A person who calls in is likely to have feelings about an issue that are consistent with the politics of the show's host. For a poll to be accurate, the sample must be chosen randomly from the larger population. The A. C. Nielsen Company uses a random sample of approximately 5000 TV households to measure the percentage of households tuned in to a television program.

BLITZER BONUS

THE UNITED STATES CENSUS

A census is a survey that attempts to include the entire population. The U.S. Constitution requires a census of the American population every ten years. The 2000 Census form was mailed to all households in the country. A Census "long form" that asked many more questions than the basic Census form was sent to a random sample of one-sixth of all households.

Although the Census generates volumes of statistics, its main purpose is to give the government block-by-block population figures to create election districts with equal population needs. The U.S. Census is not foolproof. The 1990 Census missed 1.6% of the American population, including an estimated 4.4% of the African American population, largely in inner cities. The 2000 Census had the highest participation rate, yet only 67% of households responded, even after door-to-door canvassing. About 6.4 million people were missed and 3.1 million were counted twice. For the 2010 Census, with costs estimated at $14 billion, finding and counting each person will not be an easy task, particularly with concerns about immigrants and privacy of data.

EXAMPLE 2 Selecting an Appropriate Sampling Technique

We return to the hotel owners in the large city who are interested in how the city's citizens feel about casino gambling. Which of the following would be the most appropriate way to select a random sample?

a. Randomly survey people who live in the oceanfront condominiums in the city.

b. Survey the first 200 people whose names appear in the city's telephone directory.

c. Randomly select neighborhoods of the city and then randomly survey people within the selected neighborhoods.

Solution Keep in mind that the population is the set containing all the city's citizens. A random sample must give each citizen an equal chance of being selected.

a. Randomly selecting people who live in the city's oceanfront condominiums is not a good idea. Many hotels lie along the oceanfront, and the oceanfront property owners might object to the traffic and noise as a result of casino gambling. Furthermore, this sample does not give each citizen of the city an equal chance of being selected.

b. If the hotel owners survey the first 200 names in the city's telephone directory, all citizens do not have an equal chance of selection. For example, individuals whose last name begins with a letter toward the end of the alphabet have no chance of being selected.

c. Randomly selecting neighborhoods of the city and then randomly surveying people within the selected neighborhoods is an appropriate technique. Using this method, each citizen has an equal chance of being selected.

In summary, given the three options, the sampling technique in part (c) is the most appropriate.

Surveys and polls involve data from a sample of some population. Regardless of the sampling technique used, the sample should exhibit characteristics typical of those possessed by the target population. This type of sample is called a **representative sample**.

CHECK POINT 2 Explain why the sampling technique described in Check Point 1(b) is not a random sample. Then describe an appropriate way to select a random sample of the city's homeless.

3 Organize and present data.

Frequency Distributions

After data have been collected from a sample of the population, the next task facing the statistician is to present the data in a condensed and manageable form. In this way, the data can be more easily interpreted.

Suppose, for example, that researchers are interested in determining the age at which adolescent males show the greatest rate of physical growth. A random sample of 35 ten-year-old boys is measured for height and then remeasured each year until they reach 18. The age of maximum yearly growth for each subject is as follows:

12, 14, 13, 14, 16, 14, 14, 17, 13, 10, 13, 18, 12, 15, 14, 15, 15, 14, 14, 13, 15, 16, 15, 12, 13, 16, 11, 15, 12, 13, 12, 11, 13, 14, 14.

A piece of data is called a **data item**. This list of data has 35 data items. Some of the data items are identical. Two of the data items are 11 and 11. Thus, we can say that the **data value** 11 occurs twice. Similarly, because five of the data items are 12, 12, 12, 12, and 12, the data value 12 occurs five times.

Collected data can be presented using a **frequency distribution**. Such a distribution consists of two columns. The data values are listed in one column. Numerical data are generally listed from smallest to largest. The adjacent column is labeled **frequency** and indicates the number of times each value occurs.

TABLE 2 A Frequency Distribution for a Boy's Age of Maximum Yearly Growth

Age of Maximum Growth	Number of Boys (Frequency)
10	1
11	2
12	5
13	7
14	9
15	6
16	3
17	1
18	1
Total:	$n = 35$

35 is the sum of the frequencies.

EXAMPLE 3 Constructing a Frequency Distribution

Construct a frequency distribution for the data of the age of maximum yearly growth for 35 boys:

12, 14, 13, 14, 16, 14, 14, 17, 13, 10, 13, 18, 12, 15, 14, 15, 15, 14, 14, 13, 15, 16, 15, 12, 13, 16, 11, 15, 12, 13, 12, 11, 13, 14, 14.

Solution It is difficult to determine trends in the data above in their current format. Perhaps we can make sense of the data by organizing them into a frequency distribution. Let us create two columns. One lists all possible data values, from smallest (10) to largest (18). The other column indicates the number of times the value occurs in the sample. The frequency distribution is shown in **Table 2**.

The frequency distribution indicates that one subject had maximum growth at age 10, two at age 11, five at age 12, seven at age 13, and so on. The maximum growth for most of the subjects occurred between the ages of 12 and 15. Nine boys experienced maximum growth at age 14, more than at any other age within the sample. The sum of the frequencies, 35, is equal to the original number of data items.

The trend shown by the frequency distribution in **Table 2** indicates that the number of boys who attain their maximum yearly growth at a given age increases until age 14 and decreases after that. This trend is not evident in the data in their original format.

CHECK POINT 3 Construct a frequency distribution for the data showing final course grades for students in a precalculus course, listed alphabetically by student name in a grade book:

F, A, B, B, C, C, B, C, A, A, C, C, D, C, B, D, C, C, B, C.

A frequency distribution that lists all possible data items can be quite cumbersome when there are many such items. For example, consider the following data items. These are statistics test scores for a class of 40 students.

82	47	75	64	57	82	63	93
76	68	84	54	88	77	79	80
94	92	94	80	94	66	81	67
75	73	66	87	76	45	43	56
57	74	50	78	71	84	59	76

It's difficult to determine how well the group did when the grades are displayed like this. Because there are so many data items, one way to organize these data so that the results are more meaningful is to arrange the grades into groups, or **classes**, based on something that interests us. Many grading systems assign an A to grades in the 90–100 class, B to grades in the 80–89 class, C to grades in the 70–79 class, and so on. These classes provide one way to organize the data.

Looking at the 40 statistics test scores, we see that they range from a low of 43 to a high of 94. We can use classes that run from 40 through 49, 50 through 59,

60 through 69, and so on up to 90 through 99, to organize the scores. In Example 4, we go through the data and tally each item into the appropriate class. This method for organizing data is called a **grouped frequency distribution**.

EXAMPLE 4 Constructing a Grouped Frequency Distribution

Use the classes 40–49, 50–59, 60–69, 70–79, 80–89, and 90–99 to construct a grouped frequency distribution for the 40 test scores on the previous page.

Solution We use the 40 given scores and tally the number of scores in each class.

Tallying Statistics Test Scores

Test Scores (Class)	Tally	Number of Students (Frequency)
40–49	𝍷𝍷𝍷	3
50–59	𝍸 𝍷	6
60–69	𝍸 𝍷	6
70–79	𝍸 𝍸 𝍷	11
80–89	𝍸 𝍷𝍷𝍷𝍷	9
90–99	𝍸	5

The second score in the list, 47, is shown as the first tally in this row.

The first score in the list, 82, is shown as the first tally in this row.

TABLE 3 A Grouped Frequency Distribution for Statistics Test Scores

Class	Frequency
40–49	3
50–59	6
60–69	6
70–79	11
80–89	9
90–99	5
Total:	$n = 40$

40, the sum of the frequencies, is the number of data items.

Omitting the tally column results in the grouped frequency distribution in **Table 3**. The distribution shows that the greatest frequency of students scored in the 70–79 class. The number of students decreases in classes that contain successively lower and higher scores. The sum of the frequencies, 40, is equal to the original number of data items.

The leftmost number in each class of a grouped frequency distribution is called the **lower class limit**. For example, in **Table 3**, the lower limit of the first class is 40 and the lower limit of the third class is 60. The rightmost number in each class is called the **upper class limit**. In **Table 3**, 49 and 69 are the upper limits for the first and third classes, respectively. Notice that if we take the difference between any two consecutive lower class limits, we get the same number:

$$50 - 40 = 10,\ 60 - 50 = 10,\ 70 - 60 = 10,\ 80 - 70 = 10,\ 90 - 80 = 10.$$

The number 10 is called the **class width**.

When setting up class limits, each class, with the possible exception of the first or last, should have the same width. Because each data item must fall into exactly one class, it is sometimes helpful to vary the width of the first or last class to allow for items that fall far above or below most of the data.

Use the classes in **Table 3** to construct a grouped frequency distribution for the following 37 exam scores:

73	58	68	75	94	79	96	79
87	83	89	52	99	97	89	58
95	77	75	81	75	73	73	62
69	76	77	71	50	57	41	98
77	71	69	90	75.			

TABLE 2 (repeated)
A Frequency Distribution for a Boy's Age of Maximum Yearly Growth

Age of Maximum Growth	Number of Boys (Frequency)
10	1
11	2
12	5
13	7
14	9
15	6
16	3
17	1
18	1
Total:	$n = 35$

Histograms and Frequency Polygons

Take a second look at the frequency distribution for the age of a boy's maximum yearly growth, repeated in **Table 2**. A bar graph with bars that touch can be used to visually display the data. Such a graph is called a **histogram. Figure 1** illustrates a histogram that was constructed using the frequency distribution in **Table 2**. A series of rectangles whose heights represent the frequencies are placed next to each other. For example, the height of the bar for the data value 10, shown in **Figure 1**, is 1. This corresponds to the frequency for 10 given in **Table 2**. The higher the bar, the more frequent the age. The break along the horizontal axis, symbolized by -⁄⁄-, eliminates listing the ages 1 through 9.

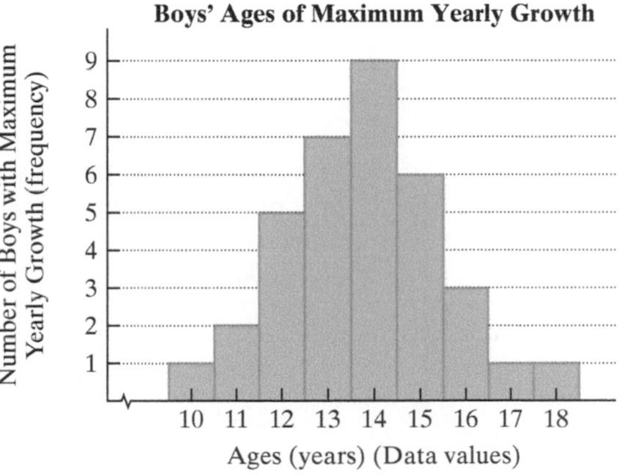

FIGURE 1 A histogram for a boy's age of maximum yearly growth

A line graph called a **frequency polygon** can also be used to visually convey the information shown in **Figure 1**. The axes are labeled just like those in a histogram. Thus, the horizontal axis shows data values and the vertical axis shows frequencies. Once a histogram has been constructed, it's fairly easy to draw a frequency polygon. **Figure 2** shows a histogram with a dot at the top of each rectangle at its midpoint. Connect each of these midpoints with a straight line. To complete the frequency polygon at both ends, the lines should be drawn down to touch the horizontal axis. The completed frequency polygon is shown in **Figure 3**.

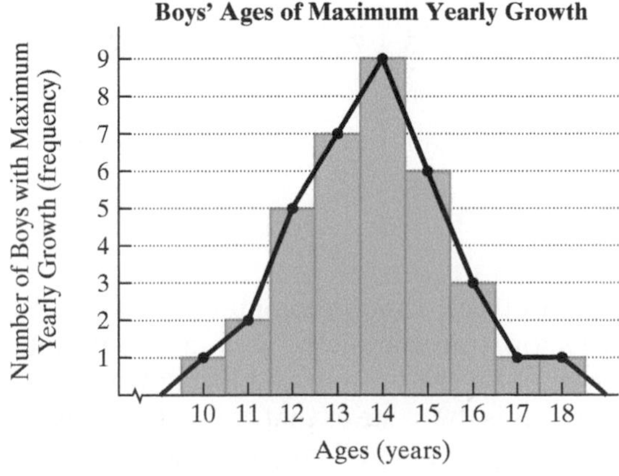

FIGURE 2 A histogram with a superimposed frequency polygon

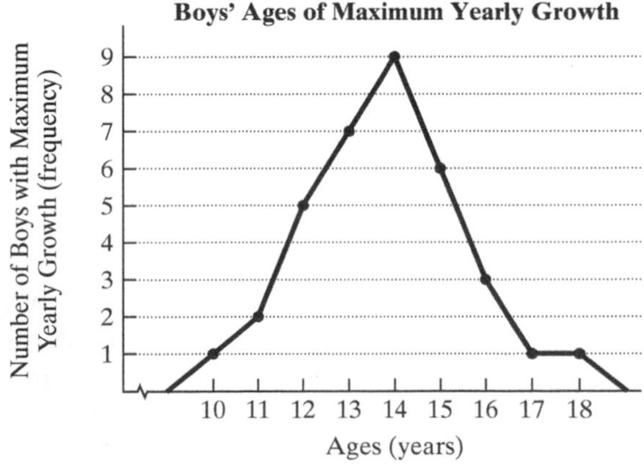

FIGURE 3 A frequency polygon

Stem-and-Leaf Plots

A unique way of displaying data uses a tool called a **stem-and-leaf plot**. Example 5 illustrates how we sort the data, revealing the same visual impression created by a histogram.

EXAMPLE 5 Constructing a Stem-and-Leaf Plot

Use the data showing statistics test scores for 40 students to construct a stem-and-leaf plot:

82	47	75	64	57	82	63	93
76	68	84	54	88	77	79	80
94	92	94	80	94	66	81	67
75	73	66	87	76	45	43	56
57	74	50	78	71	84	59	76.

Solution The plot is constructed by separating each data item into two parts. The first part is the *stem*. The **stem** consists of the tens digit. For example, the stem for the score of 82 is 8. The second part is the *leaf*. The **leaf** consists of the units digit for a given value. For the score of 82, the leaf is 2. The possible stems for the 40 scores are 4, 5, 6, 7, 8, and 9, entered in the left column of the plot.

Begin by entering each data item in the first row:

82 47 75 64 57 82 63 93.

Entering 82:

Stems	Leaves
4	
5	
6	
7	
8	2
9	

Adding 47:

Stems	Leaves
4	7
5	
6	
7	
8	2
9	

Adding 75:

Stems	Leaves
4	7
5	
6	
7	5
8	2
9	

Adding 64:

Stems	Leaves
4	7
5	
6	4
7	5
8	2
9	

Adding 57:

Stems	Leaves
4	7
5	7
6	4
7	5
8	2
9	

Adding 82:

Stems	Leaves
4	7
5	7
6	4
7	5
8	22
9	

Adding 63:

Stems	Leaves
4	7
5	7
6	43
7	5
8	22
9	

Adding 93:

Stems	Leaves
4	7
5	7
6	43
7	5
8	22
9	3

We continue in this manner and enter all the data items. **Figure 4** at the top of the next page shows the completed stem-and-leaf plot. If you turn the page so that the left margin is on the bottom and facing you, the visual impression created by the enclosed leaves is the same as that created by a histogram. An advantage over the histogram is that the stem-and-leaf plot preserves exact data items. The enclosed leaves extend farthest to the right when the stem is 7. This shows that the greatest frequency of students scored in the 70s.

A Stem-and-Leaf Plot for 40 Test Scores

Tens digit — Units digit

Stems	Leaves
4	7 5 3
5	7 4 6 7 0 9
6	4 3 8 6 7 6
7	5 6 7 9 5 3 6 4 8 1 6
8	2 2 4 8 0 0 1 7 4
9	3 4 2 4 4

FIGURE 4 A stem-and-leaf plot displaying 40 test scores

CHECK POINT 5 Construct a stem-and-leaf plot for the data in Check Point 4.

4 Identify deceptions in visual displays of data.

Deceptions in Visual Displays of Data

Benjamin Disraeli, Queen Victoria's prime minister, stated that there are "lies, damned lies, and statistics." The problem is not that statistics lie, but rather that liars use statistics. Graphs can be used to distort the underlying data, making it difficult for the viewer to learn the truth. One potential source of misunderstanding is the scale on the vertical axis used to draw the graph. This scale is important because it lets a researcher "inflate" or "deflate" a trend. For example, both graphs in **Figure 5** present identical data for the percentage of people in the United States living below the poverty level from 2001 through 2005. The graph on the left stretches the scale on the vertical axis to create an overall impression of a poverty rate increasing rapidly over time. The graph on the right compresses the scale on the vertical axis to create an impression of a poverty rate that is slowly increasing, and beginning to level off, over time.

Percentage of People in the United States Living below the Poverty Level, 2001–2005

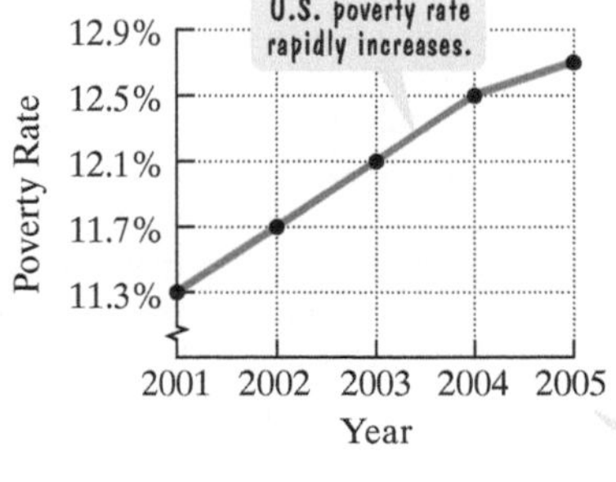

Year	Poverty Rate
2001	11.3%
2002	11.7%
2003	12.1%
2004	12.5%
2005	12.7%

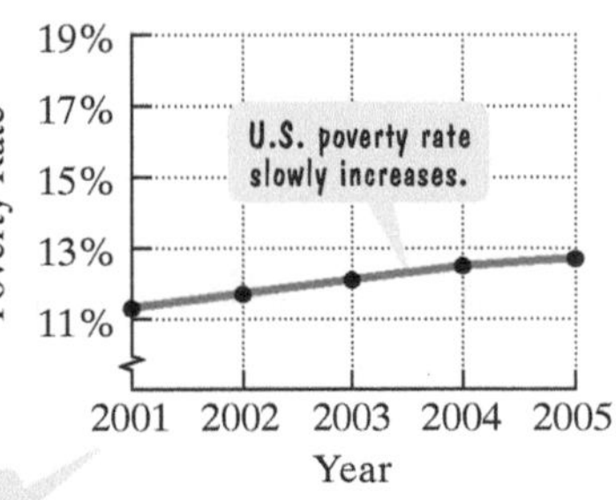

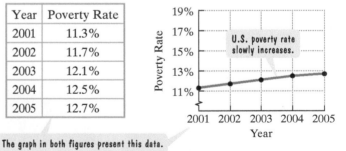

The graph in both figures present this data.

FIGURE 5
Source: U.S. Census Bureau

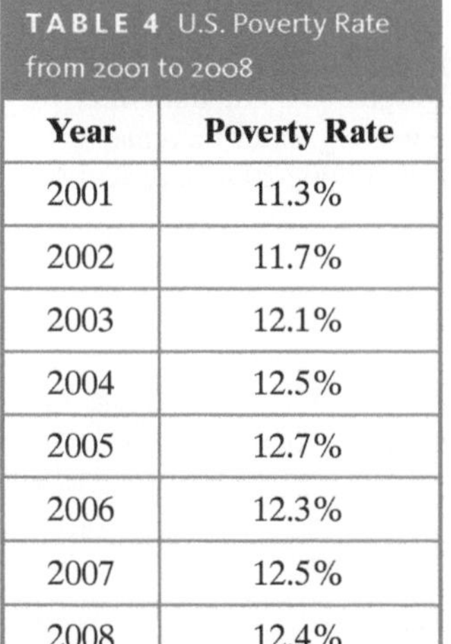

TABLE 4 U.S. Poverty Rate from 2001 to 2008

Year	Poverty Rate
2001	11.3%
2002	11.7%
2003	12.1%
2004	12.5%
2005	12.7%
2006	12.3%
2007	12.5%
2008	12.4%

There is another problem with the data in **Figure 5**. Look at **Table 4** that shows the poverty rate from 2001 through 2008. Depending on the time frame chosen, the data can be interpreted in various ways. Carefully choosing a time frame can help represent data trends in the most positive or negative light.

THINGS TO WATCH FOR IN VISUAL DISPLAYS OF DATA

1. Is there a title that explains what is being displayed?
2. Are numbers lined up with tick marks on the vertical axis that clearly indicate the scale? Has the scale been varied to create a more or less dramatic impression than shown by the actual data?
3. Do too many design and cosmetic effects draw attention from or distort the data?
4. Has the wrong impression been created about how the data are changing because equally spaced time intervals are not used on the horizontal axis? Furthermore, has a time interval been chosen that allows the data to be interpreted in various ways?
5. Are bar sizes scaled proportionately in terms of the data they represent?
6. Is there a source that indicates where the data in the display came from? Do the data come from an entire population or a sample? Was a random sample used and, if so, are there possible differences between what is displayed in the graph and what is occurring in the entire population? (We'll discuss these *margins of error* in Section 4.) Who is presenting the visual display, and does that person have a special case to make for or against the trend shown by the graph?

Table 5 contains two examples of misleading visual displays.

TABLE 5 Examples of Misleading Visual Displays

Graphic Display	Presentation Problems
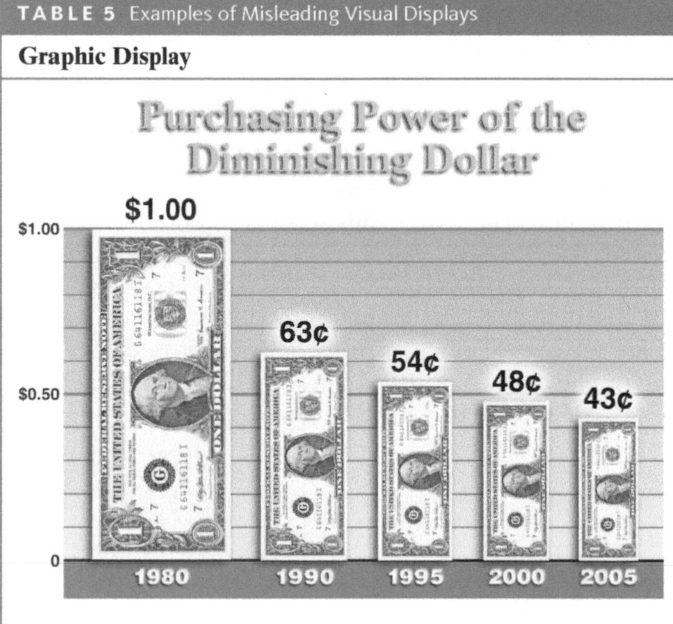 *Source:* Bureau of Labor Statistics	Although the length of each dollar bill is proportional to its spending power, the visual display varies both the length *and width* of the bills to show the diminishing power of the dollar over time. Because our eyes focus on the *areas* of the dollar-shaped bars, this creates the impression that the purchasing power of the dollar diminished even more than it really did. If the area of the dollar were drawn to reflect its purchasing power, the 2005 dollar would be approximately twice as large as the one shown in the graphic display.
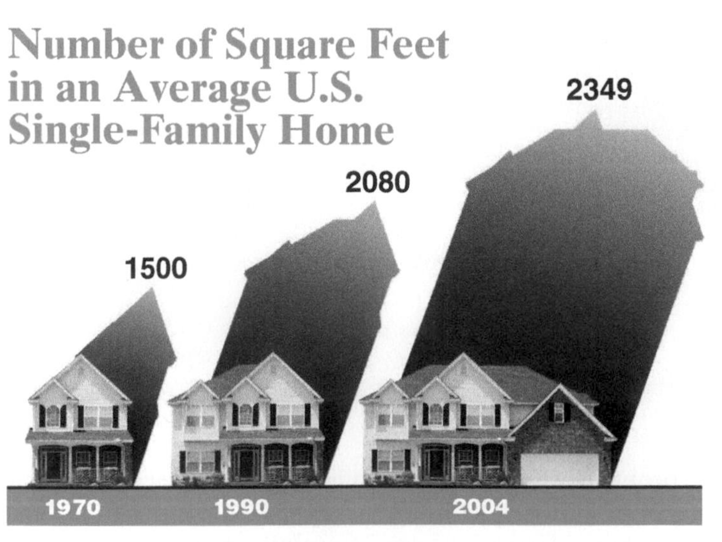 *Source:* National Association of Home Builders	Cosmetic effects of homes with equal heights, but different frontal additions and shadow lengths, make it impossible to tell if they proportionately depict the given areas. Time intervals on the horizontal axis are not uniform in size, making it appear that dwelling swelling has been linear from 1970 through 2004. The data indicate that this is not the case. There was a greater increase in area from 1970 through 1990, averaging 29 square feet per year, than from 1990 through 2004, averaging approximately 19.2 square feet per year.

Exercise Set 1

Practice and Application Exercises

1. The government of a large city needs to determine whether the city's residents will support the construction of a new jail. The government decides to conduct a survey of a sample of the city's residents. Which one of the following procedures would be most appropriate for obtaining a sample of the city's residents?
   a. Survey a random sample of the employees and inmates at the old jail.
   b. Survey every fifth person who walks into City Hall on a given day.
   c. Survey a random sample of persons within each geographic region of the city.
   d. Survey the first 200 people listed in the city's telephone directory.
2. The city council of a large city needs to know whether its residents will support the building of three new schools. The council decides to conduct a survey of a sample of the city's residents. Which procedure would be most appropriate for obtaining a sample of the city's residents?
   a. Survey a random sample of teachers who live in the city.
   b. Survey 100 individuals who are randomly selected from a list of all people living in the state in which the city in question is located.
   c. Survey a random sample of persons within each neighborhood of the city.
   d. Survey every tenth person who enters City Hall on a randomly selected day.

A questionnaire was given to students in an introductory statistics class during the first week of the course. One question asked, "How stressed have you been in the last $2\frac{1}{2}$ weeks, on a scale of 0 to 10, with 0 being not at all stressed and 10 being as stressed as possible?" The students' responses are shown in the frequency distribution. Use this frequency distribution to solve Exercises 3–6.

Stress Rating	Frequency
0	2
1	1
2	3
3	12
4	16
5	18
6	13
7	31
8	26
9	15
10	14

Source: Journal of Personality and Social Psychology, 69, 1102–1112

3. Which stress rating describes the greatest number of students? How many students responded with this rating?
4. Which stress rating describes the least number of students? How many responded with this rating?
5. How many students were involved in this study?
6. How many students had a stress rating of 8 or more?
7. A random sample of 30 college students is selected. Each student is asked how much time he or she spent on homework during the previous week. The following times (in hours) are obtained:

   16, 24, 18, 21, 18, 16, 18, 17, 15, 21, 19, 17, 17, 16, 19, 18, 15, 15, 20, 17, 15, 17, 24, 19, 16, 20, 16, 19, 18, 17.

   Construct a frequency distribution for the data.
8. A random sample of 30 male college students is selected. Each student is asked his height (to the nearest inch). The heights are as follows:

   72, 70, 68, 72, 71, 71, 71, 69, 73, 71, 73, 75, 66, 67, 75, 74, 73, 71, 72, 67, 72, 68, 67, 71, 73, 71, 72, 70, 73, 70.

   Construct a frequency distribution for the data.

A college professor had students keep a diary of their social interactions for a week. Excluding family and work situations, the number of social interactions of ten minutes or longer over the week is shown in the following grouped frequency distribution. Use this information to solve Exercises 9–16.

Number of Social Interactions	Frequency
0–4	12
5–9	16
10–14	16
15–19	16
20–24	10
25–29	11
30–34	4
35–39	3
40–44	3
45–49	3

Source: Society for Personality and Social Psychology

9. Identify the lower class limit for each class.
10. Identify the upper class limit for each class.
11. What is the class width?
12. How many students were involved in this study?
13. How many students had at least 30 social interactions for the week?
14. How many students had at most 14 social interactions for the week?
15. Among the classes with the greatest frequency, which class has the least number of social interactions?
16. Among the classes with the smallest frequency, which class has the least number of social interactions?

17. As of 2011, the following are the ages, in chronological order, at which U.S. presidents were inaugurated:

57, 61, 57, 57, 58, 57, 61, 54, 68, 51, 49, 64, 50, 48, 65, 52, 56, 46, 54, 49, 50, 47, 55, 55, 54, 42, 51, 56, 55, 51, 54, 51, 60, 62, 43, 55, 56, 61, 52, 69, 64, 46, 54, 47.

Source: Time Almanac

Construct a grouped frequency distribution for the data. Use 41–45 for the first class and use the same width for each subsequent class.

18. The IQ scores of 70 students enrolled in a liberal arts course at a college are as follows:

102, 100, 103, 86, 120, 117, 111, 101, 93, 97, 99, 95, 95, 104, 104, 105, 106, 109, 109, 89, 94, 95, 99, 99, 103, 104, 105, 109, 110, 114, 124, 123, 118, 117, 116, 110, 114, 114, 96, 99, 103, 103, 104, 107, 107, 110, 111, 112, 113, 117, 115, 116, 100, 104, 102, 94, 93, 93, 96, 96, 111, 116, 107, 109, 105, 106, 97, 106, 107, 108.

Construct a grouped frequency distribution for the data. Use 85–89 for the first class and use the same width for each subsequent class.

19. Construct a histogram and a frequency polygon for the data involving stress ratings in Exercises 3–6.

20. Construct a histogram and a frequency polygon for the data in Exercise 7.

21. Construct a histogram and a frequency polygon for the data in Exercise 8.

The histogram shows the distribution of starting salaries (rounded to the nearest thousand dollars) for college graduates based on a random sample of recent graduates.

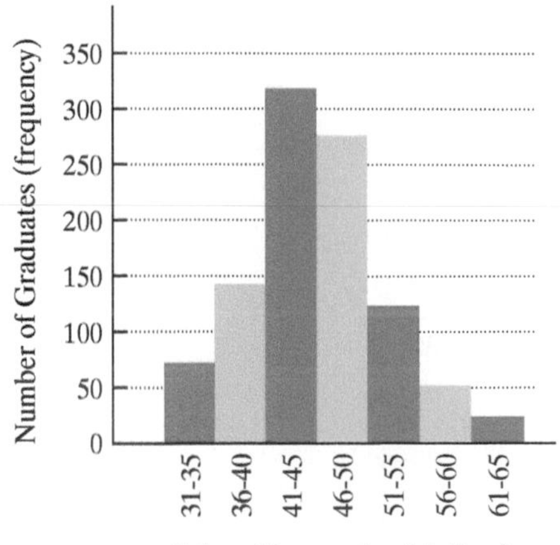

In Exercises 22–25, determine whether each statement is true or false according to the graph.

22. The graph is based on a sample of approximately 500 recent college graduates.

23. More college graduates had starting salaries in the \$51,000–\$55,000 range than in the \$36,000–\$40,000 range.

24. If the sample is truly representative, then for a group of 400 college graduates, we can expect about 28 of them to have starting salaries in the \$31,000–\$35,000 range.

25. The percentage of starting salaries falling above those shown by any rectangular bar is equal to the percentage of starting salaries falling below that bar.

The frequency polygon shows a distribution of IQ scores.

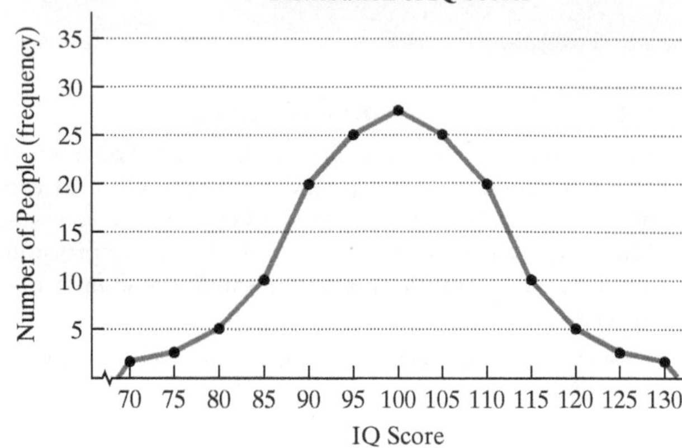

In Exercises 26–29, determine whether each statement is true or false according to the graph.

26. The graph is based on a sample of approximately 50 people.

27. More people had an IQ score of 100 than any other IQ score, and as the deviation from 100 increases or decreases, the scores fall off in a symmetrical manner.

28. More people had an IQ score of 110 than a score of 90.

29. The percentage of scores above any IQ score is equal to the percentage of scores below that score.

30. Construct a stem-and-leaf plot for the data in Exercise 17 showing the ages at which U.S. presidents were inaugurated.

31. A random sample of 40 college professors is selected from all professors at a university. The following list gives their ages:

63, 48, 42, 42, 38, 59, 41, 44, 45, 28, 54, 62, 51, 44, 63, 66, 59, 46, 51, 28, 37, 66, 42, 40, 30, 31, 48, 32, 29, 42, 63, 37, 36, 47, 25, 34, 49, 30, 35, 50.

Construct a stem-and-leaf plot for the data. What does the shape of the display reveal about the ages of the professors?

32. In "Ages of Oscar-Winning Best Actors and Actresses" (*Mathematics Teacher* magazine) by Richard Brown and Gretchen Davis, the stem-and-leaf plots shown compare the ages of 30 actors and 30 actresses at the time they won the award.

Actors	Stems	Actresses
	2	146667
98753221	3	00113344455778
88776543322100	4	11129
6651	5	
210	6	011
6	7	4
	8	0

a. What is the age of the youngest actor to win an Oscar?

b. What is the age difference between the oldest and the youngest actress to win an Oscar?

c. What is the oldest age shared by two actors to win an Oscar?

d. What differences do you observe between the two stem-and-leaf plots? What explanations can you offer for these differences?

In Exercises 33–37, describe what is misleading in each visual display of data.

33.

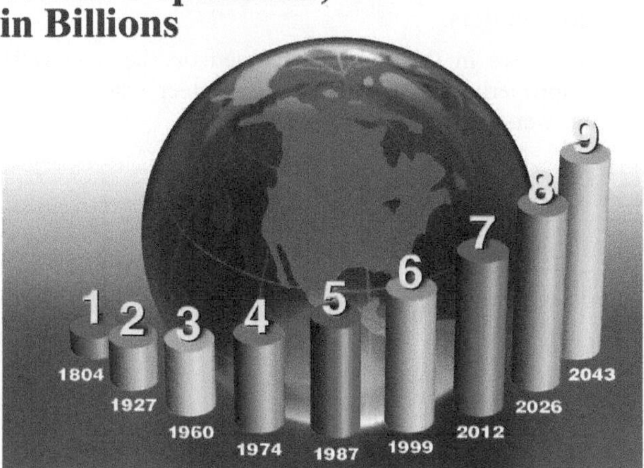

Source: U.S. Census Bureau

34.

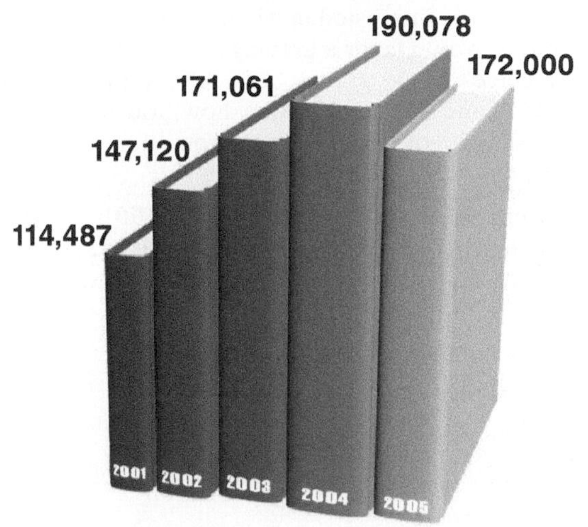

Source: R. R. Bowker

35.

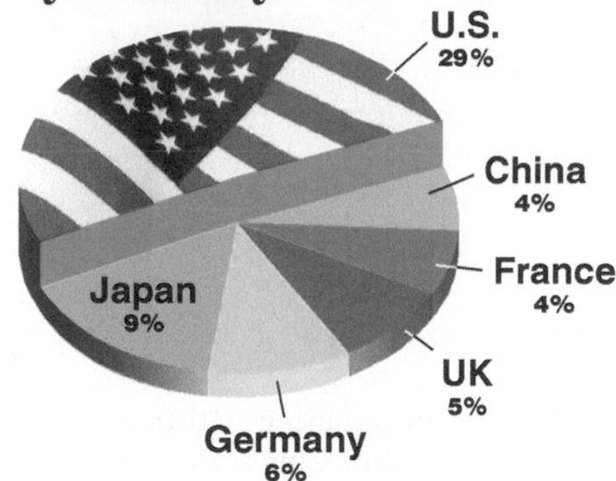

Source: Computer Industry Almanac

36.

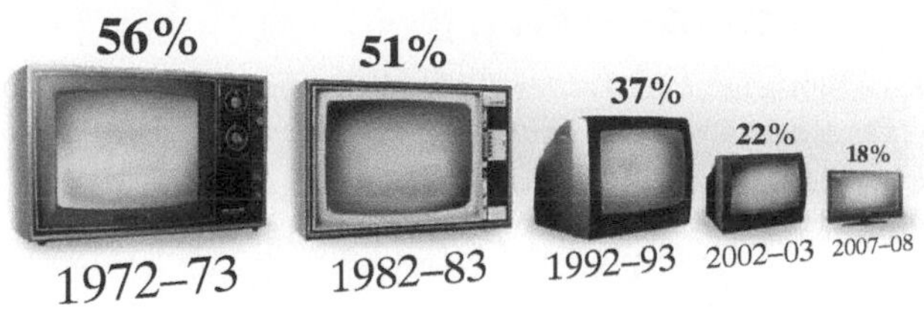

Source: Nielsen Media Research

37.

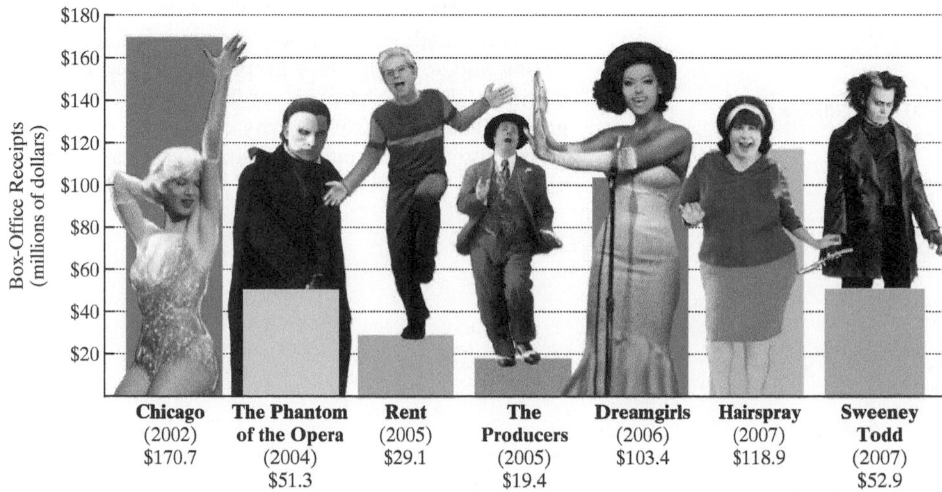

Source: Entertainment Weekly

Writing in Mathematics

38. What is a population? What is a sample?

39. Describe what is meant by a random sample.

40. Suppose you are interested in whether or not the students at your college would favor a grading system in which students may receive final grades of A+, A, A−, B+, B, B−, C+, C, C−, and so on. Describe how you might obtain a random sample of 100 students from the entire student population.

41. For Exercise 40, would questioning every fifth student as he or she is leaving the campus library until 100 students are interviewed be a good way to obtain a random sample? Explain your answer.

42. What is a frequency distribution?

43. What is a histogram?

44. What is a frequency polygon?

45. Describe how to construct a frequency polygon from a histogram.

46. Describe how to construct a stem-and-leaf plot from a set of data.

47. Describe two ways that graphs can be misleading.

Critical Thinking Exercises

Make Sense? *In Exercises 48–51, determine whether each statement makes sense or does not make sense, and explain your reasoning.*

48. The death rate from this new strain of flu is catastrophic because 25% of the people hospitalized with the disease have died.

49. The graph indicates that for the period from 2000 through 2007, the percentage of English majors among incoming college freshmen has rapidly increased.

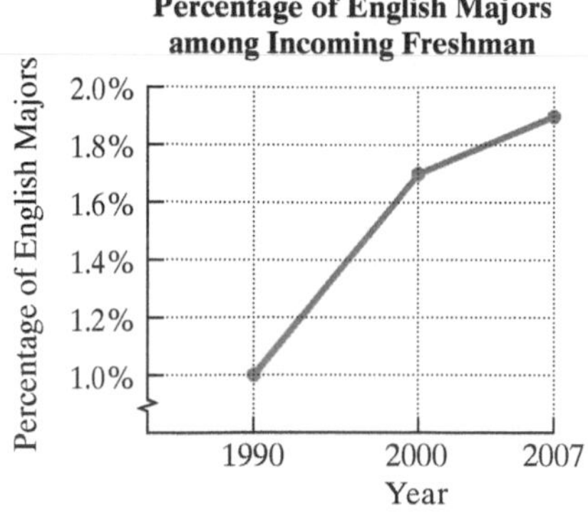

Source: Higher Education Research Institute

50. A public radio station needs to survey its contributors to determine their programming interests, so they should select a random sample of 100 of their largest contributors.

51. The joke in this cartoon is based on the observation that improperly worded questions can steer respondents toward answers that are not their own.

Creators Syndicate/John Hart Studios/Patti Hart-Pomeroy

52. Construct a grouped frequency distribution for the following data, showing the length, in miles, of the 25 longest rivers in the United States. Use five classes that have the same width.

2540	2340	1980	1900	1900
1460	1450	1420	1310	1290
1280	1240	1040	990	926
906	886	862	800	774
743	724	692	659	649

Source: U.S. Department of the Interior

Group Exercises

53. The classic book on distortion using statistics is *How to Lie with Statistics* by Darrell Huff. This activity is designed for five people. Each person should select two chapters from Huff's book and then present to the class the common methods of statistical manipulation and distortion that Huff discusses.

54. Each group member should find one example of a graph that presents data with integrity and one example of a graph that is misleading. Use newspapers, magazines, the Internet, books, and so forth. Once graphs have been collected, each member should share his or her graphs with the entire group. Be sure to explain why one graph depicts data in a forthright manner and how the other graph misleads the viewer.

OBJECTIVES

1. Determine the mean for a data set.
2. Determine the median for a data set.
3. Determine the mode for a data set.
4. Determine the midrange for a data set.

2 Measures of Central Tendency

CROCK by Bill Rechin & Brant Parker

According to researchers, "Robert," the average American guy, is 31 years old, 5 feet 10 inches, 172 pounds, works 6.1 hours daily, and sleeps 7.7 hours. These numbers represent what is "average" or "typical" of American men. In statistics, such values are known as **measures of central tendency** because they are generally located toward the center of a distribution. Four such measures are discussed in this section: the mean, the median, the mode, and the midrange. Each measure of central tendency is calculated in a different way. Thus, it is better to use a specific term (mean, median, mode, or midrange) than to use the generic descriptive term "average."

1 Determine the mean for a data set.

The Mean

By far the most commonly used measure of central tendency is the *mean*. The **mean** is obtained by adding all the data items and then dividing the sum by the number of items. The Greek letter sigma, Σ, called a **symbol of summation**, is used to indicate the sum of data items. The notation Σx, read "the sum of x," means to add all the data items in a given data set. We can use this symbol to give a formula for calculating the mean.

THE MEAN

The **mean** is the sum of the data items divided by the number of items.

$$\text{Mean} = \frac{\Sigma x}{n},$$

where Σx represents the sum of all the data items and n represents the number of items.

The mean of a sample is symbolized by $\overline{x}$ (read "x bar"), while the mean of an entire population is symbolized by μ (the lowercase Greek letter *mu*). Unless otherwise indicated, the data sets throughout this chapter represent samples, so we will use $\overline{x}$ for the mean: $\overline{x} = \frac{\Sigma x}{n}$.

EXAMPLE 1 Calculating the Mean

Table 6 shows the ten youngest male singers in the United States to have a number 1 single. Find the mean age of these male singers at the time of their number 1 single.

TABLE 6 Youngest U.S. Male Singers to Have a Number 1 Single

Artist/Year	Title	Age
Stevie Wonder, 1963	"Fingertips"	13
Donny Osmond, 1971	"Go Away Little Girl"	13
Michael Jackson, 1972	"Ben"	14
Laurie London, 1958	"He's Got the Whole World in His Hands"	14
Chris Brown, 2005	"Run It!"	15
Paul Anka, 1957	"Diana"	16
Brian Hyland, 1960	"Itsy Bitsy Teenie Weenie Yellow Polkadot Bikini"	16
Shaun Cassidy, 1977	"Da Doo Ron Ron"	17
Soulja Boy, 2007	"Crank That Soulja Boy"	17
Sean Kingston, 2007	"Beautiful Girls"	17

Source: Russell Ash, *The Top 10 of Everything*

Solution We find the mean, $\bar{x}$, by adding the ages and dividing this sum by 10, the number of data items.

$$\bar{x} = \frac{\Sigma x}{n} = \frac{13 + 13 + 14 + 14 + 15 + 16 + 16 + 17 + 17 + 17}{10} = \frac{152}{10} = 15.2$$

The mean age of the ten youngest singers to have a number 1 single is 15.2.

BLITZER BONUS

THE MEAN AMERICAN MILLIONAIRE

According to a study involving a random sample of 1300 of America's 2,270,000 millionaires, the average millionaire lives in a \$300,000 home in an upper-middle-class neighborhood, is 54 years old, drives a four-year-old American car, and had an SAT score of 1190.

Source: Stanley, *The Millionaire Next Door*

One and only one mean can be calculated for any group of numerical data. The mean may or may not be one of the actual data items. In Example 1, the mean was 15.2, although no data item is 15.2.

CHECK POINT 1 Find the mean, $\bar{x}$, for each group of data items:

a. 10, 20, 30, 40, 50 **b.** 3, 10, 10, 10, 117.

In Example 1, some of the data items were identical. We can use multiplication when computing the mean for these identical items:

$$\bar{x} = \frac{13 + 13 + 14 + 14 + 15 + 16 + 16 + 17 + 17 + 17}{10}$$

$$= \frac{13 \cdot 2 + 14 \cdot 2 + 15 \cdot 1 + 16 \cdot 2 + 17 \cdot 3}{10}$$

The data values 13, 14, and 16 each have a frequency of 2. The data value 17 has a frequency of 3.

When many data values occur more than once and a frequency distribution is used to organize the data, we can use the following formula to calculate the mean:

CALCULATING THE MEAN FOR A FREQUENCY DISTRIBUTION

$$\text{Mean} = \bar{x} = \frac{\Sigma xf}{n},$$

where

x represents a data value.

f represents the frequency of that data value.

Σxf represents the sum of all the products obtained by multiplying each data value by its frequency.

n represents the *total frequency* of the distribution.

TABLE 7 Students' Stress-Level Ratings

Stress Rating x	Frequency f
0	2
1	1
2	3
3	12
4	16
5	18
6	13
7	31
8	26
9	15
10	14

Source: Journal of Personality and Social Psychology, 69, 1102–1112

EXAMPLE 2 Calculating the Mean for a Frequency Distribution

In the previous exercise set, we mentioned a questionnaire given to students in an introductory statistics class during the first week of the course. One question asked, "How stressed have you been in the last $2\frac{1}{2}$ weeks, on a scale of 0 to 10, with 0 being not at all stressed and 10 being as stressed as possible?" **Table 7** shows the students' responses. Use this frequency distribution to find the mean of the stress-level ratings.

Solution We use the formula for the mean, $\overline{x}$:

$$\overline{x} = \frac{\Sigma xf}{n}.$$

First, we must find xf, obtained by multiplying each data value, x, by its frequency, f. Then, we need to find the sum of these products, Σxf. We can use the frequency distribution to organize these computations. Add a third column in which each data value is multiplied by its frequency. This column, shown on the right, is headed xf. Then, find the sum of the values, Σxf, in this column.

x	f	xf
0	2	$0 \cdot 2 = 0$
1	1	$1 \cdot 1 = 1$
2	3	$2 \cdot 3 = 6$
3	12	$3 \cdot 12 = 36$
4	16	$4 \cdot 16 = 64$
5	18	$5 \cdot 18 = 90$
6	13	$6 \cdot 13 = 78$
7	31	$7 \cdot 31 = 217$
8	26	$8 \cdot 26 = 208$
9	15	$9 \cdot 15 = 135$
10	14	$10 \cdot 14 = 140$
Totals:	$n = 151$	$\Sigma xf = 975$

Σxf is the sum of the numbers in the third column.

This value, the sum of the numbers in the second column, is the total frequency of the distribution.

Now, substitute these values into the formula for the mean, $\overline{x}$. Remember that n is the *total frequency* of the distribution, or 151.

$$\overline{x} = \frac{\Sigma xf}{n} = \frac{975}{151} \approx 6.46$$

The mean of the 0 to 10 stress-level ratings is approximately 6.46. Notice that the mean is greater than 5, the middle of the 0 to 10 scale.

CHECK POINT 2 Find the mean, $\overline{x}$, for the data items in the frequency distribution. (In order to save space, we've written the frequency distribution horizontally.)

Score, x	30	33	40	50
Frequency, f	3	4	4	1

2 Determine the median for a data set.

The Median

The *median* age in the United States is 35.3. The oldest state by median age is Florida (38.7) and the youngest state is Utah (27.1). To find these values, researchers begin with appropriate random samples. The data items—that is, the ages—are arranged from youngest to oldest. The median age is the data item in the middle of each set of ranked, or ordered, data.

THE MEDIAN

To find the **median** of a group of data items,

1. Arrange the data items in order, from smallest to largest.
2. If the number of data items is odd, the median is the data item in the middle of the list.
3. If the number of data items is even, the median is the mean of the two middle data items.

EXAMPLE 3 Finding the Median

Find the median for each of the following groups of data:

a. 84, 90, 98, 95, 88

b. 68, 74, 7, 13, 15, 25, 28, 59, 34, 47.

STUDY TIP

The median splits the data items down the middle, like the median strip in a road.

Solution

a. Arrange the data items in order, from smallest to largest. The number of data items in the list, five, is odd. Thus, the median is the middle number.

84, 88, 90, 95, 98

Middle data item

The median is 90. Notice that two data items lie above 90 and two data items lie below 90.

b. Arrange the data items in order, from smallest to largest. The number of data items in the list, ten, is even. Thus, the median is the mean of the two middle data items.

7, 13, 15, 25, 28, 34, 47, 59, 68, 74

Middle data items are 28 and 34.

$$\text{Median} = \frac{28 + 34}{2} = \frac{62}{2} = 31$$

The median is 31. Five data items lie above 31 and five data items lie below 31.

7 13 15 25 28 | 34 47 59 68 74

Five data items lie below 31. Five data items lie above 31.

Median is 31.

Find the median for each of the following groups of data:

a. 28, 42, 40, 25, 35 **b.** 72, 61, 85, 93, 79, 87.

If a relatively long list of data items is arranged in order, it may be difficult to identify the item or items in the middle. In cases like this, the median can be found by determining its position in the list of items.

STUDY TIP

The formula

$$\frac{n + 1}{2}$$

gives the *position* of the median, and not the actual value of the median. When finding the median, be sure to first arrange the data items in order from smallest to largest.

POSITION OF THE MEDIAN

If n data items are arranged in order, from smallest to largest, the median is the value in the

$$\frac{n + 1}{2}$$

position.

EXAMPLE 4 Finding the Median Using the Position Formula

Listed below are the points scored per season by the 13 top point scorers in the National Football League. Find the median points scored per season for the top 13 scorers.

144, 144, 145, 145, 145, 146, 147, 149, 150, 155, 161, 164, 176

Solution The data items are arranged from smallest to largest. There are 13 data items, so $n = 13$. The median is the value in the

$$\frac{n+1}{2}\text{ position} = \frac{13+1}{2}\text{ position} = \frac{14}{2}\text{ position} = \text{seventh position.}$$

We find the median by selecting the data item in the seventh position.

144, 144, 145, 145, 145, 146, 147, 149, 150, 155, 161, 164, 176

(Position 1, Position 2, Position 3, Position 4, Position 5, Position 6, Position 7)

The median is 147. Notice that six data items lie above 147 and six data items lie below it. The median points scored per season for the top 13 scorers in the National Football League is 147.

CHECK POINT 4 Find the median for the following group of data items:

1, 2, 2, 2, 3, 3, 3, 3, 3, 5, 6, 7, 7, 10, 11, 13, 19, 24, 26.

TABLE 8 Hours and Minutes per Day Spent Sleeping and Eating in Selected Countries

Country	Sleeping	Eating
France	8:50	2:15
U.S.	8:38	1:14
Spain	8:34	1:46
New Zealand	8:33	2:10
Australia	8:32	1:29
Turkey	8:32	1:29
Canada	8:29	1:09
Poland	8:28	1:34
Finland	8:27	1:21
Belgium	8:25	1:49
United Kingdom	8:23	1:25
Mexico	8:21	1:06
Italy	8:18	1:54
Germany	8:12	1:45
Sweden	8:06	1:34
Norway	8:03	1:22
Japan	7:50	1:57
S. Korea	7:49	1:36

Source: Organization for Economic Cooperation and Development

EXAMPLE 5 Finding the Median Using the Position Formula

Table 8 gives the mean number of hours and minutes per day spent sleeping and eating in 18 selected countries. Find the median number of hours and minutes per day spent sleeping for these countries.

Solution Reading from the bottom to the top of **Table 8**, the data items for sleeping appear from smallest to largest. There are 18 data items, so $n = 18$. The median is the value in the

$$\frac{n+1}{2}\text{ position} = \frac{18+1}{2}\text{ position} = \frac{19}{2}\text{ position} = 9.5\text{ position}.$$

This means that the median is the mean of the data items in positions 9 and 10.

7:49, 7:50, 8:03, 8:06, 8:12, 8:18, 8:21, 8:23, [8:25, 8:27,] 8:28, 8:29, 8:32, 8:32, 8:33, 8:34, 8:38, 8:50

(Position 1, Position 2, Position 3, Position 4, Position 5, Position 6, Position 7, Position 8, Position 9, Position 10)

$$\text{Median} = \frac{8{:}25 + 8{:}27}{2} = \frac{16{:}52}{2} = 8{:}26$$

The median number of hours per day spent sleeping for the 18 countries is 8 hours, 26 minutes.

CHECK POINT 5 Arrange the data items for eating in **Table 8** from smallest to largest. Then find the median number of hours and minutes per day spent eating for the 18 countries.

When individual data items are listed from smallest to largest, you can find the median by identifying the item or items in the middle or by using the $\frac{n+1}{2}$ formula for its position. However, the formula for the position of the median is more useful when data items are organized in a frequency distribution.

EXAMPLE 6 Finding the Median for a Frequency Distribution

The frequency distribution for the stress-level ratings of 151 students is repeated below using a horizontal format. Find the median stress-level rating.

Stress rating (x); Number of college students (f)

x	0	1	2	3	4	5	6	7	8	9	10
f	2	1	3	12	16	18	13	31	26	15	14

Total: $n = 151$

Solution There are 151 data items, so $n = 151$. The median is the value in the

$$\frac{n+1}{2} \text{ position} = \frac{151+1}{2} \text{ position} = \frac{152}{2} \text{ position} = 76\text{th position.}$$

We find the median by selecting the data item in the 76th position. The frequency distribution indicates that the data items begin with

$$0, 0, 1, 2, 2, 2, \ldots.$$

We can write the data items all out and then select the median, the 76th data item. A more efficient way to proceed is to count down the frequency column in the distribution until we identify the 76th data item:

x	f
0	2
1	1
2	3
3	12
4	16
5	18
6	13
7	31
8	26
9	15
10	14

We count down the frequency column.
1, 2
3
4, 5, 6
7, 8, 9, 10, 11, 12, 13, 14, 15, 16, 17, 18
19, 20, 21, 22, 23, 24, 25, 26, 27, 28, 29, 30, 31, 32, 33, 34
35, 36, 37, 38, 39, 40, 41, 42, 43, 44, 45, 46, 47, 48, 49, 50, 51, 52
53, 54, 55, 56, 57, 58, 59, 60, 61, 62, 63, 64, 65
66, 67, 68, 69, 70, 71, 72, 73, 74, 75, 76

Stop counting. We've reached the 76th data item.

The 76th data item is 7. The median stress-level rating is 7.

Find the median for the following frequency distribution.

Age at presidential inauguration (x); Number of U.S. presidents assuming office in the 20th century with the given age (f)

x	42	43	46	51	52	54	55	56	60	61	64	69
f	1	1	1	3	1	2	2	2	1	2	1	1

Statisticians generally use the median, rather than the mean, when reporting income. Why? Our next example will help to answer this question.

EXAMPLE 7 Comparing the Median and the Mean

Five employees in the assembly section of a television manufacturing company earn salaries of \$19,700, \$20,400, \$21,500, \$22,600, and \$23,000 annually. The section manager has an annual salary of \$95,000.

a. Find the median annual salary for the six people.

b. Find the mean annual salary for the six people.

Solution

a. To compute the median, first arrange the salaries in order:

$19,700, $20,400, $21,500, $22,600, $23,000, $95,000.

Because the list contains an even number of data items, six, the median is the mean of the two middle items.

$$\text{Median} = \frac{\$21{,}500 + \$22{,}600}{2} = \frac{\$44{,}100}{2} = \$22{,}050$$

The median annual salary is $22,050.

b. We find the mean annual salary by adding the six annual salaries and dividing by 6.

$$\text{Mean} = \frac{\$19{,}700 + \$20{,}400 + \$21{,}500 + \$22{,}600 + \$23{,}000 + \$95{,}000}{6}$$

$$= \frac{\$202{,}200}{6} = \$33{,}700$$

The mean annual salary is $33,700.

In Example 7, the median annual salary is $22,050 and the mean annual salary is $33,700. Why such a big difference between these two measures of central tendency? The relatively high annual salary of the section manager, $95,000, pulls the mean salary to a value considerably higher than the median salary. When one or more data items are much greater than the other items, these extreme values can greatly influence the mean. In cases like this, the median is often more representative of the data.

This is why the median, rather than the mean, is used to summarize the incomes, by gender and race, shown in **Figure 6**. Because no one can earn less than $0, the distribution of income must come to an end at $0 for each of these eight groups. By contrast, there is no upper limit on income on the high side. In the United States, the wealthiest 5% of the population earn about 21% of the total income. The relatively few people with very high annual incomes tend to pull the mean income to a value considerably greater than the median income. Reporting mean incomes in **Figure 6** would inflate the numbers shown, making them nonrepresentative of the millions of workers in each of the eight groups.

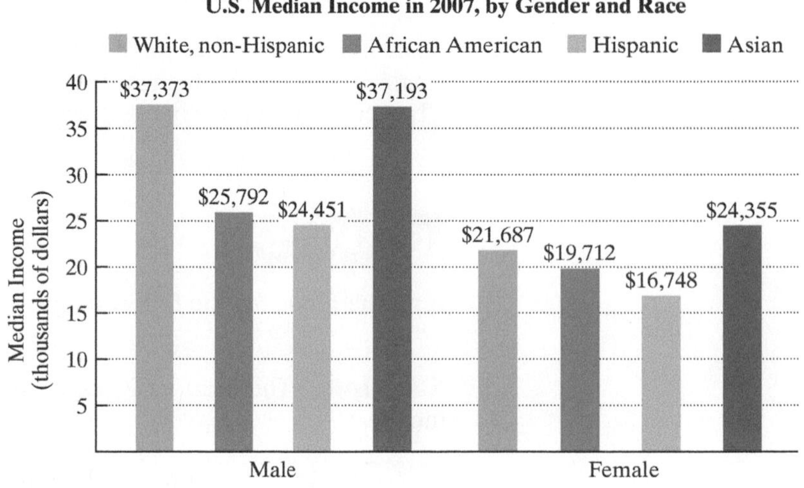

FIGURE 6
Source: U.S. Census Bureau

CHECK POINT 7 **Table 9** shows 2008 compensation (sum of salary, bonus, perks, stock and option awards) for CEOs of six U.S. companies.

TABLE 9 Executive Compensation for Six U.S. Companies

Company	Executive	Total Compensation (millions of dollars)
Apple	Steve Jobs	$0
Coca-Cola	Muhtar Kent	$19.6
IBM	Samuel Palmisano	$21.0
Exxon Mobil	Rex Tillerson	$23.9
Comcast	Brian Roberts	$24.7
Abbott Laboratories	Miles White	$25.1

Source: USA TODAY

a. Find the mean compensation, in millions of dollars, for the six CEOs.

b. Find the median compensation, in millions of dollars, for the six CEOs.

c. Describe why one of the measures of central tendency is greater than the other.

3 Determine the mode for a data set.

The Mode

Let's take one final look at the frequency distribution for the stress-level ratings of 151 college students.

Stress rating

Number of college students

x	0	1	2	3	4	5	6	7	8	9	10
f	2	1	3	12	16	18	13	31	26	15	14

7 is the stress rating with the greatest frequency.

The data value that occurs most often in this distribution is 7, the stress rating for 31 of the 151 students. We call 7 the *mode* of this distribution.

THE MODE

The **mode** is the data value that occurs most often in a data set. If more than one data value has the highest frequency, then each of these data values is a mode. If there is no data value that occurs most often, then the data set has no mode.

EXAMPLE 8 Finding the Mode

Find the mode for the following group of data:

$$7, 2, 4, 7, 8, 10.$$

Solution The number 7 occurs more often than any other. Therefore, 7 is the mode.

CHECK POINT 8 Find the mode for the following group of data:

$$8, 6, 2, 4, 6, 8, 10, 8.$$

Be aware that a data set might not have a mode. For example, no data item in 2, 1, 4, 5, 3 occurs most often, so this data group has no mode. By contrast, 3, 3, 4, 5, 6, 6 has two data values with the highest frequency, namely 3 and 6. Each of these data values is a mode and the data set is said to be **bimodal**.

4 Determine the midrange for a data set.

The Midrange

Table 10 shows the ten hottest cities in the United States. Because temperature is constantly changing, you might wonder how the mean temperatures shown in the table are obtained.

First, we need to find a representative daily temperature. This is obtained by adding the lowest and highest temperatures for the day and then dividing this sum by 2. Next, we take the representative daily temperatures for all 365 days, add them, and divide the sum by 365. These are the mean temperatures that appear in **Table 10**.

TABLE 10 Ten Hottest U.S. Cities

City	Mean Temperature
Key West, FL	77.8°
Miami, FL	75.9°
West Palm Beach, FL	74.7°
Fort Myers, FL	74.4°
Yuma, AZ	74.2°
Brownsville, TX	73.8°
Phoenix, AZ	72.6°
Vero Beach, FL	72.4°
Orlando, FL	72.3°
Tampa, FL	72.3°

Source: National Oceanic and Atmospheric Administration

Representative daily temperature,

$$\frac{\text{lowest daily temperature} + \text{highest daily temperature}}{2},$$

is an example of a measure of central tendency called the *midrange*.

THE MIDRANGE

The **midrange** is found by adding the lowest and highest data values and dividing the sum by 2.

$$\text{Midrange} = \frac{\text{lowest data value} + \text{highest data value}}{2}$$

EXAMPLE 9 Finding the Midrange

One criticism of Major League baseball is that the discrepancy between team payrolls hampers fair competition. In 2009, the New York Yankees had the greatest payroll, a record \$201,449,181 (median salary: \$5,200,000). The Florida Marlins were the worst paid team, with a payroll of \$36,834,000 (median salary: \$470,000). Find the midrange for the annual payroll of Major League baseball teams in 2009. (*Source*: usatoday.com)

Solution

$$\text{Midrange} = \frac{\text{lowest annual payroll} + \text{highest annual payroll}}{2}$$

$$= \frac{\$36{,}834{,}000 + \$201{,}449{,}181}{2} = \frac{\$238{,}283{,}181}{2} = \$119{,}141{,}590.50$$

The midrange for the annual payroll of Major League baseball teams in 2009 was \$119,141,590.50.

We can find the mean annual payroll of the 30 professional baseball teams in 2009 by adding up the payrolls of all 30 teams and then dividing the sum by 30. It is much faster to calculate the midrange, which is often used as an estimate for the mean.

In 2008, the Oakland Raiders had the greatest payroll of any team in the National Football League, a record \$152,389,371 (median salary: \$967,700). The Kansas City Chiefs were the worst paid team, with a payroll of \$83,623,776 (median salary: \$695,000). Find the midrange for the annual payroll of National Football League teams in 2008. (*Source*: usatoday.com)

EXAMPLE 10 Finding the Four Measures of Central Tendency

Suppose your six exam grades in a course are

52, 69, 75, 86, 86, and 92.

Compute your final course grade (90–100 = A, 80–89 = B, 70–79 = C, 60–69 = D, below 60 = F) using the

a. mean. **b.** median. **c.** mode. **d.** midrange.

Solution

a. The mean is the sum of the data items divided by the number of items, 6.

$$\text{Mean} = \frac{52 + 69 + 75 + 86 + 86 + 92}{6} = \frac{460}{6} \approx 76.67$$

Using the mean, your final course grade is C.

b. The six data items, 52, 69, 75, 86, 86, and 92, are arranged in order. Because the number of data items is even, the median is the mean of the two middle items.

$$\text{Median} = \frac{75 + 86}{2} = \frac{161}{2} = 80.5$$

Using the median, your final course grade is B.

c. The mode is the data value that occurs most frequently. Because 86 occurs most often, the mode is 86. Using the mode, your final course grade is B.

d. The midrange is the mean of the lowest and highest data values.

$$\text{Midrange} = \frac{52 + 92}{2} = \frac{144}{2} = 72$$

Using the midrange, your final course grade is C.

Consumer Reports magazine gave the following data for the number of calories in a meat hot dog for each of 17 brands:

173, 191, 182, 190, 172, 147, 146, 138, 175, 136, 179, 153, 107, 195, 135, 140, 138.

Find the mean, median, mode, and midrange for the number of calories in a meat hot dog for the 17 brands. If necessary, round answers to the nearest tenth of a calorie.

Exercise Set 2

Practice Exercises

In Exercises 1–8, find the mean for each group of data items.

1. 7, 4, 3, 2, 8, 5, 1, 3
2. 11, 6, 4, 0, 2, 1, 12, 0, 0
3. 91, 95, 99, 97, 93, 95
4. 100, 100, 90, 30, 70, 100
5. 100, 40, 70, 40, 60
6. 1, 3, 5, 10, 8, 5, 6, 8
7. 1.6, 3.8, 5.0, 2.7, 4.2, 4.2, 3.2, 4.7, 3.6, 2.5, 2.5
8. 1.4, 2.1, 1.6, 3.0, 1.4, 2.2, 1.4, 9.0, 9.0, 1.8

In Exercises 9–12, find the mean for the data items in the given frequency distribution.

9.

Score x	Frequency f
1	1
2	3
3	4
4	4
5	6
6	5
7	3
8	2

10.

Score x	Frequency f
1	2
2	4
3	5
4	7
5	6
6	4
7	3

11.

Score x	Frequency f
1	1
2	1
3	2
4	5
5	7
6	9
7	8
8	6
9	4
10	3

12.

Score x	Frequency f
1	3
2	4
3	6
4	8
5	9
6	7
7	5
8	2
9	1
10	1

In Exercises 13–20, find the median for each group of data items.

13. 7, 4, 3, 2, 8, 5, 1, 3
14. 11, 6, 4, 0, 2, 1, 12, 0, 0
15. 91, 95, 99, 97, 93, 95
16. 100, 100, 90, 30, 70, 100
17. 100, 40, 70, 40, 60
18. 1, 3, 5, 10, 8, 5, 6, 8
19. 1.6, 3.8, 5.0, 2.7, 4.2, 4.2, 3.2, 4.7, 3.6, 2.5, 2.5
20. 1.4, 2.1, 1.6, 3.0, 1.4, 2.2, 1.4, 9.0, 9.0, 1.8

Find the median for the data items in the frequency distribution in

21. Exercise 9.
22. Exercise 10.
23. Exercise 11.
24. Exercise 12.

In Exercises 25–32, find the mode for each group of data items. If there is no mode, so state.

25. 7, 4, 3, 2, 8, 5, 1, 3
26. 11, 6, 4, 0, 2, 1, 12, 0, 0
27. 91, 95, 99, 97, 93, 95
28. 100, 100, 90, 30, 70, 100
29. 100, 40, 70, 40, 60
30. 1, 3, 5, 10, 8, 5, 6, 8
31. 1.6, 3.8, 5.0, 2.7, 4.2, 4.2, 3.2, 4.7, 3.6, 2.5, 2.5
32. 1.4, 2.1, 1.6, 3.0, 1.4, 2.2, 1.4, 9.0, 9.0, 1.8

Find the mode for the data items in the frequency distribution in

33. Exercise 9.
34. Exercise 10.
35. Exercise 11.
36. Exercise 12.

In Exercises 37–44, find the midrange for each group of data items.

37. 7, 4, 3, 2, 8, 5, 1, 3
38. 11, 6, 4, 0, 2, 1, 12, 0, 0
39. 91, 95, 99, 97, 93, 95
40. 100, 100, 90, 30, 70, 100
41. 100, 40, 70, 40, 60
42. 1, 3, 5, 10, 8, 5, 6, 8
43. 1.6, 3.8, 5.0, 2.7, 4.2, 4.2, 3.2, 4.7, 3.6, 2.5, 2.5
44. 1.4, 2.1, 1.6, 3.0, 1.4, 2.2, 1.4, 9.0, 9.0, 1.8

Find the midrange for the data items in the frequency distribution in

45. Exercise 9.
46. Exercise 10.
47. Exercise 11.
48. Exercise 12.

Practice Plus

In Exercises 49–54, use each display of data items to find the mean, median, mode, and midrange.

49.

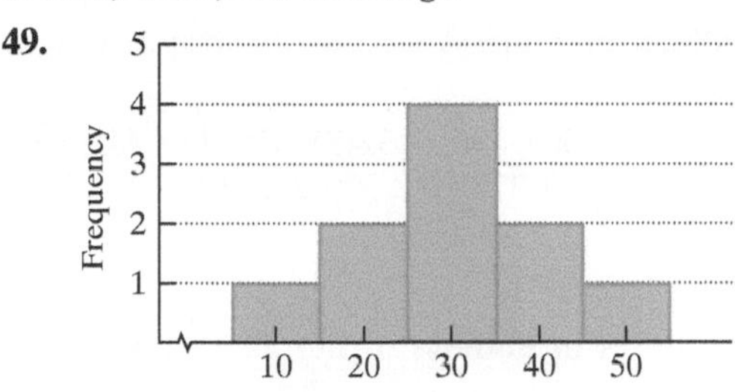

50.

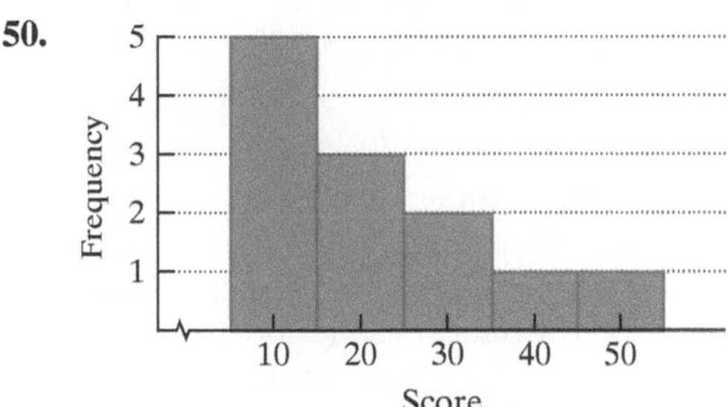

51.

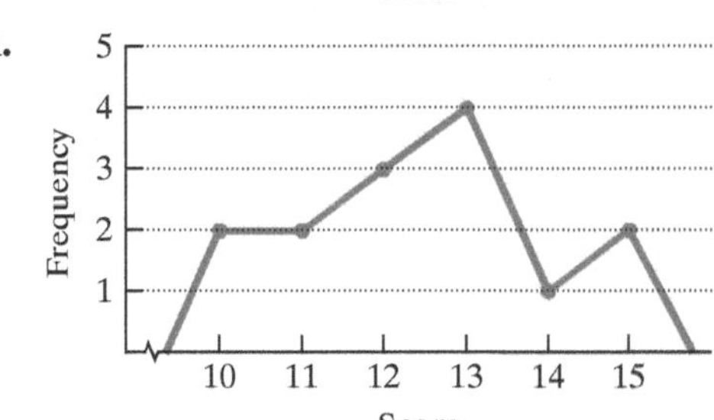

52.

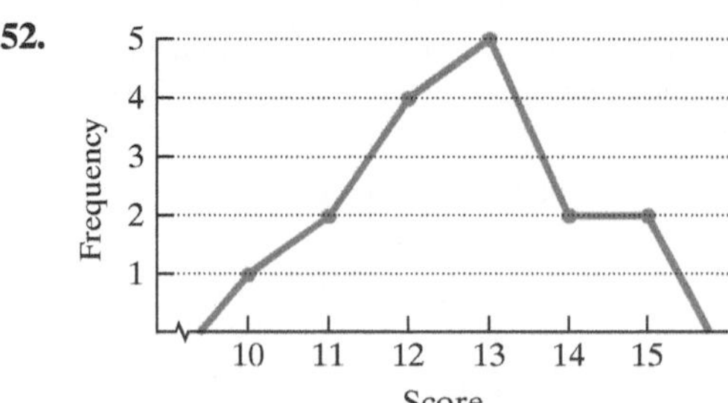

53.

Stems	Leaves			
2	1	4	5	
3	0	1	1	3
4	2	5		

54.

Stems	Leaves			
2	8			
3	2	4	4	9
4	0	1	5	7

Application Exercises

Exercises 55–57 present data on a variety of topics. For each data set described in boldface, find the

a. *mean.*

b. *median.*

c. *mode (or state that there is no mode).*

d. *midrange.*

55. **Values (in millions of dollars) of the 30 Major League Baseball Teams**

1500, 912, 833, 722, 700, 509, 496, 486, 471, 450, 446, 445, 426, 406, 406, 401, 400, 399, 390, 373, 371, 356, 353, 347, 342, 320, 319, 314, 288, 277

Source: Forbes (May 11, 2009)

56. **Revenues (in millions of dollars) of the 30 Major League Baseball Teams**

375, 269, 261, 241, 239, 216, 212, 196, 196, 195, 194, 189, 186, 186, 184, 181, 178, 177, 176, 174, 174, 173, 172, 171, 160, 160, 158, 144, 143, 139

Source: Forbes (May 11, 2009)

57. **Number of Social Interactions of College Students** In Exercise Set 1, we presented a grouped frequency distribution showing the number of social interactions of ten minutes or longer over a one-week period for a group of college students. (These interactions excluded family and work situations.) Use the frequency distribution shown to solve this exercise. (This distribution was obtained by replacing the classes in the grouped frequency distribution previously shown with the midpoints of the classes.)

Social interactions in a week

x	2	7	12	17	22	27	32	37	42	47
f	12	16	16	16	10	11	4	3	3	3

Number of college students

The weights (to the nearest five pounds) of 40 randomly selected male college students are organized in a histogram with a superimposed frequency polygon. Use the graph to answer Exercises 58–61.

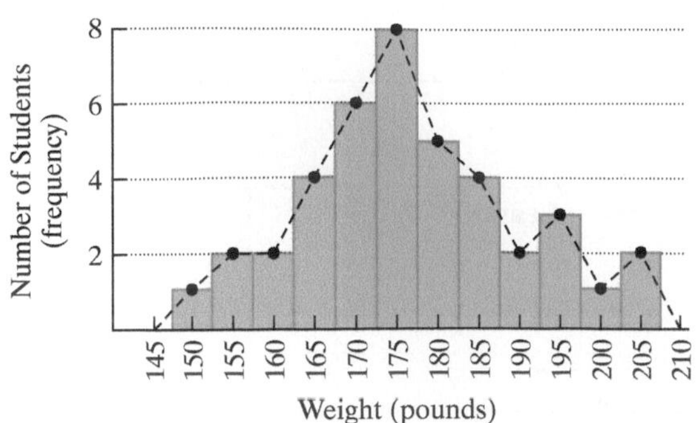

58. Find the mean weight.

59. Find the median weight.

60. Find the modal weight.

61. Find the midrange weight.

62. An advertisement for a speed-reading course claimed that the "average" reading speed for people completing the course was 1000 words per minute. Shown below are the actual data for the reading speeds per minute for a sample of 24 people who completed the course.

1000	900	800	1000	900	850
650	1000	1050	800	1000	850
700	750	800	850	900	950
600	1100	950	700	750	650

a. Find the mean, median, mode, and midrange. (If you prefer, first organize the data in a frequency distribution.)

b. Which measure of central tendency was given in the advertisement?

c. Which measure of central tendency is the best indicator of the "average" reading speed in this situation? Explain your answer.

63. In one common system for finding a grade-point average, or GPA,

$$A = 4, B = 3, C = 2, D = 1, F = 0.$$

The GPA is calculated by multiplying the number of credit hours for a course and the number assigned to each grade, and then adding these products. Then divide this sum by the total number of credit hours. Because each course grade is weighted according to the number of credits of the course, GPA is called a *weighted mean*. Calculate the GPA for this transcript:

Sociology: 3 cr. A; Biology: 3.5 cr. C; Music: 1 cr. B; Math: 4 cr. B; English: 3 cr. C.

Writing in Mathematics

64. What is the mean and how is it obtained?

65. What is the median and how is it obtained?

66. What is the mode and how is it obtained?

67. What is the midrange and how is it obtained?

68. The "average" income in the United States can be given by the mean or the median.

a. Which measure would be used in anti-U.S. propaganda? Explain your answer.

b. Which measure would be used in pro-U.S. propaganda? Explain your answer.

69. In a class of 40 students, 21 have examination scores of 77%. Which measure or measures of central tendency can you immediately determine? Explain your answer.

70. You read an article that states, "Of the 411 players in the National Basketball Association, only 138 make more than the average salary of \$3.12 million." Is \$3.12 million the mean or the median salary? Explain your answer.

71. A student's parents promise to pay for next semester's tuition if an A average is earned in chemistry. With examination grades of 97%, 97%, 75%, 70%, and 55%, the student reports that an A average has been earned. Which measure of central tendency is the student reporting as the average? How is this student misrepresenting the course performance with statistics?

72. According to the National Oceanic and Atmospheric Administration, the coldest city in the United States is International Falls, Minnesota, with a mean Fahrenheit temperature of 36.8°. Explain how this mean is obtained.

Critical Thinking Exercises

Make Sense? *In Exercises 73–76, determine whether each statement makes sense or does not make sense, and explain your reasoning.*

73. I'm working with a data set for which neither the mean nor the median is one of the data items.

74. I made a distribution of the heights of the 12 players on our basketball team. Because one player is much taller than the others, the team's median height is greater than its mean height.

75. Although the data set 1, 1, 2, 3, 3, 3, 4, 4 has a number of repeated items, there is only one mode.

76. If professors use the same test scores for a particular student and calculate measures of central tendency correctly, they will always agree on the student's final course grade.

77. Give an example of a set of six examination grades (from 0 to 100) with each of the following characteristics:

a. The mean and the median have the same value, but the mode has a different value.

b. The mean and the mode have the same value, but the median has a different value.

c. The mean is greater than the median.

d. The mode is greater than the mean.

e. The mean, median, and mode have the same value.

f. The mean and mode have values of 72.

78. On an examination given to 30 students, no student scored below the mean. Describe how this occurred.

Group Exercises

79. Select a characteristic, such as shoe size or height, for which each member of the group can provide a number. Choose a characteristic of genuine interest to the group. For this characteristic, organize the data collected into a frequency distribution and a graph. Compute the mean, median, mode, and midrange. Discuss any differences among these values. What happens if the group is divided (men and women, or people under a certain age and people over a certain age) and these measures of central tendency are computed for each of the subgroups? Attempt to use measures of central tendency to discover something interesting about the entire group or the subgroups.

80. A recent book on spotting bad statistics and learning to think critically about these influential numbers is *Damn Lies and Statistics* by Joel Best (University of California Press, 2001). This activity is designed for six people. Each person should select one chapter from Best's book. The group report should include examples of the use, misuse, and abuse of statistical information. Explain exactly how and why bad statistics emerge, spread, and come to shape policy debates. What specific ways does Best recommend to detect bad statistics?

OBJECTIVES

1 | Determine the range for a data set.

2 | Determine the standard deviation for a data set.

3 Measures of Dispersion

When you think of Houston, Texas and Honolulu, Hawaii, do balmy temperatures come to mind? Both cities have a mean temperature of 75°. However, the mean temperature does not tell the whole story. The temperature in Houston differs seasonally from a low of about 40° in January to a high of close to 100° in July and August. By contrast, Honolulu's temperature varies less throughout the year, usually ranging between 60° and 90°.

Measures of dispersion are used to describe the spread of data items in a data set. Two of the most common measures of dispersion, the *range* and the *standard deviation*, are discussed in this section.

1 Determine the range for a data set.

The Range

A quick but rough measure of dispersion is the **range**, the difference between the highest and lowest data values in a data set. For example, if Houston's hottest annual temperature is 103° and its coldest annual temperature is 33°, the range in temperature is

$$103° - 33°, \quad \text{or} \quad 70°.$$

If Honolulu's hottest day is 89° and its coldest day 61°, the range in temperature is

$$89° - 61°, \quad \text{or} \quad 28°.$$

THE RANGE

The **range**, the difference between the highest and lowest data values in a data set, indicates the total spread of the data.

$$\text{Range} = \text{highest data value} - \text{lowest data value}$$

EXAMPLE 1 Computing the Range

Figure 7 shows the number of workers, in millions, for the five countries with the largest labor forces. Find the range of workers, in millions, for these five countries.

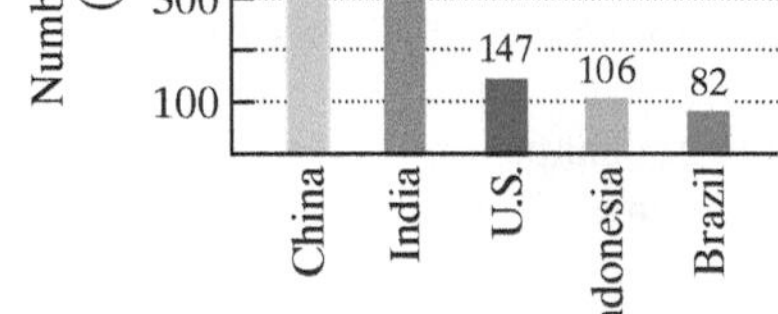

FIGURE 7

Source: Central Intelligence Agency

Solution

$$\begin{aligned}\text{Range} &= \text{highest data value} - \text{lowest data value}\\ &= 778 - 82 = 696\end{aligned}$$

The range is 696 million workers.

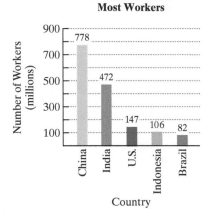

Find the range for the following group of data items:

$$4, 2, 11, 7.$$

The Standard Deviation

A second measure of dispersion, and one that is dependent on *all* of the data items, is called the **standard deviation**. The standard deviation is found by determining how much each data item differs from the mean.

In order to compute the standard deviation, it is necessary to find by how much each data item deviates from the mean. First compute the mean, $\overline{x}$. Then subtract the mean from each data item, $x - \overline{x}$. Example 2 shows how this is done. In Example 3, we will use this skill to actually find the standard deviation.

EXAMPLE 2 Preparing to Find the Standard Deviation; Finding Deviations from the Mean

Find the deviations from the mean for the five data items 778, 472, 147, 106, and 82, shown in **Figure 7**.

Solution First, calculate the mean, $\overline{x}$.

$$\overline{x} = \frac{\Sigma x}{n} = \frac{778 + 472 + 147 + 106 + 82}{5} = \frac{1585}{5} = 317$$

The mean for the five countries with the largest labor forces is 317 million workers. Now, let's find by how much each of the five data items in **Figure 7** differs from 317, the mean. For China, with 778 million workers, the computation is shown as follows:

$$\begin{aligned}\text{Deviation from mean} &= \text{data item} - \text{mean}\\ &= x - \overline{x}\\ &= 778 - 317 = 461.\end{aligned}$$

TABLE 11 Deviations from the Mean

Data item x	Deviation: data item − mean $x - \overline{x}$
778	$778 - 317 = 461$
472	$472 - 317 = 155$
147	$147 - 317 = -170$
106	$106 - 317 = -211$
82	$82 - 317 = -235$

This indicates that the labor force in China exceeds the mean by 461 million workers.

The computation for the United States, with 147 million workers, is given by

$$\begin{aligned}\text{Deviation from mean} &= \text{data item} - \text{mean}\\ &= x - \overline{x}\\ &= 147 - 317 = -170.\end{aligned}$$

This indicates that the labor force in the United States is 170 million workers below the mean.

The deviations from the mean for each of the five given data items are shown in **Table 11**.

Compute the mean for the following group of data items:

$$2, 4, 7, 11.$$

Then find the deviations from the mean for the four data items. Organize your work in table form just like **Table 11**. Keep track of these computations. You will be using them in Check Point 3.

The sum of the deviations from the mean for a set of data is always zero: $\Sigma(x - \overline{x}) = 0$. For the deviations from the mean shown in **Table 11**,

$$461 + 155 + (-170) + (-211) + (-235) = 616 + (-616) = 0.$$

This shows that we cannot find a measure of dispersion by finding the mean of the deviations, because this value is always zero. However, a kind of average of the deviations from the mean, called the **standard deviation**, can be computed. We do so by squaring each deviation and later introducing a square root in the computation. Here are the details on how to find the standard deviation for a set of data:

2 Determine the standard deviation for a data set.

COMPUTING THE STANDARD DEVIATION FOR A DATA SET

1. Find the mean of the data items.
2. Find the deviation of each data item from the mean:
$$\text{data item} - \text{mean}.$$
3. Square each deviation:
$$(\text{data item} - \text{mean})^2.$$
4. Sum the squared deviations:
$$\Sigma(\text{data item} - \text{mean})^2.$$
5. Divide the sum in step 4 by $n - 1$, where n represents the number of data items:
$$\frac{\Sigma(\text{data item} - \text{mean})^2}{n - 1}.$$
6. Take the square root of the quotient in step 5. This value is the standard deviation for the data set.
$$\text{Standard deviation} = \sqrt{\frac{\Sigma(\text{data item} - \text{mean})^2}{n - 1}}$$

The standard deviation of a sample is symbolized by s, while the standard deviation of an entire population is symbolized by σ (the lowercase Greek letter *sigma*). Unless otherwise indicated, data sets represent samples, so we will use s for the standard deviation:

$$s = \sqrt{\frac{\Sigma(x - \overline{x})^2}{n - 1}}.$$

The computation of the standard deviation can be organized using a table with three columns:

Data item x	Deviation: $x - \bar{x}$ Data item − mean	(Deviation)^2: $(x - \bar{x})^2$ (Data item − mean)^2

In Example 2, we worked out the first two columns of such a table. Let's continue working with the data for the countries with the most workers and compute the standard deviation.

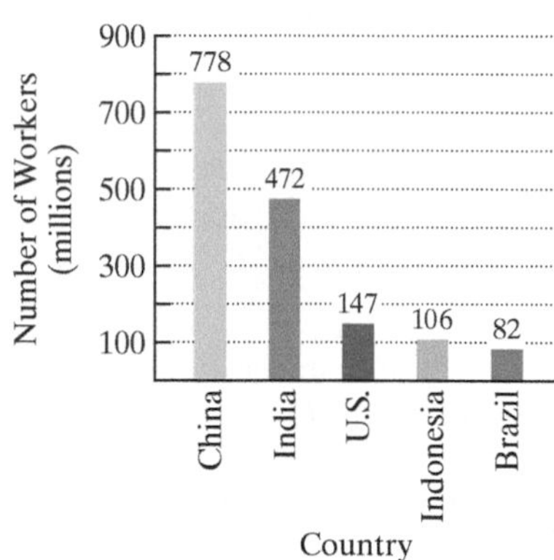

FIGURE 7 (repeated)

EXAMPLE 3 Computing the Standard Deviation

Figure 7, showing the number of workers, in millions, for the five countries with the largest labor forces, is repeated in the margin. Find the standard deviation, in millions, for these five countries.

Solution

Step 1 Find the mean. From our work in Example 2, the mean is 317: $\bar{x} = 317$.

Step 2 Find the deviation of each data item from the mean: data item − mean or $x - \bar{x}$. This, too, was done in Example 2 for each of the five data items.

Step 3 Square each deviation: (data item − mean)^2 or $(x - \bar{x})^2$. We square each of the numbers in the (data item − mean) column, shown in **Table 12**. Notice that squaring the difference always results in a nonnegative number.

TABLE 12 Computing the Standard Deviation

Data item x	Deviation: data item − mean $x - \bar{x}$	(Deviation)^2: (data item − mean)^2 $(x - \bar{x})^2$
778	$778 - 317 = 461$	$461^2 = 461 \cdot 461 = 212{,}521$
472	$472 - 317 = 155$	$155^2 = 155 \cdot 155 = 24{,}025$
147	$147 - 317 = -170$	$(-170)^2 = (-170) \cdot (-170) = 28{,}900$
106	$106 - 317 = -211$	$(-211)^2 = (-211) \cdot (-211) = 44{,}521$
82	$82 - 317 = -235$	$(-235)^2 = (-235) \cdot (-235) = 55{,}225$
Totals:	$\Sigma(x - \bar{x}) = 0$	$\Sigma(x - \bar{x})^2 = 365{,}192$

The sum of the deviations for a set of data is always zero.

Adding the five numbers in the third column gives the sum of the squared deviations: Σ(data item − mean)^2.

TECHNOLOGY

Almost all scientific and graphing calculators compute the standard deviation of a set of data. Using the data items in Example 3,

778, 472, 147, 106, 82,

the keystrokes for obtaining the standard deviation on many scientific calculators are as follows:

778 [Σ+] 472 [Σ+] 147 [Σ+]

106 [Σ+] 82 [Σ+] [2nd] [$\sigma n - 1$].

Graphing calculators require that you specify if data items are from an entire population or a sample of the population.

Step 4 Sum the squared deviations: Σ(data item − mean)^2. This step is shown in **Table 12**. The squares in the third column were added, resulting in a sum of 365,192: $\Sigma(x - \bar{x})^2 = 365{,}192$.

Step 5 Divide the sum in step 4 by $n - 1$, where n represents the number of data items. The number of data items is 5 so we divide by 4.

$$\frac{\Sigma(x - \bar{x})^2}{n - 1} = \frac{\Sigma(\text{data item} - \text{mean})^2}{n - 1} = \frac{365{,}192}{5 - 1} = \frac{365{,}192}{4} = 91{,}298$$

Step 6 The standard deviation, s, is the square root of the quotient in step 5.

$$s = \sqrt{\frac{\Sigma(x - \bar{x})^2}{n - 1}} = \sqrt{\frac{\Sigma(\text{data item} - \text{mean})^2}{n - 1}} = \sqrt{91{,}298} \approx 302.16$$

The standard deviation for the five countries with the largest labor forces is approximately 302.16 million workers.

CHECK POINT 3 Find the standard deviation for the group of data items in Check Point 2. Round to two decimal places.

Example 4 illustrates that as the spread of data items increases, the standard deviation gets larger.

EXAMPLE 4 Computing the Standard Deviation

Find the standard deviation of the data items in each of the samples shown below.

Sample A	**Sample B**
17, 18, 19, 20, 21, 22, 23	5, 10, 15, 20, 25, 30, 35

Solution Begin by finding the mean for each sample.

Sample A:

$$\text{Mean} = \frac{17 + 18 + 19 + 20 + 21 + 22 + 23}{7} = \frac{140}{7} = 20$$

Sample B:

$$\text{Mean} = \frac{5 + 10 + 15 + 20 + 25 + 30 + 35}{7} = \frac{140}{7} = 20$$

Although both samples have the same mean, the data items in sample B are more spread out. Thus, we would expect sample B to have the greater standard deviation. The computation of the standard deviation requires that we find $\Sigma(\text{data item} - \text{mean})^2$, shown in **Table 13**.

TABLE 13 Computing Standard Deviations for Two Samples

Sample A			**Sample B**		
Data item x	**Deviation: data item − mean** $x - \bar{x}$	**(Deviation)²: (data item − mean)²** $(x - \bar{x})^2$	**Data item** x	**Deviation: data item − mean** $x - \bar{x}$	**(Deviation)²: (data item − mean)²** $(x - \bar{x})^2$
17	$17 - 20 = -3$	$(-3)^2 = 9$	5	$5 - 20 = -15$	$(-15)^2 = 225$
18	$18 - 20 = -2$	$(-2)^2 = 4$	10	$10 - 20 = -10$	$(-10)^2 = 100$
19	$19 - 20 = -1$	$(-1)^2 = 1$	15	$15 - 20 = -5$	$(-5)^2 = 25$
20	$20 - 20 = 0$	$0^2 = 0$	20	$20 - 20 = 0$	$0^2 = 0$
21	$21 - 20 = 1$	$1^2 = 1$	25	$25 - 20 = 5$	$5^2 = 25$
22	$22 - 20 = 2$	$2^2 = 4$	30	$30 - 20 = 10$	$10^2 = 100$
23	$23 - 20 = 3$	$3^2 = 9$	35	$35 - 20 = 15$	$15^2 = 225$
Totals:		$\Sigma(x - \bar{x})^2 = 28$			$\Sigma(x - \bar{x})^2 = 700$

Each sample contains seven data items, so we compute the standard deviation by dividing the sums in **Table 13**, 28 and 700, by 7 − 1, or 6. Then we take the square root of each quotient.

$$\text{Standard deviation} = \sqrt{\frac{\Sigma(x - \bar{x})^2}{n - 1}} = \sqrt{\frac{\Sigma(\text{data item} - \text{mean})^2}{n - 1}}$$

Sample A:

$$\text{Standard deviation} = \sqrt{\frac{28}{6}} \approx 2.16$$

Sample B:

$$\text{Standard deviation} = \sqrt{\frac{700}{6}} \approx 10.80$$

Sample A has a standard deviation of approximately 2.16 and sample B has a standard deviation of approximately 10.80. The data in sample B are more spread out than those in sample A.

Find the standard deviation of the data items in each of the samples shown below. Round to two decimal places.

Sample A: 73, 75, 77, 79, 81, 83

Sample B: 40, 44, 92, 94, 98, 100

Figure 8 illustrates four sets of data items organized in histograms. From left to right, the data items are

Figure 8(a): 4, 4, 4, 4, 4, 4, 4

Figure 8(b): 3, 3, 4, 4, 4, 5, 5

Figure 8(c): 3, 3, 3, 4, 5, 5, 5

Figure 8(d): 1, 1, 1, 4, 7, 7, 7.

Each data set has a mean of 4. However, as the spread of the data items increases, the standard deviation gets larger. Observe that when all the data items are the same, the standard deviation is 0.

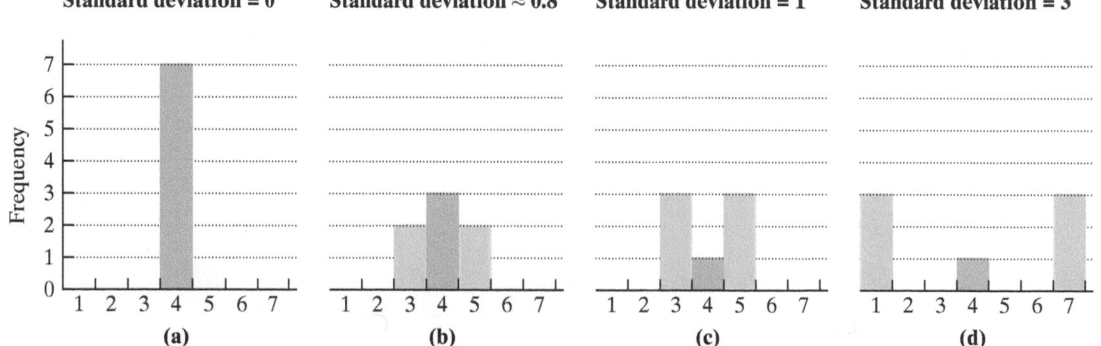

FIGURE 8 The standard deviation gets larger with increased dispersion among data items. In each case, the mean is 4.

EXAMPLE 5 Interpreting Standard Deviation

Two fifth-grade classes have nearly identical mean scores on an aptitude test, but one class has a standard deviation three times that of the other. All other factors being equal, which class is easier to teach, and why?

Solution The class with the smaller standard deviation is easier to teach because there is less variation among student aptitudes. Course work can be aimed at the average student without too much concern that the work will be too easy for some or too difficult for others. By contrast, the class with greater dispersion poses a greater challenge. By teaching to the average student, the students whose scores are significantly above the mean will be bored; students whose scores are significantly below the mean will be confused.

Shown below are the means and standard deviations of the yearly returns on two investments from 1926 through 2004.

Investment	Mean Yearly Return	Standard Deviation
Small-Company Stocks	17.5%	33.3%
Large-Company Stocks	12.4%	20.4%

Source: Summary Statistics of Annual Total Returns 1926 to 2004 Yearbook, Ibbotson Associates, Chicago

a. Use the means to determine which investment provided the greater yearly return.

b. Use the standard deviations to determine which investment had the greater risk. Explain your answer.

Exercise Set 3

Practice Exercises

In Exercises 1–6, find the range for each group of data items.

1. 1, 2, 3, 4, 5

2. 16, 17, 18, 19, 20

3. 7, 9, 9, 15

4. 11, 13, 14, 15, 17

5. 3, 3, 4, 4, 5, 5

6. 3, 3, 3, 4, 5, 5, 5

In Exercises 7–10, a group of data items and their mean are given.

a. *Find the deviation from the mean for each of the data items.*

b. *Find the sum of the deviations in part (a).*

7. 3, 5, 7, 12, 18, 27; Mean = 12

8. 84, 88, 90, 95, 98; Mean = 91

9. 29, 38, 48, 49, 53, 77; Mean = 49

10. 60, 60, 62, 65, 65, 65, 66, 67, 70, 70; Mean = 65

In Exercises 11–16, find a. the mean; b. the deviation from the mean for each data item; and c. the sum of the deviations in part (b).

11. 85, 95, 90, 85, 100

12. 94, 62, 88, 85, 91

13. 146, 153, 155, 160, 161

14. 150, 132, 144, 122

15. 2.25, 3.50, 2.75, 3.10, 1.90

16. 0.35, 0.37, 0.41, 0.39, 0.43

In Exercises 17–26, find the standard deviation for each group of data items. Round answers to two decimal places.

17. 1, 2, 3, 4, 5

18. 16, 17, 18, 19, 20

19. 7, 9, 9, 15

20. 11, 13, 14, 15, 17

21. 3, 3, 4, 4, 5, 5

22. 3, 3, 3, 4, 5, 5, 5

23. 1, 1, 1, 4, 7, 7, 7

24. 6, 6, 6, 6, 7, 7, 7, 4, 8, 3

25. 9, 5, 9, 5, 9, 5, 9, 5

26. 6, 10, 6, 10, 6, 10, 6, 10

In Exercises 27–28, compute the mean, range, and standard deviation for the data items in each of the three samples. Then describe one way in which the samples are alike and one way in which they are different.

27. Sample A: 6, 8, 10, 12, 14, 16, 18
Sample B: 6, 7, 8, 12, 16, 17, 18
Sample C: 6, 6, 6, 12, 18, 18, 18

28. Sample A: 8, 10, 12, 14, 16, 18, 20
Sample B: 8, 9, 10, 14, 18, 19, 20
Sample C: 8, 8, 8, 14, 20, 20, 20

Practice Plus

In Exercises 29–36, use each display of data items to find the standard deviation. Where necessary, round answers to two decimal places.

29.

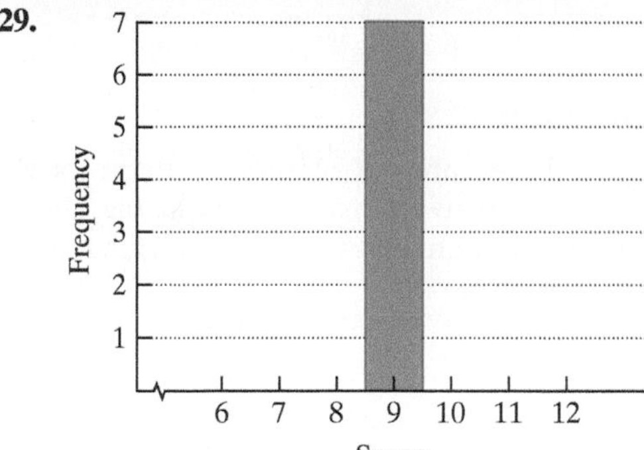

30.

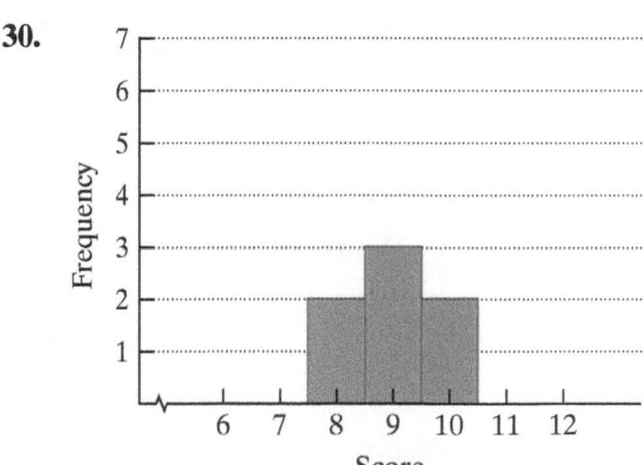

31.

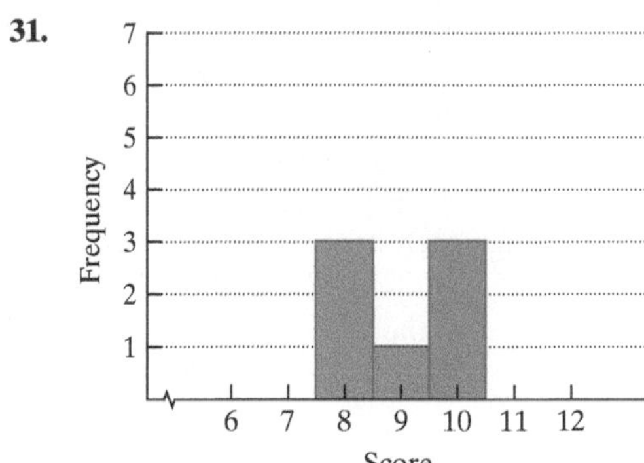

32.

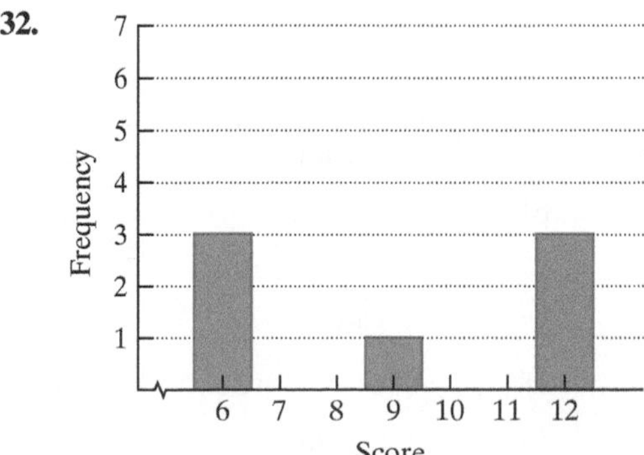

33.

Stems	Leaves
0	5
1	0 5
2	0 5

34.

Stems	Leaves
0	4 8
1	2 6
2	0

35.

Stems	Leaves
1	8 9 9 8 7 8
2	0 1 0 2

36.

Stems	Leaves
1	3 5 3 8 3 4
2	3 0 0 4

Application Exercises

37. The data sets give the number of platinum albums for the five male artists and the five female artists in the United States with the most platinum albums. (Platinum albums sell one million units or more.)

MALE ARTISTS WITH THE MOST PLATINUM ALBUMS

Artist	Platinum Albums
Garth Brooks	106
Elvis Presley	89
Billy Joel	68
Elton John	63
Michael Jackson	59

FEMALE ARTISTS WITH THE MOST PLATINUM ALBUMS

Artist	Platinum Albums
Madonna	62
Barbra Streisand	61
Mariah Carey	60
Whitney Houston	54
Celine Dion	48

Source: RIAA

a. Without calculating, which data set has the greater mean number of platinum albums? Explain your answer.

b. Verify your conjecture from part (a) by calculating the mean number of platinum albums for each data set.

c. Without calculating, which data set has the greater standard deviation? Explain your answer.

d. Verify your conjecture from part (c) by calculating the standard deviation for each data set. Round answers to two decimal places.

38. The data sets give the ages of the first six U.S. presidents and the last six U.S. presidents (through Barack Obama).

AGE OF FIRST SIX U.S. PRESIDENTS AT INAUGURATION

President	Age
Washington	57
J. Adams	61
Jefferson	57
Madison	57
Monroe	58
J. Q. Adams	57

AGE OF LAST SIX U.S. PRESIDENTS AT INAUGURATION

President	Age
Carter	52
Reagan	69
G. H. W. Bush	64
Clinton	46
G. W. Bush	54
Obama	47

Source: Time Almanac

a. Without calculating, which set has the greater standard deviation? Explain your answer.

b. Verify your conjecture from part (b) by calculating the standard deviation for each data set. Round answers to two decimal places.

Writing in Mathematics

39. Describe how to find the range of a data set.

40. Describe why the range might not be the best measure of dispersion.

41. Describe how the standard deviation is computed.

42. Describe what the standard deviation reveals about a data set.

43. If a set of test scores has a standard deviation of zero, what does this mean about the scores?

44. Two classes took a statistics test. Both classes had a mean score of 73. The scores of class A had a standard deviation of 5 and those of class B had a standard deviation of 10. Discuss the difference between the two classes' performance on the test.

45. A sample of cereals indicates a mean potassium content per serving of 93 milligrams and a standard deviation of 2 milligrams. Write a description of what this means for a person who knows nothing about statistics.

46. Over a one-month period, stock A had a mean daily closing price of 124.7 and a standard deviation of 12.5. By contrast, stock B had a mean daily closing price of 78.2 and a standard deviation of 6.1. Which stock was more volatile? Explain your answer.

Critical Thinking Exercises

Make Sense? *In Exercises 47–50, determine whether each statement makes sense or does not make sense, and explain your reasoning.*

47. The joke in this cartoon is based on the observation that the mean can be misleading if you don't know the spread of data items.

48. The standard deviation for the weights of college students is greater than the standard deviation for the weights of 3-year-old children.

49. I'm working with data sets with different means and the same standard deviation.

50. I'm working with data sets with the same mean and different standard deviations.

51. Describe a situation in which a relatively large standard deviation is desirable.

52. If a set of test scores has a large range but a small standard deviation, describe what this means about students' performance on the test.

53. Use the data 1, 2, 3, 5, 6, 7. Without actually computing the standard deviation, which of the following best approximates the standard deviation?

a. 2 **b.** 6 **c.** 10 **d.** 20

54. Use the data 0, 1, 3, 4, 4, 6. Add 2 to each of the numbers. How does this affect the mean? How does this affect the standard deviation?

Group Exercises

55. As a follow-up to Group Exercise 79, the group should reassemble and compute the standard deviation for each data set whose mean you previously determined. Does the standard deviation tell you anything new or interesting about the entire group or subgroups that you did not discover during the previous group activity?

56. Group members should consult a current almanac or the Internet and select intriguing data. The group's function is to use statistics to tell a story. Once "intriguing" data are identified, as a group
    a. Summarize the data. Use words, frequency distributions, and graphic displays.
    b. Compute measures of central tendency and dispersion, using these statistics to discuss the data.

OBJECTIVES

1 Recognize characteristics of normal distributions.
2 Understand the 68-95-99.7 Rule.
3 Find scores at a specified standard deviation from the mean.
4 Use the 68-95-99.7 Rule.
5 Convert a data item to a z-score.
6 Understand percentiles and quartiles.
7 Use and interpret margins of error.
8 Recognize distributions that are not normal.

4 The Normal Distribution

Mean Adult Heights

Source: National Center for Health Statistics

Our heights are on the rise! In one million B.C., the mean height for men was 4 feet 6 inches. The mean height for women was 4 feet 2 inches. Because of improved diets and medical care, the mean height for men is now 5 feet 10 inches and for women it is 5 feet 5 inches. Mean adult heights are expected to plateau by 2050.

1 Recognize characteristics of normal distributions.

Suppose that a researcher selects a random sample of 100 adult men, measures their heights, and constructs a histogram for the data. The graph is shown in **Figure 9 (a)** below. **Figure 9 (a)** and **(b)** illustrate what happens as the sample size increases. In **Figure 9(c)**, if you were to fold the graph down the middle, the left side would fit the right side. As we move out from the middle, the heights of the bars are the same to the left and right. Such a histogram is called **symmetric**. As the sample size increases, so does the graph's symmetry. If it were possible to measure the heights of all adult males, the entire population, the histogram would approach what is called the **normal distribution**, shown in **Figure 9(d)**. This distribution is also called the **bell curve** or the **Gaussian distribution**, named for the German mathematician Carl Friedrich Gauss (1777–1855).

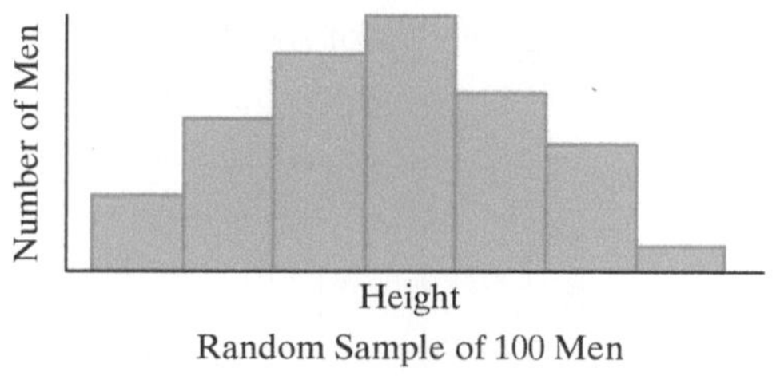

Random Sample of 100 Men
(a)

Number of Men
Height
Sample Size Increases
(b)

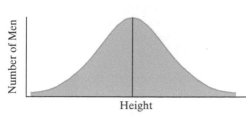

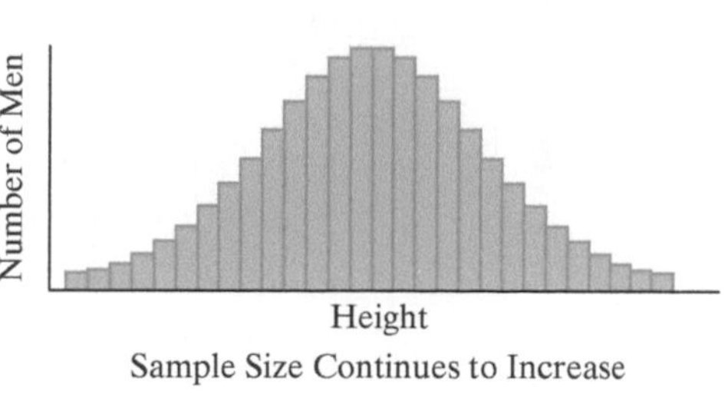

Sample Size Continues to Increase
(c)

Number of Men
Height
Normal Distribution for the Population
(d)

FIGURE 9 Heights of adult males

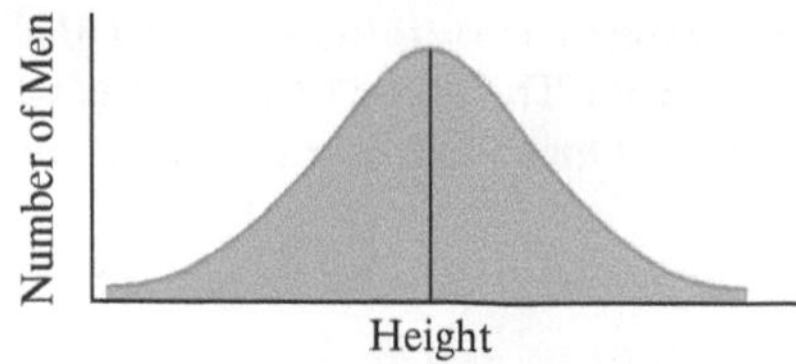

FIGURE 9(d) (repeated)

Figure 9(d) illustrates that the normal distribution is bell shaped and symmetric about a vertical line through its center. Furthermore, **the mean, median, and mode** of a normal distribution **are all equal** and located at the center of the distribution.

The shape of the normal distribution depends on the mean and the standard deviation. **Figure 10** illustrates three normal distributions with the same mean, but different standard deviations. As the standard deviation increases, the distribution becomes more dispersed, or spread out, but retains its symmetric bell shape.

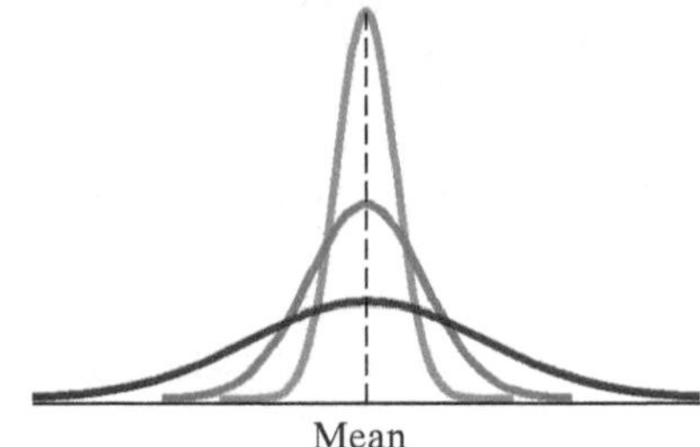

FIGURE 10

The normal distribution provides a wonderful model for all kinds of phenomena because many sets of data items closely resemble this population distribution. Examples include heights and weights of adult males, intelligence quotients, SAT scores, prices paid for a new car model, and life spans of light bulbs. In these distributions, the data items tend to cluster around the mean. The more an item differs from the mean, the less likely it is to occur.

The normal distribution is used to make predictions about an entire population using data from a sample. In this section, we focus on the characteristics and applications of the normal distribution.

BLITZER BONUS

WELL-WORN STEPS AND THE NORMAL DISTRIBUTION

Simon Warner, Photographer

These ancient steps each take on the shape of a normal distribution when the picture is viewed upside down. The center of each step is more worn than the outer edges. The greatest number of people have walked in the center, making this the mean, median, and mode for where people have walked.

2 Understand the 68–95–99.7 Rule.

The Standard Deviation and z-Scores in Normal Distributions

The standard deviation plays a crucial role in the normal distribution, summarized by the **68–95–99.7 Rule.** This rule is illustrated in **Figure 11**.

THE 68-95-99.7 RULE FOR THE NORMAL DISTRIBUTION

1. Approximately 68% of the data items fall within 1 standard deviation of the mean (in both directions).
2. Approximately 95% of the data items fall within 2 standard deviations of the mean.
3. Approximately 99.7% of the data items fall within 3 standard deviations of the mean.

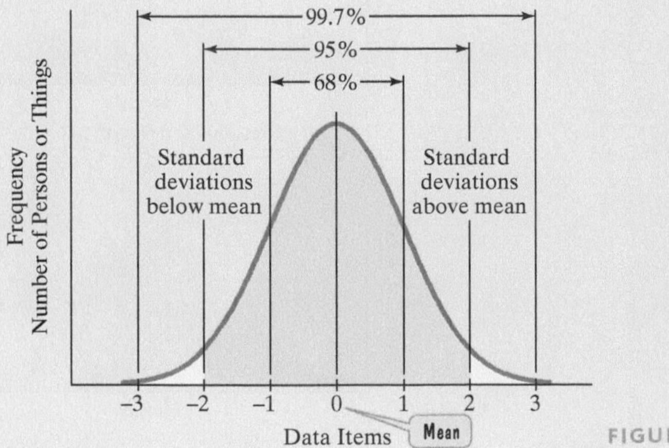

FIGURE 11

Figure 11 illustrates that a very small percentage of the data in a normal distribution lies more than 3 standard deviations above or below the mean. As we move from the mean, the curve falls rapidly, and then more and more gradually, toward the horizontal axis. The tails of the curve approach, but never touch, the horizontal axis, although they are quite close to the axis at 3 standard deviations from the mean. The range of the normal distribution is infinite. No matter how far out from the mean we move, there is always the probability (although very small) of a data item occurring even farther out.

3 Find scores at a specified standard deviation from the mean.

EXAMPLE 1 Finding Scores at a Specified Standard Deviation from the Mean

Male adult heights in North America are approximately normally distributed with a mean of 70 inches and a standard deviation of 4 inches. Find the height that is

a. 2 standard deviations above the mean.

b. 3 standard deviations below the mean.

Solution

a. First, let us find the height that is 2 standard deviations above the mean.

$$\begin{aligned}\text{Height} &= \text{mean} + 2 \cdot \text{standard deviation}\\ &= 70 + 2 \cdot 4 = 70 + 8 = 78\end{aligned}$$

A height of 78 inches is 2 standard deviations above the mean.

b. Next, let us find the height that is 3 standard deviations below the mean.

$$\begin{aligned}\text{Height} &= \text{mean} - 3 \cdot \text{standard deviation}\\ &= 70 - 3 \cdot 4 = 70 - 12 = 58\end{aligned}$$

A height of 58 inches is 3 standard deviations below the mean.

The distribution of male adult heights in North America is illustrated as a normal distribution in **Figure 12**.

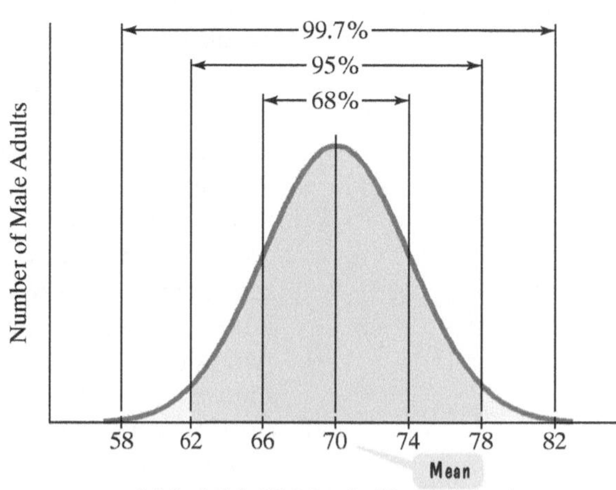

FIGURE 12

Female adult heights in North America are approximately normally distributed with a mean of 65 inches and a standard deviation of 3.5 inches. Find the height that is

a. 3 standard deviations above the mean.

b. 2 standard deviations below the mean.

4 Use the 68–95–99.7 Rule.

EXAMPLE 2 Using the 68–95–99.7 Rule

Use the distribution of male adult heights in **Figure 12** to find the percentage of men in North America with heights

a. between 66 inches and 74 inches. **b.** between 70 inches and 74 inches.

c. above 78 inches.

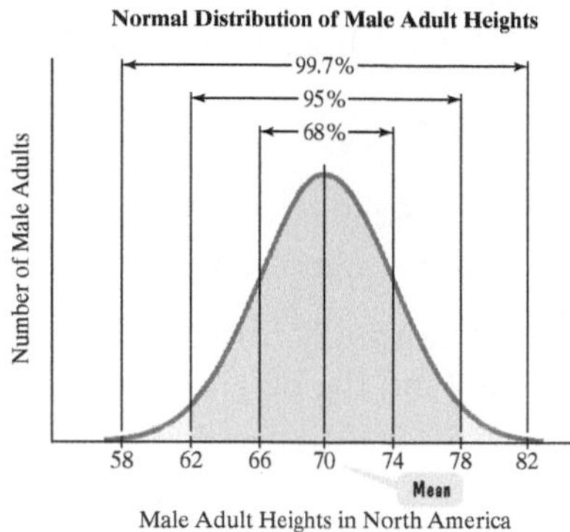

FIGURE 12 (repeated)

Solution

a. The 68–95–99.7 Rule states that approximately 68% of the data items fall within 1 standard deviation, 4, of the mean, 70.

$$\text{mean} - 1 \cdot \text{standard deviation} = 70 - 1 \cdot 4 = 70 - 4 = 66$$
$$\text{mean} + 1 \cdot \text{standard deviation} = 70 + 1 \cdot 4 = 70 + 4 = 74$$

Figure 12 shows that 68% of male adults have heights between 66 inches and 74 inches.

b. The percentage of men with heights between 70 inches and 74 inches is not given directly in **Figure 12**. Because of the distribution's symmetry, the percentage with heights between 66 inches and 70 inches is the same as the percentage with heights between 70 and 74 inches. **Figure 13** indicates that 68% have heights between 66 inches and 74 inches. Thus, half of 68%, or 34%, of men have heights between 70 inches and 74 inches.

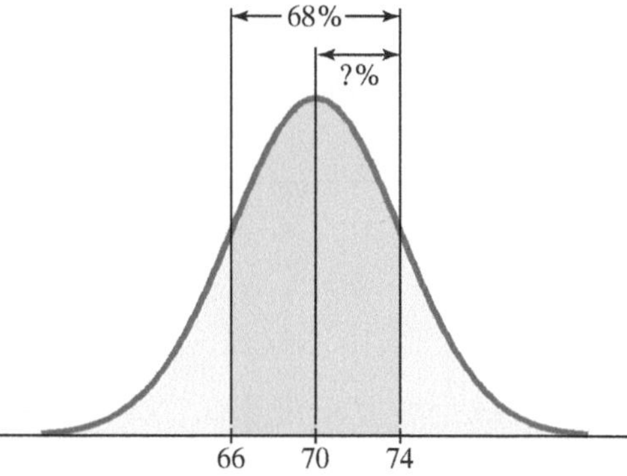

FIGURE 13 What percentage have heights between 70 inches and 74 inches?

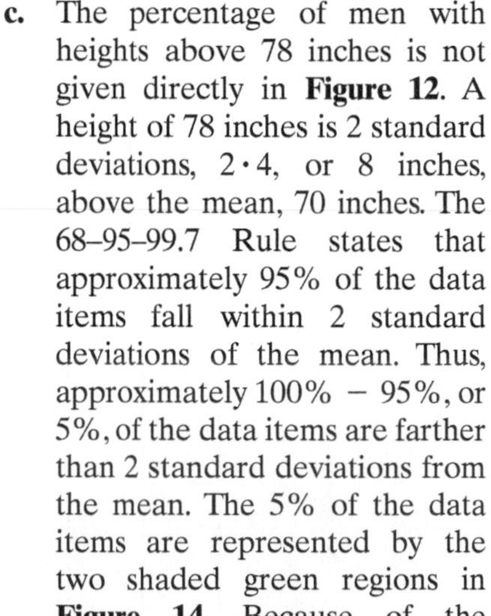

c. The percentage of men with heights above 78 inches is not given directly in **Figure 12**. A height of 78 inches is 2 standard deviations, $2 \cdot 4$, or 8 inches, above the mean, 70 inches. The 68–95–99.7 Rule states that approximately 95% of the data items fall within 2 standard deviations of the mean. Thus, approximately $100\% - 95\%$, or 5%, of the data items are farther than 2 standard deviations from the mean. The 5% of the data items are represented by the two shaded green regions in **Figure 14**. Because of the distribution's symmetry, half of 5%, or 2.5%, of the data items are more than 2 standard deviations above the mean. This means that 2.5% of men have heights above 78 inches.

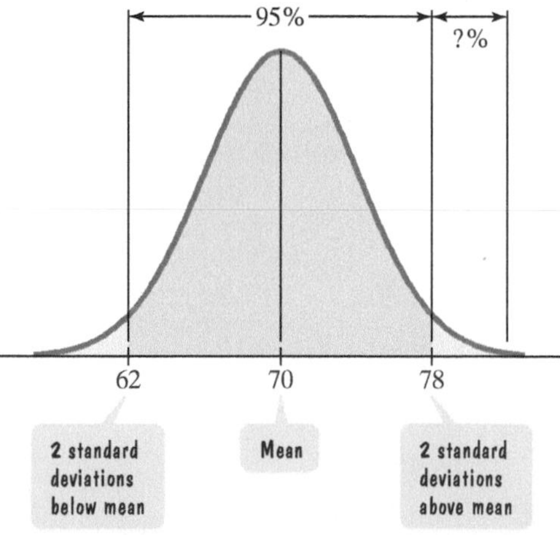

FIGURE 14 What percentage have heights above 78 inches?

CHECK POINT 2 Use the distribution of male adult heights in North America in **Figure 12** to find the percentage of men with heights

a. between 62 inches and 78 inches.

b. between 70 inches and 78 inches.

c. above 74 inches.

Because the normal distribution of male adult heights in North America has a mean of 70 inches and a standard deviation of 4 inches, a height of 78 inches lies 2 standard deviations above the mean. In a normal distribution, a **z-score** describes how many standard deviations a particular data item lies above or below the mean. Thus, the z-score for the data item 78 is 2.

The following formula can be used to express a data item in a normal distribution as a z-score:

5 Convert a data item to a z-score.

COMPUTING z-SCORES

A z-score describes how many standard deviations a data item in a normal distribution lies above or below the mean. The z-score can be obtained using

$$z\text{-score} = \frac{\text{data item} - \text{mean}}{\text{standard deviation}}.$$

Data items above the mean have positive z-scores. Data items below the mean have negative z-scores. The z-score for the mean is 0.

EXAMPLE 3 Computing z-Scores

Michael Newman\PhotoEdit Inc.

The mean weight of newborn infants is 7 pounds and the standard deviation is 0.8 pound. The weights of newborn infants are normally distributed. Find the z-score for a weight of

a. 9 pounds. **b.** 7 pounds. **c.** 6 pounds.

Solution We compute the z-score for each weight by using the z-score formula. The mean is 7 and the standard deviation is 0.8.

a. The z-score for a weight of 9 pounds, written z_9, is

$$z_9 = \frac{\text{data item} - \text{mean}}{\text{standard deviation}} = \frac{9-7}{0.8} = \frac{2}{0.8} = 2.5.$$

The z-score of a data item greater than the mean is always positive. A 9-pound infant is a chubby little tyke, with a weight that is 2.5 standard deviations above the mean.

b. The z-score for a weight of 7 pounds is

$$z_7 = \frac{\text{data item} - \text{mean}}{\text{standard deviation}} = \frac{7-7}{0.8} = \frac{0}{0.8} = 0.$$

The z-score for the mean is always 0. A 7-pound infant is right at the mean, deviating 0 pounds above or below it.

c. The z-score for a weight of 6 pounds is

$$z_6 = \frac{\text{data item} - \text{mean}}{\text{standard deviation}} = \frac{6-7}{0.8} = \frac{-1}{0.8} = -1.25.$$

The z-score of a data item less than the mean is always negative. A 6-pound infant's weight is 1.25 standard deviations below the mean.

Figure 15 shows the normal distribution of weights of newborn infants. The horizontal axis is labeled in terms of weights and z-scores.

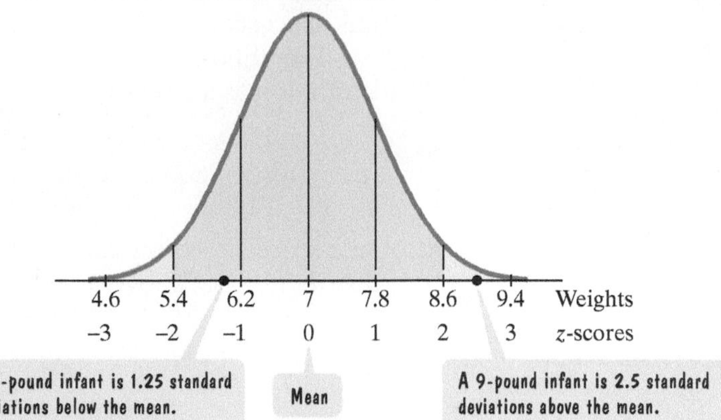

FIGURE 15 Infants' weights are normally distributed.

CHECK POINT 3 The length of horse pregnancies from conception to birth is normally distributed with a mean of 336 days and a standard deviation of 3 days. Find the z-score for a horse pregnancy of

a. 342 days. **b.** 336 days. **c.** 333 days.

In Example 4, we consider two normally distributed sets of test scores, in which a higher score generally indicates a better result. To compare scores on two different tests in relation to the mean on each test, we can use z-scores. The better score is the item with the greater z-score.

EXAMPLE 4 Using and Interpreting z-Scores

A student scores 70 on an arithmetic test and 66 on a vocabulary test. The scores for both tests are normally distributed. The arithmetic test has a mean of 60 and a standard deviation of 20. The vocabulary test has a mean of 60 and a standard deviation of 2. On which test did the student have the better score?

Solution To answer the question, we need to find the student's z-score on each test, using

$$z = \frac{\text{data item} - \text{mean}}{\text{standard deviation}}.$$

The arithmetic test has a mean of 60 and a standard deviation of 20.

$$z\text{-score for } 70 = z_{70} = \frac{70 - 60}{20} = \frac{10}{20} = 0.5$$

The vocabulary test has a mean of 60 and a standard deviation of 2.

$$z\text{-score for } 66 = z_{66} = \frac{66 - 60}{2} = \frac{6}{2} = 3$$

The arithmetic score, 70, is half a standard deviation above the mean, whereas the vocabulary score, 66, is 3 standard deviations above the mean. The student did much better than the mean on the vocabulary test.

CHECK POINT 4 The SAT (Scholastic Aptitude Test) has a mean of 500 and a standard deviation of 100. The ACT (American College Test) has a mean of 18 and a standard deviation of 6. Both tests measure the same kind of ability, with scores that are normally distributed. Suppose that you score 550 on the SAT and 24 on the ACT. On which test did you have the better score?

BLITZER BONUS

THE IQ CONTROVERSY

Is intelligence something we are born with or is it a quality that can be manipulated through education? Can it be measured accurately and is IQ the way to measure it? There are no clear answers to these questions.

In a study by Carolyn Bird (*Pygmalion in the Classroom*), a group of third-grade teachers was told that they had classes of students with IQs well above the mean. These classes made incredible progress throughout the year. In reality, these were not gifted kids, but, rather, a random sample of all third-graders. It was the teachers' expectations, and not the IQs of the students, that resulted in increased performance.

EXAMPLE 5 Understanding z-Scores

Intelligence quotients (IQs) on the Stanford-Binet intelligence test are normally distributed with a mean of 100 and a standard deviation of 16.

a. What is the IQ corresponding to a z-score of -1.5?

b. Mensa is a group of people with high IQs whose members have z-scores of 2.05 or greater on the Stanford-Binet intelligence test. What is the IQ corresponding to a z-score of 2.05?

Solution

a. We begin with the IQ corresponding to a z-score of -1.5. The negative sign in -1.5 tells us that the IQ is $1\frac{1}{2}$ standard deviations below the mean.

$$\begin{aligned} \text{IQ} &= \text{mean} - 1.5 \cdot \text{standard deviation} \\ &= 100 - 1.5(16) = 100 - 24 = 76 \end{aligned}$$

The IQ corresponding to a z-score of -1.5 is 76.

b. Next, we find the IQ corresponding to a z-score of 2.05. The positive sign implied in 2.05 tells us that the IQ is 2.05 standard deviations above the mean.

$$\begin{aligned} \text{IQ} &= \text{mean} + 2.05 \cdot \text{standard deviation} \\ &= 100 + 2.05(16) = 100 + 32.8 = 132.8 \end{aligned}$$

The IQ corresponding to a z-score of 2.05 is 132.8. (An IQ score of at least 133 is required to join Mensa.)

Use the information in Example 5 to find the IQ corresponding to a z-score of

a. -2.25.

b. 1.75.

6 Understand percentiles and quartiles.

Percentiles and Quartiles

A z-score measures a data item's position in a normal distribution. Another measure of a data item's position is its **percentile**. Percentiles are often associated with scores on standardized tests. If a score is in the 45th percentile, this means that 45% of the scores are less than this score. If a score is in the 95th percentile, this indicates that 95% of the scores are less than this score.

PERCENTILES

If n% of the items in a distribution are less than a particular data item, we say that the data item is in the ***n*th percentile** of the distribution.

STUDY TIP

A score in the 98th percentile does *not* mean that 98% of the answers are correct. Nor does it mean that the score was 98%.

EXAMPLE 6 Interpreting Percentile

The cutoff IQ score for Mensa membership, 132.8, is in the 98th percentile. What does this mean?

Solution Because 132.8 is in the 98th percentile, this means that 98% of IQ scores fall below 132.8.

A student scored in the 75th percentile on the SAT. What does this mean?

Three commonly encountered percentiles are the *quartiles*. **Quartiles** divide data sets into four equal parts. The 25th percentile is the **first quartile**: 25% of the data fall below the first quartile. The 50th percentile is the **second quartile**: 50% of the data fall below the second quartile, so the second quartile is equivalent to the median. The 75th percentile is the **third quartile**: 75% of the data fall below the third quartile. **Figure 16** illustrates the concept of quartiles for the normal distribution.

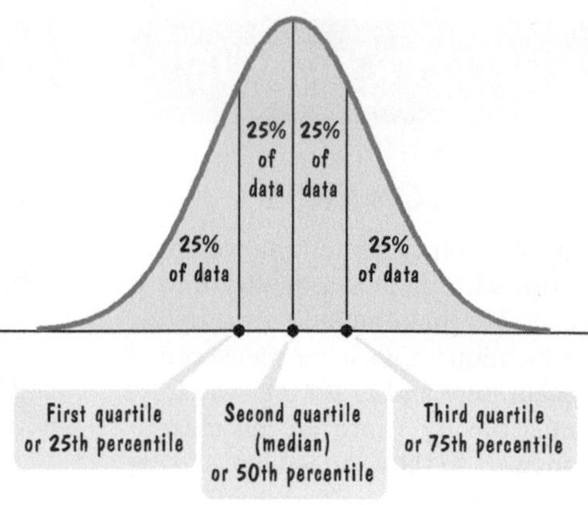

FIGURE 16 Quartiles

7 Use and interpret margins of error.

Polls and Margins of Error

When you were between the ages of 6 and 14, how would you have responded to this question:

What is bad about being a kid?

WHAT IS BAD ABOUT BEING A KID?

Kids Say	
Getting bossed around	17%
School, homework	15%
Can't do everything I want	11%
Chores	9%
Being grounded	9%

Source: Penn, Schoen, and Berland using 1172 interviews with children ages 6 to 14 from May 14 to June 1, 1999,

Note the margin of error.

In a random sample of 1172 children ages 6 through 14, 17% of the children responded, "Getting bossed around." The problem is that this is a single random sample. Do 17% of kids in the entire population of children ages 6 through 14 think that getting bossed around is a bad thing?

Statisticians use properties of the normal distribution to estimate the probability that a result obtained from a single sample reflects what is truly happening in the population. If you look at the results of a poll like the one shown in the margin, you will observe that a *margin of error* is reported. Surveys and opinion polls often give a margin of error. Let's use our understanding of the normal distribution to see how to calculate and interpret margins of error.

Suppose that $p\%$ of the population of children ages 6 through 14 hold the opinion that getting bossed around is a bad thing about being a kid. Instead of taking only one random sample of 1172 children, we repeat the process of selecting a random sample of 1172 children hundreds of times. Then, we calculate the percentage of children for each sample who think being bossed around is bad. With random sampling, we expect to find the percentage in many of the samples close to $p\%$, with relatively few samples having percentages far from $p\%$. **Figure 17** shows that the percentages of children from the hundreds of samples can be modeled by a normal distribution. The mean of this distribution is the actual population percent, $p\%$, and is the most frequent result from the samples.

Mathematicians have shown that the standard deviation of a normal distribution of samples like the one in **Figure 17** is approximately $\frac{1}{2\sqrt{n}} \times 100\%$, where n is the sample size. Using the 68–95–99.7 Rule, approximately 95% of the samples have a percentage within 2 standard deviations of the true population percentage, $p\%$:

$$\text{2 standard deviations} = 2 \cdot \frac{1}{2\sqrt{n}} \times 100\% = \frac{1}{\sqrt{n}} \times 100\%.$$

If we use a single random sample of size n, there is a 95% probability that the percent obtained will lie within two standard deviations, or $\frac{1}{\sqrt{n}} \times 100\%$, of the true population percent. We can be 95% confident that the true population percent lies between

$$\text{the sample percent} - \frac{1}{\sqrt{n}} \times 100\%$$

and

$$\text{the sample percent} + \frac{1}{\sqrt{n}} \times 100\%.$$

We call $\pm \frac{1}{\sqrt{n}} \times 100\%$ the **margin of error**.

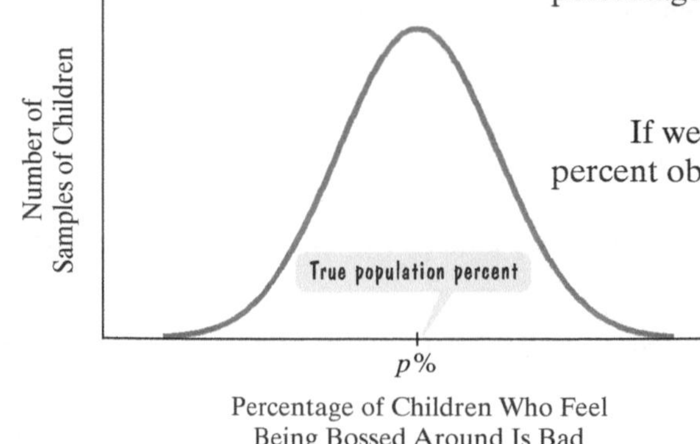

FIGURE 17 Percentage of children who feel being bossed around is bad

MARGIN OF ERROR IN A SURVEY

If a statistic is obtained from a random sample of size n, there is a 95% probability that it lies within $\frac{1}{\sqrt{n}} \times 100\%$ of the true population percent, where $\pm\frac{1}{\sqrt{n}} \times 100\%$ is called the **margin of error**.

WHAT IS BAD ABOUT BEING A KID?

Kids Say	
Getting bossed around	17%
School, homework	15%
Can't do everything I want	11%
Chores	9%
Being grounded	9%

Source: Penn, Schoen, and Berland using 1172 interviews with children ages 6 to 14 from May 14 to June 1, 1999,

EXAMPLE 7 Using and Interpreting Margin of Error

In a random sample of 1172 children ages 6 through 14, 17% of the children said getting bossed around is a bad thing about being a kid.

a. Verify the margin of error that was given for this survey.

b. Write a statement about the percentage of children in the population who feel that getting bossed around is a bad thing about being a kid.

Solution

a. The sample size is $n = 1172$. The margin of error is

$$\pm\frac{1}{\sqrt{n}} \times 100\% = \pm\frac{1}{\sqrt{1172}} \times 100\% \approx \pm 0.029 \times 100\% = \pm 2.9\%.$$

b. There is a 95% probability that the true population percentage lies between

$$\text{the sample percent} - \frac{1}{\sqrt{n}} \times 100\% = 17\% - 2.9\% = 14.1\%$$

and

$$\text{the sample percent} + \frac{1}{\sqrt{n}} \times 100\% = 17\% + 2.9\% = 19.9\%.$$

We can be 95% confident that between 14.1% and 19.9% of all children feel that getting bossed around is a bad thing about being a kid.

BLITZER BONUS

A CAVEAT GIVING A TRUE PICTURE OF A POLL'S ACCURACY

Unlike the precise calculation of a poll's margin of error, certain polling imperfections cannot be determined exactly. One problem is that people do not always respond to polls honestly and accurately. Some people are embarrassed to say "undecided," so they make up an answer. Other people may try to respond to questions in the way they think will make the pollster happy, just to be "nice." Perhaps the following caveat, applied to the poll in Example 7, would give the public a truer picture of its accuracy:

> The poll results are 14.1% to 19.9% at the 95% confidence level, but it's only under ideal conditions that we can be 95% confident that the true numbers are within 2.9% of the poll's results. The true error span is probably greater than 2.9% due to limitations that are inherent in this and every poll, but, unfortunately, this additional error amount cannot be calculated precisely. Warning: Five percent of the time—that's one time out of 20—the error will be greater than 2.9%. We remind readers of the poll that things occurring "only" 5% of the time do, indeed, happen.

We suspect that the public would tire of hearing this.

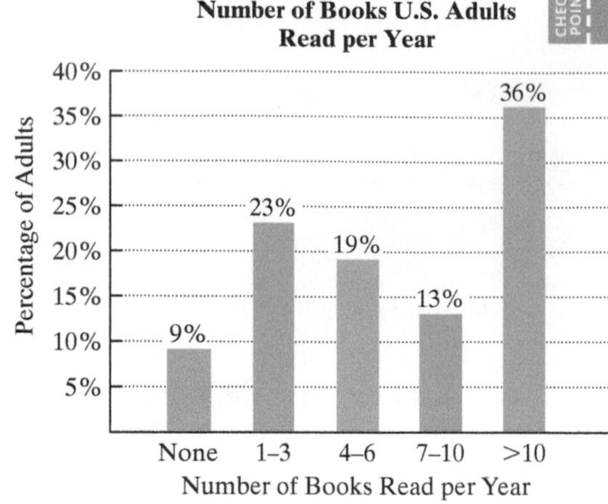

CHECK POINT 7 A Harris Poll of 2513 U.S. adults ages 18 and older asked the question

How many books do you typically read in a year?

The results of the poll are shown in **Figure 18**.

a. Find the margin of error for this survey. Round to the nearest tenth of a percent.

b. Write a statement about the percentage of U.S. adults who read more than ten books per year.

c. Why might some people not respond honestly and accurately to the question in this poll?

FIGURE 18

Source: Harris Poll of 2513 U.S. adults ages 18 and older conducted March 11 and 18, 2008

8 Recognize distributions that are not normal.

Other Kinds of Distributions

The histogram in **Figure 19** represents the frequencies of the ages of women interviewed by Kinsey and his colleagues in their study of female sexual behavior. This distribution is not symmetric. The greatest frequency of women interviewed was in the 16–20 age range. The bars get shorter and shorter after this. The shorter bars fall on the right, indicating that relatively few older women were included in Kinsey's interviews.

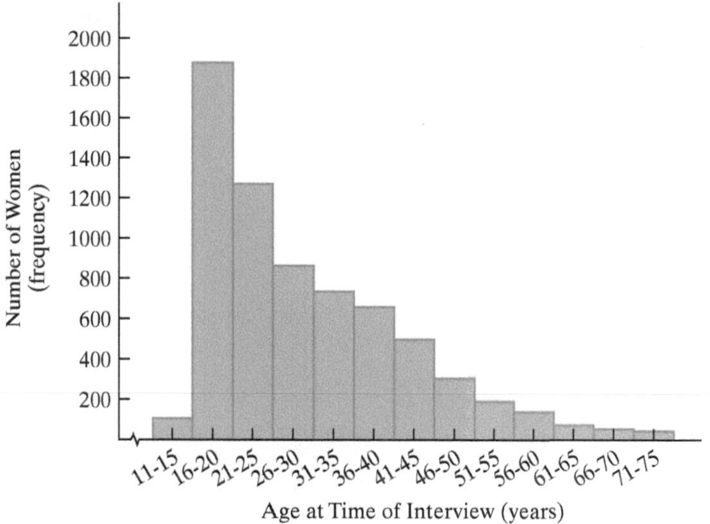

FIGURE 19 Histogram of the ages of females interviewed by Kinsey and his associates

Although the normal distribution is the most important of all distributions in terms of analyzing data, not all data can be approximated by this symmetric distribution with its mean, median, and mode all having the same value.

In our discussion of measures of central tendency, we mentioned that the median, rather than the mean, is used to summarize income. **Figure 20** illustrates the population distribution of weekly earnings in the United States. There is no upper limit on weekly earnings. The relatively few people with very high weekly incomes tend to pull the mean income to a value greater than the median. The most frequent income, the mode, occurs toward the low end of the data items. The mean, median, and mode do not have the same value, and a normal distribution is not an appropriate model for describing weekly earnings in the United States.

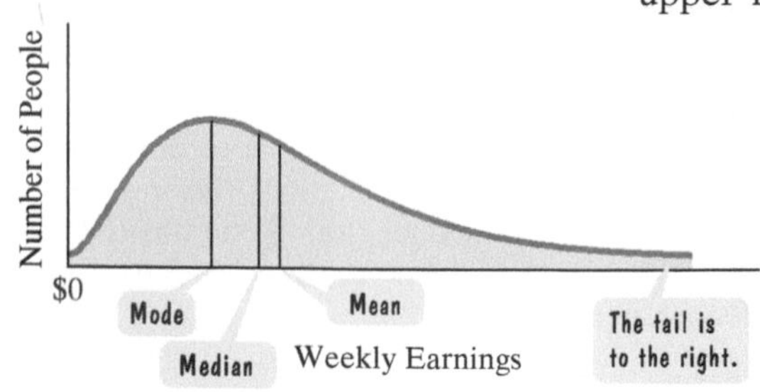

FIGURE 20 Skewed to the right

The distribution in **Figure 20** is called a *skewed distribution*. A distribution of data is **skewed** if a large number of data items are piled up at one end or the other, with a "tail" at the opposite end. In the distribution of weekly earnings in **Figure 20**, the tail is to the right. Such a distribution is said to be **skewed to the right**.

STUDY TIP

If the data are skewed to the right, the mean is greater than the median. If the data are skewed to the left, the mean is less than the median.

By contrast to the distribution of weekly earnings, the distribution in **Figure 21** has more data items at the high end of the scale than at the low end. The tail of this distribution is to the left. The distribution is said to be **skewed to the left**. In many colleges, an example of a distribution skewed to the left is based on the student ratings of faculty teaching performance. Most professors are given rather high ratings, while only a few are rated as terrible. These low ratings pull the value of the mean lower than the median.

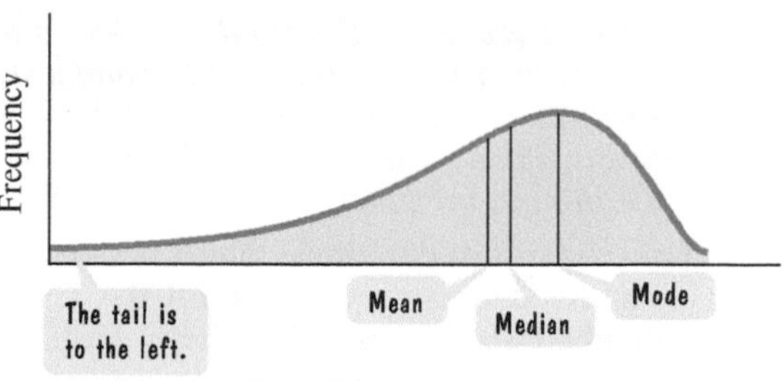

FIGURE 21 Skewed to the left

Exercise Set 4

Practice and Application Exercises

The scores on a test are normally distributed with a mean of 100 and a standard deviation of 20. In Exercises 1–10, find the score that is

1. 1 standard deviation above the mean.
2. 2 standard deviations above the mean.
3. 3 standard deviations above the mean.
4. $1\frac{1}{2}$ standard deviations above the mean.
5. $2\frac{1}{2}$ standard deviations above the mean.
6. 1 standard deviation below the mean.
7. 2 standard deviations below the mean.
8. 3 standard deviations below the mean.
9. one-half a standard deviation below the mean.
10. $2\frac{1}{2}$ standard deviations below the mean.

Not everyone pays the same price for the same model of a car. The figure illustrates a normal distribution for the prices paid for a particular model of a new car. The mean is \$17,000 and the standard deviation is \$500.

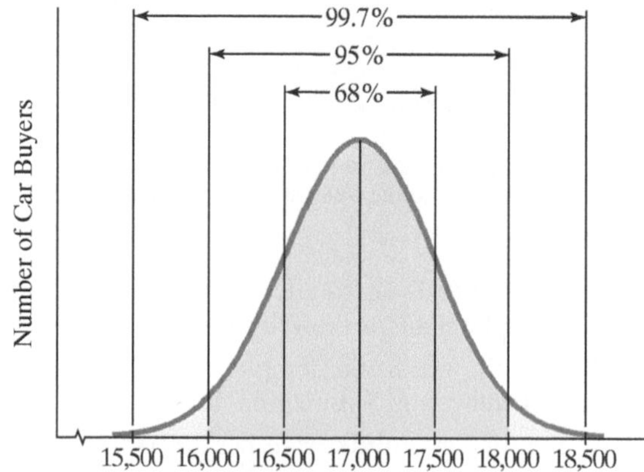

In Exercises 11–22, use the 68–95–99.7 Rule, illustrated in the figure, to find the percentage of buyers who paid

11. between \$16,500 and \$17,500.
12. between \$16,000 and \$18,000.
13. between \$17,000 and \$17,500.
14. between \$17,000 and \$18,000.
15. between \$16,000 and \$17,000.
16. between \$16,500 and \$17,000.
17. between \$15,500 and \$17,000.
18. between \$17,000 and \$18,500.
19. more than \$17,500. **20.** more than \$18,000.
21. less than \$16,000. **22.** less than \$16,500.

Intelligence quotients (IQs) on the Stanford-Binet intelligence test are normally distributed with a mean of 100 and a standard deviation of 16. In Exercises 23–32, use the 68–95–99.7 Rule to find the percentage of people with IQs

23. between 68 and 132. **24.** between 84 and 116.
25. between 68 and 100. **26.** between 84 and 100.
27. above 116. **28.** above 132.
29. below 68. **30.** below 84.
31. above 148. **32.** below 52.

A set of data items is normally distributed with a mean of 60 and a standard deviation of 8. In Exercises 33–48, convert each data item to a z-score.

33. 68 **34.** 76 **35.** 84
36. 92 **37.** 64 **38.** 72
39. 74 **40.** 78 **41.** 60
42. 100 **43.** 52 **44.** 44
45. 48 **46.** 40 **47.** 34
48. 30

Scores on a dental anxiety scale range from 0 (no anxiety) to 20 (extreme anxiety). The scores are normally distributed with a mean of 11 and a standard deviation of 4. In Exercises 49–56, find the z-score for the given score on this dental anxiety scale.

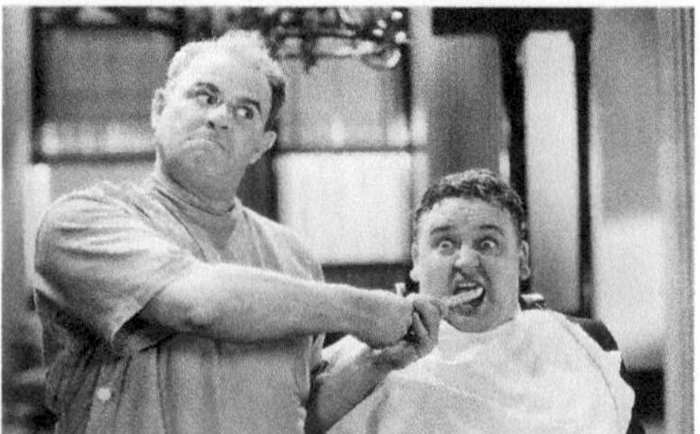

The Granger Collection, New York

49. 17 **50.** 18 **51.** 20
52. 12 **53.** 6 **54.** 8
55. 5 **56.** 1

Intelligence quotients on the Stanford-Binet intelligence test are normally distributed with a mean of 100 and a standard deviation of 16. Intelligence quotients on the Wechsler intelligence test are normally distributed with a mean of 100 and a standard deviation of 15. Use this information to solve Exercises 57–58.

57. Use z-scores to determine which person has the higher IQ: an individual who scores 128 on the Stanford-Binet or an individual who scores 127 on the Wechsler.

58. Use z-scores to determine which person has the higher IQ: an individual who scores 150 on the Stanford-Binet or an individual who scores 148 on the Wechsler.

A set of data items is normally distributed with a mean of 400 and a standard deviation of 50. In Exercises 59–66, find the data item in this distribution that corresponds to the given z-score.

59. $z = 2$ **60.** $z = 3$

61. $z = 1.5$ **62.** $z = 2.5$

63. $z = -3$ **64.** $z = -2$

65. $z = -2.5$ **66.** $z = -1.5$

67. Using a random sample of 1023 high school students 14 to 18 years old, a Ridgid survey asked respondents to name their career choice. The top five career choices and the percentage of students who named each of these careers are shown in the bar graph.

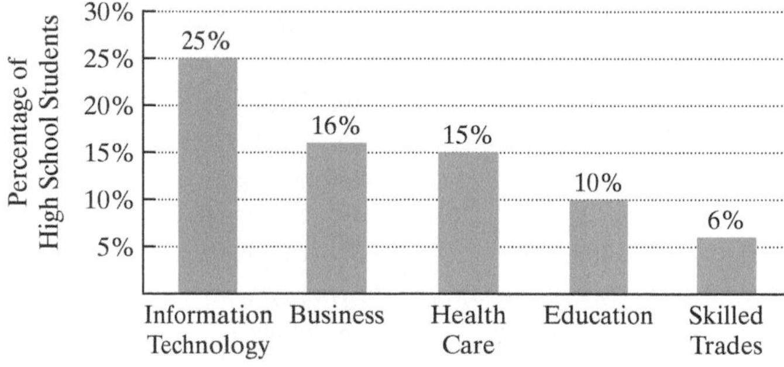

Source: Ridgid Survey

a. Find the margin of error, to the nearest tenth of a percent, for this survey.

b. Write a statement about the percentage of high school students in the population whose career choice is information technology.

68. Using a random sample of 2774 college students, an Experience.com survey asked respondents the following question:

If you had two job offers and one company was "green," would that have an impact on your decision?

The responses are shown in the circle graph.

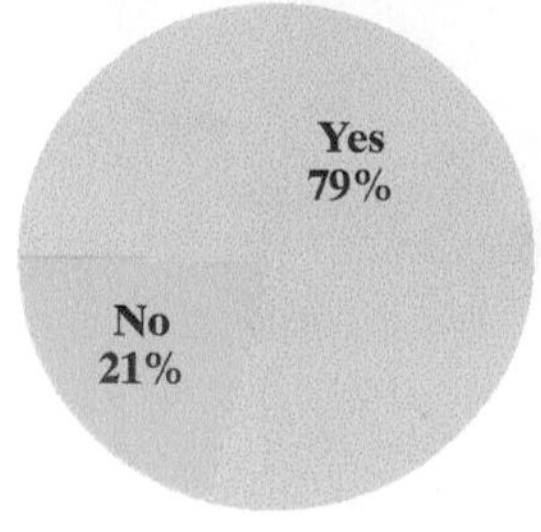

Source: Experience.com Survey.

a. Find the margin of error, to the nearest tenth of a percent, for this survey.

b. Write a statement about the percentage of college students in the population for whom a "green" company would have an impact on their decision.

69. Using a random sample of 4000 TV households, Nielsen Media Research found that 60.2% watched the final episode of *M*A*S*H*.

a. Find the margin of error in this percent.

b. Write a statement about the percentage of TV households in the population who tuned into the final episode of *M*A*S*H*.

70. Using a random sample of 4000 TV households, Nielsen Media Research found that 51.1% watched *Roots, Part 8*.

a. Find the margin of error in this percent.

b. Write a statement about the percentage of TV households in the population who tuned into *Roots, Part 8*.

71. In 1997, Nielsen Media Research increased its random sample to 5000 TV households. By how much, to the nearest tenth of a percent, did this improve the margin of error over that in Exercises 69 and 70?

72. If Nielsen Media Research were to increase its random sample from 5000 to 10,000 TV households, by how much, to the nearest tenth of a percent, would this improve the margin of error?

The histogram shows murder rates per 100,000 residents and the number of U.S. states that had these rates in 2006. Use this histogram to solve Exercises 73–74.

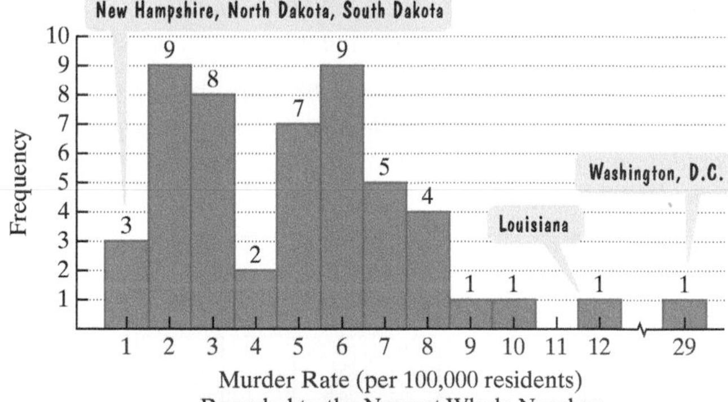

Source: FBI, *Crime in the United States*

73. a. Is the shape of this distribution best classified as normal, skewed to the right, or skewed to the left?

b. Calculate the mean murder rate per 100,000 residents for the 50 states and Washington, D.C.

c. Find the median murder rate per 100,000 residents for the 50 states and Washington, D.C.

d. Are the mean and median murder rates consistent with the shape of the distribution that you described in part (a)? Explain your answer.

e. The standard deviation for the data is approximately 4.2. If the distribution were roughly normal, what would be the z-score, rounded to one decimal place, for Washington, D.C.? Does this seem unusually high? Explain your answer.

74. a. Find the median murder rate per 100,000 residents for the 50 states and Washington, D.C.

b. Find the first quartile by determining the median of the lower half of the data. (This is the median of the items that lie below the median that you found in part (a).)

c. Find the third quartile by determining the median of the upper half of the data. (This is the median of the items that lie above the median that you found in part (a).)

d. Use the following numerical scale:

0 5 10 15 20 25 30

Murder Rate (per 100,000 residents)

Above this scale, show five points, each at the same height. (The height is arbitrary.) Each point should represent one of the following numbers:

lowest data value, first quartile, median, third quartile, highest data value.

e. A **box-and-whisker plot** consists of a rectangular box extending from the first quartile to the third quartile, with a dashed line representing the median, and line segments (or whiskers) extending outward from the box to the lowest and highest data values:

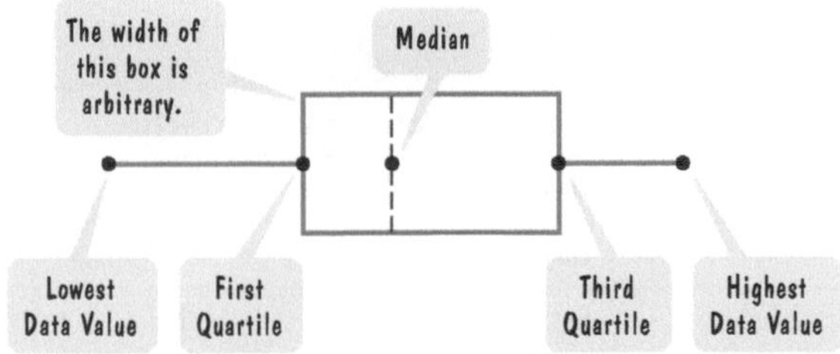

Use your graph from part (d) to create a box-and-whisker plot for U.S. murder rates per 100,000 residents.

f. If one of the whiskers in a box-and-whisker plot is clearly longer, the distribution is usually skewed in the direction of the longer whisker. Based on this observation, does your box-and-whisker plot in part (e) indicate that the distribution is skewed to the right or skewed to the left?

g. Is the shape of the distribution of scores shown by the given histogram consistent with your observation in part (f)?

Writing in Mathematics

75. What is a symmetric histogram?

76. Describe the normal distribution and discuss some of its properties.

77. Describe the 68–95–99.7 Rule.

78. Describe how to determine the z-score for a data item in a normal distribution.

79. What does a z-score measure?

80. Give an example of both a commonly occurring and an infrequently occurring z-score. Explain how you arrived at these examples.

81. Describe when a z-score is negative.

82. If you score in the 83rd percentile, what does this mean?

83. If your weight is in the third quartile, what does this mean?

84. Two students have scores with the same percentile, but for different administrations of the SAT. Does this mean that the students have the same score on the SAT? Explain your answer.

85. Give an example of a phenomenon that is normally distributed. Explain why. (Try to be creative and not use one of the distributions discussed in this section.) Estimate what the mean and the standard deviation might be and describe how you determined these estimates.

86. Give an example of a phenomenon that is not normally distributed and explain why.

Critical Thinking Exercises

Make Sense? *In Exercises 87–90, determine whether each statement makes sense or does not make sense, and explain your reasoning.*

87. The heights of the men on our college basketball team are normally distributed with a mean of 6 feet 3 inches and a standard deviation of 1 foot 2 inches.

88. I scored in the 50th percentile on a standardized test, so my score is the median.

89. A poll administered to a random sample of 1150 voters shows 51% in favor of candidate A, so I'm 95% confident that candidate A will win the election.

90. My math teacher gave a very difficult exam for which the distribution of scores was skewed to the right.

Group Exercise

91. For this activity, group members will conduct interviews with a random sample of students on campus. Each student is to be asked, "What is the worst thing about being a student?" One response should be recorded for each student.

a. Each member should interview enough students so that there are at least 50 randomly selected students in the sample.

b. After all responses have been recorded, the group should organize the four most common answers. For each answer, compute the percentage of students in the sample who felt that this is the worst thing about being a student.

c. Find the margin of error for your survey.

d. For each of the four most common answers, write a statement about the percentage of all students on your campus who feel that this is the worst thing about being a student.

OBJECTIVE

1 Solve applied problems involving normal distributions.

5 Problem Solving with the Normal Distribution

We have seen that male heights in North America are approximately normally distributed with a mean of 70 inches and a standard deviation of 4 inches. Suppose we are interested in the percentage of men with heights below 80 inches:

$$z_{80} = \frac{\text{data item} - \text{mean}}{\text{standard deviation}} = \frac{80 - 70}{4} = \frac{10}{4} = 2.5.$$

Because this z-score is not an integer, the 68–95–99.7 Rule is not helpful in finding the percentage of data items that fall below 2.5 standard deviations of the mean. In this section, we will use a table that contains numerous z-scores and their percentiles to solve a variety of problems involving the normal distribution.

1 Solve applied problems involving normal distributions.

Problem Solving Using z-Scores and Percentiles

Table 14 gives a percentile interpretation for z-scores.

Toronto Star Archives\Newscom

TABLE 14 z-Scores and Percentiles

z-Score	Percentile	z-Score	Percentile	z-Score	Percentile	z-Score	Percentile
−4.0	0.003	−1.0	15.87	0.0	50.00	1.1	86.43
−3.5	0.02	−0.95	17.11	0.05	51.99	1.2	88.49
−3.0	0.13	−0.90	18.41	0.10	53.98	1.3	90.32
−2.9	0.19	−0.85	19.77	0.15	55.96	1.4	91.92
−2.8	0.26	−0.80	21.19	0.20	57.93	1.5	93.32
−2.7	0.35	−0.75	22.66	0.25	59.87	1.6	94.52
−2.6	0.47	−0.70	24.20	0.30	61.79	1.7	95.54
−2.5	0.62	−0.65	25.78	0.35	63.68	1.8	96.41
−2.4	0.82	−0.60	27.43	0.40	65.54	1.9	97.13
−2.3	1.07	−0.55	29.12	0.45	67.36	2.0	97.72
−2.2	1.39	−0.50	30.85	0.50	69.15	2.1	98.21
−2.1	1.79	−0.45	32.64	0.55	70.88	2.2	98.61
−2.0	2.28	−0.40	34.46	0.60	72.57	2.3	98.93
−1.9	2.87	−0.35	36.32	0.65	74.22	2.4	99.18
−1.8	3.59	−0.30	38.21	0.70	75.80	2.5	99.38
−1.7	4.46	−0.25	40.13	0.75	77.34	2.6	99.53
−1.6	5.48	−0.20	42.07	0.80	78.81	2.7	99.65
−1.5	6.68	−0.15	44.04	0.85	80.23	2.8	99.74
−1.4	8.08	−0.10	46.02	0.90	81.59	2.9	99.81
−1.3	9.68	−0.05	48.01	0.95	82.89	3.0	99.87
−1.2	11.51	0.0	50.00	1.0	84.13	3.5	99.98
−1.1	13.57					4.0	99.997

TWO ENTRIES FROM TABLE 14

z-Score	Percentile
2.5	99.38
0.0	50.00

The portion of the table in the margin indicates that the corresponding percentile for a z-score of 2.5 is 99.38. This tells us that 99.38% of North American men have heights that are less than 80 inches, or $z = 2.5$.

In a normal distribution, the mean, median, and mode all have a corresponding z-score of 0. **Table 14** shows that the percentile for a z-score of 0 is 50.00. Thus, 50% of the data items in a normal distribution are less than the mean, median, and mode. Consequently, 50% of the data items are greater than or equal to the mean, median, and mode.

Table 14 can be used to find the percentage of data items that are less than any data item in a normal distribution. Begin by converting the data item to a z-score. Then, use the table to find the percentile for this z-score. This percentile is the percentage of data items that are less than the data item in question.

EXAMPLE 1 Finding the Percentage of Data Items Less Than a Given Data Item

According to the Department of Health and Education, cholesterol levels are normally distributed. For men between 18 and 24 years, the mean is 178.1 (measured in milligrams per 100 milliliters) and the standard deviation is 40.7. What percentage of men in this age range have a cholesterol level less than 239.15?

Solution If you are familiar with your own cholesterol level, you probably recognize that a level of 239.15 is fairly high for a young man. Because of this, we would expect most young men to have a level less than 239.15. Let's see if this is so. **Table 14** requires that we use z-scores. We compute the z-score for a 239.15 cholesterol level by using the z-score formula.

$$z_{239.15} = \frac{\text{data item} - \text{mean}}{\text{standard deviation}} = \frac{239.15 - 178.1}{40.7} = \frac{61.05}{40.7} = 1.5$$

A PORTION OF TABLE 14

z-Score	Percentile
1.4	91.92
1.5	93.32
1.6	94.52

A man between 18 and 24 with a 239.15 cholesterol level is 1.5 standard deviations above the mean, illustrated in **Figure 22(a)**. The question mark indicates that we must find the percentage of men with a cholesterol level less than $z = 1.5$, the z-score for a 239.15 cholesterol level. **Table 14** gives this percentage as a percentile. Find 1.5 in the z-score column in the right portion of the table. The percentile given to the right of 1.5 is 93.32. Thus, 93.32% of men between 18 and 24 have a cholesterol level less than 239.15, shown in **Figure 22(b)**.

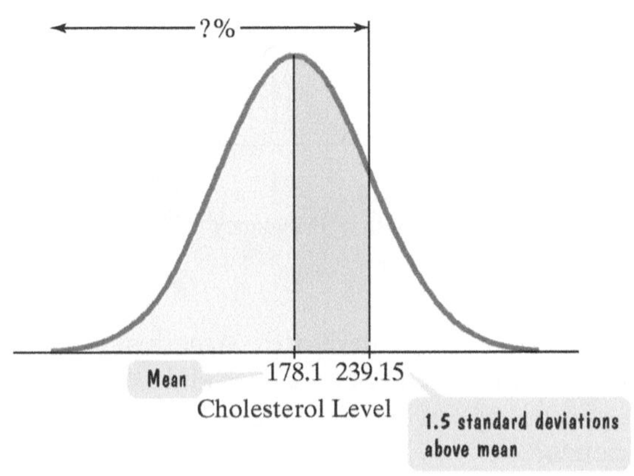

FIGURE 22(a)

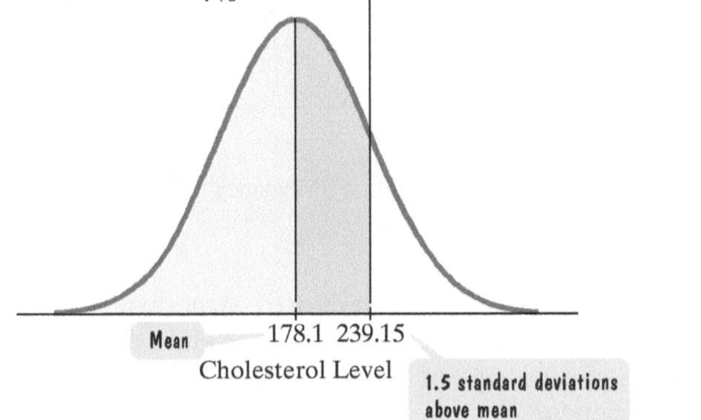

FIGURE 22(b)

CHECK POINT 1 The distribution of monthly charges for cellphone plans in the United States is approximately normal with a mean of \$62 and a standard deviation of \$18. What percentage of plans have charges that are less than \$83.60?

The normal distribution accounts for all data items, meaning 100% of the scores. This means that **Table 14** can also be used to find the percentage of data items that are greater than any data item in a normal distribution. Use the percentile in the table to determine the percentage of data items less than the data item in question. Then subtract this percentage from 100% to find the percentage of data items greater than the item in question. In using this technique, we will treat the phrases "greater than" and "greater than or equal to" as equivalent.

EXAMPLE 2 Finding the Percentage of Data Items Greater Than a Given Data Item

Lengths of pregnancies of women are normally distributed with a mean of 266 days and a standard deviation of 16 days. What percentage of children are born from pregnancies lasting more than 274 days?

A PORTION OF TABLE 14

z-Score	Percentile
0.45	67.36
0.50	69.15
0.55	70.88

Solution **Table 14** requires that we use z-scores. We compute the z-score for a 274-day pregnancy by using the z-score formula.

$$z_{274} = \frac{\text{data item} - \text{mean}}{\text{standard deviation}} = \frac{274 - 266}{16} = \frac{8}{16} = 0.5$$

A 274-day pregnancy is 0.5 standard deviation above the mean. **Table 14** gives the percentile corresponding to 0.50 as 69.15. This means that 69.15% of pregnancies last less than 274 days, illustrated in **Figure 23**. We must find the percentage of pregnancies lasting more than 274 days by subtracting 69.15% from 100%.

$$100\% - 69.15\% = 30.85\%$$

Thus, 30.85% of children are born from pregnancies lasting more than 274 days.

Norbert Schafer\CORBIS-NY

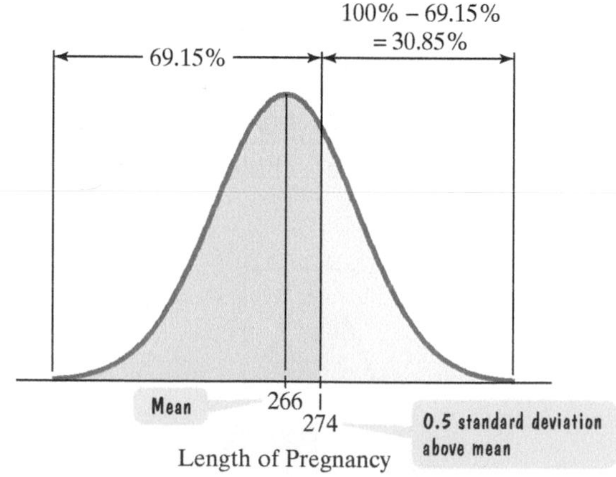

FIGURE 23

CHECK POINT 2 Female adult heights in North America are approximately normally distributed with a mean of 65 inches and a standard deviation of 3.5 inches. What percentage of North American women have heights that exceed 69.9 inches?

We have seen how **Table 14** is used to find the percentage of data items that are less than or greater than any given item. The table can also be used to find the percentage of data items *between* two given items. Because the percentile for each item is the percentage of data items less than the given item, the percentage of data between the two given items is found by subtracting the lesser percent from the greater percent. This is illustrated in **Figure 24**.

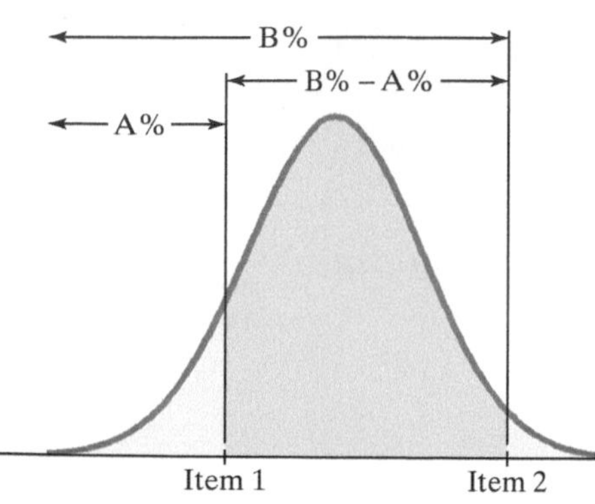

FIGURE 24 The percentile for data item 1 is A. The percentile for data item 2 is B. The percentage of data items between item 1 and item 2 is B% − A%.

FINDING THE PERCENTAGE OF DATA ITEMS BETWEEN TWO GIVEN ITEMS IN A NORMAL DISTRIBUTION

1. Convert each given data item to a z-score:
$$z = \frac{\text{data item} - \text{mean}}{\text{standard deviation}}.$$
2. Use **Table 14** to find the percentile corresponding to each z-score in step 1.
3. Subtract the lesser percentile from the greater percentile and attach a % sign.

EXAMPLE 3 Finding the Percentage of Data Items between Two Given Data Items

The amount of time that self-employed Americans work each week is normally distributed with a mean of 44.6 hours and a standard deviation of 14.4 hours. What percentage of self-employed individuals in the United States work between 37.4 and 80.6 hours per week?

Solution

Step 1 Convert each given data item to a z-score.

$$z_{37.4} = \frac{\text{data item} - \text{mean}}{\text{standard deviation}} = \frac{37.4 - 44.6}{14.4} = \frac{-7.2}{14.4} = -0.5$$

$$z_{80.6} = \frac{\text{data item} - \text{mean}}{\text{standard deviation}} = \frac{80.6 - 44.6}{14.4} = \frac{36}{14.4} = 2.5$$

A PORTION OF TABLE 14

z-Score	Percentile
−0.55	29.12
−0.50	30.85
−0.45	32.64

A PORTION OF TABLE 14

z-Score	Percentile
2.4	99.18
2.5	99.38
2.6	99.53

Step 2 Use Table 14 to find the percentile corresponding to these z-scores. The percentile given to the right of −0.50 is 30.85. This means that 30.85% of self-employed Americans work less than 37.4 hours per week.

Table 14 also gives the percentile corresponding to $z = 2.5$. Find 2.5 in the z-score column in the far-right portion of the table. The percentile given to the right of 2.5 is 99.38. This means that 99.38% of self-employed Americans work less than 80.6 hours per week.

Step 3 Subtract the lesser percentile from the greater percentile and attach a % sign. Subtracting percentiles, we obtain

$$99.38 - 30.85 = 68.53.$$

Thus, 68.53% of self-employed Americans work between 37.4 and 80.6 hours per week. The solution is illustrated in **Figure 25**.

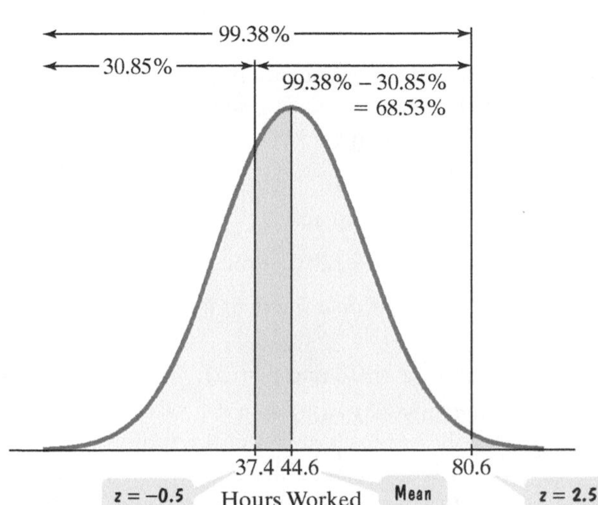

FIGURE 25

CHECK POINT 3 The distribution for the life of refrigerators is approximately normal with a mean of 14 years and a standard deviation of 2.5 years. What percentage of refrigerators have lives between 11 years and 18 years?

Our work in Examples 1 through 3 is summarized as follows:

COMPUTING PERCENTAGE OF DATA ITEMS FOR NORMAL DISTRIBUTIONS

Description of Percentage	Graph	Computation of Percentage
Percentage of data items less than a given data item with $z = b$	0 b	Use the table percentile for $z = b$ and add a % sign.
Percentage of data items greater than a given data item with $z = a$	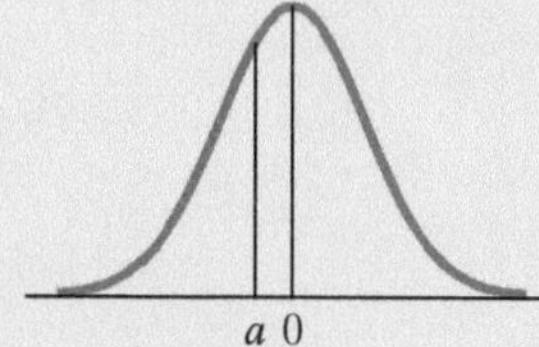	Subtract the table percentile for $z = a$ from 100 and add a % sign.
Percentage of data items between two given data items with $z = a$ and $z = b$	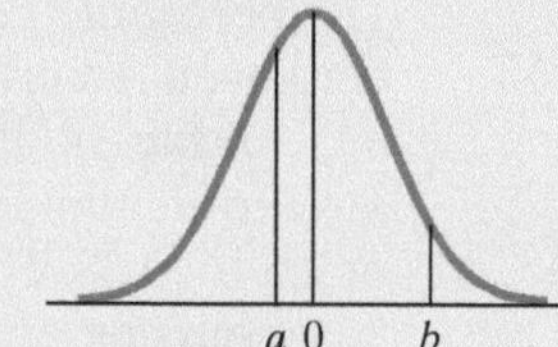	Subtract the table percentile for $z = a$ from the table percentile for $z = b$ and add a % sign.

Exercise Set 5

Practice and Application Exercises

Use **Table 14** *to solve Exercises 1–16.*

In Exercises 1–8, find the percentage of data items in a normal distribution that lie **a.** *below and* **b.** *above the given z-score.*

1. $z = 0.6$
2. $z = 0.8$
3. $z = 1.2$
4. $z = 1.4$
5. $z = -0.7$
6. $z = -0.4$
7. $z = -1.2$
8. $z = -1.8$

In Exercises 9–16, find the percentage of data items in a normal distribution that lie between

9. $z = 0.2$ and $z = 1.4$.
10. $z = 0.3$ and $z = 2.1$.
11. $z = 1$ and $z = 3$.
12. $z = 2$ and $z = 3$.
13. $z = -1.5$ and $z = 1.5$.
14. $z = -1.2$ and $z = 1.2$.
15. $z = -2$ and $z = -0.5$.
16. $z = -2.2$ and $z = -0.3$.

Systolic blood pressure readings are normally distributed with a mean of 121 and a standard deviation of 15. (A reading above 140 is considered to be high blood pressure.) In Exercises 17–26, begin by converting any given blood pressure reading or readings into z-scores. Then use **Table 14** *to find the percentage of people with blood pressure readings*

17. below 142.
18. below 148.
19. above 130.
20. above 133.
21. above 103.
22. above 100.
23. between 142 and 154.
24. between 145 and 157.
25. between 112 and 130.
26. between 109 and 133.

The weights for 12-month-old baby boys are normally distributed with a mean of 22.5 pounds and a standard deviation of 2.2 pounds. In Exercises 27–30, use **Table 14** *to find the percentage of 12-month-old baby boys who weigh*

27. more than 25.8 pounds.
28. more than 23.6 pounds.

29. between 19.2 and 21.4 pounds.
30. between 18.1 and 19.2 pounds.

Practice Plus

The table shows selected ages of licensed drivers in the United States and the corresponding percentiles.

AGES OF U.S. DRIVERS

Age	Percentile
75	98
65	88
55	77
45	60
35	37
25	14
20	5

Source: Department of Transportation

In Exercises 31–36, use the information given by the table to find the percentage of U.S. drivers who are

31. younger than 55.
32. younger than 45.
33. at least 25.
34. at least 35.
35. at least 65 and younger than 75.
36. at least 20 and younger than 65.

Writing in Mathematics

37. Explain when it is necessary to use a table showing z-scores and percentiles rather than the 68–95–99.7 Rule to determine the percentage of data items less than a given data item.
38. Explain how to use a table showing z-scores and percentiles to determine the percentage of data items between two z-scores.

Critical Thinking Exercises

Make Sense? *In Exercises 39–42, determine whether each statement makes sense or does not make sense, and explain your reasoning.*

39. I'm using a table showing z-scores and percentiles that has positive percentiles corresponding to positive z-scores and negative percentiles corresponding to negative z-scores.
40. My table showing z-scores and percentiles displays the percentage of data items less than a given value of z.
41. My table showing z-scores and percentiles does not display the percentage of data items greater than a given value of z.
42. I can use a table showing z-scores and percentiles to verify the three approximate numbers given by the 68–95–99.7 Rule.
43. Find two z-scores so that 40% of the data in the distribution lies between them. (More than one answer is possible.)
44. A woman insists that she will never marry a man as short or shorter than she, knowing that only one man in 400 falls into this category. Assuming a mean height of 69 inches for men with a standard deviation of 2.5 inches (and a normal distribution), approximately how tall is the woman?
45. The placement test for a college has scores that are normally distributed with a mean of 500 and a standard deviation of 100. If the college accepts only the top 10% of examinees, what is the cutoff score on the test for admission?

OBJECTIVES

1. Make a scatter plot for a table of data items.
2. Interpret information given in a scatter plot.
3. Compute the correlation coefficient.
4. Write the equation of the regression line.
5. Use a sample's correlation coefficient to determine whether there is a correlation in the population.

6 Scatter Plots, Correlation, and Regression Lines

Culver Pictures, Inc.

Surprised by the number of people smoking cigarettes in movies and television shows made in the 1940s and 1950s? At that time, there was little awareness of the relationship between tobacco use and numerous diseases. Cigarette smoking was seen as a healthy way to relax and help digest a hearty meal. Then, in 1964, an equation changed everything. To understand the mathematics behind this turning point in public health, we need to explore situations involving data collected on two variables.

Up to this point in the chapter, we have studied situations in which data sets involve a single variable, such as height, weight, cholesterol level, and length of pregnancies. By contrast, the 1964 study involved data collected on two variables from 11 countries—annual cigarette consumption for each adult male and deaths per million males from lung cancer. In this section, we consider situations in which there are two data items for each randomly selected person or thing. Our interest is in determining whether or not there is a relationship between the two variables and, if so, the strength of that relationship.

1 Make a scatter plot for a table of data items.

Scatter Plots and Correlation

Is there a relationship between education and prejudice? With increased education, does a person's level of prejudice tend to decrease? Notice that we are interested in two quantities—years of education and level of prejudice. For each person in our sample, we will record the number of years of school completed and the score on a test measuring prejudice. Higher scores on this 1-to-10 test indicate greater prejudice. Using x to represent years of education and y to represent scores on a test measuring prejudice, **Table 15** shows these two quantities for a random sample of ten people.

TABLE 15 Recording Two Quantities in a Sample of Ten People

Respondent	A	B	C	D	E	F	G	H	I	J
Years of education (x)	12	5	14	13	8	10	16	11	12	4
Score on prejudice test (y)	1	7	2	3	5	4	1	2	3	10

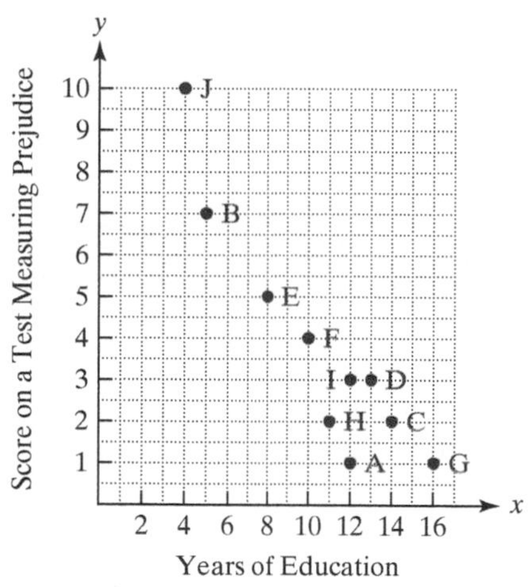

FIGURE 26 A scatter plot for education-prejudice data

When two data items are collected for every person or object in a sample, the data items can be visually displayed using a *scatter plot*. A **scatter plot** is a collection of data points, one data point per person or object. We can make a scatter plot of the data in **Table 15** by drawing a horizontal axis to represent years of education and a vertical axis to represent scores on a test measuring prejudice. We then represent each of the ten respondents with a single point on the graph. For example, the dot for respondent A is located to represent 12 years of education on the horizontal axis and 1 on the prejudice test on the vertical axis. Plotting each of the ten pieces of data in a rectangular coordinate system results in the scatter plot shown in **Figure 26**.

A scatter plot like the one in **Figure 26** can be used to determine whether two quantities are related. If there is a clear relationship, the quantities are said to be **correlated**. The scatter plot shows a downward trend among the data points, although there are a few exceptions. People with increased education tend to have a lower score on the test measuring prejudice. **Correlation** is used to determine if there is a relationship between two variables and, if so, the strength and direction of that relationship.

Correlation and Causal Connections

Correlations can often be seen when data items are displayed on a scatter plot. Although the scatter plot in **Figure 26** indicates a correlation between education and prejudice, we cannot conclude that increased education causes a person's level of prejudice to decrease. There are at least three possible explanations:

1. The correlation between increased education and decreased prejudice is simply a coincidence.
2. Education usually involves classrooms with a variety of different kinds of people. Increased exposure to diversity in the classroom setting, which accompanies increased levels of education, might be an underlying cause for decreased prejudice.
3. Education, the process of acquiring knowledge, requires people to look at new ideas and see things in different ways. Thus, education causes one to be more tolerant and less prejudiced.

STUDY TIP

The numbered list on the right represents three possibilities. Perhaps you can provide a better explanation about decreasing prejudice with increased education.

Establishing that one thing causes another is extremely difficult, even if there is a strong correlation between these things. For example, as the air temperature increases, there is an increase in the number of people stung by jellyfish at the beach. This does not mean that an increase in air temperature causes more people to be stung. It might mean that because it is hotter, more people go into the water. With an increased number of swimmers, more people are likely to be stung. In short, correlation is not necessarily causation.

2 Interpret information given in a scatter plot.

Regression Lines and Correlation Coefficients

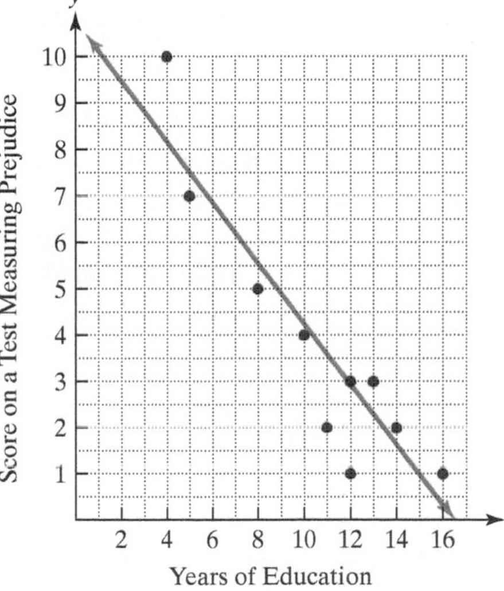

FIGURE 27 A scatter plot with a regression line

Figure 27 shows the scatter plot for the education-prejudice data. Also shown is a straight line that seems to approximately "fit" the data points. Most of the data points lie either near or on this line. A line that best fits the data points in a scatter plot is called a **regression line.** The regression line is the particular line in which the spread of the data points around it is as small as possible.

A measure that is used to describe the strength and direction of a relationship between variables whose data points lie on or near a line is called the **correlation coefficient**, designated by r. **Figure 28** shows scatter plots and correlation coefficients. Variables are **positively correlated** if they tend to increase or decrease together, as in **Figure 28(a)**, **(b)**, and **(c)**. By contrast, variables are **negatively correlated** if one variable tends to decrease while the other increases, as in **Figure 28(e)**, **(f)**, and **(g)**. **Figure 28** illustrates that a correlation coefficient, r, is a number between -1 and 1, inclusive. **Figure 28(a)** shows a value of 1. This indicates a **perfect positive correlation** in which all points in the scatter plot lie precisely on the regression line that rises from left to right. **Figure 28(g)** shows a value of -1. This indicates a **perfect negative correlation** in which all points in the scatter plot lie precisely on the regression line that falls from left to right.

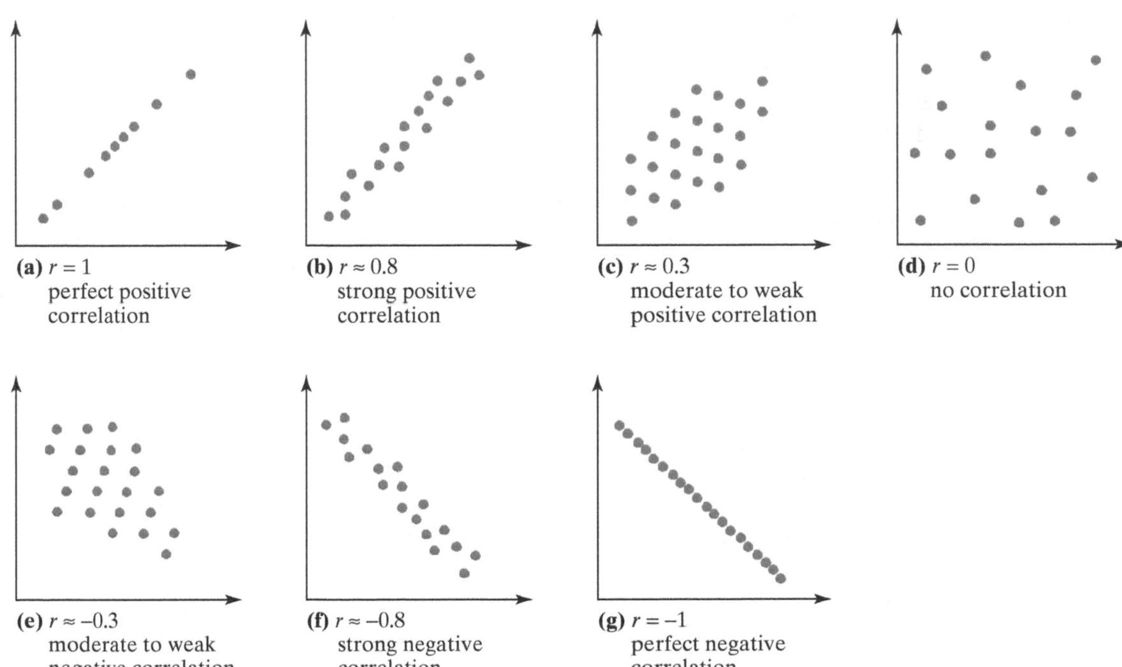

FIGURE 28 Scatter plots and correlation coefficients

Take another look at **Figure 28**. If r is between 0 and 1, as in **(b)** and **(c)** the two variables are positively correlated, but not perfectly. Although all the data points will not lie on the regression line, as in **(a),** an increase in one variable tends to be accompanied by an increase in the other.

Negative correlations are also illustrated in **Figure 28**. If r is between 0 and -1, as in **(e)** and **(f)**, the two variables are negatively correlated, but not perfectly. Although all the data points will not lie on the regression line, as in **(g)**, an increase in one variable tends to be accompanied by a decrease in the other.

BLITZER BONUS

BENEFICIAL USES OF CORRELATION COEFFICIENTS

Stuart Westmorland\Getty Images Inc. - Stone Allstock

- A Florida study showed a high positive correlation between the number of powerboats and the number of manatee deaths. Many of these deaths were seen to be caused by boats' propellers gashing into the manatees' bodies. Based on this study, Florida set up coastal sanctuaries where powerboats are prohibited so that these large gentle mammals that float just below the water's surface could thrive.
- Researchers studied how psychiatric patients readjusted to their community after their release from a mental hospital. A moderate positive correlation ($r = 0.38$) was found between patients' attractiveness and their postdischarge social adjustment. The better-looking patients were better off. The researchers suggested that physical attractiveness plays a role in patients' readjustment to community living because good-looking people tend to be treated better by others than homely people are.

EXAMPLE 1 Interpreting a Correlation Coefficient

In a 1971 study involving 232 subjects, researchers found a relationship between the subjects' level of stress and how often they became ill. The correlation coefficient in this study was 0.32. Does this indicate a strong relationship between stress and illness?

Solution The correlation coefficient $r = 0.32$ means that as stress increases, frequency of illness also tends to increase. However, 0.32 is only a moderate correlation, illustrated in **Figure 28(c)** on the previous page. There is not, based on this study, a strong relationship between stress and illness. In this study, the relationship is somewhat weak.

CHECK POINT 1 In a 1996 study involving obesity in mothers and daughters, researchers found a relationship between a high body-mass index for the girls and their mothers. (Body-mass index is a measure of weight relative to height. People with a high body-mass index are overweight or obese.) The correlation coefficient in this study was 0.51. Does this indicate a weak relationship between the body-mass index of daughters and the body-mass index of their mothers?

How to Obtain the Correlation Coefficient and the Equation of the Regression Line

The easiest way to find the correlation coefficient and the equation of the regression line is to use a graphing or statistical calculator. Graphing calculators have statistical menus that enable you to enter the x and y data items for the variables. Based on this information, you can instruct the calculator to display a scatter plot, the equation of the regression line, and the correlation coefficient.

We can also compute the correlation coefficient and the equation of the regression line by hand using formulas. First, we compute the correlation coefficient.

COMPUTING THE CORRELATION COEFFICIENT BY HAND

The following formula is used to calculate the correlation coefficient, r:

$$r = \frac{n(\Sigma xy) - (\Sigma x)(\Sigma y)}{\sqrt{n(\Sigma x^2) - (\Sigma x)^2}\sqrt{n(\Sigma y^2) - (\Sigma y)^2}}.$$

In the formula,

n = the number of data points, (x, y)
Σx = the sum of the x-values
Σy = the sum of the y-values
Σxy = the sum of the product of x and y in each pair
Σx^2 = the sum of the squares of the x-values
Σy^2 = the sum of the squares of the y-values
$(\Sigma x)^2$ = the square of the sum of the x-values
$(\Sigma y)^2$ = the square of the sum of the y-values

When computing the correlation coefficient by hand, organize your work in five columns:

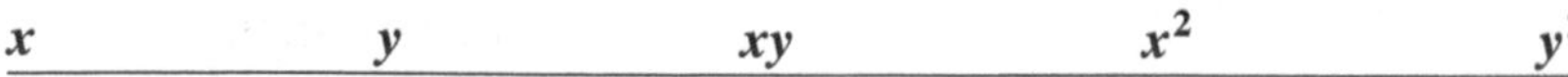

x	y	xy	x^2	y^2

Find the sum of the numbers in each column. Then, substitute these values into the formula for r. Example 2 illustrates computing the correlation coefficient for the education-prejudice test data.

3 Compute the correlation coefficient.

EXAMPLE 2 Computing the Correlation Coefficient

Shown below are the data involving the number of years of school, x, completed by ten randomly selected people and their scores on a test measuring prejudice, y. Recall that higher scores on the measure of prejudice (1 to 10) indicate greater levels of prejudice. Determine the correlation coefficient between years of education and scores on a prejudice test.

Respondent	**A**	**B**	**C**	**D**	**E**	**F**	**G**	**H**	**I**	**J**
Years of education (x)	12	5	14	13	8	10	16	11	12	4
Score on prejudice test (y)	1	7	2	3	5	4	1	2	3	10

Solution As suggested, organize the work in five columns.

x	y	xy	x^2	y^2
12	1	12	144	1
5	7	35	25	49
14	2	28	196	4
13	3	39	169	9
8	5	40	64	25
10	4	40	100	16
16	1	16	256	1
11	2	22	121	4
12	3	36	144	9
4	10	40	16	100
$\Sigma x = 105$	$\Sigma y = 38$	$\Sigma xy = 308$	$\Sigma x^2 = 1235$	$\Sigma y^2 = 218$

Add all values in the x-column. Add all values in the y-column. Add all values in the xy-column. Add all values in the x^2-column. Add all values in the y^2-column.

We use these five sums to calculate the correlation coefficient.

Another value in the formula for r that we have not yet determined is n, the number of data points (x, y). Because there are ten items in the x-column and ten items in the y-column, the number of data points (x, y) is ten. Thus, $n = 10$.

In order to calculate r, we also need to find the square of the sum of the x-values and the y-values:

$$(\Sigma x)^2 = (105)^2 = 11{,}025 \quad \text{and} \quad (\Sigma y)^2 = (38)^2 = 1444.$$

We are ready to determine the value for r.

$$r = \frac{n(\Sigma xy) - (\Sigma x)(\Sigma y)}{\sqrt{n(\Sigma x^2) - (\Sigma x)^2}\sqrt{n(\Sigma y^2) - (\Sigma y)^2}}$$

$$= \frac{10(308) - 105(38)}{\sqrt{10(1235) - 11{,}025}\sqrt{10(218) - 1444}}$$

$$= \frac{-910}{\sqrt{1325}\sqrt{736}}$$

$$\approx -0.92$$

The value for r, approximately -0.92, is fairly close to -1 and indicates a strong negative correlation. This means that the more education a person has, the less prejudiced that person is (based on scores on the test measuring levels of prejudice).

TECHNOLOGY

Graphing Calculators, Scatter Plots, and Regression Lines

You can use a graphing calculator to display a scatter plot and the regression line. After entering the x and y data items for years of education and scores on a prejudice test, the calculator shows the scatter plot of the data and the regression line.

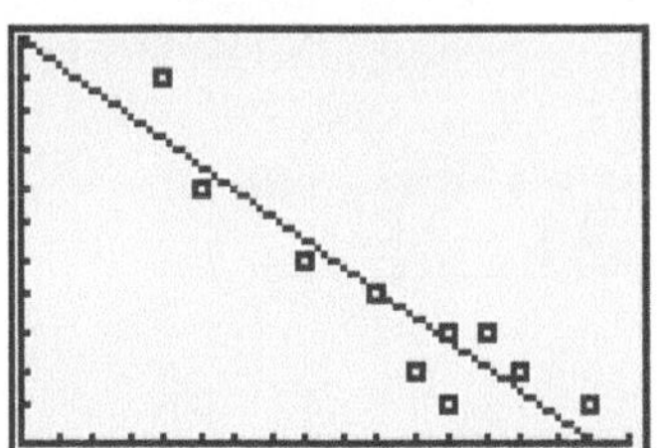

Also displayed below is the regression line's equation and the correlation coefficient, r. The slope shown below is approximately -0.69. The negative slope reinforces the fact that there is a negative correlation between the variables in Example 2.

```
LinReg
 y=ax+b
 a=-.6867924528
 b=11.01132075
 r=-.9214983162
```

CHECK POINT 2 The points in the scatter plot in **Figure 29** show the number of firearms per 100 persons and the number of deaths per 100,000 persons for the ten industrialized countries with the highest death rates. Use the data displayed by the voice balloons to determine the correlation coefficient between these variables. Round to two decimal places. What does the correlation coefficient indicate about the strength and direction of the relationship between firearms per 100 persons and deaths per 100,000 persons?

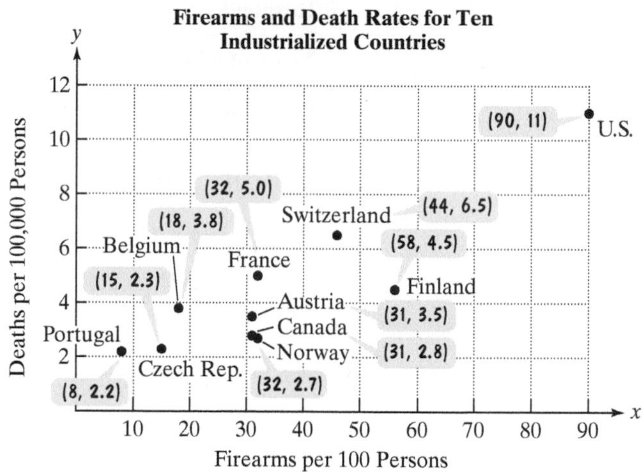

FIGURE 29
Source: International Action Network on Small Arms

Once we have determined that two variables are related, we can use the equation of the regression line to determine the exact relationship. Here is the formula for writing the equation of the line that best fits the data:

4 Write the equation of the regression line.

WRITING THE EQUATION OF THE REGRESSION LINE BY HAND

The equation of the regression line is

$$y = mx + b,$$

where

$$m = \frac{n(\Sigma xy) - (\Sigma x)(\Sigma y)}{n(\Sigma x^2) - (\Sigma x)^2} \quad \text{and} \quad b = \frac{\Sigma y - m(\Sigma x)}{n}.$$

EXAMPLE 3 Writing the Equation of the Regression Line

a. Shown, again, in **Figure 27** is the scatter plot and the regression line for the data in Example 2. Use the data to find the equation of the regression line that relates years of education and scores on a prejudice test.

b. Approximately what score on the test can be anticipated by a person with nine years of education?

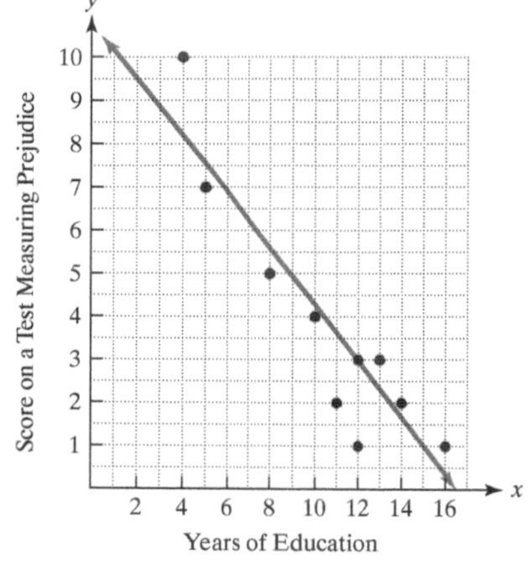

FIGURE 27 (repeated)

Solution

a. We use the sums obtained in Example 2. We begin by computing m.

$$m = \frac{n(\Sigma xy) - (\Sigma x)(\Sigma y)}{n(\Sigma x^2) - (\Sigma x)^2} = \frac{10(308) - 105(38)}{10(1235) - (105)^2} = \frac{-910}{1325} \approx -0.69$$

With a negative correlation coefficient, it makes sense that the slope of the regression line is negative. This line falls from left to right, indicating a negative correlation.

Now, we find the y-intercept, b.

$$b = \frac{\Sigma y - m(\Sigma x)}{n} = \frac{38 - (-0.69)(105)}{10} = \frac{110.45}{10} \approx 11.05$$

Using $m \approx -0.69$ and $b \approx 11.05$, the equation of the regression line, $y = mx + b$, is

$$y = -0.69x + 11.05,$$

where x represents the number of years of education and y represents the score on the prejudice test.

b. To anticipate the score on the prejudice test for a person with nine years of education, substitute 9 for x in the regression line's equation.

$$y = -0.69x + 11.05$$
$$y = -0.69(9) + 11.05 = 4.84$$

A person with nine years of education is anticipated to have a score close to 5 on the prejudice test.

Use the data in **Figure 29** of Check Point 2 to find the equation of the regression line. Round m and b to one decimal place. Then use the equation to project the number of deaths per 100,000 persons in a country with 80 firearms per 100 persons.

5 Use a sample's correlation coefficient to determine whether there is a correlation in the population.

TABLE 16 Values for Determining Correlations in a Population

n	$\alpha = 0.05$	$\alpha = 0.01$
4	0.950	0.990
5	0.878	0.959
6	0.811	0.917
7	0.754	0.875
8	0.707	0.834
9	0.666	0.798
10	0.632	0.765
11	0.602	0.735
12	0.576	0.708
13	0.553	0.684
14	0.532	0.661
15	0.514	0.641
16	0.497	0.623
17	0.482	0.606
18	0.468	0.590
19	0.456	0.575
20	0.444	0.561
22	0.423	0.537
27	0.381	0.487
32	0.349	0.449
37	0.325	0.418
42	0.304	0.393
47	0.288	0.372
52	0.273	0.354
62	0.250	0.325
72	0.232	0.302
82	0.217	0.283
92	0.205	0.267
102	0.195	0.254

The larger the sample size, n, the smaller is the value of r needed for a correlation in the population.

The Level of Significance of r

In Example 2, we found a strong negative correlation between education and prejudice, computing the correlation coefficient, r, to be -0.92. However, the sample size ($n = 10$) was relatively small. With such a small sample, can we truly conclude that a correlation exists in the population? Or could it be that education and prejudice are not related? Perhaps the results we obtained were simply due to sampling error and chance.

Mathematicians have identified values to determine whether r, the correlation coefficient for a sample, can be attributed to a relationship between variables in the population. These values are shown in the second and third columns of **Table 16**. They depend on the sample size, n, listed in the left column. If $|r|$, the absolute value of the correlation coefficient computed for the sample, is greater than the value given in the table, a correlation exists between the variables in the population. The column headed $\alpha = 0.05$ denotes a **significance level of 5%**, meaning that there is a 0.05 probability that, when the statistician says the variables are correlated, they are actually not related in the population. The column on the right, headed $\alpha = 0.01$, denotes a **significance level of 1%**, meaning that there is a 0.01 probability that, when the statistician says the variables are correlated, they are actually not related in the population. Values in the $\alpha = 0.01$ column are greater than those in the $\alpha = 0.05$ column. Because of the possibility of sampling error, there is always a probability that when we say the variables are related, there is actually not a correlation in the population from which the sample was randomly selected.

EXAMPLE 4 Determining a Correlation in the Population

In Example 2, we computed $r = -0.92$ for $n = 10$. Can we conclude that there is a negative correlation between education and prejudice in the population?

Solution Begin by taking the absolute value of the calculated correlation coefficient.

$$|r| = |-0.92| = 0.92$$

Now, look to the right of $n = 10$ in **Table 16**. Because 0.92 is greater than both of these values (0.632 and 0.765), we may conclude that a correlation does exist between education and prejudice in the population. (There is a probability of at most 0.01 that the variables are not really correlated in the population and our results could be attributed to chance.)

BLITZER BONUS

CIGARETTES AND LUNG CANCER

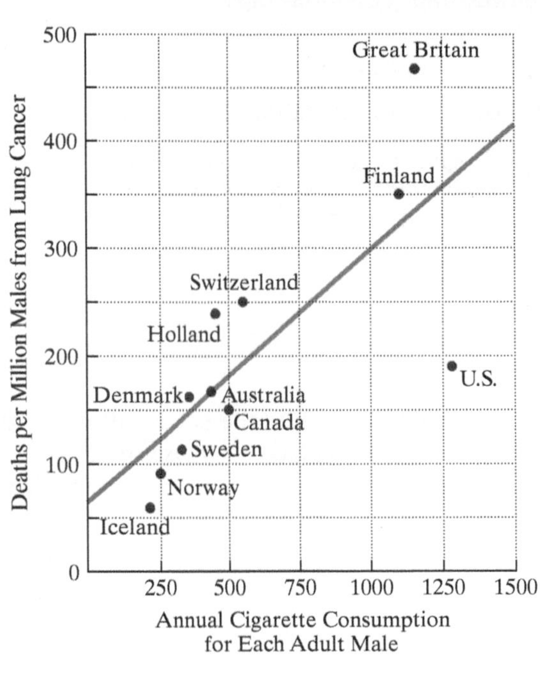

This scatter plot shows a relationship between cigarette consumption among males and deaths due to lung cancer per million males. The data are from 11 countries and date back to a 1964 report by the U.S. Surgeon General. The scatter plot can be modeled by a line whose slope indicates an increasing death rate from lung cancer with increased cigarette consumption. At that time, the tobacco industry argued that in spite of this regression line, tobacco use is not the cause of cancer. Recent data do, indeed, show a causal effect between tobacco use and numerous diseases.

Source: Smoking and Health, Washington, D.C., 1964

If you worked Check Point 2 correctly, you should have found that $r \approx 0.89$ for $n = 10$. Can you conclude that there is a positive correlation for all industrialized countries between firearms per 100 persons and deaths per 100,000 persons?

Exercise Set 6

Practice and Application Exercises

In Exercises 1–8, make a scatter plot for the given data. Use the scatter plot to describe whether or not the variables appear to be related.

1.

x	1	6	4	3	7	2
y	2	5	3	3	4	1

2.

x	2	1	6	3	4
y	4	5	10	8	9

3.

x	8	6	1	5	4	10	3
y	2	4	10	5	6	2	9

4.

x	4	5	2	1
y	1	3	5	4

5. TREASURED CHEST: FILMS OF MATTHEW MCCONAUGHEY

Film	Minutes Shirtless x	Opening Weekend Gross (millions of dollars) y
We Are Marshall	0	6.1
EDtv	0.8	8.3
Reign of Fire	1.6	15.6
Sahara	1.8	18.1
Fool's Gold	14.6	21.6

Source: Entertainment Weekly Shirley Buchan/Pacificcoastnews\Newscom

6. TELEVISION VIEWING, BY ANNUAL INCOME

Annual Income (thousands of dollars) x	Hours per Week Watching Television y
25	56.3
35	51.0
45	50.5
55	49.7
70	48.7

Source: Nielsen Media Research

7. TEENAGE DRUG USE

	Percentage Who Have Used	
Country	Marijuana x	Other Illegal Drugs y
Czech Republic	22	4
Denmark	17	3
England	40	21
Finland	5	1
Ireland	37	16
Italy	19	8
Northern Ireland	23	14
Norway	6	3
Portugal	7	3
Scotland	53	31
United States	34	24

Source: De Veaux et.al., *Intro Stats,* Pearson, 2009.

8. LITERACY AND HUNGER

	Percentage Who Are	
Country	Literate x	Undernourished y
Cuba	100	2
Egypt	71	4
Ethiopia	36	46
Grenada	96	7
Italy	98	2
Jamaica	80	9
Jordan	91	6
Pakistan	50	24
Russia	99	3
Togo	53	24
Uganda	67	19

Source: The Penguin State of the World Atlas, 2008

The scatter plot in the figure shows the relationship between the percentage of married women of child-bearing age using contraceptives and births per woman in selected countries. Use the scatter plot to determine whether each of the statements in Exercises 9–18 is true or false.

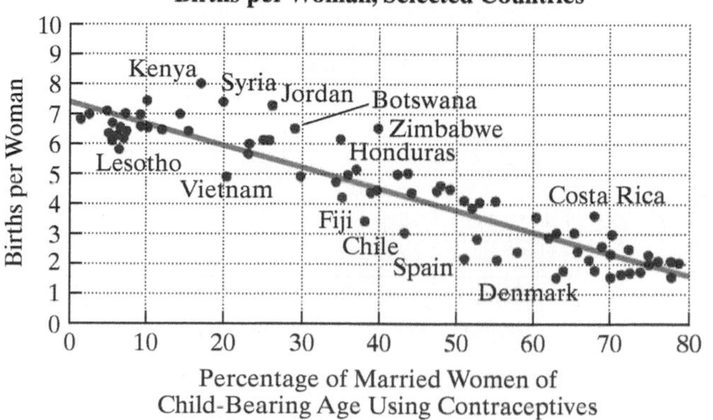

Source: Population Reference Bureau

9. There is a strong positive correlation between contraceptive use and births per woman.

10. There is no correlation between contraceptive use and births per woman.

11. There is a strong negative correlation between contraceptive use and births per woman.

12. There is a casual relationship between contraceptive use and births per woman.

13. With approximately 43% of women of child-bearing age using contraceptives, there are 3 births per woman in Chile.

14. With 20% of women of child-bearing age using contraceptives, there are 6 births per woman in Vietnam.

15. No two countries have a different number of births per woman with the same percentage of married women using contraceptives.

16. The country with the greatest number of births per woman also has the smallest percentage of women using contraceptives.

17. Most of the data points do not lie on the regression line.

18. The number of selected countries shown in the scatter plot is approximately 20.

Just as money doesn't buy happiness for individuals, the two don't necessarily go together for countries either. However, the scatter plot does show a relationship between a country's annual per capita income and the percentage of people in that country who call themselves "happy." Use the scatter plot to determine whether each of the statements in Exercises 19–26 is true or false.

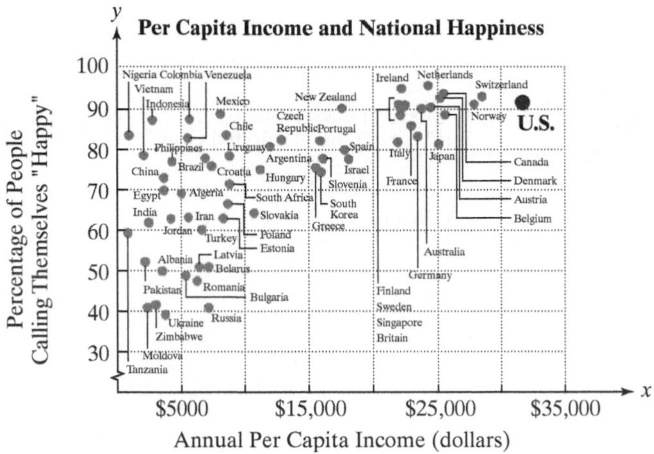

Source: Richard Layard, *Happiness: Lessons from a New Science,* Penguin, 2005.

19. There is no correlation between per capita income and the percentage of people who call themselves "happy."

20. There is an almost-perfect positive correlation between per capita income and the percentage of people who call themselves "happy."

21. There is a positive correlation between per capita income and the percentage of people who call themselves "happy."

22. As per capita income decreases, the percentage of people who call themselves "happy" also tends to decrease.

23. The country with the lowest per capita income has the least percentage of people who call themselves "happy."

24. The country with the highest per capita income has the greatest percentage of people who call themselves "happy."

25. A reasonable estimate of the correlation coefficient for the data is 0.8.

26. A reasonable estimate of the correlation coefficient for the data is -0.3.

Use the scatter plots shown, labeled (a)–(f), to solve Exercises 27–30.

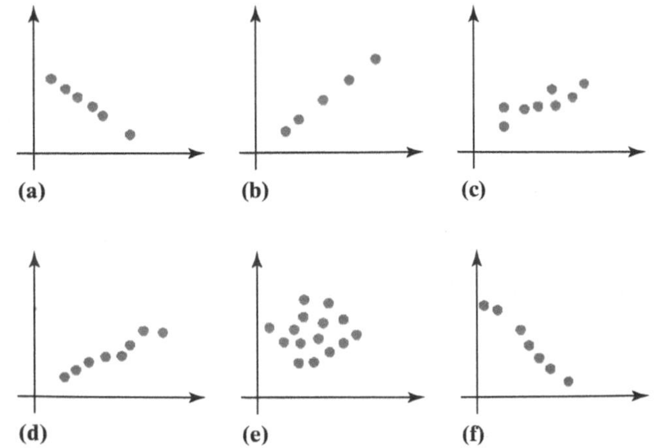

27. Which scatter plot indicates a perfect negative correlation?

28. Which scatter plot indicates a perfect positive correlation?

29. In which scatter plot is $r = 0.9$?

30. In which scatter plot is $r = 0.01$?

Compute r, the correlation coefficient, rounded to two decimal places, for the data in

31. Exercise 1.

32. Exercise 2.

33. Exercise 3.

34. Exercise 4.

35. Use the data in Exercise 5 to solve this exercise.

a. Determine the correlation coefficient, rounded to two decimal places, between the minutes Matthew McConaughey appeared shirtless in a film and the film's opening weekend gross.

b. Find the equation of the regression line for the minutes McConaughey appeared shirtless in a film and the film's opening weekend gross. Round m and b to two decimal places.

c. What opening weekend gross, to the nearest tenth of a million dollars, can we anticipate in a McConaughey film in which he appears shirtless for 20 minutes?

36. Use the data in Exercise 6 to solve this exercise.

a. Determine the correlation coefficient, rounded to two decimal places, between annual income and hours spent per week watching television.

b. Find the equation of the regression line for annual income and hours spent per week watching television. Round m and b to two decimal places.

c. Approximately how many hours per week watching television, rounded to one decimal place, can we anticipate for a person earning $100 thousand per year?

37. Use the data in Exercise 7 to solve this exercise.

a. Determine the correlation coefficient, rounded to two decimal places, between the percentage of teenagers who have used marijuana and the percentage who have used other drugs.

b. Find the equation of the regression line for the percentage of teenagers who have used marijuana and the percentage who have used other drugs. Round m and b to two decimal places.

c. What percentage of teenagers, to the nearest percent, can we anticipate using illegal drugs other than marijuana in a country where 10% of teenagers have used marijuana?

38. Use the data in Exercise 8 to solve this exercise.

a. Determine the correlation coefficient, rounded to two decimal places, between the percentage of people in a country who are literate and the percentage who are undernourished.

b. Find the equation of the regression line for the percentage who are literate and the percentage who are undernourished. Round m and b to two decimal places.

c. What percentage of people, to the nearest percent, can we anticipate are undernourished in a country where 60% of the people are literate?

In Exercises 39–45, the correlation coefficient, r, is given for a sample of n data points. Use the $\alpha = 0.05$ column in **Table 16** *to determine whether or not we may conclude that a correlation does exist in the population. (Using the $\alpha = 0.05$ column, there is a probability of 0.05 that the variables are not really correlated in the population and our results could be attributed to chance. Ignore this possibility when concluding whether or not there is a correlation in the population.)*

39. $n = 20, r = 0.5$

40. $n = 27, r = 0.4$

41. $n = 12, r = 0.5$

42. $n = 22, r = 0.04$

43. $n = 72, r = -0.351$

44. $n = 37, r = -0.37$

45. $n = 20, r = -0.37$

46. In the 1964 study on cigarette consumption and deaths due to lung cancer (see the Blitzer Bonus on page 732), $n = 11$ and $r = 0.73$. What can you conclude using the $\alpha = 0.05$ column in **Table 16**.

Writing in Mathematics

47. What is a scatter plot?

48. How does a scatter plot indicate that two variables are correlated?

49. Give an example of two variables with a strong positive correlation and explain why this is so.

50. Give an example of two variables with a strong negative correlation and explain why this is so.

51. What is meant by a regression line?

52. When all points in a scatter plot fall on the regression line, what is the value of the correlation coefficient? Describe what this means.

For the pairs of quantities in Exercises 53–56, describe whether a scatter plot will show a positive correlation, a negative correlation, or no correlation. If there is a correlation, is it strong, moderate, or weak? Explain your answers.

53. Height and weight

54. Number of days absent and grade in a course

55. Height and grade in a course

56. Hours of television watched and grade in a course

57. Explain how to use the correlation coefficient for a sample to determine if there is a correlation in the population.

Critical Thinking Exercises

Make Sense? *In Exercises 58–61, determine whether each statement makes sense or does not make sense, and explain your reasoning.*

58. I found a strong positive correlation for the data in Exercise 7 relating the percentage of teenagers in various countries who have used marijuana and the percentage who have used other drugs. I concluded that using marijuana leads to the use of other drugs.

59. I found a strong negative correlation for the data in Exercise 8 relating the percentage of people in various countries who are literate and the percentage who are undernourished. I concluded that an increase in literacy causes a decrease in undernourishment.

60. I'm working with a data set for which the correlation coefficient and the slope of the regression line have opposite signs.

61. I read that there is a correlation of 0.72 between IQ scores of identical twins reared apart, so I would expect a significantly lower correlation, approximately 0.52, between IQ scores of identical twins reared together.

62. Give an example of two variables with a strong correlation, where each variable is not the cause of the other.

Technology Exercise

63. Use the linear regression feature of a graphing calculator to verify your work in any two exercises from Exercises 35–38, parts (a) and (b).

Group Exercises

64. The group should select two variables related to people on your campus that it believes have a strong positive or negative correlation. Once these variables have been determined,

a. Collect at least 30 ordered pairs of data (x, y) from a sample of people on your campus.

b. Draw a scatter plot for the data collected.

c. Does the scatter plot indicate a positive correlation, a negative correlation, or no relationship between the variables?

d. Calculate r. Does the value of r reinforce the impression conveyed by the scatter plot?

e. Find the equation of the regression line.

f. Use the regression line's equation to make a prediction about a y-value given an x-value.

g. Are the results of this project consistent with the group's original belief about the correlation between the variables, or are there some surprises in the data collected?

65. What is the opinion of students on your campus about...? Group members should begin by deciding on some aspect of college life around which student opinion can be polled. The poll should consist of the question, "What is your opinion of...?" Be sure to provide options such as excellent, good, average, poor, horrible, or a 1-to-10 scale, or possibly grades of A, B, C, D, F. Use a random sample of students on your campus and conduct the opinion survey. After collecting the data, present and interpret it using as many of the skills and techniques learned in this chapter as possible.

Chapter Summary, Review, and Test

Summary – Definitions and Concepts

Examples

1 Sampling, Frequency Distributions, and Graphs

	Examples
a. A population is the set containing all objects whose properties are to be described and analyzed. A sample is a subset of the population.	Ex. 1
b. Random samples are obtained in such a way that each member of the population has an equal chance of being selected.	Ex. 2
c. Data can be organized and presented in frequency distributions, grouped frequency distributions, histograms, frequency polygons, and stem-and-leaf plots.	Ex. 3 Ex. 4 Figures 2 and 3 Ex. 5
d. The box at the end of this section lists some things to watch for in visual displays of data.	Table 5

2 Measures of Central Tendency

	Examples
a. The mean, $\overline{x}$, is the sum of the data items divided by the number of items: $\overline{x} = \frac{\Sigma x}{n}$.	Ex. 1
b. The mean, $\overline{x}$, of a frequency distribution is computed using $\overline{x} = \frac{\Sigma xf}{n}$, where x is a data value, f is its frequency, and n is the total frequency of the distribution.	Ex. 2
c. The median of ranked data is the item in the middle or the mean of the two middlemost items. The median is the value in the $\frac{n+1}{2}$ position in the list of ranked data.	Ex. 3 Ex. 4 Ex. 5 Ex. 6
d. When one or more data items are much greater than or much less than the other items, these extreme values greatly influence the mean, often making the median more representative of the data.	Ex. 7
e. The mode of a data set is the value that occurs most often. If there is no such value, there is no mode. If more than one data value has the highest frequency, then each of these data values is a mode.	Ex. 8
f. The midrange is computed using $\frac{\text{lowest data value} + \text{highest data value}}{2}$.	Ex. 9 Ex. 10

3 Measures of Dispersion

	Examples
a. Range = highest data value − lowest data value	Ex. 1
b. Standard deviation $= \sqrt{\frac{\Sigma(\text{data item} - \text{mean})^2}{n-1}}$. This is symbolized by $s = \sqrt{\frac{\Sigma(x-\overline{x})^2}{n-1}}$.	Ex. 2 Ex. 3 Ex. 4
c. As the spread of data items increases, the standard deviation gets larger.	Ex. 5

4 The Normal Distribution

a. The normal distribution is a theoretical distribution for the entire population. The distribution is bell shaped and symmetric about a vertical line through its center, where the mean, median, and mode are located.

b. The 68–95–99.7 Rule
Approximately 68% of the data items fall within 1 standard deviation of the mean. Approximately 95% of the data items fall within 2 standard deviations of the mean, and approximately 99.7% of the data items fall within 3 standard deviations of the mean. Ex. 1 Ex. 2

c. A z-score describes how many standard deviations a data item in a normal distribution lies above or below the mean. Ex. 3 Ex. 4 Ex. 5

$$z\text{-score} = \frac{\text{data item} - \text{mean}}{\text{standard deviation}}$$

d. If n% of the items in a distribution are less than a particular data item, that data item is in the nth percentile of the distribution. The 25th percentile is the first quartile, the 50th percentile, or the median, is the second quartile, and the 75th percentile is the third quartile. Ex. 6 Figure 6

e. If a statistic is obtained from a random sample of size n, there is a 95% probability that it lies within $\frac{1}{\sqrt{n}} \times 100\%$ of the true population statistic. $\pm\frac{1}{\sqrt{n}} \times 100\%$ is called the margin of error. Ex. 7

f. A distribution of data is skewed if a large number of data items are piled up at one end or the other, with a "tail" at the opposite end. Figure 20 Figure 21

5 Problem Solving with the Normal Distribution

a. A table showing z-scores and their percentiles can be used to find the percentage of data items less than or greater than a given data item in a normal distribution, as well as the percentage of data items between two given items. See the boxed summary on computing percentage of data items on page 724. Ex. 1 Ex. 2 Ex. 3

6 Scatter Plots, Correlation, and Regression Lines

a. A plot of data points is called a scatter plot. If the points lie approximately along a line, the line that best fits the data is called a regression line.

b. A correlation coefficient, r, measures the strength and direction of a possible relationship between variables. If $r = 1$, there is a perfect positive correlation, and if $r = -1$, there is a perfect negative correlation. If $r = 0$, there is no relationship between the variables. Table 16 indicates whether r denotes a correlation in the population. Ex. 1 Ex. 4

c. The formula for computing the correlation coefficient, r, is given in the box before Example 2. The equation of the regression line is given in the box before Example 3. Ex. 2 Ex. 3

Review Exercises

1

1. The government of a large city wants to know if its citizens will support a three-year tax increase to provide additional support to the city's community college system. The government decides to conduct a survey of the city's residents before placing a tax increase initiative on the ballot. Which one of the following is most appropriate for obtaining a sample of the city's residents?

a. Survey a random sample of persons within each geographic region of the city.

b. Survey a random sample of community college professors living in the city.

c. Survey every tenth person who walks into the city's government center on two randomly selected days of the week.

d. Survey a random sample of persons within each geographic region of the state in which the city is located.

A random sample of ten college students is selected and each student is asked how much time he or she spent on homework during the previous weekend. The following times, in hours, are obtained:

8, 10, 9, 7, 9, 8, 7, 6, 8, 7.

Use these data items to solve Exercises 2–4.

2. Construct a frequency distribution for the data.

3. Construct a histogram for the data.

4. Construct a frequency polygon for the data.

The 50 grades on a physiology test are shown. Use the data to solve Exercises 5–6.

44	24	54	81	18
34	39	63	67	60
72	36	91	47	75
57	74	87	49	86
59	14	26	41	90
13	29	13	31	68
63	35	29	70	22
95	17	50	42	27
73	11	42	31	69
56	40	31	45	51

5. Construct a grouped frequency distribution for the data. Use 0–39 for the first class, 40–49 for the second class, and make each subsequent class width the same as the second class.
6. Construct a stem-and-leaf plot for the data.
7. Describe what is misleading about the size of the barrels in the following visual display.

Source: U.S. Department of Energy

2

In Exercises 8–9, find the mean for each group of data items.

8. 84, 90, 95, 89, 98
9. 33, 27, 9, 10, 6, 7, 11, 23, 27
10. Find the mean for the data items in the given frequency distribution.

Score x	Frequency f
1	2
2	4
3	3
4	1

In Exercises 11–12, find the median for each group of data items.

11. 33, 27, 9, 10, 6, 7, 11, 23, 27
12. 28, 16, 22, 28, 34
13. Find the median for the data items in the frequency distribution in Exercise 10.

In Exercises 14–15, find the mode for each group of data items. If there is no mode, so state.

14. 33, 27, 9, 10, 6, 7, 11, 23, 27
15. 582, 585, 583, 585, 587, 587, 589
16. Find the mode for the data items in the frequency distribution in Exercise 10.

In Exercises 17–18, find the midrange for each group of data items.

17. 84, 90, 95, 88, 98
18. 33, 27, 9, 10, 6, 7, 11, 23, 27
19. Find the midrange for the data items in the frequency distribution in Exercise 10.
20. A student took seven tests in a course, scoring between 90% and 95% on three of the tests, between 80% and 89% on three of the tests, and below 40% on one of the tests. In this distribution, is the mean or the median more representative of the student's overall performance in the course? Explain your answer.
21. The data items below are the ages of U.S. presidents at the time of their first inauguration.

57 61 57 57 58 57 61 54 68 51 49 64 50 48
65 52 56 46 54 49 51 47 55 55 54 42 51 56
55 51 54 51 60 62 43 55 56 61 52 69 64 46 54 47

   a. Organize the data in a frequency distribution.
   b. Use the frequency distribution to find the mean age, median age, modal age, and midrange age of the presidents when they were inaugurated.

3

In Exercises 22–23, find the range for each group of data items.

22. 28, 34, 16, 22, 28
23. 312, 783, 219, 312, 426, 219
24. The mean for the data items 29, 9, 8, 22, 46, 51, 48, 42, 53, 42 is 35. Find **a.** the deviation from the mean for each data item and **b.** the sum of the deviations in part (a).
25. Use the data items 36, 26, 24, 90, and 74 to find **a.** the mean, **b.** the deviation from the mean for each data item, and **c.** the sum of the deviations in part (b).

In Exercises 26–27, find the standard deviation for each group of data items.

26. 3, 3, 5, 8, 10, 13
27. 20, 27, 23, 26, 28, 32, 33, 35
28. A test measuring anxiety levels is administered to a sample of ten college students with the following results. (High scores indicate high anxiety.)

10, 30, 37, 40, 43, 44, 45, 69, 86, 86

Find the mean, range, and standard deviation for the data.

29. Compute the mean and the standard deviation for each of the following data sets. Then, write a brief description of similarities and differences between the two sets based on each of your computations.

Set A: 80, 80, 80, 80 Set B: 70, 70, 90, 90

30. Describe how you would determine

a. which of the two groups, men or women, at your college has a higher mean grade point average.

b. which of the groups is more consistently close to its mean grade point average.

4

The scores on a test are normally distributed with a mean of 70 and a standard deviation of 8. In Exercises 31–33, find the score that is

31. 2 standard deviations above the mean.

32. $3\frac{1}{2}$ standard deviations above the mean.

33. $1\frac{1}{4}$ standard deviations below the mean.

The ages of people living in a retirement community are normally distributed with a mean age of 68 years and a standard deviation of 4 years. In Exercises 34–40, use the 68–95–99.7 Rule to find the percentage of people in the community whose ages

34. are between 64 and 72.

35. are between 60 and 76.

36. are between 68 and 72.

37. are between 56 and 80.

38. exceed 72.

39. are less than 72.

40. exceed 76.

A set of data items is normally distributed with a mean of 50 and a standard deviation of 5. In Exercises 41–45, convert each data item to a z-score.

41. 50

42. 60

43. 58

44. 35

45. 44

46. A student scores 60 on a vocabulary test and 80 on a grammar test. The data items for both tests are normally distributed. The vocabulary test has a mean of 50 and a standard deviation of 5. The grammar test has a mean of 72 and a standard deviation of 6. On which test did the student have the better score? Explain why this is so.

The number of miles that a particular brand of car tires lasts is normally distributed with a mean of 32,000 miles and a standard deviation of 4000 miles. In Exercises 47–49, find the data item in this distribution that corresponds to the given z-score.

47. $z = 1.5$

48. $z = 2.25$

49. $z = -2.5$

50. Using a random sample of 2281 American adults ages 18 and older, an Adecco survey asked respondents if they would be willing to sacrifice a percentage of their salary in order to work for an environmentally friendly company. The poll indicated that 31% of the respondents said "yes," 39% said "no," and 30% declined to answer.

a. Find the margin of error, to the nearest tenth of a percent, for this survey.

b. Write a statement about the percentage of American adults who would be willing to sacrifice a percentage of their salary in order to work for an environmentally friendly company.

51. The histogram indicates the frequencies of the number of syllables per word for 100 randomly selected words in Japanese.

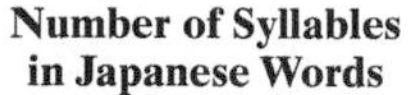

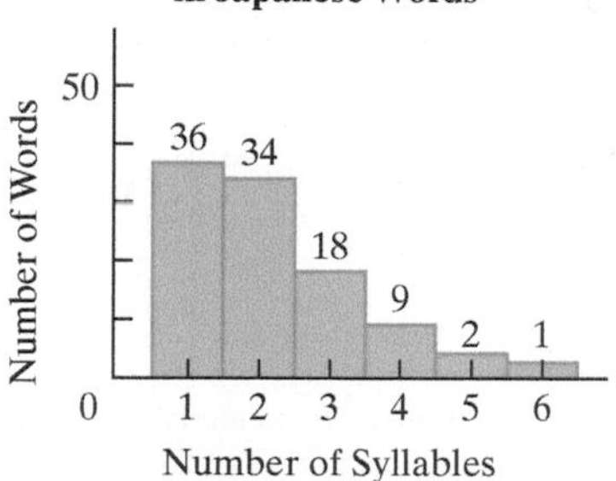

a. Is the shape of this distribution best classified as normal, skewed to the right, or skewed to the left?

b. Find the mean, median, and mode for the number of syllables in the sample of Japanese words.

c. Are the measures of central tendency from part (b) consistent with the shape of the distribution that you described in part (a)? Explain your answer.

5

The mean cholesterol level for all men in the United States is 200 and the standard deviation is 15. In Exercises 52–55, use **Table 14** *to find the percentage of U.S. men whose cholesterol level*

52. is less than 221.

53. is greater than 173.

54. is between 173 and 221.

55. is between 164 and 182.

Use the percentiles for the weights of adult men over 40 to solve Exercises 56–58.

Weight	Percentile
235	86
227	third quartile
180	second quartile
173	first quartile

Find the percentage of men over 40 who weigh

56. less than 227 pounds.

57. more than 235 pounds.

58. between 227 and 235 pounds.

6

In Exercises 59–60, make a scatter plot for the given data. Use the scatter plot to describe whether or not the variables appear to be related.

59.

x	1	3	4	6	8	9
y	1	2	3	3	5	5

60.

Country	Canada	U.S.	Mexico	Brazil	Costa Rica	Denmark	China	Egypt	Pakistan	Ban-gladesh	Aus-tralia	Japan	Russia
Life expectancy in years, x	81	78	76	72	77	78	73	72	64	63	82	82	66
Infant deaths per 1000 births, y	5.1	6.3	19.0	23.3	9.0	4.4	21.2	28.4	66.9	57.5	4.8	2.8	10.8

Source: U.S. Bureau of the Census International Database

The scatter plot in the figure shows the relationship between the percentage of adult females in a country who are literate and the mortality of children under five. Also shown is the regression line. Use this information to determine whether each of the statements in Exercises 61–67 is true or false.

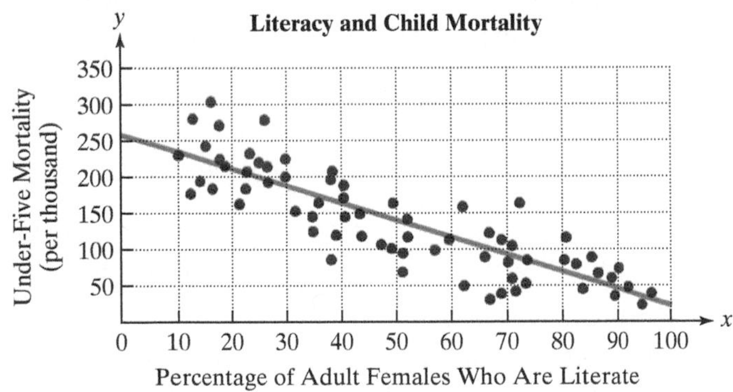

Source: United Nations

61. There is a perfect negative correlation between the percentage of adult females who are literate and under-five mortality.

62. As the percentage of adult females who are literate increases, under-five mortality tends to decrease.

63. The country with the least percentage of adult females who are literate has the greatest under-five mortality.

64. No two countries have the same percentage of adult females who are literate but different under-five mortalities.

65. There are more than 20 countries in this sample.

66. There is no correlation between the percentage of adult females who are literate and under-five mortality.

67. The country with the greatest percentage of adult females who are literate has an under-five mortality rate that is less than 50 children per thousand.

68. Which one of the following scatter plots indicates a correlation coefficient of approximately -0.9?

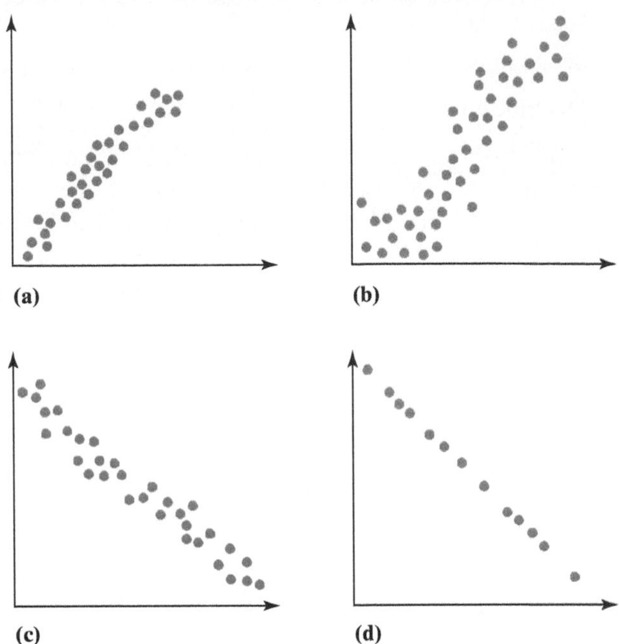

69. Use the data in Exercise 59 to solve the exercise.

a. Compute r, the correlation coefficient, rounded to the nearest thousandth.

b. Find the equation of the regression line.

70. The graph, based on Nielsen Media Research data taken from random samples of Americans at various ages, indicates that as we get older, we watch more television.

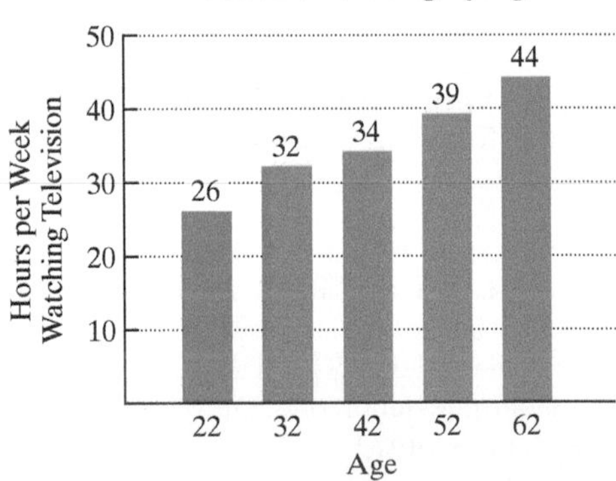

Source: Nielsen Media Research

a. Let x represent one's age and let y represent hours per week watching television. Calculate the correlation coefficient.

b. Using **Table 16** and the $\alpha = 0.05$ column, determine whether there is a correlation between age and time spent watching television in the American population.

Chapter Test

CHAPTER Test Prep VIDEOS

Step-by-step test solutions are found on the Chapter Test Prep Videos available on YouTube (search "Blitzer, Thinking Mathematically" and click on "Channels").

1. Politicians in the Florida Keys need to know if the residents of Key Largo think the amount of money charged for water is reasonable. The politicians decide to conduct a survey of a sample of Key Largo's residents. Which procedure would be most appropriate for a sample of Key Largo's residents?
   - **a.** Survey all water customers who pay their water bills at Key Largo City Hall on the third day of the month.
   - **b.** Survey a random sample of executives who work for the water company in Key Largo.
   - **c.** Survey 5000 individuals who are randomly selected from a list of all people living in Georgia and Florida.
   - **d.** Survey a random sample of persons within each neighborhood of Key Largo.

Use these scores on a ten-point quiz to solve Exercises 2–4.

8, 5, 3, 6, 5, 10, 6, 9, 4, 5, 7, 9, 7, 4, 8, 8

2. Construct a frequency distribution for the data.
3. Construct a histogram for the data.
4. Construct a frequency polygon for the data.

Use the 30 test scores listed below to solve Exercises 5–6.

79	51	67	50	78
62	89	83	73	80
88	48	60	71	79
89	63	55	93	71
41	81	46	50	61
59	50	90	75	61

5. Construct a grouped frequency distribution for the data. Use 40–49 for the first class and use the same width for each subsequent class.
6. Construct a stem-and-leaf display for the data.
7. The graph shows the percentage of students in the United States through grade 12 who were home-schooled in 1999 and 2007. What impression does the roofline in the visual display imply about what occurred in 2000 through 2006? How might this be misleading?

Source: National Center for Education Statistics

Use the six data items listed below to solve Exercises 8–11.

3, 6, 2, 1, 7, 3

8. Find the mean.
9. Find the median.
10. Find the midrange,
11. Find the standard deviation.

Use the frequency distribution shown to solve Exercises 12–14.

Score x	Frequency f
1	3
2	5
3	2
4	2

12. Find the mean.
13. Find the median.
14. Find the mode.
15. The annual salaries of four salespeople and the owner of a bookstore are

    $17,500, $19,000, $22,000, $27,500, $98,500.

    Is the mean or the median more representative of the five annual salaries? Briefly explain your answer.

According to the American Freshman, *the number of hours that college freshmen spend studying each week is normally distributed with a mean of 7 hours and a standard deviation of 5.3 hours. In Exercises 16–17, use the 68–95–99.7 Rule to find the percentage of college freshmen who study*

16. between 7 and 12.3 hours each week.
17. more than 17.6 hours each week.
18. IQ scores are normally distributed in the population. Who has a higher IQ: a student with a 120 IQ on a scale where 100 is the mean and 10 is the standard deviation, or a professor with a 128 IQ on a scale where 100 is the mean and 15 is the standard deviation? Briefly explain your answer.
19. Use the z-scores and the corresponding percentiles shown below to solve this exercise. Test scores are normally distributed with a mean of 74 and a standard deviation of 10. What percentage of the scores are above 88?

z-Score	Percentile
1.1	86.43
1.2	88.49
1.3	90.32
1.4	91.92
1.5	93.32

20. Use the percentiles in the table shown below to find the percentage of scores between 630 and 690.

Score	Percentile
780	99
750	87
720	72
690	49
660	26
630	8
600	1

21. Using a random sample of 100 students from a campus of approximately 12,000 students, 60% of the students in the sample said they were very satisfied with their professors.

a. Find the margin of error in this percent.

b. Write a statement about the percentage of the entire population of students from this campus who are very satisfied with their professors.

22. Make a scatter plot for the given data. Use the scatter plot to describe whether or not the variables appear to be related.

x	1	4	3	5	2
y	5	2	2	1	4

The scatter plot shows the number of minutes each of 16 people exercise per week and the number of headaches per month each person experiences. Use the scatter plot to determine whether each of the statements in Exercises 23–25 is true or false.

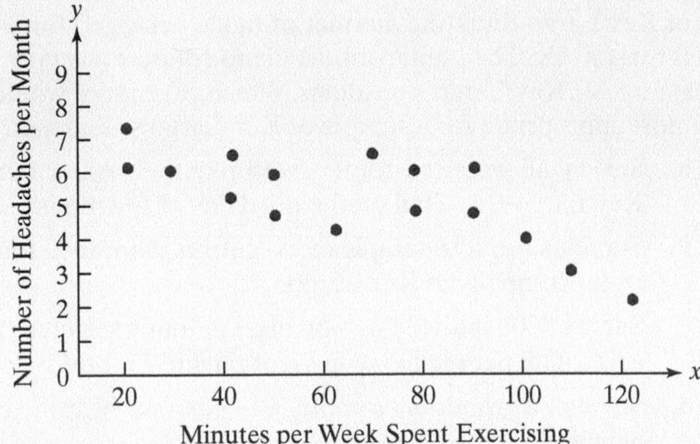

23. An increase in the number of minutes devoted to exercise causes a decrease in headaches.

24. There is a perfect negative correlation between time spent exercising and number of headaches.

25. The person who exercised most per week had the least number of headaches per month.

26. Is the relationship between the price of gas and the number of people visiting our national parks a positive correlation, a negative correlation, or is there no correlation? Explain your answer.

Answers to Selected Exercises

Section 1

Check Point Exercises

1. a. the set containing all the city's homeless **b.** no: People already in the shelters are probably less likely to be against mandatory residence in the shelters. **2.** By selecting people from a shelter, homeless people who do not go to the shelters have no chance of being selected. An appropriate method would be to randomly select neighborhoods of the city and then randomly survey homeless people within the selected neighborhood.

3.

Grade	Frequency
A	3
B	5
C	9
D	2
F	1
	20

4.

Class	Frequency
40–49	1
50–59	5
60–69	4
70–79	15
80–89	5
90–99	7
	37

5.

Stem	Leaves
4	1
5	8 2 8 0 7
6	8 2 9 9
7	3 5 9 9 7 5 5 3 3 6 7 1 7 1 5
8	7 3 9 9 1
9	4 6 9 7 5 8 0

Exercise Set 1

1. c **3.** 7; 31 **5.** 151

7.

Time Spent on Homework (in hours)	Number of Students
15	4
16	5
17	6
18	5
19	4
20	2
21	2
22	0
23	0
24	2
	30

9. 0, 5, 10, . . . , 40, 45 **11.** 5 **13.** 13 **15.** the 5–9 class

17.

Age at Inauguration	Number of Presidents
41–45	2
46–50	9
51–55	15
56–60	9
61–65	7
66–70	2
	44

19. a.

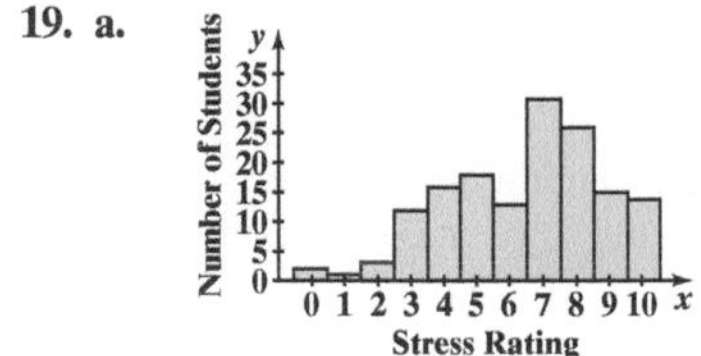

b.

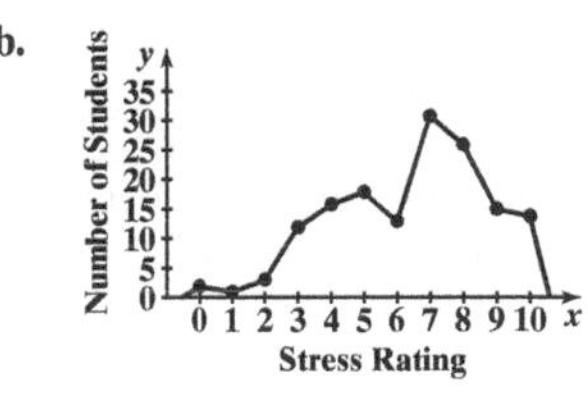

21.

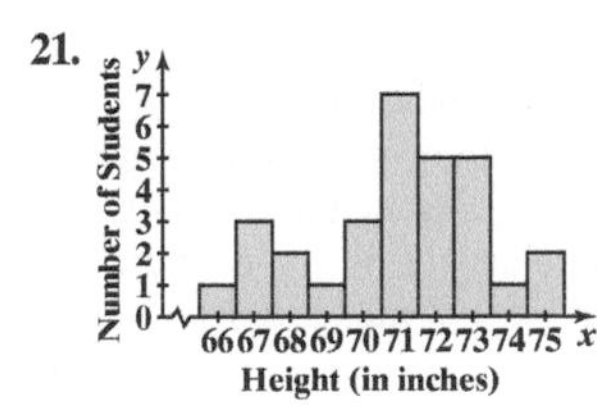

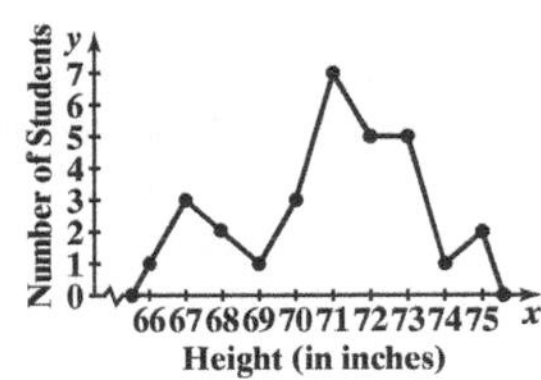

23. false **25.** false **27.** true **29.** false

31.

Stem	Leaves
2	8 8 9 5
3	8 7 0 1 2 7 6 4 0 5
4	8 2 2 1 4 5 4 6 2 0 8 2 7 9
5	9 4 1 9 1 0
6	3 2 3 6 6 3

The greatest number of college professors are in their 40s.

33. Time intervals on the horizontal axis do not represent equal amounts of time. **35.** Percentages do not add up to 100%. **37.** It is not clear whether the bars or the actors represent the box-office receipts. **49.** does not make sense **51.** makes sense

Section 2

Check Point Exercises

1. a. 30 **b.** 30 **2.** 36 **3. a.** 35 **b.** 82 **4.** 5 **5.** 1:06, 1:09, 1:14, 1:21, 1:22, 1:25, 1:29, 1:29, 1:34, 1:34, 1:36, 1:45, 1:46, 1:49, 1:54, 1:57, 2:10, 2:15; median: 1 hour, 34 minutes **6.** 54.5 **7. a.** \$19.05 million **b.** \$22.45 million **c.** One salary, \$0 million, is much smaller than the other salaries. **8.** 8 **9.** \$118,006,573.50 **10.** mean: 158.6 cal; median: 153 cal; mode: 138 cal; midrange: 151 cal

Exercise Set 2

1. 4.125 **3.** 95 **5.** 62 **7.** ≈ 3.45 **9.** ≈ 4.71 **11.** ≈ 6.26 **13.** 3.5 **15.** 95 **17.** 60 **19.** 3.6 **21.** 5 **23.** 6 **25.** 3 **27.** 95 **29.** 40 **31.** 2.5, 4.2 (bimodal) **33.** 5 **35.** 6 **37.** 4.5 **39.** 95 **41.** 70 **43.** 3.3 **45.** 4.5 **47.** 5.5 **49.** mean: 30; median: 30; mode: 30; midrange: 30 **51.** mean: approximately 12.4; median: 12.5; mode: 13; midrange: 12.5 **53.** mean: approximately 31.3;

median: 31; mode: 31; midrange: 33 **55. a.** approximately \$481.9 million **b.** \$403.5 million **c.** \$406 million **d.** \$888.5 million **57. a.** ≈ 17.27 **b.** 17 **c.** 7, 12, 17 **d.** 24.5 **59.** 175 lb **61.** 177.5 lb **63.** ≈ 2.76 **73.** makes sense **75.** makes sense **77.** Sample answers: **77. a.** 75, 80, 80, 90, 91, 94 **b.** 50, 80, 80, 85, 90, 95 **c.** 70, 75, 80, 85, 90, 100 **d.** 75, 80, 85, 90, 95, 95 **e.** 75, 80, 85, 85, 90, 95 **f.** 68, 70, 72, 72, 74, 76

Section 3

Check Point Exercises

1. 9 **2.** mean: 6;

Data item	Deviation
2	−4
4	−2
7	1
11	5

3. ≈ 3.92 **4.** sample A: 3.74; sample B: 28.06 **5. a.** small-company stocks **b.** small-company stocks; Answers will vary.

Exercise Set 3

1. 4 **3.** 8 **5.** 2

7. a.

Data item	Deviation
3	−9
5	−7
7	−5
12	0
18	6
27	15

b. 0

9. a.

Data item	Deviation
29	−20
38	−11
48	−1
49	0
53	4
77	28

b. 0

11. a. 91

b.

Data item	Deviation
85	−6
95	4
90	−1
85	−6
100	9

c. 0

13. a. 155

b.

Data item	
146	−9
153	−2
155	0
160	5
161	6

c. 0

15. a. 2.70

b.

Data item	Deviation
2.25	−0.45
3.50	0.80
2.75	0.05
3.10	0.40
1.90	−0.80

c. 0

17. ≈ 1.58 **19.** ≈ 3.46 **21.** ≈ 0.89 **23.** 3 **25.** ≈ 2.14

27. *Sample A*: mean: 12; range: 12; standard deviation: ≈ 4.32
Sample B: mean: 12; range: 12; standard deviation: ≈ 5.07
Sample C: mean: 12; range: 12; standard deviation: 6
The samples have the same mean and range, but different standard deviations.

29. 0 **31.** 1 **33.** 7.91 **35.** 1.55 **37. a.** male artists; All but one of the data items for the men are greater than the greatest data item for the women. **b.** male artists: 77; female artists: 57 **c.** male artists; There is greater spread in the data for the men. **d.** male artists: 19.91; female artists: 5.92 **47.** makes sense **49.** makes sense **53.** a

Section 4

Check Point Exercises

1. a. 75.5 in. **b.** 58 in. **2. a.** 95% **b.** 47.5% **c.** 16% **3. a.** 2 **b.** 0 **c.** −1 **4.** ACT **5. a.** 64 **b.** 128 **6.** 75% of the scores on the SAT are less than this student's score. **7. a.** $\pm$ 2.0% **b.** We can be 95% confident that between 34% and 38% of Americans read more than ten books per year. **c.** Sample answer: Some people may be embarrassed to admit that they read few or no books per year.

Exercise Set 4

1. 120 **3.** 160 **5.** 150 **7.** 60 **9.** 90 **11.** 68% **13.** 34% **15.** 47.5% **17.** 49.85% **19.** 16% **21.** 2.5% **23.** 95% **25.** 47.5% **27.** 16% **29.** 2.5% **31.** 0.15% **33.** 1 **35.** 3 **37.** 0.5 **39.** 1.75 **41.** 0 **43.** −1 **45.** −1.5 **47.** −3.25 **49.** 1.5 **51.** 2.25 **53.** −1.25 **55.** −1.5 **57.** The person who scores 127 on the Wechsler has the higher IQ. **59.** 500 **61.** 475 **63.** 250 **65.** 275 **67. a.** $\pm$ 3.1% **b.** We can be 95% confident that between 21.9% and 28.1% of high school students have information technology as their career choice. **69. a.** $\pm$ 1.6% **b.** We can be 95% confident that between 58.6% and 61.8% of all TV households watched the final episode of *M*A*S*H*. **71.** 0.2% **73. a.** skewed to the right **b.** 5.3 murders per 100,000 residents **c.** 5 murders per 100,000 residents **d.** yes; The mean is greater than the median, which is consistent with a distribution skewed to the right. **e.** 5.6; yes; For a normal distribution, almost 100% of the z-scores are between −3 and 3. **87.** does not make sense **89.** does not make sense

Section 5

Check Point Exercises

1. 88.49% **2.** 8.08% **3.** 83.01%

Exercise Set 5

1. a. 72.57% **b.** 27.43% **3. a.** 88.49% **b.** 11.51% **5. a.** 24.2% **b.** 75.8% **7. a.** 11.51% **b.** 88.49% **9.** 33.99% **11.** 15.74% **13.** 86.64% **15.** 28.57% **17.** 91.92% **19.** 27.43% **21.** 88.49% **23.** 6.69% **25.** 45.14% **27.** 6.68% **29.** 24.17% **31.** 77% **33.** 86% **35.** 10% **39.** does not make sense **41.** makes sense **45.** 630

Section 6

Check Point Exercises

1. This indicates a moderate relationship. **2.** 0.89; There is a moderately strong positive relationship between the two quantities. **3.** $y = 0.1x + 0.8$; 8.8 deaths per 100,000 people **4.** yes

Exercise Set 6

1.

There appears to be a positive correlation.

3.

There appears to be a negative correlation.

5.

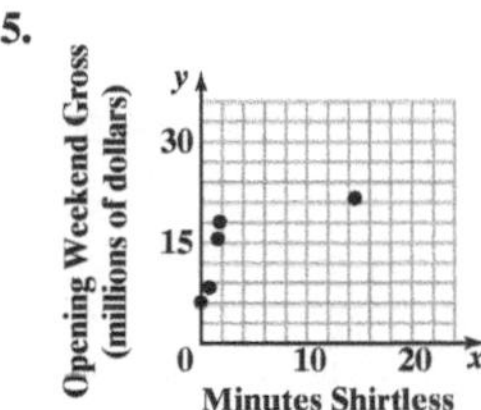

There appears to be a positive correlation.

7.

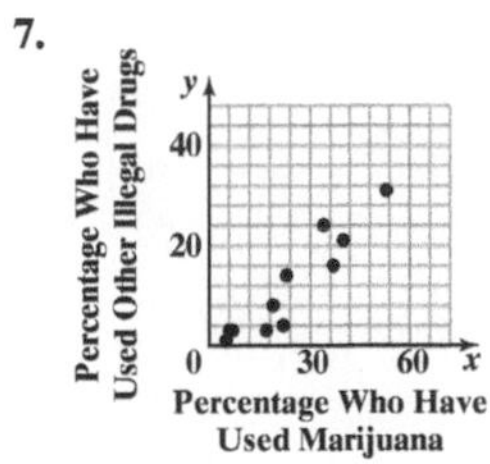

There appears to be a positive correlation.

9. false **11.** true **13.** true **15.** false **17.** true **19.** false **21.** true **23.** false **25.** false **27.** a **29.** d **31.** 0.85 **33.** −0.953 **35. a.** 0.73 **b.** $y = 0.79x + 10.97$ **c.** $26.8 million **37. a.** 0.93 **b.** $y = 0.62x - 3.07$ **c.** 3% **39.** A correlation does exist. **41.** A correlation does not exist. **43.** A correlation does exist. **45.** A correlation does not exist. **59.** does not make sense **61.** does not make sense

Chapter Review Exercises

1. a

2.

Time Spent on Homework (in hours)	Number of Students
6	1
7	3
8	3
9	2
10	1
	10

3.

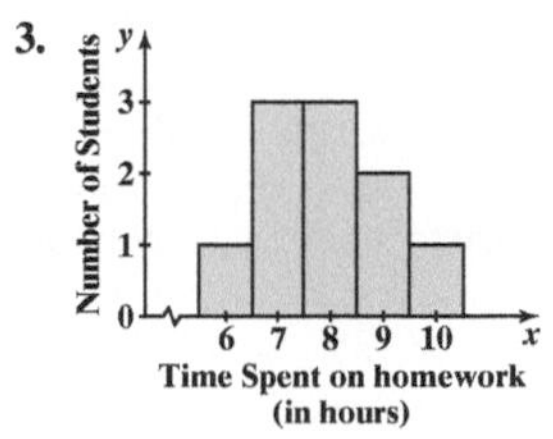

4.

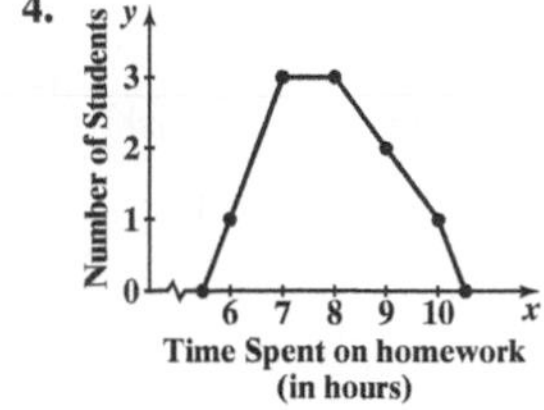

5.

Grades	Number of Students
0–39	19
40–49	8
50–59	6
60–69	6
70–79	5
80–89	3
90–99	3
	50

6.

Stem	Leaves
1	8 4 3 3 7 1
2	4 6 9 9 2 7
3	4 9 6 1 5 1 1
4	4 7 9 1 2 2 0 5
5	4 7 9 0 6 1
6	3 7 0 8 3 9
7	2 5 4 0 3
8	1 7 6
9	1 0 5

7. Sizes of barrels are not scaled proportionally in terms of the data they represent. **8.** 91.2 **9.** 17 **10.** 2.3 **11.** 11 **12.** 28 **13.** 2 **14.** 27 **15.** 585, 587 (bimodal) **16.** 2 **17.** 91 **18.** 19.5 **19.** 2.5

21. a.

Age at First Inauguration	Number of Presidents
42	1
43	1
44	0
45	0
46	2
47	2
48	1
49	2
50	1
51	5
52	2
53	0
54	5
55	4
56	3
57	4
58	1
59	0
60	1
61	3
62	1
63	0
64	2
65	1
66	0
67	0
68	1
69	1
	44

b. mean: ≈ 54.66 yr; median: 54.5 yr; mode: 51 yr, 54 yr (bimodal); midrange: 55.5 yr **22.** 18 **23.** 564

24. a.

Data item	Deviation
29	−6
9	−26
8	−27
22	−13
46	11
51	16
48	13
42	7
53	18
42	7

b. 0

25. a. 50

b.

Data item	Deviation
36	−14
26	−24
24	−26
90	40
74	24

c. 0

26. ≈ 4.05 **27.** ≈ 5.13 **28.** mean: 49; range: 76; standard deviation: ≈ 24.32 **29.** Set A: mean: 80; standard deviation: 0; Set B: mean: 80; standard deviation: ≈ 11.55; Answers will vary. **30.** Answers will vary. **31.** 86 **32.** 98 **33.** 60 **34.** 68% **35.** 95% **36.** 34% **37.** 99.7% **38.** 16% **39.** 84% **40.** 2.5% **41.** 0 **42.** 2 **43.** 1.6 **44.** −3 **45.** −1.2 **46.** vocabulary test **47.** 38,000 miles **48.** 41,000 miles **49.** 22,000 miles **50. a.** ± 2.1% **b.** We can be 95% confident that between 28.9% and 33.1% of American adults would be willing to sacrifice a percentage of their salary to work for an environmentally friendly company. **51. a.** skewed to the right **b.** mean: 2.1 syllables; median: 2 syllables; mode: 1 syllable **c.** yes; The mean is greater than the median, which is consistent with a distribution skewed to the right. **52.** 91.92% **53.** 96.41% **54.** 88.33% **55.** 10.69% **56.** 75% **57.** 14% **58.** 11%

59.

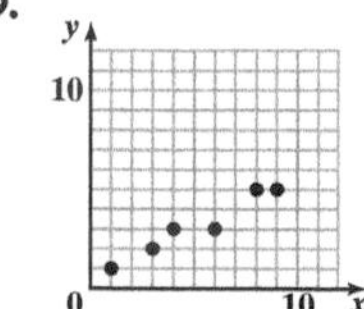

There appears to be a positive correlation.

60.

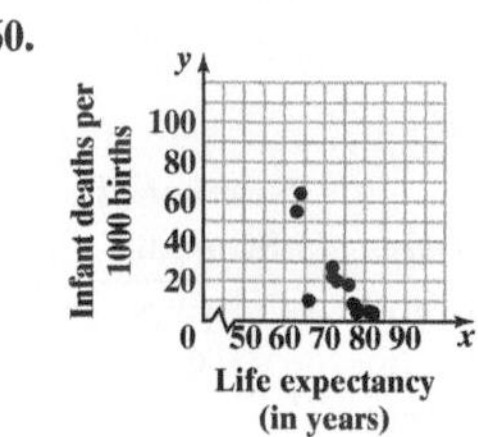

There appears to be a negative correlation.

61. false **62.** true **63.** false **64.** false **65.** true **66.** false **67.** true **68.** c **69. a.** 0.972 **b.** $y = 0.509x + 0.537$
70. a. 0.99 **b.** There is a correlation.

Chapter Test

1. d **2.**

Score	Frequency
3	1
4	2
5	3
6	2
7	2
8	3
9	2
10	1
	16

3.

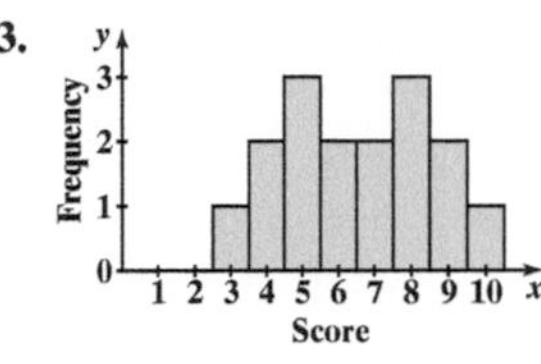

4.

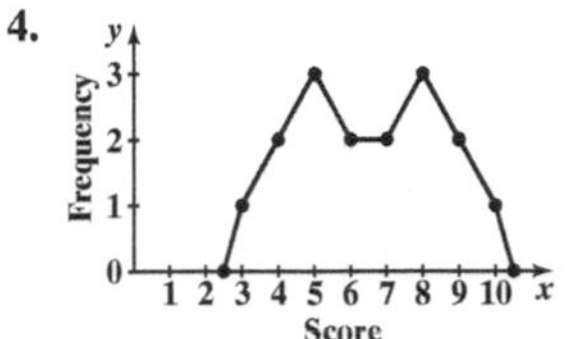

5.

Class	Frequency
40–49	3
50–59	6
60–69	6
70–79	7
80–89	6
90–99	2
	30

6.

Stem	Leaves
4	8 1 6
5	1 0 5 0 9 0
6	7 2 0 3 1 1
7	9 8 3 1 9 1 5
8	9 3 0 8 9 1
9	3 0

7. The roofline gives the impression that the percentage of home-schooled students grew at the same rate each year between the years shown which might not have happened. **8.** ≈ 3.67 **9.** 3 **10.** 4 **11.** ≈ 2.34 **12.** 2.25 **13.** 2 **14.** 2 **15.** Answers will vary. **16.** 34%
17. 2.5% **18.** student **19.** 8.08% **20.** 41%
21. a. ±10% **b.** We can be 95% confident that between 50% and 70% of all students are very satisfied with their professors.
22.

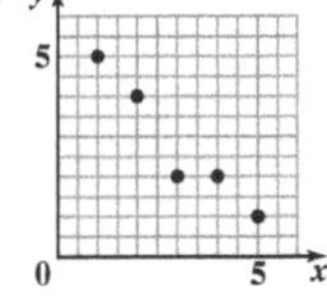

; There appears to be a strong negative correlation.
23. false **24.** false **25.** true **26.** Answers will vary.

Index

Page references followed by "f" indicate illustrated figures or photographs; followed by "t" indicates a table.